Addison-Wesley

Algebra

Teacher's Edition

Stanley A. Smith

Randall I. Charles

John A. Dossey

Mervin L. Keedy

Marvin L. Bittinger

ADDISON-WESLEY PUBLISHING COMPANY

Menlo Park, California · Reading, Massachusetts · New York

Don Mills, Ontario · Wokingham, England · Amsterdam · Bonn

Sydney · Singapore · Tokyo · Madrid · San Juan

Editorial Staff: Lila A. Nissen, Senior Editor
Robin D. Blakely
Design/Production staff: John Walker
Photo editor: Inge Kjemtrup

Cover photograph: © Paul Steel/The Stock Market

ISBN 0-201-81249-5

3 4 5 6 7 8 9 10-VH-96

Authors

Stanley A. Smith served as Coordinator, Office of Mathematics (K-12), for Baltimore County Public Schools, Maryland. He has taught junior high school mathematics and science and senior high school mathematics. He earned his M.A. degree at the University of Maryland. Mr. Smith was named Outstanding Mathematics Educator by the Maryland Council of Teachers of Mathematics in 1987. He is co-author of *Addison-Wesley Essentials of Mathematics* (1989), *Addison-Wesley Consumer Mathematics* (1989), and *Addison-Wesley Informal Geometry* (1986).

Randall I. Charles is Associate Professor of Mathematics at San Jose State University. He has taught at all levels and has been an elementary and secondary school mathematics supervisor. He has recently been involved in the development and evaluation of a nationally recognized problem-solving program. Dr. Charles holds a Ph.D. in Mathematics Education from Indiana University, and is co-author of several books, including *Addison-Wesley Mathematics* (1989) for grades 7 and 8, *Addison-Wesley Essentials of Mathematics* (1989), *Addison-Wesley Pre-Algebra* (1987), and *Problem-Solving Experiences in Mathematics* (1985).

John A. Dossey is Professor of Mathematics at Illinois State University where he teaches both mathematics and methods courses for teachers. He has taught at every level from grade 7 through graduate school and has served as K-12 supervisor of mathematics. He received his Ph.D. in Mathematics Education from the University of Illinois. During 1986–1988, Dr. Dossey served as President of the National Council of Teachers of Mathematics. He is a member of the National Research Council's Mathematical Sciences Education Board. In addition to books on both methods and content, he has published a number of research papers dealing with the Second International Study of Mathematics. He is co-author of *Addison-Wesley Essentials of Mathematics* (1989).

Mervin L. Keedy is Professor of Mathematics Emeritus at Purdue University. He received his Ph.D. at the University of Nebraska and formerly taught at the University of Maryland. He has also taught mathematics and science in junior and senior high schools. Professor Keedy is the author of many books on mathematics. Most recently he is co-author of *Addison-Wesley General Mathematics* (1986), *Addison-Wesley Applying Mathematics* (1986), and *Addison-Wesley Informal Geometry* (1986).

Marvin L. Bittinger is Professor of Mathematics Education at Indiana University-Purdue University at Indianapolis. He earned his Ph.D. at Purdue University. Dr. Bittinger is the author of many books on mathematics. Most recently, he is the author of *Calculus* (Addison-Wesley, 1984) and is co-author of *Business Mathematics* (Addison-Wesley, 1987), *Addison-Wesley General Mathematics* (1986), and *Addison-Wesley Informal Geometry* (1986).

Consultants and Reviewers

Ferrill Alderfer, Cherry Hill East High School, Cherry Hill, New Jersey

Margaret Arevalo, Memorial High School, San Antonio, Texas

Otto Bielss, Dallas Independent School District, Dallas, Texas

Bruce Burt, West Chester Area School District, West Chester, Pennsylvania

Cecile Carlton, Nashua Senior High School, Nashua, New Hampshire

Gill Choi, Board of Education, Chicago, Illinois

Jim Crawford, Manchester Memorial High School, Manchester, New Hampshire

David S. Daniels, Longmeadow High School, Longmeadow, Massachusetts

Ron Davis, Lee County Schools, Fort Myers, Florida

Paul Dillenberger, Minneapolis School District, Minneapolis, Minnesota

Charles Garabedian, Watertown High School, Watertown, Massachusetts

Susan Harder, Clark High School, Plano, Texas

Arthur C. Howard, Aldine Independent School District, Houston, Texas

Arthur Jackson, Concord High School, Concord, New Hampshire

Melleretha Johnson, City of Saginaw School District, Saginaw, Michigan

Lillian Jones, Westview Junior High School, Miami, Florida

Catherine J. Kowalski, Bellaire High School, Bellaire, Texas

Roger Larson, Anoka-Hennepin School District, Coon Rapids, Minnesota

Sandra Lindstrom, Mercer Island High School, Mercer Island, Washington

Kay Meister, Columbus School Board, Columbus, Ohio

Bert Niehius, Carlmont High School, Belmont, California

Mick O'Neil, Salem High School, Salem, New Hampshire

Sylvia Pezanowski, State College Area Intermediate High School, State College, Pennsylvania

Roy Ramos, Kennedy High School, San Antonio, Texas

Ron Schutt, Lexington High School, Lexington, Massachusetts

Robert Scott, Sweetwater High School, Sweetwater, Texas

Jim Wohlgehagen, Plano Independent School District, Plano, Texas

Contributors

Wayne S. Copes
William J. Sacco
Clifford W. Sloyer
Robert M. Stark

Associated with the University of Delaware and Advancement of Mathematical Education, Inc., Newark, Delaware

CONTENTS

1 Introduction to Algebra

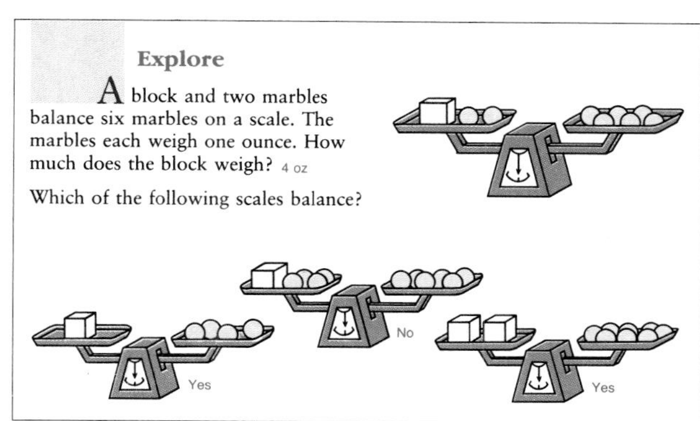

Key concepts begin with an Explore activity to promote student involvement. Suggestions for using cooperative groups are given in the Teacher's Edition.

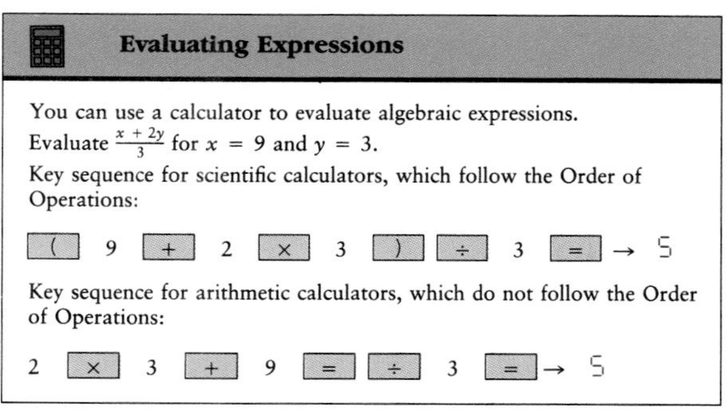

Calculator instruction is provided where the emphasis is on algebraic concepts and skills rather than arithmetic proficiency.

2 Integers and Rational Numbers

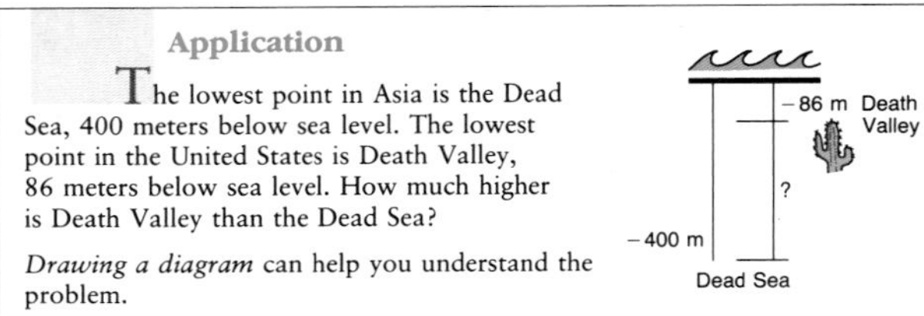

Application

The lowest point in Asia is the Dead Sea, 400 meters below sea level. The lowest point in the United States is Death Valley, 86 meters below sea level. How much higher is Death Valley than the Dead Sea?

Drawing a diagram can help you understand the problem.

Problem Solving begins in Chapter 1 and continues to be a major thrust of the instruction, using a variety of problem-solving strategies.

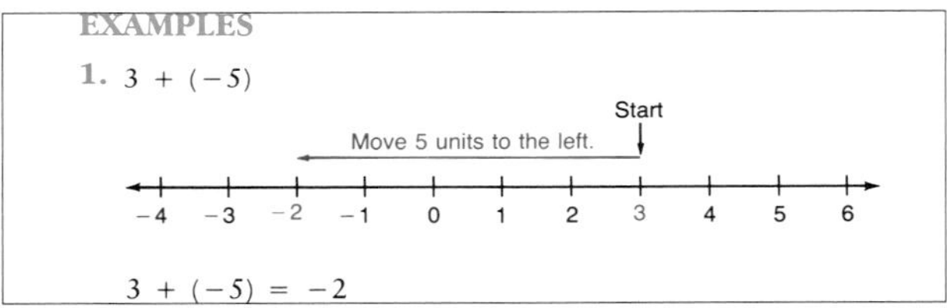

EXAMPLES

1. $3 + (-5)$

$3 + (-5) = -2$

First Pile

ⓎⓎⓎⓎ
ⓎⓎⓎⓎ

Second Pile

ⓇⓇⓇⓇ

First Pile	Second Pile	Combined Pile	Equation
8	−4	4	$8+(-4)=4$

Concepts are developed visually, with many opportunities for hands-on development provided in the Teacher's Edition or in supplemental materials.

3 Equations

Explore

The scales at the right are balanced. Suppose you have as many of each object as you want. What are five different ways you can add objects to both sides of the scale below so it remains balanced?

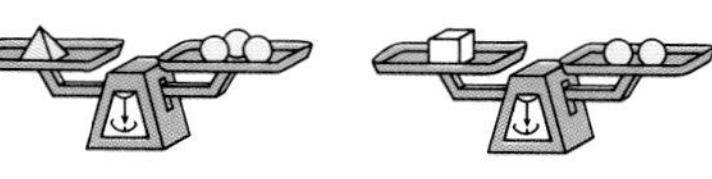

Students are encouraged to try out new concepts in groups before the lesson begins.

Application

A conservationist estimates that there are about 12 times as many deer north of a river as there are south of the river. The last count indicates that there are about 1440 deer north of the river. About how many deer are south of the river?

In this lesson you will learn how to solve equations like $12s = 1440$. This equation can be used to find out how many deer there are south of the river.

All chapters and many lessons are motivated by real-world situations.

4 Inequalities

43. ***Critical Thinking*** Give two different inequalities that each have $x \leq -5$ as a statement of all solutions.

Every exercise set includes a Critical Thinking problem, which is designed to expand students' thinking.

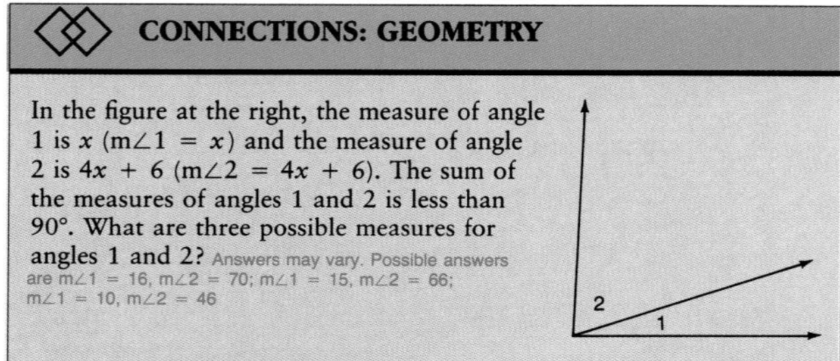

CONNECTIONS: GEOMETRY

In the figure at the right, the measure of angle 1 is x ($m\angle 1 = x$) and the measure of angle 2 is $4x + 6$ ($m\angle 2 = 4x + 6$). The sum of the measures of angles 1 and 2 is less than 90°. What are three possible measures for angles 1 and 2? Answers may vary. Possible answers are $m\angle 1 = 16$, $m\angle 2 = 70$; $m\angle 1 = 15$, $m\angle 2 = 66$; $m\angle 1 = 10$, $m\angle 2 = 46$

Mathematical connections, including connections to discrete math, are noted throughout the book by ◇◇.

5 Exponents and Polynomials

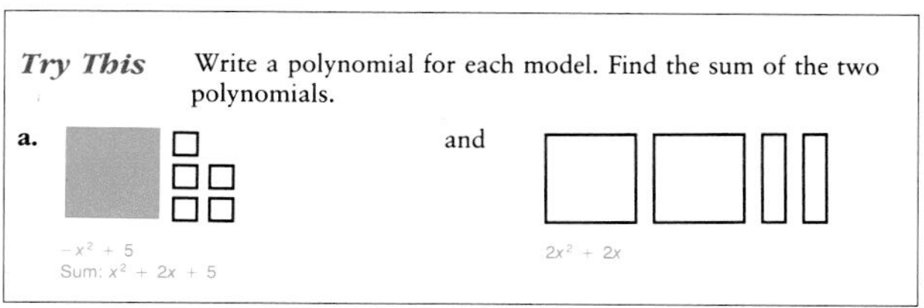

Concepts are developed visually, with opportunities for hands-on development.

6. ***Write a Convincing Argument*** Solve the problem below. Then write an argument that would convince a classmate that your solution is correct.

John was hired by a painter to paint doors. He was paid \$10 for each door that he completed that did not need repainting by the painter. For each door that needed to be redone, he was fined \$5. On a bad day, he painted 25 doors, but made a total of only \$10. How many doors did he paint that did not need to be repainted?

Students are often asked to Write a Convincing Argument.

6 Polynomials and Factoring

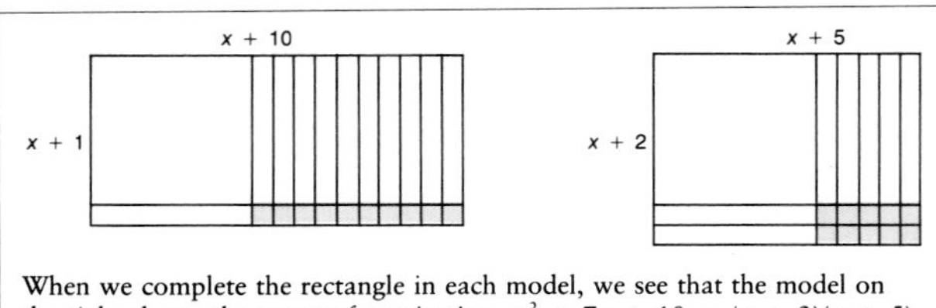

When we complete the rectangle in each model, we see that the model on the right shows the correct factorization: $x^2 + 7x + 10 = (x + 2)(x + 5)$.

Visuals are used to relate factoring to multiplying. Supplemental materials also provide hands-on experiences.

EXAMPLE 2

$0.74^2 - 0.73^2 =$
(A) 0.00147 (B) 0.0147 (C) 0.147 (D) 14.70 (E) 147.0

If we factor, we can do the arithmetic mentally.

$$\begin{aligned} 0.74^2 - 0.73^2 &= (0.74 + 0.73)(0.74 - 0.73) \\ &= (1.47)(0.01) \\ &= 0.0147 \end{aligned}$$

Factoring in Example 2 makes the computation much simpler.

Techniques, such as looking for patterns, are used to simplify problems found on standardized tests.

7 Graphs and Linear Equations

EXAMPLE Graph the equations $y = x$, $y = 2x$, $y = 3x$, and $y = 4x$ on the same axes.

- Press the [Y=] key.
- Enter Y1 = x, Y2 = $2x$, Y3 = $3x$, Y4 = $4x$ — Use the [X|T] key for x. Press [ENTER] to move the cursor to the next line.
- Press [GRAPH] and the graphs will be drawn one at a time from Y1 to Y4.

If you make an error you can use the arrow keys [◀], [▲], [▶], or [▼] to move to the error, and the insert [INS] and delete [DEL] keys as on a word processor. The [CLEAR] key can be used to blank a whole line.

Try This Graph $y = x$, $y = x + 1$, $y = x + 2$, and $y = x + 3$ on the same axes.

Opportunities for investigations using graphing utilities are provided.

We will number the Olympic Games from 1 to 10, with 1952 being number 1. We can change the winning times to seconds in order to make plotting the points easier. 3:45.2 becomes 225 s rounded to the nearest second, and so on. When all the times are converted to seconds, we plot each ordered pair (o, t) and draw a line so that there are about the same number of points above and below the line. This is called the line of best fit.

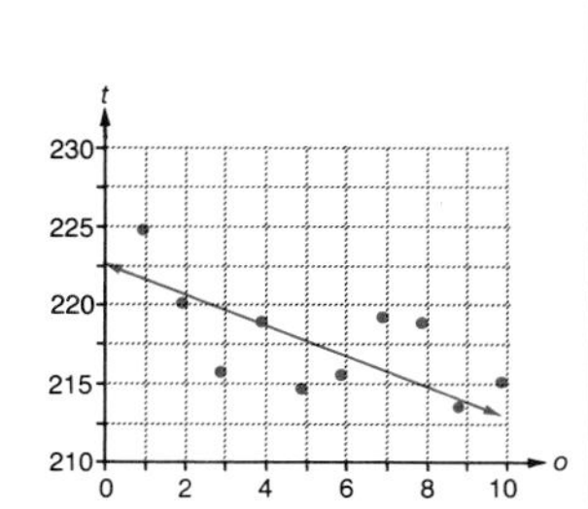

Finding the line of best fit for data is the goal of this chapter. Students learn to use the equation of the line to make predictions.

8 Systems of Equations

32. Estimate the solutions to the system of equations below by studying the graph at the right. Check your solutions using substitution in both equations.
(0, 1), (2, 1)

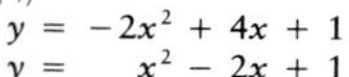

$y = -2x^2 + 4x + 1$
$y = x^2 - 2x + 1$

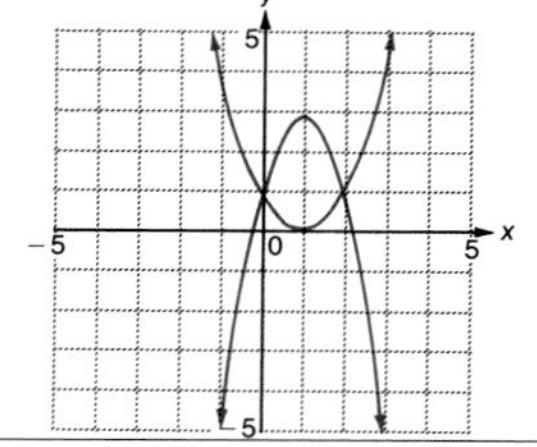

By solving systems of equations first graphically, students can visualize the solutions.

9 Inequalities and Absolute Value

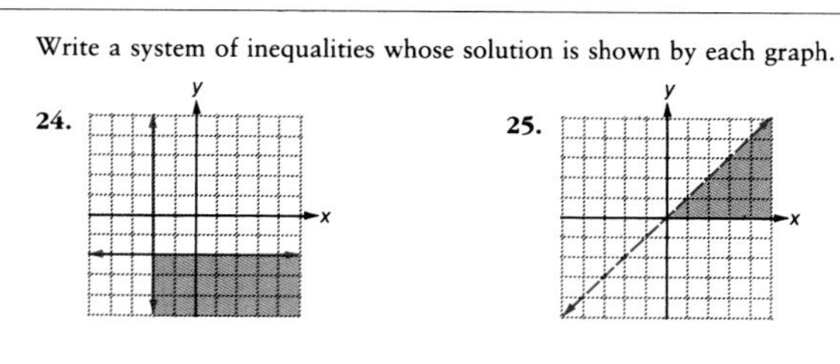

Write a system of inequalities whose solution is shown by each graph.

24.

25.

28. ***Critical Thinking*** Write a system of inequalities such that the graph of its solution forms a square region with one corner at the origin and two adjacent sides on the x- and y-axis.

Every exercise set has problems developed to stimulate thinking including a Critical Thinking Problem.

10 Rational Expressions and Equations

Explore

Geometric patterns that use repeated shapes to cover the plane without gaps or overlaps are called tessellations. Regular polygons are figures whose sides have the same length. Tessellations made up of regular polygons are often used in architecture. Not all regular polygons tessellate the plane.

Real-world situations are provided, and the relationship between the tessellation of an n-sided polygon and the rational expression $\frac{2n}{n^2}$ *is explored.*

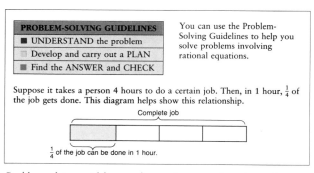

PROBLEM-SOLVING GUIDELINES
■ UNDERSTAND the problem
■ Develop and carry out a PLAN
■ Find the ANSWER and CHECK

You can use the Problem-Solving Guidelines to help you solve problems involving rational equations.

Suppose it takes a person 4 hours to do a certain job. Then, in 1 hour, $\frac{1}{4}$ of the job gets done. This diagram helps show this relationship.

Complete job

$\frac{1}{4}$ of the job can be done in 1 hour.

Problem-solving guidelines and strategies are used continuously throughout the book to reinforce problem-solving techniques.

11 Radical Expressions and Equations

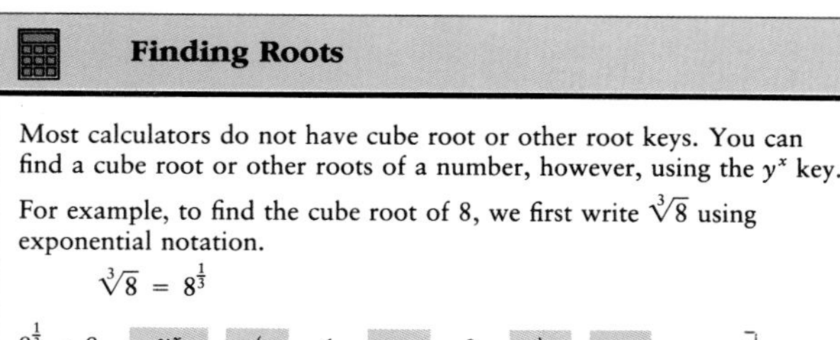
Finding Roots

Most calculators do not have cube root or other root keys. You can find a cube root or other roots of a number, however, using the y^x key.

For example, to find the cube root of 8, we first write $\sqrt[3]{8}$ using exponential notation.

$$\sqrt[3]{8} = 8^{\frac{1}{3}}$$

$8^{\frac{1}{3}} \rightarrow$ 8 [y^x] [( ] 1 [÷] 3 [ )] [=] $\rightarrow$ 2

Calculator use is stressed in this chapter, and the relationship between cube root and one-third power is a nice extension.

Injury Severity Score

Doctors in hospital emergency rooms must decide the order in which patients should be treated. Obviously, patients with the most serious injuries should be treated before those with less serious injuries. How do doctors determine the severity of an injury? Several scoring systems have been devised, the Injury Severity Score (ISS) among them. In the ISS system, each injury is assigned a severity code ranging from 1, for minor injuries, to 6, for injuries that are life-threatening. The ISS also assigns six body regions the letters A through F:

The Injury Severity Application is one of many fully-developed applications that are currently being used in industry.

12 Relations and Functions

The graph at the right shows the functions $f(x) = |2x|$ and $f(x) = |x| + 1$.

4. Graph these functions using a computer or graph paper.
   a. $f(x) = |-3x|$
   b. $f(x) = |5x|$
   c. $f(x) = |x| - 1$
   d. $f(x) = |x| + 2$
5. How are the graphs of $f(x) = |x|$ and $f(x) = |ax|$ related?
6. How are the graphs of $f(x) = |x|$ and $f(x) = |x| + c$ related?

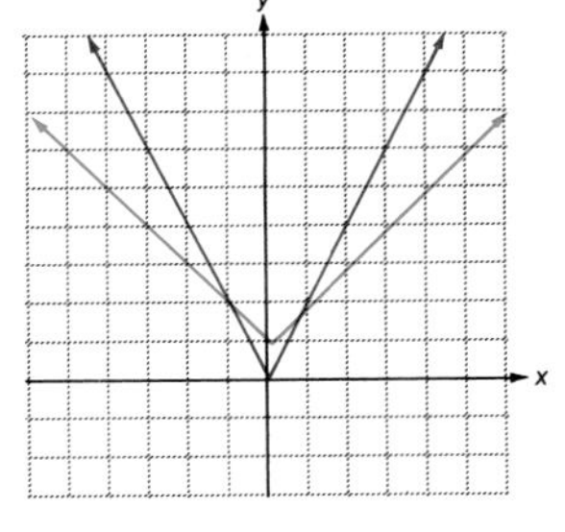

A variety of functions are presented in this chapter, and more complex functions are explored using graphing utilities.

Interval Graphs

In Chapter 7 you learned how to graph data using the Cartesian coordinate system. There are many other ways to represent data using graphs. One kind of graph, called an **interval graph,** can be used to solve problems involving the intersection of various time intervals. Interval graphs are just a collection of points, called **vertices,** and line segments, called **edges,** connecting some of the vertices.

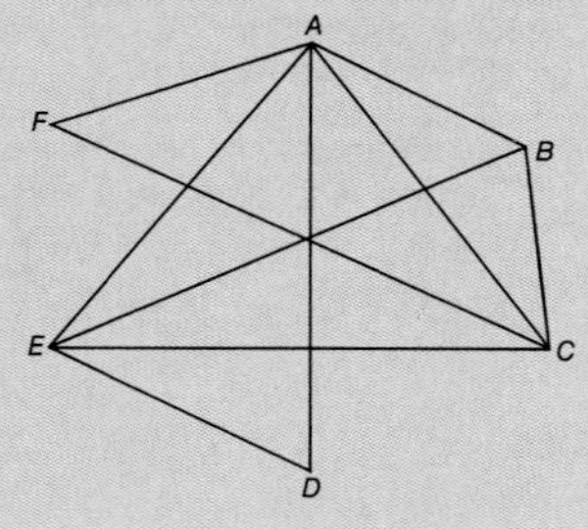

The discrete math topic, Interval Graphs, is introduced in this chapter.

13 Quadratic Equations

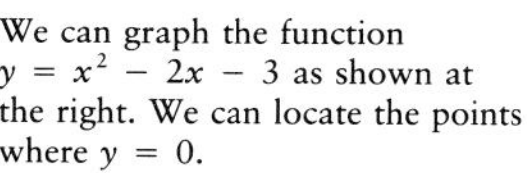
We can graph the function $y = x^2 - 2x - 3$ as shown at the right. We can locate the points where $y = 0$.

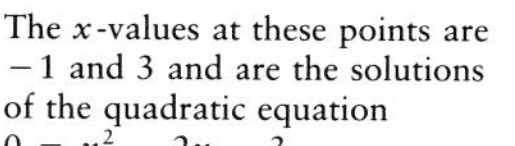
The x-values at these points are -1 and 3 and are the solutions of the quadratic equation $0 = x^2 - 2x - 3$.

Transparency 28 (*T28*) can be used with this illustration.

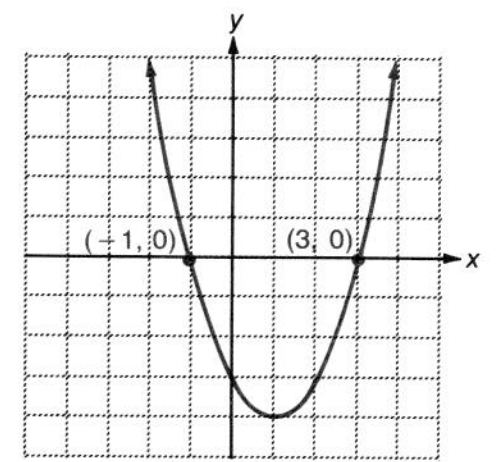

The solutions of a quadratic equation are introduced as the x-intercepts of the related quadratic function, rather than as a brand new topic.

TI–81 INVESTIGATION 3

Investigate

1. Enter the equation $y = x^2 - 2x - 8$, and view its graph. Then answer the following questions.
   - **a.** Factor the equation. What relationship do you observe between the factors and the graph of the equation?
   - **b.** What is the value of the y-coordinate where the graph of the quadratic equation crosses the x-axis?
   - **c.** What equation did you solve when you found the x-intercept?

Use of graphing utilities reinforces the relationship between equations and functions.

14 Trigonometry

Calculator Investigation

Find $(\sin R)^2$ and $(\cos R)^2$ for the triangle at the right.

1. What do you notice about the sum of these values?
2. Test other triangles to see if this relationship seems to be true for any acute angle in a right triangle.

S 1.5 T
3.22 3.55
R

The use of calculators are encouraged in this chapter to find the trigonometric values as well as to investigate the ratios.

Situational Problem

A rectangular lot, 375 ft by 500 ft, has been donated to your city to be used as a park. The park is to have one tennis court, a softball field, and at least one picnic area. Volunteers will build the park, but materials must be purchased. Your job is to suggest a layout for the park, make a scale drawing of the park, and propose a budget for the project.

Situational Problem Solving, in the last three chapters, is a culmination of all the problem-solving activities in the book, providing open-ended projects.

15 Introduction to Probability and Statistics

This chapter can be taught in its entirety any time after Chapter 7. You may also teach it in four sections throughout the year. Management guides are provided in the Teacher's Edition for both plans.

Obtain a 3×5 file card and fold it in half widthwise. Toss the folded card 100 times and determine experimental probabilities for the card falling "flat," "on edge," or "as a tent." Answers may vary.

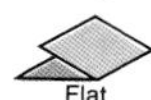

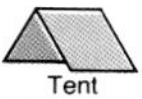

Experimental probability is explored, as well as theoretical probability.

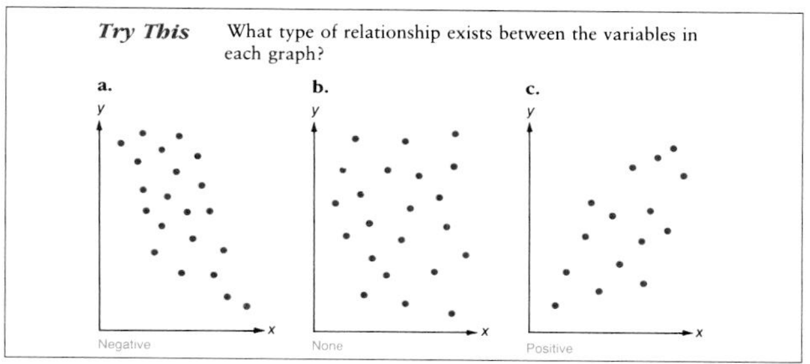

A variety of ways to present data is examined, including scatter plots, frequency distributions, stem-and-leaf diagrams, line plots, histograms, and frequency polygons.

TI-81 INVESTIGATION 5

An Introduction to Matrices

(for use with Chapter 15)

Objectives: Understand the meaning of a matrix; identify the dimensions of a matrix; solve problems by adding matrices.

Real-world data such as that shown in the chart at the right can be shown using a matrix. A matrix is a rectangular array of numbers.

Here is how the data for one company's sales of athletic shoes in the U.S. can be shown using a matrix. Notice that brackets are used to indicate a matrix.

$$\begin{bmatrix} 4.2 & 12.7 & 6.3 & 8.6 \\ 5.3 & 11.2 & 7.5 & 8.6 \\ 5.2 & 15.8 & 6.4 & 7.5 \\ 4.9 & 9.4 & 5.5 & 6.9 \end{bmatrix}$$

The number of rows and columns in a matrix determine the dimensions of the matrix. For the matrix

ATHLETIC SHOE SALES				
U.S. Sales (million $)				
Quarter	Tennis	Basket-ball	Running	Walking
1st	4.2	12.7	6.3	8.6
2nd	5.3	11.2	7.5	8.6
3rd	5.2	15.8	6.4	7.5
4th	4.9	9.4	5.5	6.9

Foreign Sales (million $)				
Quarter	Tennis	Basket-ball	Running	Walking
1st	5.6	6.4	4.2	6.2
2nd	6.1	5.8	3.1	6.2
3rd	5.9	4.6	2.7	5.9
4th	5.1	5.1	3.6	6.0

The TI-81 Investigation Appendix includes: An Introduction to Matrices and Matrix Multiplication

Addison-Wesley *meets all of your Algebra needs*

Algebra for Everyone

- An instant, lesson-correlated resource of review and reinforcement, games, cooperative activities, and assessment tools designed to raise your and your students' expectations for success in algebra.
- Includes life-skill applications, multicultural experiences, Spanish summary and review, and two-year assignment guide.
- All-in-one binder accompanies

Overhead Transparencies

Crisp and accurate, they display chalkboard examples and problem strategies. Engages visual learning, lets you maintain eye contact with students.

Multiculturalism in Mathematics, Science, and Technology

Celebrate diversity as you deepen understanding and motivate students from all backgrounds with this imaginative collection of activities.

MathTest Software

Generates tests, worksheets, and problems for assessment or cooperative learning. Programmed algorithms create an unlimited number of problems in any combination as well as answer keys. Frees you to work with students. Easy to use on IBM, Apple, or Mac. Mac users select from nonroutine questions and alternative assessment items, too.

Solutions Manual

Solutions to every exercise, parameters for every open question posed in the text, graphic solutions.

Master Grapher

An interactive graphing utility for IBM, Apple II, or Mac.

Investigative Activities for Master Grapher includes student worksheets with keystrokes and menu choices for self-guidance. Use teacher demonstration lessons with your LCD projection panel to step up the pace of learning.

Teacher's Resource Packages

Your deep-pocket resource for management and instruction comes to you as a set of eleven supplements, each addressing a different daily teaching challenge.

Four management aids support you from student placement to final evaluation.

Management and Teaching Tools

Includes record-keeping aids, student resources, and two-year assignment guide.

Lesson Plan Book

Detailed one-page lesson plans with objectives and NCTM Standards correlations.

First Five Minutes Transparency Masters

Fast class starters from the FIRST FIVE MINUTES feature in your Teacher's Edition.

Assessment

Quizzes and cumulative tests, choice of levels for chapter tests, placement and problem-solving assessment tools.

Seven instruction supplements provide a treasury of help, motivation, and creative stimulus for every student in your class.

Skills Practice and Mixed Review

Includes arithmetic and geometry review as well as lesson-correlated practice.

Problem Bank

Includes strategy problem banks and college entrance exam problems.

Enrichment

Bonus topics for *all* students. Includes critical thinking, error recognition, probability, and work with manipulatives.

Active Learning

Includes guided activities and follow-up for constructivist learning.

Technology

Calculator and spreadsheet activities; BASIC computer projects.

Investigative Activities for the TI-81 Calculator (with Teacher's Guide)

Meet the standards—yours and NCTM's—with interactive graphing explorations.

SAT Practice

For use with 1993 PSAT and 1994 SAT, includes "grid-in" practice.

Addison-Wesley Algebra's clear, consistent lesson structure

BEFORE THE CHAPTER . . .

Chapter Openers The chapter begins with an application that is solved later as an example or on a problem-solving application page.

Ready For A pretest helps identify which lessons students need to review.

DURING THE CHAPTER . . .

Lesson Openers

Explore, Application, or Math History openers offer a context for the presentation of algebraic concepts.

Objective

The objective for each section appears on the student page.

Examples

Student understanding is enhanced by fully worked examples.

Try This Exercises

Following the examples, the Try This exercises provide students with immediate reinforcement of concepts and skills and help teachers diagnose student difficulties.

7-8 Parallel and Perpendicular Lines

Master Grapher Worksheet 5 can be used with this lesson.

Explore

Graph the following equations on the same set of axes.

$y = 2x \qquad y = 2x + 3 \qquad y = 2x - 1$

$y = -\frac{1}{2}x \qquad y = -\frac{1}{2}x + 3 \qquad y = -\frac{1}{2}x - 1$

What patterns do you see?

Parallel Lines

Objective: Determine whether the graphs of two equations are parallel.

Parallel lines are lines in the same plane that never intersect. Nonvertical lines are *parallel* if they have the same slope and different y-intercepts.

The graphs at the right are for the linear equations $y = 2x + 5$ and $y = 2x - 3$. The slope of each line is 2. The coordinates of the y-intercepts are 5 and -3. The lines are parallel.

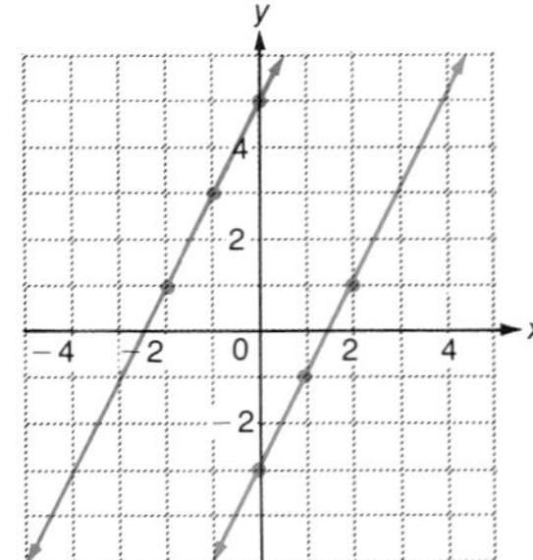

EXAMPLE 1 Determine whether the graphs of $y = -3x + 4$ and $6x + 2y = -10$ are parallel lines.

We first solve each equation for y.

$$y = -3x + 4 \qquad 6x + 2y = -10$$
$$2y = -6x - 10$$
$$y = -3x - 5$$

The graphs of these lines have the same slope and different y-intercepts. Thus the lines are parallel.

Try This Determine whether the graphs are parallel lines.

a. $3x - y = -5$ and $5y - 15x = 10$ Yes

b. $4y = -12x + 16$ and $y = 3x + 4$ No

makes rigorous content accessible to every student

A Exercises

Students can use the A exercises to reinforce their understanding of the lesson.

B Exercises

By using the B exercises, students discover connections and integrate their understanding of concepts.

9-3 EXERCISES

A

Solve.

1. $|x + 9| = 18$
2. $|x - 4| = 9$
3. $|x + 11| = 6$
4. $|m - 7| = 23$
5. $|x - 10| = -8$
6. $|x + 17| = 2$
7. $|2x - 4| = 6$
8. $|4b - 11| = 5$
9. $|7x - 2| = 5$
10. $|8x + 3| = -27$
11. $|5x - 9| = 1$
12. $|4x + 3| = 67$
13. $|2r - 1| = \frac{1}{4}$
14. $|4x + 3| = -5$
15. $|3x + 1| = 0.5$
16. $|5y + 8| = \frac{1}{2}$
17. $|2y - 6| = -9$
18. $\left|\frac{1}{3}x - 9\right| = 10$
19. $|0.2x + 1| = 0.8$
20. $|4.2x - 1.4| = 7$
21. $|5x + 0.2| = 1.2$

B

Solve.

22. $|2x + 5| - 9 = 12$
23. $|3y - 2| + 4 = 21$
24. $|2 - a| - 3 = 1$
25. $8 - |1 - y| = 7$
26. $3|y + 6| = 6$
27. $4|t + 3| = 16$
28. $8 + |2c - 1| = 4$
29. $3|b - 2| + 7 = 10$
30. $4|3 - z| - 8 = 8$
31. $10 + |5x + 2| = 7$
32. $6 - |3y - 2| = 10$
33. $-|x + 1| = -2$
34. *Critical Thinking* Make one change in the equation $|x + 3| = 5$ so that the solution set of the new equation is $\{0, -6\}$.

Challenge

Solve.

35. $|x - 4| = x - 4$
36. $|3x| = |4x - 1|$
37. $|2y| = |3y + 2| + 1$

Mixed Review

Find the slope and y-intercept of each line.

38. $x - 2y = 1$
39. $-4x - y = 7$
40. $3x = y - 4$
41. $5y + 4 = 2x - 1$
42. $3x - 5 = -4y + 7$

Factor. 43. $2x^3 - 4x^2 - 6x$ 44. $2y^2 - 9y + 4$ 45. $9a^2 - 4$

Solve. 46. $3y + 4x = -5$, $x = y + 4$ 47. $2x + y = -2$, $y - x = -5$ 48. $3x - y = 2$, $2x + y = 3$

Solve. 49. $(m + 2)(m - 1) = 0$ 50. $a(2a + 6)(a - 5) = 0$

51. Ray is 42 years old. Eight years ago, Ray was twice as old as Roy. How old is Roy today?

Critical Thinking or Write a Convincing Argument Problems

These problems provide students with opportunities to develop thinking skills and to express these skills in their own words.

Challenge Exercises

Challenge exercises motivate students to use their acquired knowledge creatively.

Mixed Review

Through daily review of the basic course material, students maintain their previously learned skills.

AFTER THE CHAPTER . . .

Chapter Summary and Review
A summary of each lesson including vocabulary is combined with its own review exercises. This unique format provides students with ideal test preparation.

Chapter Test Problems in the Chapter Test parallel those in the Chapter Summary and Review, so students can test themselves after reviewing.

Addison-Wesley Algebra Teacher's Edition provides

BEFORE THE CHAPTER . . .
Four special chapter planning guide pages provide for planning, assignment, and assessment.

Chapter Overview Provides a quick summary of the chapter's content.
Chapter Objectives List all objectives for the chapter.
Teaching Guide Provides suggestions for cooperative learning, alternative assessment, and communication ideas for each chapter. A multicultural note and possible investigations or projects are also included.
Multi-Level Management Guide Helps teachers adjust plans appropriately for different level classes. The guides include suggestions for planning each lesson and utilize all of the supplementary materials.

DURING THE CHAPTER . . .

Essential Elements

The Essential Elements are keyed to appropriate lessons.

First Five Minutes

To start every lesson, there is a quick review of skills needed for the day.

Teaching Notes

Notes and suggestions are provided to help teach every objective.

References to Technology Ancillary Materials

Math Point

This feature contains useful background information for perspective and anecdotes for human interest.

Key Questions

The key questions can be used to stimulate class discussion and promote discovery of concepts.

5-4

FIRST FIVE MINUTES

Calculate as a decimal number.
1. 10^6
   1,000,000
2. 321×1000000
   321,000,000
3. 0.0002×3000
   0.6

Simplify. Express using exponents.

4. $10^5 \cdot 10^2$
   10^7
5. $10^7 \cdot 10^{-4} \cdot 10^2$
   10^5
6. 1,000,000,000,000
   10^{12}
7. 0.1
   10^{-1}

APPLICATION

The North Star is also known as the *Pole Star* (or *Polaris*) because it is almost directly over the North Pole. Navigators have used it for thousands of years. Because of slight changes in the rotation of the earth, it will be over the pole for only a few hundred more years. Then, after about 26,000 years, it will once again be the Pole Star.

A number is in standard notation if it is expressed as a single factor, such as 34.765. A number such as 12.3×10^2 is in neither standard notation nor scientific notation.

See Computer Exploration 3 on p. 717 for the use of Scientific Notation on a computer.

Math Point
The number 10^{100} is called a *googol.* It was named by a young nephew of the American mathematician Edward Kasner. The number 10 to the googol power is called a *googolplex* and can be written $10^{10^{100}}$.

Key Questions

- Is 12.34×10^2 in scientific notation?
  No. 12.34 is not between 1 and 10.
- Is 0.237×10^3 in scientific notation?
  No. 0.237 is not between 1 and 10.
- Is 3.18×3^{10} in scientific notation?
  No. 3^{10} is not a power of ten.

5-4 Scientific Notation

Objective: Write numbers using scientific notation.

Application

The distance from Earth to the North Star is about 10,000,000,000,000,000,000 meters. The thickness of a soap bubble is about 0.0000001 meter. It is easy to make errors when working with numbers involving many zeros. If an extra zero is included, the resulting number is ten times larger or ten times smaller.

To prevent this type of error and to make it easier to work with very large and very small numbers, we can write these numbers in a form called **scientific notation.** Using scientific notation we can write a number as the product of a power of 10 and a number greater than or equal to 1, but less than 10. In scientific notation, the distance to the North Star is 1.0×10^{19} and the thickness of a soap bubble is about 1.0×10^{-6}. The numbers 10,000,000,000,000,000,000 and 0.0000001 are expressed using **standard notation.**

EXAMPLES

1. Write 4.58×10^4 using standard notation.

$4.58 \times 10^4 = 45,800$ — Multiplying 4.58 by 10^4, or 10,000, moves the decimal point 4 places to the right.

2. Write 3.4×10^{-2} using standard notation.

$$3.4 \times 10^{-2} = 3.4 \times \frac{1}{10^2} = \frac{3.4}{100} = 0.034$$

Multiplying by 10^{-2} is the same as dividing by 10^2, or 100, and moves the decimal point 2 places to the left.

Try This Write using standard notation.

a. 1.25×10^3 **b.** 7×10^5 **c.** 4.8×10^{-3}

tools for heightening teachers' effectiveness

Answers

Teacher's Edition answers are printed in blue.

Try This Solve.

e. $x^2 - x - 6 = 0$ 3, −2 **f.** $m^2 - m = 56$ 8, −7 **g.** $x^2 - 3x = 28$ 7, −4

EXAMPLES Solve.

4. $x^2 - 8x + 16 = 0$
$(x - 4)(x - 4) = 0$ Factoring the square of a binomial
$x - 4 = 0$ or $x - 4 = 0$
$x = 4$ or $x = 4$

Check: $x^2 - 8x + 16 = 0$

$4^2 - 8 \cdot 4 + 16$	0
$16 - 32 + 16$	0
0	0 ✓

There is only one solution, 4.

5. $x^2 = 5x$
$x^2 - 5x = 0$ Getting 0 on one side
$x(x - 5) = 0$ Factoring
$x = 0$ or $x - 5 = 0$
$x = 0$ or $x = 5$

Check: $x^2 = 5x$

0^2	$5 \cdot 0$
0	0 ✓

$x^2 = 5x$

5^2	$5 \cdot 5$
25	25 ✓

The solutions are 0 and 5.

6. $4x^2 = 25$
$4x^2 - 25 = 0$
$(2x - 5)(2x + 5) = 0$ Factoring a difference of two squares
$2x - 5 = 0$ or $2x + 5 = 0$
$2x = 5$ or $2x = -5$
$x = \frac{5}{2}$ or $x = -\frac{5}{2}$

Check: $4x^2 = 25$

$4\left(\frac{5}{2}\right)^2$	25
$4 \cdot \frac{25}{4}$	25
25	25 ✓

$4x^2 = 25$

$4\left(-\frac{5}{2}\right)^2$	25
$4 \cdot \frac{25}{4}$	25
25	25 ✓

The solutions are $\frac{5}{2}$ and $-\frac{5}{2}$.

Try This Solve.

h. $x^2 + 9 = 6x$ 3 **i.** $x^2 = 4x$ 0, 4 **j.** $25x^2 = 16$ $\frac{4}{5}, -\frac{4}{5}$

Avoiding Common Errors

Students may incorrectly apply the principle of zero products to products other than zero. Remind students that if the product of two factors is 12, for example, there are many pairs of numbers whose product is 12.

$3 \times 4 = 12$, $2 \times 6 = 12$, $\frac{1}{2} \times 24 = 12$, $\frac{1}{4} \times 48 = 12$, and so on.

Chalkboard Examples

1. Solve $x^2 + 7x + 12 = 0$.
Factor.
$(x + 3)(x + 4) = 0$
$x + 3 = 0$ or $x + 4 = 0$
$x = -3$ or $x = -4$
2. Solve $x^2 = -3x - 2$.
$x^2 + 3x + 2 = 0$
Factor.
$(x + 1)(x + 2) = 0$
$x + 1 = 0$ or $x + 2 = 0$
$x = -1$ or $x = -2$

LESSON ENRICHMENT

Here is a nonstandard method for finding the solution to a second-degree equation. Solve $x^2 - x - 1 = 0$. Rewrite the equation as

$$x^2 = x + 1$$

Divide both sides by x, if x is not 0.

$$x = 1 + \frac{1}{x}$$

We have solved for x in terms of x. Substitute for x in the denominator.

$$x = 1 + \frac{1}{1 + \frac{1}{x}}$$

We can substitute again, and again.

$$x = 1 + \frac{1}{1 + \frac{1}{1 + \frac{1}{1 + \ldots}}}$$

Calculate the expression shown above. Does it give an approximate solution to the equation? Yes

LESSON QUIZ

Solve.
1. $(x - 3)(x + 5) = 0$
$x = 3$ or $x = -5$
2. $(2x - 1)x = 0$
$x = \frac{1}{2}$ or $x = 0$
3. $x^2 + 4x + 3 = 0$

Avoiding Common Errors

By using these suggestions, teachers can guide students to avoid error patterns.

Chalkboard Examples

These additional examples are accompanied by worked-out answers.

Lesson Enrichment

This feature provides suggestions for extending the lesson.

Lesson Quiz

Teachers can use the quiz supplied at the end of every lesson as a quick assessment tool.

Cooperative Learning Groups

Benefits of Cooperative Learning

Students benefit in several ways from small group instruction. Progress and success are the responsibility of the group, so an individual is less likely to be frozen by anxiety about "getting the right answer." Group work also demonstrates that there is more than one way to solve a problem—one of the more important ideas students can learn.

Setting up Cooperative Learning Groups

To set up cooperative learning groups, you should first determine group size and make-up. If your students are not experienced with cooperative learning groups, you may want to begin with groups of two students. Most teachers find the optimum group size to be three or four. You should allow a group at least three sessions before making a change.

Before the first group lesson, post a set of cooperative learning rules in the room and discuss them with the class. Consistently enforce and reinforce these rules. Some possible rules are:

1. All students must participate.
2. Each group member must be willing to help any other member.
3. Show respect for one another; criticize ideas, not people.
4. Ask the teacher for help only if every member of the group has the same question.
5. Do not talk to other groups.
6. Everyone in the group must agree on the answer.

Student's Role in Cooperative Learning Groups

Each student in a group should have a designated task. Tasks can include spokesperson or reporter, writer or recorder, checker, technology person, time keeper, and others as needed. Tasks can change daily or weekly, but students should get an opportunity to routinely do every task.

Teacher's Role in Cooperative Learning Groups

When students are working in small groups, the teacher can serve as a coach. Circulate through the room, listening to group discussions and interact as needed. Observe whether all students are involved, and question those who appear to be passive.

If an entire group appears to be struggling, ask the spokesperson what the group is discussing and what is giving difficulty. Ask questions that refocus the students' attention. A question can make students discern a weak point in their approach, recognize misinterpreted information, or evaluate the reasonableness of an assumption or answer.

Using Cooperative Learning Groups with *AW Algebra*

A. Review
   1. Use the **First Five Minutes** for a review of skills needed for the day's lesson.
   2. Have students work in groups and compare their homework answers to determine errors. The **Selected Answers** can be used if the group cannot agree on an answer for an odd-numbered problem. The group should agree on one answer.
   3. Ask one member from each group to present "common errors" found in each group. Use the suggestions given in **Avoiding Common Errors** to insure understanding of the material.

B. Motivation and Development of Lesson
   1. Use the *application* presented on the opening page of each chapter to motivate topics in the chapter. Use **Explore, Math History,** and **Application** to motivate specific lessons. Exploration activities may be completed independently or with students working in small groups. Some of the **Explore** activities involve graphing and may be completed with the help of a computer or graphing calculator. Discuss the conclusions reached by the students.
   2. Focus on promoting student understanding using the suggestions found with each subsection. Use the **Key Questions** to promote student involvement. Use **Investigative Activities** to demonstrate graphing concepts.

C. Seatwork
   1. Ask student groups to work the **Try This** exercises. Have students compare answers within the group, give help where needed, and agree on an answer and method.
   2. Choose one group to present the **Try This** exercises to the class.
   3. The **Lesson Quiz** can be used to assess understanding of the day's lesson, and a bonus may be assigned to the group with the highest average score.

D. Homework Assignments
   1. Assign both reading and written assignments. Students should always read the lesson covered.
   2. The **Assignment Guide** gives suggested written assignments for three levels of classes. Writing the assignment on the chalkboard in the same place every day is an effective way to assure that an assignment is not overlooked.
   3. **Critical Thinking** exercises should be assigned whenever possible to give students the opportunity to reverse their thinking, to apply multiple skills, to analyze and synthesize, to evaluate, and to create. These exercises should be thoroughly discussed as there may be a variety of correct answers. The answers for the **Critical Thinking** exercises are never included in the student **Selected Answer** section.
   4. **Mixed Review** *exercises* should be assigned every day. They are found at the end of every lesson. In addition **Mixed Review** *worksheets* can be found in the supplemental package when further review is necessary.

Teaching Problem Solving

Developing a Positive Classroom Atmosphere

The teacher's role in creating an atmosphere conducive to successful problem solving cannot be overemphasized. Your actions affect the classroom atmosphere in several ways. First, your attitude toward problem solving will affect your students' attitudes. If you demonstrate that problem solving is not only important but also exciting and fun, students are likely to develop similar attitudes. Your own beliefs are crucial; here are some ways to convey them.

- Join enthusiastically in the problem-solving experience, exploring problems along with your students. "Think aloud" as you examine and solve, and encourage students to do the same.
- Create problems based on your students' own situations to demonstrate that problem solving is an ongoing, everyday experience.
- Encourage students to write problems themselves.
- Personalize problems from the book whenever possible (use students' names and familiar locations, for example).
- Discuss interesting inventions and games as examples of problem solving in real life.

Active Involvement

Research has shown that successful problem solvers have active involvement with problems; those who remain passive will not develop their problem-solving skills. Show that you value each student's contribution, even when his or her skills still need development. Your comments can help elicit and promote desirable problem-solving habits.

- Recognize and reinforce willingness and perseverance.
- Reward risk-takers.
- Encourage students to play hunches.
- Accept unusual solutions.
- Emphasize persistence and creativity rather than speed.
- Have students analyze their solutions; show that verification and interpretation are part of the answer process.

Evaluating Problem-Solving Performance

Problem-solving experiences provide for alternative assessment if evaluation involves the process in addition to the answer.

- Ask students to write an explanation, as well as a complete solution, for each problem situation describing why he or she thinks that this is the correct way to solve the problem. Students can keep these in a journal.
- Observe each student in a class as he or she solves problems in a whole-class setting.

A scheme for analyzing a student's problem-solving performance is provided in the **Management and Teaching Tools** supplement.

Teaching with Technology

Calculator

Students should be encouraged to use calculators when the emphasis is on algebraic concepts and skills rather than arithmetic proficiency.* The calculator boxes give simple instructions that will work on most calculators. If your students are using many different calculators, you may want to spend a day having students familiarize themselves with their calculators. The first *Calculator Worksheet* in the **Technology** supplement provides a format for "learning about your calculator." The other *Calculator Worksheets* provide additional practice using each key introduced in the book.

Graphing Calculator

Graphing calculator investigations are provided in the appendix as well in the supplement **Investigative Activities for the TI-81 Calculator**. These investigations provide opportunities for the student to investigate algebraic concepts and perceive spatial relationships of these concepts.

Through the use of the graphing calculator, students are also introduced to matrices and statistical analysis. The graphing calculator is used as a tool for learning and enhancing understanding, and is never used as simply an alternative for doing the exercises.

Computer Graphing Utility

Master Grapher is an interactive graphing software package, available for Apple, Macintosh, and IBM. This graphing utility can be used to graph equations given in *Explore* lesson openers in Chapter 7, and can be used with *Computer Explorations* in the appendix. Like the investigations for the graphing calculator, **Investigative Activities for Master Grapher** are designed to take advantage of the power of the computer by allowing the student to "discover" many algebraic concepts and relationships while making and testing their own conjectures.

Spreadsheets

The **Technology** supplement contains *Spreadsheet Activities* as well as *Calculator Worksheets* (described above), and *BASIC Computer Projects*. Each *Spreadsheet Activity* illustrates how to use a spreadsheet to work with algebraic concepts and presents problems for the student to solve and explore.

MathTest Software

This software package can generate an almost infinite number of tests, worksheets, mixed review sheets, etc. Since the test-generating software is algorithm based, you can give each student in the class a different test, if you wish, and the software will provide the answers.

Using the Assignment Guide

Assignment schedules are provided for three levels of courses—minimum, regular, and advanced. All three levels provide for 170 teaching days and include review and testing days. The Chapter Planning guide prior to each chapter gives daily assignments and optional supplementary assignments. It is not intended that all supplement pages be used. These are given to provide flexibility for individual classroom situations. The Management and Teaching Tools supplement provides a schedule for teaching Addison-Wesley Algebra over a two-year period.

Minimum Course

The minimum algebra course is for students who need extra practice and frequent review in order to master concepts. This course covers the first 13 chapters of Algebra, omitting optional lessons 2-10, 7-9, and 10-11, and includes Problem Solving: Applications, Situational Problem Solving, and College Entrance Exams. The suggested daily assignments include the A-level and the Mixed Review exercises. Minimum level chapter tests are provided for this course.

Regular Course

The regular course is for students who need skills practice and review, yet can apply these skills to higher level thinking. This course covers all but one chapter. Either Chapter 14 or Chapter 15 can be omitted. Although *Introduction to Probability and Statistics* is the last chapter in this book, it can be taught earlier. An optional Management Guide is presented on page 638C for teaching the chapter in four sections following Chapters 4, 6, 8, and 12 respectively.

The suggested daily assignments generally include half of the A and B-level exercises and the Mixed Review exercises. You may also want to assign one or two challenge problems. Three chapter tests are provided for the regular course including a multiple choice test.

Advanced Course

The advanced course covers all topics as well as Bonus Topics and is intended for students who can master concepts quickly. The suggested daily assignments include some of the A-level exercises and many of the B-level and Challenge exercises. The Mixed Review exercises are also suggested for this course. Advanced level tests are provided for this course.

The following chart summarizes the number of days allocated for each chapter for the three levels of ability.

Chapter	**1**	**2**	**3**	**4**	**5**	**6**	**7**	**8**	**9**	**10**	**11**	**12**	**13**	**14**	**15**
Minimum Course	14	13	16	9	16	17	13	12	10	15	13	10	12	0	0
Regular Course	12	12	14	8	14	12	13	12	11	17	13	10	11	11*	11*
Advanced Course	11	11	13	6	13	11	10	10	11	18	14	11	11	8	12

Semester

*The regular course covers Chapter 14 or Chapter 15.

Teachers' Answer Section

PAGE 170 READY FOR CHAPTER 4?

1. 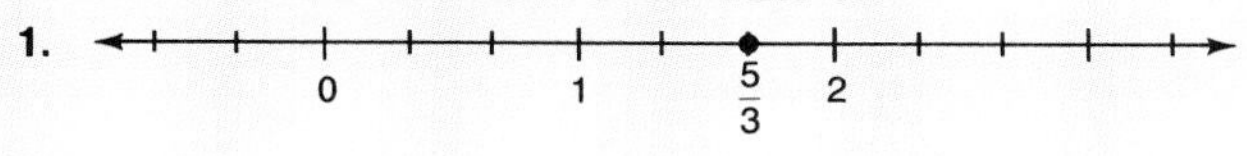

2. 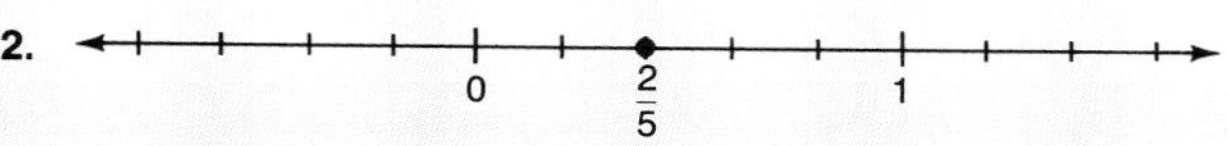

3. 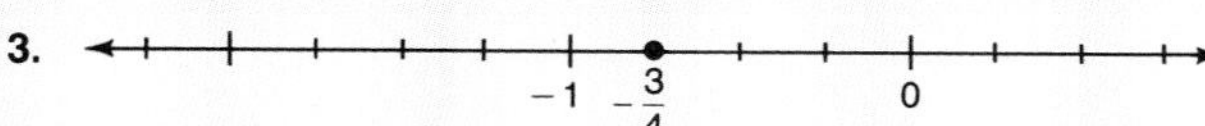

PAGE 181 TRY THIS 4-3

a. 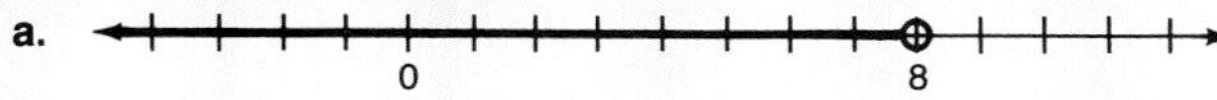

b. 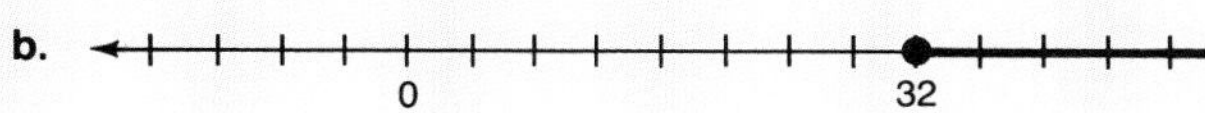

c. 0 28

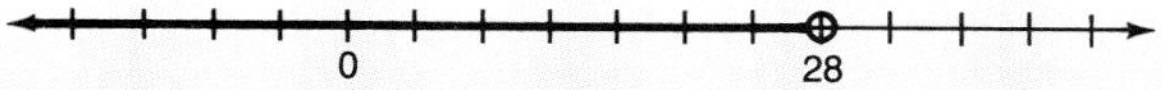

d. 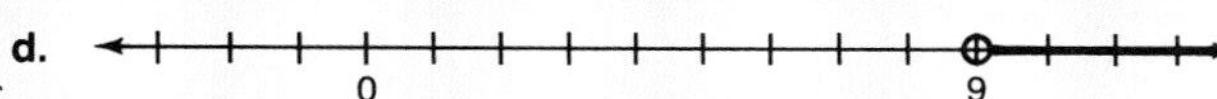

PAGE 182 EXERCISE SET 4-3

1. 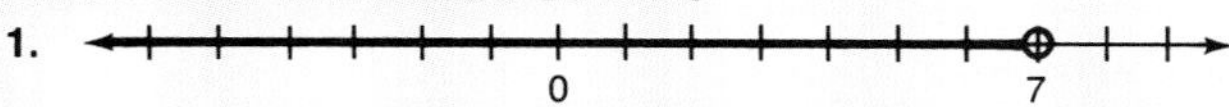

2. 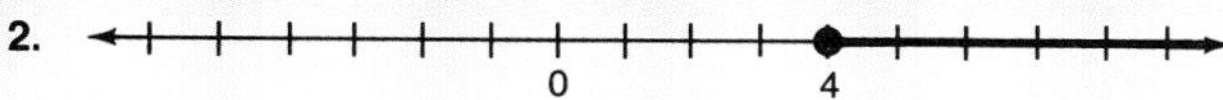

3. 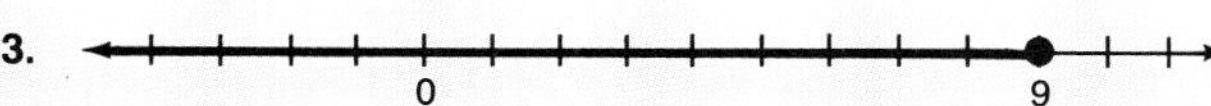

4. 0 24

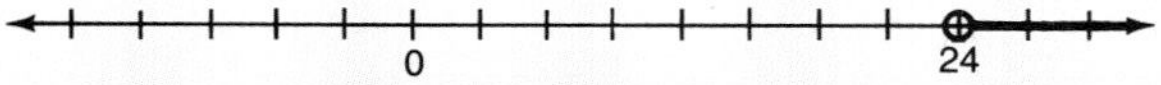

5. 0 12

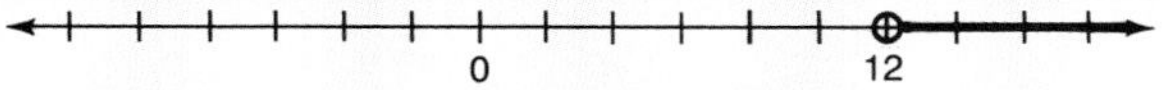

6. 0 7

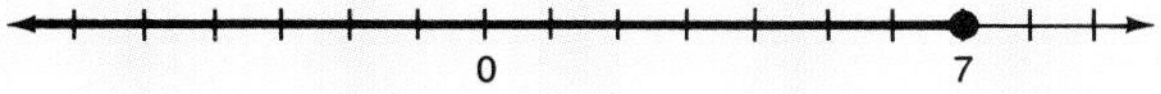

7. 0 1 $\frac{13}{7}$

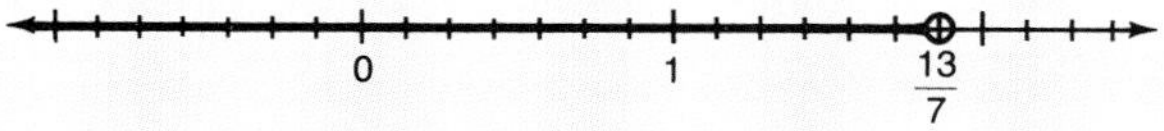

8. 0 2 $\frac{17}{8}$

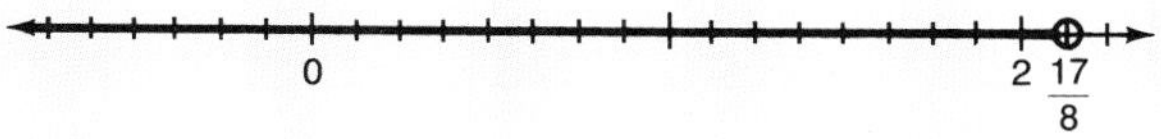

9. 0 $\frac{15}{4}$ 4

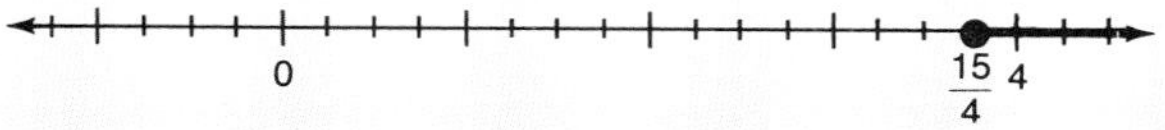

10. 0 6 $\frac{19}{3}$

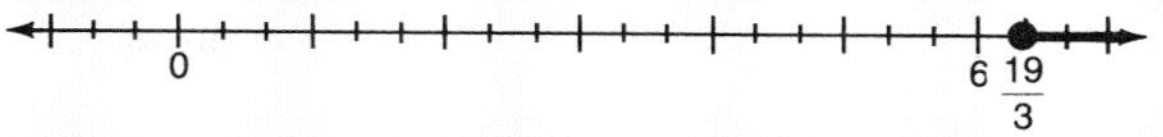

11. 0 $\frac{1}{2}$

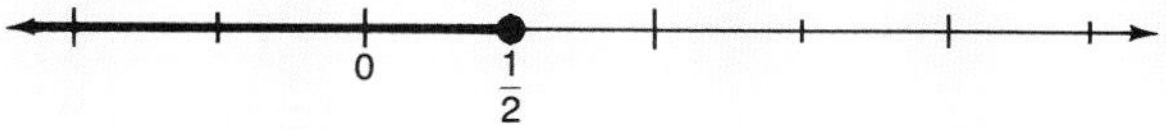

12. 0 $\frac{2}{7}$

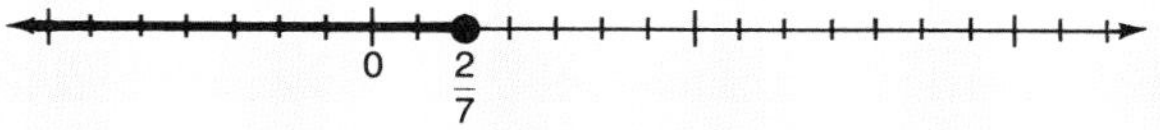

13. −3 0

14. −3 0

15. −3 0

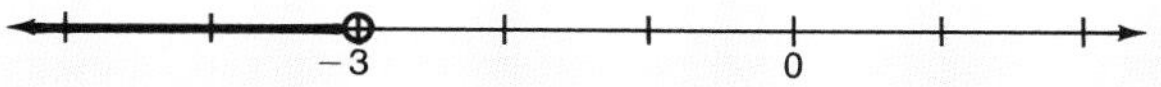

PAGE 269 EXERCISE SET 6-2

77. No; any product of the form $(x + a)(x + c)$ has 3 terms: $x^2 + (a + c)x + ac$. For the product to have 2 terms, a and c must be opposites; but if a and c are opposites, then ac must be negative, and ac cannot equal b^2 for any value of b.

Answers may vary. The answers below are examples.

78. $x(x + 2)(x + 1) = x^3 + 3x^2 + 2x$
$x(x + 2)(x - 1) = x^3 + x^2 - 2x$
79. $(x^2 - 2)(x^2 + 2) = x^4 - 4$
80. $(x + 5)(x + 1)(x - 1) = x^3 + 5x^2 - x - 5$
81. $(a + 2b)(a + b)(a - b) = a^3 - ab^2 + 2a^2b - 2b^3$
82. $(x^2 - 5)(x + 1)(x - 1) = x^4 - 6x^2 + 5$

PAGE 308 EXERCISE SET 7-1

29–35. Answers may vary. Examples are given.
29. (−3, 3), (−4, 4), (5, 5)
30. (−1, 1), (0, 0), (2, −2)
31. (4, −2), (9, 3), (1, −1)
32. (−2, −3), (0, −1), (2, 1)
33. (q, r) and (r, q) are symmetric about the line $y = x$.

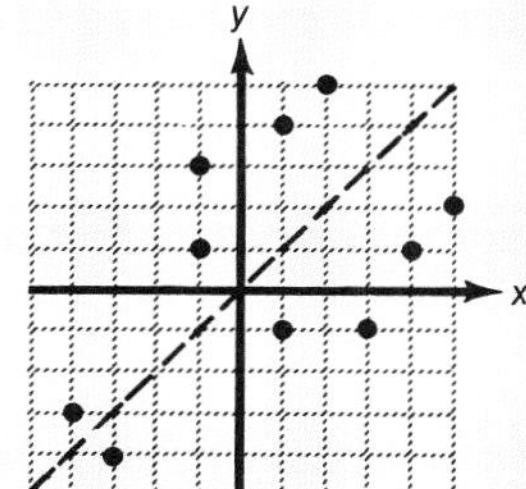

34. $(-2, -1), (1, 2), \left(4, \frac{1}{2}\right)$
35. (2, 3), (4, 1), (0, 5)

PAGE 311 EXERCISE SET 7-2

16.

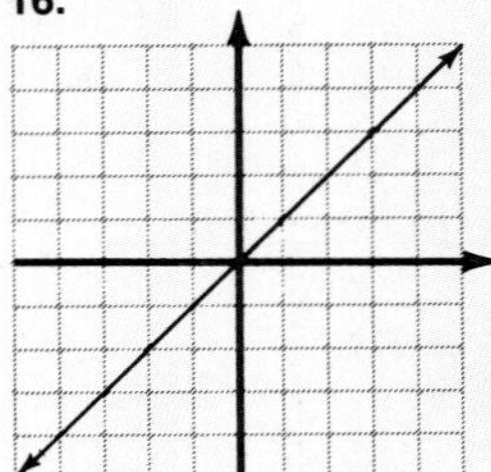

17.

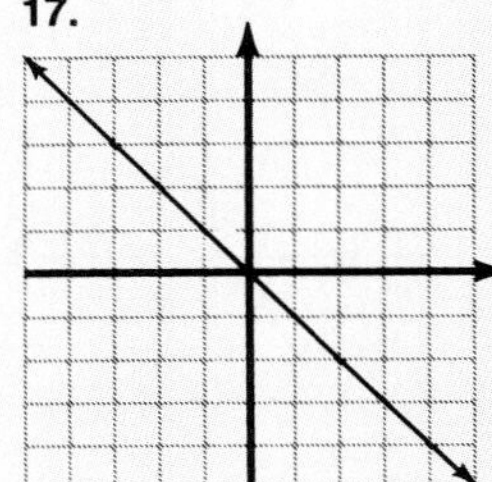

18.

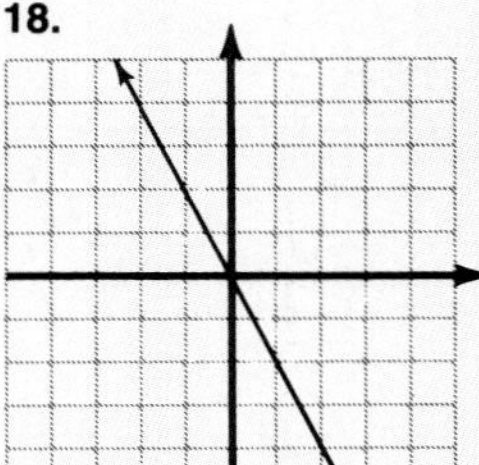

19.

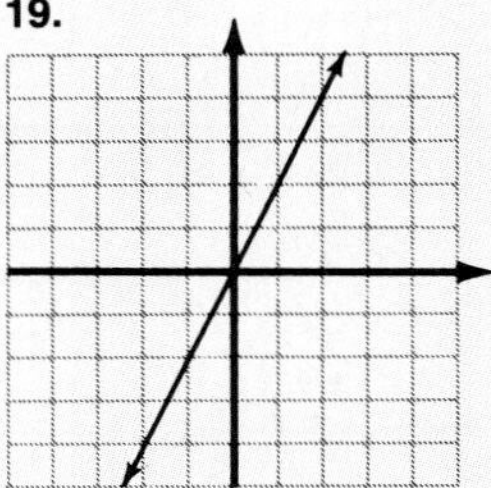

20.

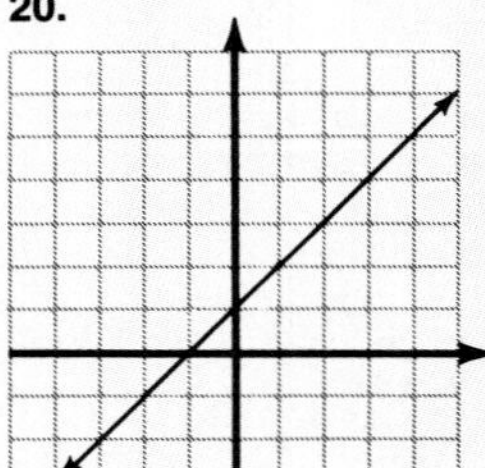

21.

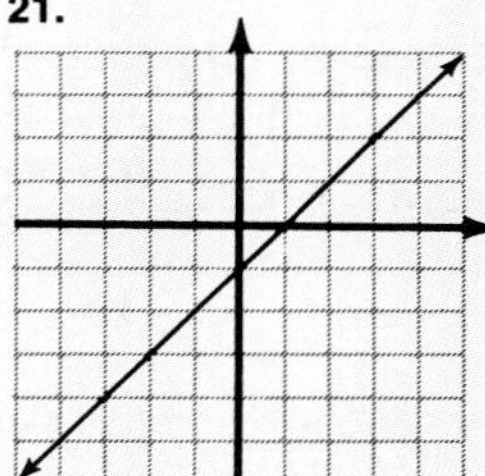

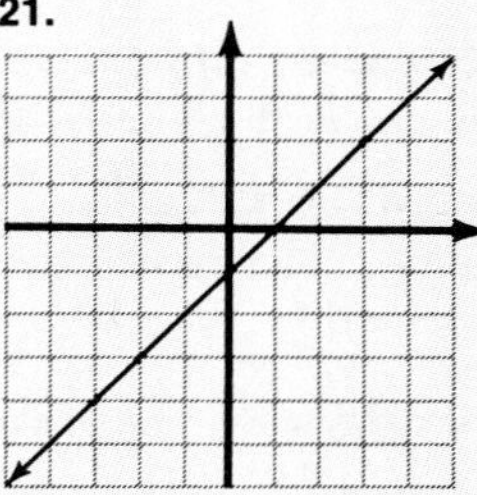

22.

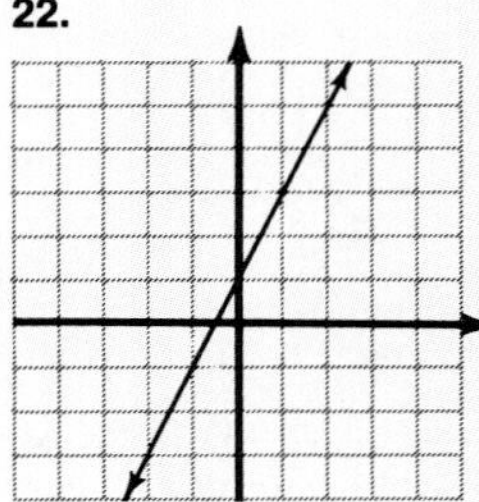

23.

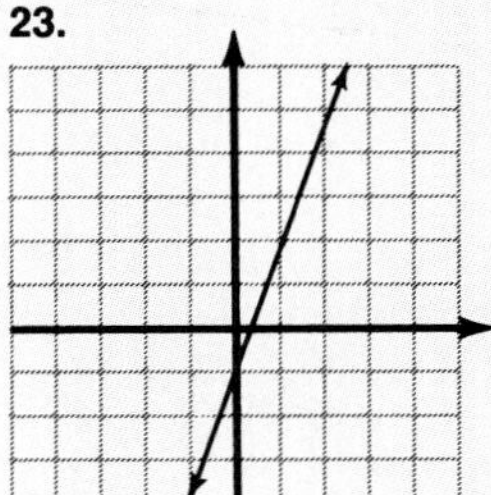

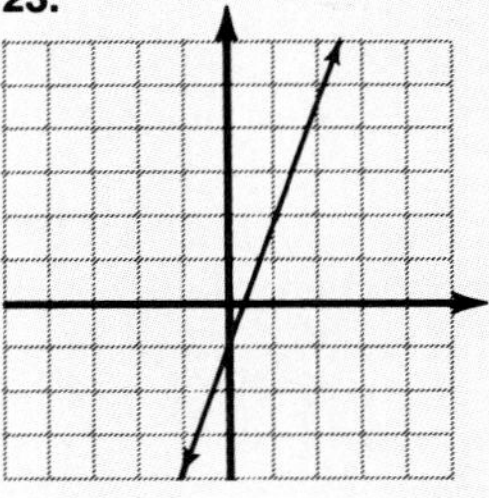

24.

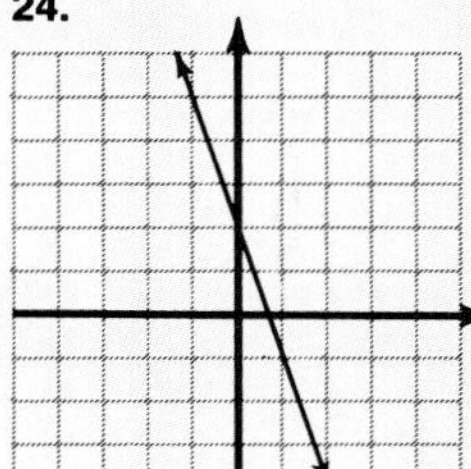

25.

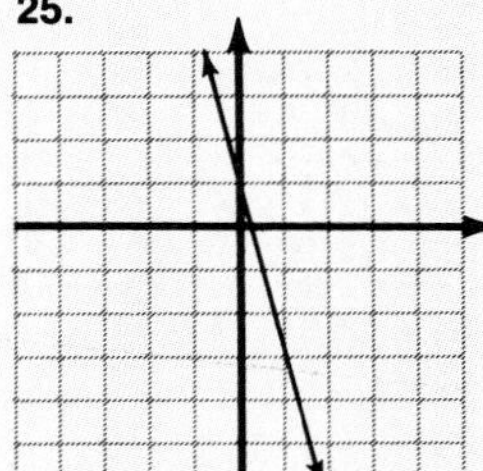

26.

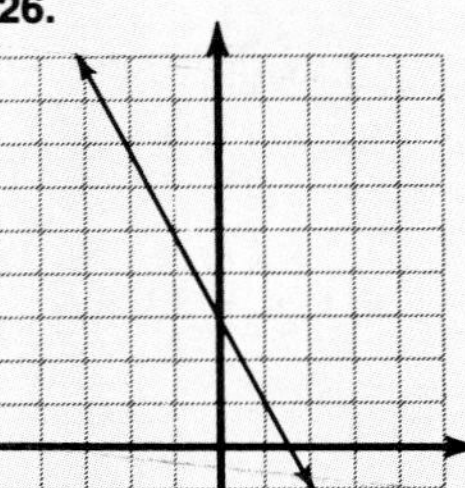

27.

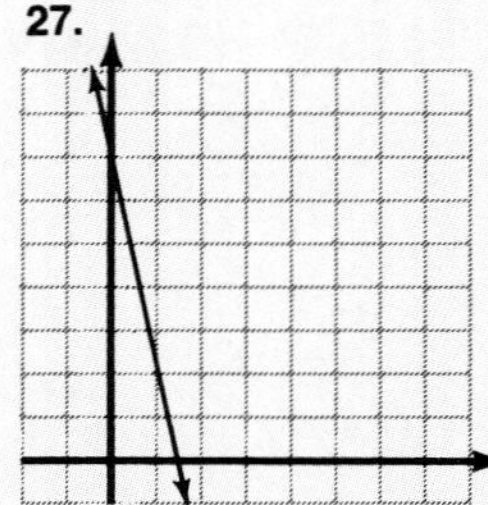

PAGE 315 LESSON QUIZ 7-3

1.

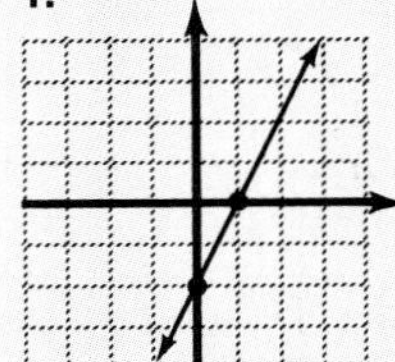

2.

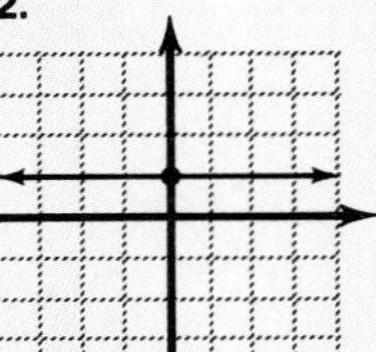

3.

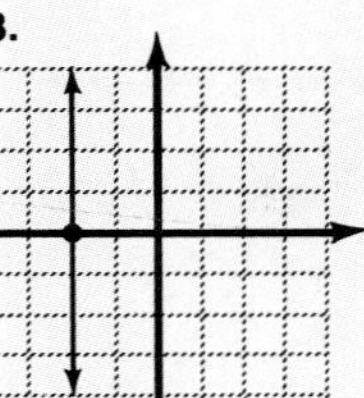

PAGE 315 TRY THIS 7-3

e.

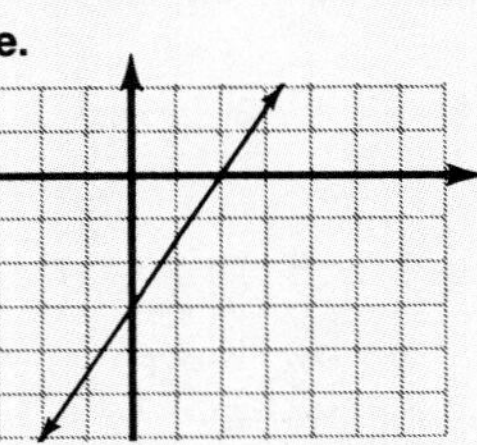

f.

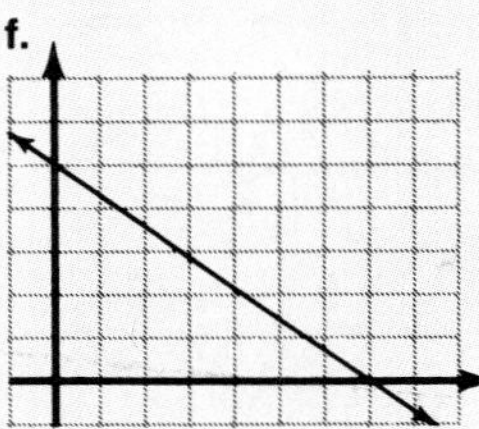

g.

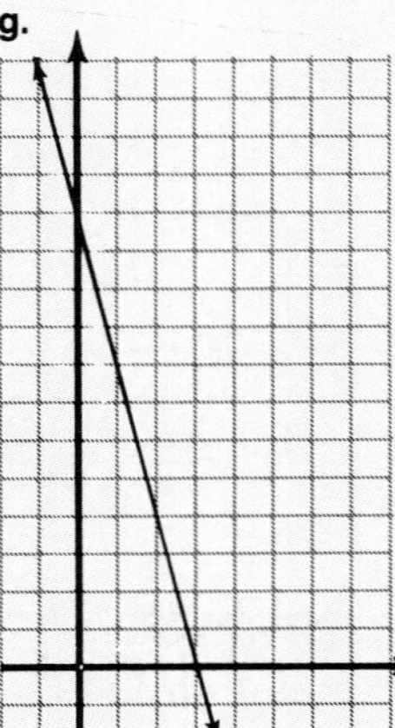

PAGE 315 TRY THIS 7-3

h.

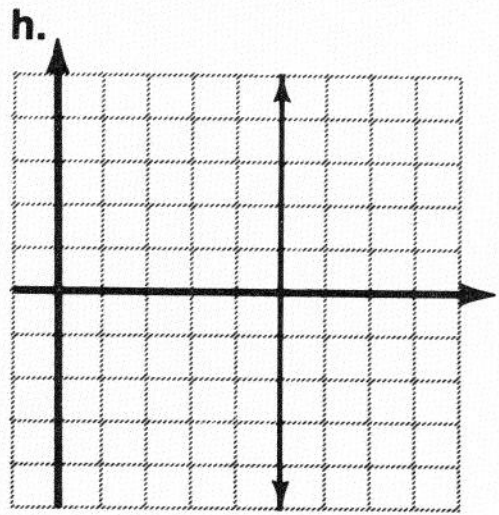

i.

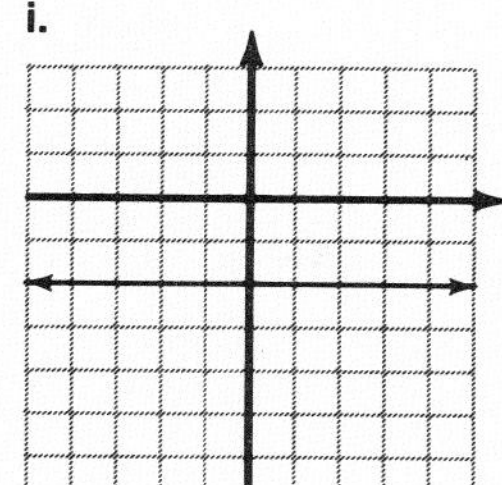

j.

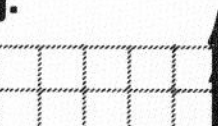

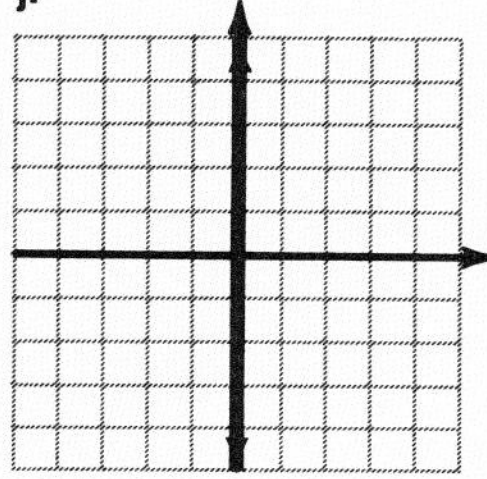

k.

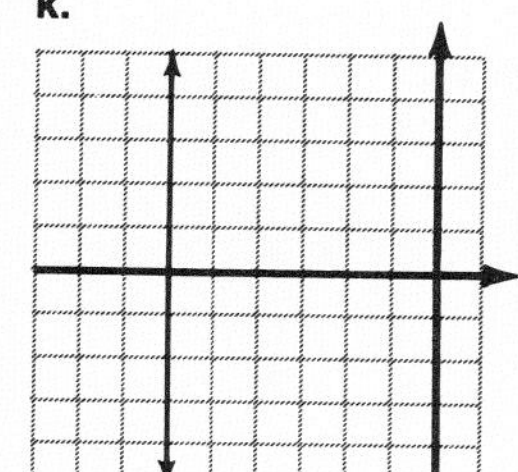

PAGE 316 EXERCISE SET 7-3

1.

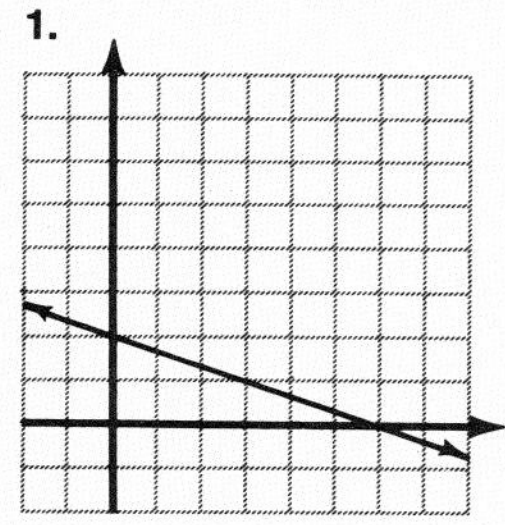

2.

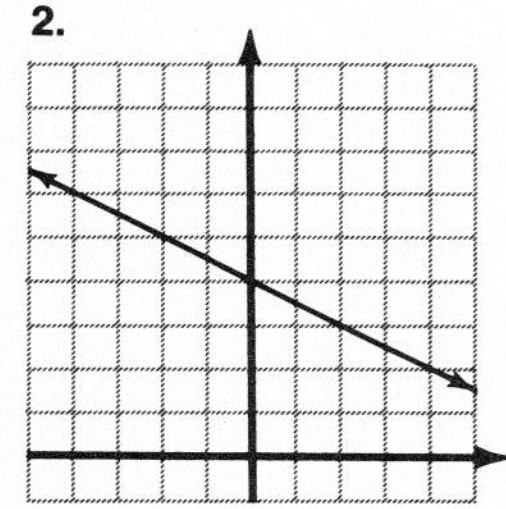

3.

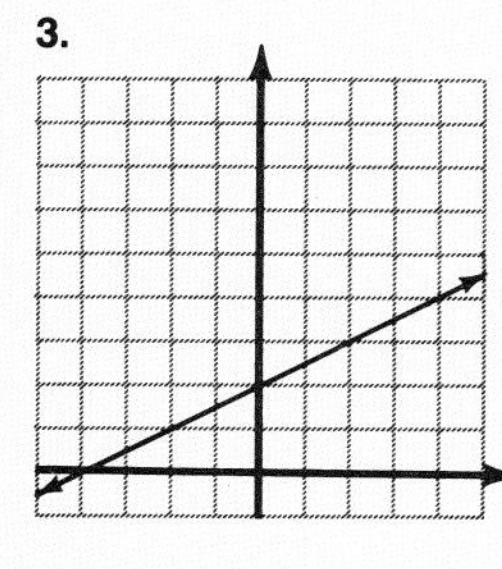

4.

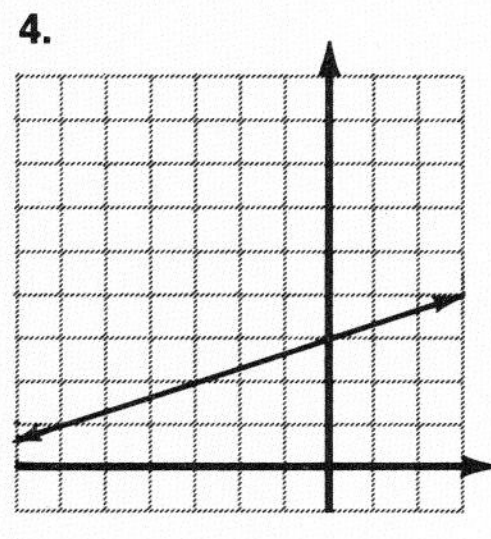

5.

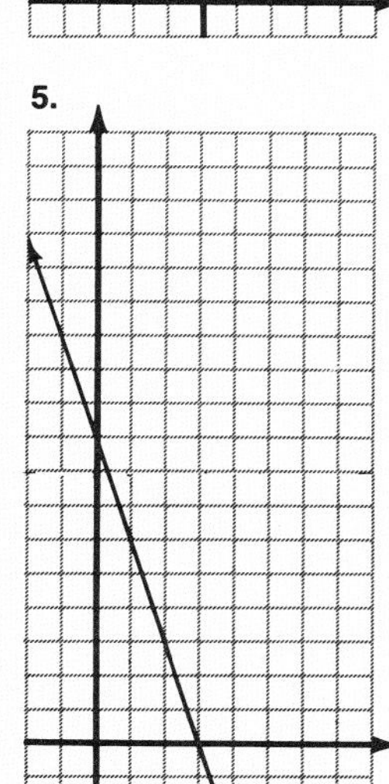

6.

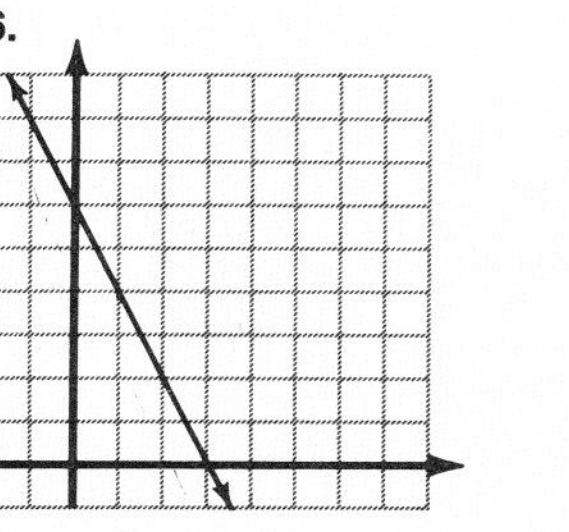

7.

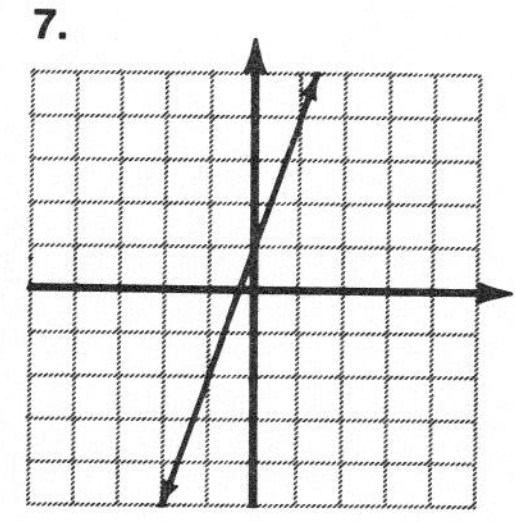

8.

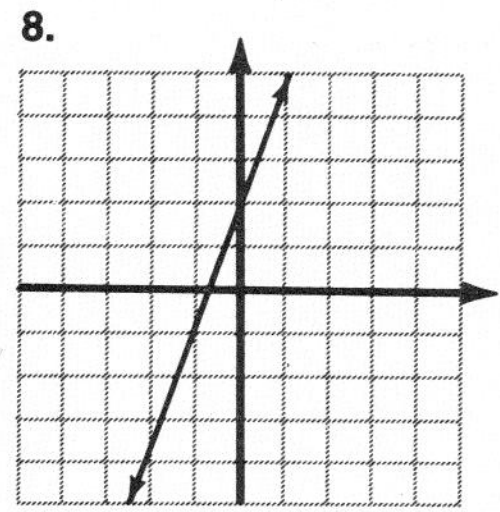

9.

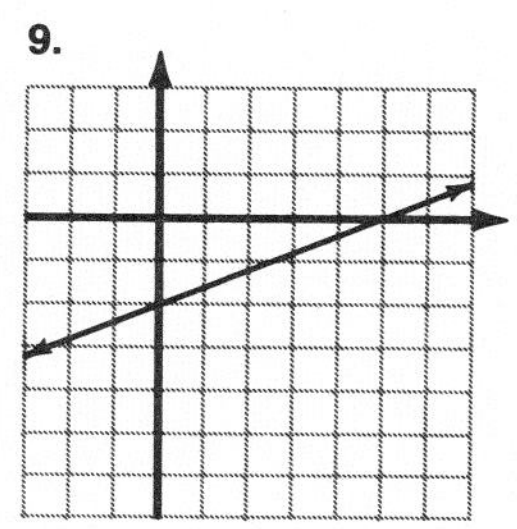

10.

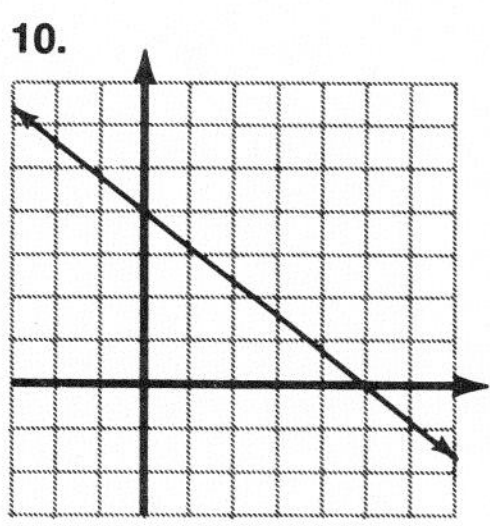

11.

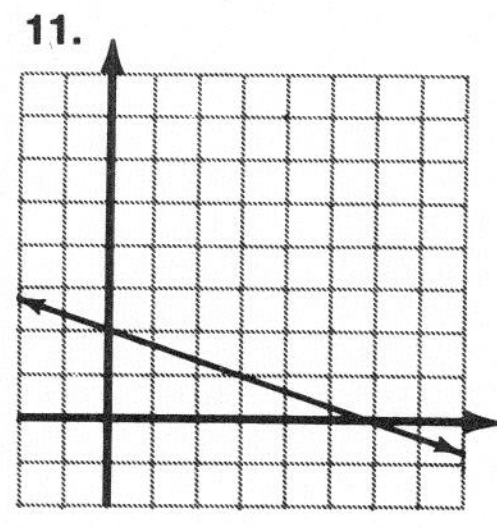

12.

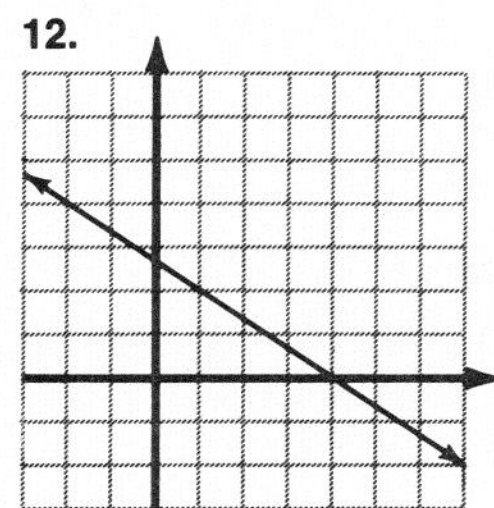

13.

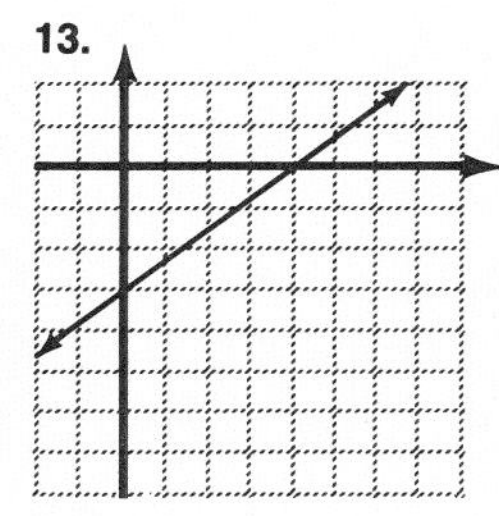

14.

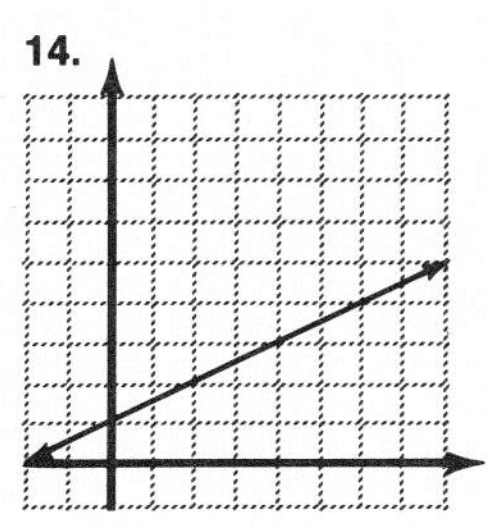

15.

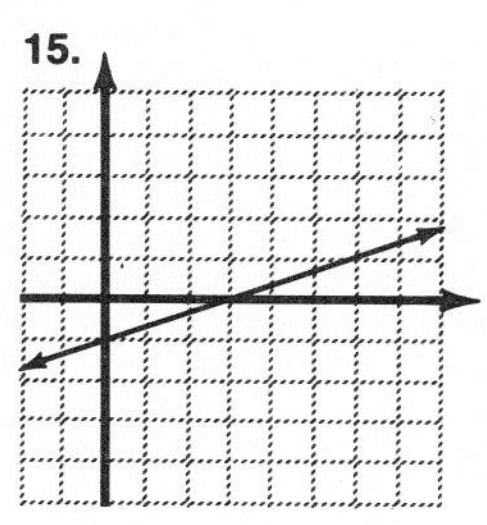

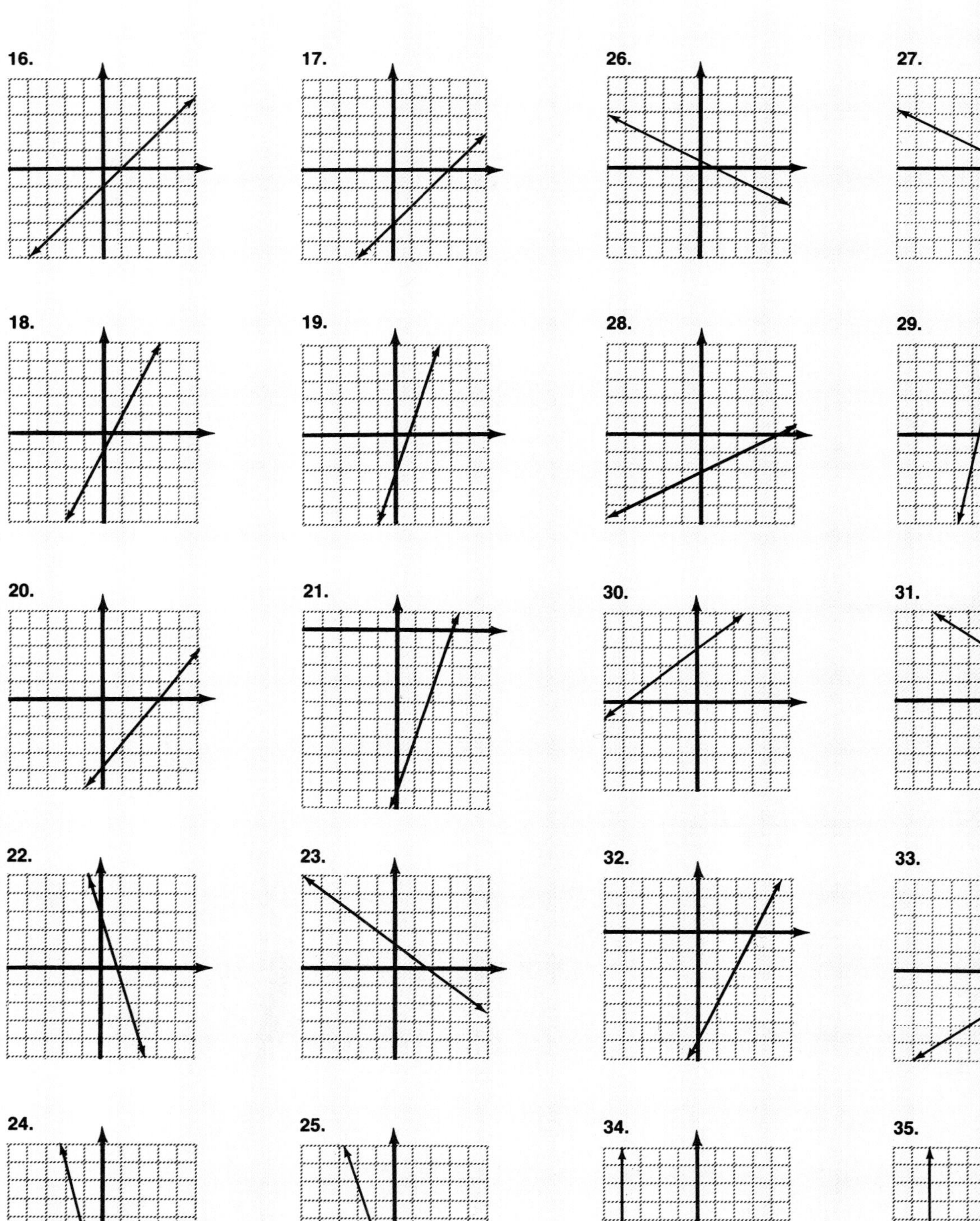
16.
17.
26.
27.
18.
19.
28.
29.
20.
21.
30.
31.
22.
23.
32.
33.
24.
25.
34.
35.

36.

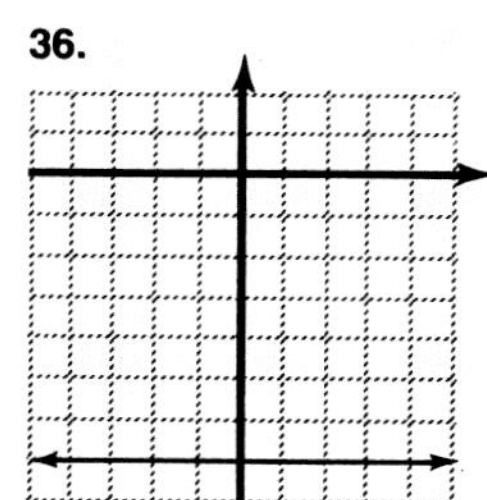

37.

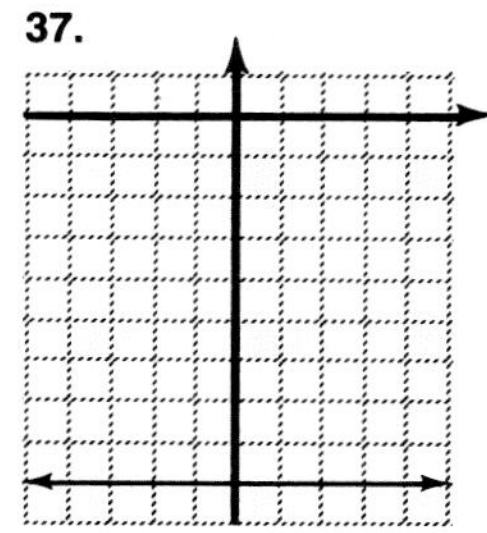

38.

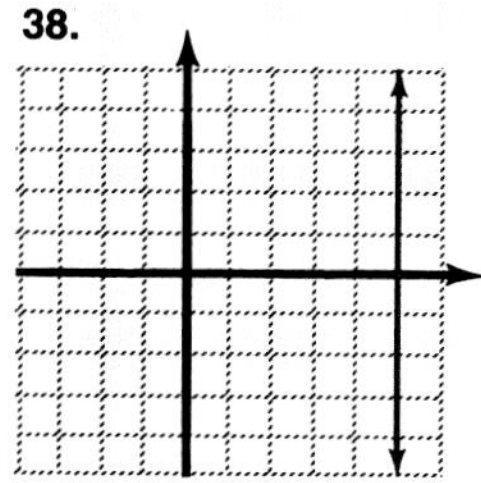

39.

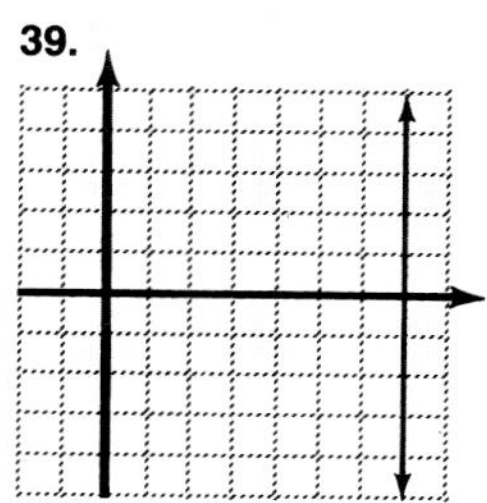

40.

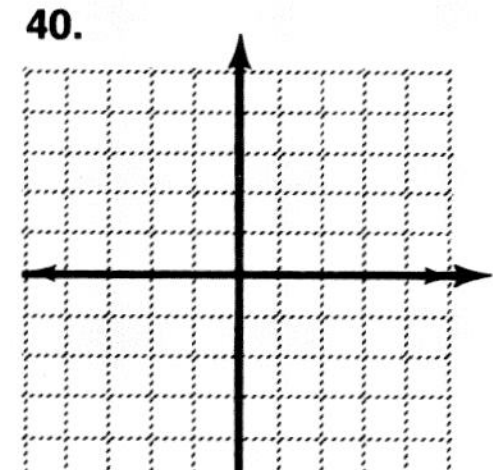

41.

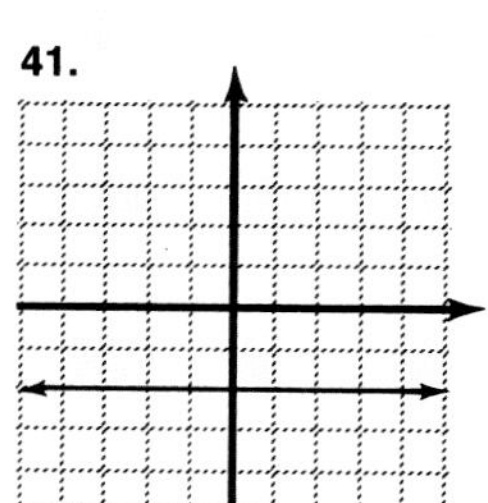

53.

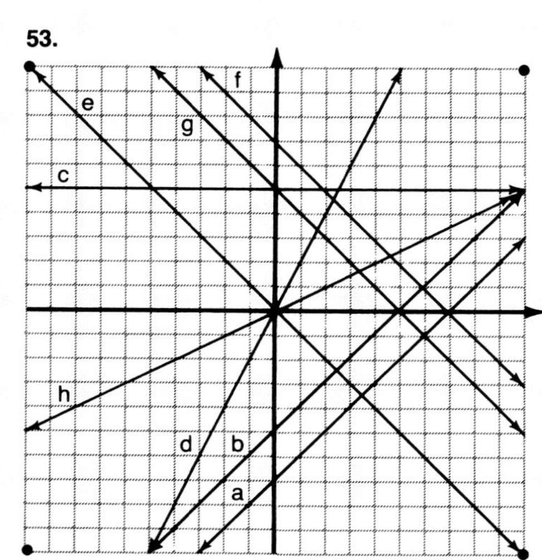

PAGE 325 TRY THIS 7-5

i.

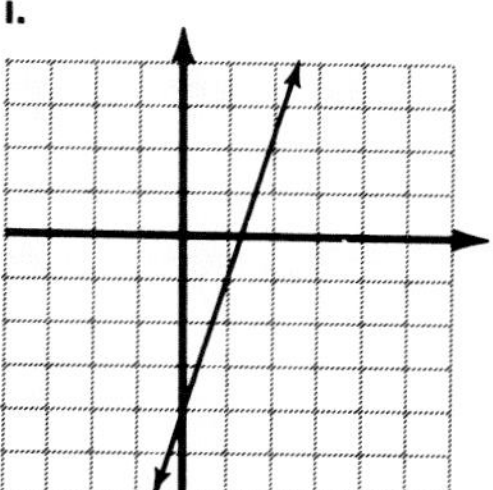

j.

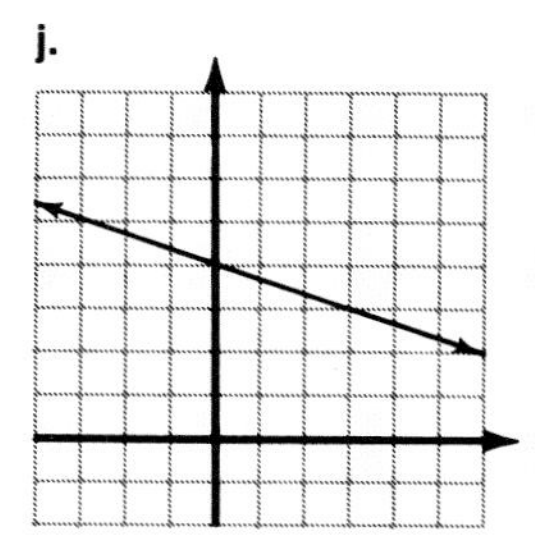

k.

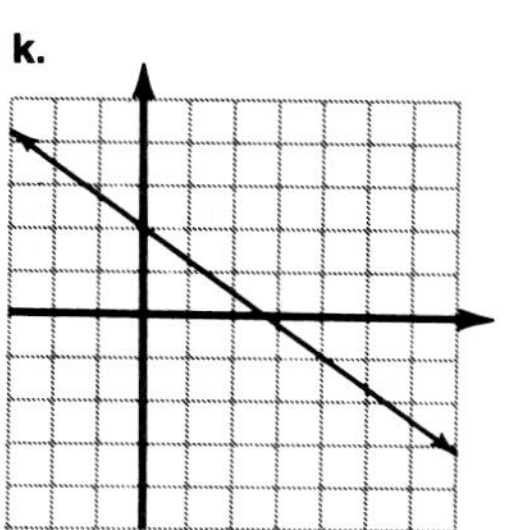

PAGE 326 EXERCISE SET 7-5

28.

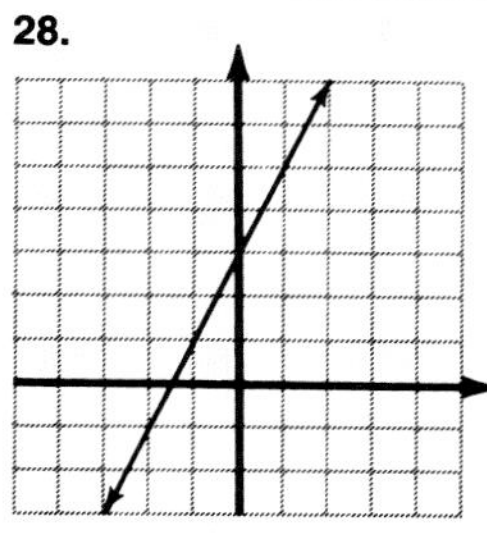

29.

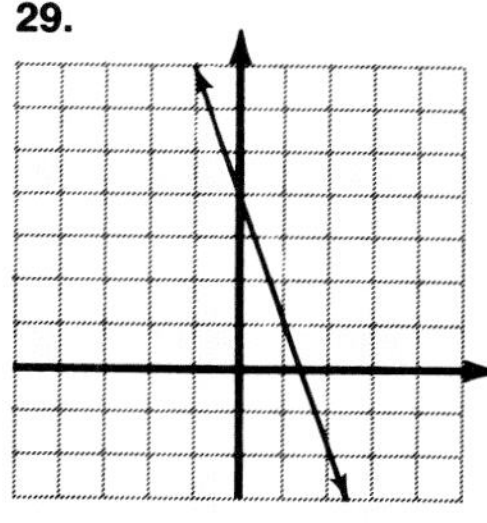

30.

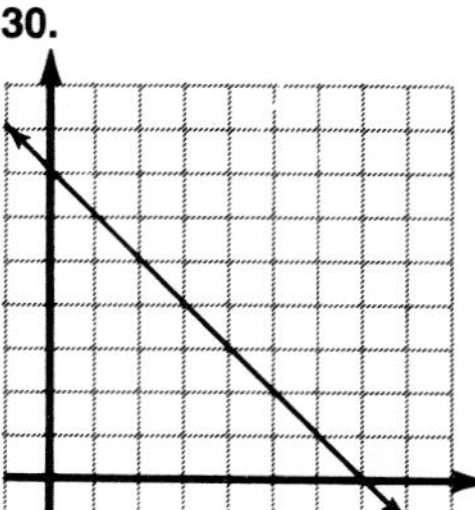

31.

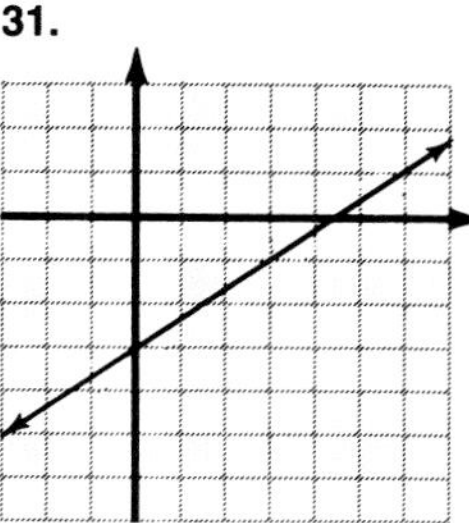

32.

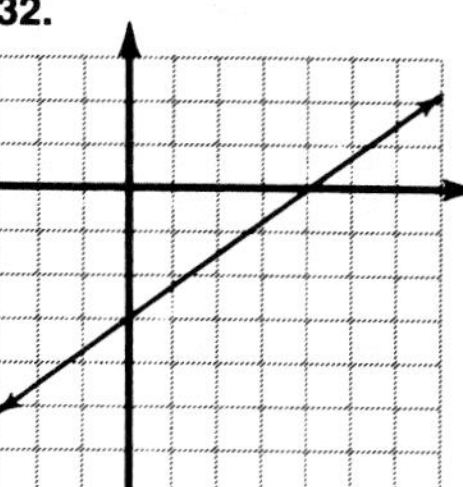

33.

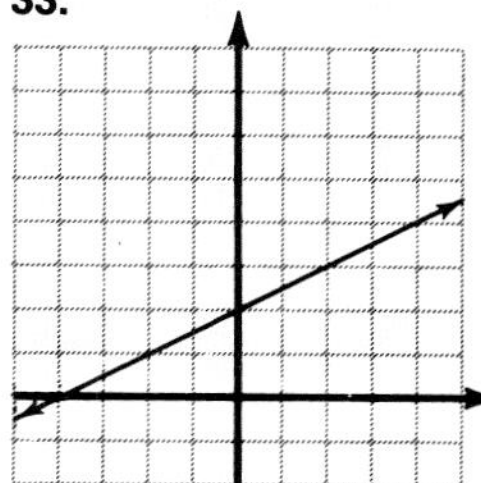

34.

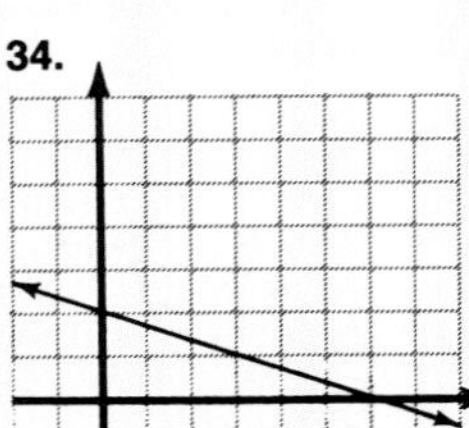

35.

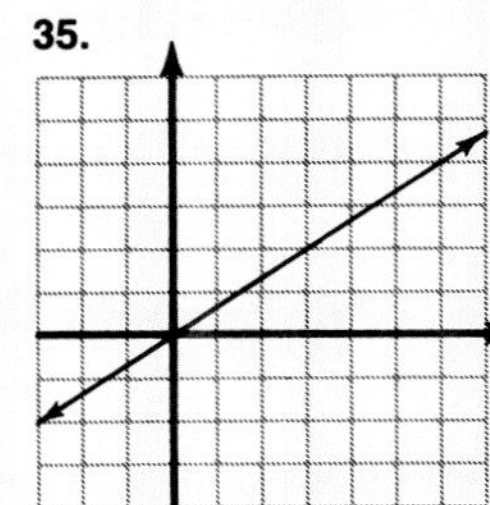

36.

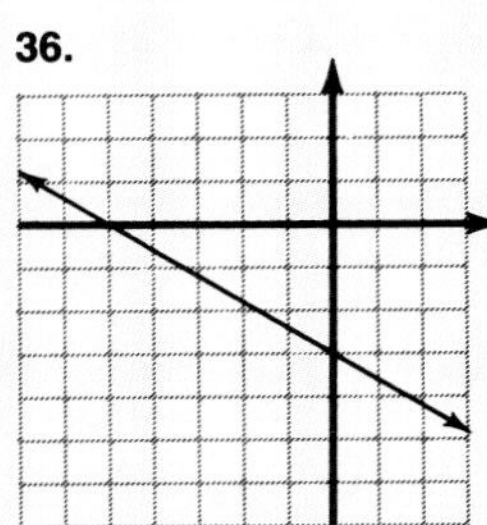

37.

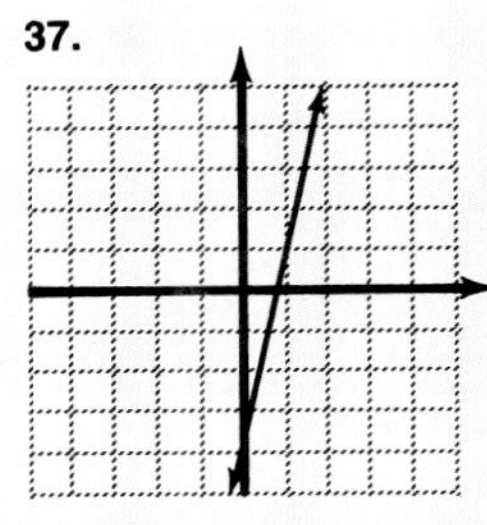

38.

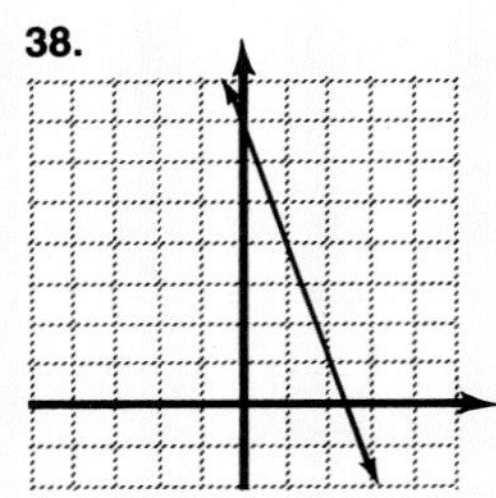

39.

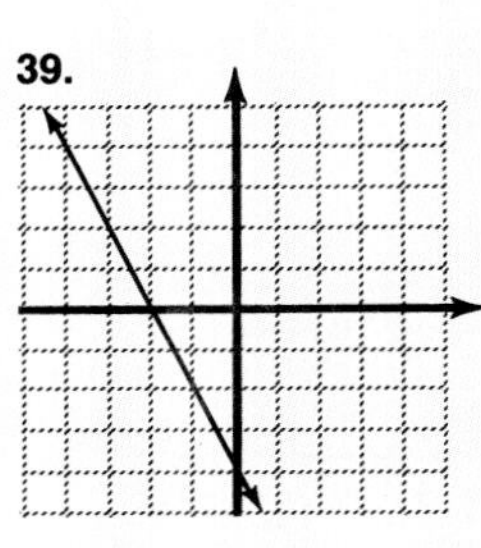

40.

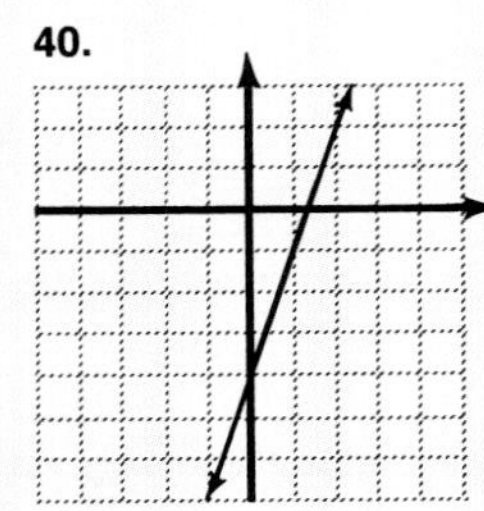

41.

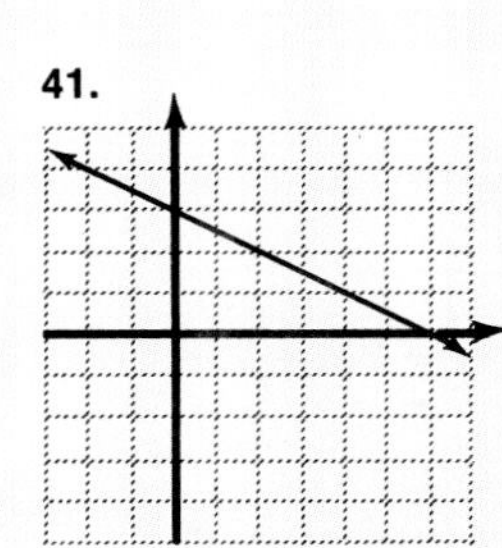

42.

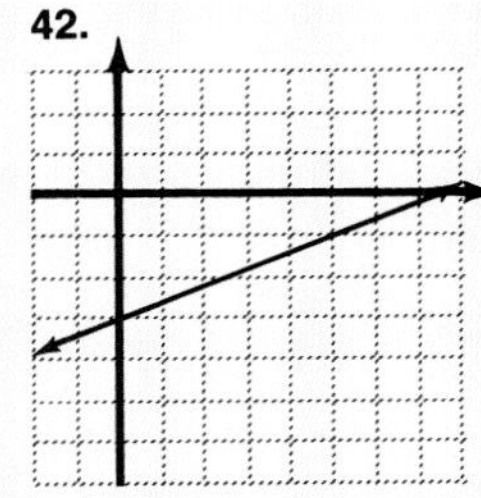

43.

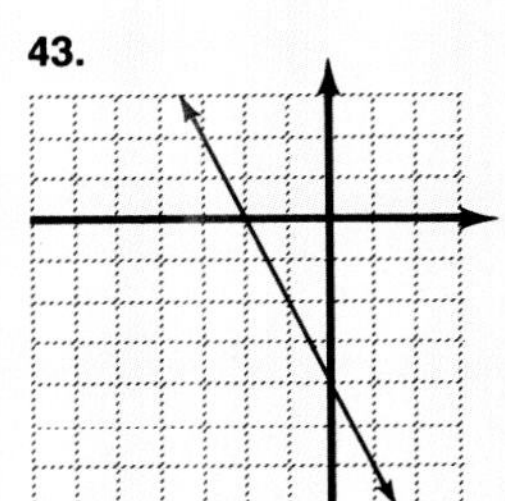

44.

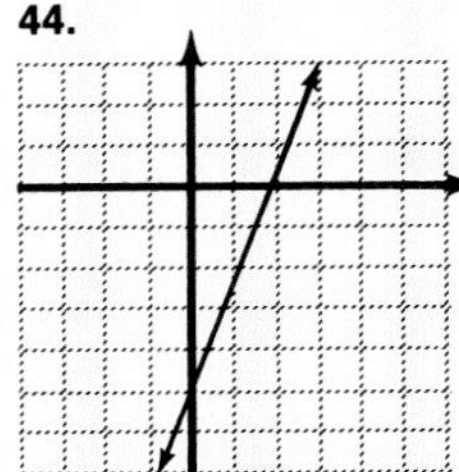

45.

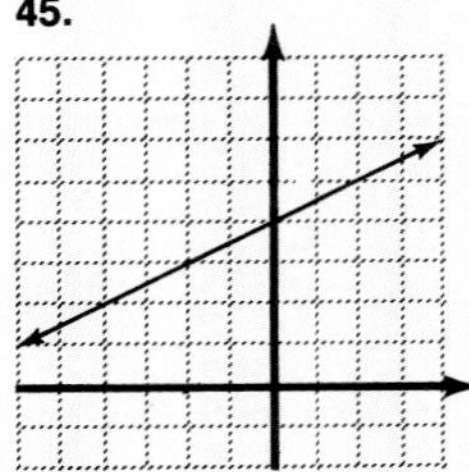

PAGE 343 EXERCISE SET 7-9

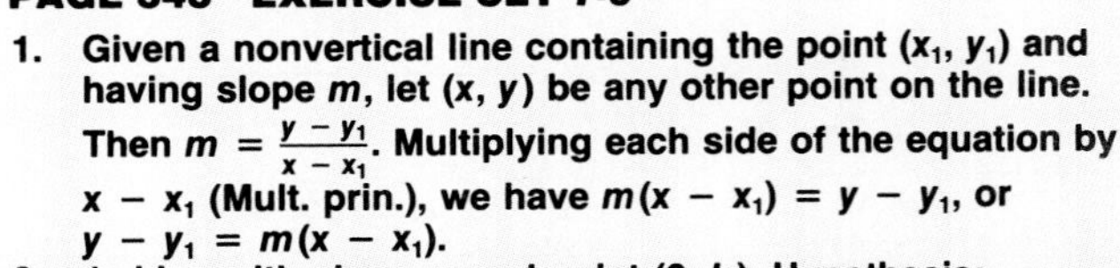

1. Given a nonvertical line containing the point (x_1, y_1) and having slope m, let (x, y) be any other point on the line. Then $m = \frac{y - y_1}{x - x_1}$. Multiplying each side of the equation by $x - x_1$ (Mult. prin.), we have $m(x - x_1) = y - y_1$, or $y - y_1 = m(x - x_1)$.
2. 1. Line with slope m and point $(0, b)$, Hypothesis;
   2. $y - y_1 = m(x - x_1)$, Point-slope equation;
   3. $y - b = m(x - 0)$, Substitution;
   4. $y = mx + b$, Add. prin.

PAGE 356 READY FOR CHAPTER 8?

19.

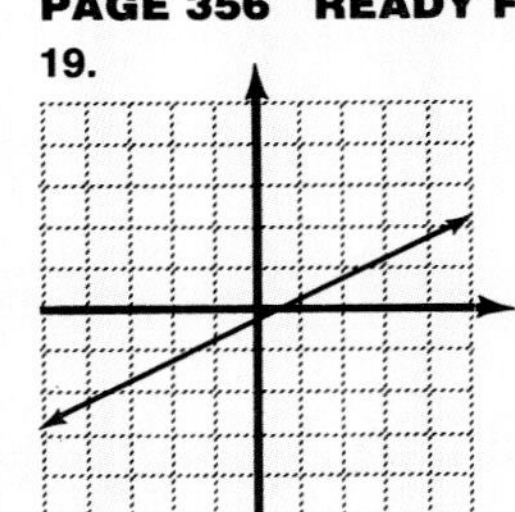

20.

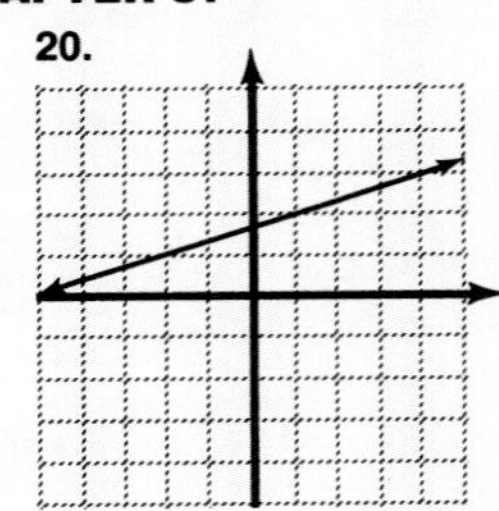

21.

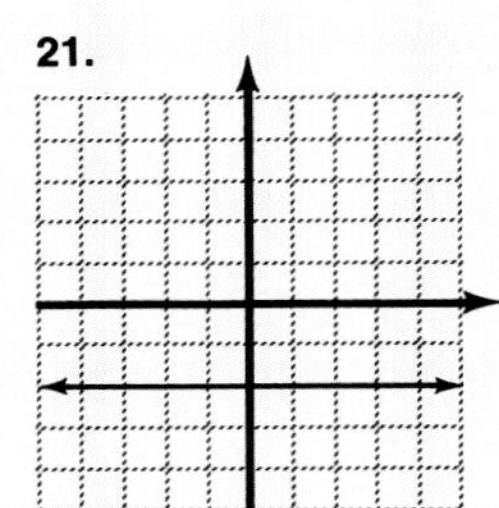

22.

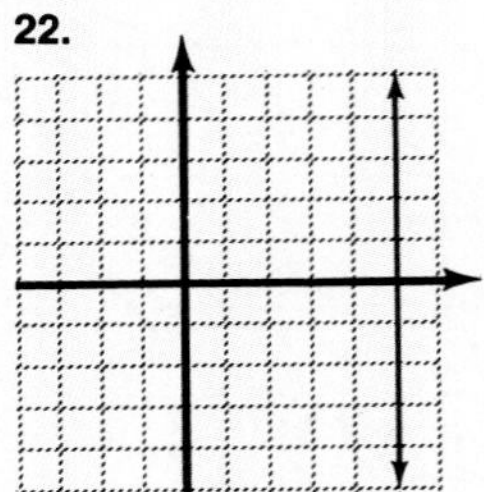

PAGE 408 EXERCISE SET 9-2

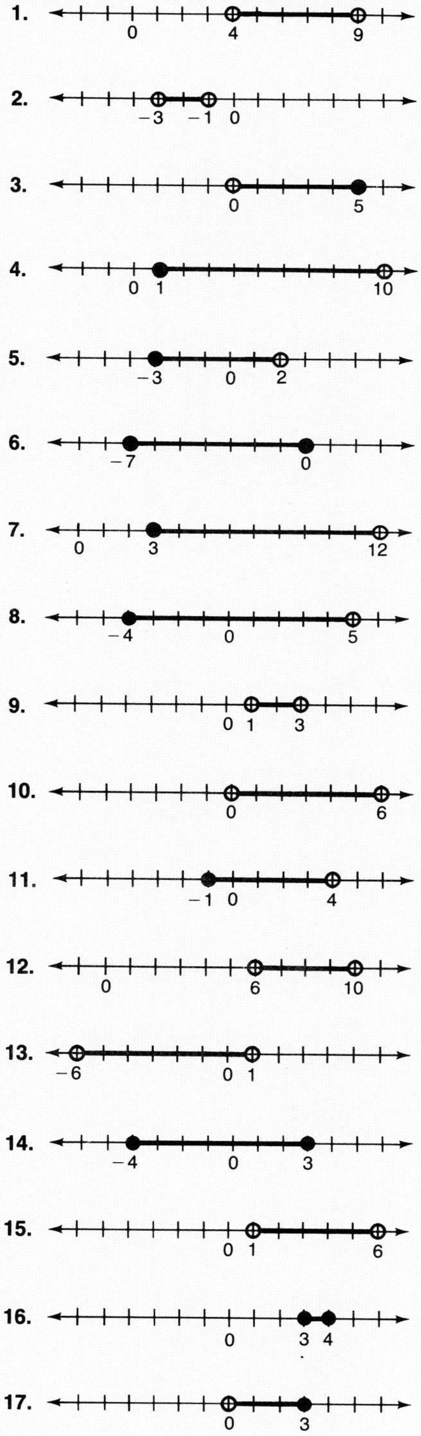

1. 0 4 9

2. −3 −1 0

3. 0 5

4. 0 1 10

5. −3 0 2

6. −7 0

7. 0 3 12

8. −4 0 5

9. 0 1 3

10. 0 6

11. −1 0 4

12. 0 6 10

13. −6 0 1

14. −4 0 3

15. 0 1 6

16. 0 3 4

17. 0 3

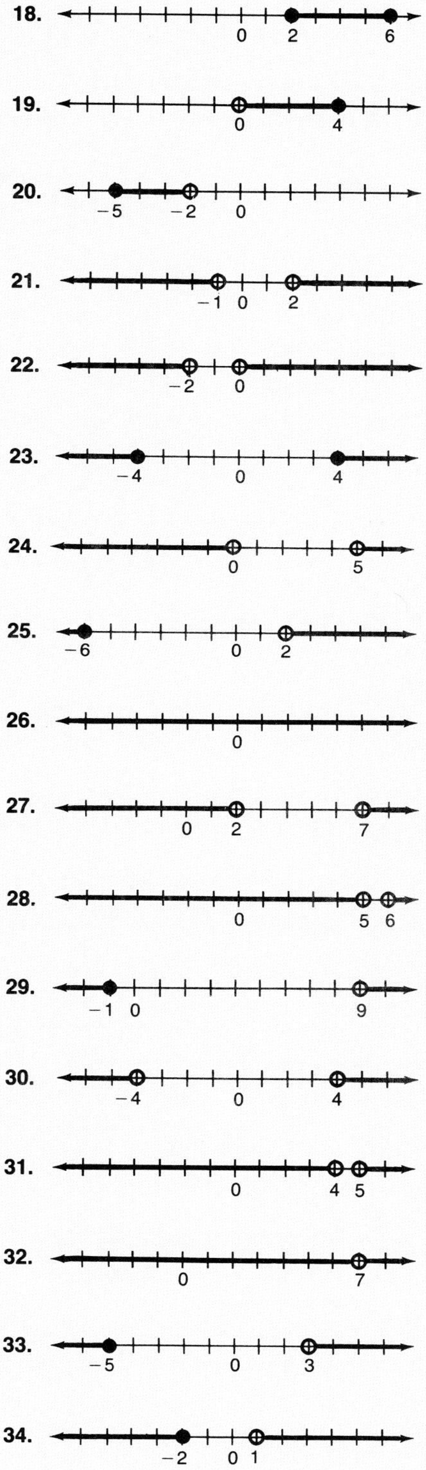

18. 0 2 6

19. 0 4

20. −5 −2 0

21. −1 0 2

22. −2 0

23. −4 0 4

24. 0 5

25. −6 0 2

26. 0

27. 0 2 7

28. 0 5 6

29. −1 0 9

30. −4 0 4

31. 0 4 5

32. 0 7

33. −5 0 3

34. −2 0 1

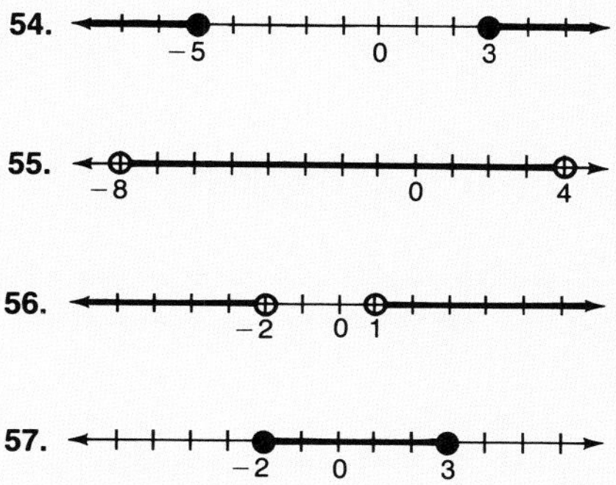

54. −5 0 3

55. −8 0 4

56. −2 0 1

57. −2 0 3

PAGE 415 TRY THIS 9-4

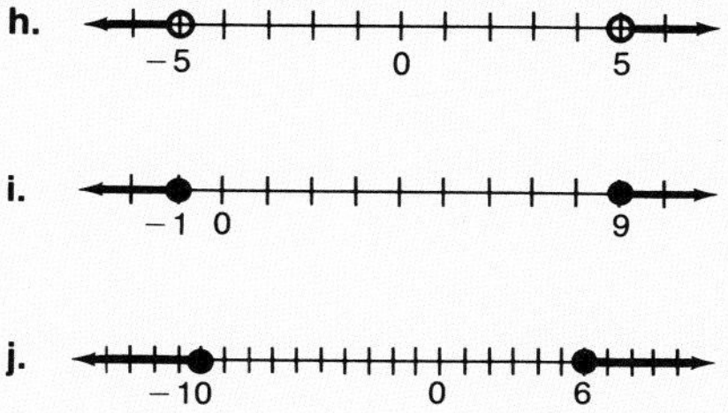

h. −5 0 5

i. −1 0 9

j. −10 0 6

PAGE 415 EXERCISE SET 9-4

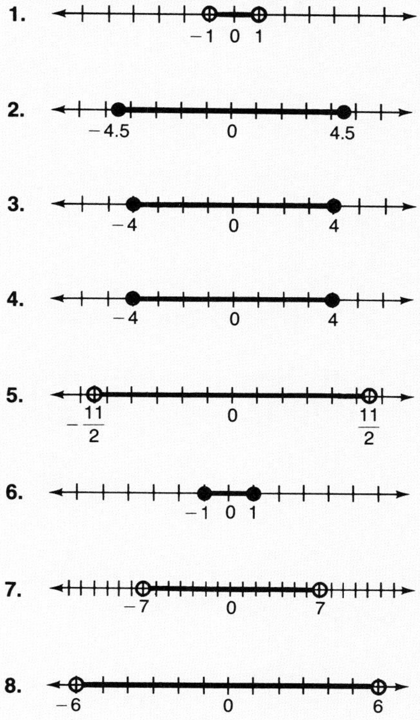

1. −1 0 1

2. −4.5 0 4.5

3. −4 0 4

4. −4 0 4

5. $-\frac{11}{2}$ 0 $\frac{11}{2}$

6. −1 0 1

7. −7 0 7

8. −6 0 6

9. −5 0 5

10. −9 0 15

11. −7 0 3

12. −2 0 12

13. −8 −4 0

14. $-\frac{3}{2}$ 0 $\frac{11}{2}$

15. $-\frac{5}{4}$ 0 $\frac{9}{4}$

16. $-\frac{14}{3}$ 0 2

17. −3 0 2

18. $-\frac{9}{2}$ 0 3

19. 0 0.989 1.011

20. −2.1 0 0.1

21. 0 1.999 2.001

22. −3 0 3

23. −4 0 4

24. −7 0 7

25. −9 0 9

26. −4 0 4

27. −6 0 6

28. −3 0 3

29. −2 0 2

30. −5 0 7

31. −14 0 4

32. −2 0 20

33. $-\frac{5}{2}$ 0 $\frac{7}{2}$

34. $-\frac{5}{3}$ 0 1

35. $-\frac{5}{2}$ 0 4

36. −2 0 $\frac{5}{3}$

37. $-\frac{15}{4}$ 0 $\frac{25}{4}$

48. −4 −2 0 2 4

PAGE 419 EXERCISE SET 9-5

4.

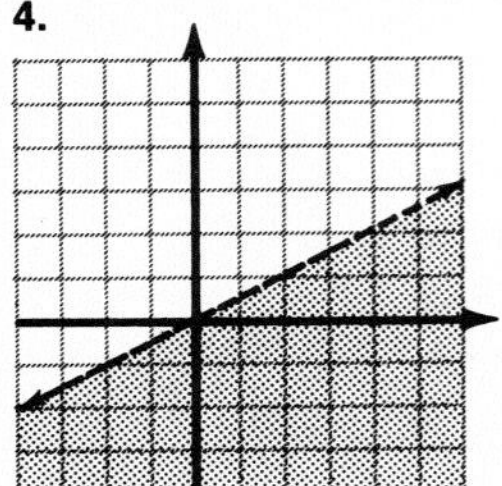

5.

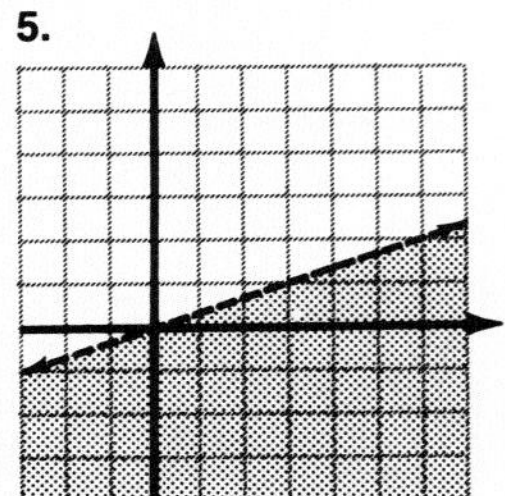

6.

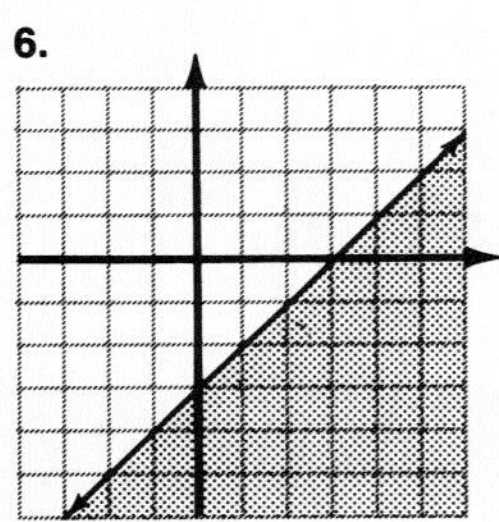

7.

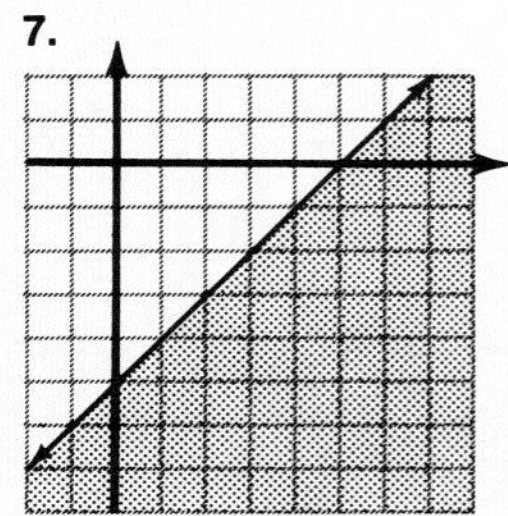

8.

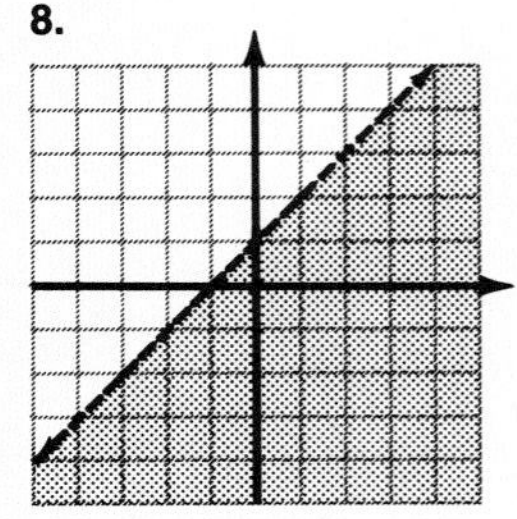

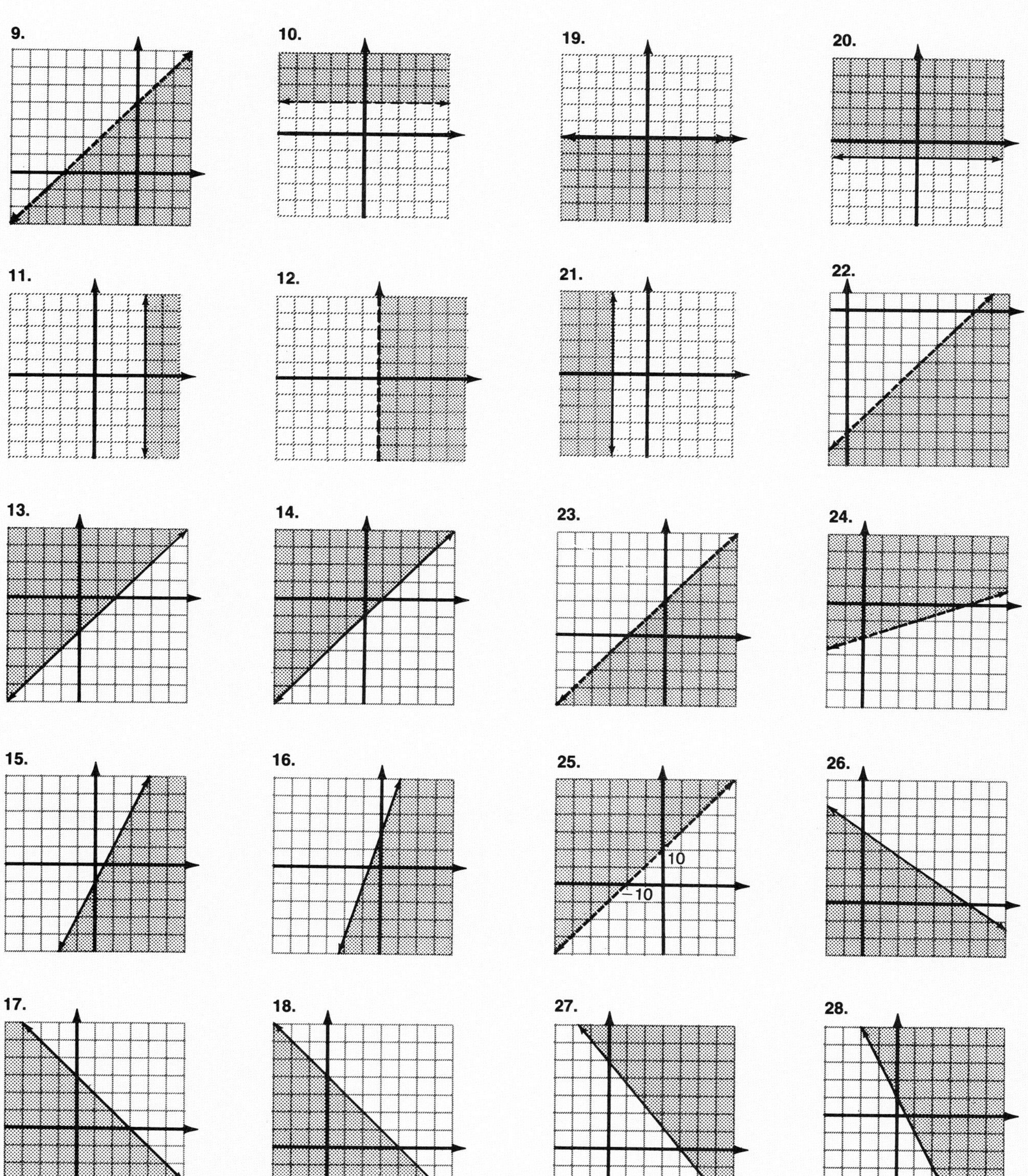
9.
10.
19.
20.
11.
12.
21.
22.
13.
14.
23.
24.
15.
16.
25.
10
−10
26.
17.
18.
27.
28.

29.

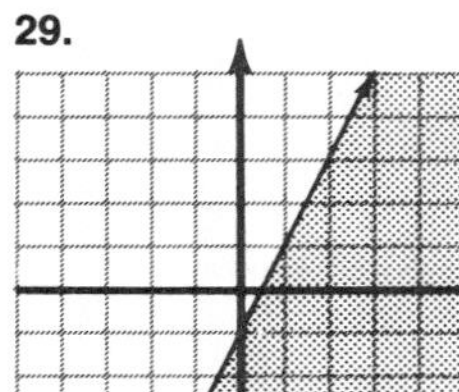

30.

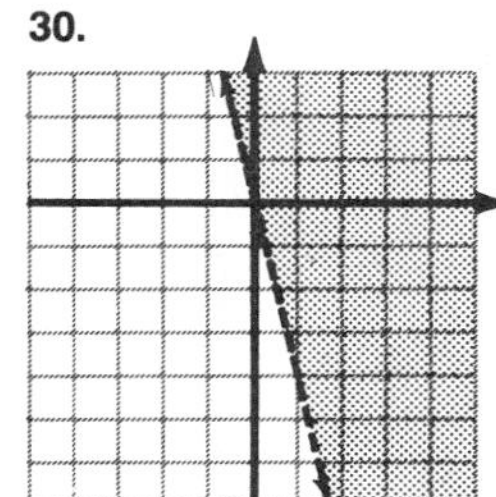

31.

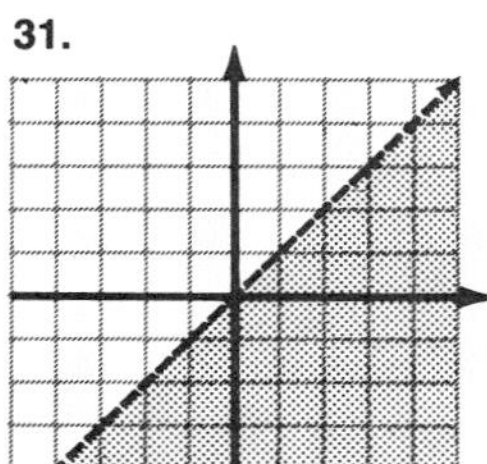

32.

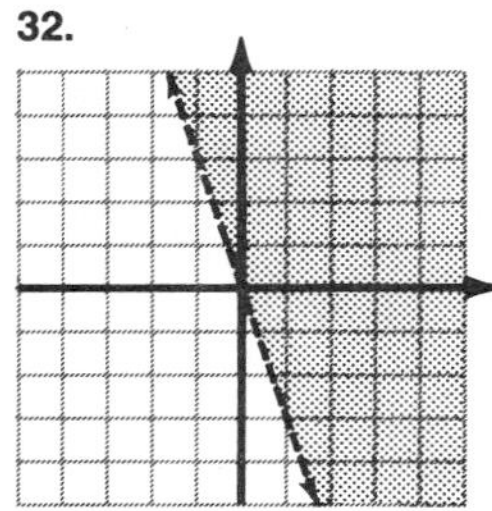

33.

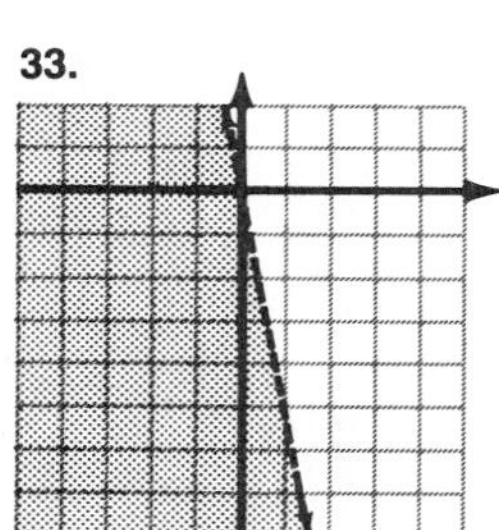

34.

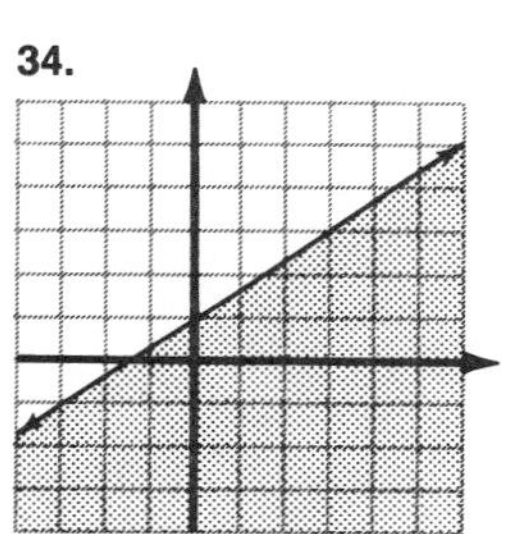

35.

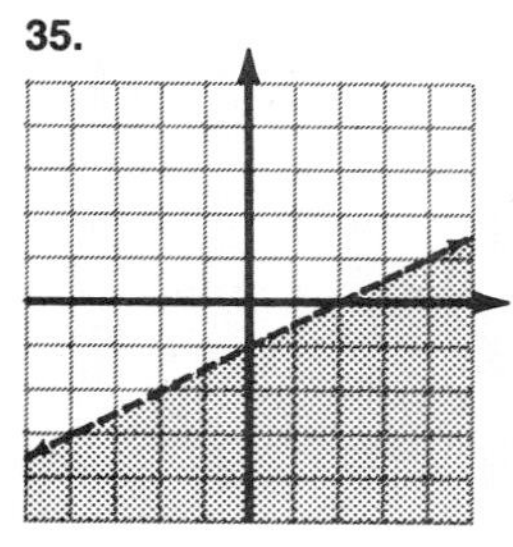

36.

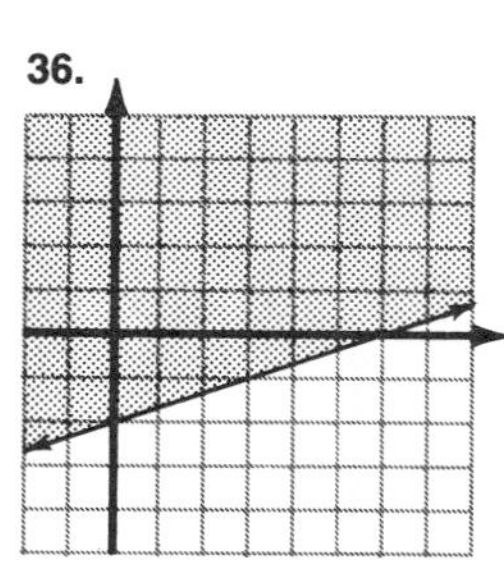

41.

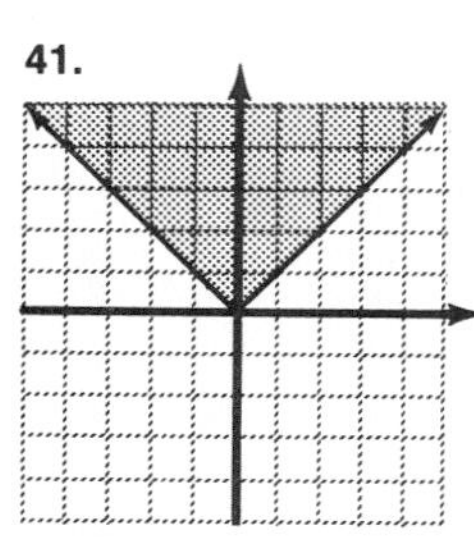

42.

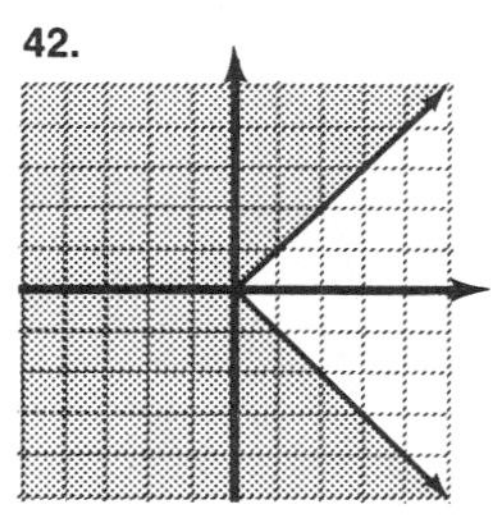

43.

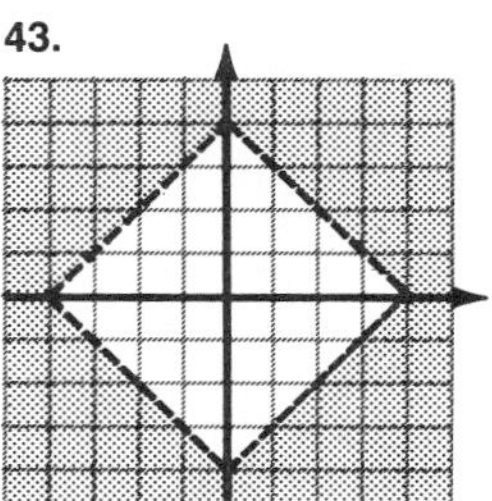

44.

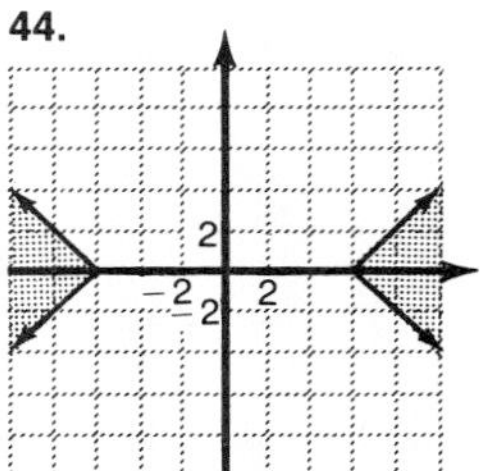

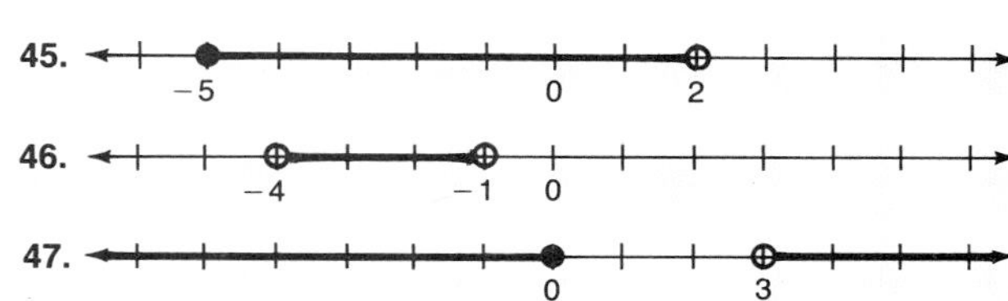

PAGE 422 TRY THIS 9-6

a.

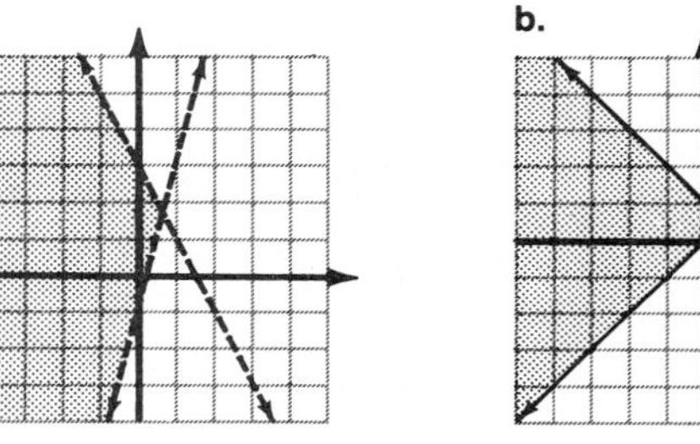

b.

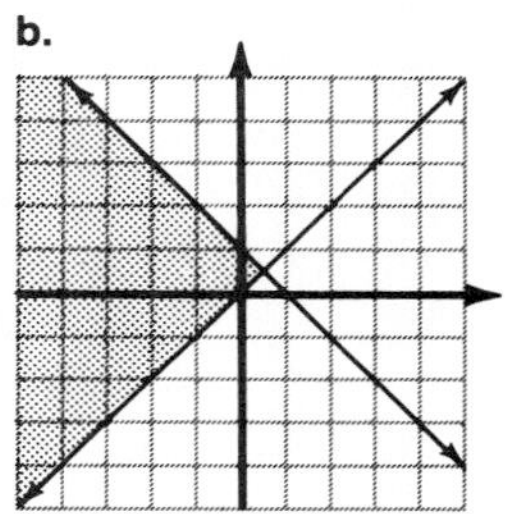

c.

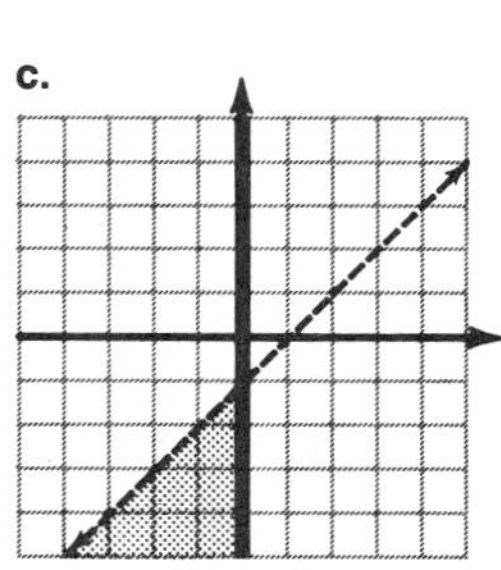

d.

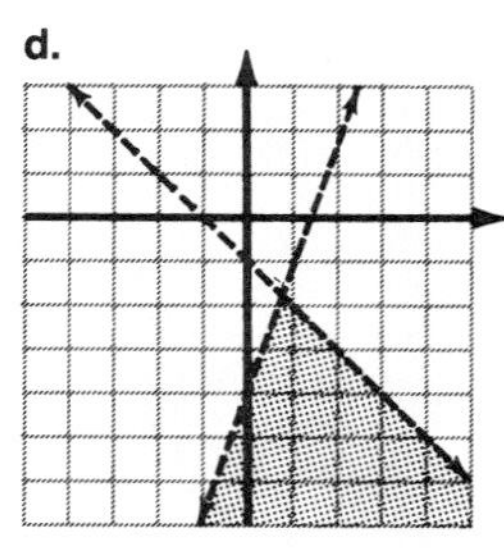

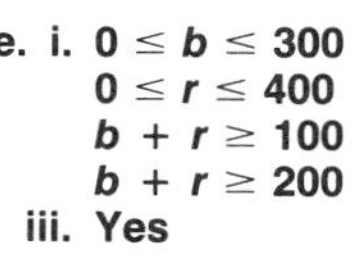

e. i. $0 \le b \le 300$
$0 \le r \le 400$
$b + r \ge 100$
$b + r \ge 200$

iii. Yes

ii.

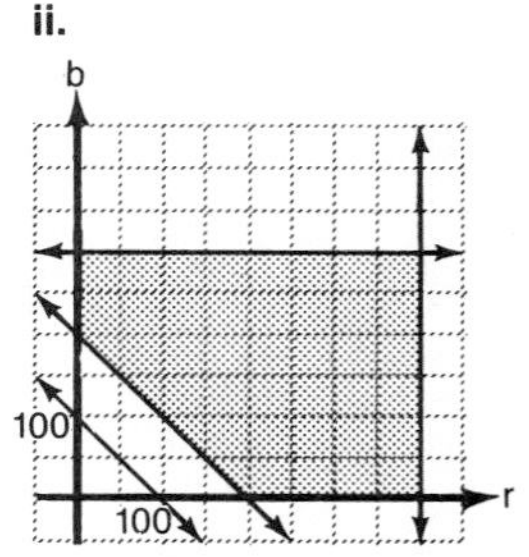

PAGE 423 EXERCISE SET 9-6

1.

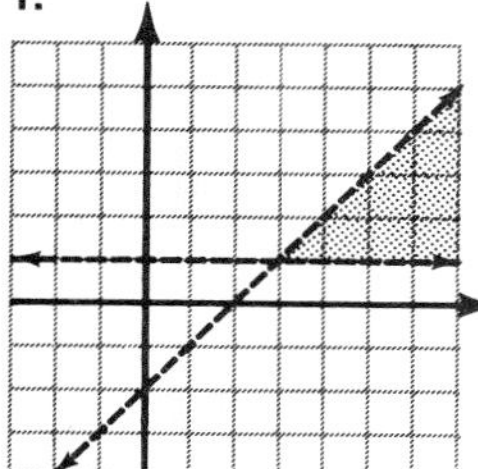

2.

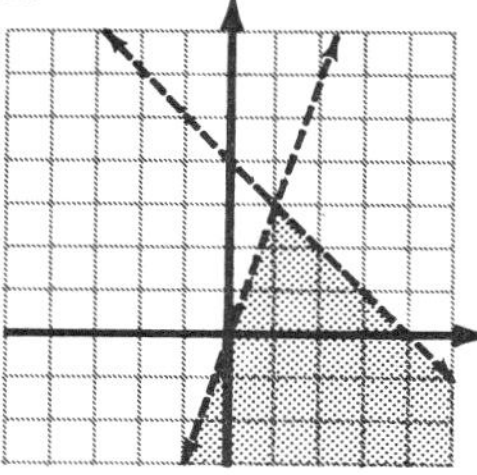

3.

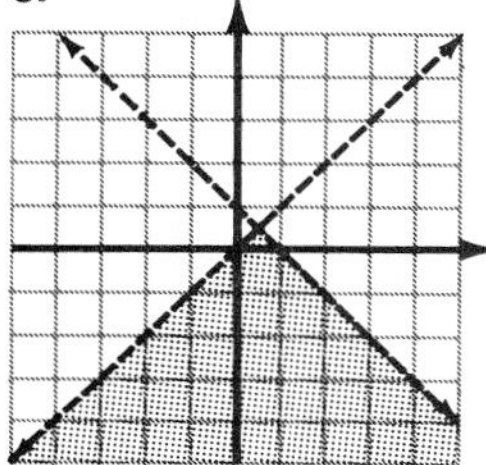

4.

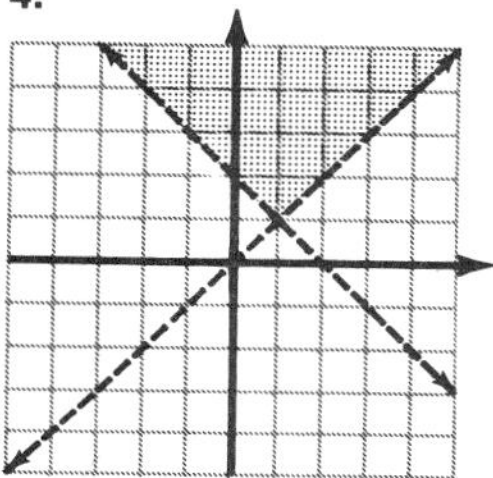

5.

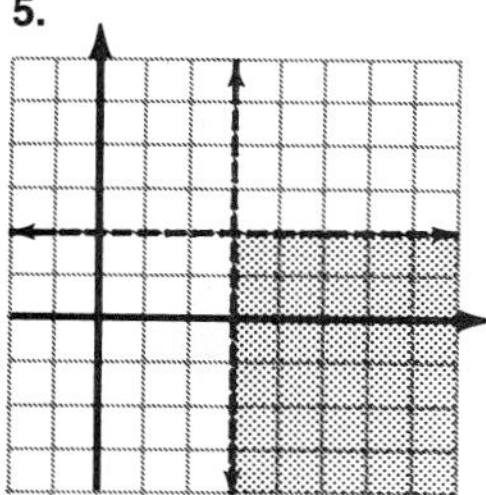

6.

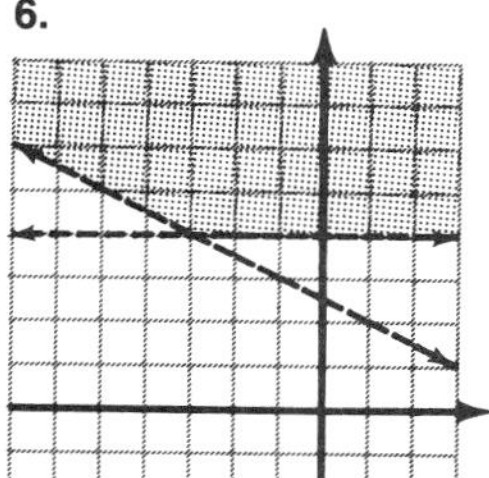

7.

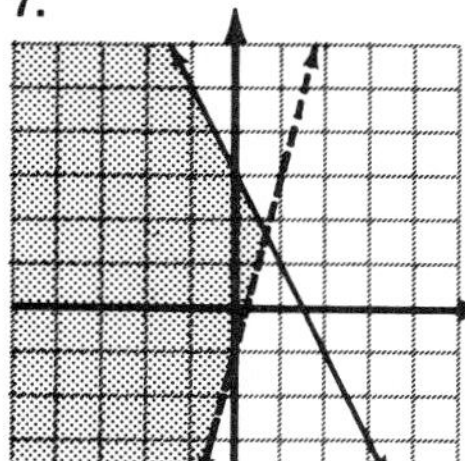

8.

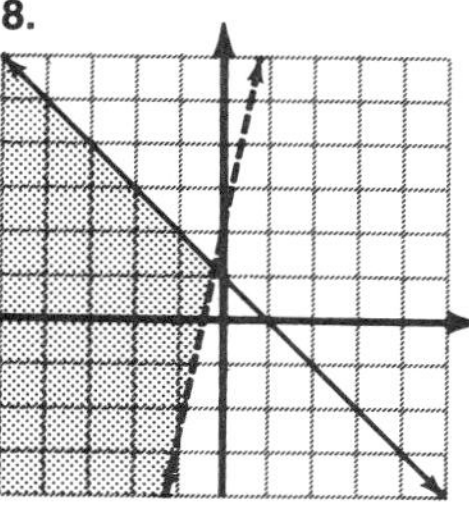

9.

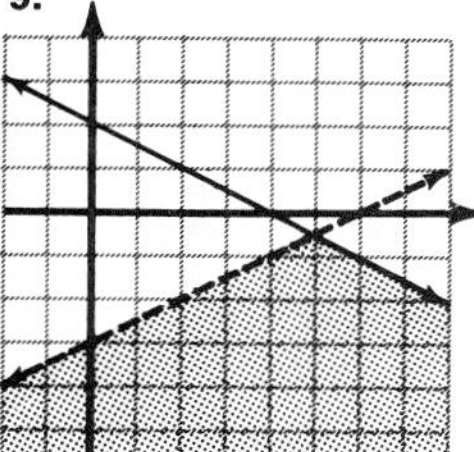

10.

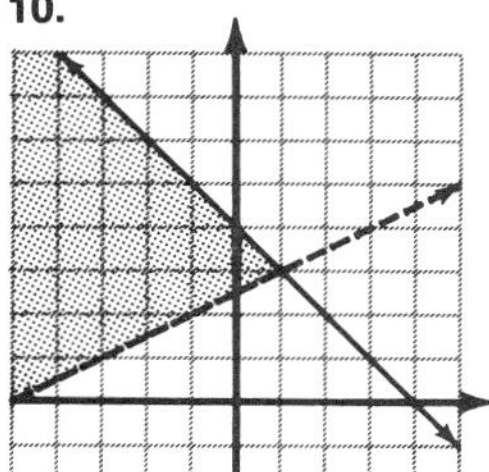

11.

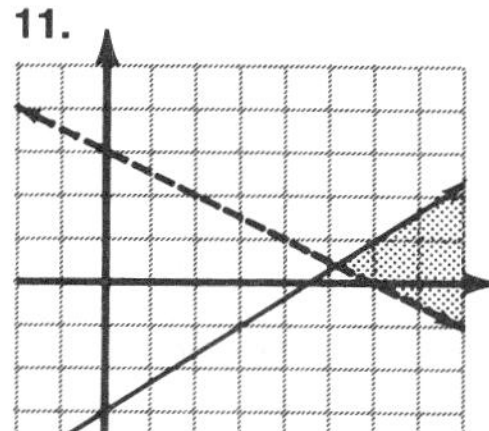

12.

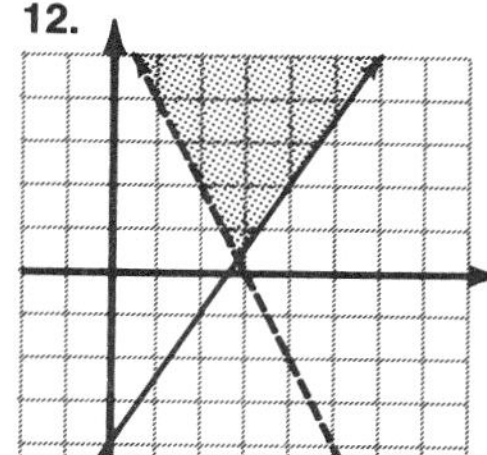

13.

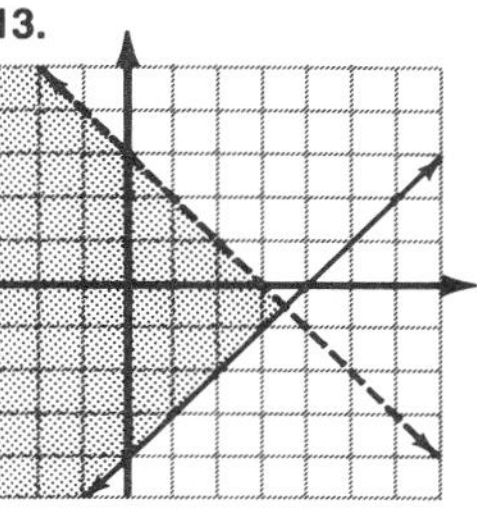

14.

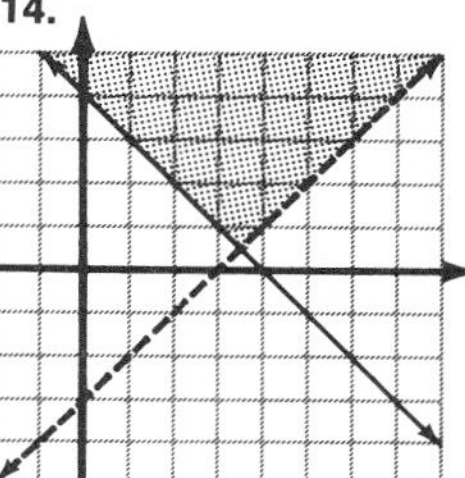

15.

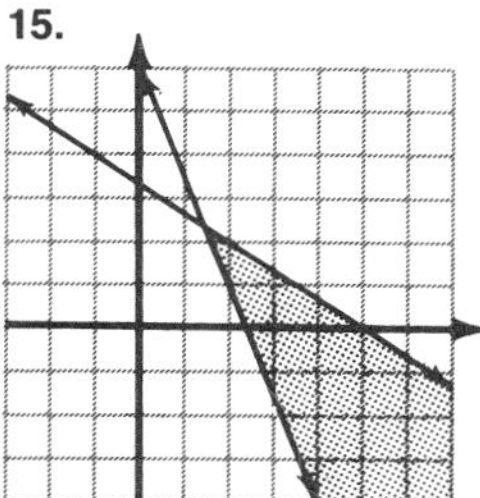

16.

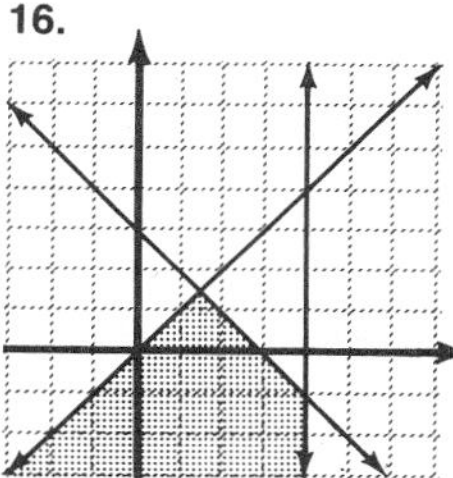

17.

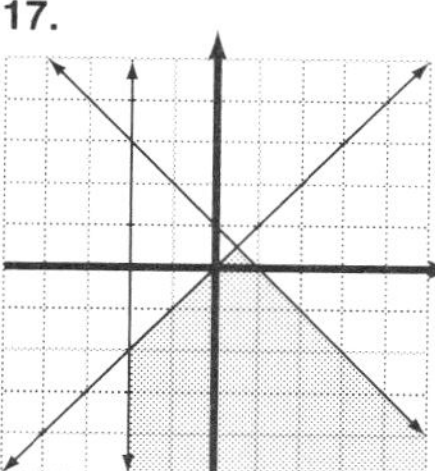

18.

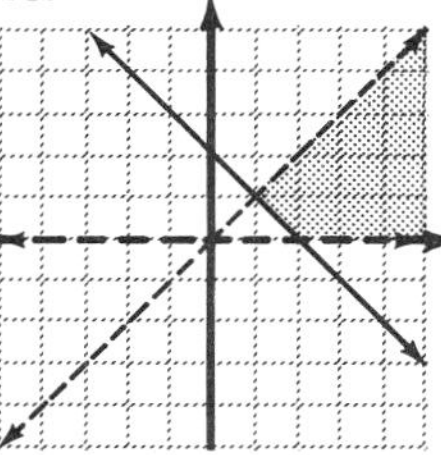

19.

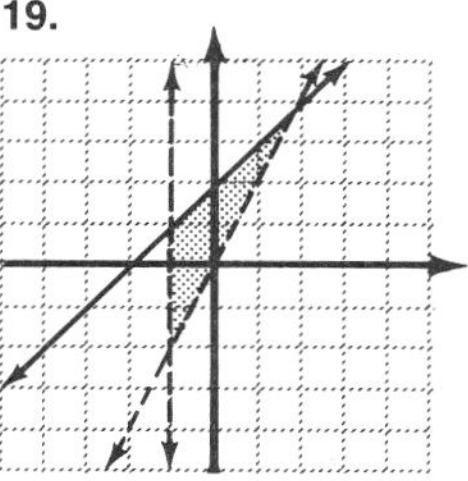

20.

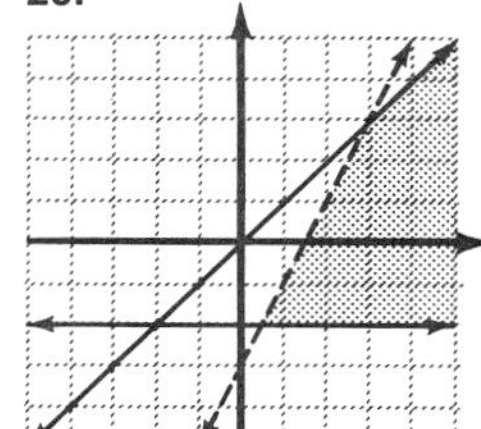

21.

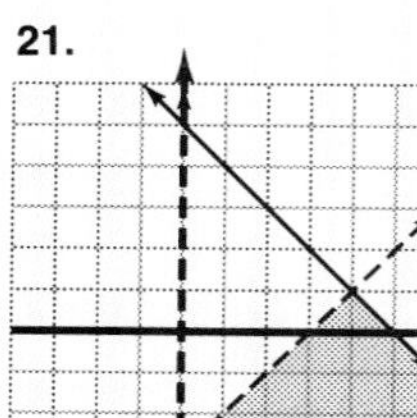

PAGE 428 SUMMARY AND REVIEW CHAPTER 9

32.

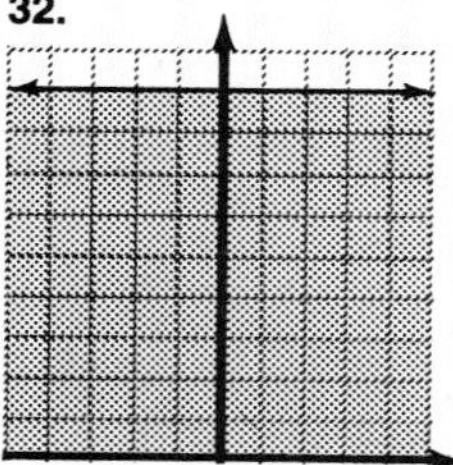

33.

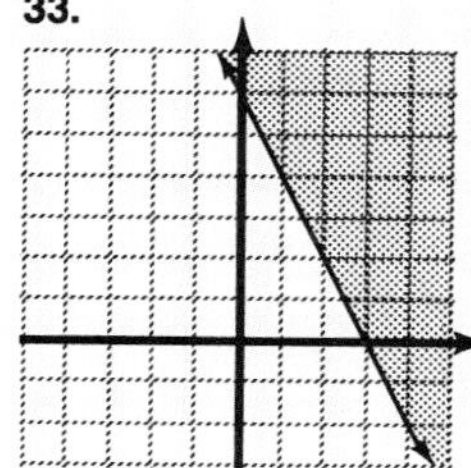

34.

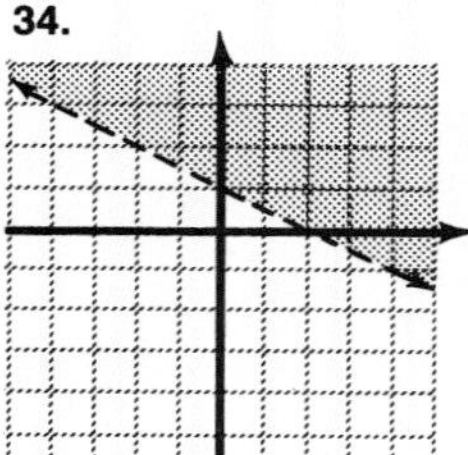

35.

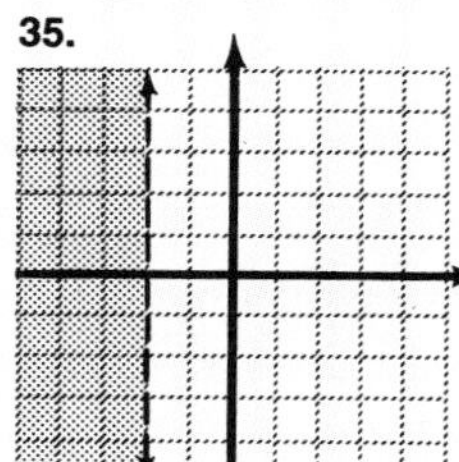

36.

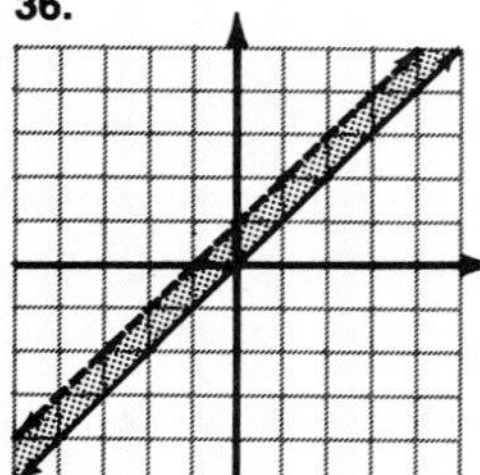

37.

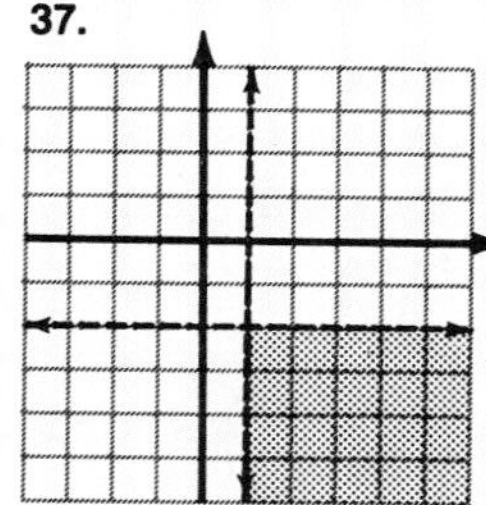

38.

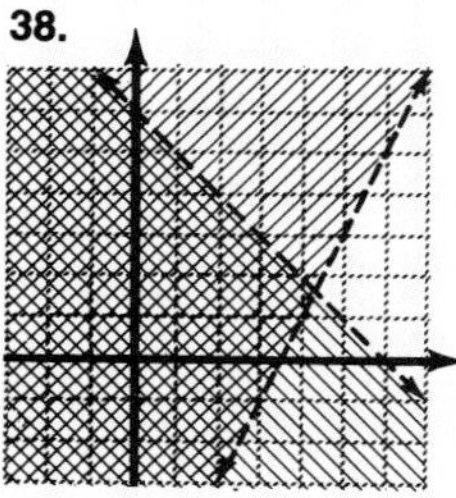

PAGE 429 CHAPTER 9 TEST

9.

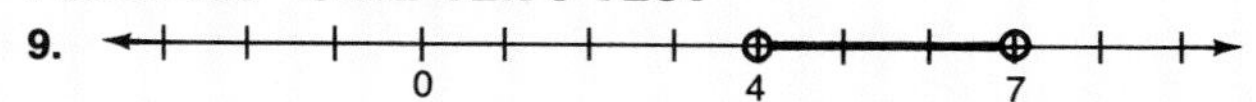

10. −5 −3 0

11. −1 0 2

12. −1 0 1

15. −7 0 7

16. −6 −2 0

17. 0 18

18. −3 0 3

19. −2 0 3

20. −2 0 6

21.

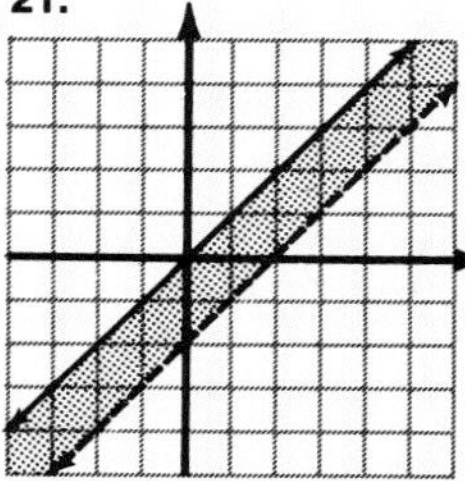

22.

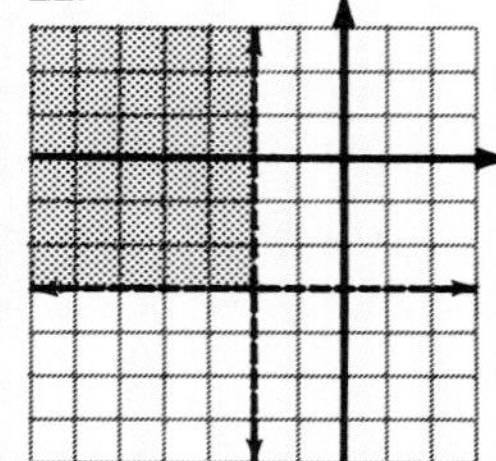

23.

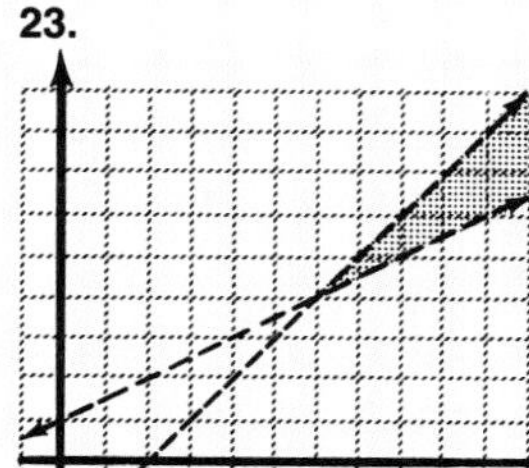

24.

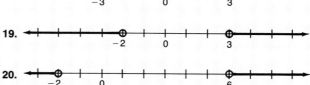

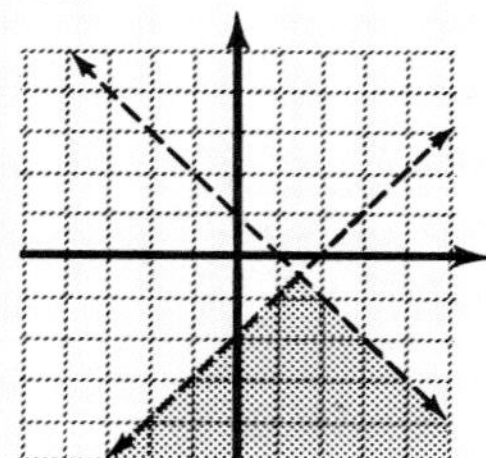

PAGE 474 EXERCISE SET 10-11

3. Show $\dfrac{1}{\frac{a}{b}} = \dfrac{b}{a}$.

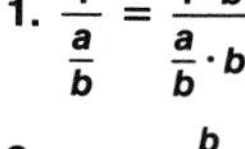

1. $\dfrac{1}{\frac{a}{b}} = \dfrac{1 \cdot b}{\frac{a}{b} \cdot b}$	1. Mult. identity; $\frac{b}{b} = 1$
2. $= \dfrac{b}{\frac{a}{b} \cdot b}$	2. Mult. identity
3. $= \dfrac{b}{\left(a \cdot \frac{1}{b}\right) \cdot b}$	3. Division theorem
4. $= \dfrac{b}{a\left(\frac{1}{b} \cdot b\right)}$	4. Associative property
5. $= \dfrac{b}{a(1)}$	5. Definition of reciprocal
6. $= \dfrac{b}{a}$	6. Mult. identity
7. $\dfrac{1}{\frac{a}{b}} = \dfrac{b}{a}$	7. Transitive property of equality

4. If $\frac{a}{b} = \frac{c}{d}$ show $ad = bc$.

1. $\frac{a}{b}(bd) = \frac{c}{d}(bd)$	1. Multiplication property of equalities
2. $\left(a \cdot \frac{1}{b}\right)(bd) = \left(c \cdot \frac{1}{d}\right)(bd)$	2. Division Theorem
3. $\left(a \cdot \frac{1}{b}\right)(bd) = \left(c \cdot \frac{1}{d}\right)(db)$	3. Commutative property
4. $a\left(\frac{1}{b} \cdot b\right)d = c\left(\frac{1}{d} \cdot d\right)b$	4. Associative property
5. $a \cdot 1 \cdot d = c \cdot 1 \cdot b$	5. Definition of Reciprocal
6. $ad = cb$	6. Mult. identity

11.

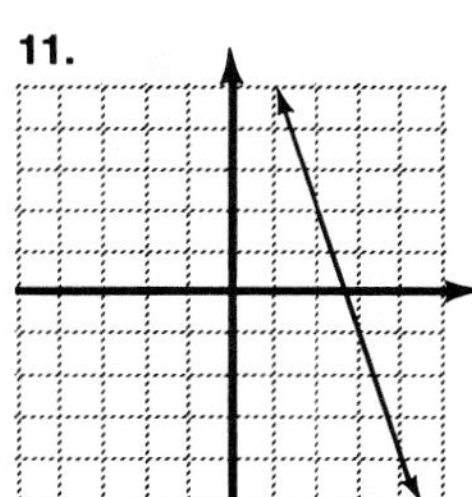

PAGE 535 READY FOR CHAPTER 12?

9.

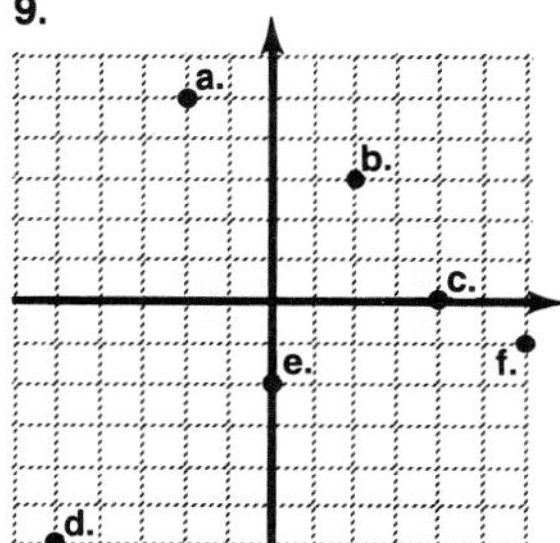

10.

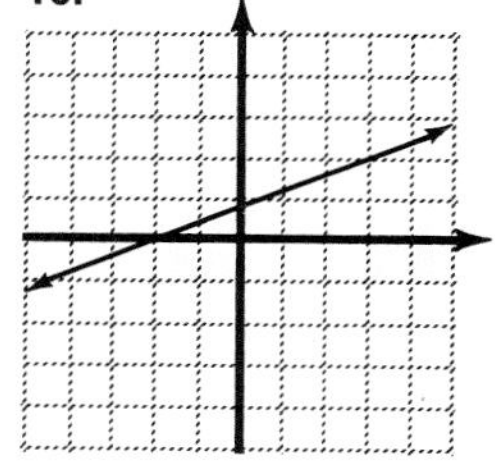

PAGE 544 EXERCISE SET 12-2

3.

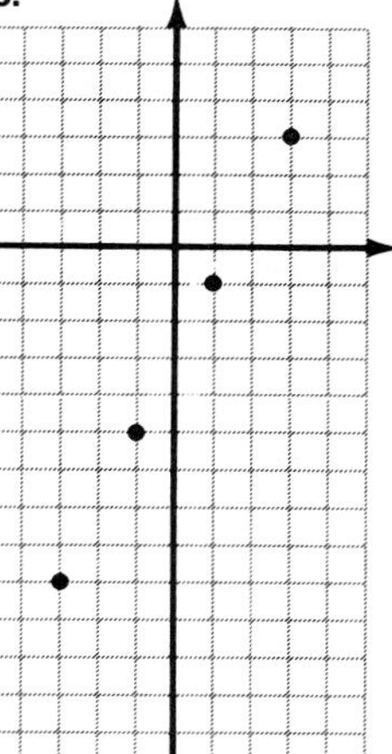

4.

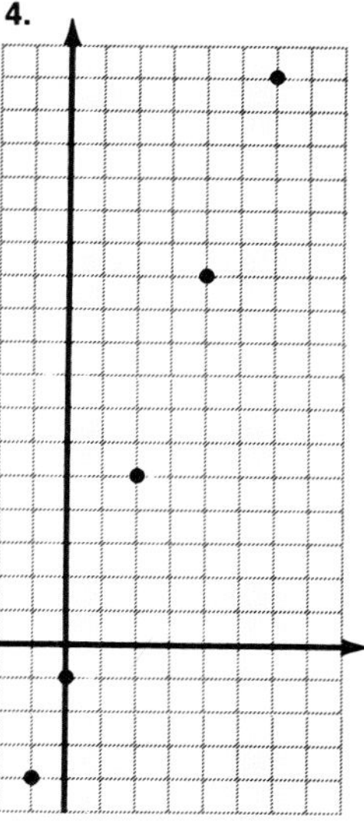

5.

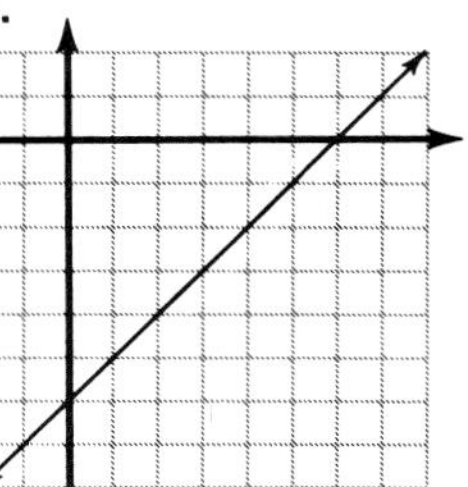

6.

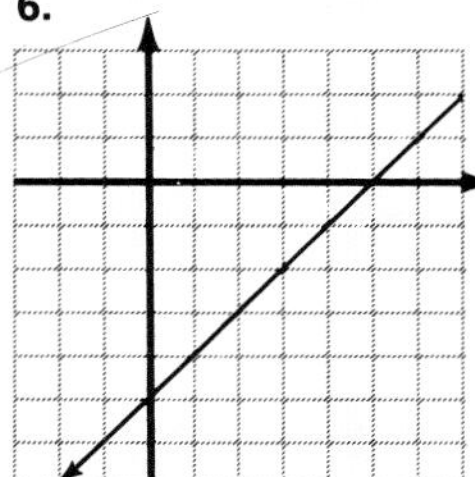

7.

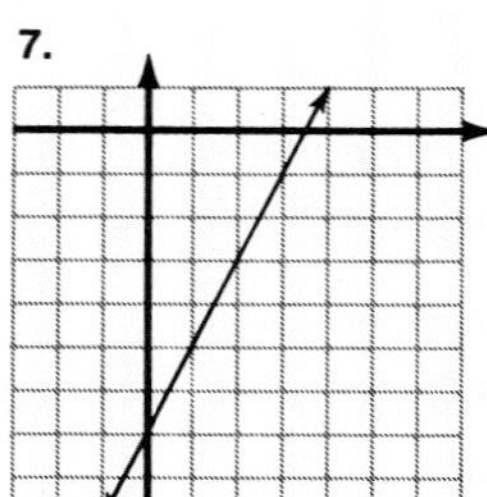

8.

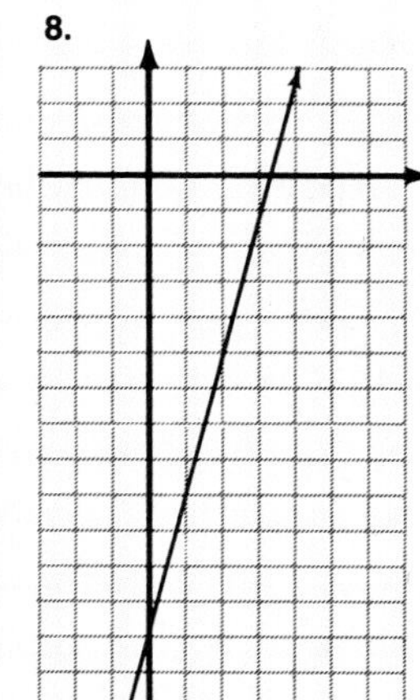

9.

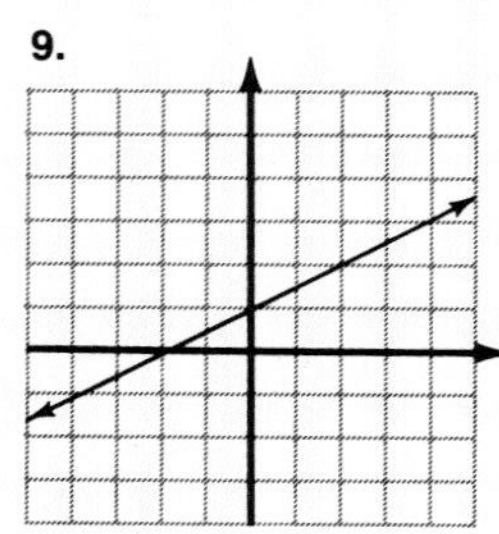

10.

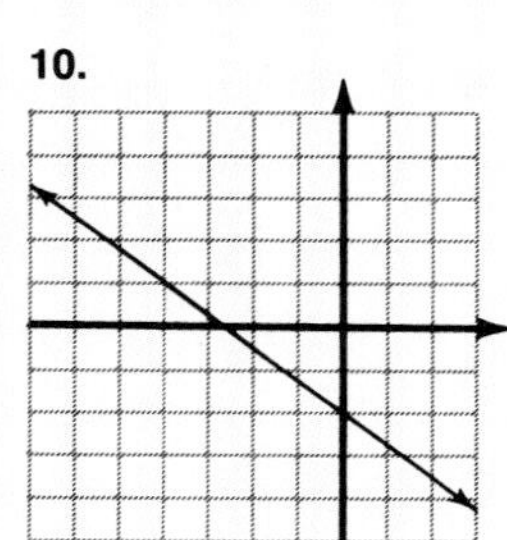

11.

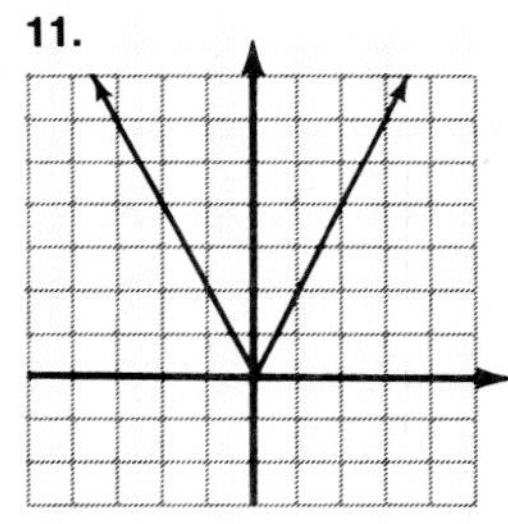

12.

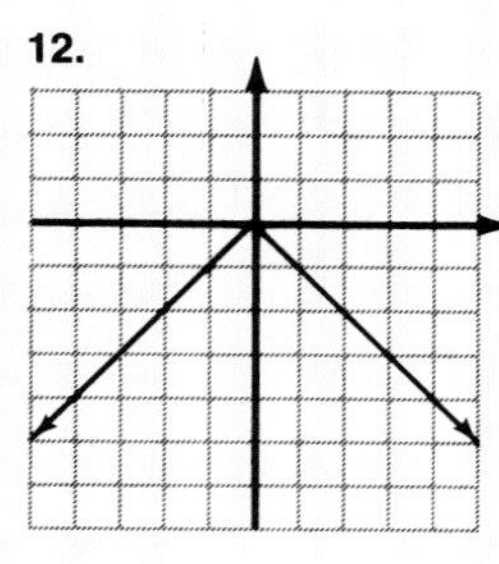

13.

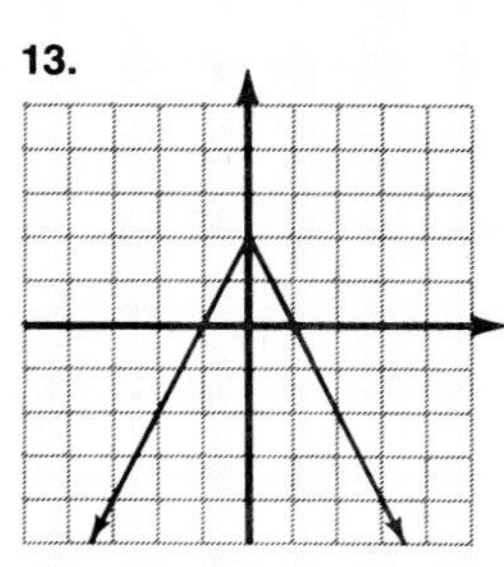

PAGE 554 EXERCISE SET 12-4

4.

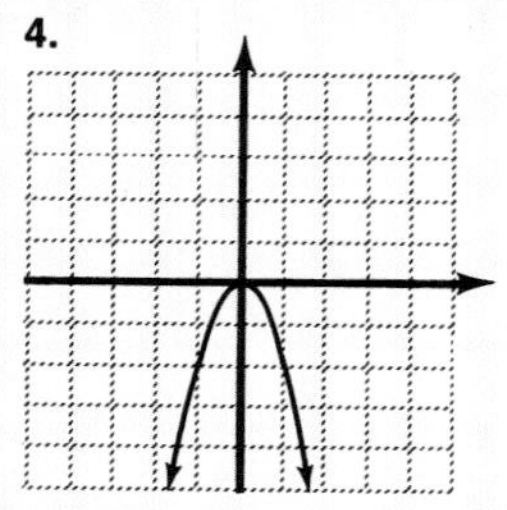

5.

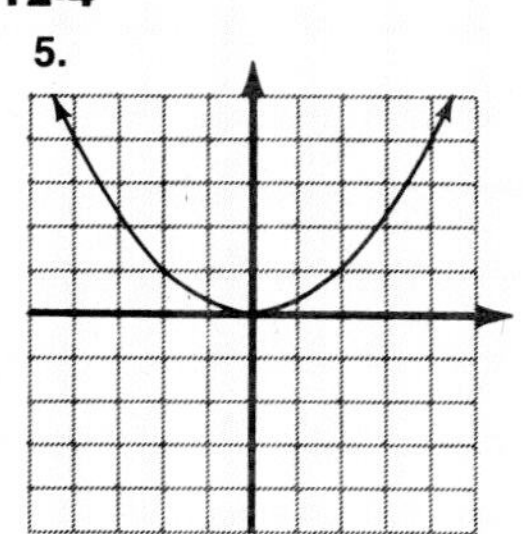

6.

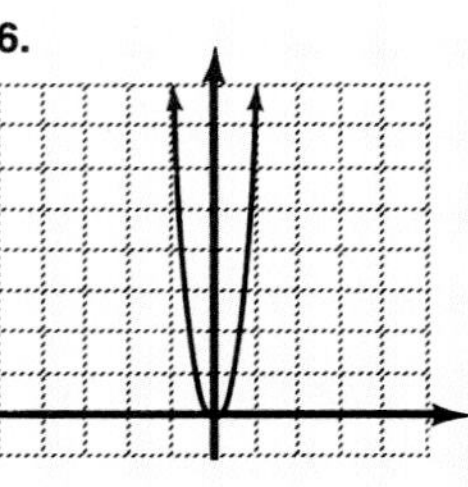

7.

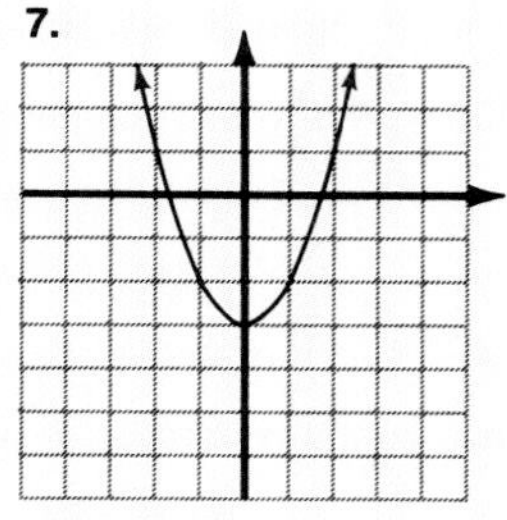

8.

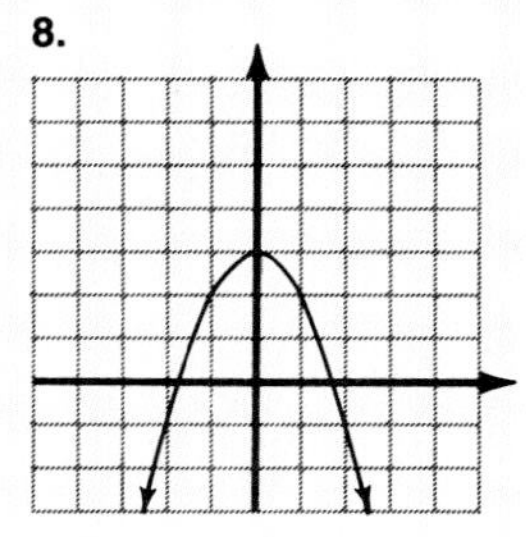

9.

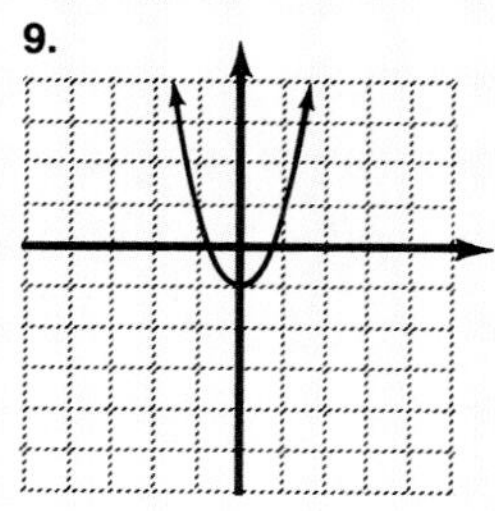

10.

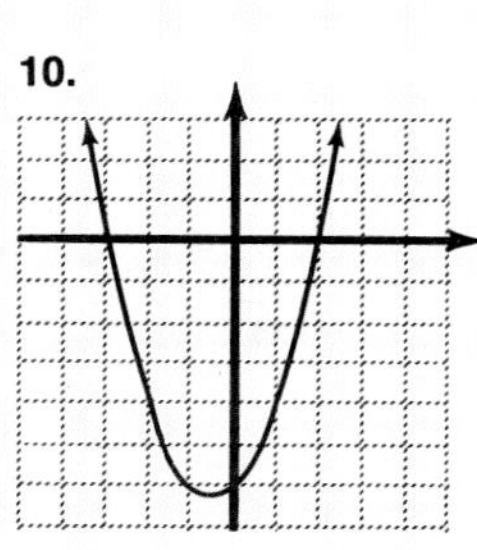

11.

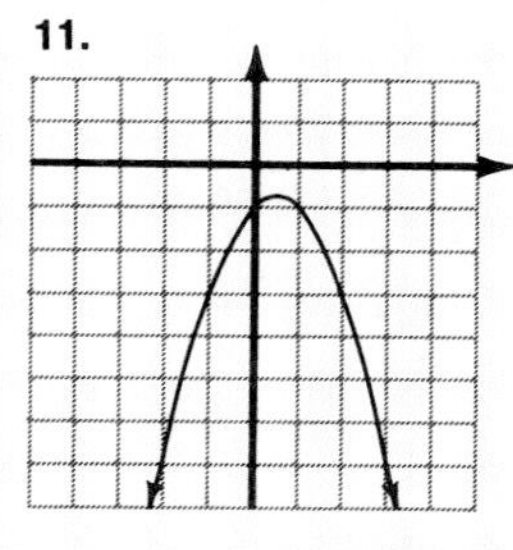

12.

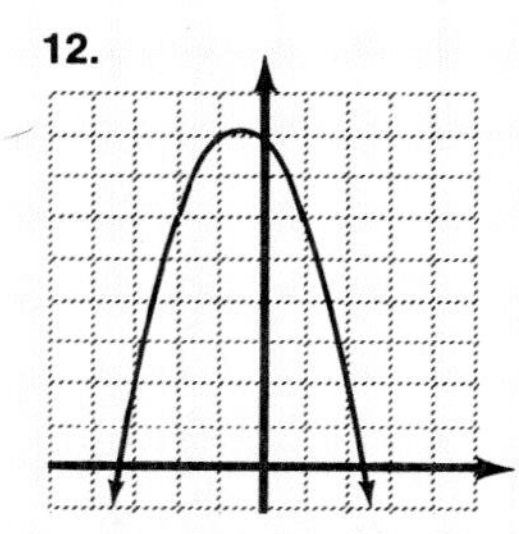

13.

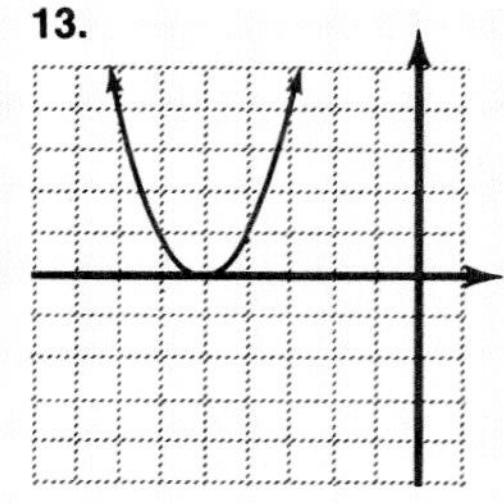

14.

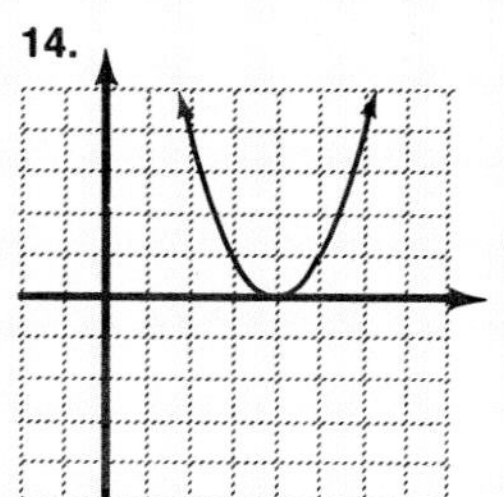

15.

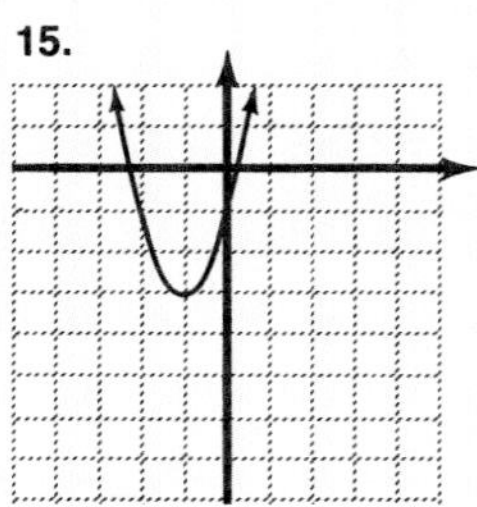

16.

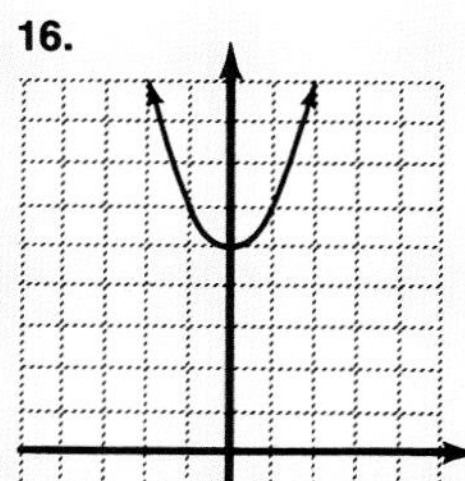

17.

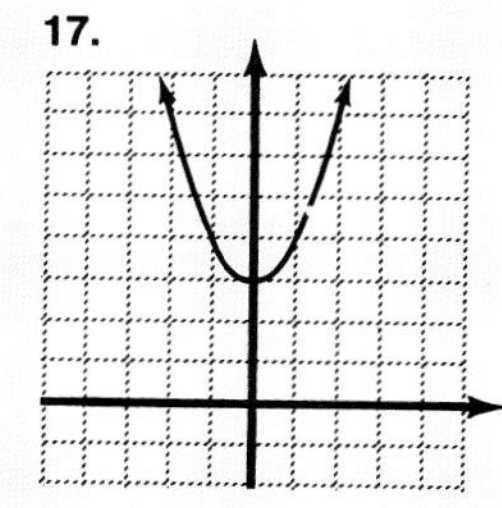

18.

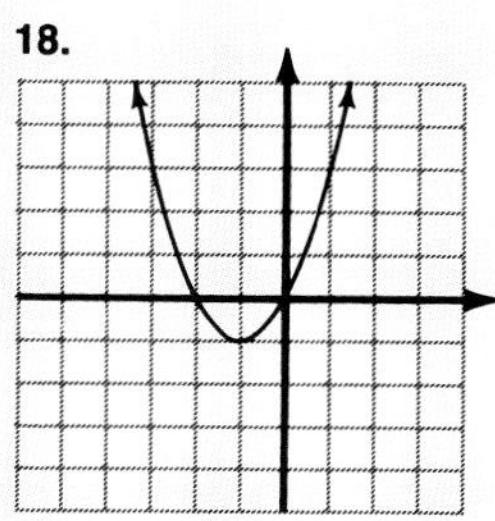

PAGE 655 EXERCISE SET 15-4

1.

Ages	Frequency
2	8
3	7
4	10
5	2

2.

No-Shows	Frequency
17	2
18	3
19	4
20	6
21	4
22	3
23	3
24	2
25	3

3.

Heights	Frequency
7800–7899	7
7900–7999	4
8000–8099	6
8100–8199	4
8200–8299	0
8300–8399	0
8400–8499	1
8500–8599	2
8600–8699	0
8700–8799	1

4.

Lengths	Frequency
2000–2249	5
2250–2499	4
2500–2749	0
2750–2999	1
3000–3249	1
3250–3499	3
3500–3749	1
3750–3999	1
4000–4249	1
4250–4499	1
4500–4749	1

5.

Stem	Leaf
15	9, 8
16	8, 5, 5, 6, 9, 5, 7, 7, 4, 3
17	7, 2, 2, 6, 4, 0, 4, 9, 8, 4, 5, 9, 6
18	0, 1, 0

6.

Stem	Leaf
10	3, 7, 8, 2, 3, 6
11	1, 9, 9
12	3, 5, 7, 3, 8, 9
13	2, 5, 8, 9, 2
14	3, 3, 6
15	4, 4, 2
16	5, 2

PAGE 660 EXERCISE SET 15-5

1.

65 70 75 80

Pulse Rate

2.

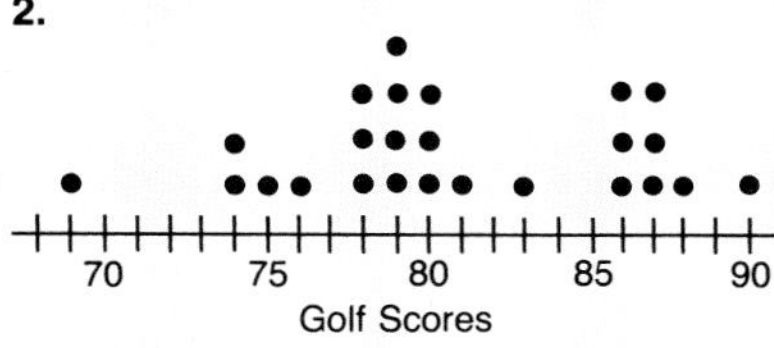

3.

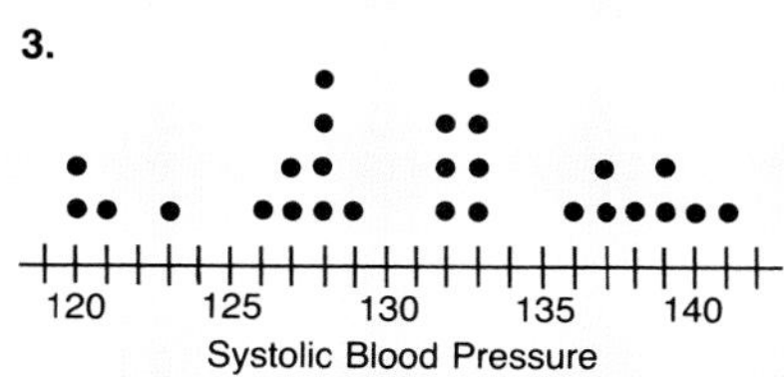

4.

0 1 2 3 4 5 6 7 8 9 10

Quiz Scores

5.

Frequency: 5 10 15 20

60 70 80 90

Pulse Rate

6.

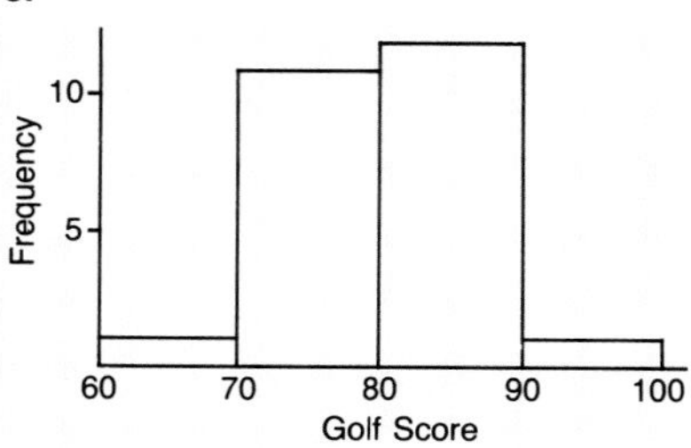

7.

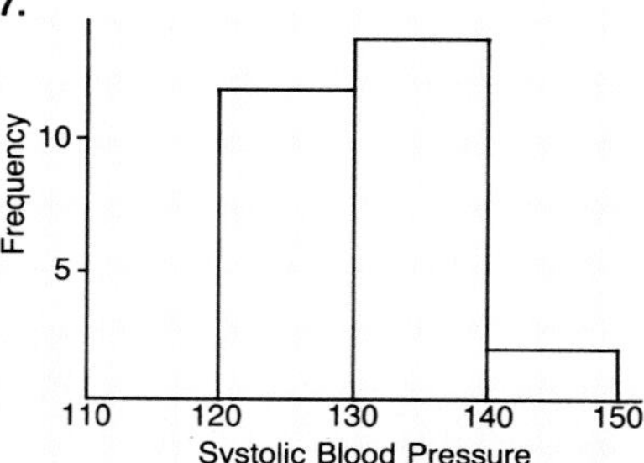

8.

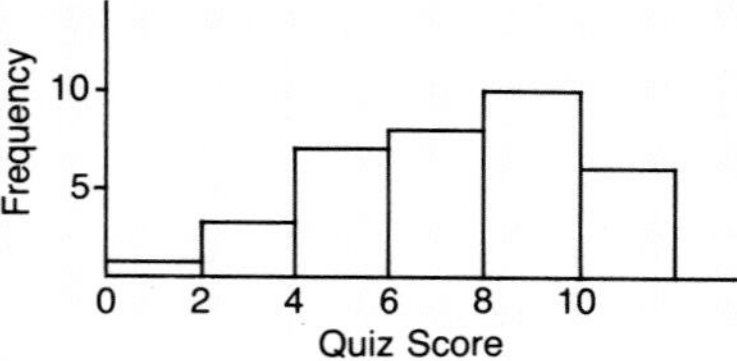

9.

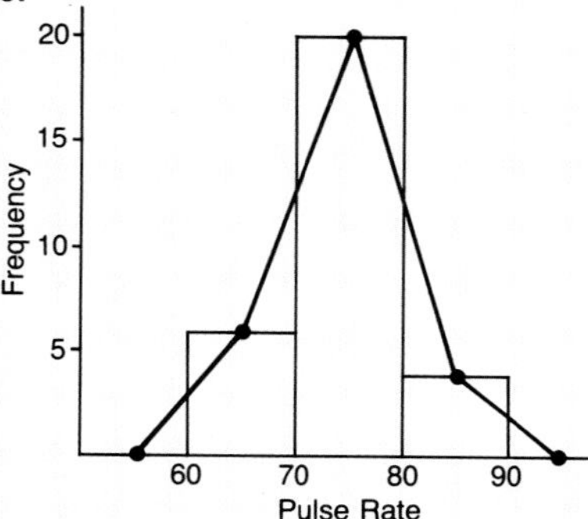

10.

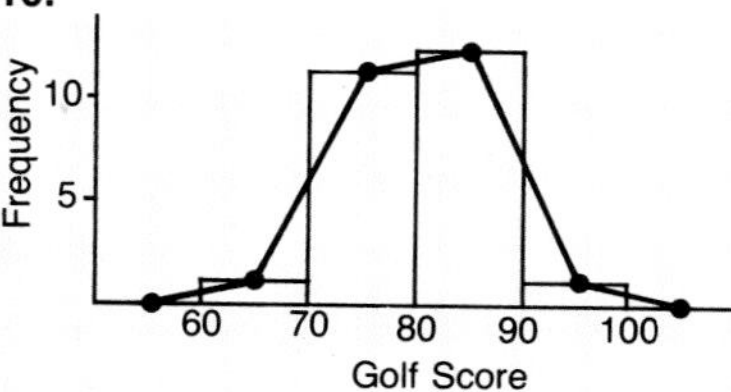

11.

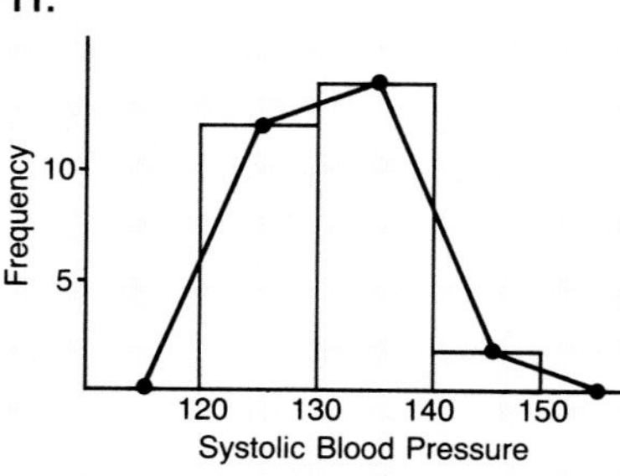

12.

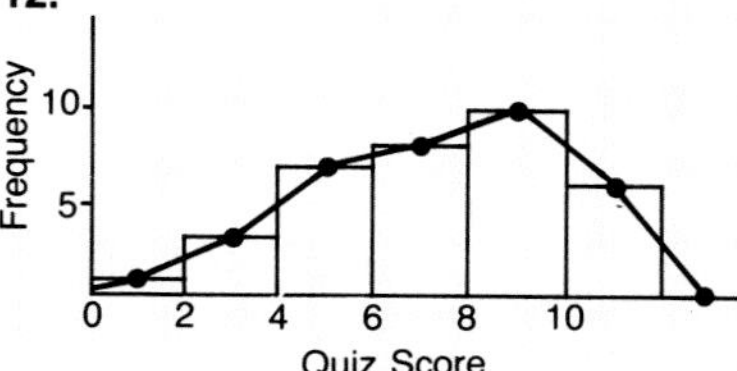

13. Answers may vary.

14. Use the stems to determine the intervals. Then the number of leaves on each stem is the frequency for the corresponding interval.

15.

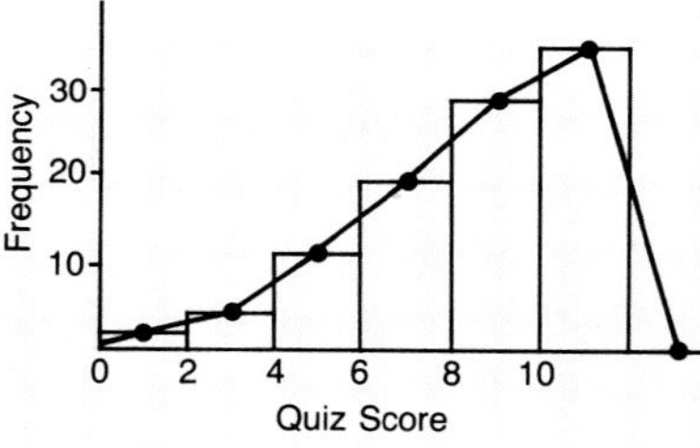

PAGE 690 MIXED PRACTICE 7

38. 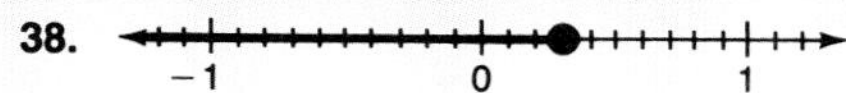

39. 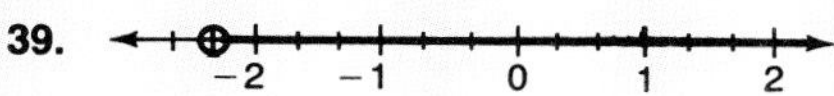

40. −3 −2 −1 0 1 2 3 4

41. −3 −2 −1 0 1 2 3 4

42. −3 −2 −1 0 1 2 3 4

43. −3 0 3 6

PAGE 697 MIXED PRACTICE 14

5.
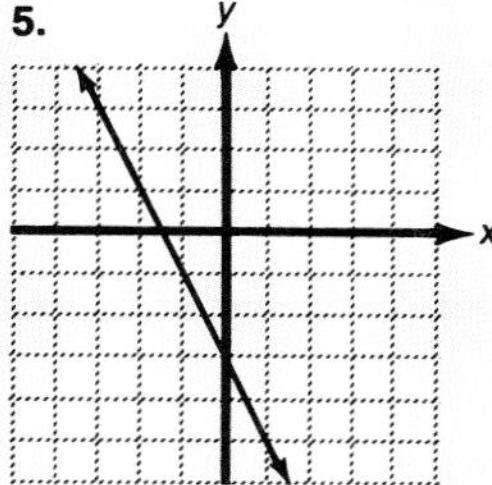

6.
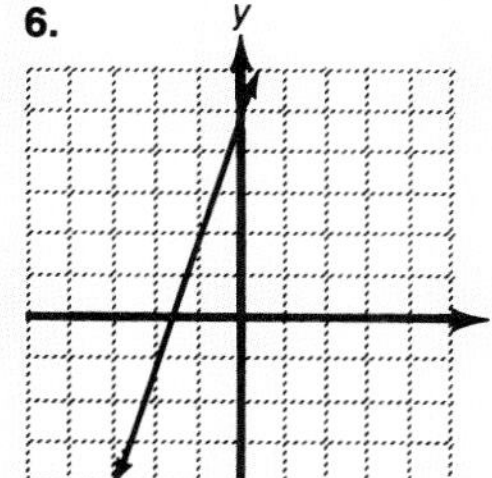

7.
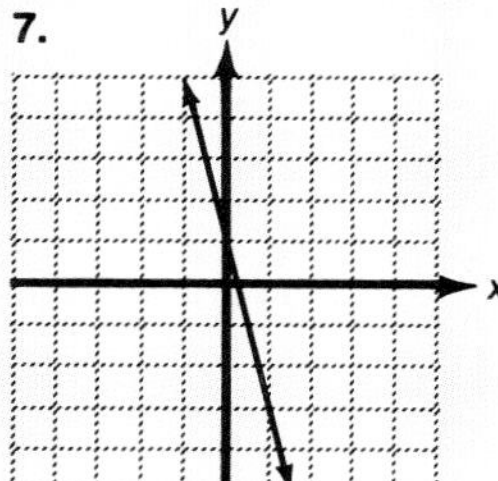

8.
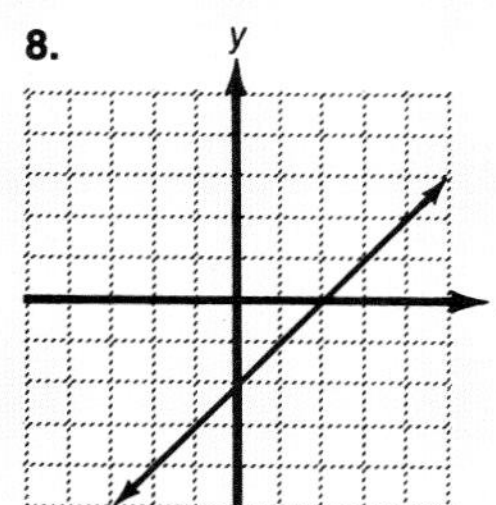

16.
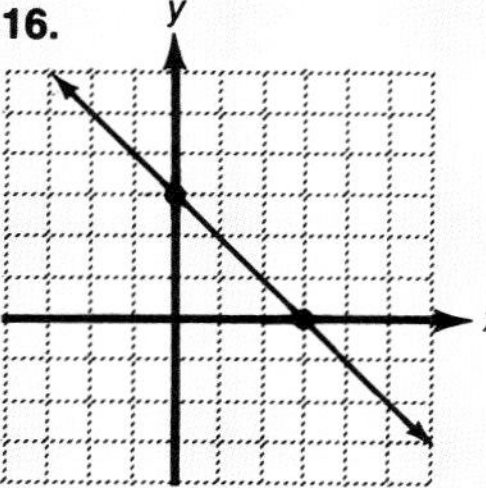

17.
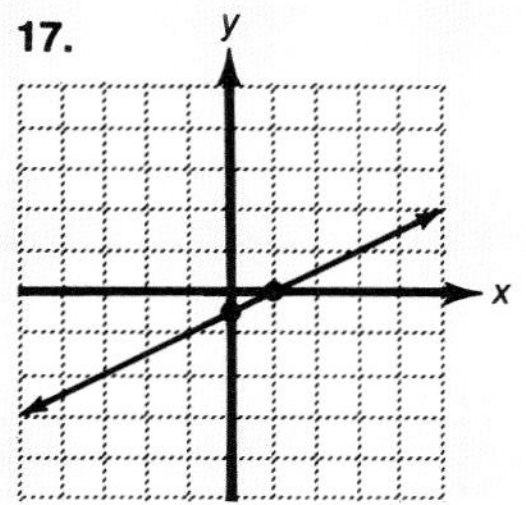

18.
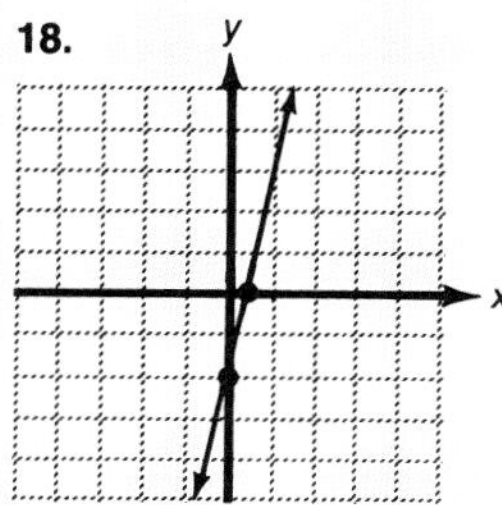

19.
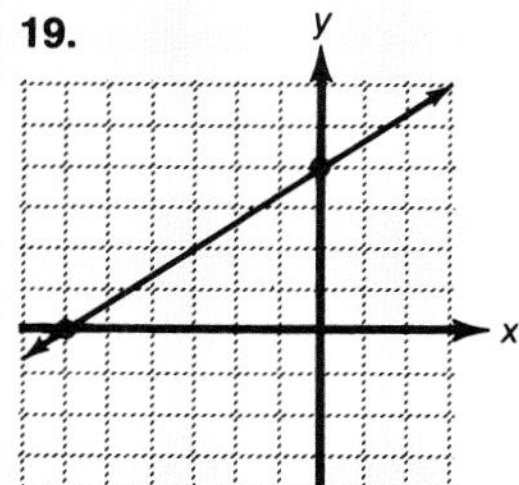

PAGE 698 MIXED PRACTICE 15

15.
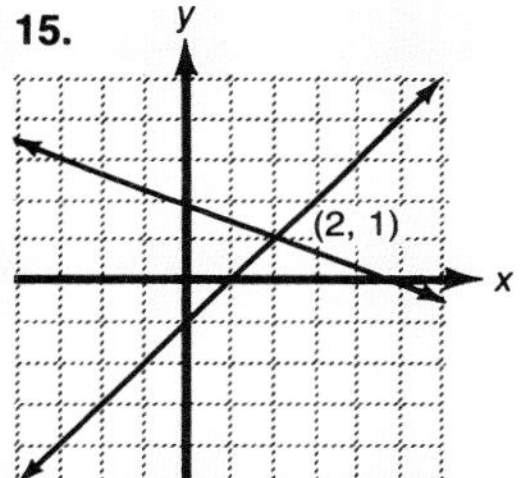

16.
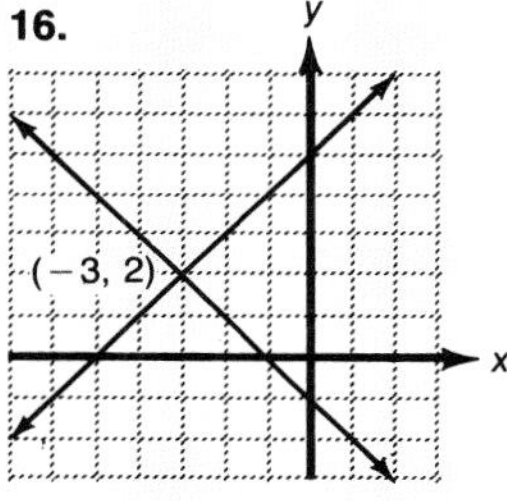

17.
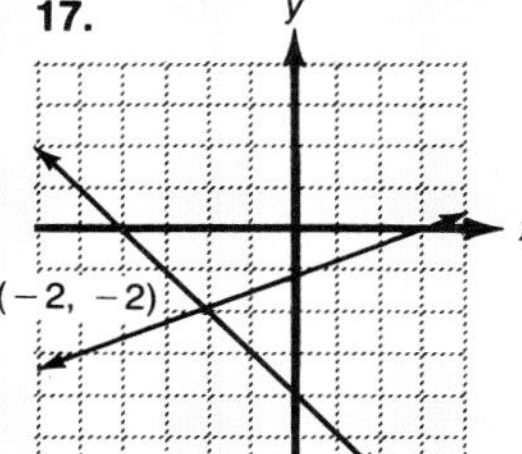

18.
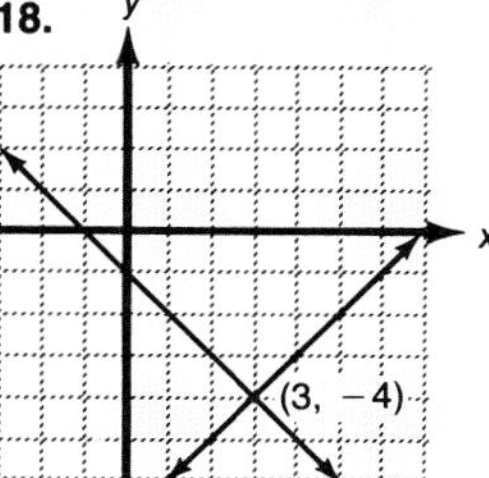

PAGE 699 MIXED PRACTICE 16

7.
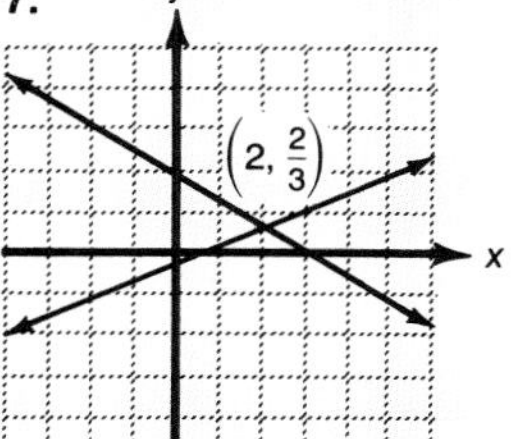

8.
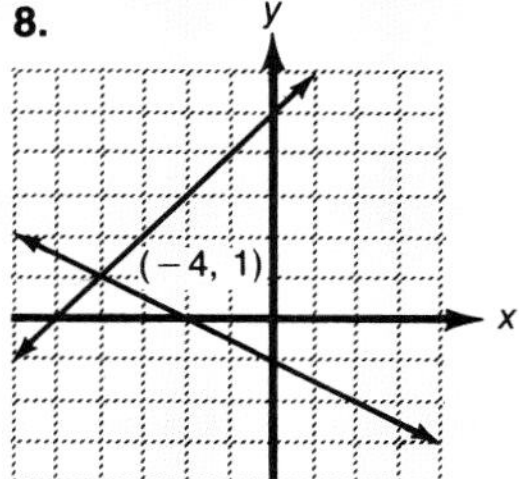

PAGE 700 MIXED PRACTICE 17

28. −6 −4 −2 0 2 4 6

29. 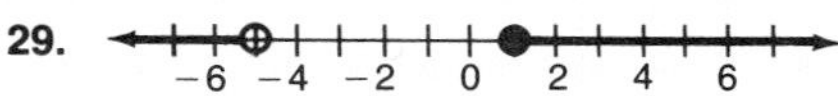

30. −6 −4 −2 0 2 4 6

31. 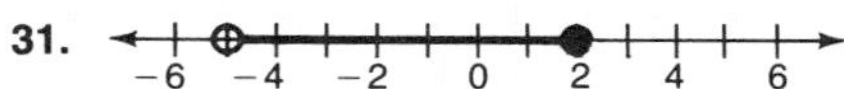

PAGE 701 MIXED PRACTICE 18

1. −10 −8 −6 −4 −2 0 2 4 6 8 10

2. −10 −8 −6 −4 −2 0 2 4 6 8 10

3. 

16. 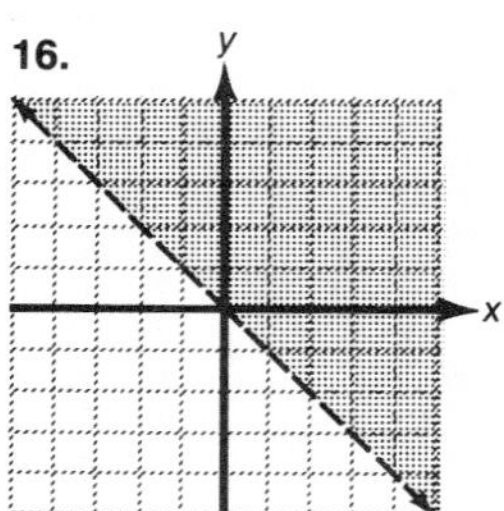

17. 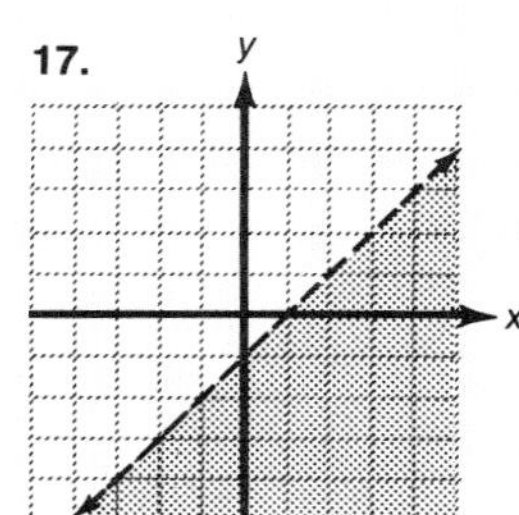

18. 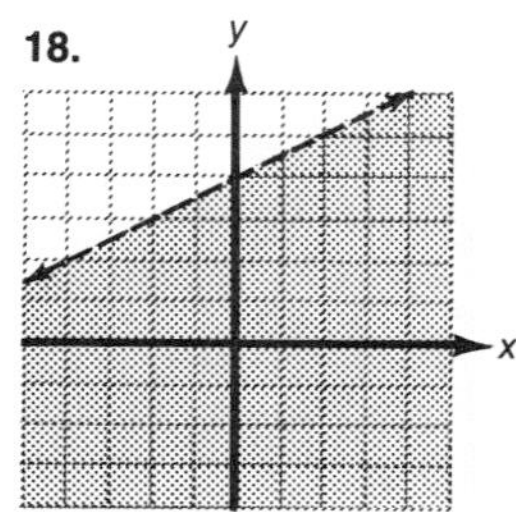

23. 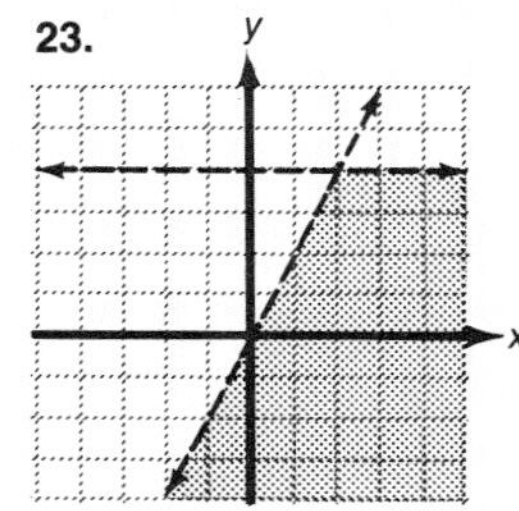

24. 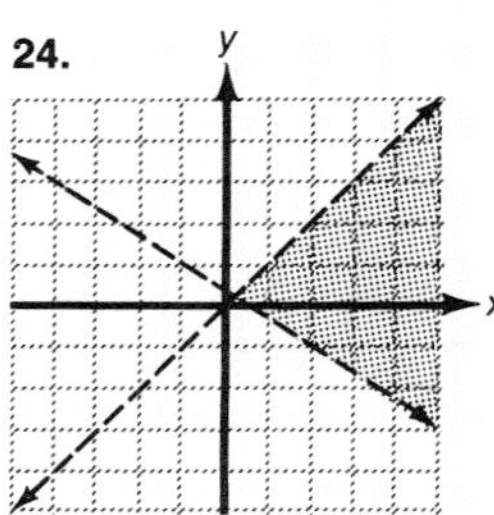

25. 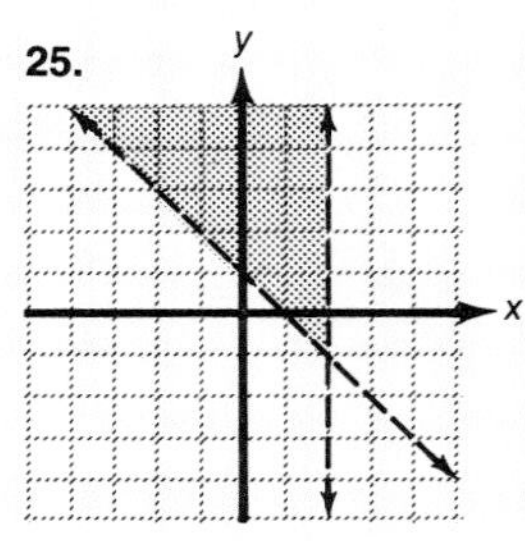

PAGE 706 MIXED PRACTICE 23

9. 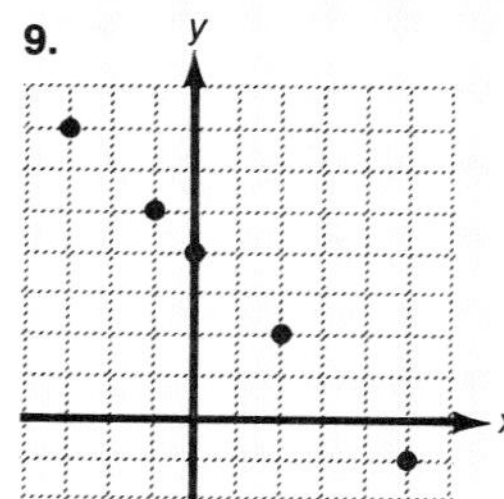

10. 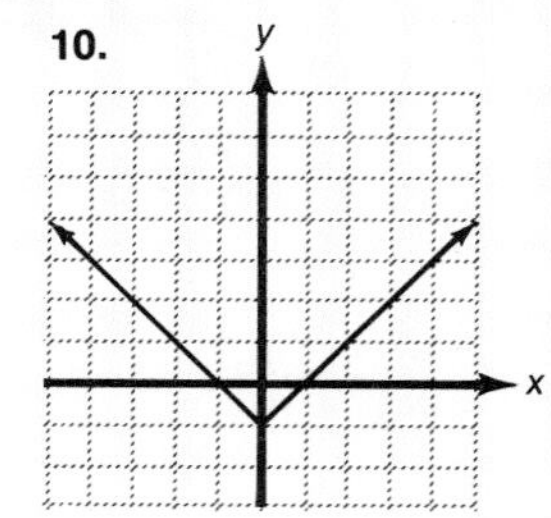

11. 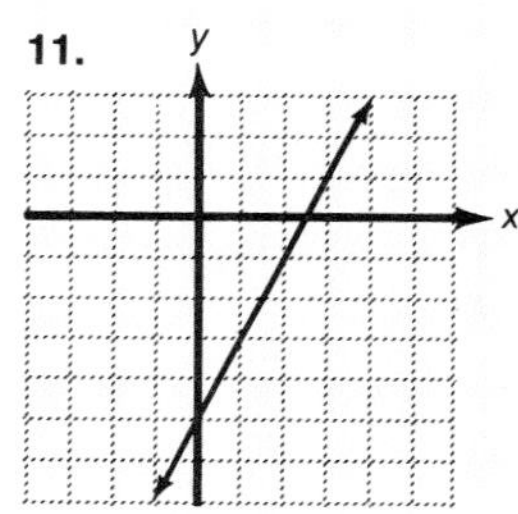

12. 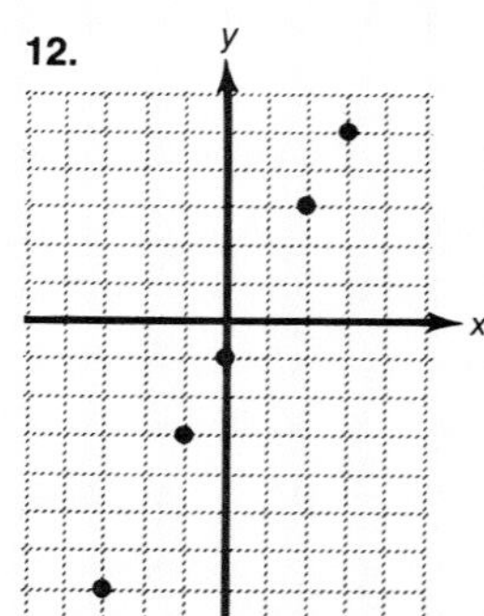

16. 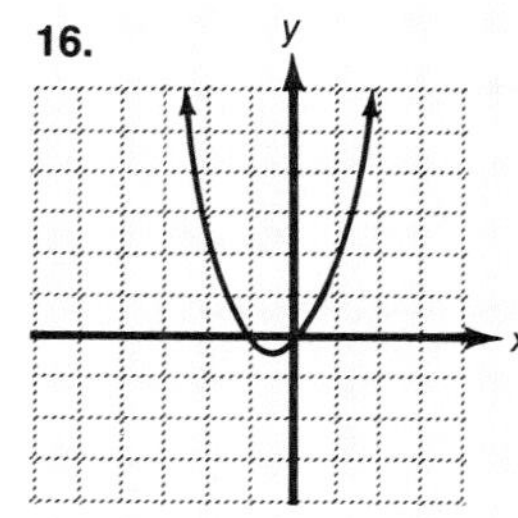

17. 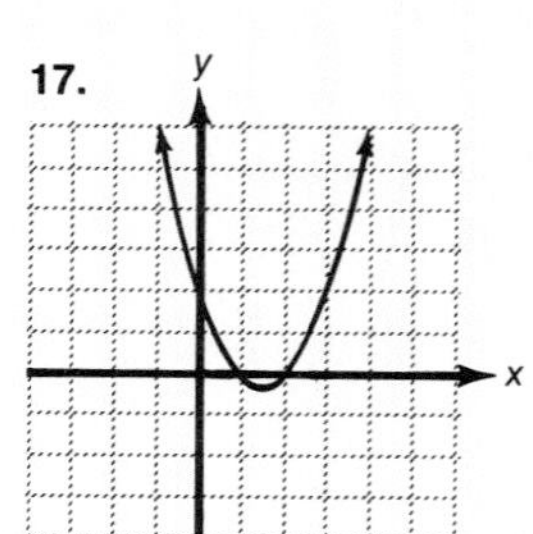

18. 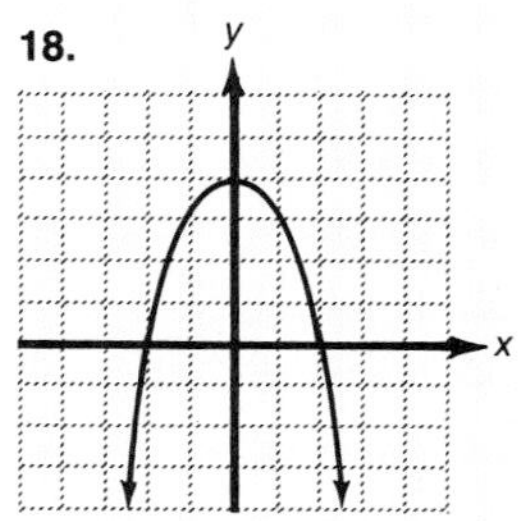

Addison-Wesley

Algebra

Stanley A. Smith
Randall I. Charles
John A. Dossey
Mervin L. Keedy
Marvin L. Bittinger

ADDISON-WESLEY PUBLISHING COMPANY
Menlo Park, California · Reading, Massachusetts · New York
Don Mills, Ontario · Wokingham, England · Amsterdam · Bonn
Sydney · Singapore · Tokyo · Madrid · San Juan

Photo Acknowledgments

Page	Credit
Cover	© Paul Steel/The Stock Market
003	David M. Doody/Tom Stack & Associates
024 L	Ardis Marshall/Tom Stack & Associates
024 R	Peter Menzel/Stock, Boston
031	Randy Wells/The Stock Market
040	David M. Doody/Tom Stack & Associates
053	John Shaw/Tom Stack & Associates
087	John Shaw/Tom Stack & Associates
101	Pete Saloutos/The Stock Market
113	Thomas Kitchin/Tom Stack & Associates
117	Bob Daemmrich/Stock, Boston
119	Thomas Kitchin/Tom Stack & Associates
123	NASA
130	Charles Feil/After-Image
171	Henley & Savage/The Stock Market
188	Henley & Savage/The Stock Market
190	Menschenfreund/The Stock Market
193	Chris Jones/The Stock Market
203	Ken Biggs/The Stock Market
217	Dan McCoy/Rainbow
227	Ken Biggs/The Stock Market
253	© Jim Karageorge
261	© David Madison
277	Brian Parker/Tom Stack & Associates
292	© David Madison
303	Focus on Sports

Page	Credit
334	Focus on Sports
357	Chris Jones/The Stock Market
376	Chris Jones/The Stock Market
386	The Bettman Archive, Inc.
394	© Harold Sund
399	Gil Garner/After-Image
414	Gil Garner/After-Image
421	Tom Stack/Tom Stack & Associates
431	Chas. Summers/Am West
432	Brian Parker/Tom Stack & Associates
461	Chas. Summers/Am West
481	William James Warren/West Light
507	Jeff Perkell/The Stock Market
520	William James Warren/West Light
535	C. Benjamin/Tom Stack & Associates
567	C. Benjamin/Tom Stack & Associates
575	Charles O'Rear/West Light
604	Charles O'Rear/West Light
607	Cameron Davidson/Bruce Coleman Inc.
608	Tim Davis*
613	Robert Rathe/After-Image
633	Robert Rathe/After-Image
634	James Holland/Black Star
639	Tim Davis
650	Tim Davis
669	© David Madison

*Photograph provided expressly for the publisher.

ISBN 0-201-81248-7

1 2 3 4 5 6 7 8 9 10-VH-96 95 94 93

Arithmetic Review

Add.

1. $\begin{array}{r} 879 \\ +412 \\ \hline \end{array}$ 1291 **2.** $\begin{array}{r} 1354 \\ 2179 \\ 6118 \\ +2771 \\ \hline \end{array}$ 12,422 **3.** $\begin{array}{r} 47.6 \\ +\ 0.8 \\ \hline \end{array}$ 48.4 **4.** $\begin{array}{r} 6.1 \\ 3.48 \\ +0.5 \\ \hline \end{array}$ 10.08

Subtract.

5. $\begin{array}{r} 75 \\ -28 \\ \hline \end{array}$ 47 **6.** $\begin{array}{r} 4003 \\ -\ 276 \\ \hline \end{array}$ 3727 **7.** $\begin{array}{r} 12.4 \\ -\ 3.63 \\ \hline \end{array}$ 8.77 **8.** $\begin{array}{r} 37.009 \\ -18.473 \\ \hline \end{array}$ 18.536

Multiply.

9. $\begin{array}{r} 709 \\ \times 807 \\ \hline \end{array}$ 572,163 **10.** $\begin{array}{r} 8342 \\ \times 7000 \\ \hline \end{array}$ 58,394,000 **11.** $\begin{array}{r} 6.09 \\ \times\ \ 4 \\ \hline \end{array}$ 24.36 **12.** $\begin{array}{r} 5.39 \\ \times\ 2.4 \\ \hline \end{array}$ 12.936

Divide.

13. $18\overline{)3006}$ 167 **14.** $290\overline{)10,150}$ 35 **15.** $2.2\overline{)0.66}$ 0.3 **16.** $0.4\overline{)3.32}$ 8.3

Add. Simplify answers if possible.

17. $\frac{4}{9} + \frac{7}{9}$ $\frac{11}{9}$ **18.** $\begin{array}{r} 8\frac{1}{6} \\ +3\frac{5}{6} \\ \hline \end{array}$ 12 **19.** $\begin{array}{r} 7\frac{1}{8} \\ +12\frac{3}{4} \\ \hline \end{array}$ $19\frac{7}{8}$ **20.** $\begin{array}{r} 2\frac{1}{2} \\ 4\frac{2}{3} \\ +6\frac{3}{4} \\ \hline \end{array}$ $13\frac{11}{12}$

Subtract. Simplify answers if possible.

21. $\begin{array}{r} \frac{7}{8} \\ -\frac{3}{8} \\ \hline \end{array}$ $\frac{1}{2}$ **22.** $\begin{array}{r} \frac{3}{4} \\ -\frac{2}{5} \\ \hline \end{array}$ $\frac{7}{20}$ **23.** $\begin{array}{r} 9\frac{1}{9} \\ -\ \frac{3}{4} \\ \hline \end{array}$ $8\frac{13}{36}$ **24.** $\begin{array}{r} 12\frac{1}{4} \\ -\ 4\frac{5}{8} \\ \hline \end{array}$ $7\frac{5}{8}$

Multiply. Simplify answers if possible.

25. $\frac{2}{7} \times \frac{2}{6}$ $\frac{2}{21}$ **26.** $\frac{4}{9} \times \frac{9}{4}$ 1 **27.** $6 \times 3\frac{1}{8}$ $18\frac{3}{4}$ **28.** $9\frac{3}{4} \times 2\frac{7}{8}$ $28\frac{1}{32}$

Divide. Simplify answers if possible.

29. $\frac{3}{7} \div \frac{3}{7}$ 1 **30.** $\frac{5}{9} \div \frac{5}{2}$ $\frac{2}{9}$ **31.** $\frac{5}{8} \div \frac{2}{5}$ $1\frac{9}{16}$ **32.** $12\frac{1}{2} \div 2\frac{3}{4}$ $4\frac{6}{11}$

CHAPTER 1 Symbols and Expressions

Chapter Overview

The basic concepts and terminology of algebra and the fundamental concept of an algebraic expression are introduced in this first chapter. The student learns that algebraic expressions may be transformed into equivalent expressions using the commutative, associative, identity, inverse, and distributive properties. The conventions for the order of operations and the use of parentheses are covered. The distributive property is used to collect like terms and to factor simple expressions.

Students begin problem solving by translating simple English phrases into algebraic notation. Students explore the concept of a balanced equation and examine replacement sets to determine the solution set of an equation. The Problem-Solving Guidelines are introduced and used to solve simple word problems mentally and by using the strategies *Draw a Diagram* and *Guess, Check, Revise.*

Objectives

1-1
- Evaluate algebraic expressions.
- Evaluate expressions using grouping symbols and the order of operations.

1-2
- Use the commutative properties for addition and multiplication of whole numbers.
- Use the identity properties for addition and multiplication of whole numbers.
- Simplify expressions.

1-3
- Evaluate and express numbers using exponential notation.
- Evaluate expressions containing exponents.

1-4
- Evaluate expressions involving parentheses.
- Write equivalent expressions using the associative properties.
- Write equivalent expressions using the commutative and associative properties.

1-5
- Use the distributive property of multiplication to write equivalent expressions.
- Factor expressions.
- Collect like terms.

1-6
- Write algebraic expressions involving one operation.

1-7
- Determine whether an equation is true, false, or open.
- Find solution sets of an equation.
- Recognize equivalent equations.

1-8
- Solve nonroutine problems using the strategy *Draw a Diagram.*

1-9
- Evaluate formulas.

1-10
- Solve problems using the strategy *Guess, Check, Revise* and other strategies.

Cooperative Learning Opportunities

The **Try This** exercises and **Explores** throughout *Addison-Wesley Algebra* provide a perfect opportunity for students to learn together in cooperative learning groups.

In Chapter 1, have students work in pairs to get used to working together. This will encourage participation from each student, which is critical for larger groups. You should assign students to groups and assign tasks to each member. Tasks should alternate so one student doesn't dominate the group. A goal for chapter 1 is for students to feel a sense of responsibility for the group's success rather than individual success. You should answer questions from a group only, not from an individual.

In addition to the **Try This** exercises, the following activities are well suited to cooperative groups:

1-1: **Order of Operations** calculator box, p. 7

1-5: **Explore**, p. 24

1-7: **Explore**, p. 33

Multicultural Note: *Al-Khowarizmi*

Did you ever wonder how algebra got its name? It is a technical word derived from Arabic, the leading language of science in the Middle Ages. Mohammed ibn Musa-al-Khowarizmi, born in what is present-day Iran, was a professor at the Arab University in Baghdad around the year 825.

Around the time he was at the university, al-Khowarizmi wrote an algebra book that became famous throughout the world. Its title gave the word algebra to the English language. The Arabic title of this book was *Al-jabr w'al muqabalah*. The spelling of *al-jabr* eventually changed to algebra.

The *al-jabr* book showed how to solve equations. It described the manipulation of terms, the balancing of equations, and the use of the quadratic formula. Al-Khowarizmi felt that his al-jabr was practical and that it might be helpful in legal disputes or in measuring land.

For more information, see page 13 of **Multiculturalism in Mathematics, Science, and Technology**.

Alternative Assessment and Communication Ideas

Order of Operations is a crucial concept for success in algebra. In lesson 1-1, have students write a rule for the order of operations or create their own mnemonic.

You may wish to have students record definitions and other key information in an algebra journal. They can record their answer to the Lesson 1-5 **Writing to Learn** activity in the journal.

Lessons 1-8 and 1-10 each include a **Write a convincing argument** exercise that can be used as authentic assessment. You may wish to have students work in groups to write an argument and allow time for each group to present their results to the class.

Investigations and Projects

Divide the class into 3 groups and assign each group one of the following properties:

Commutative,
Associative, or
Distributive.

While the class studies Chapter 1, have the groups meet periodically to make up problems using their assigned property. For example:

Commutative: $5 \cdot 3 = 3 \cdot ?$

Associative: $5+(7+3) = (5+?)+?$

Distributive: $2(3 + x) = 2(?) + 2(?)$

Have students display at least 5 problems on the bulletin board under their property name after each meeting. Between meetings, have other students solve the problems.

You may wish to rotate the properties periodically so that each group has an opportunity to find examples of each property.

MANAGING CHAPTER 1

Lesson	PACING CHART (DAYS) 2-Year* A for E	1-Year Minimum	1-Year Regular	1-Year Advanced	Opening Activity	Cooperative Activity	Seat or Group Work
1-1	2	2	1	1	First Five Minutes 1-1: ***FFMTM*** p. 1 or **TE** p. 4; Application: **SE** p. 4	Calculator Worksheet 1: ***Technology*** p. 3	Try This a–q
1-2	2	1	1	1	First Five Minutes 1-2: ***FFMTM*** p. 1 or **TE** p. 9	Critical Thinking: ***Enrichment*** p. 18	Try This a–o
1-3	2	1	1	1	First Five Minutes 1-3: ***FFMTM*** p. 1 or **TE** p. 15; Application: **SE** p. 15	Calculator Worksheet 2: ***Technology*** p. 4	Try This a–r
1-4	2	1	1	1	First Five Minutes 1-4: ***FFMTM*** p. 2 or **TE** p. 19	✂ Manipulative Activity 1: ***Enrichment*** p. 34	Try This a–q
1-5	2	2	1	1	First Five Minutes 1-5: ***FFMTM*** p. 2 or **TE** p. 24	Explore: **SE** p. 24	Try This a–j
1-6	2	1	1	1	First Five Minutes 1-6: ***FFMTM*** p. 3 or **TE** p. 29	Looking for Errors 1: ***Enrichment*** p. 50	Try This a–j
1-7	2	1	1	1	First Five Minutes 1-7: ***FFMTM*** p. 3 or **TE** p. 33	Explore: **SE** p. 33	Try This a–l
1-8	2	1	1	1	First Five Minutes 1-8: ***FFMTM*** p. 4 or **TE** p. 38; ***Overhead Transparencies*** T1, T2	Problem 1: **SE** p. 39	Problem 2: **SE** p. 39
1-9	2	1	1	1	First Five Minutes 1-9: ***FFMTM*** p. 4 or **TE** p. 40; Application: **SE** p. 40	Problem 24: **SE** p. 43; Calculator Worksheet 4: ***Technology*** p. 6	Try This a–f
1-10	2	1	1	0.5	First Five Minutes 1-10: **TE** p. 44	Problem 11: **SE** p. 45	Problems 1–4: **SE** p. 45
Review	2	1	1	0.5			
Test	1	1	1	1			

*2-Year Management Guide can be found in *Algebra for Everyone*.

FFMTM: First Five Minutes Transparency Masters

Enrichment	Review/Assess	Reteach	Technology	Lesson
Lesson Enrichment: **TE** p. 6; Calculator Worksheet 1: ***Technology*** p. 3	Lesson Quiz: **TE** p. 6		Order of Operations: **SE** p. 7; Calculator Worksheet 1: ***Technology*** p. 3	**1-1**
Critical Thinking 1: ***Enrichment*** p. 18	Lesson Quiz: **TE** p. 13			**1-2**
Lesson Enrichment: **TE** p. 17; Calculator Worksheet 2: ***Technology*** p. 4	Lesson Quiz: **TE** p. 17	Skills Practice 1: ***SPMR*** p. 9	Evaluating Expressions: **SE** p. 17; Calculator Worksheet 2: ***Technology*** p. 4	**1-3**
✂ Manipulative Activity 1: ***Enrichment*** p. 34; Calculator Worksheet 3: ***Technology*** p. 5	Mixed Review 1: ***SPMR*** p. 51; Lesson Quiz: **TE** p. 21; Quiz 1: ***Assessment*** p. 11		Evaluating Expressions: **SE** p. 20; Calculator Worksheet 3: ***Technology*** p. 5	**1-4**
BASIC Computer Project 1: ***Technology*** p. 63	Mixed Practice 1: **SE** p. 684; Lesson Quiz: **TE** p. 26	Skills Practice 2: ***SPMR*** p. 10	BASIC Computer Project 1: ***Technology*** p. 63	**1-5**
Historical Note: **SE** p. 32; Bonus Topic 1: ***Enrichment*** p. 2	Lesson Quiz: **TE** p. 30	Problem Bank 1: ***Problem Bank*** p. 18		**1-6**
Looking for Errors 1: ***Enrichment*** p. 50	Mixed Review 2: ***SPMR*** p. 52; Lesson Quiz: **TE** p. 36; Quiz 2: ***Assessment*** p. 12			**1-7**
				1-8
Problem for Programmers **SE** p. 43; Calculator Worksheet 4: ***Technology*** p. 6; Spreadsheet Activity 1: ***Technology*** p. 37	Mixed Practice 2: **SE** p. 685; Lesson Quiz: **TE** p. 41	Skills Practice 3: ***SPMR*** p. 11	Problem for Programmers **SE** p. 43; Calculator Worksheet 4: ***Technology*** p. 6; Spreadsheet Activity 1: ***Technology*** p. 37	**1-9**
Computer Exploration 1: **SE** p. 715	Assessing Strategies 1: ***Assessment*** pp. 195–196	Strategy Problem Bank 1: ***Problem Bank*** p. 2	Computer Exploration 1: **SE** p. 715	**1-10**
	Summary and Review: **SE** pp. 47–49; Test: **SE** pp. 50–51			**Review**
	Chapter 1 Exam: ***A for E*** pp. 45–46; Chapter 1 Test: ***Assessment*** pp. 43–44 (min.), 71–76 (reg.), 163–164 (adv.)			**Test**

SPMR: Skills Practice Mixed Review

The solution to the problem posed on the facing page can be found on page 40.

Ready For Introduction to Algebra?

Add or subtract. Simplify answers if possible.

1. $\frac{3}{7} + \frac{2}{7}$ $\frac{5}{7}$ **2.** $\frac{3}{8} + \frac{1}{6}$ $\frac{13}{24}$ **3.** $6\frac{3}{4} + 9\frac{5}{8}$ $16\frac{3}{8}$ **4.** $3\frac{1}{2} + 4\frac{2}{3} + 7\frac{1}{4}$ $15\frac{5}{12}$

5. $\frac{5}{9} - \frac{2}{9}$ $\frac{1}{3}$ **6.** $\frac{5}{6} - \frac{2}{5}$ $\frac{13}{30}$ **7.** $1\frac{7}{8} - \frac{3}{4}$ $1\frac{1}{8}$ **8.** $7 - \frac{5}{8}$ $6\frac{3}{8}$

Multiply. Simplify answers if possible.

9. $\frac{3}{4} \times \frac{3}{4}$ $\frac{9}{16}$ **10.** $\frac{5}{8} \times 18$ $\frac{45}{4}$ or $11\frac{1}{4}$ **11.** $4\frac{1}{5} \times 3\frac{5}{7}$ $15\frac{3}{5}$ **12.** $2\frac{3}{10} \times 3\frac{1}{3}$ $7\frac{2}{3}$

Divide. Simplify answers if possible.

13. $\frac{7}{12} \div \frac{7}{12}$ 1 **14.** $\frac{3}{4} \div 2$ $\frac{3}{8}$ **15.** $3\frac{1}{3} \div 1\frac{1}{4}$ $2\frac{2}{3}$ **16.** $3 \div \frac{1}{3}$ 9

Add.

17. 0.5 + 0.35 + 1.5 2.35 **18.** 14 + 3.75 + 8.6 26.35 **19.** 1 + 0.02 + 0.2 1.22

Subtract.

20. 7 − 4.38 2.62 **21.** 11.2 − 6.09 5.11 **22.** 8.9 − 0.76 8.14

Multiply.

23. 8.75×6 52.5 **24.** 0.75×0.003 0.00225 **25.** 7.82×7.9 61.778 **26.** 0.0004×57 0.0228

Divide. Round answers to the nearest hundredth, if necessary.

27. $7\overline{)8.1}$ 1.16 **28.** $0.08\overline{)396.7}$ 4958.75 **29.** $1.1\overline{)0.44}$ 0.4

30. $\frac{5.82}{0.6}$ 9.7 **31.** $0.065\overline{)333}$ 5123.08 **32.** $8\overline{)0.91}$ 0.11

CHAPTER 

Introduction to Algebra

What is the speed of a supersonic airplane traveling at Mach 1.5?

1-1

FIRST FIVE MINUTES

What number goes in the blank?

1. ___ + 5 = 6 1
2. 9 − ___ = 7 2
3. 2 times ___ = 10 5
4. 3· ___ + 1 = 10 3

Math Point
The formula for orbital time is $T = \frac{2\pi R}{v}$ where v is the velocity and R is the distance from the satellite to the center of the earth. In the opening discussion, R equals 300 miles plus the radius of the earth in miles. Therefore, $2\pi R \approx$ 27,000 miles.

Algebraic Expressions

Emphasize that both a variable and an expression represent a single number. The value of an expression that contains a variable depends on the value we assign the variable. We determine the exact value of the expression when we substitute and evaluate the expression.

Also, point out that of the different ways to show multiplication, the form $3a$ is the most common.

Key Questions

- In an expression such as $3 + m - 2 + m$, can the first $m = 6$ and the second $m = 4$? No
- In $a + b - 7$, can $a = 4$ and $b = 4$? Yes
- In $x + 9$ can x equal either 7 or 8? Yes

Chalkboard Examples

Evaluate each expression.

1. $3x$ for $x = 2$
   $3 \cdot 2 = 6$
2. $3(a)$ for $a = 2$
   $3(2) = 6$
3. $3 \cdot b$ for $b = 2$
   $3 \cdot 2 = 6$
4. $3 \cdot b$ for $b = 5$
   $3 \cdot 5 = 15$

1-1 Symbols and Expressions

Application

The time needed for a satellite to orbit the earth is determined by the height of the satellite above the earth's surface and the velocity of the satellite. The table below shows how to find the approximate time needed for a satellite 300 miles above the earth's surface to orbit the earth one time.

Velocity (mi/h)	Orbital time (hours)
10,000	27,000 ÷ 10,000, or 2.7
15,000	27,000 ÷ 15,000, or 1.8
20,000	27,000 ÷ 20,000, or 1.35
v	27,000 ÷ v

Algebraic Expressions

Objective: Evaluate algebraic expressions.

In algebra we use symbols to stand for various numbers. One type of symbol used is a **variable.** A variable is a letter, such as v or x or m, that represents one or more numbers. In the last line of the table above, we let the letter v stand for the velocity of the satellite.

An expression may be a number, or two or more numbers, involving operation signs. An expression, such as $27{,}000 \div v$, that contains at least one variable is called an **algebraic expression.** We can replace a variable with a number. This is called **substituting** for the variable. To **evaluate** an algebraic expression, substitute a number for each variable and calculate.

EXAMPLE 1 Evaluate $n - 7$ for $n = 15$.

$$n - 7 = 15 - 7 \quad \text{Substituting 15 for the variable } n$$
$$= 8$$

Try This Evaluate.

a. $y + 8$ for $y = 9$ 17 **b.** $2 + x$ for $x = 6$ 8 **c.** $t + 3 + t$ for $t = 4$ 11

Algebraic expressions involving multiplication can be written in several ways. For example, "3 times a" can be written as $3 \times a$, $3 \cdot a$, $3(a)$, or simply $3a$. Algebraic expressions involving division can also be written in several ways. For example, "m divided by 4" can be written as $m \div 4$ or simply as $\frac{m}{4}$. The fraction bar is a division symbol.

EXAMPLE 2 Evaluate $5y$ for $y = 6$.

$$5y = 5(6) \quad \text{Substituting 6 for the variable } y$$
$$= 30$$

Try This Evaluate.

d. $\frac{x}{12}$ for $x = 36$ 3 **e.** $6m$ for $m = 3$ 18 **f.** $\frac{18}{g}$ for $g = 2$ 9

EXAMPLE 3 Evaluate $\frac{x}{y}$ for $x = 10$ and $y = 5$.

$$\frac{x}{y} = \frac{10}{5} \quad \text{Substituting 10 for } x \text{ and 5 for } y \text{ and dividing}$$
$$= 2$$

Try This Evaluate.

g. $a + b$ for $a = 3$ and $b = 7$ 10 **h.** mn for $m = 2$ and $n = 6$ 12

We also use several different sets of numbers in algebra. Here are two you already know.

- **Natural numbers** are the numbers used for counting: 1, 2, 3, and so on.
- **Whole numbers** are the natural numbers and zero: 0, 1, 2, 3, and so on.

We will also work with numbers of the form $\frac{a}{b}$, where $b \neq 0$. Some examples are $\frac{2}{3}$, $\frac{6}{3}$, and $\frac{4}{1}$. These numbers, as well as natural and whole numbers, are contained in a set of numbers called **rational numbers.** Rational numbers are explored further in Chapter 2.

Order of Operations

Objective: Evaluate expressions using grouping symbols and the order of operations.

Parentheses are called **grouping symbols.** When an expression contains parentheses, any operation inside the parentheses should be done first. The fraction bar is also a grouping symbol. In expressions containing a fraction bar like

$$\frac{4 + 6}{2 \cdot 1}$$

all computations above the bar and below the bar should be done before dividing.

$$\frac{4 + 6}{2 \cdot 1} = \frac{10}{2} = 5$$

5. $\frac{21}{n}$ for $n = 7$
$\frac{21}{7} = 3$

6. $z + 5$ for $z = 4$
$4 + 5 = 9$

Order of Operations

Illustrate how the value of the expression

$3 + 5 \cdot 2$

depends on the order in which the operations are completed.

$(3 + 5) \cdot 2 = 16$
$3 + (5 \cdot 2) = 13$

A complete listing of the order of operations is given in Lesson 1-3.

Avoiding Common Errors

Students may rewrite $\frac{4 + 3}{7}$ as $4 + 3 \div 7$. Remind them that the fraction bar is a grouping symbol, and $\frac{4 + 3}{7} = (4 + 3) \div 7$.

Students may also tend to evaluate expressions from left to right, disregarding the order of operations. They may, for example, write

$14 + 8 \div 2 = 11$

Emphasize the need to scan through an entire expression before computing.

Key Question

- How many different answers can you get by inserting parentheses into the following expression?

$2 \cdot 4 + 3 \cdot 5$
$(2 \cdot 4) + (3 \cdot 5) = 23$
$2 \cdot (4 + 3) \cdot 5 = 70$
$2 \cdot (4 + (3 \cdot 5)) = 38$
$((2 \cdot 4) + 3) \cdot 5 = 55$

Chalkboard Examples

1. Evaluate $\frac{m + n}{3}$ for $m = 6$ and $n = 3$. 3
2. Simplify $\frac{16}{2} + 4 \cdot 2$. 16
3. Evaluate $2x + \frac{y}{4}$ for $x = 6$ and $y = 4$. 13

LESSON ENRICHMENT

Rewrite these expressions by removing as many sets of parentheses as possible without changing the value of the expression.

1. $(9 + (3 \cdot 7))$
   $9 + 3 \cdot 7$
2. $(3 \cdot 5) + (4 \cdot x)$
   $3 \cdot 5 + 4 \cdot x$ or $3 \cdot 5 + 4x$
3. $(5 - ((3 \cdot 2) + 1))$
   $5 - (3 \cdot 2 + 1)$
   The remaining set of parentheses can't be removed without changing the value of the expression.
4. $((5 + (3)))$
   $5 + 3$
   The parentheses have no effect because there is only one operation.

LESSON QUIZ

Evaluate each expression.

1. $x + 7$ for $x = 2$
   $2 + 7 = 9$
2. $7z$ for $z = 3$
   $7 \cdot 3 = 21$
3. $u - v$ for $u = 7, v = 4$
   $7 - 4 = 3$
4. $\left(\frac{12 - x}{3}\right)$ for $x = 6$
   $\left(\frac{12 - 6}{3}\right) = \frac{6}{3} = 2$

Simplify.

5. $\frac{20}{4} \cdot 3$
   $\left(\frac{20}{4}\right) \cdot 3 = 5 \cdot 3 = 15$
6. $4 + 3 \cdot 5$
   $4 + (3 \cdot 5) = 4 + 15 = 19$
7. $12 + \frac{6}{3} - 1$
   $12 + \left(\frac{6}{3}\right) - 1 = 12 + 2 - 1 = 13$

EXAMPLE 4 Evaluate $a(3 + b)$ for $a = 5$ and $b = 2$.

$$
\begin{aligned}
a(3 + b) &= 5(3 + 2) && \text{Substituting 5 for } a \text{ and 2 for } b \\
&= 5(5) && \text{Working inside parentheses} \\
&= 25
\end{aligned}
$$

Try This Evaluate.

i. $14 - (b + 5)$ for $b = 3$ 6 **j.** $\frac{x + 5}{2 \cdot 3}$ for $x = 7$ 2

k. $3 + (6x)$ for $x = 2$ 15 **l.** $s(t - 4)$ for $s = 4$ and $t = 8$ 16

We need a rule for the order in which the operations should be done.

Order of Operations

1. Compute within grouping symbols.
2. Multiply and divide in order from left to right.
3. Add and subtract in order from left to right.

EXAMPLE 5 Simplify.

$$
\begin{aligned}
8 \cdot 4 + \frac{16}{2} &= 32 + 8 && \text{Multiplying and dividing first} \\
&= 40 && \text{Adding}
\end{aligned}
$$

Try This Simplify.

m. $36 \div (4 + 5)$ 4 **n.** $24 - (12 + 3) \div 5$ 21 **o.** $4 \times 3 + 6 \div 2$ 15

EXAMPLE 6 Evaluate $\frac{2m}{n}$ for $m = 6$ and $n = 3$.

$$
\begin{aligned}
\frac{2m}{n} &= \frac{2 \cdot 6}{3} && \text{Substituting 6 for } m \text{ and 3 for } n \\
&= \frac{12}{3} \\
&= 4
\end{aligned}
$$

Try This Evaluate.

p. $3x + y$ for $x = 2$ and $y = 5$ 11 **q.** $\frac{2a + b}{5}$ for $a = 4$ and $b = 2$ 2

Order of Operations

You should determine whether or not your calculator follows the Order of Operations. Calculate 3 + 4(2).

3 [+] 4 [×] 2 [=] → ?

If your calculator displays 11, the correct answer, your calculator is programmed to follow the Order of Operations.

If your calculator displays 14, you must always enter the operations in the correct order to get the correct answer.

4 [×] 2 [+] 3 [=] → 11

For additional calculator practice, see Calculator Worksheet 1.

Assignment Guide

Minimum: Day 1: 1–25 e/o*
Day 2: 26–40 e/o, MR*

Regular: 1–30 m4,* 31–51 e/o, 52 MR

Advanced: 1–46 m4, 47–54, MR

*Codes:
- e/o Even *or* odd exercises
- m3 Exercises that are multiples of 3 (i.e., 3, 6, 9, . . .)
- m4 Exercises that are multiples of 4 (i.e., 4, 8, 12, . . .)
- MR Mixed Review exercises
- assign w. Indicates that two lessons are assigned.

1-1 EXERCISES

A

Evaluate.

1. $x + 6$ for $x = 7$ 13

2. $3 + y$ for $y = 9$ 12

3. $m - 2$ for $m = 12$ 10

4. $9 - h$ for $h = 3$ 6

5. $t + 24$ for $t = 11$ 35

6. $18 + x$ for $x = 30$ 48

7. $12 - x$ for $x = 5$ 7

8. $k - 6$ for $k = 15$ 9

9. $m + 9$ for $m = 8$ 17

10. $a + 7 + a$ for $a = 5$ 17

11. $4 - x - x$ for $x = 1$ 2

12. $k + 8 - k$ for $k = 10$ 8

13. $4h$ for $h = 12$ 48

14. $8m$ for $m = 3$ 24

15. $3t$ for $t = 9$ 27

16. $6y$ for $y = 12$ 72

17. $\frac{12}{y}$ for $y = 2$ 6

18. $\frac{p}{5}$ for $p = 30$ 6

19. $\frac{x}{6}$ for $x = 18$ 3

20. $\frac{24}{x}$ for $x = 4$ 6

21. $\frac{h}{7}$ for $h = 63$ 9

22. $\frac{x}{y}$ for $x = 16$ and $y = 4$ 4

23. $a - b$ for $a = 12$ and $b = 3$ 9

24. mn for $m = 3$ and $n = 7$ 21

25. $p + q$ for $p = 7$ and $q = 9$ 16

26. $\frac{m}{n}$ for $m = 36$ and $n = 9$ 4

Simplify.

27. $13 + 54 \div 9$ 19

28. $64 \div 16 + 8$ 12

29. $12 + 3 - 7 \cdot 2 + 8$ 9

30. $12 \div 2 \times 3 \div 9$ 2

ADDITIONAL ANSWERS

Exercises

52. Answers may vary.
Ex: $10(2 + 8 - 4 - 6) = 0$

53. 12 and 5

54. $4 - 4 = 0$

$\frac{4}{4} = 1$

$\frac{4 + 4}{4} = 2$

$4 - \frac{4}{4} = 3$

$4 = 4$

$4 + \frac{4}{4} = 5$

$4 + \frac{4 + 4}{4} = 6$

$4 + 4 - \frac{4}{4} = 7$

$4 + 4 = 8$

$4 + 4 + \frac{4}{4} = 9$

$4 + 4 + \frac{4 + 4}{4} = 10$

Mixed Review

55. 72
56. 401
57. 57
58. 1.73
59. 14.1
60. 14.896
61. $1\frac{1}{28}$
62. $\frac{7}{24}$
63. $2\frac{1}{6}$
64. 8
65. $\frac{15}{28}$

Simplify.

31. $4 + 12 \times 2 - 8 \div 4$ 26

32. $15 \div 5 \times 5 \times 0$ 0

33. $32 \div 8 + 4 \times 3$ 16

34. $18 \times 2 \div 9 - 3$ 1

Evaluate.

35. $2x + y$ for $x = 5$ and $y = 4$ 14

36. $x + 4y$ for $x = 2$ and $y = 3$ 14

37. $3m + 4n$ for $m = 2$ and $n = 6$ 30

38. $\frac{x + y}{4}$ for $x = 4$ and $y = 8$ 3

39. $\frac{a + 3b}{5}$ for $a = 4$ and $b = 2$ 2

40. $\frac{4p}{3q}$ for $p = 6$ and $q = 8$ 1

B

Evaluate.

41. $x - y$ for $x = 15$ and $y = 12$ 3

42. $3(a + 5)$ for $a = 2$ 21

43. $\frac{n}{3m}$ for $n = 12$ and $m = 4$ 1

44. $\frac{ab}{8}$ for $a = 5$ and $b = 8$ 5

45. $\frac{3x}{2y + 1}$ for $x = 7$ and $y = 3$ 3

46. $\frac{a + b}{2a}$ for $a = 5$ and $b = 15$ 2

47. $2x + 3x - 4x$ for $x = 5$ 5

48. $\frac{24}{2x} + \frac{36}{3x} + \frac{6}{x}$ for $x = 6$ 5

49. $\frac{x + y}{4} + \frac{x - y}{4}$ for $x = 12$ and $y = 8$ 6

50. $\frac{4y}{4y} + (2x + y) - 3z$ for $x = 3$, $y = 2$, and $z = 1$ 6

51. $\frac{y + x}{2} + \frac{3y}{x}$ for $x = 2$ and $y = 4$ 9

52. ***Critical Thinking*** Use each of the numbers 2, 4, 6, 8, and 10 exactly once, with any operation signs and grouping symbols, to write an expression for the smallest whole number possible.

Challenge

53. The sum of two numbers, $a + b$, is 17, and the product of these numbers, ab, is 60. What numbers do a and b represent?

54. Write as many of the whole numbers from 0 to 10 as you can, using only the digit 4 with operation signs and grouping symbols as many or as few times as you need to. For example, $\frac{(4 + 4)}{4} = 2$.

Mixed Review

Calculate. **55.** $251 - 179$ **56.** $307 + 94$ **57.** $1824 \div 32$

58. $2.66 - 0.93$ **59.** $5.74 + 8.36$ **60.** $(4.9)(3.04)$ **61.** $\frac{3}{4} + \frac{2}{7}$

62. $\frac{5}{8} - \frac{1}{3}$ **63.** $2\frac{5}{6} - \frac{2}{3}$ **64.** $4 \div \frac{1}{2}$ **65.** $1\frac{1}{4} \div 2\frac{1}{3}$

1-2 The Commutative and Identity Properties

In this lesson you will begin to study number properties as they apply to algebraic expressions. You already know that the order in which you add two numbers does not affect the sum.

$3 + 4 = 7$ and $4 + 3 = 7$

You also know that the order in which you multiply two numbers does not affect the product.

$8 \cdot 2 = 16$ and $2 \cdot 8 = 16$

You will now see how these relationships apply to algebraic expressions.

Commutative Properties

Objective: Use the commutative properties for addition and multiplication of whole numbers.

The expressions $x + 2$ and $2 + x$ have the same value for every replacement for the variable x. Similarly, the expressions $3y$ and $y(3)$ have the same value for every replacement for the variable y. The commutative properties state that these relationships will always be true.

Commutative Properties

Addition

For any numbers a and b, $a + b = b + a$. (We can change the order when adding without affecting the sum.)

Multiplication

For any numbers a and b, $ab = ba$. (We can change the order when multiplying without affecting the product.)

Expressions such as $2 + x$ and $x + 2$, which always result in the same number when we substitute any value for their variables, are called **equivalent expressions.**

EXAMPLE 1 Write an expression equivalent to $y + 5$ using a commutative property.

$y + 5 = 5 + y$ using the commutative property of addition.

1-2

FIRST FIVE MINUTES

1. Which, if either, has the greater value, $321 + 987$ or $987 + 321$? They are equal.
2. Which, if either, is larger, $21 \cdot 98$ or $98 \cdot 21$? They are equal.

Commutative Properties

Introduce the commutative properties by using numerical cases like those in the *First Five Minutes*. Have students state the generalization that the order does not matter when the only operation is addition or multiplication.

Have students evaluate Examples 1–3 for specific values to show that the commutative properties are true.

Key Questions

- For which operations does the commutative property apply? **Addition and multiplication**
- Is subtraction commutative? No; $1 - 3$ doesn't equal $3 - 1$.
- Is division commutative? No; $1 \div 3 \neq 3 \div 1$.

Chalkboard Examples

Use the commutative property to write an equivalent expression for each of the following.

1. $7 + 11$
   $11 + 7$
2. $3 + x$
   $x + 3$
3. $14 \cdot 32$
   $32 \cdot 14$
4. $5y$
   $y(5)$

Identity Properties

Point out that when you add any number to 0 you get that identical number; and when you multiply any number by 1, you get that identical number. Thus we call 0 and 1 the identity numbers for addition and multiplication respectively.

Use numerical examples to show how any nonzero number or expression divided by itself equals 1.

Avoiding Common Errors

Since $5 - 0 = 5$, students may think that 0 is the identity for subtraction. Explain that although $5 - 0 = 5$, $0 - 5 \neq 5$. They will learn the meaning of $0 - 5$ in Chapter 2.

Key Questions

- Is there an identity property for division? No; $4 \div 1 \neq 1 \div 4$.
- What are some expressions that are equivalent to 1? Answers may vary. $\frac{2}{2}, \frac{987}{987}, \frac{x}{x}$ if $x \neq 0$

Chalkboard Examples

Write an equivalent expression using the indicated expression for 1.

1. $\frac{6}{7}$ using $\frac{3}{3}$ for 1

   $\frac{6}{7} \cdot \frac{3}{3} = \frac{6 \cdot 3}{7 \cdot 3} = \frac{18}{21}$

2. $\frac{2}{3}$ using $\frac{5}{5}$ for 1

   $\frac{2}{3} \cdot \frac{5}{5} = \frac{2 \cdot 5}{3 \cdot 5} = \frac{10}{15}$

3. $\frac{x}{2}$ using $\frac{a}{a}$ for 1

   $\frac{x}{2} \cdot \frac{a}{a} = \frac{x \cdot a}{2 \cdot a} = \frac{xa}{2a}$

EXAMPLES Write an expression equivalent to each using a commutative property.

2. xy An equivalent expression is yx by the commutative property of multiplication.

3. $5 + ab$ An equivalent expression is $ab + 5$ by the commutative property of addition.

Another is $5 + ba$ by the commutative property of multiplication.

Another is $ba + 5$ by both commutative properties.

Try This Use a commutative property to write an equivalent expression.

a. $x + 9$ $9 + x$ **b.** pq qp **c.** $xy + t$ $yx + t$, $t + xy$, or $t + yx$

Identity Properties

Objective: Use the identity properties for addition and multiplication of whole numbers.

When 0 is added to any number, the sum is that number. We call 0 the **additive identity**. When any number is multiplied by 1, the product is that number. We call 1 the **multiplicative identity.**

Identity Properties

Addition

For any number a, $a + 0 = a$ and $0 + a = a$. (Adding 0 to any number gives that number.)

Multiplication

For any number a, $1 \cdot a = a$ and $a \cdot 1 = a$. (Multiplying a number by 1 gives that number.)

Recall that the bar in expressions written as $\frac{a}{b}$ means to divide.

Using this idea, we see that the expressions $\frac{5}{5}$, $\frac{3}{3}$, and $\frac{26}{26}$ all name the number 1.

Dividing a Number by Itself

For any number a, $a \neq 0$, $\frac{a}{a} = 1$.

Here are some algebraic expressions that have the value 1 for all replacements, except those that would make the denominator zero. (In Chapter 2 we will discuss why division by zero is not allowed.)

$$\frac{n}{n} \qquad \frac{m+3}{m+3} \qquad \frac{5y+4}{5y+4}$$

We can use the identity property for multiplication to write equivalent expressions. If we multiply a fraction by 1, written in the form $\frac{a}{a}$ $(a \neq 0)$, we get a fraction equivalent to the original one.

EXAMPLE 4 Write an equivalent expression for $\frac{2}{3}$ by multiplying by 1. Use $\frac{5}{5}$ for 1.

$\frac{2}{3} = \frac{2}{3} \cdot 1$ Multiplying by the identity

$= \frac{2}{3} \cdot \frac{5}{5}$ Substituting $\frac{5}{5}$ for 1

$= \frac{10}{15}$ Multiplying numerators and denominators

Try This

d. Write an equivalent expression for $\frac{7}{5}$ by multiplying by 1. Use $\frac{4}{4}$ for 1. $\frac{28}{20}$

e. Write an equivalent expression for $\frac{3}{8}$ by multiplying by 1. Use $\frac{5}{5}$ for 1. $\frac{15}{40}$

We can also use the identity property for multiplication to write equivalent algebraic expressions. In this lesson we will assume that all variables in the denominator are nonzero.

EXAMPLE 5 Write an expression equivalent to $\frac{x}{2}$ by multiplying by 1. Use $\frac{y}{y}$ for 1.

$\frac{x}{2} = \frac{x}{2} \cdot \frac{y}{y}$ Multiplying by 1

$= \frac{xy}{2y}$

The expressions $\frac{x}{2}$ and $\frac{xy}{2y}$ have the same value for all replacements for x and y, $y \neq 0$. The expressions $\frac{x}{2}$ and $\frac{xy}{2y}$ are equivalent.

Try This

f. Write an expression equivalent to $\frac{y}{2x}$ by multiplying by 1. Use $\frac{z}{z}$ for 1. $\frac{yz}{2xz}$

g. Write an expression equivalent to $\frac{2m}{n}$ by multiplying by 1. Use $\frac{p}{p}$ for 1. $\frac{2mp}{np}$

Simplifying Expressions

Review the concept of factoring by having students factor several whole numbers. Point out that it is not necessary to factor completely if common factors are identified, as in Example 7.

You may wish to introduce "cancelling" at this point.

$$\frac{10}{15} = \frac{2 \cdot 5}{3 \cdot 5} = \frac{2}{3}$$

It is important that students understand, however, that cancelling is a shortcut for the steps shown in the examples.

Key Questions

- Can all fractions and expressions be simplified? No
- Why are common factors needed above and below the fraction bar to simplify expressions? Because a factor of 1 can be removed

Chalkboard Examples

Simplify.

1. $\frac{21}{14} = \frac{3 \cdot 7}{2 \cdot 7} = \frac{3}{2} \cdot \frac{7}{7} = \frac{3}{2} \cdot 1 = \frac{3}{2}$

2. $\frac{40}{60} = \frac{10 \cdot 4}{10 \cdot 6} = \frac{10 \cdot 2 \cdot 2}{10 \cdot 2 \cdot 3} = \frac{2}{3}$

3. $\frac{4ab}{8a} = \frac{4 \cdot a \cdot b}{4 \cdot a \cdot 2} = \frac{b}{2}$

4. $\frac{y}{3xy} = \frac{y}{y \cdot 3 \cdot x} = \frac{y \cdot 1 \cdot 1}{y \cdot 3 \cdot x} = \frac{1}{3x}$

Simplifying Expressions

Objective: Simplify expressions.

When two or more numbers are multiplied to form a product, each number is called a **factor** of the product. For example, $3 \times 5 = 15$, so 3 and 5 are factors of 15. When the only common factor of the numerator and the denominator of a fraction is 1, the fraction is in **simplest form.** The process of finding the simplest form is called **simplifying.**

EXAMPLES Simplify.

6. $\frac{10}{15} = \frac{2 \cdot 5}{3 \cdot 5}$ Factoring the numerator and denominator

$= \frac{2}{3} \cdot 1$ Substituting 1 for $\frac{5}{5}$

$= \frac{2}{3}$ Using the identity property of multiplication

7. $\frac{36}{24} = \frac{6 \cdot 6}{4 \cdot 6}$ Factoring the numerator and denominator

$= \frac{3 \cdot 2 \cdot 6}{2 \cdot 2 \cdot 6}$ Further factoring

$= \frac{3}{2} \cdot 1$ Substituting 1 for $\frac{2 \cdot 6}{2 \cdot 6}$

$= \frac{3}{2}$

Try This Simplify.

h. $\frac{18}{27}$ $\frac{2}{3}$ **i.** $\frac{48}{18}$ $\frac{8}{3}$ **j.** $\frac{56}{49}$ $\frac{8}{7}$

The number of factors of the numerator and denominator may not always "match." If they do not, you can always use the factor 1.

EXAMPLES Simplify.

8. $\frac{18}{72} = \frac{2 \cdot 9}{4 \cdot 2 \cdot 9}$

$= \frac{1 \cdot 2 \cdot 9}{4 \cdot 2 \cdot 9}$ Using the identity property (inserting a factor of 1)

$= \frac{1}{4} \cdot \frac{2 \cdot 9}{2 \cdot 9}$ Factoring the fraction

$= \frac{1}{4}$

9. $\frac{72}{9} = \frac{8 \cdot 9}{1 \cdot 9}$ Factoring and inserting a factor of 1 in the denominator

$= \frac{8}{1} \cdot \frac{9}{9}$

$= \frac{8}{1}$

$= 8$

Try This Simplify.

k. $\frac{27}{54}$ $\frac{1}{2}$ **l.** $\frac{48}{12}$ 4

We can simplify algebraic expressions using the identity property for multiplication and the same procedures used above with numbers.

EXAMPLES Simplify.

10. $\frac{xy}{3y} = \frac{x \cdot y}{3 \cdot y}$ Factoring numerator and denominator

$= \frac{x}{3} \cdot \frac{y}{y}$ Factoring the fraction

$= \frac{x}{3}$ Using the identity property (removing a factor of 1)

11. $\frac{x}{5xy} = \frac{1 \cdot x}{5 \cdot x \cdot y}$ Inserting a factor of 1 in the numerator

$= \frac{1}{5y} \cdot \frac{x}{x}$ Using the commutative property and factoring the fractional expression

$= \frac{1}{5y}$

12. $\frac{4cd}{2c} = \frac{4 \cdot c \cdot d}{2 \cdot c \cdot 1}$

$= \frac{4 \cdot d}{2 \cdot 1} \cdot \frac{c}{c}$

$= \frac{2d}{1}$

$= 2d$

Try This Simplify.

m. $\frac{5xy}{3x}$ $\frac{5y}{3}$ **n.** $\frac{m}{8mn}$ $\frac{1}{8n}$ **o.** $\frac{14ab}{7b}$ $2a$

LESSON ENRICHMENT

What value for x will make the denominator zero?

1. $\frac{x + y}{3 - x}$ 3
2. $\frac{7x}{4x}$ 0
3. $\frac{2}{x - 5}$ 5

LESSON QUIZ

Use the commutative property to write an equivalent expression for each.

1. $u + v$ $v + u$
2. $1 + xy$
   $xy + 1$ or $1 + yx$ or $yx + 1$
3. Multiply $\frac{5}{s}$ by 1 to get an equivalent expression. Use $\frac{3}{3}$ for 1.
   $\frac{5}{s} \cdot \frac{3}{3} = \frac{15}{s \cdot 3} = \frac{15}{3s}$
4. Simplify $\frac{18}{15}$.
   $\frac{18}{15} = \frac{3 \cdot 6}{3 \cdot 5} = \frac{6}{5}$
5. Simplify $\frac{4x}{2y}$.
   $\frac{4x}{2y} = \frac{2 \cdot 2 \cdot x}{1 \cdot 2 \cdot y} = \frac{2x}{y}$
6. Simplify $\frac{x}{9x}$.
   $\frac{x}{9x} = \frac{1 \cdot x}{9 \cdot x} = \frac{1}{9}$
7. Simplify $\frac{2abx}{4acx}$.
   $\frac{2abx}{4acx} = \frac{2ax \cdot b}{2ax \cdot 2c} = \frac{b}{2c}$

Assignment Guide
Minimum: 1 – 29 e/o, MR

Regular: 1–38 e/o, 39, MR

Advanced: 1–29 m3, 30–40, MR

ADDITIONAL ANSWERS

Exercises

1. $8 + y$
2. $3 + x$
3. nm
4. ba
5. $9 + yx$ or $yx + 9$ or $xy + 9$
6. $ab + 11$ or $ba + 11$ or $11 + ba$
7. $c + ab$ or $c + ba$ or $ba + c$
8. $t + rs$, $t + sr$, $sr + t$

Mixed Review

41. 16
42. 1
43. 42
44. $\frac{31}{40}$
45. $\frac{15}{16}$
46. 0.062
47. 0.48

1-2 EXERCISES

A

Write an equivalent expression using a commutative property.

1. $y + 8$ **2.** $x + 3$ **3.** mn **4.** ab

5. $9 + xy$ **6.** $11 + ab$ **7.** $ab + c$ **8.** $rs + t$

Write an equivalent expression. Use the indicated expression for 1.

9. $\frac{5}{6}$ Use $\frac{8}{8}$ for 1. $\frac{40}{48}$ **10.** $\frac{9}{10}$ Use $\frac{11}{11}$ for 1. $\frac{99}{110}$ **11.** $\frac{6}{7}$ Use $\frac{100}{100}$ for 1. $\frac{600}{700}$

12. $\frac{y}{10}$ Use $\frac{z}{z}$ for 1. $\frac{yz}{10z}$ **13.** $\frac{s}{20}$ Use $\frac{t}{t}$ for 1. $\frac{st}{20t}$ **14.** $\frac{m}{3n}$ Use $\frac{p}{p}$ for 1. $\frac{mp}{3np}$

Simplify.

15. $\frac{13}{104}$ $\frac{1}{8}$ **16.** $\frac{56}{7}$ 8 **17.** $\frac{132}{11}$ 12 **18.** $\frac{5y}{5}$ y **19.** $\frac{ab}{9b}$ $\frac{a}{9}$

20. $\frac{x}{9xy}$ $\frac{1}{9y}$ **21.** $\frac{q}{8pq}$ $\frac{1}{8p}$ **22.** $\frac{8a}{3ab}$ $\frac{8}{3b}$ **23.** $\frac{9p}{17pq}$ $\frac{9}{17q}$ **24.** $\frac{3pq}{6q}$ $\frac{p}{2}$

25. $\frac{51d}{17sd}$ $\frac{3}{s}$ **26.** $\frac{9nz}{19tn}$ $\frac{9z}{19t}$ **27.** $\frac{13rv}{3vh}$ $\frac{13r}{3h}$ **28.** $\frac{9abc}{3ab}$ $3c$ **29.** $\frac{32prq}{4qrp}$ 8

B

Tell whether each pair of expressions is equivalent.

30. $3t + 5$ and $3 \cdot 5 + t$ No **31.** $4x$ and $x + 4$ No

32. $bxy + bx$ and $yxb + bx$ Yes **33.** $ab + bc$ and $ac + db$ No

34. $a + c + e + g$ and $ea + cg$ No **35.** $abc \cdot de$ and $a \cdot b \cdot c \cdot ed$ Yes

Simplify.

36. $\frac{33sba}{2 \cdot (11a)}$ $\frac{3sb}{2}$ **37.** $\frac{36 \cdot 2rh}{8 \cdot (9hg)}$ $\frac{r}{g}$ **38.** $\frac{3 \cdot (4xy) \cdot (5)}{2 \cdot (3x) \cdot (4y)}$ $\frac{5}{2}$

39. ***Critical Thinking*** Find two expressions that simplify to $\frac{4ab}{c}$.
Answers may vary. $\frac{8ab}{2c}$, $\frac{4abd}{cd}$

Challenge

40. Is there a commutative property for division of whole numbers? If not, give a counterexample. A **counterexample** is one case where a rule is false. No, $12 \div 4 \neq 4 \div 12$

Mixed Review

Simplify. **41.** $12 + 8 \div 2$ **42.** $16 \div 8 \cdot 2 \div 4$ **43.** $(3 + 4)6$

Calculate. **44.** $\frac{2}{5} + \frac{3}{8}$ **45.** $\frac{5}{8} \div \frac{2}{3}$ **46.** $(3.1)(0.02)$ **47.** $\frac{4.8}{10}$

1-3 Exponential Notation

Application

In a computer, information is read in units called "bits" and "bytes." A bit is like an on-off switch and is read by the computer as 1 (on) or 0 (off). A byte is a group of 8 bits, put together to represent one unit of data such as a letter, digit, or special character. Each byte, therefore, can represent $2 \times 2 \times 2 \times 2 \times 2 \times 2 \times 2 \times 2$ or 256 different characters.

Using Exponents

Objective: Evaluate and express numbers using exponential notation.

A product in which the factors are the same is called a **power**. We can write $2 \times 2 \times 2 \times 2 \times 2 \times 2 \times 2 \times 2$ as 2^8. The number 8 is called the **exponent**, and 2 is called the **base**. The exponent tells how many times the base is used as a factor. Similarly, we can write $a \cdot a \cdot a = a^3$. Here the exponent is 3 and the base is a. When an expression is written with exponents, we say the expression is written using **exponential notation.**

Exponent → (points to n)
Base → b^n

We read b^n as the "nth power of b," or simply "b to the nth," or "b to the n." We may also read b^2 as "b squared" and b^3 as "b cubed."

EXAMPLES What is the meaning of each expression?

1. 2^2 — 2^2 means $2 \cdot 2$
2. 3^5 — 3^5 means $3 \cdot 3 \cdot 3 \cdot 3 \cdot 3$
3. n^4 — n^4 means $n \cdot n \cdot n \cdot n$
4. $2y^3$ — $2y^3$ means $2 \cdot y \cdot y \cdot y$

Try This What is the meaning of each expression?

a. 5^4 $5 \cdot 5 \cdot 5 \cdot 5$ **b.** b^3 $b \cdot b \cdot b$ **c.** $2x^3$ $2 \cdot x \cdot x \cdot x$ **d.** $12y^4$ $12 \cdot y \cdot y \cdot y \cdot y$

EXAMPLES Write using exponential notation.

5. $7 \cdot 7 \cdot 7 \cdot 7$ can be written as 7^4
6. $n \cdot n \cdot n \cdot n \cdot n \cdot n$ can be written as n^6
7. $3 \cdot x \cdot x$ can be written as $3x^2$
8. $2 \cdot y \cdot y \cdot y \cdot y$ can be written as $2y^4$

1-3

FIRST FIVE MINUTES

1. $3 \cdot 3 \cdot 3 = ?$ 27
2. $2 \cdot 2 \cdot 2 \cdot 2 \cdot 2 = ?$ 32
3. $1 \cdot 1 \cdot 1 \cdot 1 \cdot 1 = ?$ 1
4. $10 \cdot 10 \cdot 10 = ?$ 1000

Using Exponents

Emphasize that the exponent tells you how many times the base is used as a factor. You may want to reinforce this with a diagram.

exponent → $3^5 = 3 \cdot 3 \cdot 3 \cdot 3 \cdot 3$
base → Five factors

Key Questions

In the expression 4^8,

- what is the 8 called? The exponent
- what is the 4 called? The base
- How do you read this expression? Four to the eighth

Chalkboard Examples

Write without exponential notation.

1. 2^4
   $2 \cdot 2 \cdot 2 \cdot 2 = 16$
2. x^5
   $x \cdot x \cdot x \cdot x \cdot x$
3. $6t^2$
   $6 \cdot t \cdot t$
4. 3^2x^3
   $3 \cdot 3 \cdot x \cdot x \cdot x$

Write using exponential notation.

5. $3 \cdot 3 \cdot 3 \cdot 3 \cdot 3 \cdot 3$
   3^6
6. $c \cdot c \cdot c$
   c^3
7. $2 \cdot y \cdot y \cdot y$
   $2y^3$
8. $3 \cdot 3 \cdot x \cdot x \cdot y \cdot y \cdot y$
   $3^2x^2y^3$

Evaluating Expressions

This lesson extends the order of operations to include powers.

Avoiding Common Errors

Students often assume that $2 \cdot 3^2$ means 6^2, not $2 \cdot 9$. Remind students that the exponent only affects the number it follows unless it follows parentheses. Use the following example.

$2 \cdot 3^2 = 2 \cdot 9 = 18$
$(2 \cdot 3)^2 = 6^2 = 36$

Key Questions

What number does the exponent 2 affect?

- $3 \cdot 4^2$ 4
- $(3 \cdot 4)^2$ $3 \cdot 4$, or 12

Chalkboard Examples

Evaluate.

1. x^3 for $x = 4$
   $4^3 = 4 \cdot 4 \cdot 4 = 64$
2. a^4 for $a = 2$
   $2^4 = 2 \cdot 2 \cdot 2 \cdot 2 = 16$
3. z^{100} for $z = 1$
   $1 \cdot 1 \cdot \ldots \cdot 1 = 1$
4. w^2 for $w = 0$
   $0^2 = 0 \cdot 0 = 0$
5. $a^2 + 1$ for $a = 3$
   $3^2 + 1 = 9 + 1 = 10$
6. $z^4 - 1$ for $z = 1$
   $1^4 - 1 = 1 - 1 = 0$
7. $(4x)^2$ for $x = 2$
   $(4 \cdot 2)^2 = (8)^2 = 8^2 = 64$
8. $(6r)^5$ for $r = 0$
   $(6 \cdot 0)^5 = (0)^5 = 0^5 = 0$

Try This Write using exponential notation.

e. $9 \cdot 9 \cdot 9$ 9^3 **f.** $y \cdot y \cdot y \cdot y \cdot y$ y^5 **g.** $4 \cdot n \cdot n \cdot n \cdot n \cdot n$ $4n^5$
h. $15 \cdot x \cdot x \cdot x \cdot x$ $15x^4$ **i.** $10 \cdot b \cdot b \cdot b$ $10b^3$

Here are some definitions for exponents.

Definitions

b^1 means b for any number b.

If n is a whole number greater than 1, b^n means $\overbrace{b \cdot b \cdot b \cdot b \cdot \ldots \cdot b}^{n \text{ factors}}$.

Evaluating Expressions

Objective: Evaluate expressions containing exponents.

EXAMPLES Evaluate each expression.

9. x^4 for $x = 2$

$$x^4 = 2^4 \quad \text{Substituting}$$
$$= 2 \cdot 2 \cdot 2 \cdot 2$$
$$= 16$$

10. y^2 for $y = 5$

$$y^2 = 5^2 \quad \text{Substituting}$$
$$= 5 \cdot 5$$
$$= 25$$

Try This Evaluate each expression.

j. a^2 for $a = 10$ 100 **k.** y^5 for $y = 2$ 32 **l.** x^4 for $x = 0$ 0

We now extend the rules for the order of operations to include exponents.

Order of Operations—Extended

1. Compute within grouping symbols first.
2. Compute powers.
3. Multiply and divide in order from left to right.
4. Add and subtract in order from left to right.

EXAMPLES Evaluate each expression.

11. $y^4 + 3$ for $y = 2$

$$y^4 + 3 = 2^4 + 3$$
$$= 2 \cdot 2 \cdot 2 \cdot 2 + 3$$
$$= 16 + 3$$
$$= 19$$

12. $m^3 + 5$ for $m = 4$

$$\begin{aligned} m^3 + 5 &= 4^3 + 5 \\ &= 4 \cdot 4 \cdot 4 + 5 \\ &= 64 + 5 \\ &= 69 \end{aligned}$$

Try This Evaluate each expression.

m. $x^3 + 2$ for $x = 3$ 29 **n.** $n^5 + 8$ for $n = 2$ 40

When an expression inside parentheses is raised to a power, everything inside the parentheses is the base. Compare $3a^3$ and $(3a)^3$.

$3a^3$ means $3 \cdot a \cdot a \cdot a$ — a is the base

$(3a)^3$ means $(3a)(3a)(3a)$ — $3a$ is the base

EXAMPLES Evaluate.

13. $(3a)^3$ for $a = 2$

$$\begin{aligned} (3a)^3 &= (3a)(3a)(3a) \\ &= (3 \cdot 2)(3 \cdot 2)(3 \cdot 2) \\ &= 6 \cdot 6 \cdot 6 \\ &= 216 \end{aligned}$$

14. $3a^3$ for $a = 2$

$$\begin{aligned} 3a^3 &= 3 \cdot a \cdot a \cdot a \\ &= 3 \cdot 2 \cdot 2 \cdot 2 \\ &= 24 \end{aligned}$$

Try This Evaluate.

o. $(2x)^2$ for $x = 4$ 64 **p.** $(5y)^3$ for $y = 2$ 1000

q. $3x^2$ for $x = 3$ 27 **r.** $6m^3$ for $m = 2$ 48

Evaluating Expressions Involving Exponents

You can evaluate expressions like $y^3 + 3$ for $y = 2$ on a calculator with an exponent key. Calculate $2^3 + 3$.

2 [y^x] 3 [=] [+] 3 [=] → 11

If your calculator does not have an exponent key, you can use the definition of an exponent. $2^3 + 3 = 2 \cdot 2 \cdot 2 + 3$.

2 [×] 2 [×] 2 [=] [+] 3 [=] → 11

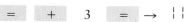

For additional calculator practice, see Calculator Worksheet 2.

LESSON ENRICHMENT

A particular kind of amoeba is found in a sample of swamp water. This amoeba splits into two amoebas after exactly one hour. After another hour, each of the two amoebas splits into two more amoebas. How many amoebas are there after 5 hours? How many after 10 hours? 32; 1024

LESSON QUIZ

Write an equivalent expression without exponents.

1. 5^3
   $5 \cdot 5 \cdot 5$
2. $2a^3$
   $2 \cdot a \cdot a \cdot a$
3. Write using exponential notation.
   $t \cdot t \cdot t \cdot t$
   t^4
4. Write using exponential notation.
   $3 \cdot 3 \cdot a \cdot a \cdot b$
   3^2a^2b
5. Simplify to a form without parentheses. $(3z)^2$
   $(3z) \cdot (3z) = 3z \cdot 3z = 3 \cdot z \cdot 3 \cdot z = 3 \cdot 3 \cdot z \cdot z = 9z^2$.
6. Evaluate s^6 for $s = 2$.
   $2^6 = 2 \cdot 2 \cdot 2 \cdot 2 \cdot 2 \cdot 2 = 64$
7. Evaluate $u^2 + 1$ for $u = 4$.
   $4^2 + 1 = 16 + 1 = 17$

Assignment Guide
Minimum: 1–33 e/o, MR

Regular: 1–40 e/o, 41, MR

Advanced: 1–33 m3, 34–45, MR

ADDITIONAL ANSWERS

Exercises

1. $2 \cdot 2 \cdot 2 \cdot 2$
2. $5 \cdot 5 \cdot 5$
3. 3
4. $4 \cdot 4 \cdot 4 \cdot 4$
5. $1 \cdot 1 \cdot 1$
6. 2
7. $a \cdot a \cdot a$
8. $m \cdot m \cdot m \cdot m \cdot m \cdot m$
9. $3 \cdot x \cdot x$
10. $5 \cdot y \cdot y \cdot y \cdot y$
11. $2 \cdot m \cdot m \cdot m$
12. $4 \cdot n \cdot n$
13. 10^6
14. 6^4
15. x^5
16. $4y^3$
17. $5m^4$
18. $2n^6$
19. 27
20. 64
21. 19
22. 0
23. 248
24. 5
25. 66
26. 22
27. 3
28. 36
29. 32
30. 512
31. 1296
32. 900
33. 20736

Mixed Review

46. 11
47. $\frac{7}{8}$
48. $\frac{1}{8}$
49. $12\frac{1}{2}$
50. 16
51. 10
52. $\frac{1}{8}$
53. 8
54. $\frac{1}{8s}$
55. $\frac{9}{y}$
56. $\frac{a}{4}$

1-3 EXERCISES

A

What is the meaning of each expression?

1. 2^4 **2.** 5^3 **3.** 3^1 **4.** 4^4 **5.** 1^3 **6.** 2^1
7. a^3 **8.** m^6 **9.** $3x^2$ **10.** $5y^4$ **11.** $2m^3$ **12.** $4n^2$

Write using exponential notation.

13. $10 \cdot 10 \cdot 10 \cdot 10 \cdot 10 \cdot 10$ **14.** $6 \cdot 6 \cdot 6 \cdot 6$ **15.** $x \cdot x \cdot x \cdot x \cdot x$
16. $4 \cdot y \cdot y \cdot y$ **17.** $5 \cdot m \cdot m \cdot m \cdot m$ **18.** $2 \cdot n \cdot n \cdot n \cdot n \cdot n \cdot n$

Evaluate each expression.

19. m^3 for $m = 3$ **20.** x^6 for $x = 2$ **21.** p^1 for $p = 19$
22. x^{19} for $x = 0$ **23.** $x^4 - 8$ for $x = 4$ **24.** $y^{15} + 4$ for $y = 1$
25. $x^3 + 2$ for $x = 4$ **26.** $y^2 - 3$ for $y = 5$ **27.** $3m^3$ for $m = 1$
28. $4x^2$ for $x = 3$ **29.** $2n^4$ for $n = 2$ **30.** $(4x)^3$ for $x = 2$
31. $(2a)^4$ for $a = 3$ **32.** $(5n)^2$ for $n = 6$ **33.** $(6y)^4$ for $y = 2$

B

34. Evaluate $(2ab)^3$ for $a = 2$ and $b = 4$. 4096

35. Evaluate $(3mn)^3$ for $m = 2$ and $n = 0$. 0

Write with a single exponent.

For example, $\frac{3^5}{3^3} = \frac{3 \cdot 3 \cdot 3 \cdot 3 \cdot 3}{3 \cdot 3 \cdot 3} = 3 \cdot 3 = 3^2$

36. $\frac{10^5}{10^3}$ 10^2 **37.** $\frac{10^7}{10^2}$ 10^5 **38.** $\frac{5^4}{5^2}$ 5^2 **39.** $\frac{8^6}{8^2}$ 8^4

40. Evaluate $x^3y^2 + zx$ for $x = 2$, $y = 1$, and $z = 3$. 14

41. ***Critical Thinking*** Does $x^y = y^x$ for all whole numbers x and y? Why? No; for example, $2^3 = 8$ and $3^2 = 9$.

Challenge

42. Find yx^{149} for $x = 13$ and $y = 0$. 0

43. Find $x^{410}y^2$ for $x = 1$ and $y = 3$. 9

44. 10^{127} is one followed by how many zeros? 127

45. Find $(x^2)^2$ if $x = 3$. 81

Mixed Review

Calculate. **46.** $8\frac{1}{3} + 2\frac{2}{3}$ **47.** $1\frac{5}{8} - \frac{3}{4}$ **48.** $\frac{3}{8} \div 3$ **49.** $5 \times 2\frac{1}{2}$

Evaluate. **50.** $2(m + n)$ for $m = 7, n = 1$ **51.** $(3 + n)n$ for $n = 2$

Simplify. **52.** $\frac{7}{56}$ **53.** $\frac{96}{12}$ **54.** $\frac{r}{8rs}$ **55.** $\frac{18x}{2xy}$ **56.** $\frac{3ab}{12b}$

1-4 The Associative Properties

Parentheses

Objective: Evaluate expressions involving parentheses.

You have learned to calculate within parentheses first. You also know that you simplify powers before doing other operations.

EXAMPLES Calculate.

1. $(3 \cdot 4)^2 = 12^2$ Working within parentheses first
$= 144$

2. $3 \cdot 4^2 = 3 \times 16$ There are no parentheses, so we find 4^2 first.
$= 48$

Try This Calculate.

a. $(3 \cdot 5)^2$ 225 **b.** $3 \cdot 5^2$ 75 **c.** $4 \cdot 2^3$ 32 **d.** $(4 \cdot 2)^3$ 512
e. $4 + 2^2$ 8 **f.** $(4 + 2)^2$ 36 **g.** $(5 - 1)^2$ 16 **h.** $5 - 1^2$ 4

EXAMPLES Evaluate each expression.

3. $(3x)^3 - 2$ for $x = 2$
$(3x)^3 - 2 = (3 \cdot 2)^3 - 2$ Substituting
$= 6^3 - 2$ Multiplying within parentheses first
$= 216 - 2$
$= 214$

4. $(2 + x)(y - 1)$ for $x = 3$ and $y = 5$
$(2 + x)(y - 1) = (2 + 3)(5 - 1)$
$= 5 \cdot 4$ Working within parentheses first
$= 20$

Try This Evaluate each expression.

i. $(4y)^2 - 5$ for $y = 3$ 139 **j.** $6(x + 12)$ for $x = 8$ 120

k. $t + \frac{6}{5t^2}$ for $t = 2$ $2\frac{3}{10}$ **l.** $(x - 4)^3$ for $x = 6$ 8

m. $(4 + y) \cdot (x - 3)$ for $y = 3$ and $x = 12$ 63

1-4

FIRST FIVE MINUTES

Simplify.
1. $(3 + 2) + 1$
6
2. $(1 + 2) - 3$
0
3. $(1 + 2) \cdot 3$
9
4. $3 \cdot (2 + 1)$
9

Parentheses

Stress that operations in parentheses are evaluated first, and that the order of operations is followed within the parentheses.

Remind students that -1^2 means $-(1^2)$, *not* $(-1)^2$.

Key Question

- How many different values can you get by inserting parentheses into the following expression?

$4 + 3 \cdot 2^2$

$4 + 3 \cdot 2^2 = 16$
$(4 + 3) \cdot 2^2 = 28$
$4 + (3 \cdot 2)^2 = 40$
$(4 + 3 \cdot 2)^2 = 100$
$((4 + 3) \cdot 2)^2 = 196$

Chalkboard Examples

Calculate.
1. $(2 \cdot 3)^2$
$= 6^2 = 36$
2. $2 \cdot 3^2$
$= 2 \cdot 9 = 18$
3. $8 - 2^2$
$= 8 - 4 = 4$

Evaluate.
4. $(5a)^2 - 1$ for $a = 2$
$(5 \cdot 2)^2 - 1 = 10^2 - 1 = 99$
5. $(2 + c)(3 - c)$ for $c = 1$
$(2 + 1)(3 - 1) = (3)(2) = 6$
6. $(x - 1)(x - 2)$ for $x = 2$
$(2 - 1)(2 - 2) = (1)(0) = 0$
7. $(y - 5)^3$ for $y = 7$
$(7 - 5)^3 = (2)^3 = 8$

Using the Associative Properties

You may wish to show that subtraction does not have the associative property.

$$8 - (5 - 2) \neq (8 - 5) - 2$$
$$8 - 3 \neq 3 - 2$$
$$5 \neq 1$$

Avoiding Common Errors

Students often assume that when a pair of equivalent expressions have parentheses in them, the associative property is being used. Stress that the associative property allows a different *association* of numbers and that the commutative property allows a different *ordering* of the numbers.

Key Questions

Can the parentheses be removed from the following expressions without changing their values?

- $(x + 3) + (3 + x)$
  Yes
- $(x + 3) + 3 + x$
  Yes
- $(3x)(3x)$
  Yes

Chalkboard Examples

Use the associative properties to write an equivalent expression.

1. $(3 + 2) + 5$
   $3 + (2 + 5)$
2. $(x + 3) + z$
   $x + (3 + z)$
3. $a + (b + c)$
   $(a + b) + c$
4. $(3 \cdot c) \cdot d$
   $3 \cdot (c \cdot d)$
5. $u(vw)$
   $(uv)w$

Evaluating Expressions

You can use a calculator to evaluate algebraic expressions.
Evaluate $\frac{x + 2y}{3}$ for $x = 9$ and $y = 3$.
Key sequence for scientific calculators, which follow the Order of Operations:

Key sequence for arithmetic calculators, which do not follow the Order of Operations:

2 [×] 3 [+] 9 [=] [÷] 3 [=] → 5

For additional calculator practice, see Calculator Worksheet 3.

Using the Associative Properties

Objective: Write equivalent expressions using the associative properties.

When addition is the only operation in an expression, the parentheses can be moved without affecting the answer. For example, the expressions $3 + (7 + 5)$ and $(3 + 7) + 5$ are equivalent.

$3 + (7 + 5)$	$(3 + 7) + 5$
$3 + 12$	$10 + 5$
15	15

When multiplication is the only operation in an expression, parentheses can be moved without affecting the answer. For example, the expressions $3 \cdot (4 \cdot 2)$ and $(3 \cdot 4) \cdot 2$ are equivalent.

$3 \cdot (4 \cdot 2)$	$(3 \cdot 4) \cdot 2$
$3 \cdot 8$	$12 \cdot 2$
24	24

The associative properties state that this will always be true.

Associative Property of Addition

For any numbers a, b, and c,

$$a + (b + c) = (a + b) + c$$

(Numbers can be grouped in any order for addition.)

Associative Property of Multiplication

For any numbers a, b, and c,

$$a \cdot (b \cdot c) = (a \cdot b) \cdot c$$

(Numbers can be grouped in any order for multiplication.)

EXAMPLES Use an associative property to write an equivalent expression.

5. $y + (z + 3) = (y + z) + 3$ Using the associative property of addition

6. $5 \cdot (x \cdot y) = (5 \cdot x) \cdot y$ Using the associative property of multiplication

Try This Use an associative property to write an equivalent expression.

n. $a + (b + 2)$ **o.** $3 \cdot (v \cdot w)$

n. $(a + b) + 2$
o. $(3 \cdot v) \cdot w$

Using the Properties Together

Objective: Write equivalent expressions using the commutative and associative properties.

If addition or multiplication is the only operation in an expression, then the associative and commutative properties allow us to group and change order as we please. For example, in a calculation like $(5 + 2) + (3 + 5) + 8$, addition is the only operation. Therefore, we can change the grouping and order to make our calculations easier.

$$(5 + 5) + (2 + 8) + 3 = 10 + 10 + 3 = 23$$

In algebra we often need to change the order or grouping of an expression. The associative and commutative properties allow us to do this.

EXAMPLE 7 Use the commutative and associative properties to write three expressions equivalent to $(x + 5) + y$.

$(x + 5) + y = x + (5 + y)$
$= x + (y + 5)$
Using the associative property first and then the commutative property

$(x + 5) + y = y + (x + 5)$
$= y + (5 + x)$
Using the commutative property and then the commutative property again

$(x + 5) + y = 5 + (x + y)$
Using the commutative property first and then the associative property

Using the Properties Together

Chalkboard Examples

Tell which property, commutative or associative, is used at each step.

1. $(x + 5) \cdot (2 \cdot y)$
   a. $= (5 + x) \cdot (2 \cdot y)$
   Commutative
   b. $= (5 + x) \cdot (y \cdot 2)$
   Commutative
   c. $= (y \cdot 2) \cdot (5 + x)$
   Commutative
   d. $= y \cdot (2 \cdot (5 + x))$
   Associative
2. $(a + b) + cd$
   a. $= a + (b + cd)$
   Associative
   b. $= a + (cd + b)$
   Commutative
   c. $= (a + cd) + b$
   Associative
   d. $= (a + dc) + b$
   Commutative

LESSON QUIZ

Calculate.

1. $3 \cdot 5^2$
   $3 \cdot 25 = 75$
2. $(3 - 1)^3$
   $2^3 = 8$

Evaluate.

3. $5(a + 2)$ for $a = 4$
   $5 \cdot (4 + 2) = 5 \cdot 6 = 30$
4. $(x - 3)(x - 5)$ for $x = 7$
   $(7 - 3)(7 - 5) = 4 \cdot 2 = 8$
5. $\frac{x^2 + 3}{2x}$ for $x = 4$
   $\frac{4^2 + 3}{2 \cdot 4} = \frac{16 + 3}{8} = \frac{19}{8}$

Use the associative property to write an equivalent expression.

6. $a + (3 + c)$
   $(a + 3) + c$
7. $(5x)y$
   $5(xy)$

Assignment Guide
Minimum: 1–43 e/o, MR

Regular: 1–43 m4, 44–53 e/o, 54, MR

Advanced: 1–53 m4, 54–57, MR

ADDITIONAL ANSWERS

Exercises

31. $a + (b + 3)$
32. $5 + (x + y)$
33. $(3 \cdot a) \cdot b$
34. $6 \cdot (x \cdot y)$
35. $(2 + b) + a$
$(2 + a) + b$
$b + (a + 2)$
36. $(y + 3) + x$
$3 + (y + x)$
$x + (3 + y)$
37. $v + (w + 5)$
$(5 + w) + v$
$w + (5 + v)$
38. $x + (y + 6)$
$y + (6 + x)$
$(x + 6) + y$
39. $(y \cdot 3) \cdot x$
$x \cdot (3 \cdot y)$
$y \cdot (x \cdot 3)$
40. $(5 \cdot a) \cdot b$
$b \cdot (a \cdot 5)$
$a \cdot (5 \cdot b)$
41. $a \cdot (b \cdot 7)$
$(a \cdot 7) \cdot b$
$b \cdot (7 \cdot a)$
42. $(x \cdot 5) \cdot y$
$(5 \cdot y) \cdot x$
$y \cdot (5 \cdot x)$
43. $c \cdot (2 \cdot d)$
$d \cdot (c \cdot 2)$
$2 \cdot (d \cdot c)$

EXAMPLE 8 Use the commutative and associative properties to write three expressions equivalent to $(3 \cdot x) \cdot y$.

$(3 \cdot x) \cdot y = 3 \cdot (x \cdot y)$
$= 3 \cdot (y \cdot x)$ — Using the associative property first and then the commutative property

$(3 \cdot x) \cdot y = y \cdot (x \cdot 3)$ — Using the commutative property twice

$(3 \cdot x) \cdot y = x \cdot (y \cdot 3)$ — Using the commutative property, then the associative property, and then the commutative property again

Try This Use the commutative and associative properties to write three equivalent expressions.

p. $4 \cdot (t \cdot u)$ **q.** $r + (2 + s)$

p. Ex. $4 \cdot (u \cdot t)$ or $u \cdot (4 \cdot t)$ or $t \cdot (4 \cdot u)$
q. Ex. $r + (s + 2)$ or $(2 + s) + r$ or $(r + s) + 2$

1-4 EXERCISES

A

Calculate.

1. $(5 \cdot 4)^2$ 400 **2.** $(6 \cdot 3)^2$ 324 **3.** $5 \cdot 4^2$ 80 **4.** $6 \cdot 3^2$ 54
5. $7 + 2^2$ 11 **6.** $5 + 3^2$ 14 **7.** $(7 + 2)^2$ 81 **8.** $(5 + 3)^2$ 64
9. $(5 - 2)^2$ 9 **10.** $(3 - 2)^2$ 1 **11.** $10 - 3^2$ 1 **12.** $16 - 4^2$ 0
13. $12 - 2^3$ 4 **14.** $30 - 3^3$ 3 **15.** $(2 + 3)^3$ 125 **16.** $3 \cdot 2^3$ 24

Evaluate each expression.

17. $5x^2 - 4$ for $x = 4$ 76
18. $3a^3 + 2$ for $a = 1$ 5
19. $(5y)^3 - 75$ for $y = 2$ 925
20. $(7x)^2 + 59$ for $x = 3$ 500
21. $3(a + 10)$ for $a = 12$ 66
22. $b(7 + b)$ for $b = 5$ 60
23. $(t + 3)^3$ for $t = 4$ 343
24. $(12 - w)^3$ for $w = 7$ 125
25. $(x + 5)(12 - x)$ for $x = 7$ 60
26. $(y - 4)(y + 6)$ for $y = 10$ 96
27. $\frac{y + 3}{2y}$ for $y = 5$ $\frac{4}{5}$
28. $\frac{(4x) + 2}{2x}$ for $x = 5$ $\frac{11}{5}$
29. $\frac{w^2 + 4}{5w}$ for $w = 4$ 1
30. $\frac{b^2 + b}{2b}$ for $b = 5$ 3

Use the associative properties to write an equivalent expression.

31. $(a + b) + 3$ **32.** $(5 + x) + y$ **33.** $3 \cdot (a \cdot b)$ **34.** $(6 \cdot x) \cdot y$

Use the commutative and associative properties to write three equivalent expressions.

35. $(a + b) + 2$ **36.** $(3 + x) + y$ **37.** $5 + (v + w)$
38. $6 + (x + y)$ **39.** $(x \cdot y) \cdot 3$ **40.** $(a \cdot b) \cdot 5$
41. $7 \cdot (a \cdot b)$ **42.** $5 \cdot (x \cdot y)$ **43.** $2 \cdot c \cdot d$

B

Use the commutative and associative properties to write two expressions equivalent to each expression.

44. $(4a + 2) + b$ **45.** $(7 \cdot m) \cdot n + 3$ **46.** $(5x^3 + 2) + 6$

47. $(6m)(np)$ **48.** $2(x + 3)y$ **49.** $5 + (3 + 7y) + 4$

Find a replacement for the variable for which the two expressions are *not* equivalent. Answers may vary.

50. $3x^2$; $(3x)^2$ Any number except 0 **51.** $(a + 2)^3$; $a^3 + 2^3$ Any number except 0 or −2

52. $\frac{x + 2}{2}$; x Any number except 2 **53.** $\frac{y^6}{y^3}$; y^2 Any number except 1. 0 is not acceptable.

54. ***Critical Thinking*** If it is true that $A + B = 25$ and $(A + C) + B = 85$, what is the value of $B + A$? $A + (B + C)$? $(A + B) + C$? C?

Challenge

55. Evaluate $a - (b - c)$ and $(a - b) - c$ for $a = 12$, $b = 7$, and $c = 4$. Is there an associative property for subtraction? 9; 1; No, $9 \neq 1$

56. Evaluate $a \div (b \div c)$ and $(a \div b) \div c$ for $a = 32$, $b = 8$, and $c = 4$. Is there an associative property for division? 16; 1; No, $16 \neq 1$

57. Suppose we define a new operation @ on the set of whole numbers as follows: a @ $b = 2a + b$. For example, 4 @ 5 = 2(4) + 5 = 13.

  a. Determine whether @ is commutative for whole numbers. That is, does a @ b = b @ a for all whole numbers a and b?

  b. Determine whether @ is associative for whole numbers. That is, does (a @ b) @ c = a @ (b @ c) for all whole numbers a, b, and c?

Mixed Review

Calculate. **58.** $12\frac{1}{4} + 7\frac{3}{8}$ **59.** $3\frac{3}{5} + 5\frac{1}{2}$ **60.** $8\frac{1}{3} + 3\frac{3}{5}$

61. $3\frac{3}{4} - 2\frac{1}{3}$ **62.** $\frac{7}{8} \times \frac{2}{3}$ **63.** $1\frac{1}{5} \times 1\frac{1}{3}$ **64.** 3.75×0.3

Simplify. **65.** $\frac{6x}{7xy}$ **66.** $\frac{12t}{24t}$ **67.** $\frac{6mn}{11mt}$ **68.** $\frac{14n}{28ny}$

Evaluate. **69.** $(3a)^3$ for $a = 5$ **70.** $4y^2$ for $y = 7$

71. $2w^3 - 9$ for $w = 2$ **72.** $4r + \frac{3t}{6}$ for $r = 4$ and $t = 8$

73. $3(m + 2n)$ for $m = 4$ and $n = 3$ **74.** $2a + 5b$ for $a = 2$ and $b = 6$

75. $\frac{3s + 7}{t}$ for $s = 1$ and $t = 5$ **76.** $\frac{x + x}{7}$ for $x = 7$

77. $\frac{w + 2z}{z}$ for $w = 6$ and $z = 3$ **78.** $\frac{6 + 3x}{6y}$ for $x = 4$ and $y = 1$

---

44. $(a \cdot 4 + b) + 2$
$(b + 4a) + 2$
45. $7 \cdot (n \cdot m) + 3$
$3 + m \cdot (7 \cdot n)$
46. $(2 + 6) + 5x^3$
$2 + (5x^3 + 6)$
47. $6(mp)n$
$m(6n)p$
48. $(x + 3)2y$
$(x + 3)y \cdot 2$
49. $(3 + 5) + 7y + 4$
$5 + 3 + (4 + 7y)$
54. 25, 85, 85, 60
57. a. No; 2 @ 3 = 7 and 3 @ 2 = 8
b. No; (1 @ 2) @ 3 = (4 @ 3) = 11 and 1 @ (2 @ 3) = 1 @ 7 = 9

Mixed Review

58. $19\frac{5}{8}$
59. $9\frac{1}{10}$
60. $11\frac{14}{15}$
61. $1\frac{5}{12}$
62. $\frac{7}{12}$
63. $\frac{8}{5}$ or $1\frac{3}{5}$
64. 1.125
65. $\frac{6}{7y}$
66. $\frac{1}{2}$
67. $\frac{6n}{11t}$
68. $\frac{1}{2y}$
69. 3375
70. 196
71. 7
72. 20
73. 30
74. 34
75. 2
76. 2
77. 4
78. 3

1-5

FIRST FIVE MINUTES

Calculate.

1. $3 \cdot (2 + 6)$
   $3 \cdot 8 = 24$
2. $3 \cdot 2 + 3 \cdot 6$
   $6 + 18 = 24$
3. $2 \cdot (1 + 2 + 3)$
   $2 \cdot 6 = 12$
4. $2 \cdot 1 + 2 \cdot 2 + 2 \cdot 3$
   $2 + 4 + 6 = 12$
5. $5 \cdot (6 + 8) - (5 \cdot 6 + 5 \cdot 8)$
   $5 \cdot 14 - (30 + 40)$
   $= 70 - 70 = 0$

EXPLORE

Have students calculate the perimeter of a rectangle that is 8 in. long and 5 in. wide using both formulas. Then have them calculate the perimeter of several different rectangles using both formulas. They should quickly see that the formulas give the same result.

Using the Distributive Property

In Example 2, remind students that the commutative property tells us that $s \cdot 6 = 6 \cdot s$. Tell them it is usual notation to write $6s$.

◇◇ symbolizes connections to other math disciplines, such as geometry.

Avoiding Common Errors

Students will often write $3 \cdot x + y$ for the expression $3 \cdot (x + y)$. Remind students that in the first expression only the x is multiplied by 3, and in the second expression both the x and the y are multiplied by 3.

Key Questions

Can you use two methods to evaluate each expression?

- $3(7 + 4)$
  $3(11) = 33$
  $21 + 12 = 33$
- $6(8 + 3)$
  $6(11) = 66$
  $48 + 18 = 66$

1-5 The Distributive Property of Multiplication Over Addition

Explore

The formula for the perimeter of a rectangle is used often by surveyors in designing land plots. One surveyor used Formula A; another used Formula B. Do both formulas give the same number for the perimeter?

Formula A: $P = (2 \cdot 5) + (2 \cdot 8)$

Formula B: $P = 2 \cdot (5 + 8)$

Using the Distributive Property

Objective: Use the distributive property of multiplication to write equivalent expressions.

The Explore activity above shows that expressions like $2 \cdot (5 + 8)$ and $(2 \cdot 5) + (2 \cdot 8)$ are equivalent. The distributive property of multiplication over addition states that this will always be true.

The Distributive Property of Multiplication Over Addition

For any numbers a, b, and c, $a(b + c) = ab + ac$.
For any numbers a, b, and c, $(b + c)a = ba + ca$.

We can omit the parentheses in expressions like $(4 \cdot 5) + (3 \cdot 7)$ and just write $4 \cdot 5 + 3 \cdot 7$, since this will not change the order of the operations. If we omit the parentheses in expressions like $2(3 + 5)$, however, we will no longer have equivalent expressions.

$2(3 + 5) = 2(8) = 16$ $\qquad$ $2 \cdot 3 + 5 = 6 + 5 = 11$

The distributive property must be used to remove the parentheses.

$2(3 + 5) = 2 \cdot 3 + 2 \cdot 5 = 6 + 10 = 16$

The following diagram illustrates the distributive property.

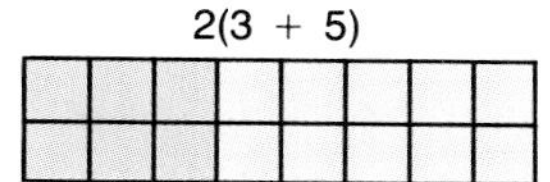

EXAMPLES Use the distributive property to write an equivalent expression.

1. $3(x + 2) = 3x + 3 \cdot 2 = 3x + 6$
2. $(s + t + w)6 = s(6) + t(6) + w(6)$
   $= 6s + 6t + 6w$ Using the commutative property
3. $4(2s + 5) = 4(2s) + 4(5)$
   $= 8s + 20$

Try This Use the distributive property to write an equivalent expression.

a. $4(x + y + z)$ $4x + 4y + 4z$ **b.** $(y + 3)5$ $5y + 15$
c. $(8a + 3)2$ $16a + 6$ **d.** $6(x + 2y + 5)$ $6x + 12y + 30$

Factoring

Objective: Factor expressions.

If the statement of the distributive property is reversed, we have the basis of a process called factoring: $ab + ac = a(b + c)$. To factor an expression, write an equivalent expression as a product of the factors.

EXAMPLES Factor.

4. $3x + 3y = 3(x + y)$ Look for a common factor. Then use the distributive property.
5. $5x + 5y + 5z = 5(x + y + z)$ The common factor is 5.
6. $7y + 14 + 21z = 7 \cdot y + 7 \cdot 2 + 7 \cdot 3z$ The common factor is 7.
   $= 7(y + 2 + 3z)$
7. $9x + 27y + 9 = 9 \cdot x + 9 \cdot 3y + 9 \cdot 1$ The common factor is 9.
   $= 9(x + 3y + 1)$

Try This Factor.

e. $5x + 10$ $5(x + 2)$ **f.** $12 + 3x$ $3(4 + x)$

g. $6x + 12 + 9y$ $3(2x + 4 + 3y)$ **h.** $5x + 10y + 5$ $5(x + 2y + 1)$

Chalkboard Examples

Use the distributive property to write an equivalent expression.

1. $6(x + y)$
   $6 \cdot x + 6 \cdot y = 6x + 6y$
2. $a(3 + b)$
   $a \cdot 3 + a \cdot b$
3. $2(x + y + z)$
   $2x + 2y + 2z$
4. $(u + v) \cdot 3$
   $u \cdot 3 + v \cdot 3$ or $3u + 3v$
5. $4(2x + 1)$
   $4 \cdot 2x + 4 \cdot 1 = 8x + 4$

Factoring

Using the distributive property to rewrite the expression

$3(x + y)$ as $3x + 3y$

can be described as "multiplying through by 3." Using the distributive property to rewrite the expression

$3x + 3y$ as $3(x + y)$

is described as "factoring out the 3."

You can also demonstrate visually how factoring relates to the distributive property.

3x + 3y = 3(x + y)

Remind students that the first step in factoring is to factor out the *largest* common factor.

Key Questions

Find the common factor.

- $9x + 9$
  9
- $9x + 27$
  9

Chalkboard Examples

Factor each expression.

1. $3a + 3b$
   $3(a + b)$
2. $6x + 12y$
   $6(x + 2y)$

Collecting Like Terms

Emphasize that there is no number property that allows the addition or subtraction of unlike terms such as x and x^2, or $3y^3$ and $2y^2$.

Key Questions

How many terms are in the following expressions?

- $2x + y$
  Two
- $2xy$
  One
- $x - \frac{1}{4}$
  Two

Chalkboard Examples

Use the distributive property to collect like terms.

1. $y + y$
   $1y + 1y = (1 + 1)y = 2y$
2. $2 \cdot a + 3 \cdot a$
   $(2 + 3) \cdot a = 5a$
3. $3c + 2c$
   $(3 + 2)c = 5c$
4. $4x + 6y + 3x + 1y$
   $4x + 3x + 6y + 1y$
   $(4 + 3)x + (6 + 1)y$
   $7x + 7y$
5. $7a^2 + 3a^2$
   $(7 + 3)a^2 = 10a^2$

Collect like terms mentally and write only the answer.

6. $3x + x + 4x$ $8x$
7. $2u + 4u + 5u$ $11u$
8. $5y^2 + 7y^2 + y^2$ $13y^2$

LESSON QUIZ

Use the distributive property to write an equivalent expression.

1. $7(x + y)$
   $7x + 7y$
2. $3(2u + 5v)$
   $6u + 15v$

Factor.

3. $6r + 6s$
   $6(r + s)$ or $(r + s) \cdot 6$
4. $2p + 6q$
   $2(p + 3q)$
5. $8a + 6b + 2c$
   $2(4a + 3b + c)$

Mentally collect like terms.

6. $8d + 2d$
   $10d$
7. $2e^2 + 5e^2$
   $7e^2$
8. $2u^2 + t + u^2 + t^2$
   $3u^2 + t^2 + t$

Factoring can be checked by multiplying. We multiply the factors to see if we get the original expression.

EXAMPLE 8 Factor and check by multiplying.

$5x + 10 = 5(x + 2)$ Check: $5(x + 2) = 5x + 5 \cdot 2 = 5x + 10$

Try This Factor and check by multiplying.

i. $9x + 3y$ **j.** $5 + 10x + 15y$

i. $3(3x + y)$
j. $5(1 + 2x + 3y)$

Collecting Like Terms

Objective: Collect like terms.

In an expression like $6s + 6t + 6w$, $6s$, $6t$, and $6w$ are called **terms.**

Terms such as $5x$ and $4x$, whose variable factors are exactly the same, are called **like terms.** Similarly, $3y^2$ and $9y^2$ are like terms. Terms such as $4y$ and $5y^2$ are not like terms. We often simplify expressions using the distributive property to collect like terms.

EXAMPLES Collect like terms.

9. $3x + 4x = (3 + 4)x$ Using the distributive property
$= 7x$

10. $x + x = 1 \cdot x + 1 \cdot x$ Using the identity property
$= (1 + 1)x$ Using the distributive property
$= 2x$

11. $2x + 3y + 5x + 2y = 2x + 5x + 3y + 2y$ Using the commutative property
$= (2 + 5)x + (3 + 2)y$ Using the distributive property
$= 7x + 5y$

12. $5x^2 + x^2 = 5x^2 + 1 \cdot x^2$ Using the identity property
$= (5 + 1)x^2$ Using the distributive property
$= 6x^2$

Try This Collect like terms.

k. $6y + 2y$ $8y$
l. $7x + 3y + 5y + 4x$ $11x + 8y$
m. $10p + 8q + 4p + 5q$ $14p + 13q$
n. $7x^2 + x^2$ $8x^2$

1-5 EXERCISES

A

Use the distributive property to write an equivalent expression.

1. $2(b + 5)$ **2.** $4(x + 3)$ **3.** $(1 + t)7$

4. $6(v + 4)$ **5.** $3(x + 1)$ **6.** $(x + 8)7$

7. $4(1 + y)$ **8.** $9(s + 1)$ **9.** $6(5x + 2)$

10. $9(6m + 7)$ **11.** $7(x + 4 + 6y)$ **12.** $(5x + 8 + 3p)4$

Factor.

13. $2x + 4$ **14.** $5y + 20$ **15.** $30 + 5y$

16. $7x + 28$ **17.** $14x + 21y$ **18.** $18a + 24b$

19. $5x + 10 + 15y$ **20.** $9a + 27b + 81$ **21.** $14c + 63d + 7$

22. $4y + 10 + 8x$ **23.** $9r + 27s + 18$ **24.** $24x + 72y + 8$

Factor and check by multiplying.

25. $9x + 27$ $9(x + 3)$ **26.** $6x + 24$ $6(x + 4)$

27. $9x + 3y$ $3(3x + y)$ **28.** $15x + 5y$ $5(3x + y)$

29. $8a + 16b + 64$ $8(a + 2b + 8)$ **30.** $5 + 20x + 35y$ $5(1 + 4x + 7y)$

31. $11x + 44y + 121$ $11(x + 4y + 11)$ **32.** $7 + 14b + 56w$ $7(1 + 2b + 8w)$

33. $5x + 10y + 45z$ $5(x + 2y + 9z)$ **34.** $9p + 3q + 27r$ $3(3p + q + 9r)$

Collect like terms.

35. $9a + 10a$ **36.** $12x + 2x$

37. $10a + a$ **38.** $16x + x$

39. $2x + 9z + 6x$ **40.** $3a + 5b + 7a$

41. $7x + 6y^2 + 9y^2$ **42.** $12m^2 + 6q + 9m^2$

43. $41a + 90 + 60a + 2$ **44.** $42x + 6 + 4x + 2$

45. $8a + 8b + 3a + 3b$ **46.** $100y + 200z + 190y + 400z$

47. $8u^2 + 3t + 10t + 6u^2 + 2$ **48.** $5 + 6h + t + 8 + 9h$

49. $23 + 5t + 7y + t + y + 27$ **50.** $45 + 90d + 87 + 9d + 3 + 7d$

51. $\frac{1}{2}b + \frac{1}{2}b$ **52.** $\frac{2}{3}x + \frac{1}{3}x$

53. $2y + \frac{1}{4}y + y$ **54.** $\frac{1}{2}a + a + 5a$

Simplify each expression. Factor and collect like terms as needed.

55. $4x + 5y + 6x$ **56.** $6z + 3k + 9z$

57. $4p^2 + 2p + 4p + 8p^2$ **58.** $2m + 3mn + 2m + mn$

59. $7xy + 3y + 6x + 2xy$ **60.** $6tp + 3t^2 + 9t^2 + 2tp$

Assignment Guide

Minimum: Day 1: 1–34 e/o
Day 2: 35–64 e/o, MR

Regular: 1–64 m4, 65–69, MR

Advanced: 1–60 m4, 61–66 e/o, 67, 68–73 e/o, MR

ADDITIONAL ANSWERS

Exercises

1. $2b + 10$
2. $4x + 12$
3. $7 + 7t$
4. $6v + 24$
5. $3x + 3$
6. $7x + 56$
7. $4 + 4y$
8. $9s + 9$
9. $30x + 12$
10. $54m + 63$
11. $7x + 28 + 42y$
12. $20x + 32 + 12p$
13. $2(x + 2)$
14. $5(y + 4)$
15. $5(6 + y)$
16. $7(x + 4)$
17. $7(2x + 3y)$
18. $6(3a + 4b)$
19. $5(x + 2 + 3y)$
20. $9(a + 3b + 9)$
21. $7(2c + 9d + 1)$
22. $2(2y + 5 + 4x)$
23. $9(r + 3s + 2)$
24. $8(3x + 9y + 1)$

35. $19a$ **36.** $14x$
37. $11a$ **38.** $17x$
39. $8x + 9z$ **40.** $10a + 5b$
41. $7x + 15y^2$ **42.** $21m^2 + 6q$
43. $101a + 92$ **44.** $46x + 8$
45. $11a + 11b$ **46.** $290y + 600z$
47. $14u^2 + 13t + 2$
48. $13 + 15h + t$
49. $50 + 6t + 8y$ **50.** $135 + 106d$
51. $1b$ or b **52.** $1x$ or x
53. $\frac{13}{4}y$ or $3\frac{1}{4}y$ **54.** $\frac{13}{2}a$ or $6\frac{1}{2}a$
55. $10x + 5y$ **56.** $15z + 3k$
57. $12p^2 + 6p$ **58.** $4mn + 4m$
59. $9xy + 6x + 3y$
60. $8pt + 12t^2$

61. $9x + 27$ 62. $14m^2 + 28$
63. $12a + 16b$ 64. $22x + 28y + 12$

72. $7x + 7xy + 7y = 7(x + xy + y)$
73. $a + ab + abc + abcd$

Mixed Review

74. 144 75. 48
76. 1 77. 0
78. $4y$ 79. $\frac{1}{3a}$
80. $\frac{1}{2}$ 81. $8x$
82. 36 83. 24
84. 5 85. 15

Writing to Learn

Students may answer in many different ways. However, they should include the idea that the commutative property can be used to change the order of $(b + c)a$ to $a(b + c)$ and to change $ab + ac$ to $ba + ca$.

B

Simplify each expression.

61. $4(x + 3) + 5(x + 3)$

62. $7(m^2 + 2) + 7(m^2 + 2)$

63. $8(a + b) + 4(a + 2b)$

64. $4(5x + 6y + 3) + 2(x + 2y)$

65. The money you deposit in a bank is called the principal. When you deposit money in a bank and earn interest, the new principal is given by the expression $P + Prt$, where P is the principal, r is the rate of interest, and t is the time. Factor the expression $P + Prt$. $P(1 + rt)$

66. a. Factor $17x + 34$. Then evaluate both expressions when $x = 10$. $17(x + 2)$; $17(10 + 2) = 17(12) = 204$; $17(10) + 34 = 170 + 34 = 204$

b. Will you get the same answer for both expressions? Why? Yes; distributive property

67. ***Critical Thinking*** Does $(x + y)^2 = x^2 + y^2$ for all whole numbers? When are they equal? No; when either x or y is 0.

Challenge

68. Find a simpler expression equivalent to $\frac{3a + 6}{2a + 4}$. $\frac{3}{2}$

69. Find a simpler expression equivalent to $\frac{4x + 12y}{3x + 9y}$. $\frac{4}{3}$

Collect like terms, if possible, and factor the result.

70. $x + 2x^2 + 3x^3 + 4x^2 + 5x$ $6x + 6x^2 + 3x^3 = 3x(2 + 2x + x^2)$

71. $q + qr + qrs + qrst$ $q(1 + r + rs + rst)$

72. $21x + 44xy + 15y - 16x - 8y - 38xy + 2x + xy$

73. Simplify $a\{1 + b[1 + c(1 + d)]\}$. (Hint: Begin with $c(1 + d)$ and work outwards.)

Mixed Review

Calculate. **74.** $(4 \cdot 3)^2$ **75.** $6 \cdot 2^3$ **76.** $(3 - 2)^3$ **77.** $8 - 2^3$

Simplify. **78.** $\frac{8xy}{2x}$ **79.** $\frac{6b}{18ab}$ **80.** $\frac{15c}{30c}$ **81.** $\frac{24xy}{3y}$

Evaluate. **82.** $6(t + 4)$ for $t = 2$ **83.** $w(5 + w)$ for $w = 3$

84. k^1 for $k = 5$ **85.** $(x + 3) \cdot (5 - x)$ for $x = 2$

WRITING TO LEARN

You know that $a(b + c) = ab + ac$ for any numbers a, b, and c. Use this fact and the properties introduced earlier to write a paragraph explaining why $(b + c)a = ba + ca$ is also true for any numbers a, b and c.

1-6 Problem Solving: Writing Expressions

Objective: Write algebraic expressions involving one operation.

Many problems can be solved by translating data given with words into algebraic expressions. To do this, you must know which phrases suggest each of the operations (addition, subtraction, multiplication, and division).

EXAMPLES Write as an algebraic expression.

1. 5 more than a number

   $n + 5$ — Think of a specific number, say 3. "5 more than 3" would be $3 + 5$, so "5 more than a number" would be $n + 5$.

2. 3 less than a number

   $n - 3$ — Think of a specific number, say 5. "3 less than 5" would be $5 - 3$, so "3 less than a number" would be $n - 3$.

3. 3 times a number

   $3n$ — Think of a specific number, say 6. "3 times 6" would be $3 \cdot 6$, so "3 times a number" would be $3n$.

4. a number divided by 5

   $\frac{n}{5}$ — Think of a specific number, say 20. "20 divided by 5" would be $\frac{20}{5}$, so "a number divided by 5" would be $\frac{n}{5}$.

Try This Write as an algebraic expression.

a. the sum of a number and 7 $n + 7$

b. the product of a number and 4 $4n$

c. 4 less than y $y - 4$

d. 6 fewer than x $x - 6$

e. the difference of m and n $m - n$

f. twice y $2y$

g. a less than b $b - a$

h. 7 times a number $7n$

EXAMPLES

5. Let L be the amount of money Lila earned. Glenn earned twice as much as Lila. Write an expression for the amount Glenn earned.

   $2L$ — "Twice as much" suggests multiplying by 2.

6. Let h be the number of hits John had in a baseball game. John had 2 more walks than hits. Write an expression for the number of walks.

   $h + 2$ — "2 more walks than hits" suggests adding 2 to the number of hits.

1-6

FIRST FIVE MINUTES

Use the distributive property to write an equivalent expression.

1. $5(x + y)$
   $5x + 5y$
2. $a(b + c)$
   $ab + ac$
3. $3(2u + v)$
   $6u + 3v$

Factor.

4. $7a + 7b$
   $7(a + b)$
5. $14c + 21d$
   $7(2c + 3d)$
6. $ax + ay + az$
   $a(x + y + z)$

The first and most important task of problem solving is to identify and name the numeric quantities in the problem so that statements can be made about them. Encourage students to use any single letter that reminds them of the quantity. For example, n is a good variable name for an unknown number, h is good for the height of a tree, and t for temperature.

Avoiding Common Errors

Students often translate expressions involving subtraction in the wrong order. Since subtraction is not commutative, the order is important.

Point out that statements such as "the difference of 5 and n" are translated in the order in which they are stated: $5 - n$. Statements that use the word "than," such as "less than" and "fewer than," are translated in reverse order. The algebraic expression for "5 less than n" is $n - 5$.

Key Question

- Write an algebraic expression for "5 more than n." $5 + n$ or $n + 5$
  Why can we write this expression both ways? Since addition is commutative, $5 + n$ and $n + 5$ are equivalent.

Chalkboard Examples

Write as an algebraic expression.

1. the sum of x and 2
   $x + 2$
2. the sum of a number and 3
   $n + 3$
   Other variables could be used instead of n.
3. six more than a number
   $n + 6$
4. nine less than a number
   $n - 9$
5. twice a number
   $2n$
6. half of a number
   $\frac{1}{2}n$ or $\frac{n}{2}$
7. the product of u and v
   uv
8. Let d be the number of dimes. There are 7 fewer nickels than dimes. Write an expression for the number of nickels.
   $d - 7$
9. Let w be the width of the table. The length is three times the width. Write an expression for the length.
   $3w$

LESSON QUIZ

Write as an algebraic expression.

1. five more than x
   $x + 5$
2. seven less than a number
   $n - 7$
3. five times a number
   $5n$
4. a number divided by 2
   $\frac{n}{2}$
5. Let m be the number of miles Malia ran. Laurel ran 3 miles further than Malia. Write an expression for the distance Laurel ran.
   $m + 3$

Assignment Guide

Minimum: 1–41 e/o, MR

Regular: 1–55 m3, 56, MR

Advanced: 1–55 m4, 56–61, MR

Try This

i. Let a be the amount of money Barbara has. Barbara divides her money among 7 people. Write an expression for the amount each person receives. $\frac{a}{7}$

j. Let c be the number of coins. Ilene has 24 fewer stamps than coins. Write an expression for the number of stamps she has. $c - 24$

1-6 EXERCISES

A

Write as an algebraic expression.

1. 6 more than b $b + 6$

2. 8 more than t $t + 8$

3. 9 less than c $c - 9$

4. 4 less than d $d - 4$

5. 6 greater than q $q + 6$

6. 11 greater than z $z + 11$

7. b more than a $a + b$

8. c more than d $d + c$

9. x less than y $y - x$

10. c less than h $h - c$

11. x added to w $w + x$

12. s added to t $t + s$

13. m subtracted from n $n - m$

14. p subtracted from q $q - p$

15. the sum of r and s $r + s$

16. the sum of d and f $d + f$

17. twice x $2x$

18. three times p $3p$

19. 5 multiplied by t $5t$

20. 9 multiplied by d $9d$

21. the product of 3 and b $3b$

22. x divided among 5 $\frac{x}{5}$

23. double h $2h$

24. half of x $\frac{x}{2}$

25. y fewer than x $x - y$

26. n more than 6 $n + 6$

27. 5 less than m $m - 5$

28. q less than p $p - q$

29. Let a be Connie's age. Robin is 5 years older than Connie. Write an expression for Robin's age. $a + 5$

30. Let p be the number of points the Tigers scored. The Lions scored double the number of points the Tigers scored. Write an expression for the number of points the Lions scored. $2p$

31. Let m be the amount of money Bob had before he went shopping. Bob spent \$4.50 while shopping. Write an expression for the amount Bob had left after shopping. $m - \$4.50$

32. Let t be the total amount Rosalie spent for blouses. Each of the 5 blouses cost the same. Write an expression for the cost of each blouse. $\frac{t}{5}$

33. Let a be the amount Greg earned last week. Greg earned \$45 more this week than last week. Write an expression for the amount he earned this week. $a + \$45$

34. Let n be the number of magazines Scotty sold. Sherry sold half as many magazines as Scotty. Write an expression for the number of magazines that Sherry sold. $\frac{n}{2}$

35. Let w be Tom's weight last week. Tom lost 2 pounds this week. Write an expression for Tom's weight this week. $w - 2$

36. Let a be the amount Gil has left after buying a record. The record cost \$8. Write an expression for the amount he had before buying the record. $a + \$8$

37. Let K be the amount Kelly earns. Geri earns three times as much as Kelly. Write an expression for the amount Geri earns. $3K$

38. Let w be the width of a racing-eight crew shell. A racing-eight shell is 25 times longer than it is wide. Write an expression for the length of a racing-eight crew shell. $25w$

39. Let t be the total amount of money collected. The total amount was divided evenly among 4 charities. Write an expression for the amount received by each charity. $\frac{1}{4}t$ or $\frac{t}{4}$

40. Let d be the distance Paul ran. Steve ran a third as far as Paul. Write an expression for the distance Steve ran. $\frac{1}{3}d$ or $\frac{d}{3}$

41. Let R be Randy's age 3 years from now. Write an expression for Randy's age now. $R - 3$

B

Write as an algebraic expression.

42. a number x increased by three times y $x + 3y$

43. a number y increased by twice x $y + 2x$

44. a number a increased by 2 more than b $a + (b + 2)$

45. a number that is 3 less than twice x $2x - 3$

46. a number x increased by itself $x + x$ or $2x$

47. the area of a rectangle with length l and width w lw

48. the perimeter of a square with side s $4s$

Evaluate.

49. $\frac{256y}{32x}$ for $y = 1$ and $x = 4$ 2

50. $\frac{y + x}{2} + \frac{3 \cdot y}{x}$ for $x = 2$ and $y = 4$ 9

51. $\frac{a + b}{4} + \frac{a \cdot b}{2}$ for $a = 3$ and $b = 4$ $\frac{31}{4}$

ADDITIONAL ANSWERS

Mixed Review

62. 144
63. 48
64. 144
65. $3(x + 2)$
66. $10(2a + 3b)$
67. $8(1 + 2x + 5y)$
68. $22c$
69. $12a + 7b$
70. c
71. $11y$
72. d
73. $9 + 7c$

Evaluate $\frac{x + y}{4}$ when

52. $y = 2$ and x is 14. 4

53. $x = 9$ and y is three times x. 9

54. $y = 8$ and x is twice y. 6

55. $x = 64$ and y is half of x. 24

56. ***Critical Thinking*** Describe a situation that could be translated to the expression $25a + 10b$. Answers may vary.

Challenge

57. Let $w + 3$ represent a whole number. Give an expression for the next whole number after it. $w + 4$

58. Let $d + 2$ represent an odd whole number. Give an expression for the preceding odd number. d

59. The difference between two numbers is 3. One number is t. What are two possible values for the other number? $t + 3, t - 3$

60. Two numbers are $v + 2$ and $v - 2$. What is their sum? $2v$

61. Two numbers are $2 + w$ and $2 - w$. What is their sum? 4

Mixed Review

Evaluate. **62.** $4c^2$ for $c = 6$ **63.** $3t^4$ for $t = 2$ **64.** $(4x)^2$ for $x = 3$

Factor. **65.** $3x + 6$ **66.** $20a + 30b$ **67.** $8 + 16x + 40y$

Collect like terms. **68.** $14c + 8c$ **69.** $4a + 7b + 8a$ **70.** $\frac{1}{3}c + \frac{2}{3}c$

71. $3y + 7y + y$ **72.** $\frac{1}{4}d + \frac{3}{4}d$ **73.** $5 + 7c + 4$

HISTORICAL NOTE

In 2000 B.C., the Babylonians used algebraic methods in solving problems. However, they used no mathematical symbols other than primitive numerals. This lack of symbolism in algebra continued for many centuries. Gradually, some of the more common words used in mathematics were abbreviated. However, it was not until almost 1500 A.D. that a symbolic algebra began to emerge.

The plus, +, and minus, −, signs first appeared in 1489 A.D. and were regularly used by 1544 A.D. The equal sign, =, was first used in 1557 by Robert Recorde in England. The raised dot, ·, and juxtaposition were first used for multiplication about 1600, and the symbol × about 1620. We find the division symbol, ÷, appearing in Rahn's *Teutsche Algebra* in 1659.

1-7 Solving Equations: An Introduction

Explore

A block and two marbles balance six marbles on a scale. The marbles each weigh one ounce. How much does the block weigh? 4 oz

Which of the following scales balance?

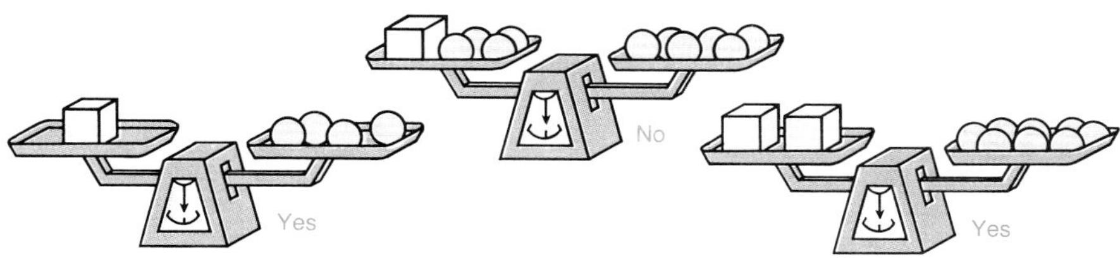

Much of your work in algebra will involve solving equations. In this lesson we introduce solving simple equations. An **equation** is a mathematical sentence that uses an equal sign to state that two expressions represent the same number or are equivalent. Here are some examples.

$3 + 2 = 5 \qquad 7 - 2 = 4 \qquad x + 15 = 12$

True, False, and Open Equations

Objective: Determine whether an equation is true, false, or open.

An equation that contains only numbers may be either true or false. For example, $3 + 2 = 5$ is true, but $7 - 2 = 4$ is false. An equation containing a variable may be neither true nor false. For example, $x + 5 = 12$ is neither true nor false because you do not know the value of the variable. An equation that contains at least one variable is called an **open sentence**.

EXAMPLES State whether each sentence is true, false, or open.

1. $18 + 32 = 50$ True
2. $42 - 15 = 25$ False
3. $12 = 4 + x$ Open

1-7

FIRST FIVE MINUTES

Write as an algebraic expression.

1. three more than z
   $z + 3$
2. twice as big as w
   $2w$
3. seven fewer than x
   $x - 7$
4. Let s be the distance from Los Angeles to New York. The distance to Omaha is half of the distance from Los Angeles to New York. Write an expression for the distance to Omaha.
   $\frac{s}{2}$
5. half the sum of a and b
   $\frac{a + b}{2}$

EXPLORE

Remind students of some facts about scales. In order to balance, each side must have the same weight. If you add or remove the same amount of weight from each side of a balanced scale, the scale will remain balanced. By removing 2 marbles from each side of the first scale, students should be able to determine that a block has the same weight as 4 marbles, or 4 ounces. They should then be able to add weights to each side to determine which of the other three scales balance.

True, False, and Open Equations

Emphasize that when an equation contains a variable, you may be unable to tell whether the equation is true or false.

Math Point
An equation that contains only numbers cannot be open; it must be true or false. An equation that contains a variable can be true, false, **or** open. For example, $x = x$ is true, $x = x + 5$ is false, and $x = 14$ is open.

Key Questions

Replace the variable x with a number that makes the sentence true.

- $x = 14$ 14
- $x + 8 = 11$ 3
- $4x = 8$ 2

Chalkboard Examples

State whether each sentence is true, false, or open.

1. $7 - 3 = 11 - 5$ False
2. $19 + 6 = x$ Open
3. $x + 1 = x + 1$ True

Equations and Solutions

A formal presentation of solving equations using the addition and multiplication properties is given in Chapter 3. This is an informal introduction, intended to give students an intuitive understanding of the concept of solution.

Key Questions

For each equation, is 9 a solution?

- $x + 3 = 6$ No
- $x - 3 = 6$ Yes
- $x = 6 + 3$ Yes
- $x + 3 + 6 = 9$ No

Chalkboard Examples

1. Solve $3x = \frac{x}{2} + 5$ for {0, 1, 2}.

$3(0) = \frac{0}{2} + 5$

$0 = 5$ False

$3(1) = \frac{1}{2} + 5$

$3 = 5\frac{1}{2}$ False

$3(2) = \frac{2}{2} + 5$

$6 = 6$ True

The solution set is {2}.

Solve mentally. The replacement set is all whole numbers.

2. $b + 7 = 15$
   $b = 8$
3. $5x = 20$
   $x = 4$
4. $z + 2 = 7$
   $z = 5$

Try This State whether each sentence is true, false, or open.

a. $3 \cdot 5 + 2 = 13$ False **b.** $4 \cdot 2 - 3 = 5$ True **c.** $y + 5 = 6$ Open

Equations and Solutions

Objective: Find solution sets of an equation.

The set of numbers from which you can select replacements for the variable is called the **replacement set.** A replacement for a variable that makes an equation true is called a **solution.** To solve an equation means to find all of its solutions. The collection of all the solutions is called the **solution set.**

When the replacement set contains a small number of elements, one way to solve the equation is to substitute each element in the set to see if it makes a true sentence.

EXAMPLE 4

Solve $2x = x + 3$ for the replacement set {0, 1, 2, 3}.

$$2x = x + 3$$

Replace the variable with each number in the replacement set.

$2(0) = 0 + 3$
$0 = 3$ False

$2(1) = 1 + 3$
$2 = 4$ False

$2(2) = 2 + 3$
$4 = 5$ False

$2(3) = 3 + 3$
$6 = 6$ True

The solution to the equation is 3. The solution set is {3}.

Try This

d. Solve $x^2 + 3 = 12$ for {0, 3, 9}. {3}

e. Solve $\frac{12}{x} = 3x$ for {2, 4, 12}. {2}

If the replacement set is large, trying numbers is not a good method for solving an equation. If an equation contains small numbers and one operation, the equation can often be solved mentally.

EXAMPLES Solve mentally. The replacement set is all whole numbers.

5. $x + 6 = 13$
$x = 7$ Think: What number added to 6 gives 13?

6. $4y = 32$
$y = 8$ Think: What number multiplied by 4 gives 32?

Try This Solve mentally. The replacement set is all whole numbers.

f. $x + 4 = 10$ $x = 6$ **g.** $\frac{y}{6} = 4$ $y = 24$

h. $14 = y + 9$ $y = 5$ **i.** $x - 5 = 12$ $x = 17$

Equivalent Equations

Objective: Recognize equivalent equations.

Two equations with the same solution set are **equivalent.**

Equivalent Equations	Solution Set	*Nonequivalent Equations*	Solution Set
$x + 4 = 10$	{6}	$x + 8 = 10$	{2}
$x + 6 = 12$	{6}	$x + 8 = 14$	{6}

An equation is like a balanced scale. If you add the same weight to both sides of the scale, it will remain balanced. Likewise, if you add the same quantity to both sides of an equation, the equations will be equivalent.

$$x + 4 = 10$$
$$x + 4 + 2 = 10 + 2 \quad \text{Adding 2 to both sides}$$
$$x + 6 = 12$$

The equation $x + 4 = 10$ is equivalent to the equation $x + 6 = 12$.

You can
add the same number to both sides of an equation,
subtract the same number on both sides of an equation,
multiply both sides of an equation by the same number, or
divide both sides of an equation by the same number
and still have an equivalent equation.

EXAMPLE 7 Each pair of equations is equivalent. What was done to the first equation to get the second one?

$x + 2 = 5$
$x + 5 = 8$ $x + 2 + 3 = 5 + 3$

Three was added to both sides of the first equation to get the second equation.

Equivalent Equations

Students can determine if two equations are equivalent by solving both and comparing the solution sets. Since there may be cases where the solution sets are different sizes, students should not merely check that each member of the solution set of one also solves the other.

Math Point
Two equations are equivalent if and only if they have the same solution set.

Chalkboard Examples

Each pair of equations is equivalent. What was done to the first equation to get the second one?

1. $3x + 1 = x$
   $3x + 2 = x + 1$
   1 was added to both sides of the equation.
2. $x + 5 = 7 - x$
   $2(x + 5) = 2(7 - x)$
   Both sides of the equation were multiplied by 2.

LESSON ENRICHMENT

1. Solve $4x - 9 = x$ for the replacement set {5, 6, 7}.
   There is no solution.
2. Solve $4x - 9 = x$ for the replacement set {1, 2, 3}.
   The solution set is {3}.
3. Can an equation have different solutions if you use different replacement sets?
   Yes
4. What must be true about the solution?
   The solution must be contained in the replacement set.

LESSON QUIZ

State whether the following sentences are true, false, or open.

1. $\frac{5}{x} = 20$
   Open
2. $5(4 + 2) = 20$
   False
3. Solve $3x - 7 = \frac{20}{x}$ for the replacement set {2, 4, 5}.
   The solution set is {4}.

Solve mentally. The replacement set is all whole numbers.

4. $x + 6 = 8$ $x = 2$
5. $6x = 36$ $x = 6$
6. $2x + 1 = 3$ $x = 1$
7. This pair of equations is equivalent. What was done to the first equation to get the second one?
   $x^2 - 3 = x$
   $x^2 - 3 - 3 = x - 3$
   3 was subtracted from both sides.

Assignment Guide
Minimum: 1–27 e/o, MR

Regular: 1–48 m3, 49, MR

Advanced: 1–48 m3, 49–51, MR

ADDITIONAL ANSWERS

Try This

j. 4 was added to both sides of the equation.
k. 5 was subtracted from both sides of the equation.
l. Both sides of the equation were divided by 2.

Exercises

19. 5 was added to both sides.
20. 3 was subtracted from both sides.
21. 10 was subtracted from both sides.

EXAMPLES Each pair of equations is equivalent. What was done to the first equation to get the second one?

8. $4x = 20$
   $x = 5$ $\quad \frac{4x}{4} = \frac{20}{4}$

Both sides of the first equation were divided by 4 to get the second equation.

9. $\frac{1}{3}x = 8$

   $\frac{2}{3}x = 16$ $\quad 2 \cdot \frac{1}{3}x = 2 \cdot 8$

Both sides of the first equation were multiplied by 2 to get the second equation.

Try This Each pair of equations is equivalent. What was done to the first equation to get the second one? See Additional Answers.

j. $x + 8 = 20$, $x + 12 = 24$ **k.** $2x - 4 = 56$, $2x - 9 = 51$ **l.** $6x = 42$, $3x = 21$

1-7 EXERCISES

A

State whether each sentence is true, false, or open.

1. $2 + 3 \cdot 5 = 25$ False **2.** $3a - 4 = 5$ Open **3.** $2^3 + 8 = 16$ True

Solve for the given replacement set.

4. $3n + 2 = 23$ {5, 7, 9} {7} **5.** $6u - 2 = 46$ {5, 6, 8} {8}

6. $2m^2 - 1 = 7 \left\{1, \frac{3}{2}, 2\right\}$ {2} **7.** $x^2 + x = 0$ {0, 100, 1000} {0}

8. $8 - n = 2n$ {1, 2, 4} No solution **9.** $t - 8 = 4t - 44$ {8, 12, 18} {12}

Solve mentally. The replacement set is all whole numbers.

10. $x + 10 = 20$ $x = 10$ **11.** $m + 7 = 30$ $m = 23$ **12.** $x - 7 = 12$ $x = 19$

13. $y - 8 = 19$ $y = 27$ **14.** $6a = 54$ $a = 9$ **15.** $8y = 72$ $y = 9$

16. $\frac{x}{6} = 5$ $x = 30$ **17.** $\frac{c}{8} = 6$ $c = 48$ **18.** $d + 98 = 100$ $d = 2$

Each pair of equations is equivalent. Tell what was done to the first equation to get the second equation.

19. $3x - 5 = 12$, $3x = 17$ **20.** $4r + 3 = 12$, $4r = 9$ **21.** $x + 5 = 12$, $x - 5 = 2$

22. $12x = 36$
$4x = 12$

23. $\frac{r}{4} = 6$
$r = 24$

24. $\frac{3y}{5} = 3$
$3y = 15$

25. $\frac{x}{8} = 4$
$x = 32$

26. $5 = \frac{n}{3}$
$15 = n$

27. $7 = \frac{2y}{4}$
$28 = 2y$

B

Simplify; then solve mentally. The replacement set is all whole numbers.

28. $5x + 3x = 24$ 29. $9y + 4y = 26$ 30. $6t + 3t = 0$

31. $\frac{y}{2} + \frac{y}{2} = 31$ 32. $\frac{2}{3}y + \frac{1}{3}y = 2$ 33. $20x - 6x = 7$

34. $\frac{10d}{5} = 10$ 35. $\frac{20k}{4} = 10$ 36. $4t^2 = 0$

What can be done to each side of the equation to get the variable alone on one side of the equal sign?

37. $x - 12 = 34$ 38. $g + 34 = 60$ 39. $3x = 23$

40. $5v = 35$ 41. $\frac{t}{8} = 12$ 42. $\frac{m}{5} = 14$

Determine whether each pair of equations is equivalent.

43. $k + 7 = 12$
$k + 7 - 4 = 12 - 4$ Yes

44. $n - 5 = 21$
$n - 5 + 5 = 21 - 5$ No

45. $\frac{x}{6} = 12$
$12 \cdot \frac{x}{6} = 6 \cdot 12$ No

46. $\frac{g}{3} = 15$
$3 \cdot \frac{g}{3} = 3 \cdot 15$ Yes

47. $4x + 3 = 15 - x$
$4x + 3 + x = 15 - x + x$ Yes

48. $5 - x = 3x + 7$
$5 - x = 3x + 7 - 3x$ No

49. *Critical Thinking* Write an equation with no solution if the replacement set is the set of all odd whole numbers. Ex. $x + 2 = 8$

Challenge

50. Write an equation that has *no* whole number solution. Ex. $3x = 2$
51. Write an equation for which *every* whole number is a solution. Ex. $x - x = 0$
52. Write an equation of the type $ax = b$ where 0 is a solution. Ex. $12x = 0$

Mixed Review

Write using exponential notation. 53. $m \cdot m \cdot m$ 54. $n \cdot n \cdot 5 \cdot n \cdot n \cdot n$

Calculate. 55. $(3 \cdot 2)^2$ 56. $(4 + 4)^2$ 57. $9 + 3^2$ 58. $(9 - 6)^3$

Factor. 59. $4x + 12$ 60. $13t + 52$ 61. $10t + 25m$

62. $16 + 8y$ 63. $8a + 16b$ 64. $9x + 3$ 65. $8 + 24c$

22. Both sides were divided by 3.
23. Both sides were multiplied by 4.
24. Both sides were multiplied by 5.
25. Both sides were multiplied by 8.
26. Both sides were multiplied by 3.
27. Both sides were multiplied by 4.
28. $x = 3$
29. $y = 2$
30. $t = 0$
31. $y = 31$
32. $y = 2$
33. $x = \frac{1}{2}$
34. $d = 5$
35. $k = 2$
36. $t = 0$
37. Add 12 to both sides.
38. Subtract 34 from both sides.
39. Divide both sides by 3.
40. Divide both sides by 5.
41. Multiply both sides by 8.
42. Multiply both sides by 5.

Mixed Review

53. m^3
54. $5n^5$
55. 36
56. 64
57. 18
58. 27
59. $4(x + 3)$
60. $13(t + 4)$
61. $5(2t + 5m)$
62. $8(2 + y)$
63. $8(a + 2b)$
64. $3(3x + 1)$
65. $8(1 + 3c)$

1-8

FIRST FIVE MINUTES

1. Joel got 87 points on his first test. That was 12 points more than Winston got. Write an algebraic expression for the number of points that Joel got.
   W + 12
2. A dozen donuts costs $3.24. Write an expression for the cost of 1 donut.
   3.24 ÷ 12
3. Corliss has $5 less than Zelma. Zelma has $38. Write an expression for how much Corliss has.
   $38 − $5
4. In San Francisco, the Transamerica Pyramid is 75 ft taller than the Bank of America Building. The Bank of America Building is 778 ft tall. Write an expression for the height of the Transamerica Pyramid.
   778 + 75

Draw a Diagram

Read the Problem-Solving Guidelines with students and discuss each phase. These guidelines are also on Overhead Transparency 1. The guidelines lead students through the problem-solving process and provide a systematic way of approaching the problem.

Many of the problem-solving strategies that will be introduced can be used to help students write an equation for solving. It is also important, however, for students to experience problems that cannot be solved by writing and solving equations and to know other strategies that can be used to solve problems.

Emphasize that drawing a diagram can be very helpful in understanding the problem. Demonstrate with the example how drawing a diagram helps you sort out and visualize the information in the problem.

Key Questions

- How long is the tunnel at the end of the first day of work? 500 ft
- How long is the tunnel at the beginning of the second day of work? 300 ft
- How long is the tunnel at the end of the second day of work? 800 ft

1-8 Problem Solving: Strategies

Draw a Diagram

Objective: Solve nonroutine problems using the strategy *Draw a Diagram.*

You can use the Problem-Solving Guidelines below to help you solve problems.

PROBLEM-SOLVING GUIDELINES

■ **Phase 1: UNDERSTAND the problem**
What am I trying to find?
What data am I given?
Have I ever solved a similar problem?

■ **Phase 2: Develop and carry out a PLAN**
What strategies might I use to solve the problem?
How can I correctly carry out the strategies I selected?

■ **Phase 3: Find the ANSWER and CHECK**
Does the proposed solution check?
What is the answer to the problem?
Does the answer seem reasonable?
Have I stated the answer clearly?

The planning phase involves selecting and carrying out one or more *strategies* for solving problems. One of the most useful strategies is to *draw a diagram* of the situation.

EXAMPLE

A mining company estimates that a crew needs to tunnel about 2000 ft into a mountain to reach the mineral deposits. Each day they are able to tunnel about 500 ft into the mountain. Each night, when they are not working, about 200 ft of their tunnel refills with rocks. At this rate, estimate how many days it will take the company to reach the mineral deposits.

■ **UNDERSTAND the problem**

Question: How many days will the mining crew need to tunnel?
Data: Each day they gain 500 ft; each night they lose 200 ft.

Develop and carry out a PLAN

We can *draw a diagram* to show the action in the problem.

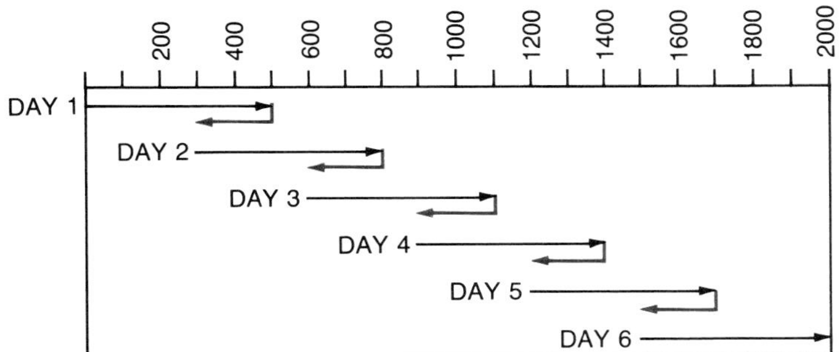

Find the ANSWER AND CHECK

The diagram shows that the crew will reach the deposit in 6 days. This answer seems reasonable, since each day the progress is 300 ft.

1-8 PROBLEMS

Solve by drawing a diagram.

1. The tip of a large underwater mountain in the Pacific Ocean is about 8700 ft from the surface. The distance from the bottom of the mountain to the water's surface is about 14,250 ft. What is the approximate height of this underwater mountain?

2. The manager of a shopping mall was asked to rope off a rectangular section of the parking lot for an automobile show. The area roped off was 250 ft by 300 ft. Posts were to be placed every 25 ft around the lot. How many posts were needed?

3. A rocket is divided into three sections: the cargo and navigation section at the top, the fuel tank in the middle, and the booster rocket at the bottom. The cargo and navigation section is one sixth as long as the booster rocket. The booster rocket is one half the total length of the rocket. The total length is 180 ft. How long is each section?

4. ***Write a convincing argument*** Solve the problem below. Then write an argument to convince a classmate that your solution is correct.

A teacher has to select 1 of her 20 students to attend a leadership conference. To be fair she places them in a circle and gives each student a number, in order, from 1 through 20. Then, starting with 1, she points to every other student, sending them back to their seats. She sends student number 2 back, student number 4 back, student number 6 back, and so on, until she goes completely around the circle. She continues skipping every other student until only 1 person is left. In which position should a student stand in order to be selected to attend the conference?

Chalkboard Example
Overhead Transparency 2 (T2)

1. In Oakville, the north-south streets are numbered consecutively and the names of the east-west streets are in alphabetical order. Amy lives at 13th and Clay, her bank is at 12th and Indio, and the grocery store is at 17th and Holly. What is the fewest number of blocks she must walk to travel from home to the bank to the store and back home again?
   Draw a diagram of Amy's neighborhood. Her home is marked H, the store is marked S, and the bank is marked with a $.

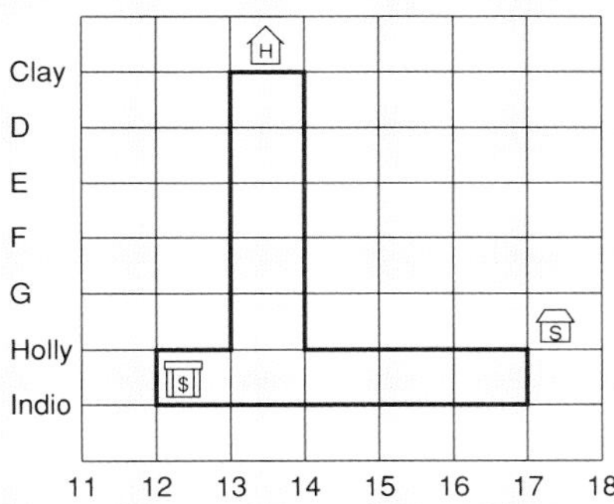

The fewest number of blocks Amy can travel is 22.

Hints for Problems

1. Draw a diagram to show the relationship between the two numbers and the unknown quantity.
2. Draw a rectangle and arrange posts. How many posts are needed for the length? the width?
3. Draw a diagram showing the three parts of the rocket. Label the total length of the rocket. How can you find the length of the booster?
4. Draw a diagram with 20 numbers around it. Act it out by drawing a line through the numbers as the students return to their seats.

ANSWERS

1. The underwater mountain is 5550 ft high.
2. Forty-four posts are needed.
3. The booster is 90 ft long, the fuel tank is 75 ft long, and the cargo and navigation section is 15 ft long.
4. A student should sit in position 9 to attend the conference.

1-9

FIRST FIVE MINUTES

Evaluate each for $x = 4$

1. $3x$ 12
2. $4x + 5$ 21
3. $3x^2$ 48
4. $(3x)^2$ 144
5. $\frac{24}{x}$ 6
6. $\frac{x}{24}$ $\frac{1}{6}$

You may wish to review formulas that students have used before. Point out to students that they can carry the units throughout each computation to determine the appropriate unit for their answer. This technique is called *dimensional analysis* and is used extensively in science.

Math Point
The speed of sound decreases at higher altitudes. At sea level at 32°F, it travels at about 740 mi/h. Supersonic airplanes are often accompanied by a sonic boom. The motion of the plane causes a variation in air pressure, or shock wave, which travels away from the plane. When this shock wave touches the ground, an explosive sound occurs.

Key Questions

What is the appropriate unit?

- $15\frac{\text{mi}}{\text{h}} \cdot 6\text{ h} = 90$ mi
- $8\frac{\text{ft}}{\text{sec}} \cdot 60\frac{\text{sec}}{\text{min}} = 480$ $\frac{\text{ft}}{\text{min}}$
- If Example 1 gave the speed of sound in feet/minute, what units would you use for the speed of the plane?
  Feet/minute
- How would you convert a speed that was given in miles/second to miles per hour?
  Multiply the number of mi/s by 3600 seconds/hour.

1-9 Using Formulas

Objective: Evaluate formulas.

Application

The speed of a supersonic airplane, which travels near or above the speed of sound, is given as a "Mach" number. The Mach number (**M**) is the quotient of the speed of the airplane (**a**) and the speed of sound (**s**). We can express this as a formula.

A **formula** is an equation that shows a relationship between two or more variables. The formula for the Mach number is $M = \frac{a}{s}$. An equivalent formula is $a = Ms$. We can evaluate this formula just as we evaluate any algebraic expression.

EXAMPLE 1

What is the speed of a supersonic airplane traveling at Mach 1.5 at an altitude where the speed of sound is 720 mi/h?

We will use the formula $a = Ms$ to find the answer, where $M = 1.5$ and $s = 720$ mi/h.

$$a = Ms$$
$$a = 1.5(720)\text{ mi/h}$$
$$a = 1080\text{ mi/h}$$

Since the speed of sound is in miles per hour, the speed of the airplane is also in miles per hour.

Try This

a. Find the speed of a supersonic airplane traveling at Mach 1.5 at an altitude where the speed of sound is 1130 km/h. 1695 km/h

b. Find the speed of a supersonic airplane traveling at Mach 2 at an altitude where the speed of sound is 685 mi/h. 1370 mi/h

The units of the quantities must always be compatible. Consider, for example, the formula $d = rt$, where d is the distance a moving object travels, r is the rate of travel, and t is the time the object travels. If the rate is given in miles per *hour,* the time must be in *hours.*

EXAMPLE 2

Find the distance (d) traveled by a moped moving at the rate (r) of 27 mi/h for the time (t) of 8 h using the formula $d = rt$.

$$d = rt$$

$$d = 27\frac{\text{mi}}{\text{h}} \cdot 8 \text{ h} \qquad \text{The units of measurement are compatible.}$$

$$d = 216 \text{ mi} \qquad \frac{\text{mi}}{\text{h}} \cdot \text{h} = \text{mi}$$

EXAMPLE 3

Find the perimeter (P) of a rectangle with length (l) of 9 ft and width (w) of 48 in. using the formula $P = 2l + 2w$.

The dimensions of the length and width must have the same units. We can easily change 48 inches to feet by dividing by 12, the number of inches in one foot. Carrying the dimensions through a computation is sometimes called **dimensional analysis.**

$$l = 9 \text{ ft} \qquad w = \frac{48 \text{ in.}}{12 \text{ in./ft}} = 4 \text{ ft} \qquad \frac{\text{in.}}{\frac{\text{in.}}{\text{ft}}} = \text{in.} \cdot \frac{\text{ft}}{\text{in.}} = \text{ft}$$

$$P = 2(9 \text{ ft}) + 2(4 \text{ ft})$$
$$P = 18 \text{ ft} + 8 \text{ ft}$$
$$P = 26 \text{ ft}$$

EXAMPLE 4

Find the amount of sales tax (T) paid on an item selling for a price (p) of \$14 using the formula $T = 0.05p$ (5% tax rate).

$$T = 0.05(\$14) \qquad \text{Substituting 14 for } p$$
$$T = \$0.70$$

Try This

c. Find the perimeter (P) of an equilateral triangle with sides (s) of 13 cm using the formula $P = 3s$. $P = 39$ cm

d. Find the area (A) of a square with sides of 7 in. using the formula $A = s^2$. $A = 49$ in.^{2}

e. Find the rate (r) at which an object is traveling if it goes a distance (d) of 63 feet in 7 seconds (t) using the velocity formula $r = \frac{d}{t}$. $r = 9$ ft/sec

f. Find the volume (V) of a toy box with length (l) of 4 ft, width (w) of 24 in., and height (h) of 30 in. using the formula $V = lwh$. $V = 20$ ft^3

Chalkboard Examples

Evaluate each formula.

1. Find the distance (d) traveled by a supersonic airplane whose speed (r) is 1080 mi/h for 15 minutes using the formula $d = rt$.
   To make units compatible, convert time to hours.
   $t = \frac{15 \text{ min}}{60 \text{ min/h}} = \frac{1}{4}\text{h}$
   $d = 1080 \frac{\text{mi}}{\text{h}} \cdot \frac{1}{4}\text{h}$
   $d = 270$ mi
2. Find the surface area of a box using the formula $S = 2(LW + LH + WH)$ if $L = 2$ ft, $W = 3$ ft, and $H = 5$ ft.
   $S = 2(2 \text{ ft} \cdot 3 \text{ ft} + 2 \text{ ft} \cdot 5 \text{ ft} + 3 \text{ ft} \cdot 5 \text{ ft})$
   $\text{ft} \cdot \text{ft} = \text{ft}^2$
   $= 2(6 \text{ ft}^2 + 10 \text{ ft}^2 + 15 \text{ ft}^2)$
   $= 2(31 \text{ ft}^2)$
   $= 62 \text{ ft}^2$
3. Find the area of a triangle whose base (b) is 17 in. and whose height (h) is 2 ft using the formula $A = \frac{1}{2}bh$.
   To make the units compatible, convert the height to in.
   $h = 2 \text{ ft} \cdot \frac{12 \text{ in.}}{\text{ft}} = 24 \text{ in.}$
   $A = \frac{1}{2} \cdot 17 \text{ in.} \cdot 24 \text{ in.}$
   $= 204 \text{ in.}^2$

LESSON QUIZ

Evaluate.

1. $D = RT$ for $R = 8$ mi/s, $T = 3$ sec
   $D = 8 \cdot 3 \frac{\text{mi}}{\text{s}} \cdot \text{s} = 24 \text{ mi}$
2. $V = LWH$ for $L = 6$ ft, $W = 3$ ft, $H = 5$ ft
   $V = 6 \cdot 3 \cdot 5 \text{ ft} \cdot \text{ft} \cdot \text{ft} = 90 \text{ ft}^3$
3. $V = LWH$ for $L = 1$ yd, $W = 5$ ft, $H = 2$ ft
   $V = (1 \text{ yd} \cdot 3 \text{ ft/yd})(5 \text{ ft})(2 \text{ ft})$
   $= 30 \text{ ft}^3$
4. $P = 2(AB - 1)$ for $A = 10$ lb, $B = 3$ lb
   $P = 2[(10 \text{ lb})(3 \text{ lb}) - 1] = 58 \text{ lb}^2$
5. $W = (X + Y)(X - Y)$ for $X = 7$ ft, $Y = 4$ ft
   $W = (7 \text{ ft} - 4 \text{ ft})(7 \text{ ft} + 4 \text{ ft})$
   $= (11 \text{ ft})(3 \text{ ft}) = 33 \text{ ft}^2$

Assignment Guide
Minimum: 1–16, MR

Regular: 1–23 e/o, 24, MR

Advanced: 1–23 e/o, 24–26, MR

1-9 EXERCISES

A

1. Find the distance (d) traveled by a truck moving at a rate (r) of 55 mi/h for the time (t) of 8 h using the formula $d = rt$. 440 mi
2. Find the area (A) of a circle with a radius (r) of 4 m using the formula $A = 3.14\,r^2$. 50.24 m²
3. Find the amount of sales tax (T) paid on an item selling for a price (p) of \$170 using the formula $T = 0.04p$ (4% tax rate). \$6.80
4. Find the number of kilometers (km) in 2500 meters (m) using the formula $\text{km} = \frac{\text{m}}{1000}$. 2.5 km
5. Find the speed of a supersonic airplane (a) traveling at Mach (M) 1.4 at an altitude where the speed of sound (s) is 1025 ft/s using the formula $a = Ms$. 1435 ft/s
6. Find the speed of a supersonic airplane (a) traveling at Mach (M) 2.3 at an altitude where the speed of sound (s) is 714 mi/h using the formula $a = Ms$. 1642.2 mi/h
7. Find the area (A) of a basketball court with length (l) of 26 m and width (w) of 1400 cm using the formula $A = lw$. 364 m²

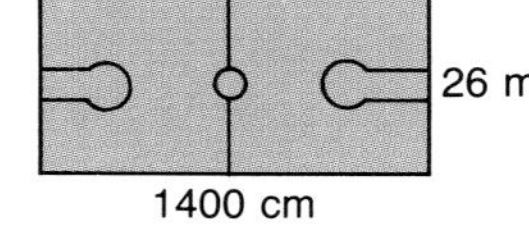

8. Find the area (A) of a triangle with a base (b) of 9 in. and a height (h) of 1 ft using the formula $A = \frac{1}{2}bh$. 54 in.² or $\frac{3}{8}$ ft²

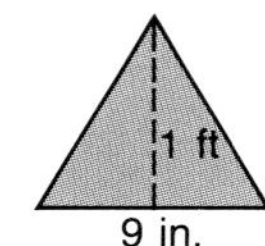

9. Find the perimeter (P) of an ice skating rink with length (l) of 66 yd and width (w) of 99 ft using the formula $P = 2(l + w)$. 198 yd or 594 ft
10. Find the temperature in degrees Celsius (C) given a temperature of 75° Fahrenheit (F) using the formula $C = \frac{5}{9}(F - 32)$. ≈24 °C
11. Find the amount of simple interest (I) paid on a principal (p) amount of \$2000 at a rate (r) of 0.15 (15% interest rate) for a term (t) of 3 years using the formula $I = prt$. \$900
12. Find the unit price (U) of a 40 oz (n) box of rice selling for a price (P) of \$2.50 using the formula $U = \frac{P}{n}$. \$0.0625 per oz

The formula below gives a rule for determining the amount of medicine a child should have if you know the age of the child (a) and the amount, or dosage, (D) of the medicine an adult would take. Find the child's dosage (d) for the given values of a and D. Round answers to the nearest tenth.

$$d = \frac{a}{a + 12} \cdot D$$

13. $a = 5$ yr, $D = 2.5$ mL 0.7 mL
14. $a = 10$ yr, $D = 8$ mL 3.6 mL
15. $a = 2$ yr, $D = 4$ mL 0.6 mL
16. $a = 1$ yr, $D = 1.5$ mL 0.1 mL

The formula below gives the approximate stopping distance (d) in feet for an automobile driving at x miles per hour (mi/h). Find the approximate stopping distance for each speed given.

$$d = x + \frac{x^2}{20}$$

17. $x = 25$ mi/h **18.** $x = 10$ mi/h **19.** 55 mi/h **20.** 50 mi/h

The formula below gives the area of a trapezoid. As shown in the picture, h is the height, b is the length of one base, and c is the length of the other base. Use this formula to find the area for the different values given below.

$$A = \frac{1}{2}h\,(b + c)$$

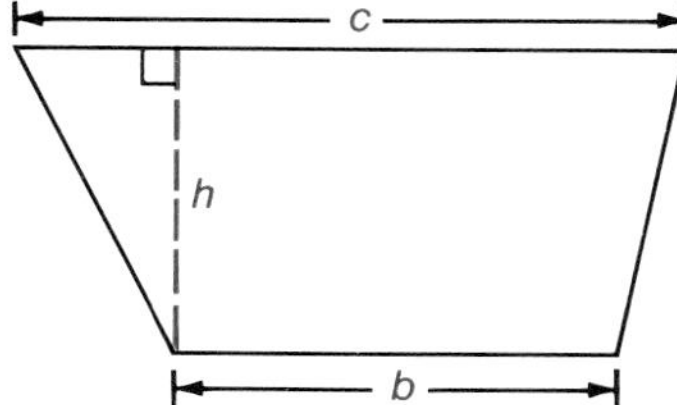

21. $h = 2$ ft, $b = 5$ ft, $c = 12$ ft

22. $h = 10$ in., $b = 8$ in., $c = 14$ in.

23. $h = 4$ m, $b = \frac{1}{2}$ m, $c = \frac{3}{4}$ m

24. ***Critical Thinking*** The length and width of a rectangle are each whole numbers. Find possible areas for this rectangle if its perimeter is 14 cm. Use the formulas $A = lw$ and $P = 2l + 2w$.

Challenge

25. Find the length of a rectangle (l) with area (A) 64 cm^2 and width (w) 16 cm. Use the formula $A = lw$.

Write a formula for the area of each figure.

26.

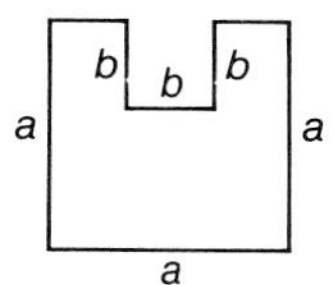

27.

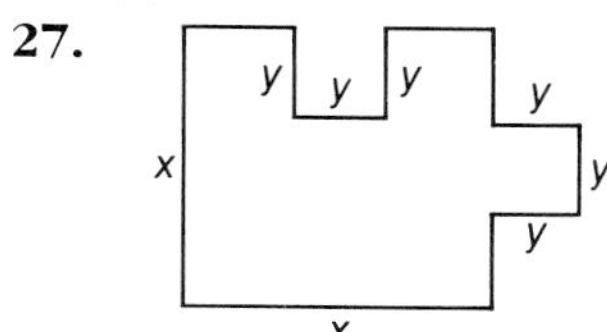

Mixed Review

Write as an algebraic expression. **28.** 5 more than t

29. the sum of x and y **30.** 3 times k **31.** 3 less than m

Collect like terms. **32.** $15c + c$ **33.** $3x + 4 + 5x$

Solve mentally. **34.** $x + 6 = 15$ **35.** $6m = 42$

Problem for Programmers

Write a program that will determine the child's dosage for medicine using the formula given with Exercises 13–16. Use Exercises 13–16 to test your program.

ADDITIONAL ANSWERS

Exercises

17. 56.25 ft
18. 15 ft
19. 206.25 ft
20. 175 ft
21. 17 ft^2
22. 110 in.^{2}
23. $2\frac{1}{2}$ m^2
24. $P = 2(l + w)$, so $l + w = 7$ cm. The dimensions of the rectangle could be 1 cm × 6 cm, 2 cm × 5 cm, or 3 cm × 4 cm. Thus, the area could be 6 cm^2, 10 cm^2, or 12 cm^2.
25. 4 cm
26. Answers may vary. Ex: $a^2 - b^2$.
27. Answers may vary. Ex: $x^2 + y^2 - y^2 = x^2$.

Mixed Review

28. $t + 5$
29. $x + y$
30. $3k$
31. $m - 3$
32. $16c$
33. $8x + 4$
34. 9
35. 7

Problem for Programmers

This program can be written using any programming language (BASIC, PASCAL, LOGO, etc.). The programming ability of the student will determine how the number is input (from the keyboard or within the program) and how the child's dosage is output (with complete sentences, in columns).

This program can also be written on a spreadsheet where each value is input in a separate column and the child's dosage calculated in a third column.

1-10

FIRST FIVE MINUTES

1. Play the game Hi-Lo. Think of a number for students to guess. The only clues you should give are "high" or "low." The first student to guess the correct number wins. Suggested numbers to use are 54, 5480, −34, 3.8.
2. Use the Hi-Lo method to approximate the square root of 200. That is, try to find a number that when multiplied by itself gives 200. $\sqrt{200} \approx 14.1421$

Guess, Check, Revise

Every day, problems are solved by the *Guess, Check, Revise* method. Emphasize that the key is to make intelligent guesses. That is, first make a "ballpark" guess based on the data in the problem, then evaluate the accuracy of that guess and use this information to make increasingly "educated" guesses and focus in on a correct answer.

See Computer Exploration 1 on p. 715 for using a computer to guess and check.

Key Question

- In Example 1, if the sum is too great, what should you do? Guess a lower number.

Chalkboard Examples

Use the Guess, Check, Revise strategy to solve the following problems.

1. $\frac{13 + \square \cdot 5}{3} = 16$

   Guess 5 and check.

   $\frac{13 + 5 \cdot 5}{3} = \frac{13 + 25}{3}$

   $= \frac{38}{3}$

   $\frac{38}{3} = 12\frac{2}{3}$: less than 16

   Guess 8 and check.

   $\frac{13 + 8 \cdot 5}{3} = \frac{53}{3}$

   $\frac{53}{3} = 17\frac{2}{3}$: greater than 16

   Guess 7 and check.

   $\frac{13 + 7 \cdot 5}{3} = \frac{48}{3}$

   $\frac{48}{3} = 16$ Correct

1-10 Problem Solving: Strategies

Guess, Check, Revise

Objective: Solve problems using the strategy *Guess, Check, Revise* and other strategies.

PROBLEM-SOLVING GUIDELINES
■ UNDERSTAND the problem
■ Develop and Carry out a PLAN
■ Find the ANSWER and CHECK

Some problems can be solved by guessing a solution, checking the guess, and, if necessary, using information gained from the check to revise the guess.

This strategy for solving problems is called Guess, Check, Revise.

EXAMPLE 1 Use the *Guess, Check, Revise* strategy to find the missing number.

$$\frac{3 \cdot \square + 7}{2} = 11$$

- Guess 8 for $\square$. Check. $\frac{3 \cdot 8 + 7}{2} = \frac{24 + 7}{2}$

  $= \frac{31}{2} = 15\frac{1}{2}$

  Since $15\frac{1}{2}$ is greater than 11, 8 was too large. Try 4.

- Guess 4 for $\square$. Check. $\frac{3 \cdot 4 + 7}{2} = \frac{12 + 7}{2}$

  $= \frac{19}{2} = 9\frac{1}{2}$

  Since $9\frac{1}{2}$ is less than 11, 4 is too small. Try 5.

- Guess 5 for $\square$. Check. $\frac{3 \cdot 5 + 7}{2} = \frac{15 + 7}{2}$

  $= \frac{22}{2} = 11$ Correct.

  The missing number is 5.

The missing number in the example was found using the *Guess, Check, Revise* strategy. The missing number also could have been found using equation-solving techniques that you will learn in later chapters. *Many problems in mathematics can be solved correctly in more than one way.*

Use the *Guess, Check, Revise* strategy to solve the following problem.

EXAMPLE 2 One number is 12 more than another number. The sum of the two numbers is 48. What are the two numbers?

- Guess 5 for the first number. $5 + 12 = 17$, the second number

  $17 + 5 = 22$ Too low, guess a higher first number.
- Guess 20 for the first number. $20 + 12 = 32$, the second number

  $20 + 32 = 52$ Too high but close. Guess a lower number.
- Guess 18 for the first number. $18 + 12 = 30$

  $18 + 30 = 48$ Correct.

The two numbers are 18 and 30.

Problem-Solving Strategies		
Draw a Diagram	Guess, Check, Revise	Write an Equation
Make an Organized List	Use Logical Reasoning	Make a Table
Look for a Pattern	Simplify the Problem	Work Backward

1-10 PROBLEMS

Solve using the *Guess, Check, Revise* strategy.

1. $\frac{4 \cdot \square - 12}{2} = 8$
2. $\frac{2 \cdot \square + 18}{4} = 6$
3. $\frac{\square \cdot 3 + 19}{2} = 20$
4. $\frac{5 \cdot 8 + \square}{4} = 12$
5. $\frac{30}{2 + \square} = 3$
6. $\frac{12}{2 + \square} = 2$
7. $7(14 - \square) = 35$
8. $5(3 + \square) = 40$
9. $2 \cdot \square - 1 = 4 + \square$
10. $6 \cdot \square + 3 = 2 \cdot \square + 11$
11. One number is 4 times larger than another number. Their sum is 60. What are the two numbers?
12. Consecutive numbers are numbers that follow each other when counting. For example, 5, 6, and 7 are consecutive numbers. Find three consecutive numbers whose sum is 72.

2. The sum of two numbers is 51. Their difference is 5. What are the two numbers?
Guess 30 for the first number. The second number is $30 - 5 = 25$. $30 + 25 = 55$ Too high
Guess 27 for the first number. The second number is $27 - 5 = 22$. $27 + 22 = 49$ Close but too low
Guess 28 for the first number. The second number is $28 - 5 = 23$. $28 + 23 = 51$
The numbers are 28 and 23.

Hints for Problems

11–19. Use the strategy guess, check, and revise.
20. Use the table to record guesses and the results of each guess.
21. Make a guess for regular hours. If she works 20 regular hours, how will you find the number of overtime hours?
22. Draw a diagram to represent the 8-day expedition. Could one person make the trip? two people?
23. Guess an amount for the first week. Check. Revise your guess.
24. Guess a number of 4-wheel lawnmowers. Check. Revise your guess. Can you find another solution?

ANSWERS

1. 7
2. 3
3. 7
4. 8
5. 8
6. 4
7. 9
8. 5
9. 5
10. 2
11. The numbers are 12 and 48.
12. 23, 24, and 25

ANSWERS

13. 24 in., 12 in.
14. 14 × 22
15. 45°, 45°, 90°
16. 30°, 60°, 90°
17. 22 and 11
18. 32 and 25
19. 59
20. 6, 11, and 30
21. Eunpyo worked 11 hours of overtime.
22. Four people are needed to start the journey.
23. Peter earned $15.25 the first week.
24. Juanita could have earned $120, $126, $132, $138, or $144 for her workday.

13. The length of a rectangle is twice as long as the width. The perimeter of the rectangle is 72 in. What are the length and width of this rectangle?

14. The length of a rectangle is 8 more than the width. The area is 308 square units. What are the dimensions of the rectangle?

15. The sum of the interior angles of a triangle is 180°. Two angles are the same. The other angle is two times as large as one of the smaller angles. What are the angles of the triangle?

16. One angle of a triangle is twice as large as the smallest. Another is three times as large as the smallest. What are the three angles?

17. The sum of two numbers is 33. Their product is 242. What are the numbers?

18. The product of two numbers is 800. Their difference is 7. What are the two numbers?

19. The sum of the digits of a two-digit number is 14. If the digits are reversed, the new number is 36 greater than the original number. What is the original two-digit number?

20. The sum of three numbers is 47. The second number is 5 more than the smallest number. The third number is 5 times larger than the smallest number. What are the three numbers? Copy and complete a table like the one below to record your guesses.

	1st Number	2nd Number	3rd Number	Sum
1st guess				
2nd guess				
3rd guess				

Solve using one or more of the strategies.

21. Eunpyo worked a total of 33 hours in 1 week. She worked half as many overtime hours as she worked regular hours. How many overtime hours did she work?

22. A photography expedition planned an 8-day crossing of an animal preserve. Each person can carry at most a 5-day supply of water. What is the smallest number of people that must start the trip in order for one member of the group to cross the preserve and the others to return safely to the starting point?

23. Peter earned $45.75 in the second week of his new job. This amount was 3 times what he earned the first week. How much did Peter earn the first week?

24. ***Write a convincing argument*** Solve the problem below. Then write an argument that would convince a classmate that your solution is correct.

Juanita installs wheels on lawnmowers. She works on 4-wheel and 5-wheel lawnmowers. One day she installed 98 wheels. She earns $6 for each lawnmower. How much money could she have earned that day?

Chapter 1 Summary and Review

1-1

To evaluate an **algebraic expression, substitute** a number for each variable and calculate the results. When an expression contains grouping symbols, any operation inside the grouping symbols must be done first. When an expression contains a fraction bar, all computations above and below the bar must be done before dividing. When no grouping symbols are used, follow the Order of Operations.

Evaluate.

1. $y + 7$ for $y = 4$
2. $n - 6$ for $n = 15$
3. $\frac{30}{x}$ for $x = 6$
4. $4t$ for $t = 8$
5. ab for $a = 8$ and $b = 9$
6. $x - y$ for $x = 19$ and $y = 11$
7. $\frac{a}{3b}$ for $a = 18$ and $b = 3$
8. $p(6 + q)$ for $p = 3$ and $q = 5$

Simplify.

9. $15 \div 3 + 6 \cdot 8$
10. $2 \cdot 10 \div 5 + 6$

Evaluate.

11. $\frac{4a}{2b + 3}$ for $a = 7$ and $b = 2$
12. $6x + \frac{3y}{2}$ for $x = 8$ and $y = 4$

1-2

The **commutative properties,** $a + b = b + a$ and $ab = ba$, and **identity properties,** $1 \cdot a = a$ and $0 + a = a$, are used to write **equivalent expressions** and to **simplify** expressions.

Write an equivalent expression using a commutative property.

13. $x + 8$
14. $11 + ab$

Write an equivalent expression. Use the indicated expression for 1.

15. $\frac{4}{5}$ Use $\frac{9}{9}$ for 1.
16. $\frac{2x}{y}$ Use $\frac{z}{z}$ for 1.

Simplify.

17. $\frac{6}{18}$
18. $\frac{56}{16}$
19. $\frac{35ab}{105bc}$
20. $\frac{96z}{24xyz}$
21. $\frac{mn}{6m}$
22. $\frac{9pq}{72p}$

ANSWERS

1. 11
2. 9
3. 5
4. 32
5. 72
6. 8
7. 2
8. 33
9. 53
10. 10
11. 4
12. 54
13. $8 + x$
14. $ab + 11$, $ba + 11$, or $11 + ba$
15. $\frac{36}{45}$
16. $\frac{2xz}{yz}$
17. $\frac{1}{3}$
18. $\frac{7}{2}$
19. $\frac{a}{3c}$
20. $\frac{4}{xy}$
21. $\frac{n}{6}$
22. $\frac{q}{8}$

23. 6^5
24. $3y^4$
25. 64
26. 72
27. 62
28. 19
29. 216
30. 100,000
31. 400
32. 55
33. 70
34. 28
35. $a + (b + 6)$ Answers may vary.
36. $7 \cdot (y \cdot x)$ Answers may vary.
37. $1 + (n + m)$
$n + (m + 1)$ Answers may
$m + (1 + n)$ vary.
38. $4 \cdot (y \cdot x)$
$y \cdot (x \cdot 4)$ Answers may vary.
$x(y \cdot 4)$
39. $7y + 35$
40. $18m + 12n + 15$
41. $6(3x + y)$
42. $4(1 + 3b + 9a)$
43. $8a + 9b$
44. $19m^2 + 12m$

1-3

We write $10 \times 10 \times 10 \times 10$ using **exponential notation** as 10^4. The **exponent**, 4, tells how many times the base, 10, is used as a factor. When an expression inside parentheses is raised to a power, everything inside the parentheses is the base.

Write using exponential notation.

23. $6 \cdot 6 \cdot 6 \cdot 6 \cdot 6$

24. $3 \cdot y \cdot y \cdot y \cdot y$

Evaluate each expression.

25. y^3 for $y = 4$

26. $2x^2$ for $x = 6$

27. $a^2 - 2$ for $a = 8$

28. $b^4 + 3$ for $b = 2$

29. $(2a)^3$ for $a = 3$

30. $(5t)^5$ for $t = 2$

1-4

The **associative properties,** $(a + b) + c = a + (b + c)$ and $(ab)c = a(bc)$, are used to write equivalent expressions. When evaluating an expression, you must simplify powers before doing other operations.

Calculate.

31. $(4 \cdot 5)^2$

32. $6 + 7^2$

Evaluate.

33. $6 + (4y)^2$ for $y = 2$

34. $(6 + a) \cdot (b - 4)$ for $a = 8$ and $b = 6$

Use an associative property to write an equivalent expression.

35. $(a + b) + 6$

36. $(7 \cdot y) \cdot x$

Use the commutative and associative properties to write three equivalent expressions.

37. $(1 + m) + n$

38. $4 \cdot (x \cdot y)$

1-5

The **distributive property of multiplication over addition,** $a(b + c) = ab + ac$, is used to write equivalent expressions and to collect like terms. We can multiply: $3(4x + 3) = 12x + 9$; factor expressions: $3xy + 9 = 3(x + 3)$; and collect like terms: $4y + 7y = 11y$.

Use the distributive property to write an equivalent expression.

39. $7(y + 5)$

40. $(6m + 4n + 5)3$

Factor.

41. $18x + 6y$

42. $4 + 12b + 36a$

Collect like terms.

43. $3a + 2b + 5a + 7b$

44. $15m^2 + 12m + 4m^2$

1-6

It is often necessary to translate data given in words into algebraic expressions. We use a variable to represent each unknown number.

Write as an algebraic expression.

45. five times a number

46. seven less than a number

47. four more than a number

48. twice a number

49. Suppose x is the amount of money Jenny earned on Monday, and she earned twice that amount on Tuesday. Write an expression for the amount Jenny earned on those two days.

50. Suppose a was Robert's age 12 years ago. Write an expression for Robert's age now.

1-7

An equation that contains only numbers may be either true or false. An equation that contains at least one variable is called an **open sentence.** A replacement for a variable that makes an equation true is called a **solution.** The collection of all the solutions is called the **solution set.** Two equations with the same solution set are **equivalent.**

Solve for the given replacement set.

51. $3n + 7 = 16 \; \{1, 3, 5\}$

52. $x^2 - x = 0 \; \{0, 1, 10\}$

Solve mentally. The replacement set is all whole numbers.

53. $5a = 35$

54. $\frac{c}{4} = 6$

Each pair of equations is equivalent. What was done to the first equation to get the second one?

55. $2x - 8 = 20$
$2x - 13 = 15$

56. $\frac{r}{5} = 10$
$2r = 100$

1-9

To evaluate a formula, substitute the given numerical values for the variables and calculate the results.

57. Find the area (A) of a figure with base (b) of 12.5 cm and height (h) of 7.5 cm using the formula $A = bh$.

58. Find the area (A) of a circle with radius (r) of 3 ft using the formula $A = 3.14r^2$.

1-8, 1-10

There are many strategies involved in solving all kinds of problems. You will use a variety of problem-solving strategies throughout your study of algebra.

45. $5n$
46. $n - 7$
47. $n + 4$
48. $2n$
49. $x + 2x$ or $3x$
50. $a + 12$
51. $\{3\}$
52. $\{0, 1\}$
53. $a = 7$
54. $c = 24$
55. 5 was subtracted from both sides.
56. Both sides were multiplied by 10.
57. 93.75 cm^2
58. 28.26 ft^2

ANSWERS

1. 14
2. 5
3. 6
4. 10
5. 10
6. 28
7. 24
8. 3
9. $3 + xy$, $3 + yx$, $yx + 3$
10. $6 + a$
11. $\frac{12}{28}$
12. $\frac{6x}{3yx}$
13. $\frac{2}{3}$
14. $\frac{9}{5}$
15. $\frac{y}{12}$
16. $\frac{3x}{5z}$
17. $2 \cdot 2 \cdot 2 \cdot 2$
18. $5 \cdot x \cdot x \cdot x$
19. 7^4
20. $8x^5$
21. 400
22. 0
23. 27
24. 48
25. 44
26. 512
27. 324
28. 33
29. 220
30. 60

Chapter 1 Test

Evaluate.

1. $p - 11$ for $p = 25$

2. $\frac{40}{x}$ for $x = 8$

3. $\frac{3x}{y}$ for $x = 10$ and $y = 5$

4. $a - 2b$ for $a = 16$ and $b = 3$

Simplify.

5. $16 \div 8 + 8$

6. $3 \cdot 4 + 2 \cdot 8$

Evaluate.

7. $3(2a + b)$ for $b = 4$ and $a = 2$

8. $\frac{2x + y}{4}$ for $x = 3$ and $y = 6$

Write an equivalent expression using a commutative property.

9. $xy + 3$

10. $a + 6$

Write an equivalent expression. Use the indicated expression for 1.

11. $\frac{3}{7}$ Use $\frac{4}{4}$ for 1.

12. $\frac{6}{3y}$ Use $\frac{x}{x}$ for 1.

Simplify.

13. $\frac{16}{24}$

14. $\frac{81}{45}$

15. $\frac{xy}{12x}$

16. $\frac{9xy}{15yz}$

What is the meaning of each expression?

17. 2^4

18. $5x^3$

Write in exponential notation.

19. $7 \cdot 7 \cdot 7 \cdot 7$

20. $8 \cdot x \cdot x \cdot x \cdot x \cdot x$

Evaluate each expression.

21. $(5x)^2$ for $x = 4$

22. $(3y)^4$ for $y = 0$

23. x^3 for $x = 3$

24. $3y^2$ for $y = 4$

25. $b^2 - 5$ for $b = 7$

26. $(4t)^3$ for $t = 2$

Calculate.

27. $(3 \cdot 6)^2$

28. $6 + 3^3$

Evaluate.

29. $(3x)^3 + 4$ for $x = 2$

30. $(r + 5)(s - 4)$ for $r = 5$ and $s = 10$

Use an associative property to write an equivalent expression.

31. $(x + y) + 5$

Use the commutative and associative properties to write three equivalent expressions.

32. $3 \cdot (a \cdot b)$

Use the distributive property to write an equivalent expression.

33. $6(4y + 3)$

Factor.

34. $8a + 12b$

35. $18x + 6y + 12$

36. $3 + 12b + 36a$

37. $8a + 4 + 12c$

Collect like terms.

38. $7a + 3b + 8a + 4b$

39. $6m + 9m^2 + 3m + 7m^2$

Write as an algebraic expression.

40. 11 fewer than x

41. half of a number

42. twice a number

43. six more than a number

44. Suppose w was Lisa's weight last week. Lisa lost 7 pounds this week. Write an expression for Lisa's weight this week.

45. Suppose t is the total amount of tickets sold to the dance. If each of the ninth, tenth, and eleventh grades sold the same number of tickets, write an expression for the number of tickets sold by each grade.

Solve for the given replacement set.

46. $5n - 4 = 11$ $\{2, 3, 4\}$

47. $x^2 - x = 2$ $\{0, 2, 4\}$

48. $7.2y = 36$ $\{5, 50, 500\}$

Each pair of equations is equivalent. What was done to the first equation to get the second one?

49. $\frac{2}{5}m = 3$

$\frac{4}{5}m = 6$

50. $2x = 10$

$2x + 4 = 14$

Evaluate.

51. Find the distance (d) traveled by a train moving at the rate (r) of 50 mi/h for the time (t) of 3 h using the formula $d = rt$.

52. Find the temperature in degrees Celsius (C) given a temperature of 77° Fahrenheit (F) using the formula $C = \frac{5}{9}(F - 32)$.

31. $x + (y + 5)$
32. $3 \cdot (b \cdot a)$
$b \cdot (a \cdot 3)$
$a \cdot (b \cdot 3)$
33. $24y + 18$
34. $4(2a + 3b)$
35. $6(3x + y + 2)$
36. $3(1 + 4b + 12a)$
37. $4(2a + 3c + 1)$
38. $15a + 7b$
39. $9m + 16m^2$
40. $x - 11$
41. $\frac{n}{2}$
42. $2n$
43. $6 + n$
44. $w - 7$
45. $\frac{t}{3}$
46. $\{3\}$
47. $\{2\}$
48. $\{5\}$
49. Both sides were multiplied by 2.
50. 4 was added to both sides.
51. 150 mi
52. 25 °C

Test Item Analysis

Item	Lesson
1–8	1-1
9–16	1-2
17–26	1-3
27–32	1-4
33–39	1-5
40–45	1-6
46–48	1-7
49, 50	1-7
51, 52	1-9

CHAPTER 2

Integers and the Number Line

Chapter Overview

Integers and rational numbers are defined, discussed, and compared using the order relations less than and greater than. Addition, subtraction, multiplication, and division with integers and rational numbers are practiced throughout the chapter. All four operations are then used to simplify expressions. Absolute value is introduced both geometrically and algebraically.

Translation of phrases into algebraic notation is discussed, and word problems are translated into equations using the problem-solving strategy *Write an Equation*.

Objectives

2-1 ▪ Give an integer that corresponds to a real-world situation.
▪ Compare integers using > or <.
▪ Find the absolute value of an integer.
2-2 ▪ Show that a number is rational.
▪ Graph rational numbers.
▪ Compare rational numbers using > or <.
2-3 ▪ Add rational numbers using a number line.
▪ Add rational numbers without a number line.
▪ Give the additive inverse.
2-4 ▪ Subtract rational numbers on a number line.
▪ Subtract rational numbers without using a number line.
2-5 ▪ Multiply rational numbers.
2-6 ▪ Divide rational numbers.
▪ Find the reciprocal of a rational number.
▪ Divide by multiplying by the reciprocal.
2-7 ▪ Multiply using the distributive property over subtraction.
▪ Factor expressions.
▪ Give the terms of an expression.
▪ Collect like terms.
2-8 ▪ Find the inverse of a sum.
▪ Simplify expressions involving parentheses.
▪ Simplify expressions containing multiple grouping symbols.
2-9 ▪ Write an equation that can be used to solve a problem.
2-10 ▪ Identify applications of the number properties.
▪ Identify the properties of equality.
▪ Prove number properties.

Cooperative Learning Opportunities

The magic square enrichment activity on page 74 of the *Teacher's Edition* works well in a cooperative setting. Assign students in pairs—one writer and one checker—and explain how a magic square works. Write the numbers from −4 through 4 on the chalkboard. Tell the groups to draw a 9-celled square and write −1 in the upper left box. Mention they may draw as many new squares as they wish. They may omit the outer lines and simply draw the "tick-tac-toe" lines.

For the first 3 minutes only the writer fills in the square. The checker watches, tells the writer where rows, columns, or diagonals do not add up, and suggests other possibilities. After 3 minutes, the roles are switched. After the second 3 minutes, if the team has not succeeded, the two students work together in any way they wish.

As a follow–up, ask students to form a magic square using the numbers −10 through −2. Mention that answers for magic squares may vary.

Multicultural Note: *Ahmes' Papyrus*

The Ahmes' Papyrus is a document written in Egypt about 1650 B.C. and named for the scribe Ahmes who wrote it. (Papyrus is a kind of paper made from the fibers of a plant.) In part, this work is about what we call fractions or rational numbers.

We take it for granted that, once we understand what a rational number is, we can work with any rational number. But it was not always so. The ancient Egyptians dealt primarily with unit fractions, that is, fractions with 1 as the numerator. To write a unit fraction, the Egyptians placed an oval or a dot over the symbol for the denominator. So, in a way, they might have been more familiar and comfortable with the reciprocals of numbers than we are.

Because of their interest in unit fractions, the Egyptians did not think of the fraction $\frac{7}{8}$ as a number in itself, but as the sum $\frac{1}{2} + \frac{1}{4} + \frac{1}{8}$. What sum might the Egyptians have used for the fraction $\frac{11}{12}$? **Ans:** $\mathbf{\frac{1}{2} + \frac{1}{4} + \frac{1}{6}}$

Alternative Assessment and Communication Ideas

In Lesson 2-2, Exercise 46 is not only a good *Critical Thinking* activity but can be expanded into an assessment. Have students use positive and negative numbers and zero to form inequalities and equations, using =, <, and ≤. Check to see that the inequalities are valid. Students might also make short true-false inequalities and exchange them with one another.

For Lesson 2-6, ask for volunteers to give real-world examples of division by a fraction. For example: Divide a 10-ft board into pieces that are $2\frac{1}{2}$ ft each.

For Lesson 2-9, ask students to write a sentence or phrase involving money or measurement for each of the following.

$120 + 2x$	$\frac{2}{3}p$
$10a + 5b$	$53{,}247x$

Investigations and Projects

Ask students, as individuals or in small groups, to gather information from encyclopedias and other sources about the history, the instruments, and the scale of numbers used for measuring a common phenomenon such as temperature, air pressure, ozone in the atmosphere, speed, blood pressure, a pulse rate, or the magnitude of an earthquake.

Ask individuals or groups to prepare a presentation that includes a description of why this type of measurement is taken, what the instrument looks like, and how it works. Ask them for information about unusual or record measurements of the phenomenon they have selected.

Have a general discussion about the many different kinds of number scales and their uses.

MANAGING CHAPTER 2

Lesson	PACING CHART (DAYS) 2-Year* A for E	1-Year Minimum	1-Year Regular	1-Year Advanced	Opening Activity	Cooperative Activity	Seat or Group Work
2-1	2	1	1	1	First Five Minutes 2-1: ***FFMTM*** p. 5 or **TE** p. 54; Application: **SE** p. 54	✂ Manipulative Activity 2: ***Enrichment*** p. 35; Connections: Geometry: **SE** p. 58	Try This a–m
2-2	2	1	1	1	First Five Minutes 2-2: ***FFMTM*** p. 5 or **TE** p. 59	Critical Thinking 2: ***Enrichment*** p. 19	Try This a–l
2-3	2	1.5	1	1	First Five Minutes 2-3: ***FFMTM*** p. 5 or **TE** p. 63; ***Overhead Transparencies*** T3	Application: **SE** p. 63; ✂ Teaching Option: **TE** p. 64	Try This a–y
2-4	2	1.5	1	1	First Five Minutes 2-4: ***FFMTM*** p. 6 or **TE** p. 71	Application: **SE** p. 71; ✂ Teaching Option: **TE** p. 72	Try This a–l
2-5	2	1	1	1	First Five Minutes 2-5: ***FFMTM*** p. 6 or **TE** p. 77	Explore: **SE** p. 77	Try This a–k
2-6	2	1	1	1	First Five Minutes 2-6: ***FFMTM*** p. 7 or **TE** p. 81	Bonus Topic: **SE** p. 86	Try This a–y
2-7	3	2	2	1	First Five Minutes 2-7: ***FFMTM*** p. 7 or **TE** p. 89	Problem Solving: Application: **SE** p. 87–88	Try This a–o
2-8	2	1	1	1	First Five Minutes 2-8: ***FFMTM*** p. 8 or **TE** p. 93	Looking for Errors 2: ***Enrichment*** p. 51	Try This a–n
2-9	2	1	1	1	First Five Minutes 2-9: ***FFMTM*** p. 8 or **TE** p. 98	Bonus Topic 2: ***Enrichment*** p. 3	Problems 1–4: **SE** p. 100
2-10	0	0	0	0.5	First Five Minutes 2-10: ***FFMTM*** p. 9 or **TE** p. 102	Problems 22–25: **SE** p. 106	Try This a–i
Review	2	1	1	0.5			
Test	1	1	1	1			

*2-Year Management Guide can be found in *Algebra for Everyone*. FFMTM: First Five Minutes Transparency Masters

Enrichment	Review/Assess	Reteach	Technology	Lesson
✂ Manipulative Activity 2: ***Enrichment*** p. 35; Connections: Geometry: **SE** p. 58	Lesson Quiz: **TE** p. 56			**2-1**
Calculator Worksheet 5: ***Technology*** p. 7	Lesson Quiz: **TE** p. 61		Calculator Worksheet 5: ***Technology*** p. 7	**2-2**
Critical Thinking 2: ***Enrichment*** p. 19	Lesson Quiz: **TE** p. 68	Skills Practice 4: ***SPMR*** p. 12; Problem Bank 2: ***Problem Bank*** p. 19		**2-3**
Lesson Enrichment: **TE** p. 74; Historical Note: **SE** p. 76	Mixed Practice 3: **SE** p. 686; Mixed Review 3: ***SPMR*** p. 53; Lesson Quiz: **TE** p. 74; Quiz 3: ***Assessment*** p. 13	Problem Bank 3: ***Problem Bank*** p. 20	Adding and Subtracting Rational Numbers: **SE** p. 73; Calculator Worksheet 6: ***Technology*** p. 8	**2-4**
Subsets of the Rational Numbers: **SE** p. 80; Computer Exploration 2: **SE** p. 716	Lesson Quiz: **TE** p. 78		Computer Exploration 2: **SE** p. 716	**2-5**
Bonus Topic: **SE** p. 86; Problem for Programmers **SE** p. 86; Calculator Worksheet 7: ***Technology*** p. 9; Spreadsheet Activity 2: ***Technology*** pp. 39–40	Lesson Quiz: **TE** p. 84	Skills Practice 5: ***SPMR*** p. 13	Problem for Programmers **SE** p. 86; Calculator Worksheet 7: ***Technology*** p. 9; Spreadsheet Activity 2: ***Technology*** pp. 39–40	**2-6**
Problem Solving: Application: **SE** pp. 87–88	Lesson Quiz: **TE** p. 91; Mixed Review 4: ***SPMR*** p. 54			**2-7**
Looking for Errors 2: ***Enrichment*** p. 51	Lesson Quiz: **TE** p. 95; Quiz 4: ***Assessment*** p. 14	Skills Practice 6: ***SPMR*** p. 14		**2-8**
Bonus Topic 2: ***Enrichment*** p. 3	Mixed Practice 4: **SE** p. 687; Assessing Strategies 2: ***Assessment*** pp. 197–198	Skills Practice 6: ***SPMR*** p. 14; Strategy Problem Bank 2: ***Problem Bank*** p. 3; Problem Bank 4: ***Problem Bank*** p. 21		**2-9**
Problems 26–27: **SE** p. 106	Lesson Quiz: **TE** p. 105			**2-10**
	Summary and Review: **SE** pp. 107–109; Test: **SE** pp. 110–111			**Review**
	Chapter 2 Exam: ***A for E*** pp. 87–88; Chapter 2 Test: ***Assessment*** pp. 45–46 (min.), 77–82 (reg.), 165–166 (adv.)			**Test**

SPMR: Skills Practice Mixed Review

The solution to the problem posed on the facing page can be found on page 87.

Ready for Integers and Rational Numbers?

1-2 Simplify.

1. $\frac{12}{27}$ $\frac{4}{9}$ **2.** $\frac{a}{4ab}$ $\frac{1}{4b}$ **3.** $\frac{13xy}{xy}$ 13 **4.** $\frac{18cd}{15d}$ $\frac{6c}{5}$

1-3 Evaluate.

5. $(4n)^2$ for $n = 2$ 64 **6.** p^1 for $p = 24$ 24 **7.** $3x^3$ for $x = 2$ 24

1-5 Multiply.

8. $5(a + b + d)$ $5a + 5b + 5d$ **9.** $11(w + 4)$ $11w + 44$ **10.** $7(3z + y + 2)$ $21z + 7y + 14$

1-5 Factor.

11. $45 + 9y$ $9(5 + y)$ **12.** $3a + 12b$ $3(a + 4b)$ **13.** $4x + 10 + 8y$ $2(2x + 5 + 4y)$

1-5 Collect like terms.

14. $5x + 3y + 2x$ $7x + 3y$ **15.** $b^2 + 3a + 4b^2$ $5b^2 + 3a$ **16.** $5t + 2 + 3t + 7$ $8t + 9$

Solve for the given replacement set.

17. $4x + 2 = 30$ {3, 5, 7} {7} **18.** $8a = 4$ {0.5, 5, 50} {0.5}

CHAPTER

2 Integers and Rational Numbers

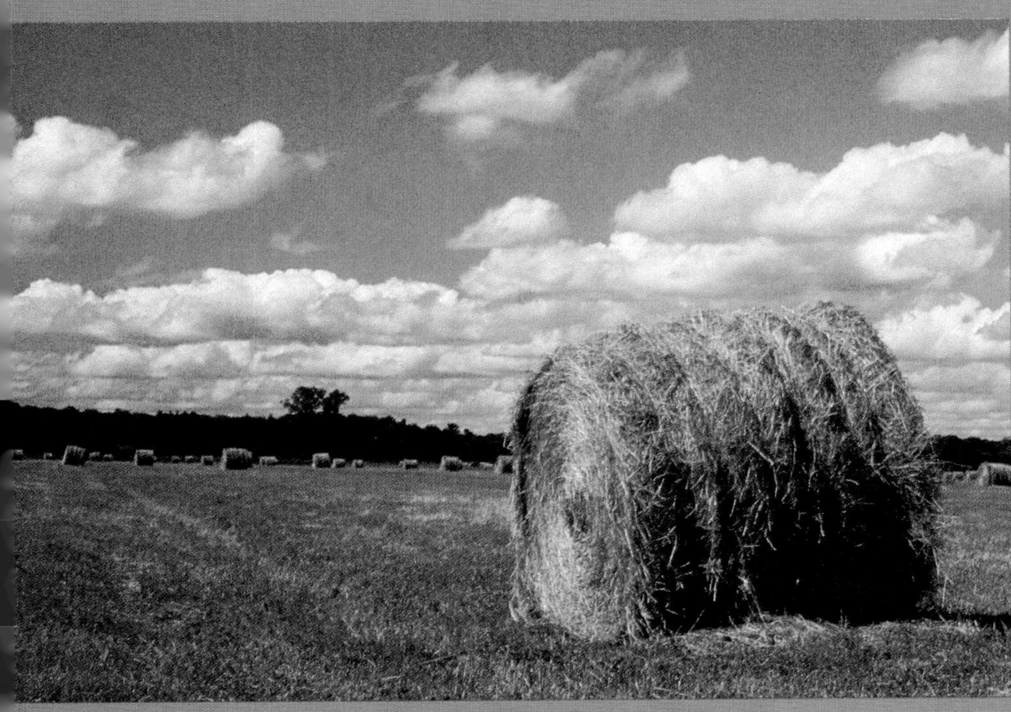

How many pounds of force are needed to lift the bale of hay?

2-1

FIRST FIVE MINUTES

True or false?

1. 0 is a positive number. F (Zero is neither positive nor negative.)
2. −8, 0, and 4 are all integers. T
3. The set of whole numbers includes all positive integers, negative integers, and 0. F

The Set of Integers

Illustrate that the set of integers includes the set of whole numbers, just as the set of students in the classroom includes the set of girls in the classroom. Have students think of other pairs of sets in which one set encloses another.

Key Questions

To which of the following sets does each number belong: integers, positive integers, negative integers, whole numbers?

- 2
  Integers, positive integers, whole numbers
- −9
  Integers, negative integers
- 0
  Integers, whole numbers

Chalkboard Examples

Name the integer suggested by each situation.

1. 1000 B.C. −1000
2. You walk forward 9 steps. 9
3. The temperature is 15 degrees above 0. 15
4. Acme Lint Company is 10 million dollars in debt. −10,000,000
5. The treasure was buried 50 feet deep. −50
6. The balloon was up 1000 feet. 1000
7. The picnic was two days ago. −2

2-1 Integers and the Number Line

Application

Most computer spreadsheets show amounts of money less than zero using parentheses. You can also write amounts less than zero using a "negative sign." ($35,000) is the same as −$35,000.

	A	B
1		October
2	Income	$129,000
3	Expenses	($164,000)
4	Balance	($35,000)

The Set of Integers

Objective: Give an integer that corresponds to a real-world situation.

We know that the set of whole numbers consists of 0, 1, 2, 3, 4, and so on. On a number line we can match each whole number with another number that is the same distance from 0 but on the opposite side of 0. Numbers such as 3 (read "positive three" or just "three") and −3 (read "negative three") that are the same distance from 0, but on opposite sides of 0, are called **opposites.** Zero is its own opposite. The set of **integers** consists of the whole numbers and their opposites. On the number line, the **positive integers** are to the right of 0, and the **negative integers** are to the left of 0. Zero is neither positive nor negative. The number line below shows some examples of opposites.

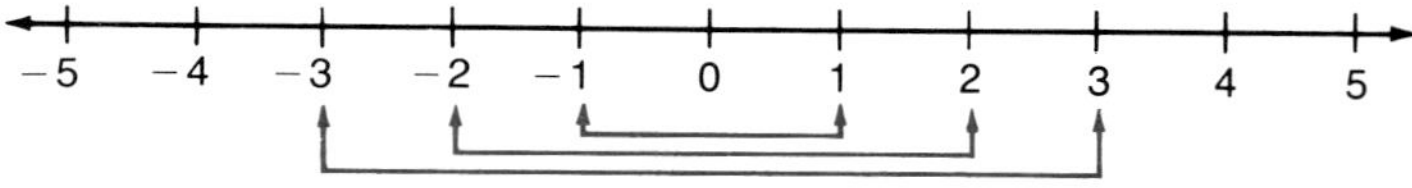

Definition

The set of **integers** consists of the positive integers, negative integers, and zero. $\{\ldots -4, -3, -2, -1, 0, 1, 2, 3, 4, \ldots\}$

EXAMPLES Name the integer that is suggested by each situation.

1. The temperature is 3° below 0.

−3 Below 0 suggests a negative integer.

2. Death Valley is 280 ft below sea level.

−280 Below sea level suggests a negative integer.

3. Mickey's juice stand made an \$18 profit on Monday.

18 A profit suggests a positive integer.

Try This Name the integer that is suggested by each situation.

a. Julia has a debt of \$12. -12

b. The halfback made a gain of 8 yd. 8

c. The quarterback lost 5 yd. -5

d. Ignition occurs 3 seconds before liftoff. -3

Order on the Number Line

Objective: Compare integers using $>$ or $<$.

We use the symbol $<$ to mean **is less than.** For example, $6 < 8$ means "6 is less than 8." The symbol $>$ means **is greater than.** For example, $2 > -4$ means "2 is greater than -4." The symbols $>$ and $<$ are called **inequality symbols.** A mathematical sentence that contains an inequality symbol is called an **inequality.** We can read an inequality in two ways. For example, the sentence $5 < 7$ means "5 is less than 7." This sentence can also be reversed and read as "7 is greater than 5." An inequality can be true or false. The sentence $12 > 2$ is true. The sentence $5 > 16$ is false.

On the number line, numbers increase as we move from left to right. For any two numbers, the one farther to the right is the greater and the one to the left is the lesser. This means that all negative numbers are less than 0 and all positive numbers are greater than 0.

EXAMPLES Write a true sentence using $>$ or $<$.

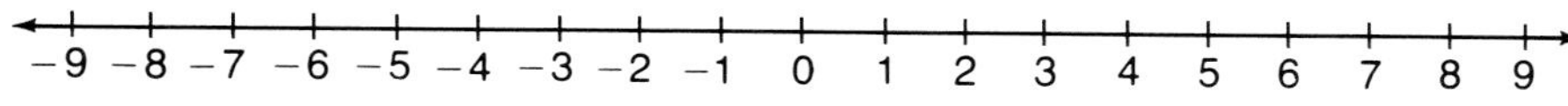

4. $2 < 9$ Since 2 is to the left of 9, 2 is less than 9.

5. $-7 < 3$ Since -7 is to the left of 3, -7 is less than 3.

6. $6 > -12$ Since 6 is to the right of -12, 6 is greater than -12.

7. $-18 < -5$ Since -18 is to the left of -5, -18 is less than -5.

Try This Write a true sentence using $>$ or $<$.

e. $14 > 7$

f. $11 > -2$

g. $-15 < -5$

Order on the Number Line

The **less than** symbol, $<$, and the **greater than** symbol, $>$, can be thought of as little "funnels." The small number is at the small end of the funnel. The big number is at the big end of the funnel.

Emphasize that a negative number is always less than a positive number.

Key Questions

True or false?

- $3 > -1$ True
- $3 < 1$ False
- $-1 < 3$ True
- $-3 > 1$ False

Chalkboard Examples

Insert the proper symbol, $<$ or $>$, to get a true statement.

1. 8 128 $<$
2. 13 713 $<$
3. -5 $7-5$ $<$
4. 14 -814 $>$
5. -10 $-5-10$ $>$
6. -4 $-11-4$ $>$

Absolute Value

Emphasize that the absolute value of a number is never negative, just as the distance between two points is never negative. It is always a positive number or zero. Also point out that $-n$, or the opposite of n, is a positive number if n is a negative number.

Key Questions

- What is the distance on the number line from 0 to 6? 6
- What is the distance on the number line from 0 to -9? 9
- What is the opposite of 12? -12
- What is the opposite of -23? 23
- Is $|15|$ greater than, less than or equal to $|-15|$? $|15| = |-15|$

Chalkboard Examples

Find the absolute value.

1. $|3|$ 3
2. $|-3|$ 3
3. $|0|$ 0
4. $|-27|$ 27

LESSON QUIZ

What integer is suggested by each situation?

1. The temperature is 60 degrees above zero. 60
2. Dorealea lost 2 pounds. -2
3. The hole was 20 feet deep. -20
4. The tree grew 5 feet. 5

Insert either < or > to make a true statement.

5. 4   9 <
6. -8 7 <
7. -14 -20 >
8. -12 -10 <
9. 4 -2 >

Find the absolute value.

10. $|-9|$ 9
11. $|12|$ 12

Absolute Value

Objective: Find the absolute value of an integer.

The integers 4 and -4 are both the same distance, 4 units, from 0 on the number line.

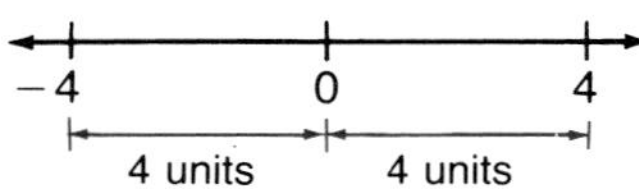

The **absolute value** of a number is its distance from 0 on the number line. We use the symbol $|n|$ to represent "the absolute value of n." The absolute value of a number is either positive or zero. The number line above shows that $|4| = 4$ and $|-4| = 4$. The absolute value of 0 is 0.

Definition

Absolute Value
For any number n,
$|n| = n$ if n is a positive number or 0, and
$|n| = -n$ if n is a negative number.

Note that $-n$ means the opposite of n. It does not necessarily stand for a negative number. For instance, the opposite of -8, written $-(-8)$, is 8. And 8 is a positive number.

EXAMPLES Find the absolute value.

8. $|12| = 12$ 12 is 12 units from 0.
Using the definition of absolute value, $|12| = 12$ since 12 is a positive number.

9. $|-7| = 7$ -7 is 7 units from 0.
Using the definition of absolute value, $|-7| =$ the opposite of $-7 = 7$. Notice that the absolute value is always nonnegative.

10. $|-3.04| = 3.04$ -3.04 is 3.04 units from 0.
Using the definition of absolute value, $|-3.04| =$ the opposite of $-3.04 = 3.04$.

Try This Find the absolute value.

h. $|17|$ 17   **i.** $|-8|$ 8
j. $|-14|$ 14   **k.** $|21|$ 21
l. $|0|$ 0   **m.** $|-21|$ 21

2-1 EXERCISES

A

Name the integer that is suggested by each situation.

1. In one game Carlos lost 12 marbles. −12
2. Jana won 5 marbles in her first game. 5
3. The temperature Wednesday was 18° above zero. 18
4. Ramona has a debt of $17. −17
5. Jane's business had a profit of $2500 in one week. 2500
6. The Dead Sea, between Jordan and Israel, is 1286 feet below sea level. −1286
7. On Friday, Vicki withdrew $125 from her savings account. −125
8. Terry's bowling team won by 34 pins. 34
9. In foreign trade, the U.S. had an excess of $3 million. 3,000,000

Write a true sentence using $<$ or $>$.

10. $5 > 0$	**11.** $9 > 0$	**12.** $-9 < 5$	**13.** $8 > -8$
14. $-6 < 6$	**15.** $0 > -7$	**16.** $-8 < -5$	**17.** $-4 < -3$
18. $-5 > -11$	**19.** $-3 > -4$	**20.** $-6 < -5$	**21.** $-10 > -14$

Find the absolute value.

22. $\|-3\|$ 3	**23.** $\|-7\|$ 7	**24.** $\|10\|$ 10	**25.** $\|11\|$ 11
26. $\|0\|$ 0	**27.** $\|-4\|$ 4	**28.** $\|-24\|$ 24	**29.** $\|325\|$ 325
30. $\|-125\|$ 125	**31.** $\|5.5\|$ 5.5	**32.** $\|-4.2\|$ 4.2	**33.** $\|-120.2\|$ 120.2
34. $\|755\|$ 755	**35.** $\|-340\|$ 340	**36.** $\|-5.8\|$ 5.8	**37.** $\|-0.3\|$ 0.3
38. $\|12.75\|$ 12.75	**39.** $\|-0.07\|$ 0.07	**40.** $\|-80\|$ 80	**41.** $\|-3.75\|$ 3.75

B

Evaluate.

42. $\|-5\| + \|-6\|$ 11	**43.** $\|17\| + \|-17\|$ 34	**44.** $\|12\| \cdot \|-3\|$ 36
45. $\|-5\| \cdot \|-6\| \cdot \|0\|$ 0	**46.** $\|-3\| \cdot \|-7\| + \|-4\|$ 25	**47.** $\|8\| \cdot \|-2\| - \|5\|$ 11

Write the following integers in order from least to greatest.

48. 13, −12, 5, −17
49. −23, 4, 0, −17
50. −24, −26, −18, −32, −5, −16
51. 15, −24, −5, −16, 12, −13, −14

Evaluate each expression.

52. $|x| + 24$ for $x = -7$ 31
53. $|t| - 15$ for $t = -36$ 21

Assignment Guide
Minimum: 1–41 e/o, MR

Regular: 1–56 m3, 57, MR

Advanced: 1–56 m4, 57–66, MR

ADDITIONAL ANSWERS

Exercises

48. −17, −12, 5, 13
49. −23, −17, 0, 4
50. −32, −26, −24, −18, −16, −5
51. −24, −16, −14, −13, −5, 12, 15

Mixed Review

67. $21m$
68. a
69. $11x^2 + 7x$
70. $6c^2 + 7c$
71. $4(m + 6c)$
72. $7(b + 2)$
73. $7(2x + 4y + 1)$
74. $\{39\}$
75. $\{361\}$
76. $\{3\}$
77. $\{2.7\}$
78. $\{3\}$
79. $x = 22$
80. $c = 55$
81. $y = 90$
82. $a = 80$
83. $x = 24$
84. $d = 140$

54. $|a| + |b|$ for $a = -5$ and $b = -12$ 17

55. $2|x| + |y|$ for $x = 8$ and $y = 15$ 31

56. $3a - |b| + |c|$ for $a = 5$, $b = -4$, $c = -12$ 23

57. ***Critical Thinking*** Find the next three numbers in each pattern by thinking about integers and the number line.

a. 13, 9, 5, 1, $\underline{-3}$, $\underline{-7}$, $\underline{-11}$

b. 6, 5, 3, 0, $\underline{-4}$, $\underline{-9}$, $\underline{-15}$

c. -3, -5, -8, -12, $\underline{-17}$, $\underline{-23}$, $\underline{-30}$

d. -1, -3, -4, -7, $\underline{-11}$, $\underline{-18}$, $\underline{-29}$

Challenge

Use <, >, or = to write a true sentence.

58. $|-3| \quad 5$ $<$ **59.** $2 \quad |-4|$ $<$ **60.** $-2 \quad |-1|$ $<$ **61.** $0 \quad |0|$ $=$

62. $|-5| \quad |-2|$ $>$ **63.** $|4| \quad |-7|$ $<$ **64.** $|x| \quad -1$ $>$ **65.** $|-8| \quad |8|$ $=$

List in order from least to greatest.

66. 7^1, -5, $|-6|$, 4, $|3|$, -100, 0, 1, $\frac{14}{4}$ $-100, -5, 0, 1, |3|, \frac{14}{4}, 4, |-6|, 7^1$

Mixed Review

Collect like terms. **67.** $6m + 11m + 4m$ **68.** $\frac{1}{2}a + \frac{1}{2}a$

69. $8x^2 + 3x^2 + 7x$ **70.** $4c^2 + 7c + 2c^2$

Factor. **71.** $4m + 24c$ **72.** $7b + 14$ **73.** $14x + 28y + 7$

Solve for the given replacement set. **74.** $y + 3 = 42$ {14, 39, 45}

75. $w + 3911 = 4272$ {361, 7183, 8183} **76.** $14t = 42$ {2, 3, 28}

77. $c + 9.7 = 12.4$ {2.7, 3.3, 22.1} **78.** $2.6n = 7.8$ {3, 5.2, 10.4}

Solve mentally. **79.** $x - 4 = 18$ **80.** $c - 25 = 30$

81. $y - 80 = 10$ **82.** $\frac{a}{4} = 20$ **83.** $\frac{x}{10} = 2.4$ **84.** $\frac{d}{7} = 20$

CONNECTIONS: GEOMETRY

A tetromino is formed by four congruent squares that share common sides.

1. How many different tetrominoes are there? 5
2. Which tetromino has the least perimeter? the square tetromino

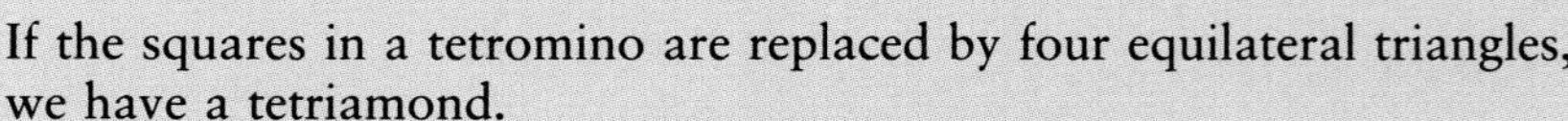

If the squares in a tetromino are replaced by four equilateral triangles, we have a tetriamond.

3. How many different tetriamonds are there? 3

2-2 Rational Numbers

Showing a Number Is Rational

Objective: Show a number is rational.

Much of your work in algebra will involve rational numbers. The word "rational" comes from the word *ratio*.

Definition

Any number that can be expressed as the ratio of two integers, $\frac{a}{b}$, where $b \neq 0$, is called a **rational number.**

There are three ways to write a negative rational number. You can write "negative three fourths" as follows.

$$-\frac{3}{4} \qquad \frac{-3}{4} \qquad \frac{3}{-4}$$

To show that a number is rational, we only have to find one way of naming it as a ratio of two integers.

EXAMPLES Show that each can be written as the ratio of two integers.

1. $3 = \frac{3}{1}$

2. $-9.2 = -\frac{92}{10}$

Try This Show that each can be written as the ratio of two integers.

a. 4.5 $\frac{45}{10}$ or $\frac{9}{2}$ **b.** -10 $-\frac{10}{1}$ **c.** -14.3 $-\frac{143}{10}$ **d.** -0.01 $-\frac{1}{100}$

Graphing Rational Numbers

Objective: Graph rational numbers.

There is a point on the number line for every rational number. The number is called the coordinate of the point. The point is the graph of the number. When we draw a point for a number on a number line, we say that we have graphed the number.

2-2

FIRST FIVE MINUTES

Simplify.

1. $\frac{4}{2}$ 2
2. $\frac{8}{16}$ $\frac{1}{2}$
3. Which is larger, $\frac{1}{2}$ or $\frac{1}{3}$? $\frac{1}{2}$
4. Write 0.1 as a fraction. $\frac{1}{10}$
5. Write 0.5 as a fraction. $\frac{1}{2}$

Showing a Number is Rational

Point out that all integers are rational numbers, but not all rational numbers are integers.

Key Questions

True or false?

- $-\frac{3}{4} = \frac{3}{-4}$
  True
- -2 is a rational number.
  True

Chalkboard Examples

Show that each number can be written as the ratio of two integers.

1. 7 — $\frac{7}{1}$ or $\frac{14}{2}$
2. 0 — $\frac{0}{1}$ or $\frac{0}{2}$
3. 0.7 — $\frac{7}{10}$
4. 81.54 — $\frac{8154}{100}$
5. -5.7 — $-\frac{57}{10}$
6. -0.001 — $-\frac{1}{1000}$

Graphing Rational Numbers

When graphing rational numbers, it is important that students divide the number line carefully into the units needed.

Key Questions

- On a number line, does $-\frac{1}{2}$ lie between -1 and -2? No
- Can any rational number be placed on the number line? Yes

Chalkboard Examples

Graph each rational number.

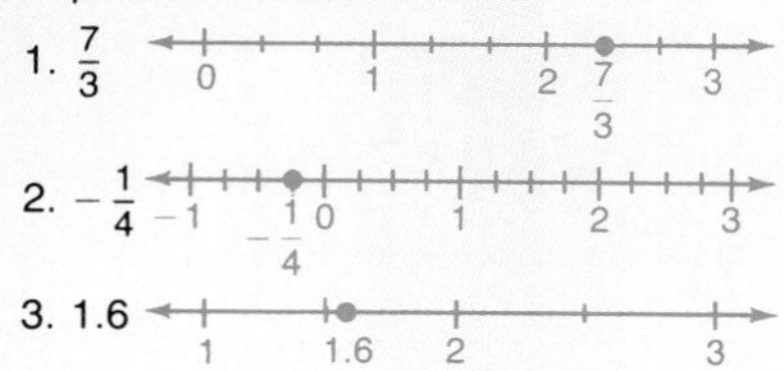

Order of the Rational Numbers

Often, the order relation between two rational numbers is not readily apparent. For example, which is smaller, $\frac{18}{33}$ or $\frac{44}{81}$? The answer is not obvious. Stress to students that in such cases they should convert the numbers to decimals.

$\frac{18}{33} = 0.545\ldots$ $\qquad$ $\frac{44}{81} = 0.543\ldots$

We observe that

$\frac{44}{81} < \frac{18}{33}$

Key Question

- What should you do to determine the order relation of a set of fractions? Convert to common denominator or to decimals

Chalkboard Examples

Insert either $<$ or $>$ to make a true statement.

1. 0.5 $\quad$ 0.1 $\qquad$ $>$
2. −2.81 $\quad$ 1.73 $\qquad$ $<$
3. −7.3 $\quad$ −1.5 $\qquad$ $<$
4. $\frac{7}{5}$ $\quad$ $\frac{9}{5}$ $\qquad$ $<$
5. $\frac{7}{5}$ $\quad$ $\frac{34}{25}$

   Convert to common denominator

   $\frac{35}{25} > \frac{34}{25}$; so $\frac{7}{5} > \frac{34}{25}$
6. $-\frac{3}{8}$ $\quad$ $-\frac{1}{3}$

   Convert to common denominator

   $-\frac{9}{24} < -\frac{8}{24}$; so $-\frac{3}{8} < -\frac{1}{3}$

EXAMPLES Graph each of these numbers.

3. $\frac{5}{2}$ The number $\frac{5}{2}$ can be named $2\frac{1}{2}$. Its graph is halfway between 2 and 3.

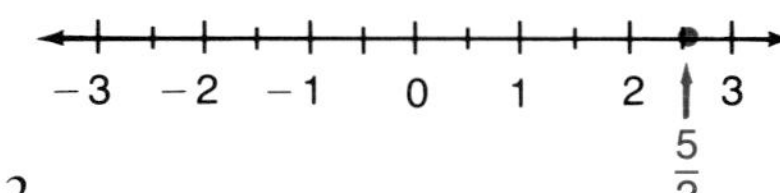

Divide the units of the number line into halves.

4. −1.2

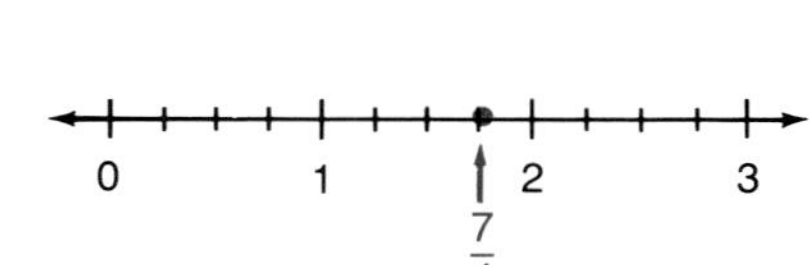

Divide the units of the number line into tenths.

5. $\frac{7}{4}$

0 $\quad$ 1 $\quad$ 2 $\quad$ 3 $\quad$ $\frac{7}{4}$

Divide the units of the number line into fourths.

Try This Graph each rational number.

e. $\frac{12}{5}$ $\qquad$ **f.** -4.8 $\qquad$ **g.** $-\frac{18}{4}$ $\qquad$ **h.** 0.5 See Additional Answers.

Order of the Rational Numbers

Objective: Compare rational numbers using $>$ or $<$.

The relations $<$ (is less than) and $>$ (is greater than) are the same for rational numbers as they are for integers. Recall that numbers on the number line increase from left to right.

EXAMPLES Use either $<$ or $>$ to write a true sentence.

6. $1.38 < 1.83$ $\qquad$ 38 hundredths is less than 83 hundredths.

7. $-3.45 < 1.32$ $\qquad$ Negative rational numbers are always less than positive rational numbers.

8. $-4.23 > -5.2$ $\qquad$ -4 is farther to the right on the number line than -5, so $-4 > -5$.

9. $\frac{3}{4}$ $\quad$ $\frac{5}{8}$

$\frac{6}{8}$ $\quad$ $\frac{5}{8}$ $\qquad$ Find a common denominator. $\frac{3}{4} = \frac{6}{8}$

$\frac{6}{8} > \frac{5}{8}$ $\qquad$ $\frac{6}{8}$ is farther to the right on the number line than $\frac{5}{8}$.

$\frac{3}{4} > \frac{5}{8}$

10. $-\frac{2}{3} \quad -\frac{5}{8}$

$-\frac{16}{24} \quad -\frac{15}{24}$ Find a common denominator. $-\frac{2}{3} = -\frac{16}{24} \quad -\frac{5}{8} = -\frac{15}{24}$

$-\frac{16}{24} < -\frac{15}{24}$ $-\frac{16}{24}$ is farther to the left on the number line than $-\frac{15}{24}$.

$-\frac{2}{3} < -\frac{5}{8}$

Try This Use either < or > to write a true sentence.

i. 4.62 > 4.26 **j.** −3.11 > −3.22 **k.** $\frac{5}{6} < \frac{7}{8}$ **l.** $-\frac{2}{3} > -\frac{4}{5}$

Rational numbers are part of a larger set of numbers called the **real numbers.** In Chapter 11, we will work with real numbers in more detail. The diagram below shows the relationships among these sets of numbers.

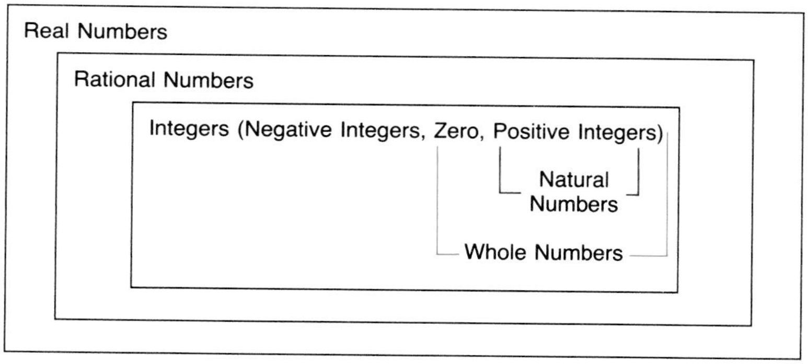

2-2 EXERCISES

A

Show that each number can be written as the ratio of two integers.

1. 14 $\frac{14}{1}$ **2.** −7 $-\frac{7}{1}$ **3.** 4.2 $\frac{42}{10}$ or $\frac{21}{5}$ **4.** 1.5 $\frac{15}{10}$ or $\frac{3}{2}$

5. −0.5 $-\frac{5}{10}$ or $-\frac{1}{2}$ **6.** −0.03 $-\frac{3}{100}$ **7.** 3.444 $\frac{3444}{1000}$ or $\frac{861}{250}$ **8.** −5.333 $-\frac{5333}{1000}$

9. −0.68 $-\frac{68}{100}$ or $-\frac{17}{25}$ **10.** −4 $-\frac{4}{1}$ **11.** $7\frac{1}{2}$ $\frac{15}{2}$ **12.** $1\frac{2}{3}$ $\frac{5}{3}$

Graph each rational number.

13. $\frac{10}{3}$ **14.** $-\frac{17}{5}$ **15.** −4.3 **16.** 6.4

LESSON QUIZ

Graph each rational number.

1. $\frac{3}{4}$

2. $\frac{7}{2}$

3. $-\frac{5}{4}$

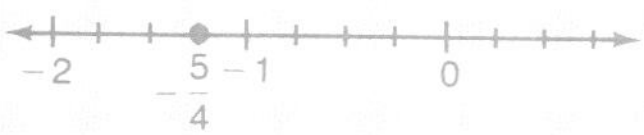

Insert either < or > to make a true statement.

4. 4.7 3.5 4.7 > 3.5
5. −2.5 −1.6 −2.5 < −1.6
6. $\frac{2}{3}$ $\frac{5}{6}$ $\frac{2}{3} < \frac{5}{6}$
7. $-\frac{3}{7}$ $-\frac{4}{5}$ $-\frac{3}{7} > -\frac{4}{5}$

Show that each number can be written as a ratio.

8. 14 $\frac{14}{1}$ 9. 1.7 $\frac{17}{10}$

10. −3.17 $-\frac{317}{100}$

Assignment Guide
Minimum: 1–37 e/o, MR

Regular: 1–45 e/o, 46, MR

Advanced: 1–45 m3, 46–48, MR

ADDITIONAL ANSWERS

Try This

e.

f.

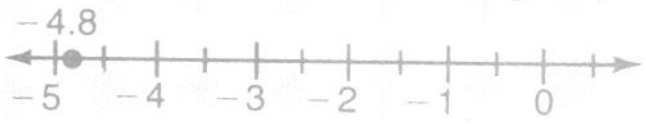

g.

h.

Exercises

13.

14.

15.

16. 

42. $-\frac{8}{8}, -\frac{4}{8}, \frac{1}{8}, \frac{3}{8}, \frac{5}{8}, \frac{7}{8}$

43. $-\frac{7}{5}, -\frac{4}{5}, -\frac{2}{5}, -\frac{1}{5}, \frac{4}{5}, \frac{6}{5}$

44. $\frac{4}{9}, \frac{4}{8}, \frac{4}{6}, \frac{4}{5}, \frac{4}{3}, \frac{4}{2}$

45. $-\frac{5}{6}, -\frac{3}{4}, -\frac{2}{3}, \frac{1}{6}, \frac{3}{8}, \frac{1}{2}$

46. Answers may vary.

$\frac{2}{3} > \frac{4}{7}, \frac{3}{2} > \frac{5}{7}, \frac{3}{2} > \frac{4}{5}, \frac{4}{5} > \frac{2}{7}, \frac{7}{2} > \frac{5}{4}$

47. $\frac{a}{b} < \frac{c}{d}$

$\frac{ad}{bd} < \frac{cb}{bd}$

$\therefore ad < cb$

48. False; $\frac{2}{3} \neq \frac{3}{4}$

Mixed Review

49. $m - 11$

50. $\frac{y}{x}$

51. $9 + t$

52. $4w$

53. 0.06

54. 2.3

55. 41

56. $\frac{1}{5}$

57. 1

58. $\frac{1}{6}$

59. 56

60. 72

61. 128

62. 22

63. 135

64. 51

65. 39

Use either $<$ or $>$ to write a true sentence.

17. $2.14 > 1.24$	**18.** $-3.3 < -2.2$	**19.** $7.075 < 7.750$
20. $-14.5 < 0.011$	**21.** $17.2 > -1.67$	**22.** $-345 > -354$
23. $-12.88 > -13$	**24.** $-14.34 > -17.88$	**25.** $-0.606 > -0.660$
26. $130.5 < 135$	**27.** $-0.99 > -0.999$	**28.** $-17.25 > -18$
29. $-4.2 < -0.42$	**30.** $23.4 > -43.5$	**31.** $124 > -300$
32. $-\frac{4}{9} < \frac{2}{5}$	**33.** $\frac{4}{11} < \frac{2}{5}$	**34.** $\frac{4}{5} < \frac{7}{8}$
35. $\frac{4}{10} > -\frac{1}{2}$	**36.** $-\frac{5}{12} < -\frac{3}{8}$	**37.** $-\frac{5}{3} < -\frac{7}{5}$

B

The **density property** of rational numbers states that between any two rational numbers, there is another rational number. Find a number between the following pairs of numbers. Answers may vary. Examples are given.

38. $\frac{1}{2}, \frac{1}{4}$ $\frac{3}{8}$ **39.** $\frac{1}{5}, \frac{2}{5}$ $\frac{3}{10}$ **40.** 0.45, 0.46 0.455 **41.** 0.012, 0.013 0.0125

Write these rational numbers in order from least to greatest.

42. $\frac{3}{8}, \frac{7}{8}, \frac{1}{8}, -\frac{4}{8}, \frac{5}{8}, -\frac{8}{8}$ **43.** $\frac{6}{5}, -\frac{4}{5}, -\frac{2}{5}, \frac{4}{5}, -\frac{7}{5}, -\frac{1}{5}$

44. $\frac{4}{5}, \frac{4}{3}, \frac{4}{8}, \frac{4}{6}, \frac{4}{9}, \frac{4}{2}$ **45.** $-\frac{2}{3}, \frac{1}{2}, -\frac{3}{4}, -\frac{5}{6}, \frac{3}{8}, \frac{1}{6}$

46. ***Critical Thinking*** Find five ways the numbers 2, 3, 4, 5, and 7 can be placed in the boxes to make a true statement. $\frac{\square}{\square} > \frac{\square}{\square}$

Challenge

47. Show that for any positive rational numbers, $\frac{a}{b}$ and $\frac{c}{d}$, if $\frac{a}{b} < \frac{c}{d}$, then $ad < cb$. (Hint: Find a common denominator.)

48. Is the following generalization true or false? $\frac{a}{b} = \frac{a + c}{b + c}$ where $b \neq 0$ and $c \neq 0$. If it is false, give a counterexample.

Mixed Review

Write as an algebraic expression. **49.** 11 less than m

50. y divided among x **51.** the sum of 9 and t **52.** 4 times w

Find the absolute value. **53.** $|0.06|$ **54.** $|-2.3|$ **55.** $|-41|$

Solve. **56.** $y + \frac{3}{5} = \frac{4}{5}$ **57.** $a - \frac{1}{7} = \frac{6}{7}$ **58.** $x + \frac{2}{3} = \frac{5}{6}$

59. $\frac{a}{7} = 8$ **60.** $\frac{c}{6} = 12$ **61.** $\frac{y}{4} = 32$ **62.** $\frac{y}{3} = 7 + \frac{1}{3}$

Evaluate. **63.** $D = r \cdot k$ for $r = 45$ and $k = 3$ **64.** $A = bh$ for $b = 10.2$ and $h = 5$ **65.** $P = 2w + 2l$ for $w = 17$ and $l = 2.5$

2-3 Addition of Rational Numbers

Application

The school refreshment stand started selling popcorn during lunch and after school. They kept a record of profits and losses for the first five days of operation. What was the total profit or loss?

Monday	Tuesday	Wednesday	Thursday	Friday
$18 profit	$7 loss	$5 loss	$11 profit	$2 loss

Profit and loss statements often involve the addition of integers. This problem can be solved by finding this sum.

$$18 + (-7) + (-5) + 11 + (-2)$$

Addition Using a Number Line

Objective: Add rational numbers using a number line.

Addition of whole numbers can be shown by moves on a number line. To add 2 and 5, we start at 2, the first number. Then we move a distance of 5 units to the right. We end up at 7, the sum.

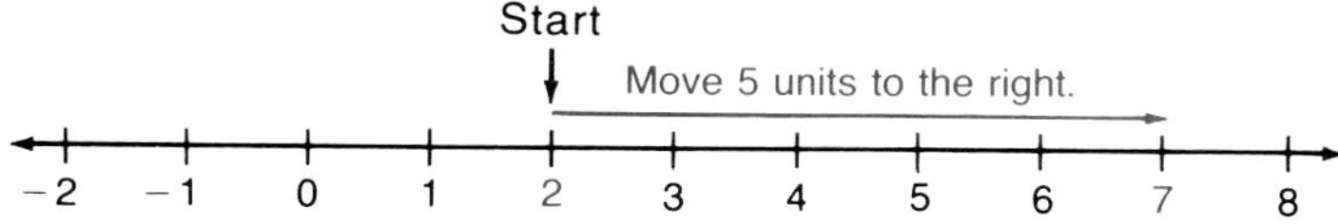

We can also add any two rational numbers using moves on the number line. When we add a negative number, however, we must move to the left. Recall that 0 plus any number is that number.

EXAMPLES Add using the number line.

1. $3 + (-5)$

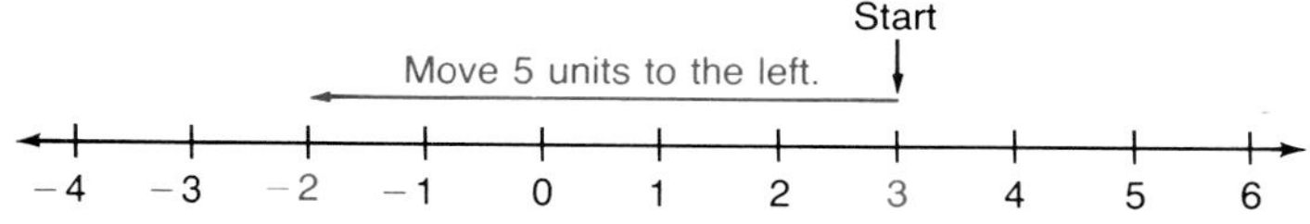

$3 + (-5) = -2$

2-3

FIRST FIVE MINUTES

In each case, tell how many jumps backward or forward would accomplish the same result.

1. forward 2, backward 1
   Forward 1
2. backward 1, forward 3
   Forward 2
3. forward 2, forward 3
   Forward 5
4. backward 3, backward 5
   Backward 8
5. backward 8, forward 2
   Backward 6

APPLICATION

The problem posed in the opening paragraph is solved in Example 9.

Addition Using a Number Line

Adding rational numbers on a number line provides a valuable illustration prior to learning rules for the addition of rational numbers.

You may wish to have students add Examples 1–4 in reverse order and then compare their answers.

Key Questions

Is starting at 5 and moving 2 to the left equivalent to

- starting at −2 and moving 5 to the right?
  Yes
- starting at 2 and moving 5 to the left?
  No

Chalkboard Examples (*T3*)

Add using the number line.

1. $2 + (-1) = ?$

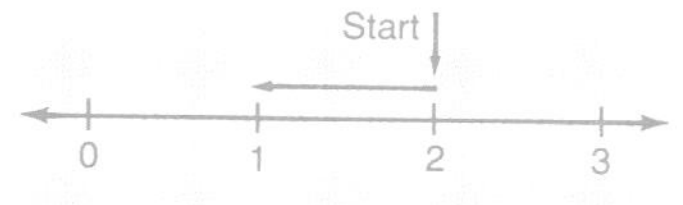

2. $-5 + 7 = ?$

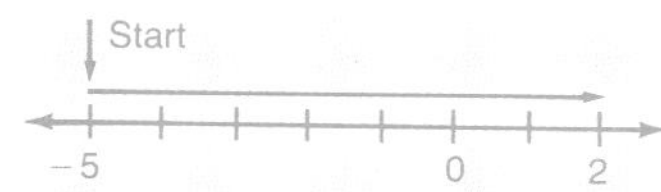

3. $-4 + (-5) = ?$

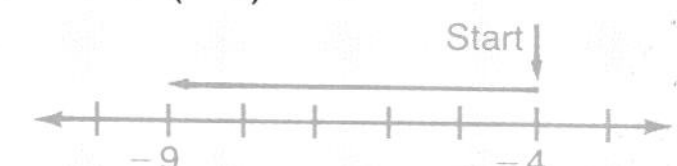

Teaching Option

The following activity provides a model that will help students gain an understanding of how to add positive and negative numbers.

Provide students with two-color counters or improvise using cardboard or buttons. Let yellow counters represent positive integers, and red counters represent negative integers. When red and yellow counters are paired, they cancel each other and both are removed.

Have students make two piles of counters, each pile consisting of only one color. They should then combine the piles, and remove pairs of counters when possible.

Students can complete several rows of a table like the one below by repeating this process several times and writing an equation that describes their actions.

First Pile ⓎⓎⓎⓎ ⓎⓎⓎⓎ

Second Pile ⓇⓇⓇⓇ

First Pile	Second Pile	Combined Pile	Equation
8	−4	4	8+(−4)=4

Encourage students to come up with rules for adding integers and list them on the blackboard.

2. $-4 + (-3)$

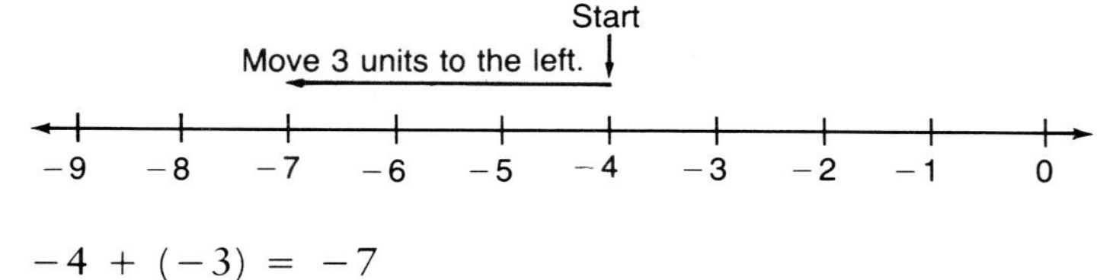

$-4 + (-3) = -7$

3. $-4 + 9$

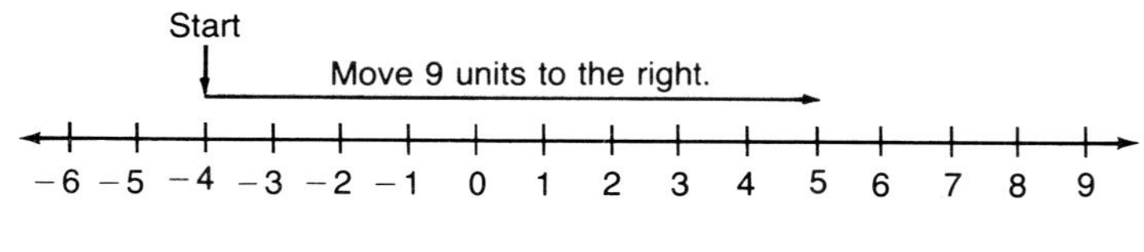

$-4 + 9 = 5$

4. $\frac{2}{3} + \left(-\frac{4}{3}\right)$

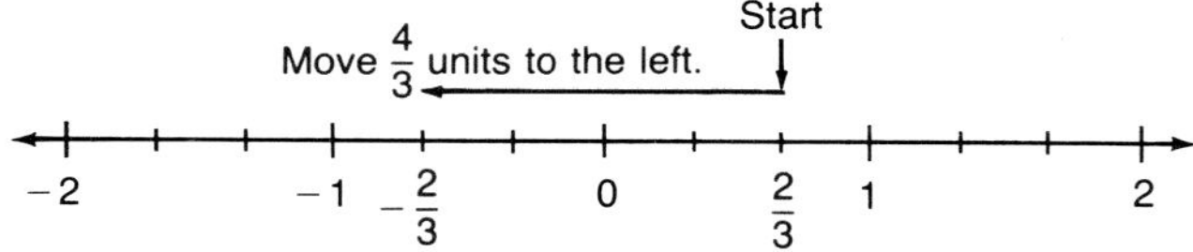

$\frac{2}{3} + \left(-\frac{4}{3}\right) = -\frac{2}{3}$

Try This Add using the number line.

a. $4 + 3$ 7 **b.** $-5 + 2$ −3 **c.** $3 + (-5)$ −2 **d.** $-4 + (-2)$ −6 **e.** $-\frac{3}{4} + \frac{7}{4}$ $\frac{4}{4}$ or 1

Addition Without a Number Line

Objective: Add rational numbers without a number line.

We can use the number line to suggest how to add rational numbers.

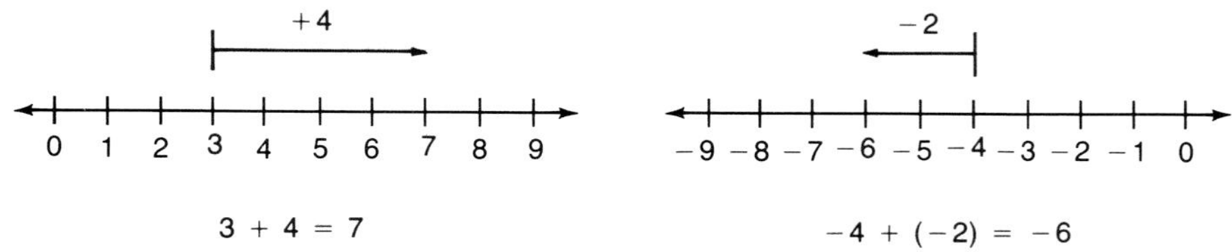

These illustrations suggest the following.

Adding Two Positive or Two Negative Numbers

Add the absolute values. The sum has the same sign as the addends.

In these illustrations, we add a positive number and a negative number.

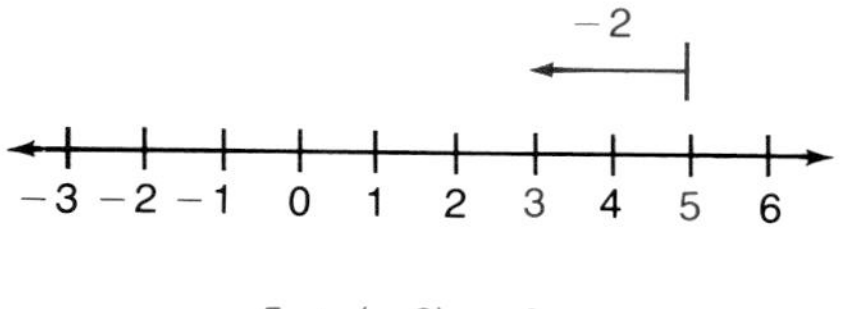

$5 + (-2) = 3$

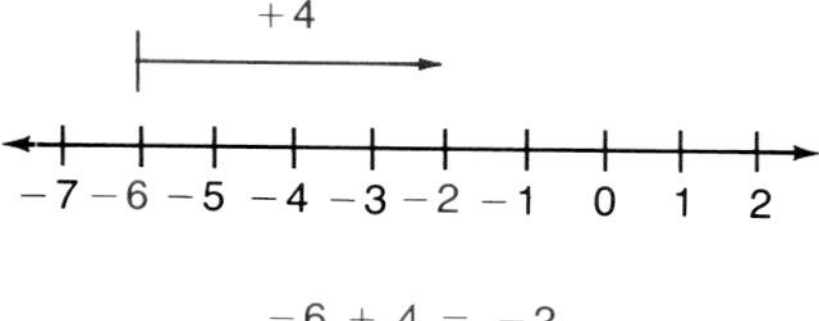

$-6 + 4 = -2$

These illustrations suggest the following.

Adding a Positive and a Negative Number

Subtract the absolute values. The sum has the sign of the addend with the greater absolute value.

EXAMPLES Add without using the number line.

5. $-12 + (-7) = -19$ Since both addends are negative, the sum is negative.

6. $-1.4 + 8.5 = 7.1$ The difference of the absolute values is 7.1. The positive addend has the greater absolute value, so the sum is positive.

7. $21 + (-36) = -15$ The difference of the absolute values is 15. The negative addend has the greater absolute value, so the sum is negative.

8. $-\frac{2}{3} + \frac{4}{5} = -\frac{10}{15} + \frac{12}{15}$

$= \frac{2}{15}$ The difference of the absolute values is $\frac{2}{15}$. The positive addend has the greater absolute value, so the sum is positive.

Try This Add without using a number line.

f. $-17 + 17$ 0 **g.** $-13 + (-7)$ −20 **h.** $-15 + (-10)$ −25

i. $-0.17 + 0.7$ 0.53 **j.** $-12 + 25$ 13 **k.** $14 + (-21)$ −7

l. $\frac{3}{4} + \left(-\frac{5}{4}\right)$ $-\frac{2}{4}$ or $-\frac{1}{2}$ **m.** $-\frac{5}{8} + \left(-\frac{1}{4}\right)$ $-\frac{7}{8}$ **n.** $-\frac{4}{5} + \frac{5}{7}$ $-\frac{3}{35}$

Addition without a Number Line

Mention to students that parentheses around negative numbers are sometimes not necessary and may be omitted when the meaning is clear. For example, (-5) can be written -5.

Key Questions

- Will the sum $-3 + -4$ be positive or negative?
  Negative
- Will the sum $-3 + 4$ be positive or negative?
  Positive
- Will the sum $3 + -4$ be positive or negative?
  Negative

Chalkboard Examples

Add without using the number line.

1. $-6 + (-5) = ?$
   -11
2. $-2.3 + (-1.4) = ?$
   -3.7
3. $7.3 + (-9.7) = ?$
   -2.4
4. $-4.6 + 9.9 = ?$
   5.3
5. $12 + (-15) = ?$
   -3
6. $-\frac{2}{7} + \left(-\frac{3}{7}\right) = ?$
   $-\frac{5}{7}$
7. $-\frac{4}{9} + \frac{1}{3} = ?$
   $-\frac{4}{9} + \frac{3}{9} = -\frac{1}{9}$

Additive Inverses

Stress that it is preferable to read $-a$ as "the additive inverse of a" or "the opposite of a." This avoids the misconception that $-a$ is necessarily a negative number.

Key Questions

- How many additive inverses does -3 have?
  One
- What is the additive inverse of 0?
  0
- Is the additive inverse of a number always negative? No

Chalkboard Examples

Find the additive inverse of each.

1. -7 7
2. 34.7 -34.7
3. -4.81 4.81
4. $-\frac{3}{7}$ $\frac{3}{7}$
5. Find $-x$ and $-(-x)$ when x is 5.
   $-x = -5$
   $-(-x) = -(-5) = 5$
6. Find $-x$ and $-(-x)$ when x is -2.
   $-x = -(-2) = 2$
   $-(-x) = -(-(-2)) = -2$
7. Find $-x$ and $-(-x)$ when x is 0.
   $-x = -0 = 0$
   $-(-x) = -(0) = 0$
8. Maria made \$13 by baby sitting paid \$11.50 for a scarf, received a \$10 bill for her birthday, and bought a snack for \$2.25. How much money does she now have?
   $13 + (-11.50) + 10 + (-2.25)$
   $= 13 + 10 + (-11.50) + (-2.25)$
   $= 23 + (-13.75)$
   $= 9.25$
   Maria now has \$9.25.

The commutative and associative properties hold for rational numbers, so we can group and order addends as we please. One way is to group the positive numbers together and group the negative numbers together.

EXAMPLE 9 Add.

$18 + (-7) + (-5) + 11 + (-2)$

$= (18 + 11) + [(-7) + (-5) + (-2)]$ Grouping the positive and the negative numbers together

$= 29 + (-14)$ Adding the results

$= 15$

Try This Add.

o. $(-15) + (-37) + 25 + 42 + (-59) + (-14)$ -58

p. $42 + (-81) + (-28) + 24 + 18 + (-31)$ -56

Additive Inverses

Objective: Give the additive inverse.

When **opposites** such as 6 and -6 are added, the sum is 0. Number pairs such as 6 and -6 are also called **additive inverses.**

Definition

Two rational numbers whose sum is 0 are called **additive inverses** of each other.

Every rational number has an additive inverse.

Property of Additive Inverses

For each rational number a, there is one and only one rational number $-a$ such that $a + (-a) = 0$.

EXAMPLES Find the additive inverse of each.

10. 34

The additive inverse is -34. $34 + (-34) = 0$

11. -2.96

The additive inverse is 2.96. $-2.96 + 2.96 = 0$

12. $-\frac{5}{4}$

The additive inverse is $\frac{5}{4}$. $-\frac{5}{4} + \frac{5}{4} = 0$

Try This Find the additive inverse of each.

q. -19 19 **r.** 54 -54 **s.** 0 0 **t.** -7.4 7.4 **u.** $-\frac{8}{3}$ $\frac{8}{3}$

The symbol -8 is usually read "negative 8." It could also be read "the additive inverse of 8" or "the opposite of 8" because the additive inverse of 8 is negative. A symbol like $-x$ should be read "the additive inverse of x" or "the opposite of x" and not "negative x," however, because we do not know if $-x$ represents a negative number, a positive number, or 0 until we know the value of x.

Inverse of the Inverse

The inverse of the inverse of a rational number is the number itself.

$$-(-n) = n$$

EXAMPLES

13. Find $-x$ and $-(-x)$ when x is 16.

If $x = 16$, then $-x = -(16)$ Replacing x with 16

$= -16$

$-(-x) = -(-16)$ Replacing x with 16

$= 16$

14. Find $-x$ and $-(-x)$ when x is -3.

If $x = -3$, then $-x = -(-3)$ Replacing x with -3

$= 3$

$-(-x) = -(-(-3))$ Replacing x with -3

$= -3$

Try This Find $-x$ and $-(-x)$ when x is each of the following.

v. 14 -14, 14 **w.** 1 -1, 1 **x.** -19 19, -19

EXAMPLE 15

A submarine is cruising at a depth of 30 m. It climbs 12 m, then dives 21 m, and then climbs 13 m. At what depth is the submarine?

$-30 + 12 + (-21) + 13 = -26$ We can represent depth with a negative number. Use a positive number to represent climbing.

The submarine is at a depth of -26 m.

LESSON QUIZ

Add.

1. $-4 + 7$
   3
2. $-7 + (-4)$
   -11
3. $-3.8 + (-4.1)$
   -7.9
4. $\frac{3}{8} + \left(-\frac{7}{8}\right)$
   $-\frac{4}{8} = -\frac{1}{2}$
5. $-\frac{1}{3} + \left(-\frac{5}{6}\right)$
   $-\frac{2}{6} + \left(-\frac{5}{6}\right) = -\frac{7}{6}$
6. $-4 + 7 + (-6) + 8$
   $-4 + (-6) + 7 + 8$
   $= -10 + 15 = 5$
7. $-12 + 8 + (-16) + (-9)$
   $-12 + (-16) + (-9) + 8$
   $= -37 + 8 = -29$

Find the additive inverse of each.

8. -14
   The additive inverse is 14.
9. $\frac{7}{3}$
   The additive inverse is $-\frac{7}{3}$.
10. Find $-x$ when x is -4.
    $-(-4) = 4$
11. A blimp rose 500 ft, fell 700 ft, fell 1300 ft, and rose 300 ft. How much did it rise or fall all together?
    $5 + (-7) + (-13) + 3$
    $= 5 + 3 + (-7) + (-13)$
    $= 8 + (-20) = -12$
    It fell 1200 ft.
12. For what number x is $-x$ equal to x?
    $-0 = 0$

Assignment Guide
Minimum: Day 1: 1–49 e/o, MR
Day 2: 50–70 e/o, assign w. 2-4
Regular: 1–79 m3, 80, MR

Advanced: 1–79 m3, 80, 81–85 e/o, MR

Try This Solve.

y. Rico carried the ball six times in the third quarter of a football game. Here are his gains and losses: 11-yd gain, 4-yd loss, 6-yd loss, 5-yd gain, 8-yd gain, 2-yd loss. What was the total number of yards he gained (or lost)? 12 yd gained

2-3 EXERCISES

A

Add using a number line.

1. $-9 + 2$ -7 **2.** $2 + (-5)$ -3 **3.** $-10 + 6$ -4 **4.** $8 + (-3)$ 5
5. $-8 + 8$ 0 **6.** $6 + (-6)$ 0 **7.** $-3 + (-5)$ -8 **8.** $-4 + (-6)$ -10

Add without using a number line.

9. $-7 + 0$ -7 **10.** $-13 + 0$ -13 **11.** $0 + (-27)$ -27
12. $0 + (-35)$ -35 **13.** $17 + (-17)$ 0 **14.** $-15 + 15$ 0
15. $-17 + (-25)$ -42 **16.** $-24 + (-17)$ -41 **17.** $-14 + (-29)$ -43
18. $-38 + (-42)$ -80 **19.** $17 + (-12)$ 5 **20.** $14 + (-25)$ -11
21. $14 + (-36)$ -22 **22.** $25 + (-8)$ 17 **23.** $-16 + 9$ -7
24. $-32 + (-9)$ -41 **25.** $-24 + 24$ 0 **26.** $-3 + (-17)$ -20
27. $5 + (-72)$ -67 **28.** $-15 + (-15)$ -30 **29.** $-\frac{3}{5} + \frac{2}{5}$ $-\frac{1}{5}$
30. $-\frac{4}{3} + \frac{2}{3}$ $-\frac{2}{3}$ **31.** $-\frac{3}{7} + \left(-\frac{5}{7}\right)$ $-\frac{8}{7}$ **32.** $-\frac{4}{9} + \left(-\frac{6}{9}\right)$ $-\frac{10}{9}$
33. $-\frac{5}{8} + \frac{1}{4}$ $-\frac{3}{8}$ **34.** $-\frac{5}{6} + \frac{2}{3}$ $-\frac{1}{6}$ **35.** $-\frac{3}{7} + \left(-\frac{2}{5}\right)$ $-\frac{29}{35}$
36. $-\frac{5}{8} + \left(-\frac{1}{3}\right)$ $-\frac{23}{24}$ **37.** $-\frac{3}{5} + \left(-\frac{2}{15}\right)$ $-\frac{11}{15}$ **38.** $-\frac{5}{9} + \left(-\frac{1}{18}\right)$ $-\frac{11}{18}$

39. $75 + (-14) + (-17) + (-5)$ 39
40. $28 + (-44) + 17 + 31 + (-94)$ -62
41. $-44 + \left(-\frac{3}{8}\right) + 95 + \left(-\frac{5}{8}\right)$ 50
42. $\frac{-3}{12} + \frac{3}{18} + \frac{-7}{6} + 2$ $\frac{3}{4}$
43. $24 + 3.1 + (-44) + (-8.2) + 63$ 37.9
44. $-17 + 28 + (-12) + (-20.5) + 16.5$ -5
45. $62 + 35 + 41 + (-8) + (-48) + (-102)$ -20

46. $24 + (-36) + 75 + (-75) + 82 + (-63)$ 7

47. $-75 + (-64) + (-58) + 105 + 210$ 118

48. $98 + (-54) + 113 + (-998) + 44 + (-612) + (-18) + 334$ -1093

49. $-455 + (-123) + 1026 + (-919) + 213 + 111 + (-874)$ -1021

Find the additive inverse of each.

50. 24 **51.** -64 **52.** -9 **53.** $\frac{7}{2}$ **54.** -26.9 **55.** 48.2

Find $-x$ when x is

56. 9 **57.** -26 **58.** $-\frac{14}{3}$ **59.** $\frac{1}{328}$ **60.** 0.101 **61.** 0

Find $-(-x)$ when x is

62. -65 -65 **63.** 29 29 **64.** $\frac{5}{3}$ $\frac{5}{3}$ **65.** -9.1 -9.1

Solve.

66. In a football game, the quarterback attempted passes with the following results. 8-yd gain

first try 13-yd gain
second try incomplete
third try 12-yd loss (tackled behind the line)
fourth try 21-yd gain
fifth try 14-yd loss
Find the total gain (or loss).

67. The average attendance at a soccer game last year was 1755 people. The table below shows the attendance for each game this year compared to last year's average. By how much was the total attendance for all 6 games above or below last year's? 542 above last year's

Game 1	Game 2	Game 3	Game 4	Game 5	Game 6
+357	−144	−250	+347	+420	−188

68. The business class kept a record of the change in the stock market for a period of 5 weeks. After 5 weeks, how many points had the market gained or lost? Up 16 points

Week 1	Week 2	Week 3	Week 4	Week 5
down 12 pts	down 15 pts	up 35 pts	down 10 pts	up 18 pts

69. In a board game, Alice started with \$1475. After these transactions how much did Alice have? \$1715

purchased properties	1700
collected rents	1640
purchased houses	900
passed start (collected money)	1200

ADDITIONAL ANSWERS

Exercises

50. -24
51. 64
52. 9
53. $-\frac{7}{2}$
54. 26.9
55. -48.2
56. -9
57. 26
58. $\frac{14}{3}$
59. $-\frac{1}{328}$
60. -0.101
61. 0

80. Answers may vary, but should include the idea that since $-n + n = 0$, the additive inverse of $-n$ is n.

Mixed Review

86. 2.4
87. 4.31
88. 12
89. $<$
90. $>$
91. $<$
92. $>$
93. $<$
94. 2
95. 4
96. 2.03
97. 0
98. 13

70. The table below shows the profits and losses of a company over a five-year period. Find the profit or loss after this period of time.

Year	Profit or loss
1984	+32,056
1985	− 2,925
1986	+81,429
1987	−19,365
1988	−13,875 77,320 profit

71. The barometric pressure at Omaha was 1012 millibars (mb). The pressure dropped 6 mb, then it rose 3 mb. After that it dropped 14 mb and then rose 4 mb. What was the pressure then? 999 mb

72. Francine received an allowance of \$2.00, bought a pen for \$0.59, gave \$0.75 to Pat, made \$4.50 baby sitting, and spent \$2.75 at a movie. How much did she have left? \$2.41

B

73. For what numbers x is $-x$ negative? When x is positive

74. For what numbers x is $-x$ positive? When x is negative

Tell whether the sum is positive, negative, or zero.

75. n is positive, m is negative. $n + (-m)$ is ____. Positive

76. n is positive, m is negative. $-n + m$ is ____. Negative

77. $n = m$, n and m are negative. $-n + (-m)$ is ____. Positive

78. $n = m$, n and m are negative. $n + (-m)$ is ____. Zero

79. Name the largest negative integer. −1

80. ***Critical Thinking*** Write an argument to convince a classmate that $-(-n) = n$.

Challenge

Solve.

81. $x + x = 0$ 0

82. $x + (-5) = x$ No value

83. $3y + (-2) = 7$ 3

84. $x + (-5) = 16$ 21

85. Does $x - y = x + (-y)$ for all numbers x and y? Yes

Mixed Review

Solve. **86.** $2.6n = 6.24$ **87.** $w - 1.07 = 3.24$ **88.** $7r = 84$

Use either $<$ or $>$ to write a true sentence. **89.** $-9 \quad 2$

90. $-4 \quad -6$ **91.** $-1 \quad 0$ **92.** $3.62 \quad 3.26$ **93.** $0 \quad 0.001$

Find the absolute value. **94.** $|2|$ **95.** $|-4|$ **96.** $|-2.03|$ **97.** $|0|$

98. Each of the members of Miss Odell's class read 8 books. If the class read 104 books in all, how many members are in the class?

2-4 Subtraction of Rational Numbers

Application

The lowest point in Asia is the Dead Sea, 400 meters below sea level. The lowest point in the United States is Death Valley, 86 meters below sea level. How much higher is Death Valley than the Dead Sea?

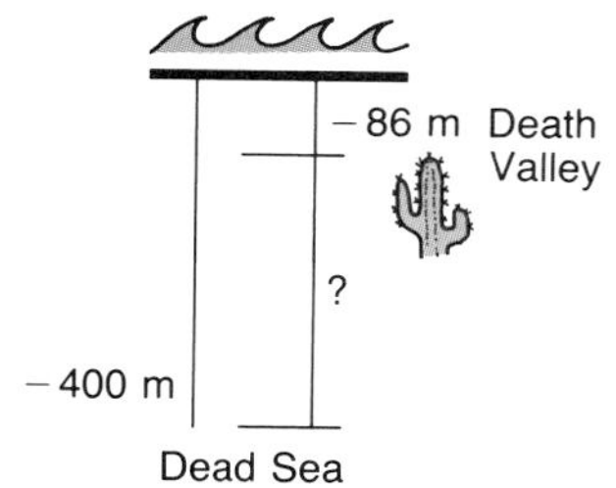

Drawing a diagram can help you understand the problem.

Let d be the difference between the altitude of Death Valley and the Dead Sea. You can solve this problem by subtracting rational numbers.

$$d = -86 - (-400)$$

Subtraction on a Number Line

Objective: Subtract rational numbers on a number line.

We can subtract rational numbers by using the definition of subtraction and a number line.

Definition

For all rational numbers a and b, the **difference** $a - b$ is the number c, such that $c + b = a$.

EXAMPLE 1 Subtract.

$10 - 12$

From the definition of subtraction, the number that can be added to 12 to get 10 will be the answer. On a number line we start at 12 and move to 10.

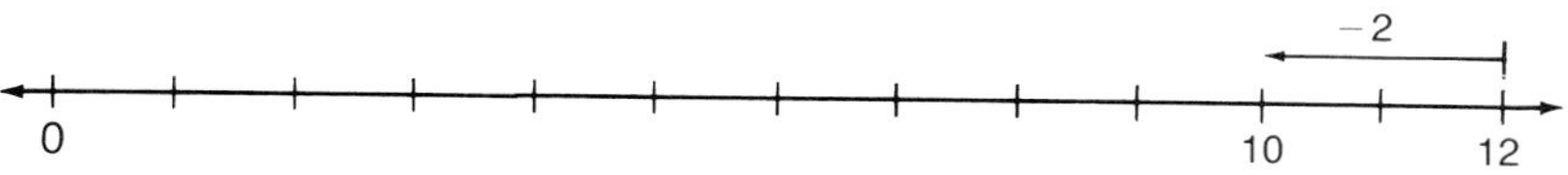

We moved 2 units in the negative direction. The answer is -2. Therefore, $10 - 12 = -2$. We can check by adding, $12 + (-2) = 10$.

2-4

FIRST FIVE MINUTES

Add.

1. $5 + (-7)$ -2
2. $-3 + (-4)$ -7
3. $-3.9 + 2.1$ -1.8
4. What is the additive inverse of -12? 12
5. What is the additive inverse of $-(-12)$? -12
6. Simplify $-(-3)$. $-(-3) = 3$
7. Add.
   $\frac{2}{7} + \left(-\frac{3}{14}\right)$
   $\frac{4}{14} + \left(-\frac{3}{14}\right) = \frac{1}{14}$

APPLICATION

In the introductory problem,

$d = -86 - (-400)$
$= 314$

Death Valley is 314 meters higher than the Dead Sea.

You may want to show students the following alternate solution.

$d = -400 - (-86)$
$d = -400 + 86$
$d = -314$

The Dead Sea is 314 meters *lower* than Death Valley.

Stress that both methods are correct, but since the question asked how much higher Death Valley is, the answer should be given in that form.

Subtraction on a Number Line

After solving $10 - 12$ in Example 1, show students that the number line solution of $10 + (-12)$ is the same diagram.

Key Question

- In Example 1, how far and in which direction would you go to move from 12 to 10?
  Move 2 in the negative direction (to the left).

Chalkboard Examples

Subtract using a number line.

1. $-3 - 7 = -10$

Start
−3 0 7

2. $-9 - (-5) = -4$

3. $10 - 7 = 3$

4. $-4 - (-6) = 2$

Teaching Option

The following cooperative learning activity models subtraction of positive and negative numbers.

Divide the class into groups of 4 or 5 students. Remind students that yellow counters represent positive numbers and that red counters represent negative numbers. Provide each group with 9 chips, including at least one of each color. Give groups the following instructions.

Your set of counters represents an integer. Determine the value of that integer. Then, beginning with your original set, show the values you can make:

- if you remove 1 counter
- if you remove 2 counters
- if you remove 3 counters

Draw a diagram to represent each action and record the value of each.

Example:

ⓎⓎⓎⓎ
ⓇⓇⓇⓇⓇ

Value: -1

Removing 2 counters:

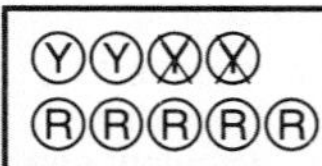

Value: -3

Value: -1

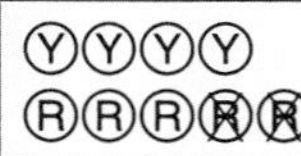

Value: $+1$

Have each group present its results to the class, then encourage students to make generalizations.

EXAMPLE 2 Subtract.

$-1 - (-5)$

We read this "negative 1 minus negative 5." From the definition of subtraction, the number that can be added to -5 to get -1 will be the answer. Start at -5 and move to -1.

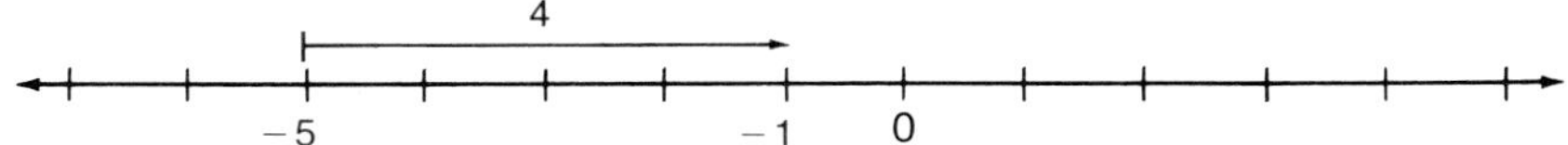

We moved 4 units in the positive direction. The answer is 4. Therefore, $-1 - (-5) = 4$. Check by adding, $-5 + 4 = -1$.

Try This Subtract using a number line.

a. $-2 - 6$ -8 **b.** $4 - 10$ -6 **c.** $-9 - (-4)$ -5

Subtraction without a Number Line

Objective: Subtract rational numbers without using a number line.

The examples below show that adding the opposite of a rational number gives the same result as subtracting the rational number.

$8 - 3 = 5$	$8 + (-3) = 5$
$4 - 7 = -3$	$4 + (-7) = -3$
$-4.5 - 2 = -6.5$	$-4.5 + (-2) = -6.5$

These examples suggest the following rule.

Subtracting Numbers

For all rational numbers a and b, $a - b = a + (-b)$.
(To subtract a rational number, add its additive inverse or opposite.)

EXAMPLES Subtract.

3. $2 - 6 = 2 + (-6)$ Writing as addition; adding the opposite of 6
$= -4$ Adding

4. $-86 - (-400) = -86 + 400$
$= 314$

5. $-4.2 - (-3.6) = -4.2 + 3.6$
$= -0.6$

6. $-\frac{1}{2} - \frac{3}{4} = -\frac{1}{2} + \left(-\frac{3}{4}\right) = -\frac{5}{4}$

Try This Subtract.

d. $4 - 9$ −5 **e.** $6 - (-4)$ 10 **f.** $-4 - 17$ −21

g. $-3 - (-12)$ 9 **h.** $\frac{3}{8} - \left(-\frac{1}{4}\right)$ $\frac{5}{8}$

When addition and subtraction occur several times, we can use the rule for subtracting rational numbers to make them all additions.

EXAMPLE 7 Simplify.

$$8 - (-4) - 2 - (-4) + 2 = 8 + 4 + (-2) + 4 + 2$$
$$= 16$$

EXAMPLE 8 Simplify.

$$-4 - (-2x) + x - (-5) = -4 + 2x + x + 5$$
$$= 3x + 1$$

Combining like terms

Try This Simplify.

i. $-6 - (-2) - (-4) - 12 + 3$ −9

j. $3 - (-7.1) + 6.3 - (-5.2)$ 21.6

k. $-8 - (-3x) + 2x - (-13)$ $5x + 5$

Adding and Subtracting Rational Numbers

If your calculator has the "change sign" key +/- , you can use it to find the opposite of a number.

$25 - (-10) - 12 + 15 \rightarrow$

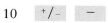

25  10   12  15  → 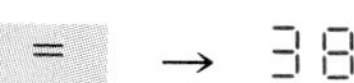 38

For additional calculator practice, see Calculator Worksheet 6.

EXAMPLE 9

Mr. Casper had \$75.50 in his checking account. He wrote a check for \$95.00. By how much has he overdrawn his checking account? Let c = the amount in his checking account.

$$c = 75.50 - 95.00$$
$$c = -19.50$$

He has overdrawn his checking account by \$19.50.

Since \$95.00 − \$75.00 = \$20.00, \$95.00 − \$75.50 should be just under \$20.00. The answer is reasonable.

Subtraction without a Number Line

It is helpful to have students practice saying "add the opposite" as you work through the chalkboard examples. Stress that in the first chalkboard example, $5 - 8$, both the 5 and the 8 are positive numbers. You may want to write $+5 - (+8)$.

Key Question

- Using the numbers 5 and 8, addition, subtraction, and additive inverses, how many different numbers can you write?
  $5 + 8 = 13$
  $5 - 8 = -3$
  $-5 + 8 = 3$
  $-5 - 8 = -13$

Chalkboard Examples

Subtract.

1. $5 - 8$
   $5 + (-8) = -3$
2. $-8 - (-5)$
   $-8 + (-(-5)) = -8 + 5 = -3$
3. $-6.7 - 9.1$
   $-6.7 + (-9.1) = -15.8$
4. $-\frac{1}{3} - \left(\frac{5}{3}\right)$
   $-\frac{1}{3} + \left(-\frac{5}{3}\right) = -\frac{6}{3} = -2$

Simplify.

5. $4 - 5 + (-3) + 1$
   $4 + (-5) + (-3) + 1$
   $= 4 + 1 + (-5) + (-3)$
   $= 5 + (-8) = -3$
6. $9.1 - (-4.2) + 3.7$
   $9.1 + (-(-4.2)) + 3.7$
   $= 9.1 + 4.2 + 3.7 = 17.0$
7. $-6 - (-3x) + 5x + 2$
   $-6 + (-(-3x)) + 5x + 2$
   $= -6 + 2 + 3x + 5x$
   $= -4 + 8x$
8. Ace Drilling is digging a well. The ground level at the surface is 112 feet above sea level. They drill down 250 feet. How far below sea level is the bottom of the well?
   Ground level is 112.
   The well depth is −250.
   $112 + (-250) = -138$
   The bottom of the well is 138 ft below sea level.

LESSON ENRICHMENT

Magic Squares With Integers

Use each of the integers -4, -3, -2, -1, 0, 1, 2, 3, and 4 exactly once to fill in a three by three table so that all the rows, columns, and diagonals add up to 0. Get students started by drawing the table and putting a -1 in the top left-hand corner and a 3 in the bottom left-hand corner. Note that answers for magic squares may vary.

-1	4	-3
-2	0	2
3	-4	1

LESSON QUIZ

Add or subtract.

1. $5 - 9$ -4
2. $-11 + 3$ -8
3. $-13 - 5$ -18
4. $12 - (-3)$
   $12 + 3 = 15$
5. $-\frac{6}{9} - \left(-\frac{2}{3}\right)$
   $= -\frac{6}{9} + \frac{2}{3}$
   $= -\frac{6}{9} + \frac{6}{9} = 0$

Simplify.

6. $14 - (-5) + 3 - 9$
   $= 14 + 5 + 3 - 9$
   $= 22 - 9 = 13$
7. $-6 - (-5x) + 4x + 3$
   $= -6 + 3 + 5x + 4x$
   $= -3 + 9x$
8. The temperature was $-12°$ at dusk and fell to $-23°$ at midnight. How much and in what direction did the temperature change?
   $-23 - (-12)$
   $= -23 + 12 = -11$
   It fell 11°.

Assignment Guide

Minimum: Day 1: 1–26 e/o, assign w. 2–3
Day 2: 27–64 e/o, MR

Regular: 1–65 m3, 66, MR

Advanced: 1–65 m3, 66, 67–77 e/0, MR

Try This Solve.

1. Juan has saved \$35 toward a new stereo system. The total cost of the system is \$125. How much more money does Juan need? \$90

2-4 EXERCISES

A

Subtract using a number line.

1. $3 - 7$ -4 **2.** $4 - 9$ -5 **3.** $0 - 7$ -7 **4.** $0 - 10$ -10

5. $5 - (-2)$ 7 **6.** $-6 - (-8)$ 2 **7.** $-10 - (-10)$ 0 **8.** $-8 - (-8)$ 0

Subtract.

9. $7 - 7$ 0 **10.** $0.9 - 0.9$ 0 **11.** $7 - (-7)$ 14

12. $4 - (-4)$ 8 **13.** $8 - (-3)$ 11 **14.** $-7 - 4$ -11

15. $-6 - 8$ -14 **16.** $6 - (-10)$ 16 **17.** $-4 - (-9)$ 5

18. $-14 - 2$ -16 **19.** $2 - 9$ -7 **20.** $1 - 8$ -7

21. $-6 - (-5)$ -1 **22.** $-4 - (-13)$ 9 **23.** $8 - (-10)$ 18

24. $15 - (-6)$ 21 **25.** $0 - 5$ -5 **26.** $0 - 0.6$ -0.6

27. $-51 - (-2)$ -49 **28.** $-39 - (-41)$ 2 **29.** $-79 - 114$ -193

30. $-197 - 216$ -413 **31.** $0 - (-500)$ 500 **32.** $500 - (-1000)$ 1500

33. $-2.8 - 0$ -2.8 **34.** $6.04 - 1.1$ 4.94 **35.** $7 - 10.53$ -3.53

36. $8 - (-9.3)$ 17.3 **37.** $\frac{1}{6} - \frac{2}{3}$ $-\frac{1}{2}$ **38.** $-\frac{3}{8} - \left(-\frac{1}{2}\right)$ $\frac{1}{8}$

39. $\frac{12}{5} - \frac{12}{5}$ 0 **40.** $-\frac{4}{7} - \left(-\frac{10}{7}\right)$ $\frac{6}{7}$ **41.** $-\frac{7}{10} - \frac{10}{15}$ $-\frac{41}{30}$

42. $-\frac{4}{18} - \left(-\frac{2}{9}\right)$ 0 **43.** $\frac{1}{13} - \frac{1}{12}$ $-\frac{1}{156}$ **44.** $-\frac{1}{7} - \left(-\frac{1}{6}\right)$ $\frac{1}{42}$

Simplify.

45. $18 - (-15) - 3 - (-5) + 2$ 37

46. $22 - (-18) + 7 + (-42) - 27$ -22

47. $-31 + (-28) - (-14) - 17$ -62

48. $-43 - (-19) - (-21) + 25$ 22

49. $-34 - 28 + (-33) - 44$ -139

50. $39 + (-88) - 29 - (-83)$ 5

51. $-93 - (-84) - 41 - (-56)$ 6

52. $84 + (-99) + 44 - (-18) - 43$ 4

53. $-5 - (-3x) + 3x + 4x - (-12)$ $10x + 7$

54. $14 + (-5x) + 2x - (-32)$ $-3x + 46$

55. $13x - (-2x) + 45 - (-21)$ $15x + 66$

56. $8x - (-2x) - 14 - (-5x) + 53$ $15x + 39$

Solve.

57. Mrs. Kang has $619.46 in her checking account. She wrote a check for $950.00. By how much did she overdraw her checking account? $330.54

58. Omar had $137.40 in his checking account. He wrote a check for $225.20. By how much has he overdrawn his checking account? $87.80

59. On a winter night the temperature dropped from −5°C to −12°C. How many degrees did the temperature drop? 7°

60. The temperature at 6 p.m. was 5°C. At 9 p.m. the temperature had dropped to −5°C. How many degrees did the temperature fall? 10°

61. There are 47 females in the band. If there is a total of 163 band members, how many males are in the band? 116 males

62. Sarah had a balance of $45 in her checking account. She wrote two checks totaling $12. How much money does she have in her checking account now? $33

63. The lowest point in Africa is Lake Assal, which is 156 m below sea level. The lowest point in South America is the Valdes Peninsula, which is 40 m below sea level. How much lower is Lake Assal than the Valdes Peninsula? 116 m

64. The deepest point in the Pacific Ocean is the Marianas Trench, which is 10,415 m deep. The deepest point in the Atlantic Ocean is the Puerto Rico Trench, whose depth is 8,648 m. How much deeper is the Marianas Trench than the Puerto Rico Trench? 1,767 m

B

65. Evaluate each expression using the values from the table.

a	b	x	y	z
5	−8	−2.3	4.1	0

a. $(a + x) - b$ 10.7
b. $z - (b - x)$ 5.7
c. $(x - y) + (a - b)$ 6.6
d. $(y - x) - (b - a)$ 19.4
e. $b - |x - a|$ −15.3
f. $|x| - a - (|b| + y)$ −14.8

66. ***Critical Thinking*** Study the first scale and then add items to the right side of the second scale so it will balance.

ADDITIONAL ANSWERS

Exercises

67. False; $3 - 0 \neq 0 - 3$
68. False; $0 - 3 \neq 3$
69. True
70. True
71. True
72. False; $3 - 3 = 0, 3 \neq -3$
73. No
74. Yes;
$a(b - c) = a[b + (-c)]$
$= ab + (-ac)$
$= ab - ac$
75. $-[-(-5)] = -5$
$-\{-[-(-5)]\} = 5$
A term with an even number of negative signs is positive. A term with an odd number of negative signs is negative.
76. Yes
77. Yes

Mixed Review

78. 49
79. 116
80. 81
81. 32
82. 243
83. 0
84. 18
85. 6
86. $y = 1$
87. $a = 8$
88. $y = \frac{1}{4}$
89. $7x^2 + 8x$
90. $2a + 8b + 4c$
91. $c(3c + 5)$
92. $6(x + 4y - 3z)$
93. $3(2m + 3p)$

Challenge

Tell whether each of the following statements is true or false for all integers m and n. If the statement is false, give a counterexample.

67. $n - 0 = 0 - n$

68. $0 - n = n$

69. If $m \neq n$, then $m - n \neq 0$.

70. If $m = -n$, then $m + n = 0$.

71. If $m + n = 0$, then m and n are additive inverses.

72. If $m - n = 0$, then $m = -n$.

73. Do the commutative and associative properties hold for subtraction of integers?

74. Does the relationship $a(b - c) = ab - ac$ hold for all rational numbers a, b, and c? Explain why it does or does not.

75. Simplify $-[-(-5)]$ and $-\{-[-(-5)]\}$. Give a rule for determining the sign of expressions like these, which involve any number of negative signs.

76. Is $a - 1 \leq a$ for all integers a?

77. Does $|a| \cdot (b + c) = |a| \cdot b + |a| \cdot c$ for all integers a, b, and c?

Mixed Review

Evaluate. **78.** $(n + 3)^2$ for $n = 4$ **79.** $(3n)^3 - 100$ for $n = 2$

80. t^4 for $t = 3$ **81.** n^5 for $n = 2$ **82.** $9y^3$ for $y = 3$

83. m^3 for $m = 0$ **84.** $3t^2 + 6$ for $t = 2$ **85.** $2|m|$ for $m = -3$

Solve mentally. **86.** $3y = 3$ **87.** $\frac{a}{2} = 4$ **88.** $4y = 1$

Combine like terms. **89.** $3x + 5x^2 + 5x + 2x^2$

90. $2a + 3b + 4c + 5b$

Factor. **91.** $3c^2 + 5c$ **92.** $6x + 24y - 18z$ **93.** $6m + 9p$

HISTORICAL NOTE

Charles Babbage was an inventor who may have been born 100 years too early. Babbage is often called the father of the computer, although he lived in the 1800s. He spent much of his life designing calculating machines. One machine had input and output mechanisms and could store one thousand 50-digit numbers. Although he spent the equivalent of $100,000 on his machines, he could never perfect a working model. Manufacturing techniques at that time could not provide the close-fitting gears he needed.

Ada Byron Lovelace worked with Babbage and set down the first examples of how a calculating machine could be programmed. She wrote of the possibility that machines could someday compose music. The programming language ADA is named for her.

2-5 Multiplication of Rational Numbers

Objective: Multiply rational numbers.

Explore

We know that one interpretation of multiplication is as repeated addition. For example, $5 \cdot 3$ can be written as $3 + 3 + 3 + 3 + 3 = 15$. Therefore, $5 \cdot 3 = 15$. Use this interpretation of multiplication to copy and complete the table below. What patterns do you see?

Factor	Factor	Repeated Addition	Product
5	4	$4 + 4 + 4 + 4 + 4$	20
5	3	$3 + 3 + 3 + 3 + 3$	15
5	2	$2 + 2 + 2 + 2 + 2$	10
5	1	$1 + 1 + 1 + 1 + 1$	5
5	0	$0 + 0 + 0 + 0 + 0$	0
5	-1	$-1 + (-1) + (-1) + (-1) + (-1)$	-5
5	-2	$-2 + (-2) + (-2) + (-2) + (-2)$	-10
5	-3	$-3 + (-3) + (-3) + (-3) + (-3)$	-15

The table above suggests the following rule.

Multiplying a Positive Number and a Negative Number

To multiply a positive number and a negative number, multiply their absolute values. The sign of the product is negative.

EXAMPLES Multiply.

1. $8(-5) = -40$ 2. $-\frac{1}{3} \cdot \frac{5}{7} = -\frac{5}{21}$ 3. $(-7.2)5 = -36.0$ or -36

Try This Multiply.

a. $(-3)6$ -18 **b.** $20(-5)$ -100 **c.** $4.5(-20)$ -90 **d.** $-\frac{2}{3}\left(\frac{9}{4}\right)$ $-\frac{3}{2}$

How do we multiply two negative numbers? Since -3 is the opposite of 3, it seems reasonable that $-3(-5)$ would be the opposite of $3(-5)$. You saw above that $3(-5) = -15$. So, $-3(-5) = 15$ (the opposite of -15). This example suggests the following rule.

2-5

FIRST FIVE MINUTES

Subtract.

1. $3 \cdot 5 - (3 \cdot 5)$ 0

Factor. Simplify, if possible.

2. $2 \cdot a + 2 \cdot b$ $2 \cdot (a + b)$
3. $2 \cdot 5 + 2 \cdot (-5)$
   $2 \cdot (5 + (-5)) = 2 \cdot 0 = 0$
4. $2 \cdot y + 2 \cdot (-y)$
   $2 \cdot (y + (-y)) = 2 \cdot 0 = 0$
5. $x \cdot y + x \cdot (-y)$
   $x \cdot y + x \cdot (-y) =$
   $x \cdot (y + (-y)) = x \cdot 0 = 0$
6. What number is its own inverse?
   $0 = -0$

EXPLORE

Ask students to make a chart like the one to the left and fill it in. Then have them complete a similar chart as follows.

$2 \cdot (-3) = -3 + (-3) = -6$
$1 \cdot (-3) =$
$0 \cdot (-3) =$
$-1 \cdot (-3) =$

The students should be able to use the pattern to determine that the product of two negative numbers is a positive number.

See Computer Exploration 2 on p. 716 for further exploration of multiplication with rational numbers.

Once students understand the rules for determining the sign of a product, you may wish to present the following:

+ times + = +
+ times − = −
− times + = −
− times − = +

Math Point

Factor and simplify the expression

$$2(5) + 2(-5) = 2(5 + -5) = 2(0) = 0$$

Hence

$$2 \cdot 5 + 2(-5) = 0$$
$$2(-5) = -(2 \cdot 5)$$

This argument works for any two numbers x and y and shows the general principle that

$$x \cdot (-y) = -(x \cdot y)$$

for any numbers x and y.

Key Questions

Which products are positive?

- $-1 \cdot 1$ No
- $-1 \cdot -1$ Yes
- $1 \cdot -1$ No
- $1 \cdot 1$ Yes

Chalkboard Examples

Multiply.

1. $3 \cdot (-2)$ -6
2. $-5 \cdot 3$ -15
3. $\left(-\frac{1}{3}\right) \cdot \left(\frac{2}{5}\right)$ $-\frac{2}{15}$
4. $3.5 \cdot (-4)$ -14
5. $876 \cdot 0$ 0
6. $\left(-\frac{3}{7}\right) \cdot \left(-\frac{4}{2}\right)$
   $\left(\frac{3}{7}\right) \cdot \left(\frac{4}{2}\right) = \frac{12}{14}$ or $\frac{6}{7}$
7. $(-4)(-2)(3)$
   $8 \cdot 3 = 24$
8. $-7 \cdot 3(-5)$
   $(-21)(-5) = 105$
9. $-2(-6)(3)(-1)$
   $12(3)(-1) = 36(-1) = -36$

LESSON QUIZ

Multiply.

1. $-7 \cdot 6$
   -42
2. $8 \cdot (-7)$
   -56
3. $(-9)(-10)$
   90
4. $\left(-\frac{1}{7}\right)\left(-\frac{3}{4}\right)$
   $\left(\frac{1}{7}\right)\left(\frac{3}{4}\right) = \frac{3}{28}$
5. $5 \cdot (-3)(-2)(4)$
   $-15 \cdot (-2)(4)$
   $= 30 \cdot 4 = 120$
6. $(-13)(-35) \cdot 0$
   0

Multiplying Two Negative Numbers

To multiply two negative numbers, multiply their absolute values. The sign of the product is positive.

We already know how to multiply two positive numbers. The only case we have not considered is multiplying by 0.

Multiplicative Property of Zero

For any rational number n, $n \cdot 0 = 0$.
(The product of 0 and any rational number is 0.)

EXAMPLES Multiply.

4. $-3(-4) = 12$ 5. $-1.6(-2) = 3.2$ 6. $-\frac{5}{6}\left(-\frac{1}{9}\right) = \frac{5}{54}$

Try This Multiply.

e. $-5(-4)$ 20 **f.** $-8(0)$ 0 **g.** $-4.2(-3)$ 12.6 **h.** $-\frac{3}{8}\left(-\frac{1}{7}\right)$ $\frac{3}{56}$

The commutative and associative properties of multiplication hold for rational numbers. We can, therefore, choose the order and grouping.

EXAMPLES Multiply.

7. $-8(2)(-3) = -16(-3)$ Multiplying the first two numbers
   $= 48$ Multiplying the results

8. $-8(2)(-3) = 24 \cdot 2$ Multiplying the negative numbers
   $= 48$

9. $-\frac{1}{2}(8)\left(-\frac{2}{3}\right)(-6) = (-4)4$
   $= -16$

Try This Multiply.

i. $-5(-6)(-3)$ -90

j. $-4(5)(-3)(2)$ 120

k. $(-7)\left(-\frac{2}{3}\right)\left(-\frac{1}{7}\right)(9)$ -6

2-5 EXERCISES

A

Multiply.

1. $-8 \cdot 2$ **2.** $-2 \cdot 5$ **3.** $-7 \cdot 6$ **4.** $-9 \cdot 2$

5. $8(-3)$ **6.** $9(-5)$ **7.** $-9 \cdot 8$ **8.** $-10 \cdot 3$

9. $-8(-2)$ **10.** $-2(-5)$ **11.** $-7(-6)$ **12.** $-9(-2)$

13. $15(-8)$ **14.** $-12(-10)$ **15.** $-14(17)$ **16.** $-13(-15)$

17. $-25(-48)$ **18.** $39(-43)$ **19.** $-3.5(-28)$ **20.** $97(-2.1)$

21. $\frac{1}{5}\left(\frac{-2}{9}\right)$ $\frac{-2}{45}$

22. $-\frac{3}{5}\left(-\frac{2}{7}\right)$ $\frac{6}{35}$

23. $-7(-21)(13)$ 1911

24. $-14 \cdot 34 \cdot 12$ −5712

25. $-4(-1.8)(7)$ 50.4

26. $-8(-1.3)(-5)$ −52

27. $-\frac{1}{9}\left(\frac{-2}{3}\right)\left(\frac{5}{7}\right)$ $\frac{10}{189}$

28. $-\frac{7}{2}\left(\frac{-5}{7}\right)\left(\frac{-2}{5}\right)$ −1

29. $4(-4)(-5)(-12)$ −960

30. $-2(-3)(-4)(-5)$ 120

31. $0.07(-7)(6)(-6)$ 17.64

32. $80(-0.8)(-90)(-0.09)$ −518.4

33. $-\frac{5}{6}\left(\frac{1}{8}\right)\left(-\frac{3}{7}\right)\left(-\frac{1}{7}\right)$ $-\frac{5}{784}$

34. $\frac{4}{5}\left(\frac{-2}{3}\right)\left(-\frac{15}{7}\right)\left(\frac{1}{2}\right)$ $\frac{4}{7}$

35. $(-14)(-27)(0)$ 0

36. $7(-6)(5)(-4)(3)(-2)(1)(0)$ 0

37. $0.02(-4)(1.3)$ −0.104

38. $-5.1(0.03)(-1.1)$ 0.1683

B

Simplify.

39. $-6[(-5) + (-7)]$ 72

40. $7[(-16) + 9]$ −49

41. $-3[(-8) + (-6)]\left(-\frac{1}{7}\right)$ −6

42. $8[17 - (-3)]\left(-\frac{1}{4}\right)$ −40

43. $-(3^5) \cdot [-(2^3)]$ 1944

44. $4(2^4) \cdot [-(3^3)] \cdot 6$ −10,368

45. $(-2)^5$ −32

46. $(-1)^{23}$ −1

Evaluate for $x = -2$, $y = -4$, and $z = 5$.

47. $xy + z$ 13

48. $-4y + 3x + z$ 15

49. $-6(3x - 5y) + z$ −79

50. $(-9z)(-5x)(-7y)$ −12,600

51. $y(x^4) - z$ −69

52. $3z^2 - xy$ 67

53. ***Critical Thinking*** Find a pair of integers with a product of −84 and a sum of 5. 12, −7

Assignment Guide

Minimum: 1–38 e/o, MR

Regular: 1–52 e/o, 53, MR

Advanced: 1–52 e/o, 53–58, MR

ADDITIONAL ANSWERS

Exercises

1. −16
2. −10
3. −42
4. −18
5. −24
6. −45
7. −72
8. −30
9. 16
10. 10
11. 42
12. 18
13. −120
14. 120
15. −238
16. 195
17. 1200
18. −1677
19. 98
20. −203.7

57. $0 < x < 2$
58. $z < 0$

Mixed Review

59. -5
60. 4
61. -4
62. 0
63. 8
64. 15
65. 59
66. $<$
67. $>$
68. $<$
69. $=$
70. $2(2x + 5 + 4y)$
71. $5(2a + 3b + 1)$
72. 24
73. 5

Challenge

54. What must be true of m and n if $-mn$ is positive? Either m or n is negative and the other is positive.
55. What must be true of m and n if $-mn$ is negative? Both m and n are positive or both are negative.
56. Is it true that for any rational numbers a and b, $|ab| = |-a||-b|$? Discuss. Yes
57. What must be true of x if $x(x - 2) < 0$?
58. What must be true of z if $|z| \cdot z < 0$?

Mixed Review

Add or subtract. **59.** $4 - 9$ **60.** $3 - (-1)$ **61.** $0 + (-4)$
62. $-8 + 8$ **63.** $6 - (-2)$ **64.** $-37 + 52$ **65.** $67 + (-8)$
Use $<$, $>$, or $=$ to write a true sentence. **66.** $-1.01 \quad -1$
67. $2.5 \quad -2.4$ **68.** $\frac{7}{2} \quad 4$ **69.** $|-3| \quad |3|$
Factor. **70.** $4x + 10 + 8y$ **71.** $10a + 15b + 5$
Evaluate. **72.** $3x^3$ for $x = 2$ **73.** $5x^3$ for $x = 1$

SUBSETS OF THE RATIONAL NUMBERS

We can use the diagram on page 61 and set notation to write subsets of the rational numbers. Consider these sets:
Natural numbers or positive integers
$N = \{1, 2, 3, \ldots\}$
Whole numbers
$W = \{0, 1, 2, 3, \ldots\}$
Integers
$I = \{\ldots, -3, -2, -1, 0, 1, 2, 3, \ldots\}$
Consider these definitions: Each number in a set is called an element or member of the set. The symbol $\in$ is read "is an element of." We write: $-3 \in$ I. Set A is a subset of set B if every element of set A is an element of set B. The symbol $\subset$ is read "is a subset of." We write: $A \subset B$.

The following are true statements.

$N \subset W$ The natural numbers are a subset of the whole numbers.
$W \subset I$ The whole numbers are a subset of the integers.
$I \subset R$ (rational numbers) The integers are a subset of the rational numbers.

1. Write at least five subset statements using the sets shown in the diagram on page 61. Answers may vary.
2. The empty set or null set, symbolized $\emptyset$, is a set with no elements. Is $\emptyset$ a subset of the rational numbers? Yes

2-6 Division of Rational Numbers

Division

Objective: Divide rational numbers.

To divide rational numbers, we can use the definition of division.

Definition

For all rational numbers a and b, the **quotient** $\frac{a}{b}$ (or $a \div b$), where $b \neq 0$, is the number c such that $cb = a$.

EXAMPLES Divide. Check your answer.

1. $14 \div (-7) = -2$ Check: $(-2)(-7) = 14$
2. $\frac{-32}{-4} = 8$ Check: $8(-4) = -32$
3. $\frac{-10}{2} = -5$ Check: $-5(2) = -10$

These examples suggest the following rule.

Dividing Positive and Negative Numbers

To divide positive and negative numbers, divide their absolute values. Use the following rules to determine the sign of the quotient.

- When we divide a positive number by a negative number or a negative number by a positive number, the quotient is negative.
- When we divide two positive numbers or two negative numbers, the quotient is positive.

Try This Divide. Check your answer.

a. $15 \div (-3)$ -5 **b.** $-21 \div (-7)$ 3 **c.** $\frac{-44}{-11}$ 4 **d.** $\frac{35}{-5}$ -7

e. $\frac{-8}{-4}$ 2 **f.** $\frac{45}{-9}$ -5 **g.** $-24 \div -8$ 3 **h.** $\frac{105}{-5}$ -21

2-6

FIRST FIVE MINUTES

Simplify.

1. $4 \cdot 5$ 20
2. $-4 \cdot 5$ -20
3. $4 \cdot (-15)$ -60
4. $-14 \cdot (-5)$ 70
5. $\frac{20}{4}$ 5
6. $\frac{20}{5}$ 4
7. $20 \cdot \frac{1}{4}$ 5
8. $\frac{0}{1}$ 0

Division

Point out that the rules to determine the sign of a quotient are similar to those for multiplication.

+ divided by + = +
+ divided by − = −
− divided by + = −
− divided by − = +

Remind students that $a \div b$, $\frac{a}{b}$, and $a \cdot \frac{1}{b}$ are all equivalent expressions.

Key Questions

- Does $\frac{0}{-1} = \frac{0}{1}$?
  Yes
- Does $\frac{1}{-1} = \frac{1}{1}$?
  No

Chalkboard Examples

Divide.

1. $\frac{21}{-3}$ -7
2. $\frac{-12}{-4}$ 3
3. $\frac{-8}{2}$ -4

Reciprocals

You may wish to use the following illustration of the property of multiplicative inverses.

$a \cdot \frac{1}{a}$

$= \frac{a}{1} \cdot \frac{1}{a}$

$= \frac{a}{a}$

$= 1$

Key Questions

- How many reciprocals of 3 are there?
  One
- What is the reciprocal of 0?
  There is none.
- Is the reciprocal of a negative number positive or negative?
  Negative

Chalkboard Examples

Find the reciprocal.

1. $\frac{3}{7}$

   The reciprocal is $\frac{7}{3}$ because

   $\frac{3}{7} \cdot \frac{7}{3} = 1$
2. -8

   The reciprocal is $\frac{1}{-8}$ because

   $-8 \cdot \frac{1}{-8} = 1$
3. 4.5

   The reciprocal is $\frac{2}{9}$ because

   $4.5 = \frac{9}{2}$ and $\frac{9}{2} \cdot \frac{2}{9} = 1$
4. $\frac{x}{y}$

   The reciprocal is $\frac{y}{x}$ because

   $\frac{x}{y} \cdot \frac{y}{x} = 1$
5. $-\frac{2}{3}$

   The reciprocal is $-\frac{3}{2}$ because

   $-\frac{2}{3} \cdot -\frac{3}{2} = 1$

We can show why we cannot divide any nonzero number by 0. For $\frac{a}{0}$, $a \neq 0$, we look for a number which, when multiplied by 0, gives a. There is no such number because the product of 0 and any number is 0. If we divide $\frac{0}{0}$, we look for a number r such that $r \cdot 0 = 0$. But $r \cdot 0 = 0$ for any number r. Thus $\frac{0}{0}$ could be any number we choose. Since for any operation there must be only one answer, we agree that we shall not divide 0 by 0. In general, we cannot divide by 0.

Reciprocals

Objective: Find the reciprocal of a rational number.

When pairs of numbers like $-\frac{1}{8}$ and -8 are multiplied, their product is 1. Number pairs such as $-\frac{1}{8}$ and -8, whose product is 1, are called multiplicative inverses or reciprocals.

Definition

Two rational numbers whose product is 1 are called **multiplicative inverses** or **reciprocals** of each other.

Any nonzero rational number has a reciprocal.

Property of Multiplicative Inverses

For each nonzero rational number a, there is one and only one rational number $\frac{1}{a}$ such that $a \cdot \frac{1}{a} = 1$.

If the rational number is named with fractional notation $\frac{a}{b}$, then its reciprocal can be named $\frac{b}{a}$. Also, the reciprocal of a positive number is positive, and the reciprocal of a negative number is negative.

EXAMPLES Find the reciprocal.

4. $\frac{7}{8}$ The reciprocal of $\frac{7}{8}$ is $\frac{8}{7}$ because $\frac{7}{8} \cdot \frac{8}{7} = 1$.

5. -5 The reciprocal of -5 is $\frac{1}{-5}$ because $-5\left(\frac{1}{-5}\right) = 1$.

6. 0.8 The reciprocal of $0.8 = \frac{8}{10}$ is $\frac{10}{8}$ because $\frac{8}{10} \cdot \frac{10}{8} = 1$.

7. $\frac{m}{n}$ The reciprocal of $\frac{m}{n}$ is $\frac{n}{m}$ because $\frac{m}{n} \cdot \frac{n}{m} = 1$.

Try This Find the reciprocal.

i. $\frac{3}{6}$ $\frac{6}{3}$ or 2 **j.** -4 $-\frac{1}{4}$ **k.** -0.5 -2 **l.** $1\frac{1}{3}$ $\frac{3}{4}$ **m.** $\frac{x}{y}$ $\frac{y}{x}$

Division and Reciprocals

Objective: Divide by multiplying by the reciprocal.

We know we can subtract a rational number by adding its inverse. Similarly, we can divide by a rational number by multiplying by its reciprocal.

Dividing Numbers

For all rational numbers a and $b (b \neq 0)$,

$$\frac{a}{b} = a \cdot \frac{1}{b}$$

EXAMPLES Rewrite each division as multiplication.

8. $-4 \div 3 = -4 \cdot \frac{1}{3}$

9. $\frac{x+2}{5} = (x+2) \cdot \frac{1}{5}$ Parentheses are necessary here.

10. $\frac{-17}{\frac{1}{b}} = -17 \cdot b$

11. $\frac{3}{5} \div \left(-\frac{9}{7}\right) = \frac{3}{5}\left(-\frac{7}{9}\right)$

Try This Rewrite each division as multiplication.

n. $-6 \div \frac{1}{5}$ $-6(5)$ **o.** $\frac{-5}{7}$ $-5\left(\frac{1}{7}\right)$ **p.** $\frac{x^2-2}{3}$ $(x^2-2)\frac{1}{3}$ **q.** $\frac{x}{y}$ $x\left(\frac{1}{y}\right)$

r. $\frac{-15}{\frac{1}{x}}$ $-15x$ **s.** $-\frac{4}{7} \div -\frac{3}{5}$ $-\frac{4}{7}\left(-\frac{5}{3}\right)$ **t.** $\frac{13}{-\frac{2}{3}}$ $13\left(-\frac{3}{2}\right)$ **u.** $\frac{a}{\frac{1}{b}}$ ab

When doing division calculations, we sometimes multiply by a reciprocal and we sometimes divide directly. With fractional notation, it is usually easier to multiply by a reciprocal. With decimal notation, it is usually easier to divide directly.

Division and Reciprocals

You may want to have students try to divide a number by zero on a calculator. Then discuss why the result is "ERROR."

According to the definition of division, if $1 \div 0 = a$, then $0 \cdot a = 1$. Since any number multiplied by 0 is 0, it is impossible to divide by 0.

Chalkboard Examples

Rewrite each division as multiplication.

1. $\frac{7}{3}$ $7 \cdot \frac{1}{3}$
2. $-\frac{5}{2}$ $-5 \cdot \frac{1}{2}$
3. $\frac{6}{-7}$ $6 \cdot \frac{1}{-7}$
4. $\frac{a+7}{4}$ $(a+7) \cdot \frac{1}{4}$

The parentheses are necessary.

Divide.

5. $\frac{9}{8} \div \frac{5}{3} = \frac{9}{8} \cdot \frac{3}{5} = \frac{27}{40}$
6. $\frac{1}{2} \div \frac{-5}{7} = \frac{1}{2} \cdot \frac{7}{-5} = \frac{7}{-10}$ or $-\frac{7}{10}$
7. $-\frac{2}{5} \div -\frac{7}{3} = -\frac{2}{5} \cdot -\frac{3}{7} = \frac{6}{35}$

LESSON QUIZ

Divide.

1. $42 \div -7$ -6
2. $\frac{-8}{-2}$ 4
3. $\frac{0}{-5}$ 0

Find the reciprocal.

4. $\frac{13}{17}$ $\frac{17}{13}$
5. 4.2 $\frac{1}{4.2}$
6. -18 $-\frac{1}{18}$
7. $-\frac{3}{7}$ $-\frac{7}{3}$

Rewrite each division as multiplication.

8. $\frac{3}{7}$ $3 \cdot \frac{1}{7}$
9. $\frac{1}{3} \div \frac{2}{7}$ $\frac{1}{3} \cdot \frac{7}{2}$

Divide.

10. $-\frac{2}{7} \div -\frac{3}{5}$

$-\frac{2}{7} \cdot -\frac{5}{3}$

$= \frac{2}{7} \cdot \frac{5}{3} = \frac{10}{21}$

> ***Assignment Guide***
> Minimum: 1–61 e/o, MR
>
> Regular: 1–71 m3, 72, MR
>
> Advanced: 1–71 m3, 72–77, MR, Assign w. Bonus Topic

EXAMPLES Divide.

12. $\frac{4}{3} \div \left(-\frac{9}{7}\right) = \frac{4}{3}\left(-\frac{7}{9}\right)$

$$= -\frac{4 \cdot 7}{3 \cdot 9} = -\frac{28}{27}$$

13. $-27.9 \div (-3) = \frac{-27.9}{-3} = 9.3$

Try This Divide.

v. $-\frac{3}{5} \div \left(-\frac{12}{11}\right)$ $\frac{11}{20}$ **w.** $-\frac{8}{5} \div \frac{2}{3}$ $-\frac{12}{5}$ **x.** $-64.8 \div 4$ -16.2 **y.** $78.6 \div (-3)$ -26.2

2-6 EXERCISES

A

Divide. Check your answer.

1. $36 \div (-6)$ -6
2. $\frac{28}{-7}$ -4
3. $\frac{26}{-2}$ -13
4. $26 \div (-13)$ -2
5. $\frac{-16}{8}$ -2
6. $-22 \div (-2)$ 11
7. $\frac{-48}{-12}$ 4
8. $-63 \div (-9)$ 7
9. $\frac{-72}{9}$ -8
10. $\frac{-50}{25}$ -2
11. $-100 \div (-50)$ 2
12. $\frac{-200}{8}$ -25
13. $-108 \div 9$ -12
14. $\frac{-63}{-7}$ 9
15. $\frac{200}{-25}$ -8
16. $(-300) \div (0)$ None
17. $\frac{75}{5}$ 15
18. $\frac{0}{-5}$ 0

Find the reciprocal. All variables represent nonzero rational numbers.

19. $\frac{15}{7}$ $\frac{7}{15}$
20. $\frac{3}{8}$ $\frac{8}{3}$
21. $\frac{47}{13}$ $\frac{13}{47}$
22. $-\frac{31}{12}$ $-\frac{12}{31}$
23. 13 $\frac{1}{13}$
24. -10 $-\frac{1}{10}$
25. 0.3 $\frac{10}{3}$
26. -0.4 $-\frac{5}{2}$
27. $1\frac{1}{2}$ $\frac{2}{3}$
28. $2\frac{2}{3}$ $\frac{3}{8}$
29. $\frac{p}{q}$ $\frac{q}{p}$
30. $\frac{s}{t}$ $\frac{t}{s}$
31. $\frac{1}{4y}$ $4y$
32. $\frac{-1}{8a}$ $-8a$
33. $\frac{2a}{3b}$ $\frac{3b}{2a}$
34. $\frac{-4y}{3x}$ $-\frac{3x}{4y}$

Rewrite each division as multiplication.

35. $3 \div 19$ **36.** $4 \div (-9)$ **37.** $\frac{6}{-13}$ **38.** $-\frac{12}{41}$

39. $\frac{13.9}{-1.5}$ **40.** $-\frac{47.3}{21.4}$ **41.** $\frac{x}{\frac{1}{y}}$ **42.** $\frac{13}{x}$

43. $\frac{3x + 4}{5}$ **44.** $\frac{4y - 8}{-7}$ **45.** $\frac{5a - b}{5a + b}$ **46.** $\frac{2x + x^2}{x - 5}$

Divide.

47. $\frac{3}{4} \div \left(-\frac{2}{3}\right)$ $-\frac{9}{8}$ **48.** $\frac{7}{8} \div \left(-\frac{1}{2}\right)$ $-\frac{7}{4}$ **49.** $-\frac{5}{4} \div \left(-\frac{3}{4}\right)$ $\frac{5}{3}$

50. $-\frac{5}{9} \div \left(-\frac{5}{6}\right)$ $\frac{2}{3}$ **51.** $-\frac{2}{7} \div \left(-\frac{4}{9}\right)$ $\frac{9}{14}$ **52.** $-\frac{3}{5} \div \left(-\frac{5}{8}\right)$ $\frac{24}{25}$

53. $-\frac{3}{8} \div \left(-\frac{8}{3}\right)$ $\frac{9}{64}$ **54.** $-\frac{5}{8} \div \left(-\frac{6}{5}\right)$ $\frac{25}{48}$ **55.** $-6.6 \div 3.3$ -2

56. $-44.1 \div (-6.3)$ 7 **57.** $-42.3 \div 0$ None **58.** $0 \div -2.5$ 0

59. $-\frac{1}{3} \div \frac{1}{3}$ -1 **60.** $-\frac{1}{4} \div \frac{1}{2}$ $-\frac{1}{2}$ **61.** $-\frac{5}{6} \div \frac{3}{4}$ $-\frac{10}{9}$

B

Simplify.

62. $\frac{(-9)(-8) + (-3)}{25}$ **63.** $\frac{-3(-9) + 7}{-4}$ **64.** $\frac{(-2)^7}{(-4)^2}$ **65.** $\frac{(-3)^4}{-9}$

66. $5\frac{3}{7} \div 4\frac{2}{5}$ **67.** $\frac{10}{7} \div 1\frac{3}{4}$ **68.** $2\frac{2}{3} \div \frac{40}{15}$ **69.** $\frac{(-4)^3}{(-8)^3}$

70. Use a calculator to find the reciprocal of -10.5. $-0.095238095238...$

71. Use a calculator to find the reciprocal of 4.2. 0.238095238

72. ***Critical Thinking*** Is it possible for a number to be its own reciprocal?

Challenge

73. Is division of rational numbers commutative? That is, does $a \div b = b \div a$ for all rational numbers a and b? No, $\frac{4}{2} \neq \frac{2}{4}$.

74. Is division of rational numbers associative? That is, does $(a \div b) \div c = a \div (b \div c)$ for all rational numbers a, b, and c? No. $(a \div b) \div c = \frac{1}{c} \cdot \left(\frac{a}{b}\right)$ $a \div (b \div c) = c \cdot \left(\frac{a}{b}\right)$

75. Is it possible for the additive inverse of a number to be its reciprocal?

ADDITIONAL ANSWERS

Exercises

35. $3\left(\frac{1}{19}\right)$

36. $4\left(\frac{-1}{9}\right)$

37. $6\left(-\frac{1}{13}\right)$

38. $-12\left(\frac{1}{41}\right)$

39. $13.9\left(-\frac{1}{1.5}\right)$

40. $47.3\left(-\frac{1}{21.4}\right)$

41. $x \cdot y$

42. $13\left(\frac{1}{x}\right)$

43. $\frac{1}{5}(3x + 4)$

44. $-\frac{1}{7}(4y - 8)$

45. $(5a - b)\left(\frac{1}{5a + b}\right)$

46. $(2x + x^2)\left(\frac{1}{x - 5}\right)$

62. $\frac{69}{25}$

63. $\frac{-17}{2}$

64. -8

65. -9

66. $\frac{95}{77}$

67. $\frac{40}{49}$

68. 1

69. $\frac{1}{8}$

72. Yes, this is true for 1 and also for -1.

75. No. A reciprocal has the same sign as the number. (Zero has no reciprocal.)

76. You get the original number.

77. $\dfrac{1}{\left(\frac{a}{b}\right)} \cdot \dfrac{\left(\frac{b}{a}\right)}{\left(\frac{b}{a}\right)} = \dfrac{\left(\frac{b}{a}\right)}{1} = \dfrac{b}{a}$

Mixed Review

78. 7
79. 7
80. 8
81. 7
82. $t + 5$
83. $2m$
84. $\frac{36}{y}$
85. $25 - x$
86. mn
87. $\frac{1}{2}$
88. $\frac{1}{4}$
89. $\frac{1}{3}$
90. $\frac{1}{2}$

Problem for Programmers

This program can be written using any programming language (BASIC, PASCAL, LOGO, etc). The programming ability of the student will determine how the number is input (from the keyboard or within the program), and how the inverses are output (with complete sentences, in columns).

This program can also be written on a spreadsheet where the number is input in one column and two other columns are used for the output of the inverses.

Bonus Topic

The calculator is useful for converting fractions to decimals. If calculators are used, however, it should be noted that many calculators round off the last digit. The decimal conversion for $\frac{3}{11}$ is displayed on many calculators as 0.2727273. Point out to students that this is the rounded answer and that 27 is the repeating decimal part. (They may need to work a few problems without the calculator to be convinced.)

76. What should happen if you enter a number on a calculator and press the reciprocal key twice? Why?

77. We know that for any nonzero rational number $\frac{a}{b}$, its reciprocal is $\frac{b}{a}$. Show that $\dfrac{1}{\left(\frac{a}{b}\right)}$ also names the reciprocal.

Mixed Review

Simplify. **78.** $6 + (-3) - 5 - (-9)$ **79.** $12 - 7 - (-4) + (-2)$
80. $9 + (11) + (-8) - 4$ **81.** $8 + (-15) - 4 - (-18)$

Write as an algebraic expression. **82.** 5 more than t **83.** twice m
84. 36 divided among y **85.** x less than 25 **86.** m times n

Solve. **87.** $12 = 24p$ **88.** $20n = 5$ **89.** $42x = 14$ **90.** $3 = 6y$

Problem for Programmers

Write a program that will find the additive inverse and the multiplicative inverse for any input number. Test your program using the numbers 500, -0.01, and 1. What happens if you input 0?

Bonus Topic: Terminating and Repeating Decimals

We have learned that a rational number can be expressed as the ratio of two integers. A rational number can also be expressed as either a **terminating decimal** or a **repeating decimal.** When we divide the integer a by the integer b in the rational number $\frac{a}{b}$, the resulting decimal will either terminate or repeat.

$\frac{3}{8} = 0.375$ The decimal ends or terminates in the thousandths place.

$\frac{3}{11} = 0.272727 = 0.\overline{27}$ The digits 27 repeat. We use a bar to indicate which digits repeat.

A decimal that neither terminates nor repeats, such as 2.35335333533335... names an **irrational number.**

Exercises

Write as a decimal. If the decimal repeats, use a bar for the repeating decimal part.

1. $\frac{4}{11}$ $0.\overline{36}$ **2.** $\frac{7}{20}$ 0.35 **3.** $\frac{23}{9}$ $2.\overline{5}$ **4.** $\frac{5}{18}$ $0.2\overline{7}$ **5.** $\frac{4}{9}$ $0.\overline{4}$ **6.** $\frac{2}{13}$ $0.\overline{153846}$

Problem Solving: Application

Moment Problems

The principles that allow small forces to lift heavy bridges and provide for movement on playground teeter-totters also provide ways for small forces to move heavy loads. Consider the problem of lifting a 1500-pound bale of hay. If a farmer uses a tower boom crane to lift the bale of hay, how many pounds of force are needed to lift the bale with the crane?

The problem is like the problem of lifting a person off the ground on a seesaw. A force needs to be applied to the opposite side of the seesaw or to the opposite side of the boom on the crane.

You can use integers to predict what will happen when forces are applied to a seesaw or boom. Both of these situations are examples of **levers.** The diagram represents the physical situation involved.

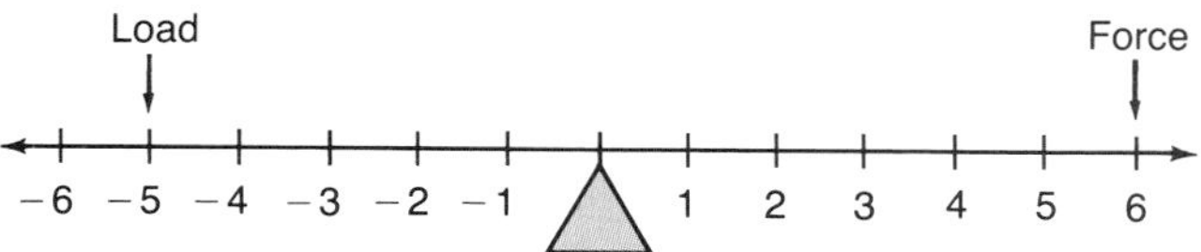

The 0 point, where the lever pivots, is called the **fulcrum.** The **moment,** or **torque,** for both the load and the force, is the product of the force each exerts and its distance from the fulcrum: Moment = (force)(distance). Downward forces, such as weight or force applied, are negative. Distances to the left of the fulcrum can be thought of as negative, and distances to the right can be thought of as positive, as on a number line.

The farmer uses a hydraulic jack to pull on the end of the other side of the boom to lift the bale. He notes that the force required was 750 pounds to lift and balance the bale. This force caused the moments of the two sides to be equal.

−20 −15 −10 −5 5 10

750 1500

Farmer's moment: $(-750)(-20) = 15{,}000$
Bale's moment: $(-1500)(10) = -15{,}000$
Sum of the two moments: $15{,}000 + (-15{,}000) = 0$

When the sum of the moments is 0, the boom balances.

Problem Solving: Application

Discuss the unlimited potential of the lever: The greater the distance from the fulcrum, the less is the force required to shift a given weight. The Greek mathematician Archimedes (287–212 B.C.) analyzed the principle of the lever. Fascinated by its potential, he said, "Give me a place to stand and I will move the world."

Equilibrium is derived from the Latin "equal weights." Any system under stress of forces is in equilibrium when the forces cancel each other out. Discuss this concept and its application to moment problems.

Mechanics is the branch of physics dealing with motions and forces. The study of forces in equilibrium is *statics,* from the Greek, "to cause to stand."

Use a doorknob to demonstrate advantageous uses of leverage. The door is a lever, with the hinge as its fulcrum. What happens when a doorknob is placed in the center of the door? What would happen if it were placed just an inch from the hinge?

ANSWERS

1. Answers may vary. Some examples are 15 ft, 1000 lb; and 30 ft, 500 lb.
2. 120 ft
3. 600 lb
4. 180 lb
5. The fulcrum would have to be 60 cm from the 10-kg weight and 40 cm from the 15-kg weight.

The Principle of Moments

When several parallel forces act on an object, it will be in balance if the sum of the moments is 0.

To move an object using a lever and fulcrum, the moment on one side of the fulcrum has to exceed the moment created by the load to be moved. Exact solutions of such problems must also take into account the mass of the lever.

EXAMPLE

To lift a heavy load, one end of an eight-foot pry bar is placed two feet beyond a pivot point and inserted into a chain link. How many pounds of force are needed to balance the chain link if 200 pounds of force are placed on the other end of the pry bar?

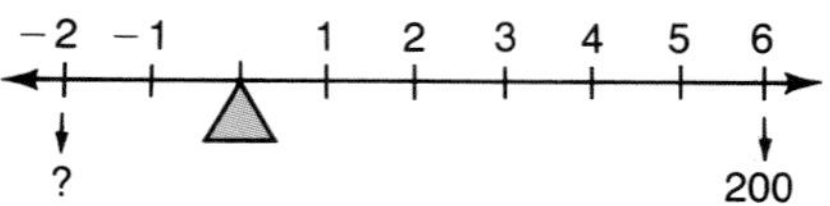

The force of 200 pounds acting downward at a distance of 6 feet from the fulcrum creates a moment of $(-200)(6)$ or -1200. The chain link end is acting through a distance of 2 feet on the negative side of the fulcrum. If f represents the force exerted here, we have a moment of $-2f$ being in balance with the moment on the other side of -1200. Hence, f must equal 600 pounds.

Problems

Solve. Use the conditions in the hay bale problem for Problems 1–3.

1. Show two other places the farmer could hook the jack to the boom and lift the hay bale. Give the force required to balance the bale for each of these points.
2. How long a boom on the farmer's side would be required to balance the bale with a force of 125 pounds?
3. Suppose the hay bale was attached at a point 8 feet from the fulcrum. How much force would be required 20 feet from the fulcrum to balance the bale?
4. One end of a 10-foot pry bar is inserted under a 420-pound rock. If the fulcrum is 3 feet from the rock, how many pounds of force have to be exerted on the other end of the bar to balance the rock?
5. A meter bar has a 10-kg weight on one end and a 15-kg weight on the other end. Where would the fulcrum have to be placed to balance the loads?

2-7 Using the Distributive Property

The Distributive Property Over Subtraction

Objective: Multiply using the distributive property over subtraction.

In Chapter 1 you learned how to use the distributive property over addition with whole numbers. The distributive property over addition applies to all rational numbers.

The Distributive Property of Multiplication Over Addition

For any rational numbers a, b, and c, $a(b + c) = ab + ac$, and $(b + c)a = ba + ca$

We can use the basic properties and previous definitions to show that the distributive property holds for subtraction as well.

The Distributive Property of Multiplication Over Subtraction

For any rational numbers a, b, and c, $a(b - c) = ab - ac$, and $(b - c)a = ba - ca$

We refer to these relationships as the distributive property over subtraction.

EXAMPLES Multiply.

1. $9(x - 5) = 9x - 9(5)$
   $= 9x - 45$

2. $-3(y - 3) = -3y - (-3)(3)$
   $= -3y + 9$

3. $\frac{4}{3}(s - t + w) = \frac{4}{3}s - \frac{4}{3}t + \frac{4}{3}w$

4. $-4(x - 2y + 3z) = -4 \cdot x - (-4)(2y) + (-4)(3z)$
   $= -4x - (-8y) + (-12z) = -4x + 8y - 12z$

Try This Multiply.

a. $8(y - 7)$ **b.** $\frac{5}{6}(x - y + 7z)$ **c.** $-5(x - 3y + 8z)$

a. $8y - 56$
b. $\frac{5}{6}x - \frac{5}{6}y + \frac{35}{6}z$
c. $-5x + 15y - 40z$

2-7

FIRST FIVE MINUTES

Use the distributive property to multiply.
1. $3(x + 1)$ $3x + 3$
2. $a(b + 2)$ $ab + 2a$
3. $x(y + z)$ $xy + xz$
4. $5(x + (-2))$
   $5x + 5(-2) = 5x - 10$

Use the distributive property to factor.
5. $2a + 2b$ $2(a + b)$
6. $ax + ay$ $a(x + y)$
7. $3x + 3(-y)$
   $3[x + (-y)] = 3(x - y)$

The Distributive Property Over Subtraction

You may wish to illustrate the distributive property over subtraction with an arithmetic example. For instance,

$7(8 - 3) = 7 \cdot 8 - 7 \cdot 3 = 35$
$7(8 - 3) = 7(5) = 35$

Math Point
The distributive property is the *only* property that relates addition and subtraction to multiplication.

Chalkboard Examples

Multiply.
1. $7(a - 2)$ $7a - 14$
2. $-5(u - v)$
   $-5u - (-5)v = -5u + 5v$
3. $\frac{1}{2}(r + s - t)$
   $\frac{1}{2}r + \frac{1}{2}s - \frac{1}{2}t$
4. $-6(2e - 3f - g)$
   $(-6)2e - (-6)3f - (-6)g$
   $= -12e + 18f + 6g$

Factoring

Illustrate that factoring is the reverse of the distributive property. For instance, Example 5:

Factor $5x - 5y$.
$5(x - y)$
Multiply $5(x - y)$.
$5x - 5y$

Chalkboard Examples

Factor.

1. $3z - 3y$
   $3(z - y)$
2. $10u - 30$
   $10(u - 3)$
3. $ua - ub - uc$
   $u(a - b - c)$
4. $5x - 35y - 10$
   $5(x) - 5(7y) - 5(2)$
   $= 5(x - 7y - 2)$
5. $-6u - 4v - 8w$
   $-2(3u + 2v + 4w)$
6. $14u - 21w - 28$
   $7(2u - 3w - 4)$
7. $\frac{2}{3}p - \frac{1}{3}q + \frac{5}{3}r$
   $\frac{1}{3}(2p - q + 5r)$

Terms and Factors

Chalkboard Examples

What are the terms of each expression?

1. $4a - 2b - 5c$
   The terms are $4a$, $-2b$, $-5c$.
2. $-8x + y - 7z$
   The terms are $-8x$, y, $-7z$.
3. $\frac{1}{7}a - \frac{3}{5}b$
   The terms are $\frac{1}{7}a$, $-\frac{3}{5}b$.

Factoring

Objective: Factor expressions.

Recall that when we reverse the statement of the distributive property, we are factoring.

$$ab + ac = a(b + c)$$
$$ab - ac = a(b - c)$$

EXAMPLES Factor.

5. $5x - 5y = 5(x - y)$
6. $8x - 16 = 8 \cdot x - 8 \cdot 2 = 8(x - 2)$
7. $ax - ay + az = a(x - y + z)$
8. $9x - 27y - 9 = 9(x) - 9(3y) - 9(1)$
   $= 9(x - 3y - 1)$
9. $-3x + 6y - 9z = 3(-x + 2y - 3z)$ or $-3(x - 2y + 3z)$
10. $18z - 12x - 24 = 6(3z - 2x - 4)$
11. $\frac{1}{2}x + \frac{3}{2}y - \frac{1}{2} = \frac{1}{2}(x + 3y - 1)$

Try This Factor.

d. $4x - 8$ **e.** $3x - 6y - 15$ **f.** $bx - by + bz$
g. $-2y + 8z - 2$ **h.** $12z - 16x - 4$

d. $4(x - 2)$
e. $3(x - 2y - 5)$
f. $b(x - y + z)$
g. $-2(y - 4z + 1)$ or $2(-y + 4z - 1)$
h. $4(3z - 4x - 1)$

Terms and Factors

Objective: Give the terms of an expression.

When we have only additions in an expression, the terms are separated by addition signs. If there are subtractions, we can think of an equivalent expression without subtraction signs.

EXAMPLE 12

What are the terms of $3x - 4y + 2z$?

The terms are $3x$, $-4y$, and $2z$. Think $3x + (-4y) + 2z$.

In the first term, $3x$, 3 and x are the factors. In the second term, $-4y$, -4 and y are the factors. In the last term, $2z$, 2 and z are the factors.

Try This What are the terms of each expression?

i. $5a - 4b + 3$ **j.** $-5y - 3x + 5z$

i. $5a$, $-4b$, 3
j. $-5y$, $-3x$, $5z$

Collecting Like Terms

Objective: Collect like terms.

We can collect like terms by using the distributive property of multiplication over addition or subtraction to factor.

EXAMPLES Collect like terms.

13. $2x + 3y - 5x - 2y = 2x - 5x + 3y - 2y$
$= (2 - 5)x + (3 - 2)y$ Factoring x and factoring y
$= -3x + y$

14. $3x - x = (3 - 1)x = 2x$

15. $x - 0.24x = 1 \cdot x - 0.24x = (1 - 0.24)x = 0.76x$

16. $x - 6x = 1 \cdot x - 6x = (1 - 6)x = -5x$

Try This Collect like terms.

k. $6x - 3x$ $3x$ **l.** $7y - y$ $6y$ **m.** $m - 0.44m$ $0.56m$

n. $5x + 4y - 2x - y$ $3x + 3y$ **o.** $3x - 7x - 11 + 8y - 4 - 13y$ $-4x - 5y - 15$

2-7 EXERCISES

A

Multiply.

1. $7(x - 2)$
2. $5(x - 8)$
3. $-7(y - 2)$
4. $-9(y - 7)$
5. $-9(-5x - 6y + 8)$
6. $-7(-2x - 5y + 9)$
7. $-4(x - 3y - 2z)$
8. $8(2x - 5y - 8z)$
9. $3.1(-1.2x + 3.2y - 1.1)$
10. $-2.1(-4.2x - 4.3y - 2.2)$
11. $\frac{2}{3}(3a - 6b + 9)$
12. $\frac{1}{2}(4c + 5d - 6)$
13. $-\frac{4}{5}\left(-\frac{1}{2}x + \frac{2}{3}y - 1\right)$
14. $-\frac{7}{8}\left(\frac{2}{3}x - \frac{1}{2}y - 8\right)$

Factor.

15. $8x - 24$
16. $-10x - 50$
17. $32 - 4y$
18. $24 - 6m$
19. $8x + 10y - 22$
20. $-9a + 6b - 15$
21. $ax - 7a$
22. $by - 9b$
23. $ax - ay - az$
24. $cx + cy - cz$
25. $\frac{3}{4}x - \frac{1}{4}y - \frac{1}{4}$
26. $\frac{2}{3}x - \frac{1}{3}y + \frac{1}{3}$

Collecting Like Terms

Chalkboard Examples

Collect like terms.

1. $-7x + 2x - 3x$
$(-7 + 2 - 3)x$
$= -8x$
2. $5x - 2y - 2x + 6y$
$5x - 2x - 2y + 6y$
$= (5 - 2)x + (-2 + 6)y$
$= 3x + 4y$
3. $3.4a - 2.1a + 1.0a$
$(3.4 - 2.1 + 1.0)a$
$= 2.3a$
4. $-6a + 5b + 4a - b$
$-6a + 4a + 5b - b$
$= (-6 + 4)a + (5 - 1)b$
$= -2a + 4b$

LESSON QUIZ

Multiply.

1. $8(a - 3)$ $8a - 24$
2. $-2(x - 7)$
$-2x - (-2)7$
$= -2x + 14$
3. $4(3z - 2w)$ $12z - 8w$
4. $-7(3x - 2y - w)$
$-21x + 14y + 7w$

Factor.

5. $7x - 21y$ $7(x - 3y)$
6. $af - ag - ah$ $a(f - g - h)$

Collect like terms.

7. $9x - 2x + x$ $(9 - 2 + 1)x = 8x$
8. $3a - 7b - 2a + 12b$
$3a - 2a - 7b + 12b$
$= (3 - 2)a + (-7 + 12)b$
$= a + 5b$

Assignment Guide

Minimum: 1–52 e/o, MR

Regular: 1–52 m3, 53–56 e/o, 57, MR

Advanced: 1–56 m3, 57–59, MR

ADDITIONAL ANSWERS

Exercises

1. $7x - 14$
2. $5x - 40$
3. $-7y + 14$
4. $-9y + 63$
5. $45x + 54y - 72$
6. $14x + 35y - 63$
7. $-4x + 12y + 8z$
8. $16x - 40y - 64z$
9. $-3.72x + 9.92y - 3.41$
10. $8.82x + 9.03y + 4.62$

11. $2a - 4b + 6$
12. $2c + \frac{5}{2}d - 3$
13. $\frac{2}{5}x - \frac{8}{15}y + \frac{4}{5}$
14. $-\frac{7}{12}x + \frac{7}{16}y + 7$
15. $8(x - 3)$
16. $-10(x + 5)$ or $10(-x - 5)$
17. $4(8 - y)$
18. $6(4 - m)$
19. $2(4x + 5y - 11)$
20. $-3(3a - 2b + 5)$ or $3(-3a + 2b - 5)$
21. $a(x - 7)$
22. $b(y - 9)$
23. $a(x - y - z)$
24. $c(x + y - z)$
25. $\frac{1}{4}(3x - y - 1)$
26. $\frac{1}{3}(2x - y + 1)$
27. $4x, 3z$
28. $8x, -1.4y$
29. $7x, 8y, -9z$
30. $8a, 10b, -18c$
31. $12x, -13.2y, \frac{5}{8}z, -4.5$
32. $3ab, -4cd$
33. $-2x$
34. $-8t$
35. $5n$
36. $-16y$
37. $4x + 2y$
38. $12y - 3z$
39. $7x + y$
40. $11a + 5b$
41. $0.8x + 0.5y$
42. $2.6a + 1.4b$
43. $-2y - 3x$
44. $-3n$
45. $-9t + 5p$
46. $3q + 5p$
47. $32a - 17b - 17c$
48. $8.5m - 10.5n$
49. $8.5d + 3a$
50. $12z - y$
51. $\frac{3}{5}x + \frac{3}{5}y$
52. $x + \frac{1}{4}y$

Mixed Review

60. $\frac{15}{2}$
61. $-\frac{11}{6}$
62. $\frac{1}{4}$
63. $3c$
64. -17
65. $12x$
66. $\frac{8}{15}$
67. $-\frac{3}{16}$
68. $-\frac{4}{3}$
69. 2

What are the terms of each expression?

27. $4x + 3z$
28. $8x - 1.4y$
29. $7x + 8y - 9z$
30. $8a + 10b - 18c$
31. $12x - 13.2y + \frac{5}{8}z - 4.5$
32. $3ab - 4cd$

Collect like terms.

33. $x - 3x$
34. $9t - 17t$
35. $6n - n$
36. $y - 17y$
37. $9x + 2y - 5x$
38. $8y - 3z + 4y$
39. $11x + 2y - 4x - y$
40. $13a + 9b - 2a - 4b$
41. $2.7x + 2.3y - 1.9x - 1.8y$
42. $6.7a + 4.3b - 4.1a - 2.9b$
43. $5y - 3x - 7y$
44. $13m + 5m - 3n - 18m$
45. $-8t + p + 4p - t$
46. $q + q + q + 5p$
47. $17a - 17b - 17c + 15a$
48. $6m - 3.5n + 2.5m - 7n$
49. $5.5d - 1.2a + 3d + 4.2a$
50. $17z + 3x - 2y + y - 5z - 3x$
51. $\frac{1}{5}x + \frac{4}{5}y + \frac{2}{5}x - \frac{1}{5}y$
52. $\frac{7}{8}x + \frac{5}{8}y + \frac{1}{8}x - \frac{3}{8}y$

B

Write as an algebraic expression. Simplify.

53. eight times the difference of x and y $8(x - y)$
54. nine times the difference of y and z, increased by $3z$ $9(y - z) + 3z$ or $9y - 6z$
55. three times the sum of a and b, decreased by $7a$ $3(a + b) - 7a$ or $3b - 4a$
56. the total cost if you buy x cassette tapes at \$2.95 on Monday and y cassettes at the same price on Wednesday $2.95(x + y)$
57. ***Critical Thinking*** For all rational numbers a, b, and c, does $a \cdot (b - c) = a - (b \cdot c)$? Explain. No; $1 \cdot (3 - 2) = 1$, $1 - (3 \cdot 2) = -5$

Challenge

58. If the temperature is C degrees Celsius, it is $\frac{9}{5}C + 32$ degrees Fahrenheit. What is the Fahrenheit temperature if the Celsius temperature drops 5°? $\frac{9}{5}(C - 5) + 32$ or $\frac{9}{5}C + 23$
59. Jill has 5420 shares of a stock that she bought at $41\frac{1}{8}$. The stock is now worth $37\frac{3}{4}$. Show two ways of determining how much she has lost. Solve. $5420\left(41\frac{1}{8} - 37\frac{3}{4}\right)$ or $5420\left(41\frac{1}{8}\right) - 5420\left(37\frac{3}{4}\right)$; \$18,292.50

Mixed Review

Find the reciprocal. **60.** $\frac{2}{15}$ **61.** $-\frac{6}{11}$ **62.** 4 **63.** $\frac{1}{3c}$

Simplify. **64.** $11 - |-3| + (-9) - 16$ **65.** $4x - (-9x) - x$

Calculate. **66.** $\frac{4}{5}\left(\frac{2}{3}\right)$ **67.** $-\frac{3}{8}\left(\frac{1}{2}\right)$ **68.** $\frac{2}{3} \div -\frac{1}{2}$ **69.** $\frac{4}{5} \div \frac{2}{5}$

2-8 Inverse of a Sum and Simplifying

Inverse of a Sum

Objective: Find the inverse of a sum.

What happens when we multiply a rational number by -1?

$$-1 \cdot 7 = -7 \qquad -1 \cdot (-5) = 5 \qquad -1 \cdot 0 = 0$$

The product is the additive inverse of the number.

The Property of −1

For any rational number a,

$$-1 \cdot a = -a.$$

(Negative one times a is the additive inverse of a.)

The property of -1 enables us to find an equivalent expression for the additive inverse of a sum.

EXAMPLES Rename each additive inverse without parentheses.

1. $-(3 + x) = -1(3 + x)$ Using the property of -1
$= -1 \cdot 3 + (-1)x$ Using a distributive property
$= -3 + (-x)$ Using the property of -1
$= -3 - x$ Using the subtraction rule

2. $-(3x + 2y + 4) = -1(3x + 2y + 4)$
$= -1(3x) + (-1)(2y) + (-1)4$
$= -3x - 2y - 4$

Try This Rename each additive inverse without parentheses.

a. $-(x + 2)$ $-x - 2$ **b.** $-(5x + 2y + 8)$ $-5x - 2y - 8$

c. $-(a - 7)$ $-a + 7$ **d.** $-(3c - 4d + 1)$ $-3c + 4d - 1$

2-8

FIRST FIVE MINUTES

1. $(-1)(-1)$ 1
2. $(-1)x$ $-x$
3. $(-1)2y$ $-2y$
4. $(-1)(x + 2)$
$(-1)x + (-1)2 = -x - 2$

Simplify.

5. $[(3 + 5) + 7] + 1$
$(8 + 7) + 1 = 15 + 1 = 16$
6. $(2x + 4x) - 4x$
$6x - 4x = 2x$
7. $2 + 3(5 + 4)$
$2 + 3 \cdot 9 = 2 + 27 = 29$
8. $[(7x - 3x) - 2x] + 5x$
$(4x - 2x) + 5x$
$2x + 5x = 7x$

Inverse of a Sum

Point out that the inverse of a sum can be found by changing the sign of each term.

Key Questions

- Is the additive inverse of 3 equal to the additive inverse of -3?
No
- What is the additive inverse of 0?
0
- Write the additive inverse of $x \cdot y$ in 3 different ways.
$-(x \cdot y)$, $(-x) \cdot (y)$, and $(x) \cdot (-y)$

Chalkboard Examples

Multiply.

1. $-1 \cdot 12$ -12
2. $-1 \cdot (-4)$ 4
3. $0(-1)$ 0

Rename each additive inverse without parentheses.

4. $-(2y + 3)$
$-1(2y + 3)$
$= (-1)2y + (-1)3$
$= -2y - 3$
5. $-(a - 2)$
$-1(a - 2) = -1 \cdot a + (-1)(-2)$
$= -a + 2$
6. $-(5y - 3z + 4w)$
$-1(5y - 3z + 4w) =$
$(-1)5y + (-1)(-3)z + (-1)4w$
$= -5y + 3z - 4w$

Simplifying Expressions Involving Parentheses

You may wish to use an arithmetic example to show students that

$a - (b + c) = a - b - c$

For example,

$3 - (2 + 1) = 3 - 3 = 0$ and
$3 - (2 + 1) = 3 - 2 - 1 = 0$

Chalkboard Examples

Do the following mentally.

1. $-(8x - 3y - 2z)$
   $-8x + 3y + 2z$
2. $-(-4a + 7b - 3c)$
   $4a - 7b + 3c$
3. $-(4ab - 5ac + 6bc)$
   $-4ab + 5ac - 6bc$

Simplify.

4. $3 - (x + 1)$
   $3 + [-(x + 1)]$
   $3 + (-x - 1)$
   $3 + (-x) + (-1)$
   $2 - x$
5. $x - (2x - 3y)$
   $x - 2x + 3y$
   $-x + 3y$
6. $3z - 2y - (4z + 5y)$
   $3z - 2y - 4z - 5y$
   $= -z - 7y$
7. $7u - 3(7u + v)$
   $7u - 21u - 3v$
   $-14u - 3v$
8. $-2(e - f) - (2e + 5f)$
   $-2e + 2f - 2e - 5f$
   $-4e - 3f$

Examples 1 and 2 illustrate an important property of rational numbers.

The Inverse of a Sum Property

For any rational numbers a and b,

$$-(a + b) = -a + (-b)$$

(The additive inverse of a sum is the sum of the additive inverses.)

The inverse of a sum property holds for differences as well as sums because any difference can be expressed as a sum. It also holds when there is a sum or difference of more than two terms. When we apply the inverse of a sum property we sometimes say that we "change the sign of every term."

EXAMPLES Rename each additive inverse without parentheses.

3. $-(5 - y) = -5 + y$ Changing the sign of every term

4. $-(2a - 7b - 6) = -2a + 7b + 6$

Try This Rename each additive inverse without parentheses.

e. $-(6 - t)$ $-6 + t$ **f.** $-(-4a + 3t - 10)$ $4a - 3t + 10$ **g.** $-(18 - m - 2n + 4t)$ $-18 + m + 2n - 4t$

Simplifying Expressions Involving Parentheses

Objective: Simplify expressions involving parentheses.

When an expression inside parentheses is added to another expression as in $5x + (2x + 3)$, the associative property allows us to move the parentheses and simplify the expression to $7x + 3$. When an expression inside parentheses is subtracted from another expression as in $3x - (4x + 2)$, we can subtract by adding the inverse. Then we can use the inverse of a sum property and simplify.

EXAMPLE 5 Simplify.

$$\begin{aligned} 3x - (4x + 2) &= 3x + (-(4x + 2)) && \text{Using the definition of subtraction} \\ &= 3x + (-4x - 2) && \text{Using the inverse of a sum property} \\ &= 3x - 4x - 2 \\ &= -x - 2 && \text{Collecting like terms} \end{aligned}$$

We can combine the first two steps of Example 5 by changing the sign of every term inside the parentheses.

EXAMPLES Simplify.

6. $5y - (3y + 4) = 5y - 3y - 4$ Changing the sign of the terms inside parentheses
$= 2y - 4$ Collecting like terms

7. $3y - 2 - (2y - 4) = 3y - 2 - 2y + 4$
$= y + 2$

Try This Simplify.

h. $5x - (3x + 9)$ $2x - 9$ **i.** $5x - 2y - (2y - 3x - 4)$ $8x - 4y + 4$

Next consider subtracting an expression consisting of several terms preceded by a number.

EXAMPLES Simplify.

8. $x - 3(x + y) = x + (-3(x + y))$ Adding the inverse of $3(x + y)$
$= x + (-3x - 3y)$ Using the distributive property
$= x - 3x - 3y$
$= -2x - 3y$ Collecting like terms

9. $3y - 2(4y - 5) = 3y + (-2(4y - 5))$ Adding the inverse of $2(4y - 5)$
$= 3y + (-8y + 10)$
$= 3y - 8y + 10$
$= -5y + 10$

Try This Simplify.

j. $y - 9(x + y)$ **k.** $5a - 3(7a - 6)$

j. $-9x - 8y$
k. $-16a + 18$

Grouping Symbols

Objective: Simplify expressions containing multiple grouping symbols.

Some expressions contain more than one grouping symbol. **Parentheses** ( ), **brackets** [ ], and **braces** { } are all grouping symbols we use in algebra. When an expression contains more than one grouping symbol, the computations in the innermost grouping symbols should be done first.

EXAMPLES Simplify.

10. $[3 - (7 + 3)] = [3 - 10]$ Computing 7 + 3
$= -7$

11. $\{8 - [9 - (12 + 5)]\} = \{8 - [9 - 17]\}$ Computing 12 + 5
$= \{8 - [-8]\}$ Computing 9 − 17
$= 16$

Grouping Symbols

Point out that brackets and braces are used to clarify expressions that require several sets of grouping symbols.

Key Question

- How many different values can you give the expression $9 \cdot 2 + 5 \cdot 4$ by inserting grouping symbols?
  $9 \cdot 2 + 5 \cdot 4 = 38$
  $9 \cdot (2 + 5) \cdot 4 = 252$
  $(9 \cdot 2 + 5) \cdot 4 = 92$
  $9 \cdot (2 + 5 \cdot 4) = 198$

Chalkboard Examples

Simplify.

1. $[5 + (3 + 1)]$
   $[5 + 4] = 9$
2. $\{6 - [3 + (5 - 2)]\}$
   $\{6 - [3 + 3]\}$
   $= \{6 - 6\} = 0$
3. $[3(2x - 1) + 1] - (3x + 1)$
   $[(6x - 3) + 1] - 3x - 1$
   $= 6x - 3 + 1 - 3x - 1$
   $= 3x - 3$

LESSON QUIZ

Rename each additive inverse without parentheses.

1. $-(4x + 7)$ $-4x - 7$
2. $-(-6a + 3b - 7c)$
   $6a - 3b + 7c$

Simplify.

3. $12y - (2y - 1)$
   $12y - 2y + 1$
   $= 10y + 1$
4. $(-5x + 2) - (-2x - 3)$
   $-5x + 2 + 2x + 3$
   $= -5x + 2x + 2 + 3$
   $= -3x + 5$

Simplify.

5. $[3 - (5 - 3)]$
   $[3 - 2] = 1$
6. $[3(x + 4) + 1] - (x - 5)$
   $[3x + 12 + 1] - x + 5$
   $= 3x + 12 + 1 - x + 5$
   $= 3x - x + 12 + 1 + 5$
   $= 2x + 18$

Assignment Guide
Minimum: 1–40 e/o, MR

Regular: 1–46 e/o, 47, MR

Advanced: 1–46 m3, 47–51, MR

ADDITIONAL ANSWERS

Exercises

13. $5x - 3$
14. $5y - 9$
15. $-3a + 9$
16. $8n + 7$
17. $5x - 6$
18. $a - 7$
19. $-19x + 2y$
20. $-a - 4b$
21. $9y - 25z$
22. $-16a + 27b - 32c$
23. $-2x + 6y$
24. $-7a - 5b$
25. $3m - 6n$
26. $-6p + 2q$
27. 0
28. $12m + 5n$
29. $a + 4b$
30. $6x - 4y$

EXAMPLES Simplify.

12. $4(2 + 3) - \{7 - [4 - (8 + 5)]\}$
$= 4 \cdot 5 - \{7 - [4 - 13]\}$ Working with innermost parentheses first
$= 20 - \{7 - [-9]\}$ Computing $4 \cdot 5$ and $4 - 13$
$= 20 - 16$ Computing $7 - [-9]$
$= 4$

13. $[5(x + 2) - 3x] - [3(y + 2) - 7(y - 3)]$
$= [5x + 10 - 3x] - [3y + 6 - 7y + 21]$ Working with innermost parentheses first
$= [2x + 10] - [-4y + 27]$ Collecting like terms
$= 2x + 10 + 4y - 27$
$= 2x + 4y - 17$

Try This Simplify.

l. $[9 - (6 + 4)]$ -1 **m.** $3(4 + 2) - \{7 - [4 - (6 + 5)]\}$ 4

n. $[3(4 + 2) + 2x] - [4(y + 2) - 3(y - 2)]$ $2x - y + 4$

2-8 EXERCISES

A

Rename each additive inverse without parentheses.

1. $-(2x + 7)$ $-2x - 7$
2. $-(3x + 5)$ $-3x - 5$
3. $-(5x - 8)$ $-5x + 8$
4. $-(6x - 7)$ $-6x + 7$
5. $-(4a - 3b + 7c)$ $-4a + 3b - 7c$
6. $-(5x - 2y - 3z)$ $-5x + 2y + 3z$
7. $-(6x - 8y + 5)$ $-6x + 8y - 5$
8. $-(8x + 3y + 9)$ $-8x - 3y - 9$
9. $-(3x - 5y - 6)$ $-3x + 5y + 6$
10. $-(6a - 4b - 7)$ $-6a + 4b + 7$
11. $-(-8x - 6y - 43)$ $8x + 6y + 43$
12. $-(-2a + 9b - 5c)$ $2a - 9b + 5c$

Simplify.

13. $9x - (4x + 3)$
14. $7y - (2y + 9)$
15. $2a - (5a - 9)$
16. $11n - (3n - 7)$
17. $2x + 7x - (4x + 6)$
18. $3a + 2a - (4a + 7)$
19. $2x - 4y - 3(7x - 2y)$
20. $3a - 7b - 1(4a - 3b)$
21. $15x - y - 5(3x - 2y + 5z)$
22. $4a - b - 4(5a - 7b + 8c)$
23. $(3x + 2y) - (5x - 4y)$
24. $(-6a - b) - (4b + a)$
25. $6m - n - 4m - (5n - m)$
26. $7p - (q + 8p) - 5p + 3q$
27. $-(7u - 8v) - (8v - 7u)$
28. $7m + 8n - (4n - 5m) + n$
29. $5a - 3b - (-6b + 4a) - (-b)$
30. $-(-4x - 3y) - 6y + 3x - x - y$

Simplify.

31. $[9 - 2(5 - 4)]$ 7

32. $[6 - 5(8 - 4)]$ −14

33. $8[7 - 6(4 - 2)]$ −40

34. $10[7 - 4(7 - 5)]$ −10

35. $[4(9 - 6) + 11] - [14 - (6 + 4)]$ 19

36. $[7(8 - 4) + 16] - [15 - (7 + 3)]$ 39

37. $[10(x + 3) - 4] + [2(x - 1) + 6]$ $12x + 30$

38. $[9(x + 5) - 7] + [4(x - 12) + 9]$ $13x - 1$

39. $[7(x + 5) - 19] - [4(x - 6) + 10]$ $3x + 30$

40. $[6(x + 4) - 12] - [5(x - 8) + 11]$ $x + 41$

B

Find an equivalent expression for each of the following by enclosing the last three terms in parentheses preceded by a minus sign.

41. $x - y - a - b$

42. $6y + 2x - 3a + c$

43. $6m + 3n - 5m + 4b$

44. $3q - 2p + 4q - 5$

Simplify.

45. $3a + 4 - \{-2 - [-3 - (a - 1)]\}$ $2a + 4$

46. $2s + 2 - \{-3 - [2 - (3 - s)]\}$ $3s + 4$

47. *Critical Thinking* If $-(a + b)$ is $-a + (-b)$, what should be the sum of $(a + b)$ and $-a + (-b)$? Show that your answer is correct.
$0; a + b + (-a) + (-b) = a + (-a) + b + (-b) = 0$

Challenge

Simplify.

48. $z - \{2z - [3z - (4z - 5z) - 6z] - 7z\} - 8z$

49. $\{x - [f - (f - x)] + [x - f]\} - 3x$

50. $x - \{x - 1 - [x - 2 - (x - 3 - \{x - 4 - [x - 5 - (x - 6)]\})]\}$

51. A bar, or vinculum, can be used as a grouping symbol. Simplify the following.

$$\{y - [y + (3 - y)] - \overline{y + 1}\} + 5y$$

Mixed Review

Factor. 52. $3x + 12y$ 53. $2a - 6b + 12$ 54. $an + 2a$

Evaluate for $x = 3$, $y = 2$, and $z = 5$. 55. $2x^3$ 56. $-3z^2$

57. $6x + 2y^4$ 58. $2x^2 + 3z$ 59. $x + 2y - 3z$

Calculate. 60. $\frac{2}{3} + \frac{1}{4} - \left(-\frac{3}{8}\right)$ 61. $\frac{1}{2}\left(\frac{4}{5}\right) + \left(\frac{5}{6}\right)\left(-\frac{2}{3}\right)$

Collect like terms. 62. $8b + 7b + b$ 63. $x^2 + x + x^2$

Write as an algebraic expression. 64. a number squared plus 3

65. five less than three times a number

41. $x - (y + a + b)$
42. $6y - (-2x + 3a - c)$
43. $6m - (-3n + 5m - 4b)$
44. $3q - (2p - 4q + 5)$

48. $-4z$
49. $-2x - f$
50. $x - 3$
51. $5y - 4$

Mixed Review

52. $3(x + 4y)$
53. $2(a - 3b + 6)$
54. $a(n + 2)$
55. 54
56. −75
57. 50
58. 33
59. −8
60. $\frac{31}{24}$
61. $-\frac{7}{45}$
62. $16b$
63. $2x^2 + x$
64. $x^2 + 3$
65. $3x - 5$

2-9

FIRST FIVE MINUTES

Write as an algebraic expression.

1. Six less than five times n.
   $5n - 6$
2. One third the sum of p and q.
   $\frac{1}{3}(p + q)$
3. Doug is five years more than 3 times Lee's age. Let L be Lee's age. Write an expression for Doug's age.
   $3L + 5$
4. Let d be the number of miles Jay runs each week. Nina runs 5 less than twice as far as Jay. Write an expression for the distance Nina runs each week.
   $2d - 5$

Write an Equation

To clarify a problem, it often helps to underline the phrases that refer to quantities, then replace the phrases with variables that suggest the quantities.

Note that if the equation is set up correctly for these easier problems, the solution to the equation is usually the answer to the problem. In later chapters, however, the answer to the problem will not always be the solution to the equation.

This lesson is meant to give students practice in writing equations to solve problem situations. It is not necessary for students to actually solve the equations. It is fine if they do, as long as they have set up the equation properly.

As always, have students check that their answers are reasonable and that they have included units, if any.

Avoiding Common Errors

When writing an equation, students often have difficulty determining whether to add or subtract and to which side. In Example 1, students may want to add 1700 to 23,400 rather than to p.

Ask students to visualize the equation as a scale. Since Jose made more this year than last year, the side of the scale showing this year's salary will be heavier. In order to balance the scale, the student must add to the lighter side, so the equation will be $23{,}400 = p + 1700$.

2-9 Problem Solving: Strategies

Write an Equation

Objective: Write an equation that can be used to solve a problem.

In the past you have been introduced to strategies that you can use to solve mathematical problems. A powerful strategy is *Write an Equation.* Many of the problems you will work with in your study of algebra can be solved by writing and solving an equation.

PROBLEM-SOLVING GUIDELINES
■ UNDERSTAND the problem
■ Develop and carry out a PLAN
■ Find the ANSWER and CHECK

The Problem-Solving Guidelines were introduced in Chapter 1. The three phases can help you solve many kinds of problems.

The planning phase involves selecting and carrying out strategies for solving problems. Here are some tips you can use when your plan involves writing an equation.

PLANNING to write and solve an equation

Can I use a variable to represent an unknown number?
Can I represent other conditions in terms of the variable?
Can I find equivalent expressions?
Can I write and solve an equation?

EXAMPLE 1 Which equation(s) can be used to solve the problem?

Jose's salary this year is \$23,400. This is \$1700 more than he made last year. What was his salary last year?

(A) $l - 1700 = 23{,}400$ (B) $1700 + l = 23{,}400$
(C) $l = 23{,}400 - 1700$

■ **UNDERSTAND the problem**

Question: What was Jose's salary last year?
Data: Jose earned \$23,400 this year. This is \$1700 more than he made last year.

Clarifying the question and identifying the data given

■ **Develop and carry out a PLAN**

Let l = last year's salary.

Using a variable to represent what you are trying to find

Our data tell us that 23,400 is 1700 more than l. This is the same as equation (B). We can also say that last year's salary was 1700 less than this year's salary. This is the same as equation (C).

Either (B) or (C) are correct equations.

EXAMPLE 2 Write an equation that could be used to solve the problem.

A solid-state color television set uses about 420 kilowatt hours (kWh) of electric energy in a year. That is 3.5 times the amount of energy used by a black-and-white set. How many kWh does a black-and-white set use in a year?

■ **UNDERSTAND the problem**

Question: How many kWh does a black-and-white set use in 1 year?

Data: A color set uses 420 kWh a year. This amount is 3.5 times as much as the amount used by a black-and-white set.

Clarifying the question and identifying the data given

■ **Develop and carry out a PLAN**

Let b = number of kWh used by a black-and-white set.

Using a variable to represent what you are trying to find

$3.5b$ = number of kWh used by a color set

3.5 times the number of kWh for a black-and-white TV equals the amount used by a color TV.

$(3.5)b = 420$

EXAMPLE 3 Write an equation that could be used to solve the problem.

In baseball, a player's batting average multiplied by the number of times at bat equals the number of hits. A player had 125 at-bats and 36 hits. What was this player's batting average?

■ **UNDERSTAND the problem**

Question: What was this player's batting average?

Data: A player had 125 at-bats and 36 hits.

Clarifying the question and identifying the data given

■ **Develop and carry out a PLAN**

Let b = player's batting average.

$125b$ = player's batting average after 125 at-bats

Using a variable to represent what you are trying to find

$(125)b = 36$

Math Point

Ordinary language is efficient. The fewest possible words are used to express facts. This is good for ordinary communication, but it can be bad for doing algebra. Word problems often need to be rephrased and expanded to make their meaning clear.

Key Questions

- In Example 1, is Jose earning more or less than he earned last year? More
- In Example 2, does a color television use more or less energy than a black-and-white television? More
- What unit is energy measured in? Kilowatt hours
- Write a different equation that can be used to solve Example 2. $b = 420 \div 3.5$

Chalkboard Examples

1. In the year after Anne-Marie bought a used car, she drove 12,500 miles. At the end of the year the mileage of the car was 42,800. Write an equation for the mileage of the car when Anne-Marie bought it.
   Let m = mileage when Anne-Marie bought the car.
   $m + 12,500 = 42,800$
2. On one tank of gas, Anne-Marie can drive 238 miles. The gas tank in her car holds $9\frac{1}{2}$ gallons. Write an equation for the number of miles per gallon her car gets.
   Let m = miles per gallon.
   $m = 238 \text{ miles} \div 9\frac{1}{2} \text{ gallons}$

ANSWERS

1. (B) or (C)
2. (A)
3. (A) or (B)
4. (B)
5. (B) or (C)
6. (A) or (C)

Problems 7–24: Answers may vary.

7. Let d = the number of tickets sold on the first day.
   $127 + d = 318$
8. Let a = the amount of money Alberto has.
   $a = 115 - 48$
9. Let c = the cost of a single bagel.
   $12c = 3.12$
10. Let p = the price of a ticket.
    $117p = 438.75$
11. Let c = the amount of hours the consultant worked.
    $80c = 53{,}400$
12. Let a = the area of Lake Ontario.
    $4a = 78{,}114$

2-9 PROBLEMS

Which equation(s) can be used to solve each problem?

1. Nita had 25 points on the second quiz. That was 8 more points than she had on the first quiz. How many points did she have on the first quiz?
   Let x = number of points on the first quiz.
   (A) $x - 25 = 8$ **(B)** $x + 8 = 25$ **(C)** $x = 25 - 8$
2. A golfer hit two shots for a total of 375 yards. Her first shot was 240 yards. How far was her second shot?
   Let s = length of the second shot.
   (A) $240 + s = 375$ **(B)** $s - 240 = 375$ **(C)** $s = 375 + 240$
3. There are 775 dogs and cats in an animal shelter. There are 423 dogs in the shelter. How many cats are there?
   Let c = number of cats.
   (A) $775 - 423 = c$ **(B)** $423 + c = 775$ **(C)** $c - 423 = 775$
4. The San Francisco Giants won 39 more games than the St. Louis Cardinals. The Giants won 101 games. How many games did the Cardinals win?
   Let c = number of games the Cardinals won.
   (A) $c - 39 = 101$ **(B)** $c + 39 = 101$ **(C)** $101 + 39 = c$
5. A game board has 64 squares. If you win 35 squares, how many does your opponent get?
   Let o = number of squares your opponent got.
   (A) $o - 35 = 64$ **(B)** $35 + o = 64$ **(C)** $o = 64 - 35$
6. A dozen balloons costs $3.50. How much is each balloon?
   Let b = the cost of each balloon.
   (A) $3.50 \div 12 = b$ **(B)** $3.50 - b = 12$ **(C)** $12b = 3.50$

Write an equation that can be used to solve the problem.

7. Dennis sold a total of 318 tickets in two days. He sold 127 tickets the second day. How many did he sell the first day?
8. Alberto has $48 less than Mariana. Mariana has $115. How much does Alberto have?
9. A bakery charges $3.12 for a dozen bagels. How much does it cost to buy a single bagel?
10. A movie theater took in $438.75 from 117 customers. What was the price of a ticket?
11. A consultant charges $80 an hour. How many hours did the consultant work to make $53,400?
12. The area of Lake Superior is about 4 times the area of Lake Ontario. The area of Lake Superior is 78,114 km^2. What is the area of Lake Ontario?

13. It takes a 60-watt bulb about 16.6 hours to use 1 kWh of electricity. That is about 2.5 times as long as it takes a 150-watt bulb to use 1 kWh. How long does it take a 150-watt bulb to use 1 kWh?

14. The area of Alaska is about 483 times the area of Rhode Island. The area of Alaska is 1,519,202 km^2. What is the area of Rhode Island?

15. The boiling point of ethyl alcohol is 78.3° C. That is 13.5° C higher than the boiling point of methyl alcohol. What is the boiling point of methyl alcohol?

16. The height of the Eiffel Tower is 295 m, which is about 203 m higher than the Statue of Liberty. What is the height of the Statue of Liberty?

17. The distance from the earth to the sun is about 150,000,000 km. That is about 391 times the distance from the earth to the moon. What is the distance from the earth to the moon?

18. In three-way light bulbs, the highest wattage is the sum of the two lower wattages. If the lowest is 30 watts and the highest is 150 watts, what is the middle wattage?

19. The distance traveled (D) equals the rate of travel (r) times the time traveled (t). How long would it take a boat traveling 50 miles per hour to travel 325 miles, assuming there are no stops?

20. A roll of film costs $3.14 and developing costs $10.39. What is the total cost for each of the 36 prints?

21. The dryers at Franklin Laundry cost a quarter for 7 minutes. How many quarters will you have to use to dry your clothes for 45 minutes?

22. One inch equals 2.54 centimeters. A meter is 100 centimeters. How many inches are there in a meter?

23. Sound travels at 1087 feet per second. How long does it take the sound of an airplane to reach you when it is 10,000 feet overhead?

24. In baseball, a player's batting average multiplied by the number of times at bat equals the number of hits. A player had 125 at-bats and 36 hits. What was this player's batting average?

Write a problem that can be solved using the given equations. Specify what the variable represents.

25. Let x = ?
$x - 2 = 32$

26. Let a = ?
$a + 24 = 42$

27. Let r = ?
$42 - r = 11$

28. Let m = ?
$m + 2m = 18$

13. Let t = the time it takes a 150-watt bulb to use 1 kWh.
$2.5t = 16.6$
14. Let a = the area of Rhode Island.
$483a = 1{,}519{,}202$
15. Let b = the boiling point of methyl alcohol.
$b + 13.5 = 78.3$
16. Let h = the height of the Statue of Liberty.
$h + 203 = 295$
17. Let d = the distance from the earth to the moon.
$391d = 150{,}000{,}000$
18. Let m = the middle wattage of a three-way light bulb.
$m + 30 = 150$
19. Let t = time.
$325 = 50t$
20. Let c = the cost of each print.
$36c = 13.53$
21. Let q = the number of quarters required.
$7q = 45$
22. Let x = the number of inches in a meter.
$x = 2.54 \cdot 100$
23. Let t = the time it takes the sound to reach you.
$1087t = 10{,}000$
24. Let b = batting average.
$125b = 36$
25–28. Answers will vary.

2-10

FIRST FIVE MINUTES

True or false? (A statement that can be both true and false should be marked false.)

1. $10 = 10$
   True; any number equals itself.
2. $(3 + 2) + 1 = 3 + (2 + 1)$
   True, by the associative property
3. $x + 3 = 1$
   False; depends on the value of x
4. $\frac{a}{0} = 1$
   False; division by 0 is undefined.
5. $x - y = y - x$
   False; depends on x, y
6. There is a number x such that $\frac{2}{53} + x = 0$
   True; $x = -\frac{2}{53}$ (Every number has an additive inverse.)

Number Properties and Definitions

Students may have difficulty with the closure properties, as this is probably their first exposure to them. As another example, you may wish to show that the rational numbers do not have the closure property of division: 1 and 0 are rational, but $\frac{1}{0}$ is not.

Key Questions

- Do axioms lead to theorems or do theorems lead to axioms?
  Axioms lead to theorems.
- Do we need to prove an axiom?
  No
- Does the closure property of subtraction hold for whole numbers?
  No; $1 - 2 = -1$, not a whole number
- Does the multiplicative inverse property hold for integers?
  No
- Are the integers a field?
  No

2-10 Number Properties and Proofs (Optional)

Number Properties and Definitions

Objective: Identify applications of the number properties.

Number properties are important in algebra because they allow us to write equivalent expressions. For example, the associative property allows us to write $(x + 3) + 5$ and $x + (3 + 5)$ and know they are equivalent.

How do we know that the properties we have used so far are true? We accept some number properties as obvious, and then, using these properties, we prove the rest. The properties that we accept without proof are called **axioms.** The properties that we prove are called **theorems.**

We try to choose the more obvious properties as axioms, but different mathematicians may make different choices. Following is a list of properties that we will accept as axioms.

Axioms for Rational Numbers

For any rational numbers a, b, and c,

- The Closure Properties
  1. Addition: $a + b$ is a rational number.
  2. Multiplication: ab is a rational number.
- The Commutative Properties
  3. Addition: $a + b = b + a$
  4. Multiplication: $ab = ba$
- The Associative Properties
  5. Addition: $a + (b + c) = (a + b) + c$
  6. Multiplication: $a(bc) = (ab)c$
- The Identity Properties
  7. Addition: $a + 0 = a$
  8. Multiplication: $a \cdot 1 = a$
- The Inverse Properties
  9. Addition: For each a, there is an additive inverse, $-a$, such that $a + (-a) = 0$.
  10. Multiplication: For each $a (a \neq 0)$, there is a multiplicative inverse, $\frac{1}{a}$ such that $a \cdot \frac{1}{a} = 1$.
- The Distributive Property of Multiplication over Addition
  11. $a(b + c) = ab + ac$

These axioms hold for rational numbers, and they also hold in some other number systems. Any number system with two operations defined in which these axioms hold is called a **field.** Hence the axioms above are known as the **field axioms.**

EXAMPLES Which axiom guarantees the truth of each statement?

1. $2(y + 3) = 2y + 2 \cdot 3$ Distributive property
2. $(3m)n = 3(mn)$ Associative property for multiplication

Try This Which axiom guarantees the truth of each statement?

a. $4 + (5 + x) = (4 + 5) + x$ Assoc. prop. of addition.

b. $7\left(\frac{1}{7}\right) = 1$ Inverse prop. of mult.

c. $-12 + 12 = 0$ Inverse prop. of addition.

d. $2(m + n) = (m + n)2$ Comm. prop. of mult.

Here are some important definitions.

Definitions

Subtraction

The difference $a - b$ is the number c such that $c + b = a$.

Division

The quotient $\frac{a}{b}$, or $a \div b, b \neq 0$ is the number c such that $c \cdot b = a$.

Equality

A sentence $a = b$ states that a and b are expressions for the same number.

Properties of Equality

Objective: Identify the properties of equality.

The following are some important properties related to equality.

Properties of Equality

For any rational numbers a, b, and c,

Reflexive Property	Symmetric Property	Transitive Property
$a = a$ is always true.	If $a = b$, then $b = a$.	If $a = b$ and $b = c$, then $a = c$.

Chalkboard Examples

Which axiom guarantees the truth of each statement?

1. $3 \cdot x = x \cdot 3$
   Commutative for multiplication
2. $(2a)b = 2(ab)$
   Associative for multiplication
3. $a(x + b) = ax + ab$
   Distributive
4. $7 + (-7) = 0$
   Inverse for addition
5. $9 \cdot \left(\frac{1}{9}\right) = 1$
   Inverse for multiplication
6. $(-a) + (-b) = (-b) + (-a)$
   Commutative for addition
7. $\frac{1}{2} + \left(\frac{3}{5} + \frac{4}{7}\right) = \left(\frac{1}{2} + \frac{3}{5}\right) + \frac{4}{7}$
   Associative for addition
8. $\left(x + \frac{3}{2}\right) + 0 = \left(x + \frac{3}{2}\right)$
   Identity element for addition

Properties of Equality

Chalkboard Examples

Which property of equality guarantees the truth of each statement?

1. $3x + 2 = 3x + 2$
   Reflexive property
2. $x - 3 = 2$, hence $2 = x - 3$
   Symmetric property
3. $a + 2 = b$ and $b = c - 7$, therefore $a + 2 = c - 7$.
   Transitive property
4. $2y + 4x = 16$, therefore $16 = 2y + 4x$.
   Symmetric property
5. $\frac{6}{5}\left(\frac{1}{2}x - \frac{4}{7}\right) = \frac{6}{5}\left(\frac{1}{2}x - \frac{4}{7}\right)$
   Reflexive property

Theorems and Proofs

You may wish to explain that algebra is like a game in which the rules are axioms and logic. The axioms and logic allow certain equations to be written down. Other axioms allow expressions to be rewritten in alternate forms. It is not clear at the outset what can and cannot be written down. Every equation that can be derived using the axioms and logic is called a *theorem.*

A proof is a careful record of the "moves" made to show a theorem is true. In the examples on this page, each property is mentioned as it is used. Note that other moves might lead to the same result.

Chalkboard Example

Theorem: $(a + b) - b = a$

Complete the proof of this theorem by supplying the missing reasons.

Proof

1. $(a + b) - b = (a + b) + (-b)$	Subtract. rule
2. $= a + [b + (-b)]$	Assoc. Prop. of add.
3. $= a + 0$	Additive Inverses
4. $= a$	Additive Identity
5. $(a + b) - b = a$	Transitive Prop. of Eq.

EXAMPLES Which property of equality justifies each statement?

3. $a(b + c) = ab + ac$, so $ab + ac = a(b + c)$ — Symmetric property

4. $2x^3 = 2x^3$ — Reflexive property

5. If $5xy^2 = 5y^2x$ and $5y^2x = 5 \cdot y \cdot y \cdot x$ then $5xy^2 = 5 \cdot y \cdot y \cdot x$. — Transitive property

Try This Which property of equality justifies each statement?

e. $3a + 5b = 3a + 5b$ Reflexive

f. $(b + c)a = a(b + c)$ and $a(b + c) = ab + ac$. Therefore, $(b + c)a = ab + ac$. Transitive

g. If $a(b - c) = ab - ac$, then $ab - ac = a(b - c)$. Symmetric

Theorems and Proofs

Objective: Prove number properties.

We now consider some number properties that can be proved. The first theorem is a restatement of the distributive property. To prove this theorem, we write a sequence of statements. Each statement must be supported by a reason, which can be an axiom or a definition.

Theorem

For any rational numbers a, b, and c, $(b + c)a = ba + ca$.

EXAMPLE 6 Prove the above theorem.

Statement	Reason
1. $(b + c)a = a(b + c)$	1. Commutative property of mult.
2. $= ab + ac$	2. Distributive property
3. $= ba + ca$	3. Commutative property of mult.
4. $(b + c)a = ba + ca$	4. Transitive property of equality

Here is another theorem dealing with the distributive property. It involves three addends.

Theorem

For any rational numbers a, b, c, and d, $a(b + c + d) = ab + ac + ad$.

Try This

h. Complete the following proof by supplying the missing reasons.

Statement	Reason
1. $a(b + c + d) = a[(b + c) + d]$	1. Associative property of add.
2. $\qquad = a(b + c) + ad$	2. Distributive property
3. $\qquad = ab + ac + ad$	3. Distributive property
4. $a(b + c + d) = ab + ac + ad$	4. Transitive property of equality

The next theorem concerns a rule for multiplying by 0.

Theorem

For any rational number a, $a \cdot 0 = 0$.

Try This

i. Complete the following proof by supplying the missing reasons.

1. $a \cdot 0 = a \cdot 0 + 0$	1. Additive identity
2. $\qquad = a \cdot 0 + a + (-a)$	2. Additive inverse
3. $\qquad = a \cdot 0 + a \cdot 1 + (-a)$	3. Multiplicative identity
4. $\qquad = a(0 + 1) + (-a)$	4. Distributive property
5. $\qquad = a \cdot 1 + (-a)$	5. Additive identity
6. $\qquad = a + (-a)$	6. Multiplicative identity
7. $\qquad = 0$	7. Additive inverses
8. $a \cdot 0 = 0$	8. Transitive property of equality

2-10 EXERCISES

A

Which axiom guarantees each statement?

1. $a + b = b + a$

2. $(a + b) + c = c + (a + b)$

3. $x(y + z) = xy + xz$

4. $3(b + c) = 3b + 3c$

5. $y + [x + (-x)] = y + 0$

6. $3x(x + 2) = 3x^2 + 6x$

7. $-(x - 3) = -x + 3$

8. $6x - 3y = 3(2x - y)$

Which axiom or property guarantees the truth of each statement?

9. $(a \cdot b)c = a(b \cdot c)$

10. $(a + b) \cdot 1 = a + b$

11. $17(2b + 1) = 34b + 17$

12. $(2a + 3b) + 19 = 19 + (3b + 2a)$

LESSON QUIZ

Which axioms, properties or definitions guarantee that these are true?

1. $3(x + a) = 3x + 3a$
   Distributive property
2. $7 + (3 + x) = (7 + 3) + x$
   Associative for addition
3. $(x + 3) \cdot \frac{1}{x + 3} = 1$
   Inverse for multiplication
4. $u(vw) = (uv)w$
   Associative for multiplication
5. $(ax - 2) + [-(ax - 2)] = 0$
   Inverse for addition
6. $x - 7 = x - 7$
   Reflexive property of equality
7. $x = a$ and $a = 3$, thus $x = 3$
   Transitive property of equality
8. $-1 \cdot a + (a + (-a))$
   $= (-1 \cdot a + a) + (-a)$
   Associative for addition
9. $2y + u = 7x + 3$, therefore
   $7x + 3 = 2y + u$
   Symmetric property of equality
10. $x - y = x + (-y)$
    Definition of subtraction

Assignment Guide

Minimum: omit

Regular: omit

Advanced: 1–27 e/o, MR

ADDITIONAL ANSWERS

Exercises

1. Commutative property of addition
2. Commutative property of addition
3. Distributive property of multiplication over addition
4. Distributive property of multiplication over addition
5. Additive inverses
6. Distributive property of multiplication over addition
7. Additive inverses
8. Distributive property of multiplication over subtraction
9. Associative property of multiplication
10. Multiplicative identity
11. Distributive property of multiplication over addition
12. Commutative property of addition

13. Multiplicative inverse
14. Additive inverse
15. Reflexive property of equality
16. Symmetric property of equality
17. Commutative property of multiplication
18. Symmetric property of equality
19. Reflexive property of equality
20. Commutative property of multiplication

26.

Statement	Reason
1. $(-a)b = (-1 \cdot a)b$	Property of -1
2. $= -1(ab)$	Assoc. property of mult.
3. $= -ab$	Property of -1
4. $(-a)b = -ab$	Transitive property of equality

27.

Statement	Reason
1. $-(a - b) = -[a + (-b)]$	Subtraction rule
2. $= -a + -(-b)$	Inverse of a sum
3. $= -a + b$	Inverse of inverse
4. $= b + -a$	Comm. property of addition
5. $= b - a$	Subtraction rule
6. $-(a - b) = b - a$	Transitive property of equality

Mixed Review

28. $c = \frac{4.80 + 8.35}{36}$
29. $16(a - 3)$
30. $2(4y - 5 + 6x)$
31. $15(3 - n)$
32. $9c - 2a$
33. $9 - 17c$

Which axiom or property guarantees the truth of each statement?

13. $\frac{1}{x + y} \cdot (x + y) = 1$
14. $-(a + b) + (a + b) = 0$
15. $3x(y + z) = 3x(y + z)$
16. $\frac{1}{x} \cdot x = 1$. Thus $1 = \frac{1}{x} \cdot x$
17. $3(xy) = (xy)3$
18. $x + 5 = 12$, so $12 = x + 5$
19. $4ab = 4ab$
20. $5(a + b) = (a + b)5$

Complete the following proof by supplying the missing reasons.

21. Property of -1. For any number a, $-1 \cdot a = -a$.

1. $-1 \cdot a = -1 \cdot a + 0$	1. Additive identity
2. $= -1 \cdot a + (a + (-a))$	2. Additive inverse
3. $= (-1 \cdot a + a) + (-a)$	3. Associative property of addition
4. $= (-1 \cdot a + 1 \cdot a) + (-a)$	4. Multiplicative identity
5. $= (-1 + 1) \cdot a + (-a)$	5. Distributive property
6. $= 0 \cdot a + (-a)$	6. Additive inverse
7. $= 0 + -a$	7. Mult. property of zero
8. $= -a$	8. Additive identity
9. $-1 \cdot a = -a$	9. Transitive property of equality

B

22. The set of rational numbers is *closed* under addition since the sum of any two rational numbers is a rational number. Consider the set of even whole numbers {0, 2, 4, 6, 8, 10, . . .}. Is the set of even whole numbers closed under addition? Yes

23. Is the set of odd whole numbers {1, 3, 5, 7, 9, . . .} closed under addition? No. $1 + 3 = 4$. 4 is not in the set of odd whole numbers.

24. The set of rational numbers is closed under multiplication, since the product of any two rational numbers is a rational number. Consider the set of multiples of three {0, 3, 6, 9, 12, . . .}. Is this set closed under multiplication? Yes

25. Determine whether the set {0, 1} is closed under multiplication. Yes

Challenge

26. Prove that for any numbers a and b, $(-a)b = -ab$.

27. Prove that for any numbers a and b, $-(a - b) = b - a$. (Hint: Use the definition of subtraction and the inverse of a sum property.)

Mixed Review

Write an equation. **28.** A roll of film costs \$4.80 and developing costs \$8.35. What is the total cost for each of the 36 prints?

Factor. **29.** $16a - 48$ **30.** $8y - 10 + 12x$ **31.** $45 - 15n$

Collect like terms. **32.** $6a + 9c - 8a$ **33.** $7 + 8c - 25c + 2$

Chapter 2 Summary and Review

2-1

The set of **integers** consists of the **positive integers**, the **negative integers**, and zero. Numbers that are the same distance from 0, but on opposite sides of 0 on the number line, are called **opposites**. For any two numbers on the number line, the one farther to the right is greater. The **absolute value** of a number is its distance from 0 on the number line.

Name the integer suggested by each situation.

1. Tanya's mom owes \$25.

2. Keiko deposited \$50 in her savings account.

Find the absolute value.

3. $|-38|$ **4.** $|91|$ **5.** $|-0.02|$

2-2

A **rational number** can be expressed as the ratio of two integers, $\frac{a}{b}$, where $b \neq 0$. There is a point on the number line for every rational number. The number is called the **coordinate** of the point, and the point is the **graph** of the number.

Graph each rational number on a number line.

6. -2.5 **7.** $\frac{4}{3}$ **8.** $-\frac{16}{5}$

Use $<$ or $>$ to write a true sentence.

9. $-2.25 \quad -4.5$ **10.** $-\frac{2}{3} \quad -\frac{1}{10}$ **11.** $-\frac{1}{2} \quad \frac{3}{5}$

Show that each number can be written as the ratio of two integers.

12. -4.2 **13.** $1\frac{3}{5}$ **14.** -8

2-3

To add two positive numbers or two negative numbers, add the absolute values; the sum has the same sign as each addend. To add a positive number and a negative number, subtract the absolute values; the sum has the same sign as the addend with the greater absolute value. Number pairs whose sum is 0 are called **additive inverses**.

Add.

15. $-6 + (-13)$ **16.** $\frac{3}{4} + \left(-\frac{9}{4}\right)$ **17.** $-3.9 + 7.4$

18. $6 + (-9) + (-8) + 7$ **19.** $-3.8 + 5.1 + (-12) - (-4.3)$

ANSWERS

1. -25
2. $+50$
3. 38
4. 91
5. 0.02

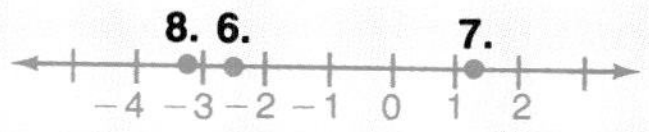

9. $>$
10. $<$
11. $<$
12. $-\frac{42}{10}$
13. $\frac{8}{5}$
14. $-\frac{8}{1}$
15. -19
16. $-\frac{6}{4}$ or $-\frac{3}{2}$
17. 3.5
18. -4
19. -6.4

20. -27
21. 7.45
22. $\frac{7}{3}$
23. 34
24. 5
25. 8 yd gain
26. -2
27. -4
28. $-\frac{14}{10}$ or $-\frac{7}{5}$
29. 19
30. $11y - 16$
31. 4000 ft
32. $16.95
33. -24
34. $-\frac{2}{7}$
35. 210
36. -3
37. 5
38. $-\frac{7}{10}$

Find the additive inverse of each.

20. 27 **21.** -7.45 **22.** $-\frac{7}{3}$

23. Find $-x$ when x is -34. **24.** Find $-(-x)$ when x is 5.

25. On a first, second, and third down a football team had these gains and losses: 5-yd gain, 12-yd loss, and a 15-yd gain. Find the total number of yards gained or lost.

2-4

To subtract a rational number, add its inverse. When addition and subtraction occur several times, use the rule for subtracting rational numbers to make them all additions.

Subtract.

26. $5 - 7$ **27.** $-7 - (-3)$ **28.** $-\frac{9}{10} - \frac{1}{2}$

Simplify.

29. $13 - 4 + 8 - (-2)$ **30.** $4y - 19 - (-7y) + 3$

31. An airplane is 2500 ft above the rim of the Grand Canyon at a point where the Grand Canyon is 1500 ft deep. How high is the plane above the floor of the canyon?

32. Mr. Jones had a balance of $89.00 in his checking account. He wrote a check for $105.95. By how much has he overdrawn his checking account?

2-5

When you multiply a positive number and a negative number, the product is negative. When you multiply two negative numbers or two positive numbers, the product is positive. The product of 0 and a rational number is 0.

Multiply.

33. $6(-4)$ **34.** $\frac{2}{3}\left(-\frac{3}{7}\right)$ **35.** $3(-7)(-2)(5)$

2-6

When you divide a positive number by a negative number or a negative number by a positive number, the quotient is negative. When you divide two negative numbers, the quotient is positive. Two numbers are **multiplicative inverses** or **reciprocals** if their product is 1. To divide by a rational number, multiply by its reciprocal.

Divide.

36. $21 \div (-7)$ **37.** $\frac{-45}{-9}$ **38.** $-\frac{7}{8} \div \frac{5}{4}$

2-7

The **distributive property of multiplication over subtraction** is used to multiply and factor algebraic expressions and to collect like terms.

Multiply.

39. $2(6x - 1)$ **40.** $-7(1 + 4x)$ **41.** $-3(2a - 3b + c)$

Factor.

42. $9a - 9$ **43.** $8x - 32y - 8$ **44.** $42z - 21x + 7$

Collect like terms.

45. $5x + 3x - x$ **46.** $5a - 3a$ **47.** $8m - 6m + 6$

2-8

The **property of** -1 states that $-1 \cdot a = -a$. The property of -1 and the distributive property allow us to rename the inverse of a sum as the sum of the inverses, $-(a + b) = -a + -b$.

Rename each additive inverse without parentheses.

48. $-(x + 7)$ **49.** $-(7a + 12b + c)$ **50.** $-(6 - z)$

When an expression contains more than one grouping symbol, you must do the computation in the innermost grouping symbols first.

Simplify.

51. $3a - (8a + 3)$ **52.** $7x - 5 - (10x - 4)$

53. $a - 5(a + b)$ **54.** $3p - 4(8p - 3)$

Simplify.

55. $[12 - (8 + 3)]$ **56.** $15 - [9 - (11 + 4)]$

2-9

Write an equation is a powerful strategy for many of the problems you will encounter while studying algebra. You should use the Problem-Solving Guideline, Develop and carry out a PLAN, when you need to write an equation.

Which equation(s) can be used to solve the problem?

57. A dozen roses costs $30. How much does each rose cost? Let r = the cost of one rose.

(A) $\frac{30}{12} = r$ **(B)** $30 - r = 12$ **(C)** $12r = 30$

Write an equation that could be used to solve the problem.

58. A professional baseball player made $289,170 for the 1988 baseball season. His team played 162 games in the season. How much did the player make per game?

39. $12x - 2$
40. $-7 - 28x$
41. $-6a + 9b - 3c$
42. $9(a - 1)$
43. $8(x - 4y - 1)$
44. $7(6z - 3x + 1)$
45. $7x$
46. $2a$
47. $2m + 6$
48. $-x - 7$
49. $-7a - 12b - c$
50. $-6 + z$
51. $-5a - 3$
52. $-3x - 1$
53. $-4a - 5b$
54. $-29p + 12$
55. 1
56. 21
57. (A) or (C)
58. $162a = 289{,}170$

ANSWERS

1. -16
2. $+9000$
3. 6.5
4. 105.5

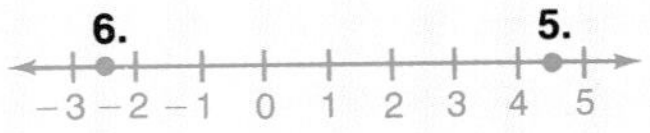

7. $<$
8. $<$
9. $-\frac{35}{10}$
10. $\frac{7}{3}$
11. -1.6
12. $-\frac{7}{5}$
13. -8
14. $-\frac{2}{3}$
15. 1.4
16. \$48
17. $-\frac{1}{3}$
18. 10
19. -2.5
20. 12
21. $7y + 23$
22. 12°
23. $-$\$130
24. -48
25. $\frac{3}{16}$
26. 240

Chapter 2 Test

Name the integer suggested by each situation.

1. Ed lost 16 points in a card game.

2. The highest points on the Grand Canyon are 9000 ft above sea level.

Find the absolute value.

3. $|6.5|$ **4.** $|-105.5|$

Graph each rational number on a number line.

5. $\frac{9}{2}$ **6.** -2.5

Use $>$ or $<$ to write a true sentence.

7. $-3.2 \quad 1.2$ **8.** $-\frac{3}{4} \quad -\frac{5}{8}$

Show that each number can be written as the ratio of two integers.

9. -3.5 **10.** $2\frac{1}{3}$

Add.

11. $3.1 + (-4.7)$ **12.** $-\frac{3}{5} + \left(-\frac{4}{5}\right)$ **13.** $-8 + 4 + (-7) + 3$

Find the additive inverse of each.

14. $\frac{2}{3}$ **15.** -1.4

16. Wendy had \$43 in her savings account. She withdrew \$25. Then she made a deposit of \$30. How much money does she have in her savings account now?

Subtract.

17. $\frac{1}{3} - \frac{2}{3}$ **18.** $2 - (-8)$ **19.** $3.2 - 5.7$

Simplify.

20. $6 + 7 - 4 - (-3)$ **21.** $3y + 16 - (-4y) + 7$

22. On a winter night the temperature dropped from 5°C to -7°C. How many degrees did the temperature drop?

23. Your total assets are \$170. You borrow \$300 to go on vacation. What is your net worth now?

Multiply.

24. $4(-12)$ **25.** $\left(-\frac{1}{2}\right)\left(-\frac{3}{8}\right)$ **26.** $5(-4)(-6)(2)$

Divide.

27. $-35 \div 7$ **28.** $\frac{-54}{-9}$ **29.** $\frac{-125}{25}$

Find the reciprocal.

30. $-\frac{8}{7}$ **31.** $-\frac{24}{7}$ **32.** $3y$

Divide.

33. $\frac{4}{9} \div \left(\frac{-7}{3}\right)$ **34.** $\frac{-15}{\frac{1}{x}}$ **35.** $\frac{-3}{5} \div \left(-\frac{5}{6}\right)$

Multiply.

36. $-7(x + 3)$ **37.** $\left(\frac{5}{3}\right)(x - 2y + z)$ **38.** $-7(-3a - 2b - 8)$

Factor.

39. $4x - 12$ **40.** $4a + 12b - 16$ **41.** $\frac{2x}{3} - \frac{y}{3}$

Collect like terms.

42. $-5x - 6x + 4x$ **43.** $q + t - 2t + q$ **44.** $4m - m + 3$

Multiply.

45. $(-1)(-21)$ **46.** $-1 \cdot 17$

Rename each additive inverse without parentheses.

47. $-(y - 8)$ **48.** $-(2a + 5b - c)$

Simplify.

49. $5n - (2n + m)$ **50.** $4x - 3(y + 2x)$

51. $50 - [12 - (16 + 5)]$ **52.** $6(9 - 4) - [10 - (6 + 8)]$

Which equation(s) can be used to solve the problem?

53. Saturnina got a 92 on the Chapter 2 test. That was 9 more points than she got on the Chapter 1 test. What was her score on the Chapter 1 test?

(A) $n - 92 = 9$ **(B)** $n = 92 + 9$ **(C)** $n + 9 = 92$

Write an equation that can be used to solve the problem.

54. A museum took in \$3456 from 576 patrons. What was the price of admittance to the museum?

55. Marta rode her bike 57 miles in two days. She rode 31 miles the first day. How far did she ride the second day?

27. -5
28. 6
29. -5
30. $-\frac{7}{8}$
31. $-\frac{7}{24}$
32. $\frac{1}{3y}$
33. $-\frac{4}{21}$
34. $-15x$
35. $\frac{18}{25}$
36. $-7x - 21$
37. $\frac{5}{3}x - \frac{10}{3}y + \frac{5}{3}z$
38. $21a + 14b + 56$
39. $4(x - 3)$
40. $4(a + 3b - 4)$
41. $\frac{1}{3}(2x - y)$
42. $-7x$
43. $2q - t$
44. $3m + 3$
45. 21
46. -17
47. $-y + 8$
48. $-2a - 5b + c$
49. $3n - m$
50. $-2x - 3y$
51. 59
52. 34
53. C
54. $576p = 3456$ or $p = \frac{3456}{576}$
55. $d + 31 = 57$ or $d = 57 - 31$

Test Item Analysis

Item	Lesson
1–4	2-1
5–10	2-2
11–16	2-3
17–23	2-4
24–26	2-5
27–35	2-6
36–44	2-7
45–52	2-8
53–55	2-9

CHAPTER 3

Equations

Chapter Overview

Solving equations in one variable is now formally introduced using the addition and multiplication properties. Skills learned in chapters one and two are extended in this chapter to solving equations. Simple equations involving absolute value are introduced and solved. Equations involving proportions and percents are presented.

Translation of phrases into algebraic notation is discussed, and word problems are translated into equations and solved using the Problem-Solving Guidelines. The problem-solving strategy *Make an Organized List* is introduced as another method of solving problems.

Objectives

3-1
- Use the addition property to solve equations.
- Solve problems using an equation.

3-2
- Use the multiplication property of equality to solve equations.
- Solve problems using an equation.

3-3
- Solve equations using the addition and multiplication properties.
- Solve equations by first collecting like terms.
- Solve equations containing parentheses.

3-4
- Translate phrases to algebraic expressions.
- Solve problems by writing and solving equations.

3-5
- Solve equations by first getting all variables on the same side of the equation.
- Solve equations that contain parentheses.

3-6
- Clear an equation of fractions or decimals.

3-7
- Solve for a given variable in a formula.

3-8
- Solve equations involving absolute value.

3-9
- Solve proportions.
- Solve problems involving proportions.

3-10
- Express decimals and fractions as percents and vice versa.
- Solve percent problems.
- Solve problems involving applications of percent.

3-11
- Translate compound phrases into algebraic expressions.
- Solve problems by writing and solving equations.

3-12
- Solve problems using the strategy *Make an Organized List* and other strategies.

Cooperative Learning Opportunities

The systematic approach to problem solving, derived from Pólya and presented in Lesson 3-4, is still the most logical method for analyzing and solving mathematical problems. But it is not easy to get students to follow this plan. Most would rather jump in than stand back for a moment and judge the depth of the water. Cooperative groups can help instill the problem-solving approach.

Display the **Problem-Solving Guidelines** on the chalkboard or by using Overhead Transparency T1. Arrange students in pairs. Assign roles A and B by flipping coins or by an odd–even count. Student A writes the answers to each of the nine questions in the guidelines. Student B performs the mathematical work.

Assign different problems from Exercises 13–24 on pages 134 and 135. After each problem, switch roles.

Multicultural Note: *Benjamin Banneker*

Proportion is an important practical topic that appears at all levels of mathematics. Most students are interested in scale drawing, an application of proportion. In Lesson 3-9, this interest can provide the opportunity for a multicultural and historical connection, the work of Benjamin Banneker.

Benjamin Banneker was an African-American mathematician and astronomer who lived during the founding years of the United States. Banneker was part of a six-person surveying team that worked on the plans for Washington, D.C. As the astronomer on the team, Banneker helped determine the outline for the city. Furthermore, when the plan for the city was suddenly lost, it is said that Banneker reproduced the entire city plan from memory. Banneker also prepared one of the first American almanacs and this made his name known throughout Europe.

For more information, see page 25 of **Multiculturalism in Mathematics, Science, and Technology**.

Alternative Assessment and Communication Ideas

Research and reporting assignments provide occasions to assess skills, concepts, and problem-solving abilities.

Ask students individually or in groups to choose one of the formulas on page 143. Find out what it means, what the variables stand for, and in what career fields it is applied. Students should find real-world applications of the formula or interview a person who needs the formula in his or her work. Reporting may be done by oral presentation to the class or from group to group, or through a creative scrapbook or bulletin board of clippings or drawings.

Some examples: Area is used in carpentry and interior and landscape design; $F = ma$ (force = mass × acceleration) is used in auto design and ballistics; $I = prt$ is used in banking and estate planning.

The **Write a convincing argument** exercise in Lesson 3-12 provides an opportunity for students to make brief written or oral presentations.

Investigations and Projects

As mentioned in the multicultural note, many students are interested in scale drawings and maps. Making a scale drawing can give students a realistic sense of how proportions work.

Have students, as individuals or in pairs, make a scale drawing of one floor of a house or other building. Explain that the drawing should show the shape, size, and position of each room and account for all space on that floor. Use a sketch to show what this means.

The project should be done following these steps.

(1) Draw a rough floor plan, showing the partitions of each room and closet, ignoring furniture and fixtures.
(2) Measure and record on the floor plan the dimensions of each room. Account for all space.
(3) Determine a scale so that a carefully drawn plan will fit on the paper.
(4) Calculate the reduced-scale units for each dimension.
(5) Do the scale drawing.
(6) Check the scale drawing against the floor plan for accuracy.

MANAGING CHAPTER 3

Lesson	PACING CHART (DAYS) 2-Year* A for E	1-Year Minimum	1-Year Regular	1-Year Advanced	Opening Activity	Cooperative Activity	Seat or Group Work
3-1	2	1	1	1	First Five Minutes 3-1: ***FFMTM*** p. 9 or **TE** p. 114	Explore: **SE** p. 114	Try This a–d
3-2	2	1	1	1	First Five Minutes 3-2: ***FFMTM*** p. 10 or **TE** p. 119	Appilcation: **SE** p. 119	Try This a–j
3-3	2	2	1	1	First Five Minutes 3-3: ***FFMTM*** p. 10 or **TE** p. 125	Connections: Geometry **SE** p. 129; ✂ Manipulative Activity 3: ***Enrichment*** p. 36	Try This a–i
3-4	2	1	1	1	First Five Minutes 3-4: ***FFMTM*** p. 11 or **TE** p. 130	Appilcation: **SE** p. 130	Try This a–i
3-5	2	1	1	1	First Five Minutes 3-5: ***FFMTM*** p. 11 or **TE** p. 136	Bonus Topic 3: ***Enrichment*** p. 4	Try This a–f
3-6	2	1	1	1	First Five Minutes 3-6: ***FFMTM*** p. 12 or **TE** p. 139	Problem 25: **SE** p. 141	Try This a–d
3-7	2	1	1	1	First Five Minutes 3-7: ***FFMTM*** p. 12 or **TE** p. 142; Application: **SE** p. 142	Looking for Errors 3: ***Enrichment*** p. 52	Try This a–d
3-8	2	1	1	1	First Five Minutes 3-8: ***FFMTM*** p. 12 or **TE** p. 145	Looking for Errors: **SE** p. 147	Try This a–c
3-9	2	1	1	1	First Five Minutes 3-9: ***FFMTM*** p. 13 or **TE** p. 148	Critical Thinking 3: ***Enrichment*** p. 20	Try This a–e
3-10	2	2	1	1	First Five Minutes 3-10: ***FFMTM*** p. 13 or **TE** p. 152; Math History: **SE** p. 152	Problems 50–51: **SE** p. 157	Try This a–p
3-11	2	1	1	1	First Five Minutes 3-11: ***FFMTM*** p. 14 or **TE** p. 158	Problem 26: **SE** p. 161	Try This a–e
3-12	2	1	1	0.5	First Five Minutes 3-11: ***FFMTM*** p. 14 or **TE** p. 163	Problem 2: **SE** p. 164	Problem 1: **SE** p. 164
Review	2	1	1	0.5			
Test	1	1	1	1			

*2-Year Management Guide can be found in *Algebra for Everyone*.

FFMTM: First Five Minutes Transparency Masters

Enrichment	Review/Assess	Reteach	Technology	Lesson
	Lesson Quiz: **TE** p. 116	Problem Bank 5: ***Problem Bank*** p. 22		**3-1**
Calculator Worksheet 8: ***Technology*** p. 10	Lesson Quiz: **TE** p. 122	Problem Bank 6: ***Problem Bank*** p. 23	Calculator Worksheet 8: ***Technology*** p. 10	**3-2**
✂ Manipulative Activity 3: ***Enrichment*** p. 36; Lesson Enrichment: **TE** p. 127	Lesson Quiz: **TE** p. 127	Skills Practice 7: ***SPMR*** p. 15		**3-3**
Problem for Programmers **SE** p. 135; Lesson Enrichment: **TE** p. 132	Mixed Review 5: ***SPMR*** p. 55; Lesson Quiz: **TE** p. 133; Quiz 5: ***Assessment*** p. 15		Problem for Programmers **SE** p. 135	**3-4**
Bonus Topic 3: ***Enrichment*** p. 4	Mixed Practice 5: **SE** p. 688; Lesson Quiz: **TE** p. 137			**3-5**
Critical Thinking 3: ***Enrichment*** p. 20	Lesson Quiz: **TE** p. 140	Skills Practice 8: ***SPMR*** p. 16		**3-6**
Calculator Worksheet 9: ***Technology*** p. 11	Lesson Quiz: **TE** p. 143 Quiz 6: ***Assessment*** p. 16	Problem Bank 7: ***Problem Bank*** p. 24	Calculator Worksheet 9: ***Technology*** p. 11	**3-7**
Looking for Errors: **SE** p. 147	Lesson Quiz: **TE** p. 146			**3-8**
Lesson Enrichment: **TE** p. 149	Mixed Review 6: ***SPMR*** p. 56; Lesson Quiz: **TE** p. 150	Problem Bank 8: ***Problem Bank*** p. 25	Calculator Worksheet 10: ***Technology*** p. 12	**3-9**
Calculator Worksheet 11: ***Technology*** p. 13	Lesson Quiz: **TE** p. 155	Skills Practice 9: ***SPMR*** p. 17; Problem Bank 9: ***Problem Bank*** p. 26	Percents: **SE** p. 154; Calculator Worksheet 11: ***Technology*** p. 13	**3-10**
BASIC Computer Project 2: ***Technology*** p. 64	Mixed Practice 6: **SE** p. 689; Lesson Quiz: **TE** p. 159	Problem Bank 10: ***Problem Bank*** p. 27	BASIC Computer Project 2: ***Technology*** p. 64	**3-11**
College Entrance Exam 1: ***Problem Bank*** pp. 47–51	Assessing Strategies 3: ***Assessment*** pp. 199–200	Strategy Problem Bank 3: ***Problem Bank*** p. 4		**3-12**
	Summary and Review: **SE** pp. 165–168; Test: **SE** pp. 168–169			**Review**
	Chapter 3 Exam: ***A for E*** pp. 141–142; Chapter 3 Test: ***Assessment*** pp. 47–48 (min.), 83–88 (reg.), 167–168 (adv.)			**Test**

SPMR: Skills Practice Mixed Review

The solution to the problem posed on the facing page can be found on pages 119 and 120.

Ready for Equations?

2-3 Add.

1. $-3 + (-8)$ -11 **2.** $8 + (-3) + (-11)$ -6 **3.** $-3.1 + 6.8$ 3.7

2-4 Subtract.

4. $9 - (-13)$ 22 **5.** $-7.2 - (-10.1)$ 2.9 **6.** $\frac{2}{3} - \frac{9}{10}$ $-\frac{7}{30}$

2-5 Multiply.

7. $9 \cdot (-4)$ -36 **8.** $\frac{3}{2} \cdot \frac{-4}{7}$ $-\frac{6}{7}$ **9.** $-\frac{2}{3} \cdot \frac{5}{8}$ $\frac{-5}{12}$

10. $-6 \cdot 8$ -48 **11.** $-11(-3)$ 33 **12.** $-7(-5)$ 35

2-6 Divide.

13. $\frac{3}{4} \div -\frac{1}{8}$ -6 **14.** $-\frac{7}{9} \div -\frac{2}{3}$ $\frac{7}{6}$ **15.** $-9.37 \div -0.1$ 93.7

2-7 Factor.

16. $9y - 45$ $9(y - 5)$ **17.** $bw + bx - by$ $b(w + x - y)$

18. $3y + 15 - 21x$ $3(y + 5 - 7x)$ **19.** $6w - 12x + 10$ $2(3w - 6x + 5)$

2-7 Multiply.

20. $3(x - 5)$ $3x - 15$ **21.** $8(4 + w)$ $32 + 8w$

2-8 Simplify.

22. $5x - (6 + 3x)$ $2x - 6$ **23.** $7w - 3 - (4w - 8)$ $3w + 5$

24. $[3(5 - 2) + 18] - [12 - (3 + 4)]$ 22

25. $[2(4x + 7) - 3] + [5(3 + x) + 2x]$ $15x + 26$

CHAPTER

Equations 3

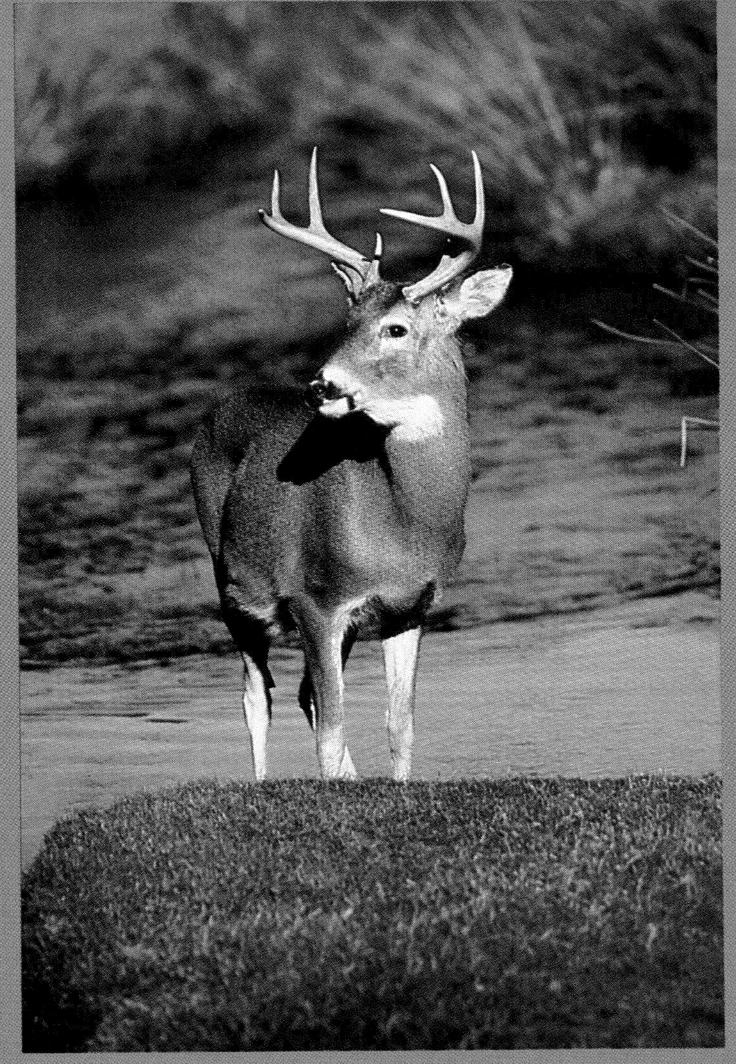

A conservationist estimates that there are about 12 times as many deer north of a river as there are south of the river. The last count indicates that there are about 1440 deer north of the river. How many deer are south of the river?

FIRST FIVE MINUTES

Fill in the missing number.

1. $2a + 4 + 3 = 2a + ?$ 7
2. $8x - 2x + 9 = ? + 9$ 6x
3. If $x = 9$, then $x + 5 = ? + 5$ 9
4. If $x = 2$, then $x + 5 = 2 + ?$ 5
5. If $a + 7 = 2 + 7$, then $a = ?$ 2

EXPLORE

Students should realize that there are many ways of balancing the scales. Some students will come up with obvious ones; others will be more creative. To check whether their scales balance, students should substitute. They should replace each pyramid with three balls and each cube with two balls. If they end up with the same number of balls on each side, the scale balances.

Using the Addition Property of Equality

This chapter presents a formal approach to solving equations.

Note that the direction "Solve" includes checking. Students can be asked to write formal checks, to use a calculator, or to check mentally.

You may wish to introduce the concept of "undoing" an equation. Students should look at the variable and determine what has been done to it. If something has been added to it, they can "undo" the addition by adding the inverse to both sides. Emphasize that the goal is to isolate the variable on one side of the equation.

Key Questions

- If $m + 4 = 7$, does $m = 4 + 7$? No
- If $a = b$, then does $a + 3 = b + 3$? Yes

3-1 The Addition Property of Equality

Explore

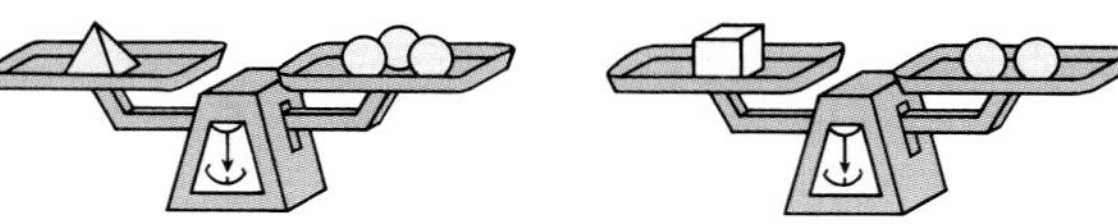

The scales at the right are balanced. Suppose you have as many of each object as you want. What are five different ways you can add objects to both sides of the scale below so it remains balanced?

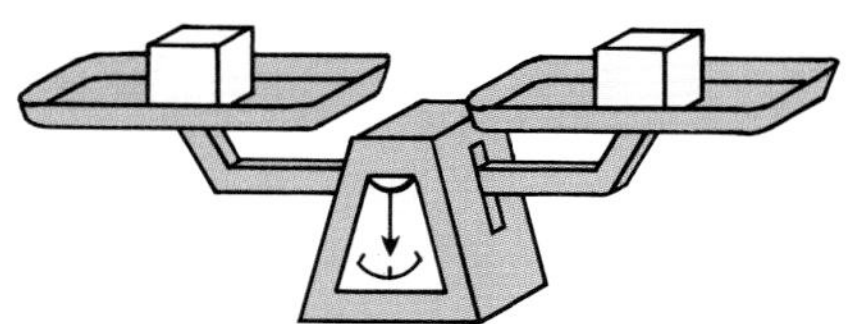

Using the Addition Property of Equality

Objective: Use the addition property to solve equations.

In Chapter 1 you learned two ways to solve equations: using mental math and the problem-solving strategy *Guess, Check, and Revise.* Recall that replacements that make an equation true are called solutions and that to solve an equation means to find all of its solutions.

You also learned that you can add the same number to both sides of an equation and get an equivalent equation. We call this the **addition property of equality.**

The Addition Property of Equality

For all rational numbers a, b, and c, if $a = b$, then $a + c = b + c$.

To solve an equation like $x + 5 = -7$, we need to get the variable alone on one side of the equation. In this equation, we have to add a number to 5 to "get rid of" the 5. Since -5 is the additive inverse, or the opposite of 5, $5 + (-5) = 0$. If we add -5 to both sides of the equation, we will get the variable alone. The following example shows these steps.

EXAMPLES Solve.

1.

$x + 5 = -7$ — We must add -5, the opposite of 5.

$x + 5 + (-5) = -7 + (-5)$ — Using the addition property to add -5 to both sides

$x + 0 = -12$ — Using the additive inverse property

$x = -12$ — Using the additive identity property

Check: $x + 5 = -7$

$-12 + 5$	-7
-7	-7 ✓

Substituting -12 for x

The solution is -12.

2.

$-6 = y - 8$ — Using the addition property to add 8 to both sides of the equation

$-6 + 8 = y - 8 + 8$ — Using the addition property to add 8 to both sides of the equation

$2 = y$

Check: $-6 = y - 8$

-6	$2 - 8$
-6	-6 ✓

Substituting 2 for y

The solution is 2.

3.

$x - 5.4 = 2.3$ — We must add 5.4, the opposite of -5.4.

$x - 5.4 + 5.4 = 2.3 + 5.4$ — Using the addition property to add 5.4 to both sides of the equation

$x = 7.7$

The solution is 7.7.

Substitution will show that 7.7 checks.

Try This Solve.

a. $x + 7 = 2$ -5 **b.** $y - 8 = -3$ 5 **c.** $5 = -4 + a$ 9

Problem Solving

Objective: Solve problems using an equation.

PROBLEM-SOLVING GUIDELINES
■ UNDERSTAND the problem
■ Develop and carry out a PLAN
■ Find the ANSWER and CHECK

You have seen in Chapters 1 and 2 that many problems can be solved by translating the situation into an equation and then solving the equation.

Chalkboard Examples

Solve using the addition principle.

1. $y + 9 = 15$
   $y + 9 + (-9) = 15 + (-9)$
   $y + 0 = 6$
   $y = 6$
2. $-4 = z + 3$
   $-4 + (-3) = z + 3 + (-3)$
   $-7 = z + 0$
   $-7 = z$
3. $a - 7 = -3$
   $a - 7 + 7 = -3 + 7$
   $a + 0 = 4$
   $a = 4$
4. $z + \frac{1}{2} = -\frac{3}{2}$
   $z + \frac{1}{2} + \left(-\frac{1}{2}\right) = -\frac{3}{2} + \left(-\frac{1}{2}\right)$
   $z + 0 = -\frac{4}{2} = -2$
   $z = -2$

Problem Solving

When translating from a problem to an equation, students should first assign a variable, or "unknown," to the quantity that they want to know. Encourage students to use estimation to determine whether an answer is reasonable.

Chalkboard Examples

Translate into an equation and solve.

1. Jerry owed \$9, but made enough money by washing cars so that he had \$15 left after paying off his debt. How much did he make by washing cars?
   Let w be the amount Jerry made by washing cars.
   $w - 9 = 15$
   $w - 9 + 9 = 15 + 9$
   $w = 24$
   He made \$24.
2. A herd of elephants grew by 23 last year to a total of 97. How many elephants were there originally?
   Let e be the original number of elephants.
   $e + 23 = 97$
   $e + 23 + (-23) = 97 + (-23)$
   $e + 0 = 74$
   $e = 74$

LESSON QUIZ

Solve.

1. $x + 7 = 12$
   $x = 5$
2. $t - 8 = 3$
   $t = 11$
3. $z + 8 = -9$
   $z = -17$
4. $-4 + y = 14$
   $y = 18$
5. Translate to an equation and solve. From dawn to noon, the temperature increased 14°F to reach 64°F. What was the temperature at dawn?
   Let d be the temperature at dawn.
   $d + 14 = 64$
   $d = 50$
   The temperature was 50°F.

Assignment Guide
Minimum: 1–52 e/o, MR

Regular: 1–60 m3, 61, MR

Advanced: 1–60 m3, 61–68, MR

EXAMPLE 4

In a basketball game Paula scored 18 points. This was 4 points higher than her average. What is her average?

Let a = Paula's average.

Paula's average plus 4 points is 18 points.

$$a + 4 = 18 \quad \text{Translating to an equation}$$
$$a + 4 + (-4) = 18 + (-4) \quad \text{Adding } -4 \text{ to both sides}$$
$$a + 0 = 14$$
$$a = 14$$

Paula's average was 14 points.
The answer is reasonable, since 14 is less than 18.

Try This Translate to an equation and solve.

d. The weekly rent on an ocean-front apartment was increased by \$32. The new rental cost is \$475. What was the previous rent? $x + 32 = 475$; \$443

3-1 EXERCISES

A

Solve.

1. $x + 2 = 6$ 4
2. $x + 5 = 8$ 3
3. $x + 15 = 26$ 11
4. $y + 9 = 43$ 34
5. $x + 6 = -8$ −14
6. $t + 9 = -12$ −21
7. $x + 16 = -2$ −18
8. $y + 25 = -6$ −31
9. $x - 9 = 6$ 15
10. $x - 8 = 5$ 13
11. $x - 7 = -21$ −14
12. $x - 3 = -14$ −11
13. $5 + t = 7$ 2
14. $8 + y = 12$ 4
15. $-7 + y = 13$ 20
16. $-9 + z = 15$ 24
17. $-3 + t = -9$ −6
18. $-6 + y = -21$ −15
19. $14 + x = 27$ 13
20. $-9 + y = -32$ −23
21. $m + 18 = 45$ 27
22. $b - 31 = 12$ 43
23. $24 = x + 5$ 19
24. $-18 = y - 4$ −14
25. $34 = t + 15$ 19
26. $-14 = p + 6$ −20
27. $a - 18 = 19$ 37
28. $a + 1.5 = 3$ 1.5
29. $n - 0.6 = 4$ 4.6
30. $x + 3.2 = 7$ 3.8
31. $4.7 = x - 1.2$ 5.9
32. $3.6 = m + 1$ 2.6
33. $c + 4 = -2.5$ −6.5
34. $s + 8.1 = 10$ 1.9
35. $x + 5.7 = 15$ 9.3
36. $s - 10 = -3.1$ 6.9
37. $r + \frac{1}{3} = \frac{8}{3}$ $\frac{7}{3}$
38. $t + \frac{3}{8} = \frac{5}{8}$ $\frac{1}{4}$
39. $m + \frac{5}{6} = -\frac{11}{12}$ $-\frac{7}{4}$
40. $x + \frac{2}{3} = -\frac{5}{6}$ $\frac{-3}{2}$
41. $x - \frac{5}{6} = \frac{7}{8}$ $\frac{41}{24}$
42. $y - \frac{3}{4} = \frac{5}{6}$ $\frac{19}{12}$
43. $x - \frac{3}{8} = \frac{1}{4}$ $\frac{5}{8}$
44. $a + \frac{4}{5} = \frac{1}{10}$ $-\frac{7}{10}$
45. $m + \frac{2}{9} = \frac{2}{3}$ $\frac{4}{9}$

Translate to an equation and solve.

46. Six more than a number is 57. Find the number.

47. A number decreased by 18 is -53. Find the number.

48. Four less than a number is eleven. Find the number.

49. A number increased by 42 is -100. Find the number.

50. In Churchill, Manitoba, the average daily low temperature in January is $-35°C$. This is 55° less than the average daily low temperature in Key West, Florida. What is the average daily low temperature in Key West in January?
Let t = the average low temperature for Key West in January.
   a. Write an expression using t that represents the average low temperature in Churchill.
   b. What is the average low temperature in Churchill in January?
   c. What are you asked to find in this problem?
   d. Write an equation using the information you know.
   e. Solve the equation and answer the problem.

51. In 1980 a TV magazine had a circulation of 18,870,730. That was 15,918,215 more than the circulation of a certain newspaper. What was the newspaper's circulation?
Let c = circulation for the newspaper.
   a. Write an expression using c for the circulation of the magazine.
   b. What was the actual circulation for the TV magazine?
   c. What are you asked to find in this problem?
   d. Write an equation using the information you know.
   e. Without solving the equation, decide whether the circulation for the newspaper will be more or less than the circulation for the magazine.
   f. Solve the equation and answer the problem.

52. In San Antonio, Texas, the Tower of the Americas has a height of 622 ft. This is 313 ft higher than the State Capitol Building located in Austin, Texas. What is the height of the State Capitol Building?
Let h = height of the State Capitol Building.
   a. Write an expression that represents the height of the Tower of the Americas.
   b. What is the height of the Tower of the Americas?
   c. What are you asked to find?
   d. Write an equation using the information you know.
   e. Without solving the equation, decide whether the height of the State Capitol Building will be greater than or less than the height of the Tower of Americas Building.
   f. Solve the equation and answer the problem.

ADDITION ANSWERS

Exercises

46. $x + 6 = 57$; 51
47. $x - 18 = -53$; -35
48. $x - 4 = 11$; 15
49. $x + 42 = -100$; -142
50. a. $t - 55$
b. $-35°$
c. The average daily low temperature in Key West in January
d. $t - 55 = -35$
e. $t = 20°$
51. a. $c + 15{,}918{,}215$
b. 18,870,730
c. The newspaper's circulation
d. $c + 15{,}918{,}215 = 18{,}870{,}730$
e. Less
f. $c = 2{,}952{,}515$
52. a. $h + 313$
b. 622 ft
c. The height of the State Capitol Building
d. $h + 313 = 622$
e. Less
f. $h = 309$ ft

Mixed Review

69. $7y - 4$
70. $-c - 2$
71. $-7w + 24$
72. $-7c$
73. $51 - 12y$
74. $-3 - 4t$
75. 100
76. 20
77. 32
78. -15
79. $\frac{1}{5}$
80. -24
81. -2
82. $-\frac{16}{21}$
83. $-\frac{98}{75}$
84. $\frac{1}{2}a = 5.52$ or $2(5.52) = a$

B

Solve each equation for x.

53. $8 - 25 = 8 + x - 21$ -4

54. $16 + x - 22 = -16$ -10

55. $x + 5 = x - (3 + x)$ -8

56. $x + 3 = 3 + a - b$ $a - b$

57. $x + 7 = b + 10$ $b + 3$

58. $1 - c = a + x$ $1 - c - a$

Solve.

59. At the end of the month the computer inventory indicated that there were 319 blank video cassettes in stock. This was after sales of 142 and a restock of 75. How many cassettes were in stock at the beginning of the month? 386

60. After totaling her checkbook at the end of the week, Andrea found that she has \$124.23 in her checking account. She had written checks for \$12.24, \$15.05, and \$22.00, and she had deposited \$55.12. How much was in her checking account at the beginning of the week? \$118.40

61. ***Critical Thinking*** Write an equation for which the solution $-\frac{7}{12}$ is found using addition. Answers may vary.

Challenge

62. Suppose k is a solution of some equation. Can $-k$ ever be a solution of this equation? Yes, e.g. $|x| = 3$, $3x = 0$, $x^2 = 4$.

63. Tell why it is not necessary to state a subtraction property for equation solving. Subtraction is the addition of inverses.

64. Solve $x - 1 + 2x - 2 + 3x - 3 = 30 + 4x$. 18

65. If $x - 4720 = 1634$, find $x + 4720$. 11,074

66. Solve $x + x = x$. 0

67. Solve $x + 3 = 3 + x$. Any value

68. One student solved the equation $6 - x = 10$ by subtracting 6 from both sides and got 4. Explain what that student did wrong.
The student solved for $-x$. $x = -4$.

Mixed Review

Simplify. **69.** $9y - (2y + 4)$ **70.** $7c - (8c + 2)$

71. $8w - 3(5w - 8)$ **72.** $6a + 2c - 3(2a + 3c)$

73. $3[5 + 4(3 - y)]$ **74.** $5t - (3 + 9t)$

Evaluate. **75.** $(5a)^2$ for $a = 2$ **76.** $5a^2$ for $a = 2$ **77.** s^1 for $s = 32$

Multiply. **78.** $3(-5)$ **79.** $\left(-\frac{1}{3}\right)\left(-\frac{3}{5}\right)$ **80.** $4(-2)(-1)(-3)$

Divide. **81.** $-4 \div 2$ **82.** $\frac{2}{7} \div \left(-\frac{3}{8}\right)$ **83.** $-\frac{14}{15} \div \frac{5}{7}$

84. Mario spent half of his weekly allowance to buy a book. The book cost \$5.52. Write an equation to find Mario's allowance.

3-2 The Multiplication Property of Equality

Application

A conservationist estimates that there are about 12 times as many deer north of a river as there are south of the river. The last count indicates that there are about 1440 deer north of the river. About how many deer are south of the river?

In this lesson you will learn how to solve equations like $12s = 1440$. This equation can be used to find out how many deer there are south of the river.

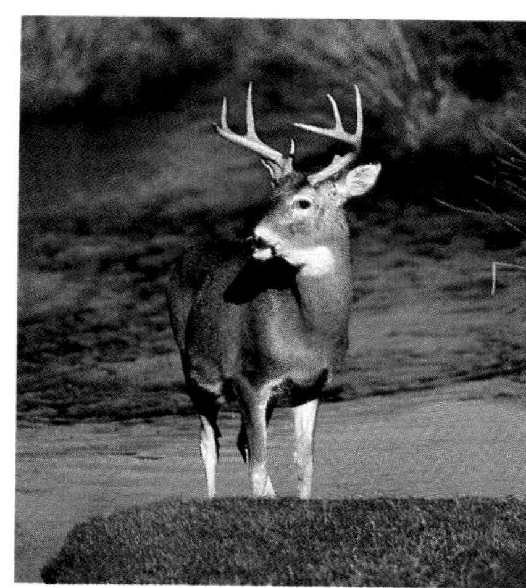

Using the Multiplication Property of Equality

Objective: Use the multiplication property of equality to solve equations.

Equations such as $12s = 1440$ can be solved using the multiplication property of equality.

The Multiplication Property of Equality
For all rational numbers a, b, and c, if $a = b$, then $ac = bc$.

When using the multiplication property of equality, we can say that "we multiply both sides of the equation by the same number."

To solve an equation like $12s = 1440$, we need to get the variable alone on one side of the equal sign. In this equation, we have to multiply $12s$ by some number to "get rid of" the 12. Since $\frac{1}{12}$ is the multiplicative inverse or reciprocal of 12, $\frac{1}{12} \cdot 12 = 1$. Therefore, if we multiply both sides of the equation by $\frac{1}{12}$, we will get the variable alone. The following example shows these steps.

3-2

FIRST FIVE MINUTES

Find the number that goes in the blank.

1. $2 \cdot 3 = 3 \cdot \underline{2}$
2. $3x = \underline{3}\,x$
3. $a \cdot 5 = a \cdot \underline{5}$
4. $(x \cdot 7) \cdot \frac{1}{7} = (x \cdot 7) \cdot \underline{\frac{1}{7}}$
5. If $x = 5$, then $3 \cdot x = \underline{3} \cdot 5$
6. If $4u = 9$, then $\underline{\frac{1}{4}} \cdot 4u = \frac{1}{4} \cdot 9$

APPLICATION

You may want to ask students to translate this problem to an equation. The problem will be solved in Example 1.

Using the Multiplication Property of Equality

Remind students that $-\frac{2}{3} = \frac{2}{-3} = \frac{-2}{3}$. The rules for multiplying and dividing integers guarantee that these numbers are equivalent.

Emphasize again that the goal is to isolate the variable, and that this can be attained by "undoing" the multiplication using the multiplication property of equality.

In Example 1, you can show that "multiplying by $\frac{1}{3}$" is equivalent to "dividing by 3," as shown in Chapter 1.

Key Questions

- If $d = e$, does $7d = 7e$? Yes
- Which of the following are reciprocals of $-\frac{3}{4}$?

$-\frac{4}{3}$ Yes

$\frac{-4}{3}$ Yes

$\frac{3}{-4}$ No

$\frac{4}{-3}$ Yes

$-\frac{16}{9}$ Yes

Chalkboard Examples

Solve and check.

1. $5x = 30$

$\frac{1}{5} \cdot 5x = \frac{1}{5} \cdot 30$

$1x = 6$

$x = 6$

2. $-6z = 42$

$\frac{1}{-6} \cdot (-6z) = \frac{1}{-6} \cdot 42$

$1z = \frac{42}{-6}$

$z = -7$

3. $\frac{3}{5}v = \frac{2}{7}$

$\frac{5}{3} \cdot \frac{3}{5}v = \frac{5}{3} \cdot \frac{2}{7}$

$1v = \frac{10}{21}$

$v = \frac{10}{21}$

Solve.

4. $\frac{z}{4} = 12$

$4 \cdot \frac{z}{4} = 4 \cdot 12$

$z = 48$

5. $\frac{w}{13} = -2$

$13 \cdot \frac{w}{13} = 13 \cdot (-2)$

$w = -26$

6. $\frac{r}{-3} = -7$

$-3 \cdot \frac{r}{-3} = -3 \cdot (-7)$

$r = 21$

EXAMPLE 1 Solve.

$12s = 1440$ We must multiply by $\frac{1}{12}$, the reciprocal of 12.

$\frac{1}{12} \cdot 12s = \frac{1}{12} \cdot 1440$ Using the multiplication property to multiply both sides of the equation by $\frac{1}{12}$

$1 \cdot s = 120$ Using the multiplicative inverse property

$s = 120$ Using the multiplicative identity property

Check:

$12s$	1440
$12 \cdot 120$	1440
1440	1440 ✓

Substituting 120 for s

The solution is 120.

This is the solution to the application on page 119; there are 120 deer south of the river.

EXAMPLE 2 Solve.

$-x = 9$ We think of $-x$ as $-1 \cdot x$. We must multiply by -1, the reciprocal of -1.

$-1(-x) = -1(9)$ Using the multiplication property to multiply both sides by -1

$1 \cdot x = -9$ $-1(-x) = -1(-1 \cdot x) = (-1 \cdot -1)x = 1 \cdot x$

$x = -9$ Using the multiplicative identity property

Check:

$-x$	9
$-(-9)$	9
9	9 ✓

Substituting -9 for x

The solution is -9.

EXAMPLE 3 Solve.

$$\frac{3}{8} = -\frac{5}{4}x$$

$$-\frac{4}{5} \cdot \frac{3}{8} = -\frac{4}{5}\left(-\frac{5}{4}x\right)$$

Using the multiplication property to multiply both sides by $-\frac{4}{5}$, the reciprocal of $-\frac{5}{4}$

$$-\frac{3}{10} = x$$

Check:

$\frac{3}{8}$	$-\frac{5}{4}x$
$\frac{3}{8}$	$-\frac{5}{4}\left(-\frac{3}{10}\right)$
$\frac{3}{8}$	$\frac{3}{8}$ ✓

Substituting $-\frac{3}{10}$ for x

The solution is $-\frac{3}{10}$.

Try This Solve.

a. $5x = 25$ 5 **b.** $4a = -7$ $-\frac{7}{4}$ **c.** $-3y = -42$ 14

d. $-\frac{1}{3}y = 4$ −12 **e.** $\frac{5}{6} = -\frac{2}{3}x$ $-\frac{5}{4}$ **f.** $-x = 6$ −6

An equation like $\frac{y}{9} = 14$ can also be solved using the multiplication property. In Chapter 2 you learned that $\frac{y}{9}$ can be written

$$\frac{y}{9} = \frac{1}{9} \cdot y$$

We know that the multiplicative inverse of $\frac{1}{9}$ is 9, since $\frac{1}{9} \cdot 9 = 1$. Example 4 shows how to use this relationship to solve the equation $\frac{y}{9} = 14$.

EXAMPLE 4 Solve.

$$\frac{y}{9} = 14$$

$$9 \cdot \frac{y}{9} = 9 \cdot 14$$

$$y = 126$$

Check: $\frac{y}{9} = 14$

$\frac{126}{9}$	14
14	14 ✓

The solution is 126.

Try This Solve.

g. $\frac{x}{5} = 10$ 50 **h.** $\frac{m}{-3} = -12$ 36 **i.** $\frac{-t}{4} = 6$ −24

Problem Solving

Objective: Solve problems using an equation.

PROBLEM-SOLVING GUIDELINES
■ UNDERSTAND the problem
■ Develop and carry out a PLAN
■ Find the ANSWER and CHECK

After translating a problem to an equation, we may need to use the multiplication property to solve the equation.

EXAMPLE 5 Solve.

In 1982, the metropolitan population of Lubbock, Texas, was 216,700. That was about one fifth of the metropolitan population of Arlington, Texas. What was the approximate metropolitan population of Arlington?

Let a = population of Arlington.

"The population of Lubbock . . . about $\frac{1}{5}$ of the population of Arlington" can be written as $\frac{1}{5}a$.

$\frac{1}{5}a$ = population of Lubbock

Problem Solving

Chalkboard Examples

1. Kayla bought twelve identical bowling balls, which weighed a total of 90 pounds. How much did each ball weigh?
   Let b be the weight of one bowling ball.
   $12b = 90$
   $\frac{1}{12} \cdot 12b = \frac{1}{12} \cdot 90$
   $b = \frac{90}{12} = 7.5$
   Each ball weighs 7.5 lb.
2. If 16 turnips cost a total of $4, how much does one turnip cost?
   Let r be the cost of one turnip.
   $16r = 4$
   $\frac{1}{16} \cdot 16r = \frac{1}{16} \cdot 4$
   $r = \frac{4}{16} = 0.25$
   One turnip costs $0.25.

LESSON QUIZ

Solve.

1. $7x = 56$

   $x = \frac{56}{7} = 8$

2. $8y = -72$

   $y = -\frac{72}{8} = -9$

3. $-5m = -8$

   $m = \frac{-8}{-5} = \frac{8}{5}$

4. $3.5n = 17.5$

   $n = \frac{17.5}{3.5} = 5$

5. $\frac{m}{6} = 13$

   $m = 6 \cdot 13 = 78$

Assignment Guide
Minimum: 1–45 e/o, MR

Regular: 1–55 m3, 56, MR

Advanced: 1–55 m4, 56–58, MR

We can write the following equation.

$$\frac{1}{5}a = 216{,}700 \qquad \frac{1}{5}a \text{ and } 216{,}700 \text{ both represent the population of Lubbock.}$$

$$5 \cdot \frac{1}{5}a = 5 \cdot 216{,}700 \qquad \text{Using the multiplication property}$$

$$a = 1{,}083{,}500$$

There are about 1,083,500 people in metropolitan Arlington. If we estimate using 1,000,000 rather than 1,083,500, we get $1{,}000{,}000 \cdot \frac{1}{5} = 200{,}000$, which is close to 216,700. Therefore, the number 1,083,500 seems reasonable.

Try This Solve.

j. Penny bought a 12-bottle case of juice on sale for \$6.72. What was the price for each bottle? $12x = \$6.72$; \$0.56

3-2 EXERCISES

A

Solve.

1. $6x = 36$ 6	**2.** $3x = 39$ 13	**3.** $5x = 45$ 9
4. $9x = 72$ 8	**5.** $84 = 7x$ 12	**6.** $56 = 8x$ 7
7. $-x = 40$ −40	**8.** $100 = -x$ −100	**9.** $-x = -1$ 1
10. $-68 = -r$ 68	**11.** $7x = -49$ −7	**12.** $9x = -36$ −4
13. $-12x = 72$ −6	**14.** $-15x = 105$ −7	**15.** $-21x = -126$ 6
16. $-13x = -104$ 8	**17.** $\frac{t}{7} = -9$ −63	**18.** $\frac{y}{-8} = 11$ −88
19. $\frac{3}{4}x = 27$ 36	**20.** $\frac{4}{5}x = 16$ 20	**21.** $\frac{-t}{3} = 7$ −21
22. $\frac{-x}{6} = 9$ −54	**23.** $-\frac{m}{3} = \frac{1}{5}$ $-\frac{3}{5}$	**24.** $\frac{1}{9} = -\frac{z}{7}$ $-\frac{7}{9}$
25. $-\frac{3}{5}r = -\frac{9}{10}$ $\frac{3}{2}$	**26.** $-\frac{2}{5}y = -\frac{4}{15}$ $\frac{2}{3}$	**27.** $-\frac{3}{2}r = -\frac{27}{4}$ $\frac{9}{2}$
28. $\frac{5}{7}x = -\frac{10}{14}$ −1	**29.** $6.3x = 44.1$ 7	**30.** $2.7y = 54$ 20
31. $-3.1y = 21.7$ −7	**32.** $-3.3y = 6.6$ −2	**33.** $38.7m = 309.6$ 8
34. $29.4x = 235.2$ 8	**35.** $-\frac{2}{3}y = -30$ 45	**36.** $-\frac{9}{7}y = 3$ $-\frac{7}{3}$

Translate to an equation and solve.

37. Eighteen times a number is -1008. Find the number.

38. Some number multiplied by negative eight is 744. Find the number.

39. Katha paid the same price for each of 8 tickets to a concert. If she paid a total of \$170, what was the price of each ticket?
Let p = price of each ticket.
   a. Write an expression using p that represents the price of all 8 tickets.
   b. What did she pay for all 8 tickets?
   c. What are you asked to find in this problem?
   d. Write an equation using the information you know.
   e. Without solving the equation decide whether the price of each ticket is more or less than \$30? How do you know?
   f. Solve the equation and answer the problem.

40. In 1969 Apollo 10 reached a speed of 24,790 mi/h. That is 37 times the speed of the first supersonic flight in 1947. What was the speed of the 1947 flight?
Let s = speed of first supersonic flight in 1947.
   a. Write an expression using s that represents the speed of Apollo 10.
   b. What was the speed of Apollo 10?
   c. What are you asked to find in this problem?
   d. Write an equation using the information you know.
   e. Without solving the equation, estimate the speed of the first supersonic flight.
   f. Solve the equation and answer the problem.

41. In 1980 the population of Las Vegas, the largest city in Nevada, was 164,275. That was about 30 times the population of Ely, Nevada's ninth largest city. What was the population of Ely?
Let e = population of Ely, Nevada.
   a. Write an expression using e for the population of Las Vegas in 1980.
   b. What was the population of Las Vegas in 1980?
   c. What are you asked to find in this problem?
   d. Write an equation using the information you know.
   e. Without solving the equation, estimate the population in Ely, Nevada, in 1980.
   f. Solve the equation and answer the problem.

42. A case of a dozen video cassette tapes costs \$191.40. Find the cost of a single tape.

ADDITIONAL ANSWERS

Exercises

37. $18x = -1008$; -56
38. $-8x = 744$; -93
39. **a.** $8p$
b. \$170
c. The price of one ticket
d. $8p = 170$
e. Less; if each ticket costs \$30, 8 tickets would cost \$240.
f. $p = \$21.25$
40. **a.** $37s$
b. 24,790 mi/h
c. The speed of the 1947 flight
d. $37s = 24{,}790$
e. Answers may vary. ≈ 600 mi/h
f. $s = 670$ mi/h
41. **a.** $30e$
b. 164,275
c. The population of Ely
d. $30e = 164{,}275$
e. Answers may vary. ≈ 6000
f. $e \approx 5476$
42. $12t = 191.40$; \$15.95

43. $1131 = \frac{1}{3}f$; 3393

44. $\frac{9}{10}n = 7{,}028{,}000$; $\approx 7{,}808{,}889$

45. $\frac{3}{5}a = 16{,}856$; $\approx 28{,}093$

Mixed Review

59. $4x + 9y$
60. $-4a - 4$
61. $5r - 5s$
62. 0
63. -80
64. 0
65. 2.52
66. -42
67. -44
68. 18.6
69. 17
70. 216
71. 24
72. 3
73. -3
74. $4(x + 2y - 3z)$
75. $3(2a - 4b - 3c)$

43. A wildlife expert estimates that in a certain year the number of male fawns born will be about $\frac{1}{3}$ the number of adult female deer. Suppose 1131 male fawns are born. About how many female deer are there?

44. The population of London, England, is about 7,028,000. This is about $\frac{9}{10}$ of the population of New York City. What is the population of New York City?

45. Roger Staubach completed 16,856 passes in his pro football career. This is about $\frac{3}{5}$ the number he attempted. About how many passes did he attempt?

B

Use the first equation to find the missing value or expression in the second equation.

46. $6a + 6b = 72$
$a + b = ??$ 12

47. $\frac{x}{3} + 2 = 12$
$x + 6 = ??$ 36

48. $\frac{2m}{5} - 2 = 12$
$2m - 10 = ??$ 60

49. $\frac{2a^2}{3} + 1 = 8$
$2a^2 + 3 = ??$ 24

Solve each equation for x.

50. $ax = 5a$ 5

51. $3x = \frac{b}{a} (a \neq 0)$ $\frac{b}{3a}$

52. $cx = a^2 + 1$ $\frac{a^2 + 1}{c}$

53. $abx = 1$ $\frac{1}{ab}$

54. $0 \cdot x = 0$ Any value

55. $0 \cdot x = 9$ No value

56. ***Critical Thinking*** If a, b, and c are rational numbers such that $a = b$ and $c = 0$, does $ac = bc$? Explain. Yes; $ac = 0$ and $bc = 0$

Challenge

57. Explain why it is not necessary to have a division property for solving equations. Division is multiplication by reciprocal.

58. Write two different equations that each have the solution 2 and could be solved using the multiplication property. Answers may vary.

Mixed Review

Simplify. **59.** $8x + 4y - (4x - 5y)$ **60.** $3 - (4a + 7)$

61. $7r - (s + 2r) - 4s$ **62.** $(2a + 4b) - (2a + 4b)$

Multiply. **63.** $-5 \cdot 8 \cdot 2$ **64.** $(-7) \cdot (-24) \cdot 0$ **65.** $(-2.1)(-1.2)$

66. $(-3)(-7)(-2)$ **67.** $(-4)(-2.2)(-5)$ **68.** $(-2)(-3.1)3$

Evaluate. **69.** $t^4 + 1$ for $t = 2$ **70.** $8y^3$ for $y = 3$

71. $3|x|$ for $x = -8$ **72.** $y^2 + 2y$ for $y = -3$

73. $4z + |z|$ for $z = -1$

Factor. **74.** $4x + 8y - 12z$ **75.** $6a - 12b - 9c$

3-3 Using the Properties Together

Applying Both Properties

Objective: Solve equations using the addition and multiplication properties.

To solve some equations, you may need to use both the addition property and the multiplication property.

EXAMPLE 1 Solve.

$$3x + 4 = 13$$

$$3x + 4 + (-4) = 13 + (-4)$$ Using the addition property to add -4 to both sides

$$3x = 9$$

$$\frac{1}{3} \cdot 3x = \frac{1}{3} \cdot 9$$ Using the multiplication property to multiply both sides by $\frac{1}{3}$

$$x = 3$$

Check:

$3x + 4$	$= 13$
$3(3) + 4$	13
$9 + 4$	13
13	13 ✓

The solution is 3.

EXAMPLE 2 Solve.

$$-5x + 6 = 16$$

$$-5x + 6 + (-6) = 16 + (-6)$$ Using the addition property to add -6 to both sides

$$-5x = 10$$

$$-\frac{1}{5} \cdot (-5x) = -\frac{1}{5} \cdot 10$$ Using the multiplication property to multiply both sides by $-\frac{1}{5}$

$$x = -2$$

Check:

$-5x + 6$	$= 16$
$-5(-2) + 6$	16
$10 + 6$	16
16	16 ✓

The solution is -2.

FIRST FIVE MINUTES

Solve.

1. $x - 13 = 17$ $x = 30$
2. $-5 + z = 21$ $z = 26$
3. $8a = 7$ $a = \frac{7}{8}$
4. $\frac{3}{5}y = \frac{1}{2}$ $y = \frac{5}{6}$

Applying Both Properties

Point out that when the equation is in the form $ax + b = c$, it is usually easier to use the addition property before using the multiplication property.

When students become proficient with the addition and multiplication properties, they may take shortcuts, such as subtracting instead of adding the inverse and dividing instead of multiplying by the reciprocal. They may also skip steps, going directly from $3x = 15$ to $x = 5$. You may want to allow students to skip steps as long as they demonstrate that they understand the process.

Key Question

- Solve $ax + b = c$ for x.

$$ax + b + (-b) = c + (-b)$$
$$ax = c - b$$
$$\frac{1}{a} \cdot ax = \frac{1}{a}(c - b)$$
$$x = \frac{c - b}{a}$$

Chalkboard Examples

Solve.

1. $7x + 6 = 13$
   $7x + 6 + (-6) = 13 + (-6)$
   $7x = 7$
   $x = 1$
2. $-4y + 3 = 12$
   $-4y = 9$
   $y = -\frac{9}{4}$
3. $34 - 3z = 14$
   $-3z = -20$
   $z = \frac{-20}{-3}$
   $z = \frac{20}{3}$
4. $5 = 4x - 12$
   $17 = 4x$
   $\frac{17}{4} = x$

Collecting Like Terms in Equations

Stress the need to simplify before beginning to solve an equation.

Chalkboard Examples

Solve.

1. $7x - 3x + 4 = 6$
$4x + 4 = 6$
$4x = 2$
$x = \frac{2}{4}$
$x = \frac{1}{2}$

2. $-2a + 3 + 6a = 14$
$4a + 3 = 14$
$4a = 11$
$a = \frac{11}{4}$

3. $-7z + 2z - 3z - 7 = 17$
$-8z - 7 = 17$
$-8z = 24$
$z = -3$

Equations Containing Parentheses

Explain to students that in some places parentheses must be used, and in some places parentheses are optional. The parentheses in the expression

$2(x + 1)$

are necessary, although the expression can be rewritten in an equivalent form that doesn't use parentheses. The parentheses in the expression

$(-3)x$

can be removed without changing the meaning of the expression. Parentheses are often a matter of style.

Key Questions

Would the expression change in meaning if the parentheses were removed?

- $3(x)$ No
- $3(x + 1)$ Yes
- $7(-x)$ Yes

Try This Solve.

a. $9x + 6 = 51$ 5 **b.** $-8y - 4 = 28$ −4

c. $-18 - 3x = -57$ 13 **d.** $4 - 8x = 12$ −1

Collecting Like Terms in Equations

Objective: Solve equations by first collecting like terms.

If there are like terms on one side of an equation, we collect them before using the properties.

EXAMPLE 3 Solve.

$$6x + 2x = 15$$
$$8x = 15 \quad \text{Collecting like terms}$$
$$\frac{1}{8} \cdot 8x = \frac{1}{8} \cdot 15 \quad \text{Multiplying both sides by } \frac{1}{8}$$
$$x = \frac{15}{8}$$

Substitution will show that $\frac{15}{8}$ checks.
The solution is $\frac{15}{8}$.

Try This Solve.

e. $4c + 3c = 21$ 3 **f.** $9x - 4x = 20$ 4

Equations Containing Parentheses

Objective: Solve equations containing parentheses.

Equations containing parentheses can often be solved by first using the distributive property.

EXAMPLE 4 Solve.

$$2(2y + 3) = 14$$
$$4y + 6 = 14 \quad \text{Using the distributive property}$$
$$4y + 6 + (-6) = 14 + (-6) \quad \text{Using the addition property}$$
$$4y = 8$$
$$\frac{1}{4} \cdot 4y = \frac{1}{4} \cdot 8 \quad \text{Using the multiplication property}$$
$$1 \cdot y = 2$$
$$y = 2$$

Substitution will show that 2 checks.
The solution is 2.

EXAMPLE 5 Solve.

$$
\begin{aligned}
4(3x - 2) + 12x &= 40 \\
12x - 8 + 12x &= 40 && \text{Using the distributive property} \\
24x - 8 &= 40 && \text{Collecting like terms} \\
24x - 8 + 8 &= 40 + 8 && \text{Using the addition property} \\
24x &= 48 \\
\frac{1}{24} \cdot 24x &= \frac{1}{24} \cdot 48 && \text{Using the multiplication property} \\
1 \cdot x &= 2 \\
x &= 2
\end{aligned}
$$

Substitution will show that 2 checks.
The solution is 2.

Try This Solve.

g. $9 = 3(x + 6)$ -3 **h.** $24 - 2(2m + 1) = -6$ 7

i. $3a + 5(a - 2) = 6$ 2

3-3 EXERCISES

A

Solve.

1. $5x + 6 = 31$ 5

2. $3x + 6 = 30$ 8

3. $8x + 4 = 68$ 8

4. $7z + 9 = 72$ 9

5. $4x - 6 = 34$ 10

6. $6x - 3 = 15$ 3

7. $3x - 9 = 33$ 14

8. $5x - 7 = 48$ 11

9. $7x + 2 = -54$ -8

10. $5x + 4 = -41$ -9

11. $6y + 3 = -45$ -8

12. $9t + 8 = -91$ -11

13. $-4x + 7 = 35$ -7

14. $-5x - 7 = 108$ -23

15. $-7x - 24 = -129$ 15

16. $-6z - 18 = -132$ 19

17. $-4x + 71 = -1$ 18

18. $-8y + 83 = -85$ 21

Solve.

19. $5x + 7x = 72$ 6

20. $4x + 5x = 45$ 5

21. $8x + 7x = 60$ 4

22. $3x + 9x = 96$ 8

23. $4x + 3x = 42$ 6

24. $6x + 19x = 100$ 4

25. $4y - 2y = 10$ 5

26. $8y - 5y = 48$ 16

27. $-6y - 3y = 27$ -3

28. $-4y - 8y = 48$ -4

29. $-7y - 8y = -15$ 1

30. $-10y - 3y = -39$ 3

31. $10.2y - 7.3y = -58$ -20

32. $6.8y - 2.4y = -88$ -20

Chalkboard Examples

Solve.

1. $8(3x + 2) = 30$
 $24x + 16 = 30$
 $24x = 14$
 $x = \frac{14}{24}$ or $\frac{7}{12}$

2. $5x + 5(4x - 1) = 20$
 $5x + 20x - 5 = 20$
 $25x - 5 = 20$
 $25x = 25$
 $x = 1$

LESSON ENRICHMENT

Have students solve the following equation by two different methods.

$4(x - 2) = 4$

$4x - 8 = 4$	$(x - 2) = \frac{4}{4}$
$4x = 12$	$x - 2 = 1$
$x = 3$	$x = 3$

LESSON QUIZ

Solve.

1. $4z + 5 = 13$
 $4z = 8$
 $z = 2$

2. $9u - 3 = -4$
 $9u = -1$
 $u = -\frac{1}{9}$

3. $-2y + 7y = 6$
 $5y = 6$
 $y = \frac{6}{5}$

4. $4(x + 2) + 2 = 8$
 $4x + 8 + 2 = 8$
 $4x + 10 = 8$
 $4x = -2$
 $x = -\frac{2}{4}$ or $-\frac{1}{2}$

Assignment Guide
Minimum: Day 1: 1–32 e/o
Day 2: 33–50 e/o, MR
Regular: 1–60 m3, 61, MR

Advanced: 1–60 m3, 61–63, MR

Solve.

33. $5(3x - 2) = 35$ 3

34. $3(2y - 3) = 27$ 6

35. $4(2m - 3) = 28$ 5

36. $40 = 5(3x + 2)$ 2

37. $9 = 3(5x - 2)$ 1

38. $6(3 + 2m) = -18$ -3

39. $-2(4y - 3) = 6$ 0

40. $(4 + 3x)(-3) = -9$ $-\frac{1}{3}$

41. $2(3 + 4m) - 9 = 45$ 6

42. $3(5 + 3m) - 8 = 88$ 9

43. $12 - 3(x - 5) = 21$ 2

44. $5 - 2(y + 1) = 21$ -9

45. $5r - 2(2r + 8) = 16$ 32

46. $6b - 4(2b + 8) = 16$ -24

47. $2(2x - 4) + 3x = -1$ 1

48. $-5a + 4(2 + 2a) = -1$ -3

49. $\frac{1}{3}x + 2\left(\frac{1}{3}x + 5\right) = 12$ 2

50. $3\left(\frac{1}{8}m - \frac{1}{2}\right) + \frac{3}{4}m = \frac{3}{2}$ $\frac{8}{3}$

B

Provide a reason justifying each step in the solution.

51. $6(2x - 8) = 36$

a. $\frac{1}{6} \cdot 6(2x - 8) = \frac{1}{6} \cdot 36$ — Using the multiplication property

b. $2x - 8 = 6$ — Simplifying

c. $2x - 8 + 8 = 6 + 8$ — Using the addition property

d. $2x = 14$ — Simplifying

e. $\frac{1}{2} \cdot 2x = \frac{1}{2} \cdot 14$ — Using the multiplication property

$x = 7$

52. $7y + (8 + 3y) = 38$

a. $7y + (3y + 8) = 38$ — Using the commutative property

b. $(7y + 3y) + 8 = 38$ — Using the associative property

c. $10y + 8 = 38$ — Collecting like terms

d. $10y + 8 - 8 = 38 - 8$ — Using the addition property

e. $10y = 30$ — Simplifying

f. $\frac{1}{10} \cdot 10y = \frac{1}{10} \cdot 30$ — Using the multiplication property

g. $y = 3$ — Simplifying

53. $9m - 2(2m + 6) = 28$

a. $9m - 4m - 12 = 28$ — Using the distributive property

b. $5m - 12 = 28$ — Collecting like terms

c. $5m - 12 + 12 = 28 + 12$ — Using the addition property

d. $5m = 40$ — Simplifying

e. $\frac{1}{5} \cdot 5m = \frac{1}{5} \cdot 40$ — Using the multiplication property

f. $m = 8$ — Simplifying

Solve.

54. $(0.26 + y) + 3y = 0.98$ 0.18 **55.** $0 = y - (-14) - (-3y)$ $-\frac{7}{2}$

56. $12 - (-5m) + 3m + 12 = 0$ -3 **57.** $4a + 5a - 2(2a) + 35 = 0$ -7

58. $4(a - 2) + 3(2a + 1) = 5$ 1 **59.** $2(3x + 5) + 3(2x + 5) = 1$ -2

60. Rafael spent $2011 to operate his car last year. He drove 7400 miles. He paid $972 for insurance and $114 for the registration fee. Rafael's only other expense was for gas. How much did the gas cost per mile?

61. ***Critical Thinking*** Solve $4x - 8 = 32$ by using the multiplication property first. Then solve it using the addition property first. Are the results the same?

Challenge

Solve the first equation for x and substitute this number into the second equation. Then solve for y.

62. $9x - 5 = 22$
$4x + 2y = 2$

63. $9x + 2 = -1$
$4x - y = \frac{11}{3}$

Mixed Review

Use > or < to write a true sentence. **64.** $-5.2 \quad 4$ **65.** $-2.3 \quad 2.2$

66. $\frac{2}{3} \quad \frac{3}{5}$ **67.** $\frac{1}{5} \quad -\frac{3}{5}$ **68.** $-6.7 \quad -3.9$

Divide. **69.** $\frac{5}{12} \div \frac{3}{4}$ **70.** $-\frac{2}{5} \div -\frac{5}{6}$ **71.** $\frac{2}{9} \div -\frac{1}{2}$

Solve. **72.** $x + 10 = 25$ **73.** $t - 84 = 72$ **74.** $5y = 30$

Factor. **75.** $4t + 4n - 12m$ **76.** $3a - 3c - 3d$ **77.** $4c - 12d$

Multiply. **78.** $4(3x - 4y)$ **79.** $3(2q - r - 4)$

CONNECTIONS: GEOMETRY

Find the length of each side given the perimeter.

1. a rectangle with perimeter 36 inches
   5 inches, 13 inches

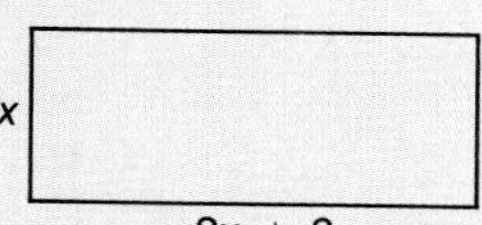

2. a square with perimeter 64 feet
   16 feet

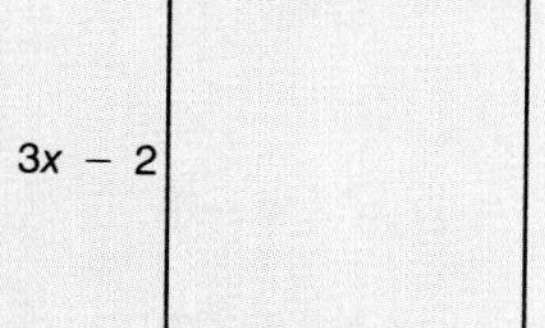

ADDITIONAL ANSWERS

Exercises

60. Let x = cost of gas per mile.
$972 + 114 + 7400x = 2011$
$7400x = 925$
$x = 0.125$
$0.125/mi or 12.5¢ per mile

61. $4x - 8 = 32$ $\qquad$ $4x - 8 = 32$
$\frac{1}{4}(4x - 8) = \frac{1}{4}(32)$ $\qquad$ $4x = 40$
$x - 2 = 8$ $\qquad$ $x = 10$
$x = 10$
Yes

62. $x = 3,\ y = -5$

63. $x = -\frac{1}{3},\ y = -5$

Mixed Review

64. <
65. <
66. >
67. >
68. <
69. $\frac{5}{9}$
70. $\frac{12}{25}$
71. $-\frac{4}{9}$
72. $x = 15$
73. $t = 156$
74. $y = 6$
75. $4(t + n - 3m)$
76. $3(a - c - d)$
77. $4(c - 3d)$
78. $12x - 16y$
79. $6q - 3r - 12$

3-4

FIRST FIVE MINUTES

Write an algebraic expression for each of the following.

1. twice the number n $2n$
2. half of the number n $\frac{1}{2}n$
3. 5 more than a number $n + 5$

Translate to an equation and solve.

4. Arthur is two years younger than Chan. Arthur is 21. How old is Chan?
   Let c be the age of Chan.
   The age of Arthur is $c - 2$.
   $c - 2 = 21$
   $c = 21 + 2 = 23$
5. The number of salted peanuts in a nut mix is 13 times the number of cashews. There are 52 peanuts. How many cashews are there?
   Let c be the number of cashews.
   $13c = 52$
   $c = 4$

APPLICATION

Students will solve this problem in Try This **h.**

Phrases to Algebraic Expressions

Remind students that "3 less than x" is equivalent to $x - 3$, not $3 - x$.

Also, stress that the same expression can represent two phrases. For example, $8 + x$ can represent "the sum of 8 and some number" and "8 more than some number."

Key Questions

Translate to a phrase.

- $6n - 9$
  9 less than 6 times a number
- $\frac{x + 3}{2}$
  half the sum of a number and 3

Chalkboard Examples

Write as an algebraic expression.

1. 3 times a number, plus 5
   $3n + 5$
2. 12 less than 4 times a number
   $4n - 12$
3. 8 less than half a number
   $\frac{1}{2}n - 8$

3-4 Problem Solving: Expressions and Equations

Application

The total length of a new road will be 18 miles. The first 3 miles of this new road have been paved. The same number of miles will be paved each day. How many miles should be paved each day to complete the road in the next 5 days?

In this lesson you will learn techniques for solving similar problems.

Phrases to Algebraic Expressions

Objective: Translate phrases to algebraic expressions.

In Chapters 1 and 2 you translated simple phrases like "5 more than a number" to algebraic expressions. In this lesson you will translate more difficult phrases to algebraic expressions.

EXAMPLES Write as an algebraic expression.

1. 4 more than 6 times a number

$6n + 4$ — "6 times a number" translates to $6n$, and "4 more than . . ." translates to $6n + 4$.

2. 14 less than 3 times a number

$3n - 14$ — "3 times a number" translates to $3n$, and "14 less than . . ." translates to $3n - 14$.

3. 2 times the sum of a number and 4

$2(n + 4)$ — "The sum of a number and 4" translates to $n + 4$, and "2 times the sum . . ." translates to $2(n + 4)$.

Try This Write as an algebraic expression.

a. 3 less than twice a number $2n - 3$

b. $\frac{1}{2}$ of the difference of a number and 1 $\frac{1}{2}(n - 1)$

c. 5 less than a number divided by 3 $\frac{n}{3} - 5$

d. 2 fewer than 10 times a number $10n - 2$

EXAMPLE 4

Jason's weekly salary is $35 less than twice David's weekly salary. Let D = David's weekly salary. Write an expression for Jason's weekly salary.

David's weekly salary $= D$
Jason's weekly salary $= 2D - 35$ "Twice David's weekly salary" translates to $2D$, and "$35 less than . . ." translates to $2D - 35$.

Try This

e. This year Todd sold five less than twice as much as he sold last year. Let n = the number he sold last year. Write an expression for the number he sold this year. $2n - 5$

f. Ellen Ikeda scored two points more than half the number scored by the whole team. Let t = the number of points scored by the whole team. Write an expression for the number of points Ellen scored. $\frac{1}{2}t + 2$

g. On Monday Janice drove 80 miles more than half the distance she drove on Sunday. Let S = the number of miles driven on Sunday. Write an expression for the number of miles she drove on Monday. $\frac{1}{2}S + 80$

Using Equations to Solve Problems

Objective: Solve problems by writing and solving equations.

You can use the Problem-Solving Guidelines below to help you solve problems when your plan involves writing and solving an equation.

PROBLEM-SOLVING GUIDELINES

■ **Phase 1: UNDERSTAND the problem**

What am I trying to find?
What data am I given?
Have I ever solved a similar problem?

■ **Phase 2: Develop and carry out a PLAN**

What strategies might I use to solve the problem?
How can I correctly carry out the strategies I selected?

■ **Phase 3: Find the ANSWER and CHECK**

Does the proposed solution check?
What is the answer to the problem?
Does the answer seem reasonable?
Have I stated the answer clearly?

4. This week Belinda worked 3 more than twice as many hours as last week. Let h be the hours worked last week. Write an expression for the hours worked this week.
$2h + 3$

5. The depth of the new well is 4 ft less than three times the depth of the old well. Let w be the depth of the old well. Write an expression for the depth of the new well.
$3w - 4$

Using Equations to Solve Problems

Remind students to clearly label what the variable represents. You may want students to write their answers in complete sentences. This helps them to determine whether the answer is reasonable or not.

Chalkboard Examples

1. A case of 24 boxes of cereal costs $31. There is also an added shipping cost per case. The total cost for each box of cereal is $1.40. What is the shipping cost per case?
Let c be the shipping cost per case.
The total cost per case is $c + 31$.
The cost per box is the total cost divided by 24, hence
$$\frac{c + 31}{24} = 1.40$$
$$c + 31 = 33.60$$
$$c = 2.60$$
The shipping cost is $2.60 per case.

2. A rectangular garden is 40 ft longer than it is wide. The total length of the fence that surrounds the garden is 1000 ft. How wide is the garden?
Let w be the width of the garden.
The length is $w + 40$.
The fence is twice the width plus twice the length and equals 1000 ft. Hence
$$2w + 2(w + 40) = 1000$$
$$2w + 2w + 80 = 1000$$
$$4w + 80 = 1000$$
$$4w = 920$$
$$w = 230$$
The width is 230 ft.

3. On a committee of 18 persons, there were four more women than men. How many men were on the committee?
Let m be the number of men.
The number of women is $m + 4$.
The total of men and women is 18, hence

$$m + (m + 4) = 18$$
$$2m + 4 = 18$$
$$2m = 14$$
$$m = \frac{14}{2} = 7$$

There were 7 men on the committee.

LESSON ENRICHMENT

Write a problem that can be solved using each of the following equations. Then solve the problem. Was your answer realistic? Answers may vary.

1. $5x + 18 = 98$ $x = 16$
2. $\frac{3m + 2}{2} = 10$ $m = 6$
3. $4(c - 6) = 26$ $c = \frac{50}{4}$
4. $3p - \frac{2p - 24}{3} = 1$ $p = -3$

EXAMPLE 5

The number of girls in the band is 6 more than twice the number of boys. There are 88 girls in the band. How many boys are in the band?

UNDERSTAND the problem

Question: How many boys are there in the band?
Data: The number of girls is 6 more than twice the number of boys; 88 girls are in the band.

Clarifying the question and identifying the data given in the problem

Develop and carry out a PLAN

Let b = the number of boys in the band. *(Choosing a variable)*
$2b + 6$ = the number of girls in the band *(The number of girls is given in terms of the number of boys.)*

$$2b + 6 = 88$$ *Finding equivalent expressions*
$$2b + 6 + (-6) = 88 + (-6)$$ *Using the addition property*
$$2b = 82$$
$$\frac{1}{2} \cdot 2b = \frac{1}{2} \cdot 82$$ *Using the multiplication property*
$$1 \cdot b = 41$$
$$b = 41$$

Find the ANSWER and CHECK

There are 41 boys in the band. If there were 40 boys in the band, $2 \cdot 40 + 6 = 86$, so 41 is a reasonable answer.

Estimating to check whether the answer is reasonable

EXAMPLE 6

Kara has driven 75 miles. She averages 55 mi/h. How many more hours must Kara drive to have traveled a total of 350 miles?

UNDERSTAND the problem

Question: How many additional hours must Kara drive?
Data: She averages 55 mi/h; she has already traveled 75 mi; she wants to travel a total of 350 mi.

Develop and carry out a PLAN

Let h = the number of additional hours she must drive.
$55h$ = the additional distance she must travel

Drawing a diagram can often help you understand a problem.

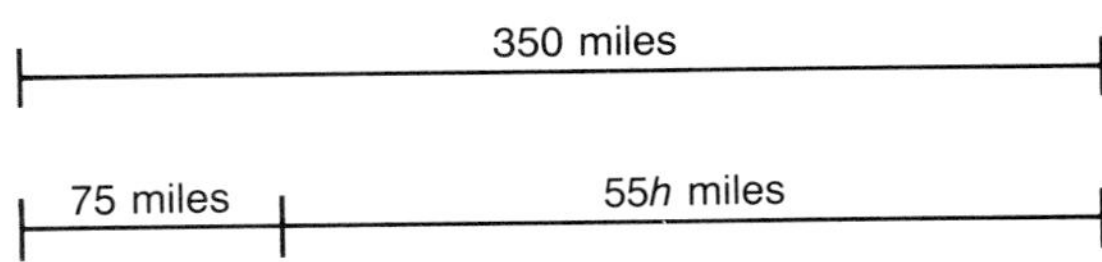

$55h + 75 =$ the total distance for the trip
Since $55h + 75$ represents the total distance for the trip, and we know that the total distance is 350 miles, we have the equation

$$55h + 75 = 350$$

We can solve this equation.

$$\begin{aligned} 55h + 75 &= 350 \\ 55h + 75 + (-75) &= 350 + (-75) \\ 55h &= 275 \\ \frac{1}{55} \cdot 55h &= \frac{1}{55} \cdot 275 \\ h &= 5 \end{aligned}$$

Find the ANSWER and CHECK

Kara must drive for 5 more hours.
$5 \cdot 55 = 275$ miles. This plus 75 miles gives the total of 350 miles. The answer checks.

Try This Solve.

h. When Jill sells 2 more buckets, she will have sold 3 times as many buckets as Jack sold. Jill has sold 19 buckets. How many buckets has Jack sold? 7

i. The total length of a new road will be 18 miles. The first 3 miles of this new road have been paved. The same number of miles will be laid each day. How many miles should be laid each day to complete the road in the next 5 days? 3

3-4 EXERCISES

A

Write as an algebraic expression.

1. 3 less than 5 times a number
2. 5 more than twice a number
3. 18 fewer than half a number
4. 12 more than half a number
5. 3 less than a number divided by 5 $\frac{n}{5} - 3$
6. 3 more than the quotient of a number and 2 $\frac{n}{2} + 3$
7. 4 times the difference of a number and 1 $4(n - 1)$
8. 2 times the sum of a number and 4 $2(n + 4)$
9. $\frac{1}{2}$ the sum of a number and 6 $\frac{1}{2}(n + 6)$

LESSON QUIZ

Write as an algebraic expression.

1. 7 more than three times a number
$3n + 7$
2. twice the sum of a number and 6
$2(n + 6)$
3. 9 less than twice a number
$2n - 9$
4. The repair bill totaled \$150 for labor and parts. The labor cost was twice the parts cost. What did the parts cost?
Let p be the parts cost.
The labor cost is $2p$.
The total 150 is the sum of the parts and labor costs, hence
$$\begin{aligned} p + 2p &= 150 \\ 3p &= 150 \\ p &= \frac{150}{3} = 50 \end{aligned}$$
The parts cost \$50.
5. There are 3 more women than men in the Glee Club. There are 45 people in the club altogether. How many men are in the club?
Let m be the number of men.
The number of women is $m + 3$.
The number of men plus the number of women equals 45, hence
$$\begin{aligned} m + (m + 3) &= 45 \\ 2m + 3 &= 45 \\ 2m &= 42 \\ m &= \frac{42}{2} = 21 \end{aligned}$$
There are 21 men in the club.

Assignment Guide
Minimum: 1–20 e/o, MR

Regular: 1–24 e/o, 25, MR

Advanced: 1–24 e/o, 25–28, MR

ADDITIONAL ANSWERS

Exercises

1. $5n - 3$
2. $2n + 5$
3. $\frac{1}{2}n - 18$
4. $\frac{1}{2}n + 12$

19. a.

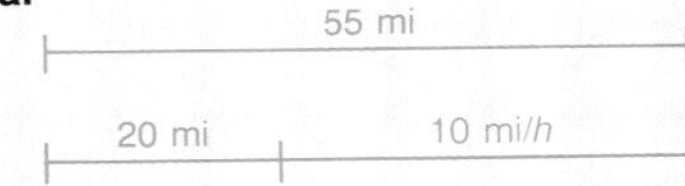

b. $10h + 20$
c. the number of additional hours that Elena must ride
d. $10h + 20 = 55$
e. $h = 3\frac{1}{2}$

Elena must ride $3\frac{1}{2}$ hours more.

20. a. the total number of vans in the railroad cars
b. $8v + 2$
c. $8v + 2 = 122$
d. $v = 15$
There are 15 vans in each railroad car.

10. $\frac{3}{4}$ the difference of a number and 3 $\frac{3}{4}(n - 3)$

11. 4 less than a third of a number $\frac{1}{3}n - 4$

12. 7 greater than half a number $\frac{1}{2}n + 7$

13. Today Harvey ran 2 km more than twice as far as he ran yesterday. Let y = the number of kilometers he ran yesterday. Write an expression for the number of kilometers he ran today. $2y + 2$

14. Darrell sold 3 fewer subscriptions than 4 times the number Brenda sold. Let B = the number Brenda sold. Write an expression for the number Darrell sold. $4B - 3$

15. The cost of a small television is \$25 more than half the cost of a large television. Let c = the cost of a large television. Write an expression for the cost of the small television. $\frac{1}{2}c + 25$

16. Lyle has left \$2 more than half of his allowance. Let a = the amount of his allowance. Write an expression for the amount he has left. $\frac{1}{2}a + 2$

17. Last year Chu found 3 more customers than Ralph found. This year Chu found 2 times as many customers as he found last year. Let r = the number of customers Ralph found last year. Write an expression for the number of customers Chu found this year. $2(r + 3)$

18. Large drinks cost 15¢ more than small drinks. Let s = the cost of a small drink. Write an expression for what it would cost to buy 5 large drinks. $5(s + 15)$

19. Elena has ridden 20 mi on her bike so far. She travels at an average rate of 10 mi/h. How many more hours will she have to ride to have gone a total of 55 mi?

Let h = number of additional hours of travel needed.
$10h$ = distance traveled in h hours

a. Draw a diagram that shows this problem.
b. Write an expression using h that represents 55 miles.
c. What are you asked to find in this problem?
d. Write an equation using the information you know.
e. Solve the equation and answer the problem.

20. One hundred twenty-two vans were supposed to be shipped by railroad, but 2 vans could not fit on the railroad cars. There were 8 railroad cars, each holding the same number of vans. How many vans were on each car?

Let v = vans in each railroad car.

a. What does the expression $8v$ represent?
b. Write an expression using v that represents the 122 vans.
c. Write an equation using the information you know.
d. Solve the equation and answer the problem.

B

21. The number of boys in the tennis club is 10 more than half the number of girls. There are 30 boys in the tennis club. All together, how many boys and girls are in the club? 70

22. A salesman rented a car that could get 35 miles per gallon. He paid \$19.50 a day for the car plus \$0.18 per mile. He rented the car for 1 day and paid \$33. How many miles did he travel? 75

23. Bowling at Sunset Lanes cost Danny and Zorina \$9. This included shoe rental of \$0.75 a pair. How much did each game cost if Danny bowled 3 games and Zorina bowled 2 games? \$1.50

24. Popcorn costs \$0.75 a box. Carl and Diane each bought 1 box of popcorn at the ball game. Carl bought 3 cans of juice and Diane bought 2 cans of juice during the game. Each can cost the same. They spent a total of \$3.25. What did they pay for each can of juice? \$0.35

25. *Critical Thinking* If you add 2 to a certain number, multiply the result by 3, subtract 1 from the product, and divide the difference by 2, you get 10. Find the number. 5

Challenge

26. Ronald can do a job alone in 3 days. His assistant can do the same job alone in 6 days. How long would it take Ronald and his assistant to do the same job together? (Hint: Determine how much work each can do in one day.) 2 days

27. One cashier works at a rate of 3 minutes per customer and a second cashier works at a rate of 2 customers per minute. How many customers do they serve in 1 hour? 140 customers

28. Ruth has some money in a savings account. After the bank adds 5% interest to her account she has \$126. How much was in her account before the interest was added? \$120

Mixed Review

Solve. **29.** $3x + 2x = 15$ **30.** $-\frac{1}{2}x + 3 = 1$ **31.** $3(4y - 2) = 18$

Write using exponential notation. **32.** $4 \cdot n \cdot n \cdot m \cdot 3 \cdot m \cdot n$

33. $y \cdot y \cdot y \cdot x$ **34.** $5 \cdot t \cdot 3 \cdot t \cdot 2 \cdot t$ **35.** $2 \cdot 6 \cdot r \cdot r$

Solve. **36.** $\frac{w}{-5} = -4$ **37.** $\frac{1}{2} = -\frac{1}{8}c$ **38.** $\frac{5}{7} = \frac{2}{3}x$ **39.** $\frac{4}{9}y = 2$

Problem for Programmers

Write a program that will solve an equation of the form $ax + b = c$. Test your program using the equations in Lesson 3-3.

Mixed Review

29. 3
30. 4
31. 2
32. $12n^3m^2$
33. y^3x
34. $30t^3$
35. $12r^2$
36. 20
37. -4
38. $\frac{15}{14}$
39. $\frac{9}{2}$

Problem for Programmers

This program can be written using any programming language (BASIC, PASCAL, LOGO, etc.). The programming experience of the student will determine how the solution is output.

This program can also be written on a spreadsheet where *a*, *b*, and *c* are each input in a separate column and the solution is computed in another column.

3-5

FIRST FIVE MINUTES

Solve.

1. $2x + 1 = 9$
   $2x = 8$
   $x = 4$
2. $3y + 2y - 4 = 6$
   $5y = 10$
   $y = 2$
3. $4(x + 3) = 7$
   $4x + 12 = 7$
   $4x = -5$
   $x = -\frac{5}{4}$
4. $2z + 3(4z + 5) = 20$
   $2z + 12z + 15 = 20$
   $14z + 15 = 20$
   $14z = 5$
   $z = \frac{5}{14}$

Variables on Both Sides

Stress that there is more than one correct way to solve each of these equations. Some students may choose to keep the variables on the left, while others may choose to move the variable with the smaller coefficient, regardless of where it is, to the other side.

Chalkboard Examples

1. $5x = 8 + x$
   $5x - x = 8 + x - x$
   $4x = 8$
   $x = 2$
2. $8a + 1 = 3a + 7$
   $8a + 1 - 1 = 3a + 7 - 1$
   $8a = 3a + 6$
   $8a - 3a = 3a - 3a + 6$
   $5a = 6$
   $a = \frac{6}{5}$
3. $8w + 4 - 2w = w + 1$
   $6w + 4 = w + 1$
   $6w + 4 - 4 = w + 1 - 4$
   $6w = w - 3$
   $6w - w = w - w - 3$
   $5w = -3$
   $w = -\frac{3}{5}$

3-5 More on Solving Equations

Variables on Both Sides

Objective: Solve equations by first getting all variables on the same side of the equation.

If there are variable terms on opposite sides of the equation, we can get them on the same side by using the addition property. Then we collect like terms.

EXAMPLE 1 Solve.

$$2x - 2 = -3x + 3$$

$$2x + 3x - 2 = -3x + 3x + 3 \quad \text{Using the addition property; adding } 3x \text{ to both sides}$$

$$5x - 2 = 3 \quad \text{Collecting like terms and simplifying}$$

$$5x - 2 + 2 = 3 + 2 \quad \text{Using the addition property}$$

$$5x = 5$$

$$\frac{1}{5} \cdot 5x = \frac{1}{5} \cdot 5 \quad \text{Using the multiplication property}$$

$$x = 1$$

Substitution will show that 1 checks.
The solution is 1.

If there are like variable terms on the same side of the equation, they should be collected first.

EXAMPLE 2 Solve.

$$6m + 5 - 7m = 10 - 5m + 3$$

$$-m + 5 = 13 - 5m \quad \text{Collecting like terms}$$

$$-m + m + 5 = 13 - 5m + m \quad \text{Using the addition property; adding } m \text{ to both sides}$$

$$5 = 13 - 4m \quad \text{Collecting like terms and simplifying}$$

$$-13 + 5 = -13 + 13 - 4m \quad \text{Using the addition property}$$

$$-8 = -4m$$

$$-\frac{1}{4}(-8) = -\frac{1}{4}(-4m) \quad \text{Using the multiplication property}$$

$$2 = m$$

Substitution will show that 2 checks.
The solution is 2.

Try This Solve.

a. $7y + 5 = 2y + 10$ 1 **b.** $5 - 2p = 3p - 5$ 2

c. $7x - 17 + 2x = 2 - 8x + 15$ 2 **d.** $3n - 15 = 5n + 3 - 4n$ 9

Equations Containing Parentheses

Objective: Solve equations that contain parentheses.

Some equations containing parentheses can be solved by first using the distributive property.

EXAMPLE 3 Solve.

$$
\begin{aligned}
3(n - 2) - 1 &= 2 - 5(n + 5) \\
3n - 6 - 1 &= 2 - 5n - 25 && \text{Using the distributive property} \\
3n - 7 &= -5n - 23 && \text{Simplifying} \\
3n + 5n - 7 &= -5n + 5n - 23 && \text{Using the addition property} \\
8n - 7 &= -23 \\
8n - 7 + 7 &= -23 + 7 && \text{Using the addition property} \\
8n &= -16 \\
\frac{1}{8} \cdot 8n &= \frac{1}{8} \cdot -16 && \text{Using the multiplication property} \\
n &= -2
\end{aligned}
$$

Substitution will show that -2 checks.
The solution is -2.

Try This Solve.

e. $3(7 + 2x) = 30 + 7(x - 1)$ -2 **f.** $4(3 + 5y) - 4 = 3 + 2(y - 2)$ $-\frac{1}{2}$

3-5 EXERCISES

A

Solve.

1. $4x - 7 = 3x$ 7 **2.** $9x - 6 = 3x$ 1

3. $8x - 1 = 23 - 4x$ 2 **4.** $5y - 2 = 28 - y$ 5

5. $2x - 1 = 4 + x$ 5 **6.** $5x - 2 = 6 + x$ 2

7. $6x + 3 = 2x + 11$ 2 **8.** $5y + 3 = 2y + 15$ 4

9. $5 - 2x = 3x - 7x + 25$ 10 **10.** $10 - 3x = 2x - 8x + 40$ 10

11. $4 + 3x - 6 = 3x + 2 - x$ 4 **12.** $5 + 4x - 7 = 4x + 3 - x$ 5

Equations Containing Parentheses

Remind students that their first objective is to simplify the equation, using the distributive property to remove parentheses and collect like terms and using the addition property to move variables to the same side of the equation. Once the equation is in the form $ax + b = c$, it can be solved as before.

Key Questions

- Does $3 - (x - 4) = 3 - x - 4$? No
- Does $3 + (x - 4) = 3 + x - 4$? Yes

Chalkboard Examples

1. $3(4x - 2) = 5x$

$$
\begin{aligned}
12x - 6 &= 5x \\
12x - 6 + 6 &= 5x + 6 \\
12x &= 5x + 6 \\
12x - 5x &= 5x - 5x + 6 \\
7x &= 6 \\
x &= \frac{6}{7}
\end{aligned}
$$

2. $7x + 2(5x + 1) = 14x$

$$
\begin{aligned}
7x + 10x + 2 &= 14x \\
17x + 2 &= 14x \\
17x + 2 - 2 &= 14x - 2 \\
17x &= 14x - 2 \\
17x - 14x &= 14x - 14x - 2 \\
3x &= -2 \\
x &= -\frac{2}{3}
\end{aligned}
$$

LESSON QUIZ

Solve.

1. $7x - 2 = 4x$ $x = \frac{2}{3}$
2. $4y + 3 = 6y + 8$ $y = -\frac{5}{2}$
3. $5(2z + 1) = 4z + 12$ $z = \frac{7}{6}$
4. $8u + 3(u + 2) = 7(2u - 1)$ $u = \frac{-13}{-3} = \frac{13}{3}$

Assignment Guide
Minimum: 1–30 e/o, MR

Regular: 1–35 e/o, 36, MR

Advanced: 1–35 m3, 36–38, MR

ADDITIONAL ANSWERS

Mixed Review

39. $-\frac{1}{5}x + \frac{3}{7}y$

40. $\frac{1}{2}m - \frac{1}{2}n$

41. $\frac{1}{3}a + \frac{1}{3}$

42. $3 + 2n$

43. $5(n - 2)$

44. $\frac{n}{2} + 4$

Solve.

13. $5r - (2r + 8) = 16$ 8

14. $6b - (3b + 8) = 16$ 8

15. $3g - 3 = 3(7 - g)$ 4

16. $3d - 10 = 5(d - 4)$ 5

17. $6 - 2(3x - 1) = 2$ 1

18. $10 - 3(2x - 1) = 1$ 2

19. $5(d + 4) = 7(d - 2)$ 17

20. $9(t + 2) = 3(t - 2)$ −4

21. $5(x + 2) = 3(x - 2)$ −8

22. $5(y + 4) = 3(y - 2)$ −13

23. $8(3t - 2) = 4(7t - 1)$ −3

24. $7(5x - 2) = 6(6x - 1)$ −8

25. $3(r - 6) + 2 = 4(r + 2) - 21$ −3

26. $5(t + 3) + 9 = 3(t - 2) + 6$ −12

27. $19 - (2x + 3) = 2(x + 3) + x$ 2

28. $13 - (2c + 2) = 2(c + 2) + 3c$ 1

29. $\frac{1}{4}(8y + 4) - 17 = \frac{-1}{2}(4y - 8)$ 5

30. $\frac{1}{3}(6x + 24) - 20 = \frac{-1}{4}(12x - 72)$ 6

B

Solve.

31. $\frac{2x + 4}{4} = 3x - 4$ 2

32. $\frac{3x - 14}{-2} = 3x - 2$ 2

33. $5(x - 1) = \frac{2(x + 4)}{-2}$ $\frac{1}{6}$

34. $-4(2x + 2) = \frac{-4(x + 1)}{4}$ −1

Solve.

35. Terry has walked 3 miles. He averages 4 miles an hour. In how many more hours will he have traveled 13 miles? $2\frac{1}{2}$ hours

36. *Critical Thinking* An **identity** is an equation that is true for all acceptable replacements. Which of the following is an identity? a

a. $2x + 4 + x = 4 + 3x$ **b.** $2(x - 3) + 5 = 3(x - 2) + 5$

Challenge

Solve for x. Assume that all variables represent positive numbers.

37. $a - b(x + c) = d$ $x = \frac{bc + d - a}{-b}$

38. $a(bx - c) = d - (x + e)$ $\frac{d - e + ac}{ab + 1}$

Mixed Review

Collect like terms. **39.** $\frac{2}{5}x + \frac{1}{7}y - \frac{3}{5}x + \frac{2}{7}y$

40. $\frac{3}{8}m - \frac{7}{8}n + \frac{1}{8}m + \frac{3}{8}n$ **41.** $\frac{2}{3}a - \frac{1}{3}a + \frac{4}{9} - \frac{1}{9}$

Write as an algebraic expression.

42. 3 more than twice a number

43. 5 times the difference of a number and 2

44. 4 more than the quotient of a number and 2

3-6 Clearing an Equation of Fractions or Decimals

Objective: Clear an equation of fractions or decimals.

In equations containing fractions, you can use the multiplication property to make the equation easier to solve. To clear the equation of fractions, multiply both sides of the equation by the least common denominator of all the fractions in the equation.

EXAMPLE 1 Solve.

$$\frac{2}{3}x + \frac{1}{2}x = \frac{5}{6} + 2x$$

The number 6 is the least common denominator.

$$6\left(\frac{2}{3}x + \frac{1}{2}x\right) = 6\left(\frac{5}{6} + 2x\right) \quad \text{Multiplying both sides by 6}$$

$$6 \cdot \frac{2}{3}x + 6 \cdot \frac{1}{2}x = 6 \cdot \frac{5}{6} + 6 \cdot 2x \quad \text{Using the distributive property}$$

$$4x + 3x = 5 + 12x$$
$$7x = 5 + 12x$$
$$7x - 12x = 5 + 12x - 12x$$
$$-5x = 5$$
$$x = -1$$

Substitution will show that -1 checks.
The solution is -1.

If you wish to clear the decimals in an equation, multiply on both sides by the appropriate power of 10.

EXAMPLE 2 Solve.

$$16.3 - 7.2y = -8.18 \quad \text{Multiplying by 100 will clear the decimals.}$$

$$100(16.3 - 7.2y) = 100(-8.18)$$
$$100(16.3) - 100(7.2y) = 100(-8.18) \quad \text{Using the distributive property}$$
$$1630 - 720y = -818$$
$$-720y = -818 - 1630$$
$$-720y = -2448$$
$$y = \frac{-2448}{-720}$$
$$y = 3.4$$

Substitution will show that 3.4 checks.
The solution is 3.4.

3-6

FIRST FIVE MINUTES

Simplify.

1. $3 \cdot \frac{1}{3}x$

   x

2. $2\left(\frac{1}{2}y + \frac{3}{2}\right)$

   $2 \cdot \frac{1}{2}y + 2 \cdot \frac{3}{2} = y + 3$

3. $10(1.2u + 0.5)$

   $12u + 5$

When clearing an equation of decimal coefficients, have students choose the smallest power of ten that will convert all coefficients to integers. Show students that a larger power of ten will work, but will create coefficients that are more difficult to work with.

Key Questions

Can you find a multiplier that will simplify the equations?

- $0.21x + 4.52 = -0.73 - 0.84x$ 100
- $\frac{3}{4}x - 7 = 8 + \frac{2}{3}x$ 12

Chalkboard Examples

Solve.

1. $\frac{1}{3}p + \frac{1}{6} = \frac{3}{2}$

   The least common denominator is 6.

   $$6\left(\frac{1}{3}p + \frac{1}{6}\right) = 6 \cdot \frac{3}{2}$$
   $$6 \cdot \frac{1}{3}p + 6 \cdot \frac{1}{6} = 9$$
   $$2p + 1 = 9$$
   $$2p = 8$$
   $$p = 4$$

2. $0.5r + 1.5 = 3.0$

   Multiply by 10 to clear the decimals.

   $$10(0.5r + 1.5) = 10 \cdot 3.0$$
   $$10 \cdot 0.5r + 10 \cdot 1.5 = 30$$
   $$5r + 15 = 30$$
   $$5r = 15$$
   $$r = 3$$

LESSON QUIZ

Solve. Clear fractions first, if necessary.

1. $\frac{2}{3}x - \frac{1}{3} = \frac{5}{3}x + \frac{7}{3}$

   Multiply by 3 to clear the fractions.

   $x = -\frac{8}{3}$

2. $\frac{1}{5}z + \frac{1}{10} = \frac{4}{5}z + \frac{2}{10}$

   Multiply by 10 to clear the fractions.

   $z = -\frac{1}{6}$

3. $0.8a + 0.2 = 0.4a + 0.7$

   Multiply by 10 to clear the decimals.

   $a = \frac{5}{4}$

Assignment Guide

Minimum: 1–18 e/o, MR

Regular: 1–24 e/o, 25, MR

Advanced: 1–24 m3, 25–27, MR

ADDITIONAL ANSWERS

Exercises

1. -1
2. -3
3. -2
4. -3
5. 4
6. 23
7. $\frac{1}{2}$
8. $-\frac{4}{3}$
9. $-\frac{2}{3}$
10. $\frac{2}{5}$
11. 28
12. $\frac{32}{7}$
13. -4
14. $\frac{5}{3}$ or 1.67
15. 0.8
16. 1
17. 3
18. 70

Try This Solve.

a. $\frac{7}{8}x + \frac{3}{4} = \frac{1}{2}x + \frac{3}{2}$ 2

b. $\frac{5}{6}x + \frac{1}{2} = \frac{2}{3}x + 4$ 21

c. $26.45 = 4.2x + 1.25$ 6

d. $41.68 = 4.7 - 8.6y$ -4.3

The following summarizes the steps for solving an equation.

Solving Equations

1. Multiply both sides to clear fractions or decimals, if necessary.
2. Collect like terms on each side, if necessary.
3. Use the addition property to move the variable to one side and all other terms to the other side of the equation.
4. Collect like terms again, if necessary.
5. Use the addition and multiplication properties to solve for the variable.

3-6 EXERCISES

A

Solve. Clear the fractions first, if necessary.

1. $\frac{7}{2}x + \frac{1}{2}x = 3x + \frac{3}{2} + \frac{5}{2}x$

2. $\frac{1}{2} + 4m = 3m - \frac{5}{2}$

3. $\frac{5}{3} + \frac{2}{3}x = \frac{25}{12} + \frac{5}{4}x + \frac{3}{4}$

4. $1 - \frac{2}{3}y = \frac{9}{5} - \frac{y}{5} + \frac{3}{5}$

5. $\frac{4}{5}x - \frac{3}{4}x = \frac{3}{10}x - 1$

6. $\frac{8}{5}y - \frac{2}{3}y = 23 - \frac{1}{15}y$

7. $\frac{7}{8}x - \frac{1}{4} + \frac{3}{4}x = \frac{1}{16} + x$

8. $\frac{2}{3} + \frac{1}{4}t = \frac{1}{3}$

9. $-\frac{3}{2} + x = -\frac{5}{6} - \frac{4}{3}$

10. $\frac{2}{3} + 3y = 5y - \frac{2}{15}$

11. $\frac{2}{7}x + \frac{1}{2}x = \frac{3}{4}x + 1$

12. $\frac{5}{16}y + \frac{3}{8}y = 2 + \frac{1}{4}y$

13. $2.1x + 45.2 = 3.2 - 8.4x$

14. $0.96y - 0.79 = 0.21y + 0.46$

15. $1.03 - 0.62x = 0.71 - 0.22x$

16. $1.7t + 8 - 1.62t = 0.4t - 0.32 + 8$

17. $0.42 - 0.03y = 3.33 - y$

18. $0.7n - 15 + n = 2n - 8 - 0.4n$

B

Solve.

19. $7\frac{1}{2}x - \frac{1}{2}x = 3\frac{3}{4}x + 39$ 12

20. $\frac{1}{5}t - 0.4 + \frac{2}{5}t = 0.6 - \frac{1}{10}t$ $\frac{10}{7}$

21. $\frac{1}{4}(8y + 4) - 17 = -\frac{1}{2}(4y - 8)$ 5

22. $\frac{1}{3}(6x + 24) - 20 = -\frac{1}{4}(12x - 72)$ 6

23. $30{,}000 + 20{,}000x = 55{,}000$ $\frac{5}{4}$

24. $25{,}000(4 + 3x) = 125{,}000$ $\frac{1}{3}$

25. ***Critical Thinking*** After the death of Diophantus, a famous Greek mathematician, someone described his life as a puzzle.
He was a boy for $\frac{1}{6}$ of his life.
After $\frac{1}{12}$ more, he acquired a beard.
After another $\frac{1}{7}$, he married.
In the fifth year after his marriage his son was born.
The son lived half as many years as his father.
Diophantus died 4 years after his son.
How old was Diophantus when he died? 84 yr

Challenge

26. Apples are collected in a basket for six people. One third, one fourth, one eighth, and one fifth are given to four people, respectively. The fifth person gets ten apples with one apple remaining for the sixth person. Find the original number of apples in the basket. 120

27. Carol shared a package of graph paper with 3 of her friends. She gave $\frac{1}{4}$ of the pack to Willy. Sara got $\frac{1}{3}$ of what was left. Then Marcy took $\frac{1}{6}$ of what was left in the package. Carol kept the remaining 30 sheets. How many sheets were in the package to start? 72

Mixed Review

Write a true sentence using < or >. **28.** 7.301 7.310
29. 5.4 $|-5.5|$ **30.** -0.783 -0.781 **31.** $|6|$ $|-7|$
Write as an algebraic expression. **32.** 7 more than half a number
33. 5 less than twice a number **34.** twice the sum of a number and 3
Solve. **35.** $-4(2t + 7) = -4$ **36.** $3a + 2(2a + 5) = 3$
37. $x + \frac{1}{3}x = 8$ **38.** $x + \frac{1}{4}x = 10$ **39.** $\frac{3}{8}y + \frac{3}{4}y = 3$
Evaluate each expression for $x = -2$. **40.** $9x^2 - 4$ **41.** $\frac{1}{2}x^3 + 32$

Mixed Review
28. <
29. <
30. <
31. <
32. $\frac{n}{2} + 7$
33. $2n - 5$
34. $2(n + 3)$
35. -3
36. -1
37. 6
38. 8
39. $\frac{8}{3}$
40. 32
41. 28

3-7

FIRST FIVE MINUTES

Solve.

1. $7 = 2t$

   $\frac{7}{2} = t$

2. $8 = \frac{5h}{2}$

   $16 = 5h$

   $\frac{16}{5} = h$

3. $14 = w \cdot 7$

   $\frac{14}{7} = w$

   $w = 2$

Formulas allow us to process large amounts of data quickly. By programming a formula like the one in Example 3 into a computer, a sportswriter can enter values for the variables for every pitcher in a league and immediately find each one's earned run average.

Remind students that solving equations for a given variable means getting that variable by itself on one side of the equation, and that solving a formula is the same as solving an equation.

Chalkboard Examples

1. Solve for h where $A = \frac{bh}{2}$.

   $2A = bh$

   $\frac{2A}{b} = h$

2. Solve for L where $P = 2L + 2W$.

   $P - 2W = 2L$

   $\frac{1}{2}(P - 2W) = L$

3. Solve for E where $I = \frac{E}{R}$.

   $IR = E$

3-7 Formulas

Objective: Solve for a given variable in a formula.

Application

Computers are used by air traffic controllers to quickly determine the flight times of thousands of airplanes. The computer program must include a formula that will compute the time given the rate and distance for each flight. The formula that is needed is based on the formula for distance, $d = rt$, where d is the distance, r is the rate, and t is the time.

We can solve the formula $d = rt$ for the variable t using the same rules as for solving equations.

EXAMPLES

1. Solve $d = rt$ for t.

$$d = rt$$

$$\frac{1}{r} \cdot d = \frac{1}{r} \cdot rt$$

Using the multiplication property to multiply both sides by the multiplicative inverse of r, $\frac{1}{r}$

$$\frac{d}{r} = t$$

2. A formula for the average A of three numbers, a, b, and c is

$$A = \frac{a + b + c}{3}$$

Solve for a.

$$A = \frac{a + b + c}{3}$$

$$3A = a + b + c$$

Using the multiplication property to multiply both sides by 3

$$3A - b - c = a$$

Try This

a. Solve $C = 2\pi r$ for r. $r = \frac{C}{2\pi}$ **b.** Solve $P = 2l + 35$ for l. $l = \frac{P - 35}{2}$

c. A formula for the average A of four numbers a, b, c, and d is

$$A = \frac{a + b + c + d}{4}$$

Solve for c. $c = 4A - a - b - d$

EXAMPLE 3

A formula for computing the earned run average A of a pitcher who has given up R earned runs in I innings of pitching is

$$A = \frac{9R}{I}$$

Solve for I.

$$A = \frac{9R}{I}$$

$$AI = 9R \quad \text{Multiplying both sides by } I$$

$$I = \frac{9R}{A} \quad \text{Multiplying both sides by } \frac{1}{A}$$

Try This

d. A formula for a football player's rushing average r with a total of y yards rushed in n carries of the ball is $r = \frac{y}{n}$.
Solve for n. $n = \frac{y}{r}$

3-7 EXERCISES

A

Solve.

1. $A = bh$, for b (an area formula) $\frac{A}{h}$

2. $A = bh$, for h $\frac{A}{b}$

3. $d = rt$, for r (a distance formula) $\frac{d}{t}$

4. $d = rt$, for t $\frac{d}{r}$

5. $I = Prt$, for P (an interest formula) $\frac{I}{rt}$

6. $I = Prt$, for t $\frac{I}{Pr}$

7. $F = ma$, for a (a physics formula) $\frac{F}{m}$

8. $F = ma$, for m $\frac{F}{a}$

9. $P = 2l + 2w$, for w (a perimeter formula) $\frac{P - 2l}{2}$

10. $P = 2l + 2w$, for l $\frac{P - 2w}{2}$

11. $A = \pi r^2$, for r^2 (an area formula) $\frac{A}{\pi}$

12. $A = \pi r^2$, for π $\frac{A}{r^2}$

13. $A = \frac{1}{2}bh$, for b (an area formula) $\frac{2A}{h}$

14. $A = \frac{1}{2}bh$, for h $\frac{2A}{b}$

15. $E = mc^2$, for m (a relativity formula) $\frac{E}{c^2}$

16. $E = mc^2$, for c^2 $\frac{E}{m}$

17. $A = \frac{a + b + c}{3}$, for b $3A - a - c$

18. $A = \frac{a + b + c}{3}$, for c $3A - a - b$

19. $v = \frac{3k}{t}$, for t $\frac{3k}{v}$

20. $P = \frac{ab}{c}$, for c $\frac{ab}{P}$

LESSON QUIZ

Solve.

1. $I = Prt$, for r

 $\frac{I}{Pt} = r$

2. $Q = \frac{2s}{t}$, for s

 $Qt = 2s$

 $\frac{Qt}{2} = s$

3. $A = \frac{a + b}{2}$, for b

 $2A = a + b$

 $2A - a = b$

4. $e = 3f + 2g$, for g

 $e - 3f = 2g$

 $\frac{1}{2}(e - 3f) = g$

Assignment Guide

Minimum: 1–8, 9–24 e/o, MR

Regular: 1–31 e/o, 32, MR

Advanced: 1–31 m3, 32, 33–40 e/o, MR

ADDITIONAL ANSWERS

Exercises

31. $t = \frac{R - 3.85}{-0.00625}$ or $-160R + 616$

32. by taking the square root of D^2; $D = \sqrt{\frac{2.5H}{N}}$

33. $\frac{g - 40n}{20}$

34. $8h - 4r$

35. $\frac{y}{1 - b}$

36. $\frac{x - b}{1 - 2b}$

37. $\frac{1}{d} - e$

38. $\frac{xz^2}{t}$

39. $\frac{m - ax^2 - c}{x}$

40. No, a may be $-b$.

Mixed Review

41. $4(x + 3)$
42. $3(c + 4d - 3)$
43. $3y - 2x$
44. $6a - 3c + 4$
45. 3
46. 4
47. 5
48. $\frac{1}{5}$
49. 3
50. 4

A formula for the area of a sector of a circle is $A = \frac{\pi r^2 S}{360}$ where r is the radius and S is the central angle measure of the sector. ◇◇

21. Solve for S. $\frac{360A}{\pi r^2}$

22. Solve for r^2. $\frac{360A}{\pi S}$

A formula to find the horsepower H of an N-cylinder engine is

$$H = \frac{D^2N}{2.5}$$

23. Solve for D^2. $\frac{2.5H}{N}$

24. Solve for N. $\frac{2.5H}{D^2}$

B

Solve.

25. $ax + b = cb$, for b $\frac{ax}{c - 1}$

26. $a^2 = b^2 + 2xc$, for x $\frac{a^2 - b^2}{2c}$

27. $l = a + (n - 1)d$, for n $\frac{d - a + l}{d}$

28. $A = \frac{1}{R}$, for R $\frac{1}{A}$

29. $\frac{s}{t} = \frac{t}{v}$, for s $\frac{t^2}{v}$

30. $\frac{a}{b} = \frac{c}{d}$, for $\frac{a}{c}$ $\frac{b}{d}$

31. The formula $R = -0.00625t + 3.85$ can be used to estimate the world record in the 1500 m run t years after 1930. Solve for t.

32. ***Critical Thinking*** In Exercise 23, you solved for D^2. How might you solve for D?

Challenge

Solve.

33. $g = 40n + 20k$, for k

34. $r = 2h - \frac{1}{4}f$, for f

35. $y = a - ab$, for a

36. $x = a + b - 2ab$, for a

37. $d = \frac{1}{e + f}$, for f

38. $x = \frac{\left(\frac{y}{z}\right)}{\left(\frac{z}{t}\right)}$, for y

39. $m = ax^2 + bx + c$, for b

40. If $a^2 = b^2$, does $a = b$?

Mixed Review

Factor. **41.** $4x + 12$ **42.** $3c + 12d - 9$

Collect like terms. **43.** $2x + 3y - 4x$ **44.** $8a - 3c + 4 - 2a$

Solve. **45.** $16 - 2c = 4c - 2$ **46.** $1.7m + 16.8 = 25.8 - 0.55m$

47. $\frac{1}{2}(8m + 4) + 2 = \frac{1}{3}(18m - 18)$ **48.** $\frac{2}{5} + 3y = 10y - 1$

49. $15.4 - 9.1t = 2.4t - 19.1$ **50.** $27 - 3(t + 4) = 9(t - 2) - 15$

3-8 Solving Equations Involving Absolute Value

Objective: Solve equations involving absolute value.

In Chapter 2 you learned that the absolute value of a number is its distance from zero on a number line. You also learned that the absolute value of a number is always positive or zero. In this lesson you will solve equations involving absolute value.

EXAMPLES Solve.

1. $|x| = 6$

$x = 6$ or $x = -6$ — 6 and -6 are both 6 units from 0 on the number line.

Check:

$\|x\|$	$= 6$
$\|6\|$	6
6	6 ✓

$\|x\|$	$= 6$
$\|-6\|$	6
6	6 ✓

The solutions are 6 and -6.

2.
$$|x| + 2 = 12$$
$$|x| + 2 + (-2) = 12 + (-2) \quad \text{Using the addition property}$$
$$|x| = 10$$
$$x = 10 \text{ or } x = -10$$

Check:

$\|x\| + 2$	$= 12$
$\|10\| + 2$	12
$10 + 2$	12
12	12 ✓

$\|x\| + 2$	$= 12$
$\|-10\| + 2$	12
$10 + 2$	12
12	12 ✓

The solutions are 10 and -10.

3.
$$3|b| - 4 = 2$$
$$3|b| - 4 + 4 = 2 + 4 \quad \text{Using the addition property}$$
$$3|b| = 6$$
$$\frac{1}{3} \cdot 3|b| = \frac{1}{3} \cdot 6 \quad \text{Using the multiplication property}$$
$$|b| = 2$$
$$b = 2 \text{ or } b = -2$$

Substitution will show that the numbers 2 and -2 check. The solutions are 2 and -2.

Try This Solve.

a. $|y| = 17$ 17, -17 **b.** $|y| - 5 = 1$ 6, -6 **c.** $2|x| + 1 = 15$ 7, -7

3-8

FIRST FIVE MINUTES

Evaluate.

1. $|3|$
   3
2. $|-5|$
   5
3. $|3 - 5|$
   $|-2| = 2$
4. $|-4| + |4|$
   $4 + 4 = 8$
5. $|x - 7|$ when $x = 3$
   $|3 - 7| = |-4| = 4$

Emphasize that there are two numbers that have a distance of 6 from 0: 6 and -6.

Key Questions

- How many numbers are there whose absolute value is 3?
  Two: 3, -3
- How many numbers are there whose absolute value is 0?
  One: 0
- How many numbers are there whose absolute value is -3?
  None

Chalkboard Examples

Solve.

1. $|y| = 3$
   $y = 3$ or $y = -3$
2. $|x| + 5 = 12$
   $|x| = 12 - 5$
   $|x| = 7$
   $x = 7$ or $x = -7$
3. $5|a| + 3 = 10$
   $5|a| = 10 - 3$
   $5|a| = 7$
   $|a| = \frac{7}{5}$
   $a = \frac{7}{5}$ or $a = -\frac{7}{5}$

LESSON QUIZ

Solve.

1. $|x| = 2$
   $x = 2$ or $x = -2$
2. $|a| = |-4|$
   $|a| = 4$
   $a = 4$ or $a = -4$
3. $|y| + 5 = 9$
   $|y| = 9 - 5$
   $|y| = 4$
   $y = 4$ or $y = -4$
4. $3|x| + 7 = 13$
   $3|x| = 13 - 7$
   $3|x| = 6$
   $|x| = \frac{6}{3} = 2$
   $x = 2$ or $x = -2$
5. $\frac{2}{5}|b| + |-2| = 5$
   $\frac{2}{5}|b| + 2 = 5$
   $\frac{2}{5}|b| = 5 - 2$
   $\frac{2}{5}|b| = 3$
   $\frac{5}{2} \cdot \frac{2}{5}|b| = \frac{5}{2} \cdot 3$
   $|b| = \frac{15}{2}$
   $b = \frac{15}{2}$ or $b = -\frac{15}{2}$

Assignment Guide

Minimum: 1–34 e/o, MR

Regular: 1–48 e/o, 49, MR

Advanced: 1–48 m3, 49, 50–58 e/o, MR

3-8 EXERCISES

A

Solve.

1. $|x| = 19$ 19, −19
2. $|y| = 9$ 9, −9
3. $4 = |m|$ 4, −4
4. $|n| = 7$ 7, −7
5. $|h| = 0$ 0
6. $3 = |a|$ 3, −3
7. $|b| = 12$ 12, −12
8. $|x| = 15$ 15, −15
9. $|a| = |-2|$ 2, −2
10. $|-20| = |-x|$ 20, −20
11. $|y| = 12 - 5$ 7, −7
12. $|y| + 5 = 16$ 11, −11
13. $|a| - 7 = 21$ 28, −28
14. $4 + |m| = 9$ 5, −5
15. $-2 + |n| = 0$ 2, −2
16. $|x| + 3 + 9 = 15$ 3, −3
17. $5 + |x| - 9 = 2$ 6, −6
18. $|x| - 23 = 34$ 57, −57
19. $|-4| + |-6| + |m| = 10$ 0
20. $|-8| + |x| = |-8| + |-3|$ 3, −3
21. $5|x| = 35$ 7, −7
22. $3|y| = 27$ 9, −9
23. $2|x| + 6 = 12$ 3, −3
24. $4|r| - 2 = 18$ 5, −5
25. $\frac{|m|}{4} = 5$ 20, −20
26. $\frac{|t|}{-2} = -9$ 18, −18
27. $-4|x| = -5$ $\frac{5}{4}, -\frac{5}{4}$
28. $-7 = \frac{|y|}{-3}$ 21, −21
29. $4|x| + |-4| = |-6|$ $\frac{1}{2}, -\frac{1}{2}$
30. $-3|a| - 5 = -17$ 4, −4
31. $-2|b| + 4 = 2$ 1, −1
32. $\frac{|x|}{5} + 7 = 42$ 175, −175
33. $\frac{2}{3}|k| + 5 = 7$ 3, −3
34. $\frac{1}{4} + \frac{1}{2}|x| = \frac{5}{8}$ $\frac{3}{4}, -\frac{3}{4}$

B

Solve.

35. $-|x| = -4$ 4, −4
36. $-12 = -|y|$ 12, −12
37. $-2|a| + 5 = 1$ 2, −2
38. $2|x| + 3|x| + 4 = 24$ 4, −4
39. $-3|m| + 5|m| - 3 = 1$ 2, −2
40. $|n| - 3 + 5|n| = 15$ 3, −3
41. $|x| + 12 = 5|x| - 4$ 4, −4
42. $6 - 3|a| = 2|a| + 1$ 1, −1
43. $-\frac{2}{3}|m| - \frac{4}{5} = -4$ $\frac{24}{5}, -\frac{24}{5}$
44. $-\frac{1}{3}|y| + \frac{5}{6} = \frac{1}{6}$ 2, −2
45. $|3m| = 6$ $m = 2, -2$
46. $|2a| = 8$ $a = 4, -4$
47. $|-m| = 5$ $m = 5, -5$
48. $|-x| = 7$ $x = 7, -7$

49. *Critical Thinking* For what values of x is $|x| > x$? For $x < 0$

Challenge

Complete.

50. If $x > 0$, $|x| = ?$ x **51.** If $x < 0$, $|x| = ?$ $-x$ **52.** If $x = 0$, $|x| = ?$ 0

Solve.

53. $|x + 2| = 7$ 5, −9 **54.** $|m - 4| = 1$ 5, 3 **55.** $|2a + 1| = 5$ 2, −3

56. If $|x| > |y|$, what is the most you know about x and y? $x \neq y, x \neq 0$

57. Can $|x| + |y| = 0$ if $x \neq y$? No

58. For what values of x does $|x| = |-x|$? All values

Mixed Review

Solve. **59.** $-12t - 4 = 32$ **60.** $3m + 2m + 15 = 35$

61. $x + 0.75x = 21$ **62.** $\frac{1}{2}n + \frac{2}{5}n = -\frac{9}{10}$ **63.** $\frac{2}{5}(m - 4) = 4$

Collect like terms. **64.** $2x - \frac{1}{2}x + \frac{3}{4}x - 4x$

65. $3a - \frac{2}{5}b - \frac{1}{2}a - 6b$ **66.** $5x + \frac{2}{3}y - \frac{1}{4}x + y$

Translate to an equation and solve. **67.** The sum of two consecutive even integers is 94. What are the integers? **68.** The sum of three consecutive odd integers is 123. What are the integers? **69.** One angle of a triangle is 3 times as large as another. The measure of the third angle is 60° less than the sum of the other two angles. Find the measure of each angle. **70.** The length of a rectangle is twice the width. The perimeter is 24 m. Find the length and the width.

LOOKING FOR ERRORS

Each exercise has an error commonly made by algebra students. Find and correct the error.

1. Solve $4 - 3x = 5$.

$$3x = 9$$
$$x = 3$$

The correct solution is $x = -\frac{1}{3}$.

2. Solve $ax - b = c$ for b.

$$ax = b + c$$
$$x = \frac{b + c}{a}$$

The correct solution is $b = ax - c$.

3. Solve $4|c| - 3 = 1$.

$4|c| - 3 = 1$ or $4|c| - 3 = -1$

$4|c| = 4$ or $4|c| = 2$

$|c| = 1$ or $|c| = \frac{1}{2}$

$c = 1$ or $c = -1$ $c = \frac{1}{2}$ or $c = -\frac{1}{2}$

The correct solution is $c = 1$ or $c = -1$.

4. Solve $|x| = -3$.

$x = 3$ or $x = -3$

There is no solution.

ADDITIONAL ANSWERS

Mixed Review

59. -3
60. 4
61. 12
62. -1
63. 14
64. $-\frac{7}{4}x$
65. $\frac{5}{2}a - \frac{32}{5}b$
66. $\frac{19}{4}x + \frac{5}{3}y$
67. 46, 48
68. 39, 41, 43
69. 30°, 60°, 90°
70. $8m$, $4m$

3-9

FIRST FIVE MINUTES

Simplify.

1. $\frac{14}{21}$ $\frac{2}{3}$
2. $\frac{15}{25}$ $\frac{3}{5}$
3. $\frac{16}{8}$ 2
4. $\frac{4a}{2b}$ $\frac{2a}{b}$
5. $\frac{x \cdot 3}{x}$ 3

Solving Proportions

You may want to introduce cross multiplication as a way of checking proportions. In Example 1 the solution is 14. Substituting 14 for x,

$$\frac{14}{63} = \frac{2}{9}$$
$$14 \cdot 9 = 2 \cdot 63$$
$$126 = 126$$

The solution, 14, checks.

Key Questions

- If one ratio in a proportion is less than 1, must the other ratio also be less than 1? Yes
- Is $\frac{8}{13}$ a proportion? No

Chalkboard Examples

Solve.

1. $\frac{x}{21} = \frac{3}{7}$

$$21 \cdot \frac{x}{21} = 21 \cdot \frac{3}{7}$$
$$x = 9$$

2. $\frac{4}{7} = \frac{24}{x}$

Multiply by $7x$ to clear the fractions.

$$7x \cdot \frac{4}{7} = 7x \cdot \frac{24}{x}$$
$$x \cdot 4 = 168$$
$$x = \frac{168}{4}$$
$$x = 42$$

3-9 Problem Solving: Proportions

Solving Proportions

Objective: Solve proportions.

The ratio of two quantities is their quotient. For example, the ratio of the age of a 34-year-old parent to that of a 10-year-old child is 34 to 10. The ratio of 34 to 10 can be expressed in several ways.

$$34{:}10 \qquad 34 : 10 \qquad \frac{34}{10} \qquad 3.4$$

An equation that states that two ratios are equal is called a **proportion.** These are proportions.

$$\frac{2}{3} = \frac{6}{9} \qquad \frac{5}{7} = \frac{25}{35} \qquad \frac{x}{24} = \frac{2}{3} \qquad \frac{9}{y} = \frac{32}{81}$$

Since proportions are equations, we can use equation-solving properties to solve them.

EXAMPLE 1 Solve.

$$\frac{x}{63} = \frac{2}{9}$$
$$63 \cdot \frac{x}{63} = 63 \cdot \frac{2}{9} \quad \text{Using the multiplication property}$$
$$x = 14$$

EXAMPLE 2 Solve.

$$\frac{65}{10} = \frac{13}{x}$$
$$10x \cdot \frac{65}{10} = 10x \cdot \frac{13}{x} \quad \text{Using the multiplication property; multiplying by } 10x \text{ to clear fractions}$$
$$65x = 130$$
$$\frac{1}{65} \cdot 65x = \frac{1}{65} \cdot 130 \quad \text{Using the multiplication property}$$
$$x = 2$$

Try This Solve.

a. $\frac{3}{5} = \frac{12}{y}$ 20 **b.** $\frac{1}{2} = \frac{x}{5}$ $\frac{5}{2}$ **c.** $\frac{m}{4} = \frac{7}{6}$ $\frac{14}{3}$

Problem Solving

Objective: Solve problems involving proportions.

PROBLEM-SOLVING GUIDELINES
■ UNDERSTAND the problem
■ Develop and carry out a PLAN
■ Find the ANSWER and CHECK

Some problems can be solved by writing and solving a proportion. Use the Problem-Solving Guidelines to help you solve the following problems.

EXAMPLE 3

The property tax on a house is \$8 per \$1000 assessed valuation. What is the tax on a house assessed at \$65,000?

$$\frac{8}{1000} = \frac{x}{65{,}000}$$

Think: \$8 is to \$1000 as x dollars is to \$65,000.

$$\frac{8}{1000} \cdot 65{,}000 = \frac{x}{65{,}000} \cdot 65{,}000$$

$$520 = x$$

The tax is \$520.

EXAMPLE 4

A certain car can travel 180 miles on 12 gallons of gasoline. How far can this car travel on 20 gallons of gasoline?

$$\frac{180}{12} = \frac{x}{20}$$

Think: 180 is to 12 as x miles is to 20.

$$\frac{180}{12} \cdot 20 = \frac{x}{20} \cdot 20$$

$$\frac{180 \cdot 20}{12} = x$$

$$300 = x$$

The car can travel 300 miles.

Try This Solve.

d. The scale on a map says that 0.5 cm represents 25 km. On the map the measurement between two cities is 5 cm. What is the actual distance between these two cities? 250 km

e. According to the scale on a road map, 3 inches represent 40 miles. If two cities measure 10 inches apart on the map, how many miles apart are they? $133\frac{1}{3}$ miles

Problem Solving

For Example 3, explain to students that "assessed valuation" simply refers to the rated value of a house.

Math Point
The study of proportions is one of the oldest and most useful areas of mathematics. Around the year 550 BC, the philosopher Pythagoras discovered that if one string on a musical instrument was twice the length of another, their sounds would go well together. Today we call this musical interval an octave. Pythagoras was deeply impressed that the *ratios* were important rather than the actual lengths of each string. He and his followers believed that by studying ratios one could understand the nature of the world. In fact, the word "rational" comes from the word ratio. It was believed that a rational person is one who has a sense of proportion.

Chalkboard Example

1. If a car moving at constant speed travels 55 miles in 2 hours, how many miles will it travel in 7 hours? Let x be the distance traveled in 7 hours. Since the rate is constant, the rate can be computed either as $\frac{55}{2}$ or as $\frac{x}{7}$, hence

$$\frac{55}{2} = \frac{x}{7}$$

$$7 \cdot \frac{55}{2} = 7 \cdot \frac{x}{7}$$

$$192.5 = x$$

The car will travel 192.5 miles.

LESSON ENRICHMENT

Make up a problem whose answer can be found by writing and solving the proportion $\frac{x}{400} = \frac{4}{500}$. Then solve the problem. $x = 3.2$

LESSON QUIZ

Solve these proportions.

1. $\frac{a}{3} = \frac{5}{6}$

   $a = \frac{5}{2}$

2. $\frac{4}{x} = \frac{8}{3}$

   $x = \frac{3}{2}$

3. $\frac{6}{7} = \frac{2}{z}$

   $z = \frac{14}{6} = \frac{7}{3}$

4. On a certain map, 2 inches represent 5 miles. 9 inches represent how many miles?
   Let m be the number of miles. Since the scale proportion remains constant, the scale is equal to $\frac{2}{5}$ and to $\frac{9}{x}$, hence

   $\frac{2}{5} = \frac{9}{x}$

   Multiply by 5x.

   $5x \cdot \frac{2}{5} = 5x \cdot \frac{9}{x}$

   $x \cdot 2 = 45$

   $x = \frac{45}{2}$

   9 inches represents $22\frac{1}{2}$ miles.

Assignment Guide

Minimum: 1–34 e/o, MR

Regular: 1–38 e/o, 39, MR

Advanced: 1–38 m3, 39–43, MR

3-9 EXERCISES

A

Solve these proportions.

1. $\frac{y}{3} = \frac{9}{27}$ 1	**2.** $\frac{7}{8} = \frac{m}{4}$ $\frac{7}{2}$	**3.** $\frac{9}{x} = \frac{2}{3}$ $\frac{27}{2}$	**4.** $\frac{25}{75} = \frac{1}{x}$ 3
5. $\frac{2}{y} = \frac{5}{9}$ $\frac{18}{5}$	**6.** $\frac{16}{m} = \frac{1}{4}$ 64	**7.** $\frac{8}{5} = \frac{40}{y}$ 25	**8.** $\frac{12}{15} = \frac{t}{5}$ 4
9. $\frac{y}{4} = \frac{5}{8}$ $\frac{5}{2}$	**10.** $\frac{3}{8} = \frac{12}{x}$ 32	**11.** $\frac{5}{x} = \frac{9}{11}$ $\frac{55}{9}$	**12.** $\frac{2}{7} = \frac{5}{y}$ $\frac{35}{2}$
13. $\frac{x}{40} = \frac{3}{5}$ 24	**14.** $\frac{n}{20} = \frac{3}{4}$ 15	**15.** $\frac{18}{c} = \frac{2}{7}$ 63	**16.** $\frac{24}{x} = \frac{4}{3}$ 18
17. $\frac{15}{y} = \frac{10}{8}$ 12	**18.** $\frac{63}{144} = \frac{u}{16}$ 7	**19.** $\frac{12}{30} = \frac{10}{k}$ 25	**20.** $\frac{5}{3} = \frac{y}{42}$ 70
21. $\frac{7}{b} = \frac{4}{9}$ $\frac{63}{4}$	**22.** $\frac{100}{a} = \frac{90}{45}$ 50	**23.** $\frac{4}{5} = \frac{28}{h}$ 35	**24.** $\frac{y}{18} = \frac{150}{126}$ $\frac{150}{7}$

Solve.

25. A car travels 150 km on 12 L of gasoline. How many liters of gasoline are needed to travel 500 km? 40

26. A baseball pitcher strikes out an average of 3.6 batters per 9 innings. At this rate, how many batters would the pitcher strike out in 315 innings? 126

27. A watch loses 2 minutes every 15 hours. How much time will it lose in 2 hours? $\frac{4}{15}$ minute

28. A school has a policy that 2 adults must accompany every group of 15 students on school trips. How many adults are needed to take 180 students on a trip? 24

29. Four shovels of sand are used for every 5 shovels of gravel in making cement. How many shovels of gravel are needed for 64 shovels of sand? 80

30. The ratio of foreign students to American students at a college is 2 to 35. How many foreign students attend this college if there are 1575 American students? 90

31. The members of a loading crew estimated that they could load 8 boxes in 20 minutes. At this rate, how many boxes could they load in 1 hour? 24

32. On a map, 1 cm represents 3.27 km. It is 24.5 cm between two cities on this map. What is the actual distance between the two cities? 80.115 km

33. A television station found that 145 out of the 350 people surveyed watched a program on education on Monday night. If this survey is representative of the total viewing area (12,250 people), about how many people watched the television special? 5075

34. A survey of 250 people in a city found that Channel 5 was the favorite station of 52 people. If this survey was representative of the city's population of 35,000, about how many people in this city favor Channel 5? 7280

B

Solve.

35. An automobile engine crankshaft revolves 3000 times per minute. How long does it take to revolve 50 times? 1 second

36. A refrigerator goes on a defrost cycle 1 hour out of every 14 hours of operation. How many hours is it on the defrost cycle each week? 12

37. The ratio of boys to girls in a school is 4:5. If there are 125 girls, what is the total number of students in this school? 225

38. The ratio of full seats to empty seats in an auditorium is 5 to 2. If there are 120 empty seats, what is the seating capacity of this auditorium? 420

39. ***Critical Thinking*** $9m = 5n$. Find the ratio $m:n$. 5:9

Challenge

40. Alena wants to guess the number of marbles in an 8-gal jar in order to win a moped. She knows there are 128 oz in a gallon, and she finds that 46 marbles fill an 8-oz jar. How many marbles should she guess?

41. If it takes 12 minutes to cut a log into 4 pieces, how long would it take to cut a log into 8 pieces?

42. A scale model of an experimental airplane measures 2.5 m from wing tip to wing tip. The actual plane will measure 60 m from wing tip to wing tip. If the highest point on the model will just fit under a $\frac{1}{2}$ m workbench, how tall does the airplane hangar have to be?

43. It has taken Sheryl 10 minutes to type two thirds of a page of her paper. If she continues to type at her present rate, how much longer will it take her to finish her seven-page term paper?

Mixed Review

Divide. **44.** $\frac{-32}{-8}$ **45.** $-\frac{7}{8} \div \frac{1}{4}$ **46.** $\frac{1}{6} \div -\frac{2}{3}$

Solve. **47.** $9a - 6 = 30 - 3a$ **48.** $17 - 5c = 2c + 3$

49. $-11w = -132$ **50.** $|x| = 15$ **51.** $|c| + 9 = 12$

52. $6|m| = 24$ **53.** $|n| = 0$ **54.** $4(3x - 12) = 12$

55. $\frac{x}{3} + 5 = \frac{3x}{5} - \frac{7}{3}$ **56.** $0.3r - 2.8 = 3.2 - 0.2r$

Solve for the given variable. **57.** $y = mx + b$ for m

58. $PV = nRT$ for T **59.** $I = Prt$ for r

Simplify. **60.** $2w - (3w - 1)$ **61.** $2[3x - 2(3x + 4)]$

ADDITIONAL ANSWERS

Exercises

40. 5888 marbles
41. 28 minutes
42. 12 meters
43. 95 minutes, or 1 hour 35 minutes

Mixed Review

44. 4
45. $-\frac{7}{2}$ or $-3\frac{1}{2}$
46. $-\frac{1}{4}$
47. 3
48. 2
49. 12
50. ± 15
51. ± 3
52. ± 4
53. 0
54. 5
55. $x = \frac{55}{2}$
56. $r = 12$
57. $m = \frac{y - b}{x} = \frac{y}{x} - \frac{b}{x}$
58. $T = \frac{PV}{nR}$
59. $r = \frac{I}{Pt}$
60. $-w + 1$
61. $-6x - 16$

3-10

FIRST FIVE MINUTES

Write as a decimal.

1. $\frac{23}{100}$ 0.23
2. $\frac{475}{100}$ 4.75
3. $\frac{2}{100}$ 0.02
4. $\frac{0.5}{100}$ 0.005

Write as a fraction with 100 in the denominator.

5. 0.67 $\frac{67}{100}$
6. 1.98 $\frac{198}{100}$
7. 0.01 $\frac{1}{100}$
8. 0.001 $\frac{0.1}{100}$

Percent

Emphasize that each of the three ways to write a percent,

$$5\% = 0.05 = \frac{5}{100}$$

is useful in different situations. We can remember numbers like 5%. We can add and compare sizes with the decimal form 0.05. We can multiply and divide easily with the fractional form $\frac{5}{100}$.

Avoiding Common Errors

Too often, .11 becomes 11 and .54 becomes 54. Remind students that when writing decimals, like 0.54, they are to write the leading 0 before the decimal point. The leading 0 makes the decimal point more visible.

Key Questions

- What is 10% of 10? 1
- What is 10% of 50? 5
- What is 50% of 10? 5
- What is 100% of 315? 315

Chalkboard Examples

Write as a decimal.

1. 41% 0.41
2. 2% 0.02
3. 150% 1.50
4. 0.5% 0.005

Express as a percent.

5. 0.62

$$0.62 = \frac{62}{100} = 62\%$$

6. $\frac{1}{4} = 0.25 = \frac{25}{100} = 25\%$
7. $\frac{6}{5} = 1.20 = \frac{120}{100} = 120\%$
8. $1 = \frac{100}{100} = 100\%$

3-10 Problem Solving: Using Percent

Math History

The idea of percent was used as early as the Roman Empire. The Roman Emperor Augustus levied a tax at a rate of $\frac{1}{100}$ of the selling price on all goods. In the 15th century, Italian manuscripts used expressions such as "20 p 100" and "xx p cento" to indicate 20 percent. Near the end of that century, phrases such as "viii in x perceto" (8 percent) were used to express percent. The percent symbol (%), probably came from a symbol introduced in Italy at the end of the 15th century, " ⁀ᵒ ". By 1650, the symbol "per $\frac{o}{o}$ " was used for percent. Later, the "per" was dropped, leaving the symbol used today.

Percent

Objective: Express decimals and fractions as percents and vice versa.

The ratio of a number to 100 is called **percent.** The word "percent" means *per one hundred*, and is represented by the symbol **%.** We can write a percent as a fraction or as a decimal.

$$78.5\% = 78.5 \times \frac{1}{100} = \frac{78.5}{100} = 0.785$$

$$4\% = 4 \times \frac{1}{100} = \frac{4}{100} = 0.04$$

To solve problems involving percent, we must first change the percent to a decimal.

EXAMPLES Write as a decimal.

1. 35% = 0.35 — The hundredths place is the second place to the right of the decimal point.
2. 5% = 0.05
3. 138% = 1.38
4. 0.8% = 0.008

Try This Write as a decimal.

a. 48% 0.48 **b.** 3% 0.03 **c.** 145% 1.45 **d.** 0.5% 0.005

Some problems require that we change a fraction to a percent. The easiest way to do this is usually to change the fraction to a decimal first.

EXAMPLES Express as a percent. Round to the nearest tenth of a percent if necessary.

5. $\frac{2}{3} = 0.666\bar{6}$ — $2 \div 3 = 0.666\bar{6}$ The bar shows that the digit six repeats.

$= 0.667$ — Rounding to the nearest thousandth

$= \frac{66.7}{100}$ — Writing as a fraction with a denominator of 100

$= 66.7\%$

6. $\frac{5}{4} = 1.25$ — $5 \div 4 = 1.25$

$= \frac{125}{100}$

$= 125\%$

Try This Express as a percent. Round to the nearest tenth of a percent if necessary.

e. $\frac{3}{4}$ 75% f. $\frac{3}{8}$ 37.5% g. $\frac{24.5}{5}$ 490%

h. $\frac{12.4}{25}$ 49.6% i. $\frac{0.02}{500}$ 0.004% j. $\frac{3}{40}$ 7.5%

Percent Problems

Objective: Solve percent problems.

We can solve problems involving percent by using a proportion or by translating to an equation and solving. When fractional percents are used, translating to an equation is usually the better method.

EXAMPLE 7 Solve.

15.5% of 60 is what number?

15.5%	of	60	is	what number
↓	↓	↓	↓	↓
0.155	·	60	=	n

Translating to an equation

$15.5\% = \frac{15.5}{100} = 0.155$

$9.3 = n$

15.5% of 60 is 9.3.

Percent Problems

You may want to show students how to solve problems involving percent using a proportion.

Example 7
15.5% of 60 is what number?

$\frac{n}{60} = \frac{15.5}{100}$

$n = (60)\left(\frac{15.5}{100}\right)$

$n = 9.3$

Example 8
24 is what percent of 120?

$\frac{24}{120} = \frac{p}{100}$

$100\left(\frac{24}{120}\right) = p$

$20\% = p$

You may wish to illustrate the three basic types of percent problems with the same phrase. For example, in Example 9, we have

25% of 60 is 15

This leads to the following.
1) 25% of 60 is what number?
2) 15 is what percent of 60?
3) 25% of what number is 15?

You can also illustrate that many sentences have the same translation. For example,
1) What percent of 150 is 30?
2) 30 is what percent of 150?
Both translate to $30 = p \cdot 150$.

Chalkboard Examples

Solve.

1. What is 20% of 90?
   20% of 90 = $0.20 \cdot 90 = 18$
2. 12% of 40 is what number?
   $0.12 \cdot 40 = 4.8$
3. What percent of 60 equals 12?
   Let p be the percent, expressed as a decimal.
   $p \cdot 60 = 12$
   $p = \frac{12}{60} = 0.20 = 20\%$
4. 35% of what number equals 1.4?
   $0.35 \cdot x = 1.40$
   $x = \frac{1.40}{0.35} = \frac{140}{35} = 4$

EXAMPLE 8 Solve.

24 is what percent of 120?

24	is	what percent	of	120?
↓	↓	↓	↓	↓
24	=	p	·	120

Translating to an equation

Let p represent the percent expressed as a decimal.

$$\frac{24}{120} = p$$

$$0.2 = p$$

$$p = 0.2 \text{ or } 20\%$$

Express the decimal as a percent.

24 is 20% of 120.

EXAMPLE 9 Solve.

25% of what number is 15?

25%	of	what number	is	15?
↓	↓	↓	↓	↓
0.25	·	n	=	15

Translating to an equation

Let n be the number you are trying to find. $25\% = \frac{25}{100} = 0.25$

$$n = \frac{15}{0.25}$$

$$n = 60$$

25% of 60 is 15.

Try This Solve.

k. What percent of 40 is 15? 37.5%

l. 3 is 16% of what number? 18.75

m. 7.5% of 80 is what number? 6

n. What number is 12.5% of 40? 5

Percents

Most calculators have a [%] key that can be used to transform a percent to a decimal when performing calculations. (On some calculators, you have to push [=] after [%].)

Find 30% of 200. 30 [%] [×] 200 [=] 60

For additional calculator practice, see Calculator Worksheet 11.

Problem Solving

Objective: Solve problems involving applications of percent.

PROBLEM-SOLVING GUIDELINES
■ UNDERSTAND the problem
■ Develop and carry out a PLAN
■ Find the ANSWER and CHECK

You can use the Problem-Solving Guidelines to help you solve problems involving percent.

EXAMPLE 10

The tax on an automobile was 6%. What was the original price of this car if the tax was \$633?

■ UNDERSTAND the problem

Question: What was the price of the car?
Data: The tax was 6% of the price.

Clarifying the question and identifying the given data

■ Develop and carry out a PLAN

Let p = the price of the car.

Using a variable to represent the price of the car.

$(0.06)p = 633$

The tax, \$633, is 6% of the price.

$$p = \frac{633}{0.06}$$

$$p = 10{,}550$$

■ Find the ANSWER and CHECK

The price of the car was \$10,550. If we find 6% of \$10,550, we get \$633. The answer checks.

Since 5% of 10,000 is 500, the answer is reasonable.

Try This Solve.

o. Ms. Pelligrini received a \$750 bonus with her monthly paycheck. Her regular monthly pay is \$2500. What percent of her regular monthly pay is her bonus? 30%

p. Truong's college expenses were \$5000 last year. She spent \$1500 on tuition, \$2250 on room and board, and \$1250 on miscellaneous expenses. What percent of her college expenses went toward tuition? 30%

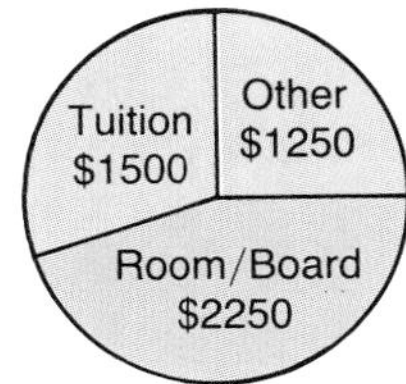

Problem Solving

Chalkboard Examples

Solve.

1. The population decreased to 90% of last year's population. The population is now 270. What was it last year?
   Let p be last year's population.
   $0.90p = 270$
   $p = \frac{270}{0.90} = 300$
2. The stock market index is now at 1560, which is 130% of last year's value. What was the value last year?
   Let s be the stock market index for last year.
   $1.30s = 1560$
   $s = \frac{1560}{1.30} = 1200$

LESSON QUIZ

Write as a decimal.

1. 54% 0.54
2. 4% 0.04
3. 104% 1.04
4. 0.3% 0.003

Express as a percent.

5. $\frac{7}{5}$
   $\frac{7}{5} = 1.4 = \frac{140}{100} = 140\%$

Solve.

6. What number is 40% of 120?
   $0.40 \cdot 120 = 48$
7. 18 is what percent of 20?
   $18 = \frac{p}{100} \cdot 20$
   $p = 90$; 90%

Assignment Guide
Minimum: Day 1: 1–34 e/o, MR
Day 2: 35–42

Regular: 1–48 e/o, 49, MR

Advanced: 1–47 m4, 48–53, MR

3-10 EXERCISES

A

Write as a decimal.

1. 41% 0.41 **2.** 60% 0.6 **3.** 7% 0.07 **4.** 1% 0.01 **5.** 125% 1.25
6. 180% 1.8 **7.** 0.8% 0.008 **8.** 0.6% 0.006 **9.** 1.5% 0.015 **10.** 2.8% 0.028

Express as a percent. Round to the nearest tenth of a percent if necessary.

11. $\frac{3}{4}$ 75% **12.** $\frac{1}{25}$ 4% **13.** $\frac{24}{25}$ 96% **14.** $\frac{3}{8}$ 37.5% **15.** $\frac{1}{3}$ 33.3%
16. $\frac{3}{25}$ 12% **17.** $\frac{5}{8}$ 62.5% **18.** $\frac{5}{6}$ 83.3% **19.** $\frac{3}{16}$ 18.8% **20.** $\frac{1}{20}$ 5%

Solve.

21. What percent of 68 is 17? 25%
22. What percent of 75 is 36? 48%
23. What percent of 125 is 30? 24%
24. What percent of 300 is 57? 19%
25. 45 is 30% of what number? 150
26. 20.4 is 24% of what number? 85
27. 0.3 is 12% of what number? 2.5
28. 7 is 175% of what number? 4
29. What percent of 80 is 100? 125%
30. What percent of 10 is 205? 2050%
31. What is 2% of 40? 0.8
32. What is 40% of 2? 0.8
33. 2 is what percent of 40? 5%
34. 40 is 2% of what number? 2000

35. On a test of 88 items, a student got 76 correct. What percent of the items were correct? 86.4%

36. A baseball player had 13 hits in 25 times at bat. What percent of his times at bat were hits? 52%

37. A family spent $208 one month for food. This was 26% of its income. What was its monthly income? $800

38. The sales-tax rate in New York City is 8%. How much tax would be charged on a purchase of $428.86? How much will the total cost of the purchase be? $34.31; $463.17

39. Water volume increases 9% when it freezes. If 400 cm^3 of water are frozen, how much will the volume increase? What will be the volume of the ice? 36 cm^3 436 cm^3

40. Sales tax in Freeberg is 5%. What would the sales tax be on a motorbike that cost $775? What was the total cost for the motorbike, including tax? $38.75; $813.75

41. A Shea tape player costs $12 more this year than last year. This represents a 40% increase in the cost of the item. How much did this tape player cost last year? $30

42. A salesperson's quota was set at $7500 for one month. Last month this salesperson sold $10,000. What percent of the quota did the salesperson sell? 133.3%

B

43. A meal came to \$16.41 without tax. Calculate a 6% sales tax, and then calculate a 15% tip based on the sum of the meal and the tax. What is the total cost of the meal? \$20

44. Rollie's Records charges \$7.99 for an album. Warped Records charges \$9.95, but you have a coupon for a \$2.00 discount. A sales tax of 7% is charged on the *regular* prices. How much does the record cost at each store? \$8.55; \$8.65

To find the **percent of increase** (or **decrease**), divide the amount of increase (or decrease) by the original amount.

45. Wendi worked for \$5 an hour for the first month she was on the job. She then earned a raise and was making \$5.20 an hour. What was the percent of increase of her raise? 4%

46. A car stereo that originally cost \$175 was on sale for \$150. What was the percent of decrease for the car stereo? 14.3%

47. The dimensions of a rectangular design are 7.5 cm by 12.5 cm. This has been reduced to $37\frac{1}{2}$% of the original design. What were the dimensions of the original design? 20 cm by 33.3 cm

48. The new price of a car is 25% higher than the old price of \$8800. The old price is what percent lower than the new price? 20%

49. ***Critical Thinking*** If x is 160% of y, y is what percent of x? 62.5%

Challenge

50. A store has a 30% discount on every item in stock. Would a customer be better off if the 5% sales tax were applied before or after the discount?

51. Which is better, a discount of 40% or successive discounts of 20% and 20%?

52. Which is better, successive discounts of 10%, 10%, and 20% or 20%, 10%, and 10%?

53. A bank offered two plans for an investment of \$400 if the money was not withdrawn for two years. One was 5% the first year and 10% the second year. The other was 10% the first year and 5% the second year. Which investment plan is better? Equal. Both earn \$62 interest over two years.

Mixed Review

Give the additive inverse. **54.** 4.1 **55.** -9 **56.** 16

Simplify. **57.** $-4 - (-2x) + 6x + x + 9$ **58.** $8c + 8 - (-2c)$

59. $-6 + 5x - (-2x) - 4x$ **60.** $2t - (-13) - 3t - (-6t) - 19$

Calculate. **61.** $-6(3.4)(-1)$ **62.** $-3.2(0)$ **63.** $-2(-8)(-2)$

64. $99 \div (-3)$ **65.** $-72 \div 3$ **66.** $45 \div (-15)$

ADDITIONAL ANSWERS

Exercises

50. No difference;
$x - 0.30x + 0.05(x - 0.30x) = 0.735x$
$x + 0.05x - 0.30(x + 0.05x) = 0.735x$

51. 40%. Successive 20% discounts mean you pay 80% of 80%, or 64%, which is only a 36% discount.

52. Equal. Both are 35.2% discounts, since $(0.9)(0.9)(0.8) = (0.8)(0.9)(0.9)$.

Mixed Review

54. -4.1
55. 9
56. -16
57. $9x + 5$
58. $10c + 8$
59. $3x - 6$
60. $5t - 6$
61. 20.4
62. 0
63. -32
64. -33
65. -24
66. -3

3-11

FIRST FIVE MINUTES

Write as an algebraic expression.

1. the sum of x and the quantity three times x
   $x + 3x$
2. the difference between c and one third of c
   $c - \frac{1}{3}c$
3. the integer one greater than the integer n
   $n + 1$
4. the product of s and the quantity s plus 5
   $s(s + 5)$
5. three times the number n
   $3n$

Phrases to Algebraic Expressions

Stress that there may be more than one way to translate a phrase to an algebraic expression. It may vary depending on which quantity we let the variable represent.

You may wish to have students give answers in simplified form. Answers in this lesson will be given in both simplified and unsimplified forms.

Key Questions

- Simplify the answer to Example 1.
  $4b$
- Simplify the answer to Example 2.
  $4x + 3$
- Suppose we let $m =$ the cost of the main floor seat in Example 1. What would be the expression for the total cost of one of each type of seat?
  $\frac{1}{3}m + m$ or $\frac{4}{3}m$

Chalkboard Examples

1. Write an expression for the sum of two consecutive integers.
   Let n represent the first integer. The next integer is $n + 1$. The sum is $n + (n + 1)$ or $2n + 1$.
2. Write an expression for the sum of an even integer and the next even integer.
   Assume x is an even integer. Then $x + 2$ is the next even integer and the sum is $x + (x + 2)$ or $2x + 2$.

3-11 Problem Solving: More Expressions and Equations

Some problems contain two or more unknowns. To solve such problems, you must first decide which unknown quantity the variable will represent and then express the other unknown quantities in terms of that variable.

Phrases to Algebraic Expressions

Objective: Translate compound phrases into algebraic expressions.

EXAMPLE 1

The cost of a main floor seat is three times as much as the cost of a balcony seat. Write an expression showing the total cost for one of each type of seat.

Let $b =$ cost of a balcony seat.
$3b =$ cost of a main floor seat

The cost of a main floor seat is expressed in terms of the cost of a balcony seat. Therefore, let the variable b represent the cost of a balcony seat, and express the cost of a main floor seat in terms of b.

$b + 3b =$ total cost

To find the total cost, add the cost of each seat.

Try This

a. There are half as many boys in a certain club as there are girls. Write an expression for the total number of boys and girls in the club. $\frac{1}{2}g + g$ or $2b + b$

The integers 22, 23, and 24 are **consecutive integers**. These numbers follow each other when we count by ones. The integers 6, 8, and 10 are **consecutive even integers**. These numbers follow each other when we count by twos, beginning with the number 6. The integers 7, 9, and 11 are **consecutive odd integers** because they follow each other when we count by twos, beginning with the number 7.

EXAMPLE 2

Write an expression for the sum of an integer and three times the next larger integer.

Let $x =$ an integer.
$(x + 1) =$ the next integer
$x + 3(x + 1) =$ the sum of an integer and three times the next integer

Try This

b. Write an expression for the sum of three consecutive odd integers.
$x + x + 2 + x + 4 = 3x + 6$

Using Equations to Solve Problems

Objective: Solve problems by writing and solving equations.

You can use the Problem-Solving Guidelines on page 155 to help solve problems when your plan involves writing and solving an equation.

EXAMPLE 3

Manuel scored 35 points fewer in his second bowling game than in his first game. His total score for two games was 395. How many points did he score in each game?

■ **UNDERSTAND the problem**

Question: How many points did Manuel score in each game?
Data: The total for the 2 games was 395. In the second game, he scored 35 points fewer than in the first.

We can show this in a *diagram*.

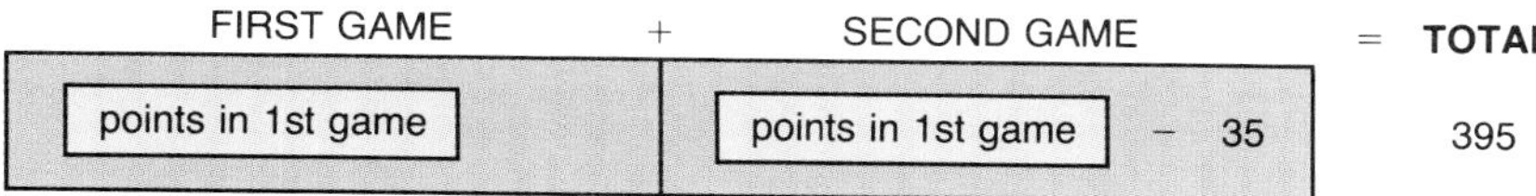

■ **Develop and carry out a PLAN**

Let f = points in the first game.

The points for the second game are expressed in terms of points for the first game. Therefore, let the variable represent the points in the first game.

$f - 35$ = points in the second game

$$f + (f - 35) = 395$$
$$2f - 35 = 395$$
$$2f - 35 + 35 = 395 + 35$$
$$2f = 430$$
$$\frac{1}{2} \cdot 2f = \frac{1}{2} \cdot 430$$
$$f = 215$$

Second game $= f - 35 = 215 - 35 = 180$

■ **Find the ANSWER and CHECK**

Manuel scored 215 points in the first game and 180 points in the second game.

If we estimate by rounding we get $200 + 200 = 400$. The answer seems reasonable.

Using Equations to Solve Problems

Remind students to estimate whether their answers are reasonable and to see that they are labeled correctly.

Before working Try This Exercise **c**, students may need to review the formula for finding the perimeter of a rectangle.

Key Question

- Ask students to estimate answers and give units, if any, for Try This Exercises **c, d,** and **e**.

Chalkboard Example

1. The local bank pays 8% yearly interest on deposits. The interest is added into the account at the end of the year. How much money should be invested now, in order to have $972 at the end of the year?
   Let p be the amount of dollars to be invested. At the end of one year there will be
   $p + 0.08p$
   in the account, hence
   $p + 0.08p = 972$
   $1.08p = 972$
   $p = \frac{972}{1.08} = 900$
   $900 should be invested now.

LESSON QUIZ

1. The height of a table is 1.5 times the height of the seat of a chair. Write an expression for the difference between the height of the table and the height of the chair.
   Let c be the height of the chair.
   $1.5c - c$ or $0.5c$
2. Write an expression for the sum of an integer plus twice the next integer.
   Let n be the integer.
   $n + 2(n + 1)$ or $3n + 2$
3. If you add one fifth of a number to that number you get 42. What is the number?
   Let n be the number.
   $\frac{1}{5}n + n = 42$
   $\frac{6}{5}n = 42$
   $n = \frac{5}{6} \cdot 42 = 35$

Assignment Guide
Minimum: 1–31 e/o, MR

Regular: 1–36 m3, 37, MR

Advanced: 1–36 m4, 37, 38–42 e/o, MR

ADDITIONAL ANSWERS

Exercises

Answers may vary depending on which quantity the variable represents.

1. Let r = cost of one record. $r + (r - 3.50)$ or $2r - 3.50$ Let t = cost of one tape. $t + (t + 3.50)$ or $2t + 3.50$
2. Let t = points on first test. $t + \frac{1}{2}t$ or $\frac{3}{2}t$ Let s = points on second test. $s + 2s$ or $3s$
3. Let e = # of English books. $e + (e - 9)$ or $2e - 9$ Let m = # of math books. $m + (m + 9)$ or $2m + 9$
4. Let s = # of science books. $s + (s + 12)$ or $2s + 12$ Let h = # of history books. $h + (h - 12)$ or $2h - 12$
5. Let p = cost of paperback book. $p + 3(p + 7)$ or $4p + 21$ Let h = cost of hardback book. $3h + (h - 7)$ or $4h - 7$
6. Let s = cost of small drink. $3s + 2(s + 50)$ or $5s + 100$ Let l = cost of large drink. $2l + 3(l - 50)$ or $5l - 150$
7. $x + (x + 2) = 2x + 2$
8. $x + (x + 2) = 2x + 2$
9. $x + 2(x + 2) = 3x + 4$
10. $x + 3(x + 1) = 4x + 3$
11. $x + (x + 2) + (x + 4) = 3x + 6$
12. $\frac{1}{4}x + \frac{1}{5}(x + 1) + \frac{1}{2}(x + 2) = \frac{19}{20}x + \frac{6}{5}$
13. $x + \frac{1}{2}(x + 2) + \frac{1}{4}(x + 4) = \frac{7}{4}x + 2$
14. $x + \frac{3}{4}(x + 2) + 2(x + 4) = \frac{15}{4}x + \frac{19}{2}$
15. $2x + \frac{2}{3}(x + 1) + 3(x + 2) = \frac{17}{3}x + \frac{20}{3}$

Try This Solve.

c. The perimeter of a rectangle is 150 cm. The length is 15 cm greater than the width. Find the dimensions. Width is 30 cm; length is 45 cm

d. The sum of an integer and twice the next consecutive integer is 29. What are the integers? 9, 10

e. Mrs. Lee deposited a sum of money in a savings account that pays 11% interest per year. At the end of one year, Mrs. Lee has a total of \$9990 in the account. How much did she invest originally? \$9000

3-11 EXERCISES

A

1. A record cost \$3.50 more than a tape. Write an expression for the total cost of 1 record and 1 tape.
2. The second math test was worth half as many points as the first test. Write an expression for the total number of points on the 2 tests.
3. There were 9 fewer math books than English books. Write an expression for the total number of books.
4. There are 12 more history books than science books. Write an expression for the total number of books.
5. A hardback book cost \$7 more than a paperback book. Write an expression for the total cost of 1 paperback book and 3 hardback books.
6. A large drink costs 50¢ more than a small drink. Write an expression for the total cost of 3 small drinks and 2 large drinks.

Write an expression for each of the following.

7. the sum of an even integer and the next even integer
8. the sum of an odd integer and the next odd integer
9. the sum of an even integer and two times the next even integer
10. the sum of an integer and three times the next integer
11. the sum of an even integer and the next two even integers
12. the sum of $\frac{1}{4}$ of an integer, $\frac{1}{5}$ of the next integer, and $\frac{1}{2}$ of the following integer
13. the sum of an even integer, $\frac{1}{2}$ of the next even integer, and $\frac{1}{4}$ of the following even integer
14. the sum of an odd integer, $\frac{3}{4}$ of the next odd integer, and two times the following odd integer
15. the sum of two times an integer, $\frac{2}{3}$ of the next integer, and three times the following integer

Solve.

16. If you add $\frac{2}{5}$ of a number to the number itself, you get 56. What is the number? 40

17. If you add one third of a number to the number itself, you get 48. What is the number? 36

18. The sum of two consecutive odd integers is 76. What are the integers? 37, 39

19. The sum of two consecutive even integers is 106. What are the integers? 52, 54

20. The sum of three consecutive integers is 126. What are the integers? 41, 42, 43

21. The sum of three consecutive odd integers is 189. What are the integers? 61, 63, 65

22. The perimeter of a rectangle is 310 m. The length is 25 m greater than the width. What are the length and the width of this rectangle? 65 m, 90 m

23. One angle of a triangle is 4 times as large as another. The third angle is equal to the sum of the other two angles. What is the measure of the smallest angle? (Hint: The sum of the measures of the angles of a triangle equals 180°.) 18°

24. The combined lengths of the Nile and Amazon rivers is 13,108 km. If the Amazon were 234 km longer, it would be as long as the Nile. What is the length of each river? Amazon 6437 km, Nile 6671 km

25. In 1984 tennis players John McEnroe and Martina Navratilova earned a total of $3,462,665. If McEnroe had earned $884,447 more, he would have earned the same as Navratilova. How much did each earn? McEnroe: $1,289,109; Navratilova: $2,173,556

26. A 48-ft wire is cut into three pieces. The second piece is three times as long as the first piece. The third piece is four times as long as the second piece. How long is each piece? 3 ft, 9 ft, 36 ft

27. Mrs. Gutierrez borrowed some money. At the end of the year, she repaid the loan plus 10.5% of the original amount for interest. She paid back a total of $8287.50. How much money did she borrow originally? $7500

28. Mr. Horvath put some money in a savings account and deposited no more into this account for one year. At the end of the year, there was $6272 in the account, including 6% of the original amount for interest. How much did he deposit originally? $5916.98

29. After a 20% discount, an item was sold for $9600. What was the original price of the item? $12,000

30. The population of the United States in 1980 was 224 million. This was a 48% increase over the population in 1950. What was the population in 1950 to the nearest million? 151,000,000

31. The number of students, ages 5 to 17 years, enrolled in school in the year 1950 was 25 million. The number of students enrolled in 1980 was 64% greater than in 1950. How many students were enrolled in 1980? 41 million

37. $4s + 7 = 1863 - 1776$; $s = 20$
38. 30
39. $1.09p = 10.00$, $p = \$9.17$, not $9.10
40. 7.5%
41. $1056
42. 5 half dollars, 10 quarters, 20 dimes, 60 nickels

Mixed Review

43. $\frac{10}{7}$
44. -3
45. 9
46. 2
47. 4
48. 12
49. 36
50. -20

B

$0.25x = x - 12$, $x = 16$, $0.25x = 4$

32. One number is 25% of another. The larger number is 12 more than the smaller. Both numbers are positive. What are the numbers?

33. If the daily rental for a car is $18.90, and a person must drive 190 miles and stay within a $55.00 budget, what is the highest price per mile the person can afford? 19¢

34. Jane scored 78 on a test that had 4 seven-point fill-ins and 24 three-point multiple-choice questions. She had one fill-in wrong. How many multiple-choice answers did she get right? 19

35. The width of a rectangle is $\frac{3}{4}$ the length. The perimeter of the rectangle becomes 50 cm when the length and width are each increased by 2 cm. Find the length and width. 12 cm, 9 cm

36. A phone company charges $13.72 per month plus 13¢ per call and 8¢ per minute. How much did it cost Helga one month to make 35 calls that totaled 172 minutes? $32.03

37. *Critical Thinking* Abraham Lincoln's 1863 Gettysburg Address refers to the year 1776 as "four score and seven years ago." Write an equation and solve for a score.

Challenge

38. In a basketball league, the Falcons won 15 of their first 20 games. If they win only half the time from now on, how many more games will they have to play in order to win 60% of the total games?

39. In one city, a sales tax of 9% was added to the price of gasoline as registered on the pump. Suppose a driver asked for $10 worth of regular. The attendant filled the tank until the pump read $9.10 and charged the driver $10.00. Something was wrong. Use algebra to correct the error.

40. The buyer of a piano priced at $2000 is given the choice of paying cash at the time of purchase or $2150 at the end of one year. What rate of interest is being charged if payment is made at the end of one year?

41. If you receive 7% interest on savings, but 20% tax is charged on the interest, how much do you have left from an initial $1000 deposit?

42. A storekeeper goes to the bank to get $10 worth of change. He requests twice as many quarters as half dollars, twice as many dimes as quarters, three times as many nickels as dimes, and no pennies or dollars. How many of each coin did the storekeeper get?

Mixed Review

Solve. **43.** $7x = 10$ **44.** $7a - 9a = 6$ **45.** $-8w + 13w = 45$

46. $8c + 6 = 6c + 10$ **47.** $15 - (5m - 6) = 1$ **48.** $\frac{3}{4}b = 9$

Solve. **49.** $\frac{3}{4}a - 6 = 3 + \frac{1}{2}a$ **50.** $\frac{3}{5}y + 2 = \frac{1}{2}y$

3-12 Problem Solving: Strategies

Make an Organized List

Objective: Solve problems using the strategy *Make an Organized List* and other strategies.

PROBLEM-SOLVING GUIDELINES
■ UNDERSTAND the problem
■ Develop and carry out a PLAN
■ Find the ANSWER and CHECK

Some problems can be solved by listing information in a systematic or organized way. This strategy for solving problems is called Make an Organized List.

EXAMPLE Use the strategy *Make an Organized List* to solve this problem. The first team to win 3 out of 5 possible games will be the winner of a basketball tournament. In how many ways can a team win 3 out of the 5 games?

We can solve this problem by first listing all of the ways to win if there are no losses. Next we will list the ways if there is 1 loss and then the ways with 2 losses. Listing the possibilities according to the number of losses keeps the list organized. After the list is organized, we can tell when we have listed all possibilities.

WWW — 1 way to win 3 games with 0 losses

LWWW
WLWW
WWLW — 3 ways to win 3 games with 1 loss

LLWWW
LWLWW
LWWLW
WLLWW
WLWLW
WWLLW — 6 ways to win 3 games with 2 losses

1 + 3 + 6 = 10 — There are 10 ways to win 3 out of 5 games.

Problem-Solving Strategies		
Draw a Diagram	Guess, Check, Revise	Write an Equation
Make an Organized List	Use Logical Reasoning	Make a Table
Look for a Pattern	Simplify the Problem	Work Backward

3-12

FIRST FIVE MINUTES

1. Jody drives 10 miles north, 20 miles east, 10 miles south, and 5 miles west. How far is she from where she started? 15 miles

Make an Organized List

Stress that the key to a successful list is organization. It may be necessary for students to try several different ways of organizing data before they find a way that leads to a solution. Use the example in the text to show an organized approach to making a list.

Key Questions

- How many games must a team win to win the tournament? 3
- What is the most number of games a team could lose and still win the tournament? 2
- What is the fewest number of games a team could play in order to win? 3, if it wins all 3

Chalkboard Example

1. In Mr. Dismond's math class there are 4 tests and a final exam. To get an A in the class, a student must get an A on the final exam and on at least 2 tests, and a B or better on the remaining tests. How many ways are there to get an A?
   First, list the ways to get an A if the student gets no Bs. Then list the ways if the student gets one B, then the ways if the student gets 2 Bs. The student must get an A on the final exam, so the italicized grade is always an A.
   AAAA*A*
   BAAA*A* ABAA*A* AABA*A* AAAB*A*
   AABB*A* ABAB*A* BAAB*A* ABBA*A*
   BABA*A* BBAA*A*
   There are 11 ways to get an A in the class.

Hints for Problems

1. Make an organized list of all the teams each team would play. How many times does each team play the other team?
2. Guess a number of cartons with 2 rackets in each. Check and revise your guess.

3. Draw diagrams to represent different tile arrangements.
4. Make an organized list of different combinations.
5. Guess two factors of 120 as dimensions, check perimeter, and guess again. Compare the perimeters.
6. Guess five items, check cost, revise your guess. Can you find more than one solution?
7. Draw a calendar. Circle each day off that Charles has. Mark each day off that Eva has.
8. Guess a number for large calculators, then find the number of small calculators and the total cost. Revise your guess.

ANSWERS

1. There will be 72 games played when each team has played each other team twice.
2. Fourteen cartons of 2 rackets each and 24 cartons of 3 rackets each were used to pack 100 rackets.
3. The 5 orange tiles can be arranged 12 different ways.
4. There are 7 different combinations possible.
5. The garden's measurements were 10 m by 12 m.
6. Some possible solutions:
   a. soccer shoes ($25) + leg weights ($45) + sweat shirt ($15) + softball bat ($15) + basketball ($20) = $120
   b. tennis outfit ($50) + basketball ($20) + swimsuit ($10) + sweat shirt ($15) + soccer shoes ($25) = $120
   c. tennis outfit ($50) + basketball ($20) + swimsuit ($10) + softball bat ($15) + soccer shoes ($25) = $120
   d. racquetball racket ($40) + basketball ($20) + jogging suit ($35) + swimsuit ($10) + softball bat ($15) = $120
   e. racquetball racket ($40) + basketball ($20) + jogging suit ($35) + swimsuit ($10) + sweat shirt ($15) = $120
7. Charles and Eva will both be off on a Monday five weeks later.
8. The club sold 24 large calculators and 72 small ones.

3-12 PROBLEMS

Solve using one or more problem-solving strategies.

1. There are 9 teams that play in a soccer league. During the season each team will play each other team in the league twice. How many games will be played?

2. Tennis rackets can be packaged in cartons holding 2 rackets each or in cartons holding 3 rackets each. Yesterday's packing slip showed that 38 cartons were used to pack a total of 100 rackets. How many cartons of each size were used yesterday?

3. Mrs. Smith is having her shower retiled. The tiles are square and all are tan, except for 5 that are orange. She asked the tileman to arrange the orange tiles in a decorative design in which at least one side of each tile is completely touching that of another, and all 5 tiles are adjacent. How many different designs can he possibly show her?

4. A vending machine had to be programmed to accept any combination of nickels, dimes, and quarters that totals 40¢. How many different combinations are possible?

5. A garden plot has an area of 120 square meters. The measure of the length and width are whole numbers. The length and width of the garden were selected so that the least amount of fencing was required to enclose the garden. What are the dimensions of this garden?

6. A sporting goods store was having a sale. One customer bought 5 different items and paid $120, not including tax. He could have chosen any of the items listed in the chart below. What combinations of 5 items could he have bought?

■ soccer shoes $25	■ jogging suits $35	■ sweat shirts $15
■ basketballs $20	■ swimsuits $10	■ softball bats $15
■ leg weights $45	■ racquetball racket $40	■ tennis outfit $50

7. Charles and his girlfriend Eva want to have a party for their friends. Both work at night. Charles has every ninth night off from work, and Eva has every fifth night off. Today is Sunday and Charles is off work. Eva has tomorrow night off. When is the first night they would both be available to have the party?

8. ***Write a convincing argument*** Solve the problem below. Then write an argument that would convince a classmate that your solution is correct.

A school club sold calculators to raise money for a field trip. The members sold small calculators for $5 each and large desk-top calculators for twice as much as the small calculators. At the end of the sale, they sold three times as many small calculators as large calculators for a total of $600. How many of each size calculator did they sell?

Chapter 3 Summary and Review

3-1

To solve an equation using the **addition property of equality**, you add the same number to both sides of the equation.

Solve.

1. $x + 12 = -8$
2. $-7 = y - 11$
3. $x - 11 = 14$
4. $w + \frac{3}{7} = -\frac{5}{7}$

Translate to an equation and solve.

5. A color TV sold for $629 in May. This was $38 more than the price in January. Find the January price.
6. In La Ciudad Fría the average daily high temperature in the winter is $-65°$F. This is 150° less than the average daily high temperature in Ciudad Caliente. What is the average daily high temperature in Ciudad Caliente in the winter?

3-2

To solve an equation using the **multiplication property of equality**, you multiply both sides of the equation by the same number.

Solve.

7. $6x = 24$
8. $-\frac{x}{4} = 48$
9. $\frac{3}{5} = \frac{-2}{5}x$
10. $-11x = 121$

Translate to an equation and solve.

11. Rosita gets a $4 commission for each appliance that she sells. One week she got $108 in commissions. How many appliances did she sell?

3-3

To solve an equation, you may need to use both the addition and multiplication properties of equality. Collect like terms on each side of the equation before using the properties. You may need to use the distributive property to remove parentheses before collecting like terms.

Solve and check.

12. $2x + 5 = 13$
13. $-8x + 3 = 27$
14. $50 - 4x = 14$
15. $7x + 8x = 45$
16. $4(3y + 2) = 44$
17. $6(3a - 2) + 5a = 57$

ANSWERS

1. -20
2. 4
3. 25
4. $-\frac{8}{7}$
5. $591
6. 85°
7. 4
8. -192
9. $-\frac{3}{2}$
10. -11
11. 27
12. 4
13. -3
14. 9
15. 3
16. 3
17. 3

18. $2n + 6$
19. $5n - 18$
20. $\frac{1}{3}n - 6$
21. $\frac{1}{2}(n + 10)$
22. $2n - 3$
23. $2x + 10$
24. 40
25. 4 h 10 min or 250 min
26. 38
27. 2
28. −12
29. 6
30. 12
31. −1
32. −2.8
33. 7
34. −3

3-4

Use the Problem-Solving Guidelines to help you understand a problem, write an equation, and check your solution.

Write as an algebraic expression.

18. 6 more than twice a number

19. 18 less than five times a number

20. 6 less than $\frac{1}{3}$ of the number

21. $\frac{1}{2}$ of the sum of a number and 10

22. Betsy swims every day. She swam 3 fewer laps today than twice the number of laps she swam yesterday. Write an expression for the number of laps she swam today.

23. After 8 weeks at the exercise club, Nadia could lift 10 pounds more than twice what she could lift before joining the club. Write an expression for the weight Nadia could lift after 8 weeks at the club.

24. The number of girls in the swim club is 5 less than twice the number of boys. There are 75 girls in the club. How many boys are in the club?

25. Chris has ridden his bike 10 miles. He averages 12 mi/h. How many more minutes must he ride before he has traveled 60 miles?

26. If the Menlo High football team scored 4 more points in Friday night's game, they would have tripled the score of Woodside High. Woodside scored 14 points. How many points did Menlo score?

3-5

To solve an equation, you must get all variable terms on the same side of the equation. If the equation contains parentheses, you may need to use the distributive property first.

Solve.

27. $6x - 5 = -2x + 11$

28. $3y - 6 - 7y = 12 - 2y + 6$

29. $4(x + 3) = 36$

30. $8(x - 2) = 5(x + 4)$

3-6

To clear an equation of fractions, multiply both sides of the equation by the least common denominator. To clear an equation of decimals, multiply both sides of the equation by a power of 10.

Solve.

31. $\frac{3}{4}x + \frac{1}{2}x + \frac{1}{4} = 1 + 2x$

32. $12.21 - 4.3a = 24.25$

33. $\frac{4}{9}y - \frac{4}{3} = \frac{1}{6}y + \frac{11}{18}$

34. $0.83w + 0.29 = 0.5w - 0.7$

3-7

To solve a formula for a given variable, use the same rules you use to solve equations.

Solve.

35. $V = Bh$ for h

36. $b = \frac{3A}{r}$ for A

37. $P = 2x + 2w$ for x

38. $V = \frac{1}{3}Ar$ for A

3-8

To solve an equation involving absolute value, remember that the absolute value of a number is its distance from 0 on a number line. If $|a| = 3$, then $a = 3$ or -3.

Solve.

39. $|x| = 5$

40. $|x| - 4 = 6$

41. $-9 + 3|y| = 24$

3-9

An equation that states two **ratios** are equal is called a **proportion.** Some problems can be solved by writing and solving a proportion.

Solve.

42. $\frac{b}{42} = \frac{6}{7}$

43. $\frac{45}{15} = \frac{30}{x}$

Translate to a proportion and solve.

44. The winner of an election for class president won by a vote of 3 to 2, having received 324 votes. How many votes did the loser get?

45. A student traveled 234 km in 14 days. At this rate, how far would the student travel in 42 days?

3-10

The ratio of a number to 100 is called **percent.** When solving problems involving percent, the percent should be expressed as a fraction or a decimal.

Write as a decimal.

46. 48%

47. 7%

48. 150%

Express as a percent. Round off to the nearest tenth if necessary.

49. $\frac{1}{3}$

50. $\frac{7}{8}$

51. 0.012

Solve.

52. 60 is what percent of 150?

53. 75% of what number is 187.5?

54. Sales tax in a certain city is 6.5%. What would the sales tax be on a motorcycle that costs $850?

35. $h = \frac{V}{B}$
36. $A = \frac{br}{3}$
37. $x = \frac{P - 2w}{2}$
38. $A = \frac{3V}{r}$
39. 5, −5
40. 10, −10
41. 11, −11
42. 36
43. 10
44. 216
45. 702 km
46. 0.48
47. 0.07
48. 1.5
49. 33.3%
50. 87.5%
51. 1.2%
52. 40%
53. 250
54. $55.25

55. $2x + x = 3x$
56. $x + x + 2 = 2x + 2$
57. 57, 59
58. 11 cm, 17 cm

ANSWERS

1. 8
2. 26
3. -6
4. 4
5. -40
6. $\frac{2}{5}$
7. 3
8. 7
9. 7
10. 5
11. -12
12. -5
13. -7
14. 2
15. 5, -5
16. 6, -6
17. $7x$
18. $15 - 4n$
19. $2x + 1$
20. $\frac{1}{5}x - 2$
21. $r = \frac{A}{2\pi h}$
22. $A = \frac{bh}{2}$
23. $x = \frac{P - 2w}{2}$
24. $r = \frac{3V}{A}$

3-11

To solve a problem with more than one unknown quantity, you may be able to represent all of the unknown quantities in terms of one variable. First decide which unknown quantity the variable will represent.

55. An adult's ticket to the movie theater costs twice as much as a child's ticket. Write an expression for the cost of admission for one child and one adult.

56. Write an expression for the sum of two consecutive even integers.

Translate to an equation and solve.

57. The sum of two consecutive odd integers is 116. Find the integers.

58. The perimeter of a rectangle is 56 cm. The width is 6 cm less than the length. Find the width and the length.

Chapter 3 Test

Solve.

1. $x + 7 = 15$

2. $t - 9 = 17$

3. $3x = -18$

4. $-7x = -28$

5. $-\frac{x}{8} = 5$

6. $-\frac{2}{3}y = -\frac{4}{15}$

7. $8a + 11 = 35$

8. $-4y + 7 = -21$

9. $3(x + 2) = 27$

10. $45 - 3x = 30$

11. $3t + 7 = 2t - 5$

12. $-3x + 6(x + 4) = 9$

13. $0.51m + 0.03 = 0.4m - 0.74$

14. $\frac{1}{2}x - \frac{3}{5} = \frac{1}{10} + \frac{3}{10}$

15. $|x| + 3 = 8$

16. $2|y| - 4 = 8$

Write as an algebraic expression.

17. the number of days in x weeks

18. fifteen decreased by four times a number

19. the sum of two consecutive integers

20. two less than one fifth of a number

Solve the formulas for the given letter.

21. $A = 2\pi rh$ for r

22. $b = \frac{2A}{h}$ for A

23. $P = 2x + 2w$ for x

24. $V = \frac{1}{3}Ar$ for r

Solve.

25. $\frac{16}{3} = \frac{c}{12}$

26. $\frac{21}{x} = \frac{105}{5}$

Translate to a proportion and solve.

27. A sample of 184 light bulbs contained 6 defective bulbs. At this rate, how many defective bulbs would you expect to find in a sample of 1288 light bulbs?

28. In traveling 350 miles, Raul used 21 gallons of gas. How many gallons of gas would Raul use on a trip of 525 miles if his car consumed gas at the same rate?

Write as a decimal.

29. 89%

30. 3%

31. 200%

Express as a percent. Round off to the nearest tenth of a percent if necessary.

32. $\frac{2}{5}$

33. $\frac{2}{3}$

Solve.

34. 96 is what percent of 150?

35. 90% of what number is 45?

36. 87.5% of 200 is what number?

37. A family spends $660 a month for rent. This is 30% of the family's monthly income. What is their monthly income?

Translate to an equation and solve.

38. Jim scored 22 points in a basketball game. That was six points more than Frank scored. How many points did Frank score?

39. A carpenter worked on a job for 5 days and earned $440. How much did he earn per day?

40. Marisa and Lisa earned a total of $65 babysitting during the month of November. Marisa earned $5 more than $\frac{1}{2}$ of what Lisa earned. How much did they each earn?

41. The perimeter of a rectangle is 36 cm. The length is 4 cm greater than the width. Find the width and the length.

42. Money is invested in a savings account at 12% simple interest. After one year, there is $840 in the account. How much was originally invested?

ANSWERS

25. 64
26. 1
27. 42 defective bulbs
28. 31.5 gallons
29. 0.89
30. 0.03
31. 2.00 or 2
32. 40%
33. 66.7%
34. 64%
35. 50
36. 175
37. $2200
38. 16
39. $88
40. Lisa $40, Marisa $25
41. 7 cm, 11 cm
42. $750

Test Item Analysis

Item	Lesson
1,2	3-1
3–6	3-2
7–10	3-3
11–12	3-5
13–14	3-6
15–16	3-8
17–20	3-4
21–24	3-7
25–28	3-9
29–37	3-10
38–42	3-11

CHAPTER 4

Inequalities

Chapter Overview

The properties of inequalities make up the core of Chapter 4. Inequalities in one variable are solved using the multiplication and addition properties. It is noted that most inequalities have infinite solutions and that all solutions cannot be checked. A simple test is introduced to check computational errors. If-then statements and logical reasoning are discussed as a discrete math topic.

Translation of simple expressions involving inequalities is introduced and word problems are translated and solved. The problem-solving strategy *Use Logical Reasoning* is added to the students' problem-solving repertoire.

Objectives

4-1 ■ Determine whether a given number is a solution of an inequality.
■ Graph inequalities on the number line.
4-2 ■ Solve inequalities using the addition property.
4-3 ■ Solve inequalities using the multiplication property.
4-4 ■ Solve inequalities using the addition and multiplication properties.
4-5 ■ Translate phrases to mathematical expressions.
■ Solve problems by translating and solving inequalities.
4-6 ■ Solve problems using the strategy *Use Logical Reasoning* and other strategies.

Cooperative Learning Opportunities

Partner Checking is an easy way to introduce paired cooperative learning. There are several ways to go about Partner Checking.

One method is to use the **First Five Minutes**, **Try This**, or **Lesson Quiz** Exercises. Divide the exercise set you are using into two halves, A and B.

Duplicate the halves separately and place the answers to the A Exercises on the B page and the B answers on the A page.

After students have done the exercises, form groups with an A and a B student in each group. Students check each others answers and work together to redo exercises in which the answers were wrong.

A second method of paired checking is for each student to do all the exercises, keeping his or her work. You then put the answers on the chalkboard and have students work in pairs to find the reasons for mistakes.

Multicultural Note: *The Bernoullis*

Does mathematical ability run in families? Sometimes it seems so. Through six generations, from about 1650 until 1860, more than a dozen members of the Swiss family Bernoulli made important contributions to mathematics and physics. They were all direct descendants of Nicolaus Bernoulli.

In 1689, Jacques Bernoulli wrote a paper in which he stated that "Bernoulli Inequality." This inequality, although rooted in the study of infinite series, is itself quite simple and can be used to give students experience working with an inequality. The inequality has several conditions attached to it.

The Bernoulli Inequality is $(1 + x)^n > 1 + nx$, with the conditions $x > -1$, $x \neq 0$, and n is an integer greater than 1.

Have students try different numbers to see that this inequality is valid.

Most of the mathematical contributions of Jacques and his brother John are found in the areas of curves and calculus.

Alternative Assessment and Communication Ideas

The chapter emphasizes solving and graphing inequalities. But understanding can be checked by working in reverse.

Using Exercises 25–31 on page 174, ask students to write the inequality that correctly describes each of the graphs.

After students have completed their inequalities, ask for volunteers to come forward to explain the answers. Ask each student to draw the graph and write the inequality on the chalkboard. The student should then explain how each part of the graph corresponds to a part of the inequality.

For the *Write a convincing argument* exercise in Lesson 4-6 ask students to do a chart as shown but write a reason for each "yes" or "no" entered.

Investigations and Projects

Very often, parents or other adults at home like to be involved in school work. This is particularly true when the activity is related to the adult's everyday experience. The topic of inequalities is a natural in this regard.

Ask students to explain the general idea of inequalities to a parent or other adult (or older sibling). Suggest that students use words such as "more than," "at least," and "enough." Then they should ask the adults to describe situations in their experience that involve inequalities. Situations might involve time and money for shopping, distance and time for travel, saving money, time required to accomplish work. Ask the students to get as much detail as possible about a situation.

Ask for volunteers to share their findings with the class. Ask whether, in everyday life, inequalities seem to be used more frequently than equations, and why.

MANAGING CHAPTER 4

Lesson	PACING CHART (DAYS) 2-Year* A for E	1-Year Minimum	1-Year Regular	1-Year Advanced	Opening Activity	Cooperative Activity	Seat or Group Work
4-1	2	1	1	1	First Five Minutes 4-1: ***FFMTM*** p. 14 or **TE** p. 172; Application: **SE** p. 172	Lesson Enrichment: **TE** p. 173	Try This a–d
4-2	2	1	1	0.5	First Five Minutes 4-2: ***FFMTM*** p. 15 or **TE** p. 175; ***Overhead Transparencies*** T4	Connections: Geometry **SE** p. 179	Try This a–h
4-3	2	1	1	0.5	First Five Minutes 4-3: ***FFMTM*** p. 15 or **TE** p. 180; ***Overhead Transparencies*** T5	Lesson Enrichment: **TE** p. 181	Try This a–l
4-4	2	1	1	0.5	First Five Minutes 4-4: ***FFMTM*** p. 15 or **TE** p. 183	✂ Manipulative Activity 4: ***Enrichment*** p. 37	Try This a–d
4-5	2	2	1	1.5	First Five Minutes 4-5: ***FFMTM*** p. 16 or **TE** p. 187	Problem Solving: Application: **SE** p. 193	Try This a–h
4-6	2	1	1	0.5	First Five Minutes 4-6: ***FFMTM*** p. 16 or **TE** p. 194	Problem 2: **SE** p. 195	Problem 1: **SE** p. 195
Review	2	1	1	0.5			
Test	1	1	1	1			
Cum. Review	2	0	0	0			
Mid-Year Test	1	0	0	0			

*2-Year Management Guide can be found in *Algebra for Everyone*.

FFMTM: First Five Minutes Transparency Masters

MANAGING CHAPTER 4

Enrichment	Review/Assess	Reteach	Technology	Lesson
Lesson Enrichment: **TE** p. 173; Bonus Topic 4: ***Enrichment*** p. 5	Lesson Quiz: **TE** p. 173		BASIC Computer Project 3: ***Technology*** p. 65	**4-1**
Connections: Geometry: **SE** p. 179	Mixed Review 7: ***SPMR*** p. 57; Lesson Quiz: **TE** p. 177; Quiz 7: ***Assessment*** p. 17		BASIC Computer Project 4: ***Technology*** p. 66	**4-2**
Lesson Enrichment: **TE** p. 181	Lesson Quiz: **TE** p. 181	Mixed Practice 7: **SE** p. 690; Skills Practice 10: ***SPMR*** p. 18		**4-3**
Biographical Note: George Pólya: **SE** p. 186; ✂ Manipulative Activity 4: ***Enrichment*** p. 37	Mixed Review 8: ***SPMR*** p. 58; Lesson Quiz: **TE** p. 184; Quiz 8: ***Assessment*** p. 18		Calculator Worksheet 12: ***Technology*** p. 14	**4-4**
Problem Solving: Application: **SE** p. 193; Connections: Discrete Math: **SE** p. 192; Looking for Errors 4: ***Enrichment*** p. 53	Lesson Quiz: **TE** p. 189	Skills Practice 11: ***SPMR*** p. 19; Problem Bank 11: ***Problem Bank*** p. 28	Problem for Programmers: **SE** p. 191	**4-5**
Critical Thinking 4: ***Enrichment*** p. 21	Assessing Strategies 4: ***Assessment*** pp. 201–202	Mixed Practice 8: **SE** p. 691; Strategy Problem Bank 4: ***Problem Bank*** p. 5	BASIC Computer Project 5: ***Technology*** p. 67	**4-6**
	Summary and Review: **SE** pp. 196–197; Test: **SE** p. 197; Cumulative Review: **SE** p. 198–201			**Review**
	Chapter 4 Exam: ***A for E*** pp. 169–170; Chapter 4 Test: ***Assessment*** pp. 49–50 (min.), 89–94 (reg.), 169–170 (adv.)			**Test**
	Cumulative Review: **SE** pp. 198–201			**Cum. Review**
	Cumulative Exam: ***Algebra for Everyone*** pp. T59-T62			**Mid-Year Test**

SPMR: Skills Practice Mixed Review

The solution to the problem posed on the facing page can be found on page 188.

Ready for Inequalities?

2-2 Graph each number on the number line. See Teacher's Answer Section.

1. $\frac{5}{3}$ **2.** $\frac{2}{5}$ **3.** $-\frac{3}{4}$

Use the proper symbol $>$ or $<$.

4. $-\frac{3}{4} < -\frac{2}{5}$ **5.** $-1.5 < 0.65$ **6.** $\frac{3}{4} > -2$

3-3 Solve.

7. $3x - 2 = 7$ 3
8. $-6x + 4 = 28$ −4
9. $40 - 2x = 26$ 7
10. $5x + 3x = 64$ 8
11. $2(5y + 3) = 56$ 5
12. $8(3a + 5) + a = 65$ 1

3-4 Write as an algebraic expression.

13. the sum of three consecutive even integers $n + n + 2 + n + 4$
14. one half the number plus 12 $\frac{1}{2}n + 12$
15. thirty-two less than twice the number $2n - 32$
16. two greater than 3 times a number $3n + 2$

3-5 Solve.

17. $2x + 20 + 33x = 80 + 15x$ 3
18. $3(2x - 1) + 4 = x + 25$ $\frac{24}{5}$
19. $14p - 10 = 8 + 2p$ $\frac{3}{2}$
20. $4(2x + 1) = 3(x + 13)$ 7

Solve.

21. $\frac{b}{3} - 2 = 6$ 24
22. $\frac{2}{9}b + \frac{1}{3}b = \frac{4}{9} - \frac{1}{3}b$ $\frac{1}{2}$
23. $0.9x - 0.5x = 6$ 15
24. $0.32y = 0.3y + 32$ 1600

CHAPTER

Inequalities 4

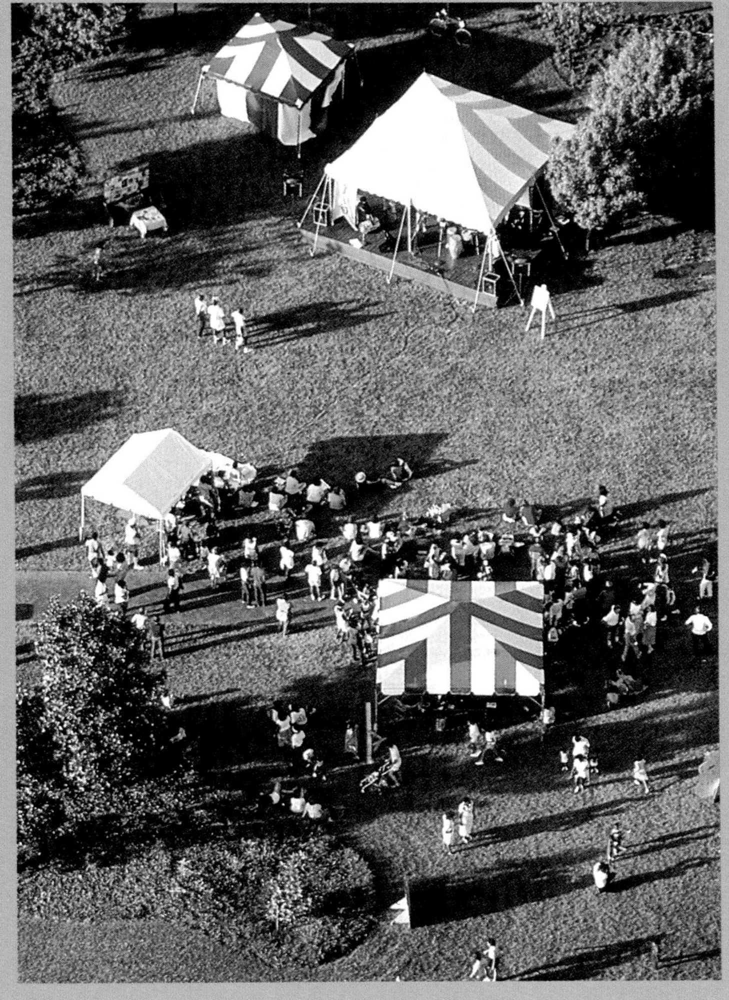

Black angus calves weigh approximately 75 pounds at birth and gain around 2 pounds per day for the first few weeks. How many days will it take until Ruth Anne's calf weighs at least 200 pounds?

4-1

FIRST FIVE MINUTES

Fill in the blank with <, >, or = to make each statement true.

1. 2 __ 3 $2 < 3$
2. 5 __ 4 $5 > 4$
3. 3 __ −1 $3 > -1$
4. 5 __ $\frac{10}{2}$ $5 = \frac{10}{2}$
5. −7 __ −4 $-7 < -4$
6. −2 __ −5 $-2 > -5$
7. $\frac{4}{7}$ __ $\frac{11}{21}$ $\frac{4}{7} > \frac{11}{21}$

Solutions of Inequalities

Point out that there can be infinite solutions for an inequality.

Key Questions

- Is the statement $0 \leq 0$ true? Yes
- Is the statement $0 \geq 0$ true? Yes
- Is the statement $-1 \geq 1$ true? No
- Is the statement $1 > 1$ true? No

Chalkboard Examples

1. Determine whether each number is a solution of $x \leq 7$.
   a. 3 Yes, because $3 \leq 7$ is true.
   b. −2 Yes, because $-2 \leq 7$ is true.
   c. 9 No, because $9 \leq 7$ is false.
   d. 7 Yes, because $7 \leq 7$ is true.

Graphing Inequalities

Chalkboard Examples

1. Graph $x > 5$ on the number line.

The solution is all points to the right of 5. Note that 5 is not included.

2. Graph $x \leq -1$ on the number line.

The solution is all points to the left of −1. Note that −1 is included.

4-1 Inequalities and Their Graphs

Application

The phrases italicized below are statements of **inequality**. An inequality tells the relationship between two numbers or expressions.

- Motorized vehicles must be able to maintain a speed *greater than or equal to* 35 miles per hour to travel on most freeways.
- Tire pressure on some bicycles should be *greater than* 50 psi but *less than* 75 psi.
- Most elevators can carry a load *less than or equal to* 2000 pounds.

Solutions of Inequalities

Objective: Determine whether a given number is a solution of an inequality.

In Chapter Two you learned the meaning of the symbols < (is less than) and > (is greater than). We now include the symbols ≤ and ≥.

We read ≤ as "is less than or equal to."
We read ≥ as "is greater than or equal to."

Mathematical sentences containing <, >, ≤, or ≥ are called **inequalities**.

A **solution** of an inequality is any number that makes the inequality true.

EXAMPLE 1 Determine whether each number is a solution of $x \geq 5$.

5 Yes, 5 is a solution because $5 \geq 5$ is true.
12 Yes, 12 is a solution because $12 \geq 5$ is true.
−7 No, −7 is not a solution because $-7 \geq 5$ is not true.

Try This Determine whether the given number is a solution of the inequality.

a. $x < 3$ (1) 2 Yes (2) 0 Yes (3) −5 Yes (4) 15 No (5) 3 No
b. $x \geq 6$ (1) 6 Yes (2) 0 No (3) −4 No (4) 25 Yes (5) −6 No

Graphing Inequalities

Objective: Graph inequalities on the number line.

A graph of an inequality in one variable is a picture of all its solutions on a number line.

EXAMPLE 2 Graph $x < 2$ on a number line.

The solutions of $x < 2$ are all numbers less than 2. They are shown by shading all points to the left of 2 on a number line.

Note that 2 is not a solution. We indicate this by an open circle at 2. The darkened arrow indicates that all points to the left of 2 are solutions of the inequality.

EXAMPLE 3 Graph $x \geq -3$ on a number line.

The solutions of $x \geq -3$ are -3 and all points to the right of -3.

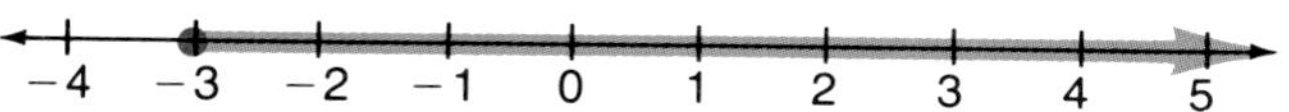

Note that -3 is a solution. We indicate this by a closed circle at -3. The darkened arrow indicates that all points to the right are also solutions of the inequality.

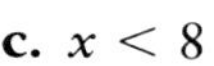 Graph on a number line.

c. $x < 8$ **d.** $y \geq -5$

4-1 EXERCISES

A

Determine whether the given number is a solution of the inequality.

	a.	b.	c.	d.
1. $x > 4$	4 No	0 No	-4 No	6 Yes
2. $y < 5$	0 Yes	5 No	-1 Yes	-5 Yes
3. $x \geq 6$	-6 No	0 No	6 Yes	8 Yes
4. $x \leq 10$	4 Yes	-10 Yes	0 Yes	11 No
5. $x < -8$	0 No	-8 No	-9 Yes	-7 No
6. $x \geq 0$	2 Yes	-3 No	0 Yes	3 Yes
7. $y \geq -5$	0 Yes	-4 Yes	-5 Yes	-6 No
8. $y \leq -\frac{1}{2}$	-1 Yes	$-\frac{2}{3}$ Yes	0 No	-0.5 Yes

Graph on a number line.

9. $x < 5$ **10.** $y < 0$ **11.** $t < -3$ **12.** $h < -5$

13. $y > 6$ **14.** $m > 4$ **15.** $k \geq -4$ **16.** $n \geq -2$

17. $x \leq 5$ **18.** $g \leq 8$ **19.** $b \leq -3$ **20.** $c \leq -1$

LESSON ENRICHMENT

True or false. Assume that x, y, and z are rational numbers.

a. $x < x$ False

b. If $x < y$ then $x \leq y$. True

c. If $x < y$, then there is some z such that $x < z$ and $z < y$.
True. This says there is some z between x and y.

d. For any x, there is a y such that $y > x$.
True. This says that there is always a bigger number y.

LESSON QUIZ

Determine whether each given number is a solution of the inequality.

1. $y \leq 4$ a. 4, b. 0, c. 8
Yes, yes, no
2. $a > -1$ a. 5, b. 0, c. -1
Yes, yes, no

Graph on a number line.

3. $x < 3$

4. $z \geq -2$

Assignment Guide

Minimum: 1–20 e/o, MR

Regular: 1–31 e/o, 32, MR

Advanced: 1–31 e/o, 32–36, MR

ADDITIONAL ANSWERS

Exercises

9. 

10. 

11. 

12. 

13. 

14. 0 4

15. −4 0

16. −2 0

17. 0 5

18. 0 8

19. −3 0

20. −1 0

32. The solutions to $|x - 2| = 5$ are symmetrically located about 2.

33. −1 0 3

34. No points meet requirements.

35. 0 2 5

36. −4 0 4

Mixed Review

37. $-\frac{1}{6}$ 38. 3

39. 12 40. 3

41. ±15 42. ±9

43. No solution 44. 5 in., 10 in.

45. 6

B

Classify each statement as true or false.

21. $3 \le 3$ T **22.** $\left|-\frac{1}{4}\right| \ge 0$ T **23.** $|-10| \le 4$ F **24.** $|-.08| \le 0.4$ T

Write the inequality shown by each graph.

25.  $x \ge 2$

26. −5 0 5 $x \le -5$

27. −5 0 5 $x \le -2$

28. −5 0 5 $x < 4$

29. −5 0 5 $x < 0$

30. −5 0 5 $x \ge 3$

31. −5 0 5 $x \le 7$

32. ***Critical Thinking*** The solutions to $|x| = 5$ are the same distance from 0. What can you say about the solutions to $|x - 2| = 5$?

Challenge

Graph on a number line.

33. all values of x such that $x < 3$ and $x > -1$

34. all values of x such that $x \ge 4$ and $x \le 1$

35. all values of x such that $x > 2$ and $x < 5$

36. all values of x such that $|x| \ge 4$

Mixed Review

Solve. **37.** $\frac{1}{3} + 8m = 3m - \frac{1}{2}$ **38.** $5x - (2x + 7) = 2$

39. $7.5y - 0.5y = 3.75y + 39$ **40.** $16 - 2w = 10w - 2 - 6w$

41. $|y| + 6 = 21$ **42.** $|a| = |-9|$ **43.** $|x| = -6$

Write as an algebraic expression.

44. The perimeter of a rectangle is 30 in. The length is 5 in. greater than the width. Find the dimensions.

45. Maury bought concert tickets at the Ticket Outlet. He paid $12 for each ticket, plus a $5 service charge for the whole set of tickets. The total cost was $77. How many tickets did he buy?

4-2 The Addition Property of Inequalities

Objective: Solve inequalities using the addition property.

We can use a scale to think about inequalities. We know that the inequality $3 < 7$ is true. If we add the same number to both sides of the inequality, we get another true inequality in the same direction.

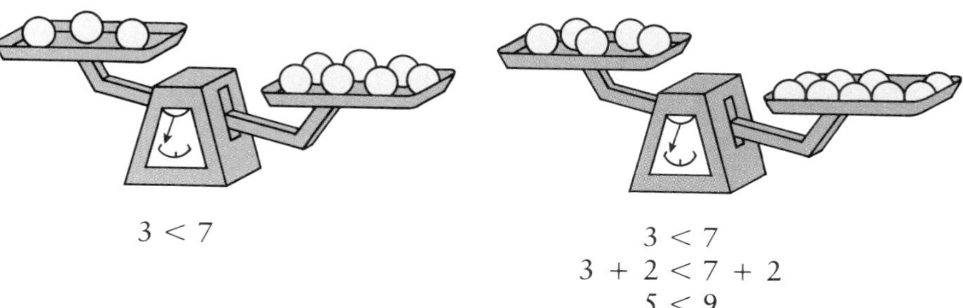

$3 < 7$

$$\begin{aligned} 3 &< 7 \\ 3 + 2 &< 7 + 2 \\ 5 &< 9 \end{aligned}$$

We can state this observation as a property.

The Addition Property of Inequalities

For all rational numbers a, b, and c,
if $a < b$, then $a + c < b + c$
if $a > b$, then $a + c > b + c$
Similar statements hold for $\leq$ and $\geq$.

We use the addition property of inequalities when solving inequalities just as we use the addition property of equality when solving equations.

EXAMPLE 1 Solve and graph the solution.

$$x + 3 > 4$$
$$x + 3 + (-3) > 4 + (-3) \quad \text{Using the addition property}$$
$$x > 1$$

−2 −1 0 1 2 3 4 5 6

Since there are an infinite number of solutions to an inequality, it is not possible to "check" the solution. It is possible, however, to check whether the computations used in solving the inequality were done correctly.

4-2

FIRST FIVE MINUTES

For which numbers is the inequality true?

1. $x > -1$ a. 3, b. 0, c. 1
   Yes, yes, yes
2. $a \leq 3$ a. 3, b. 4, c. 1
   Yes, no, yes
3. $b \geq -3$ a. 3, b. −4, c. −1
   Yes, no, yes
4. Graph the inequality $x \geq -1$.

Just as a balanced scale can represent an equation, an unbalanced scale can represent an inequality. Add the same amount to both sides and the scale remains unbalanced in the same direction.

Math Point

The triangle inequality states that for any numbers a and b, $|a + b| \leq |a| + |b|$. One application of this shows that the sum of two sides of a triangle must always be greater than the length of the third side. The inequality can be extended to state that the absolute value of the sum is less than or equal to the sum of the absolute values for any list of numbers.

Key Questions

- If $x < y$, is $x + 50 < y + 50$?
  Yes
- If $z > 15$, is $z - 5 > 15 - 5$?
  Yes
- If $m > 9$, can $m = 9$?
  No
- If $x \leq -5$, can $x = -5$?
  Yes

Chalkboard Examples (*T4*)

Solve and graph the solution set.

1. $x + 7 \le 9$

   $x + 7 + (-7) \le 9 + (-7)$

   $x \le 2$

   To check the answer, try $x = 2$ in the original inequality.

   $(2) + 7 \le 9$

   $9 \le 9$

2. $8z + 6 - 7z \ge 16$

   $z + 6 \ge 16$

   $z \ge 10$

3. $y - \frac{1}{4} \le \frac{1}{2}$

   $y \le \frac{1}{4} + \frac{1}{2}$

   $y \le \frac{3}{4}$

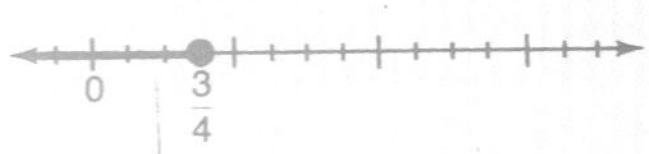

4. $5x + 2 \le 4x + 7$

   $5x + 2 - 2 \le 4x + 7 - 2$

   $5x \le 4x + 5$

   $5x - 4x \le 4x - 4x + 5$

   $x \le 5$

Write the equation $x + 3 = 4$ for the inequality $x + 3 > 4$. Then substitute 1, the boundary point of the solution, into the equation. If the computations were done correctly, the equation will check.

Check the computation.
Use $x = 1$ to check the computation.

$$x + 3 = 4$$
$$1 + 3 = 4 \quad \text{Substituting 1 for } x$$
$$4 = 4 \checkmark$$

We can also check whether the inequality symbol in the solution is correct. Choose any number greater than 1. Substitute this number into the original inequality. An easy number to use is 3.

Check the inequality symbol.

$$x + 3 > 4$$
$$3 + 3 > 4 \quad \text{Substituting 3 for } x$$
$$6 > 4 \checkmark$$

Any number greater than 1 is a solution.

Try This Solve and graph the solution. For graphs, see Additional Answers.

a. $x + 3 > 5$ $x > 2$

b. $x - 5 \le 8$ $x \le 13$

c. $x - 2 \ge 7$ $x \ge 9$

d. $x + 1 < 3$ $x < 2$

EXAMPLE 2 Solve and graph the solution.

$$x + \frac{1}{3} \ge \frac{3}{4}$$

$$x + \frac{1}{3} + \left(-\frac{1}{3}\right) \ge \frac{3}{4} + \left(-\frac{1}{3}\right) \quad \text{Using the addition property}$$

$$x \ge \frac{3}{4} - \frac{1}{3}$$

$$x \ge \frac{9}{12} - \frac{4}{12}$$

$$x \ge \frac{5}{12}$$

We can check the computation and the inequality symbol to ensure that the answer is correct.

Check the computation.
Use $\frac{5}{12}$, the boundary point.

$$x + \frac{1}{3} = \frac{3}{4}$$
$$\frac{5}{12} + \frac{4}{12} = \frac{3}{4}$$
$$\frac{9}{12} = \frac{3}{4}$$
$$\frac{3}{4} = \frac{3}{4} \checkmark$$

Check the inequality symbol.
Use any number greater than $\frac{5}{12}$, say 1.

$$x + \frac{1}{3} \geq \frac{3}{4}$$
$$1 + \frac{1}{3} \geq \frac{3}{4}$$
$$1\frac{1}{3} \geq \frac{3}{4} \checkmark$$

Any number greater than or equal to $\frac{5}{12}$ is a solution.

Try This Solve and graph the solution. For graphs, see Additional Answers.

e. $y + \frac{1}{8} < -\frac{3}{8}$ $y < -\frac{1}{2}$

f. $\frac{3}{10} \leq -\frac{1}{5} + y$ $y \geq \frac{1}{2}$

As in solving equations, you should collect like terms on the same side of the inequality symbol first. Then solve the inequality.

EXAMPLE 3 Solve and graph the solution.

$$3y + 1 - 2y < -3$$
$$y + 1 < -3 \quad \text{Collecting like terms}$$
$$y + 1 + (-1) < -3 + (-1) \quad \text{Using the addition property}$$
$$y < -4$$

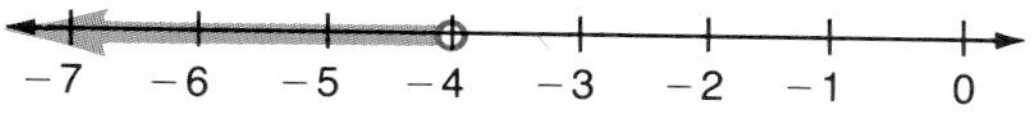

Check the computation.
Use -4, the boundary point.

$$3y + 1 - 2y = -3$$
$$3(-4) + 1 - 2(-4) = -3$$
$$-12 + 1 + 8 = -3$$
$$-3 = -3 \checkmark$$

Check the inequality symbol.
Choose any number less than -4, say -6.

$$3y + 1 - 2y < -3$$
$$3(-6) + 1 - 2(-6) < -3$$
$$-18 + 1 + 12 < -3$$
$$-5 < -3 \checkmark$$

Any number less than -4 is a solution.

Try This Solve and graph the solution. For graphs, see Additional Answers.

g. $5y + 2 - 4y \leq -1$ $y \leq -3$

h. $-4x + 5x + 1 < -2$ $x < -3$

LESSON QUIZ

Solve and graph the solution set.

1. $x + 3 < 8$
   $x < 5$

2. $z - 4 \leq 3$
   $z \leq 7$

Solve.

3. $6m - 7 - 5m \geq 3$
   $m \geq 10$
4. $y + \frac{2}{3} \leq \frac{1}{6}$
   $y \leq -\frac{1}{2}$

Assignment Guide
Minimum: 1–28 e/o, MR

Regular: 1–42 e/o, 43, MR

Advanced: 1–42 m4, 43, 44–49 e/o, MR, assign w. 4-3

ADDITIONAL ANSWERS

Try This

a. 0 2

b. 0 13

c. 0 9

d. 0 2

e. −1 $-\frac{1}{2}$ 0

f. 0 $\frac{1}{2}$ 1

g. −3 0

h. −3 0

Exercises

1. −5 0

2. −3 0

3. 0 3

4. 0 2

5. −19 −18

6. −22 −21

7. −6 0

8. −13 −12

9. 15 16

10. 16 17

4-2 EXERCISES

A

Solve and graph the solution.

1. $x + 7 > 2$ $x > -5$
2. $x + 6 > 3$ $x > -3$
3. $y + 5 > 8$ $y > 3$
4. $y + 7 > 9$ $y > 2$
5. $x + 8 \leq -10$ $x \leq -18$
6. $x + 9 \leq -12$ $x \leq -21$
7. $a + 12 < 6$ $a < -6$
8. $a + 20 < 8$ $a < -12$
9. $x - 7 \leq 9$ $x \leq 16$
10. $x - 3 \leq 14$ $x \leq 17$
11. $x - 6 > 2$ $x > 8$
12. $x - 9 > 4$ $x > 13$
13. $y - 7 > -12$ $y > -5$
14. $y - 10 > -16$ $y > -6$
15. $4m - 3m < 2$ $m < 2$
16. $2x + 3 - x > 5$ $x > 2$

Solve.

17. $3x - 2x + 9 \leq 6$ $x \leq -3$
18. $-2y + 3y + 10 \leq 8$ $y \leq -2$
19. $5n - 6 - 4n < -2$ $n < 4$
20. $-5x + 6x - 8 < -9$ $x < -1$
21. $3y + 4 - 2y \leq -7$ $y \leq -11$
22. $4a - 3a + 5 \geq -8$ $a \geq -13$

Solve.

23. $m + \frac{1}{4} \leq \frac{1}{2}$ $m \leq \frac{1}{4}$
24. $y + \frac{1}{3} \geq \frac{5}{6}$ $y \geq \frac{1}{2}$
25. $x - \frac{1}{3} > \frac{1}{4}$ $x > \frac{7}{12}$
26. $b - \frac{1}{8} > \frac{1}{2}$ $b > \frac{5}{8}$
27. $c + \frac{4}{5} \leq \frac{3}{10}$ $c \leq -\frac{1}{2}$
28. $\frac{2}{3} + a \geq \frac{5}{6}$ $a \geq \frac{1}{6}$

B

Solve.

29. $3(r + 2) - 2r < 4$ $r < -2$
30. $4(r + 5) - 3r \geq 7$ $r \geq -13$
31. $3a + 6 + 2a \geq -19$ $a \geq -5$
32. $-5 \leq 3m - 10 - 2m$ $m \geq 5$
33. $4(x + 3) - 3x > 4$ $x > -8$
34. $5(y - 2) - 4(y - 1) < 0$ $y < 6$
35. $-6(a + 2) + 7a \leq -12$ $a \leq 0$
36. $-2(a - 3) + 3(a + 2) < 4$ $a < -8$

Use the first inequality to find the unknown number or expression in the second inequality.

37. $y + 2 + 3y > 9$
 $y + 3y > ??$ 7
38. $a^2 + 4 - b \leq -2$
 $a^2 - b \leq ??$ −6
39. $m + n - 4 \leq n$
 $m - 4 \leq ??$ 0
40. $p + q + z \geq -2$
 $p + z \geq ??$ $-2 - q$
41. $a + b < 2a - 4$
 $b < ??$ $a - 4$
42. $x - y > 7 + y$
 $x > ??$ $7 + 2y$

43. ***Critical Thinking*** Give two different inequalities that each have $x \leq -5$ as a statement of all solutions.

Challenge

Determine whether the following statements are true or false.

44. $x + c < y + d$ when $x < y$ and $c < d$. True

45. $x - c > y - d$ when $x > y$ and $c > d$. False

46. If x is an integer, write a statement equivalent to $x > 5$ using $\geq$. $x \geq 6$

47. If y is an integer, write a statement equivalent to $y < 5$ using $\leq$. $y \leq 4$

48. Does the transitive property hold for $>$? Does it hold for $\leq$?

49. Other inequality symbols include $\ngtr$, which means "is not greater than," $\nless$, "is not less than," and $\neq$, "is not equal to." Write statements equivalent to each of the following using $>$, $<$, $\geq$, $\leq$, or $=$.

a. $x \ngtr 5$ **b.** $x \nless -3$ **c.** $x \neq -\frac{3}{2}$

d. $x \nless y$ **e.** $x \ngtr -y$ **f.** $-x \neq y$

Mixed Review

Solve each proportion. **50.** $\frac{m}{8} = \frac{3}{4}$ **51.** $\frac{21}{m} = \frac{7}{3}$ **52.** $\frac{4}{6} = \frac{m}{9}$

Solve. **53.** $-84x = 4$ **54.** $-3 = 9c$ **55.** $|t| - 4 = 21$

56. $3 - |m| = 1$ **57.** $\frac{2}{3} + \frac{1}{8}m = \frac{5}{12}m - \frac{19}{24}$ **58.** $\frac{2}{3} \cdot |y| = 8$

59. Write an algebraic expression for 3 more than twice a number.

60. A certain cruise ship must have 1 lifeboat for every 16 passengers. How many lifeboats are needed to accommodate 144 passengers?

61. A certain mixed-nut snack uses 6 oz peanuts for every 4 oz of almonds and cashews. How many ounces of peanuts are needed for 28 oz of almonds and cashews?

CONNECTIONS: GEOMETRY

In the figure at the right, the measure of angle 1 is x ($m\angle 1 = x$) and the measure of angle 2 is $4x + 6$ ($m\angle 2 = 4x + 6$). The sum of the measures of angles 1 and 2 is less than 90°. What are three possible measures for angles 1 and 2? Answers may vary. Possible answers are $m\angle 1 = 16$, $m\angle 2 = 70$; $m\angle 1 = 15$, $m\angle 2 = 66$; $m\angle 1 = 10$, $m\angle 2 = 46$

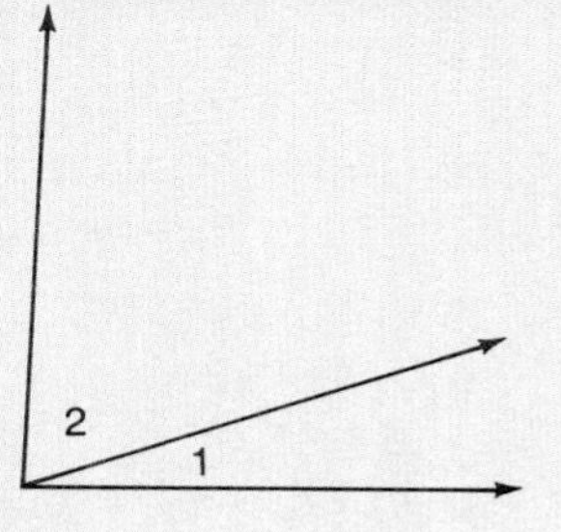

11. 0 8

12. 13 14

13. −5 0

14. −6 0

15. 0 2

16. 0 2

43. Answers may vary. Example: $x + 7 \leq 2$, $2x - 6 \leq -16$

48. Yes, if $a > b$ and $b > c$, $a > c$; Yes, if $a \leq b$ and $b \leq c$, $a \leq c$.

49. a. $x \leq 5$ **b.** $x \geq -3$

c. $x < \frac{-3}{2}$ or $x > \frac{-3}{2}$

d. $x \geq y$ **e.** $x \leq -y$

f. $-x > y$ or $-x < y$

Mixed Review

50. 6
51. 9
52. 6
53. $-\frac{1}{21}$
54. $-\frac{1}{3}$
55. ± 25
56. ± 2
57. 5
58. ± 12
59. $2x + 3$
60. 9
61. 42

4-3

FIRST FIVE MINUTES

Solve.

1. $x + 7 < 12$
   $x < 12 - 7$
   $x < 5$
2. $z - 4 \geq 1$
   $z \geq 1 + 4$
   $z \geq 5$
3. $-a + 6 + 2a \leq 8$
   $a \leq 8 - 6$
   $a \leq 2$
4. $3(x + 1) = 15$
   $x + 1 = 5$
   $x = 5 - 1$
   $x = 4$

Illustrate the multiplication property of inequalities with an arithmetic example. For instance, $2 < 5$.
Multiply both sides by 2. $4 < 10$ is true.
Multiply both sides by -2. $-4 < -10$ is false, but $-4 > -10$ is true.

Avoiding Common Errors

Students often forget to reverse the inequality sign when they multiply by a negative number. If they check a number in the solution set of the original inequality, they can find and correct this type of error.

Key Questions

- If both sides of a true inequality are multiplied by 3, is the inequality still true? Yes
- If both sides of a true inequality are multiplied by -3, is the inequality still true? No

Chalkboard Examples (*T5*)

Solve and graph the solution.

1. $6x > 24$ $\quad \frac{1}{6}(6x) > \frac{1}{6} \cdot 24$
   $x > 4$

2. $7y \leq 21$ $\quad \frac{1}{7}(7y) \leq \frac{1}{7} \cdot 21$
   $y \leq 3$

4-3 The Multiplication Property of Inequalities

Objective: Solve inequalities using the multiplication property.

Consider the true inequality.

$$3 < 7$$

If we multiply both numbers by 2, we get another true inequality.

$$6 < 14 \qquad \text{True}$$

If we multiply both numbers by -3, we get a false inequality.

$$-9 < -21 \qquad \text{False}$$

If we reverse the inequality symbol, however, we get a true inequality.

$$-9 > -21 \qquad \text{True}$$

The Multiplication Property of Inequalities

For all rational numbers a, b, and c,

where c is positive,	where c is negative,
if $a < b$, then $ac < bc$	if $a < b$, then $ac > bc$
if $a > b$, then $ac > bc$	if $a > b$, then $ac < bc$

Similar statements hold for $\leq$ and $\geq$.

EXAMPLE 1 Solve and graph the solution.

$$4x < 28$$

$$\frac{1}{4}(4x) < \frac{1}{4} \cdot 28 \qquad \text{Multiplying both sides by } \frac{1}{4}$$

$$x < 7 \qquad \text{Since } \frac{1}{4} \text{ is positive, do not change the inequality symbol.}$$

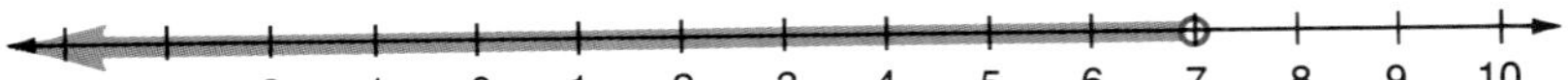

Check the computation.
Use 7 to check the computation.

$$4x = 28$$
$$4 \cdot 7 = 28$$
$$28 = 28 \checkmark$$

Check the inequality symbol.
Choose any number less than 7, say 0.

$$4x < 28$$
$$4 \cdot 0 < 28$$
$$0 < 28 \checkmark$$

Any number less than 7 is a solution.

Try This Solve and graph the solution. For graphs, see Teacher's Answer Section.

a. $8x < 64$ $x < 8$ **b.** $5y \geq 160$ $y \geq 32$ **c.** $2t < 56$ $t < 28$ **d.** $9s > 81$ $s > 9$

EXAMPLE 2 Solve and graph the solution.

$$-2y < 18$$

$$-\frac{1}{2}(-2y) > -\frac{1}{2} \cdot 18 \qquad \text{Multiplying both sides by } -\frac{1}{2} \text{ and reversing the inequality symbol}$$

$$y > -9$$

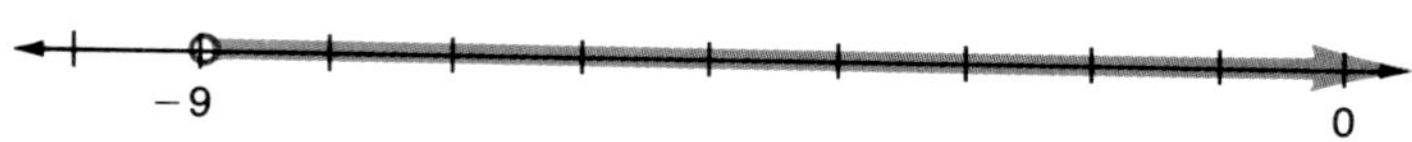

Check the computation.
Use -9 to check the computation.

$$-2y = 18$$
$$-2 \cdot -9 = 18$$
$$18 = 18 \checkmark$$

Check the inequality symbol.
Choose any number greater than -9, say 0.

$$-2y < 18$$
$$-2 \cdot 0 < 18$$
$$0 < 18 \checkmark$$

Any number greater than -9 is a solution.

Try This Solve and graph the solution. For graphs, see Additional Answers.

e. $-4x \geq 24$ **f.** $-5y < 13$ **g.** $-t < -5$ **h.** $-n > 2$

e. $x \leq -6$
f. $y > -\frac{13}{5}$
g. $t > 5$
h. $n < -2$

EXAMPLE 3 Solve and graph the solution.

$$-3x \geq \frac{5}{6}$$

$$-\frac{1}{3}(-3x) \leq -\frac{1}{3} \cdot \frac{5}{6} \qquad \text{Multiplying both sides by } -\frac{1}{3} \text{ and reversing the inequality sign}$$

$$x \leq -\frac{5}{18}$$

Any number less than or equal to $-\frac{5}{18}$ is a solution.

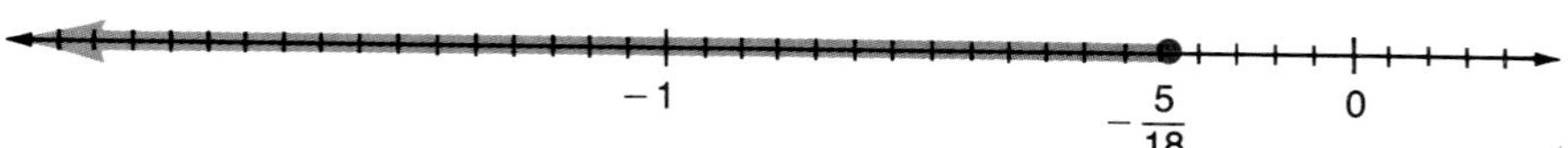

Try This Solve and graph the solution.

i. $-y \geq \frac{1}{2}$ **j.** $-3x < \frac{1}{6}$ **k.** $-2x \leq \frac{5}{8}$ **l.** $-4y \geq -\frac{3}{7}$

For graphs, see Additional Answers.

i. $y \leq -\frac{1}{2}$
j. $x > -\frac{1}{18}$
k. $x \geq -\frac{5}{16}$
l. $y \leq \frac{3}{28}$

---

3. $-5x > 35$ $\quad -\frac{1}{5}(-5x) < -\frac{1}{5} \cdot 35$
   $x < -7$

4. $-z \geq -9$ $\quad -1(-z) \leq -1 \cdot -9$
   $z \leq 9$

LESSON ENRICHMENT

Use the correct inequality symbol, $<$, $=$, or $>$, that will make the statement $5x$? $6x$ true for each replacement.

$x = 4$ $\quad 5x < 6x$
$x = 7$ $\quad 5x < 6x$
$x = 0$ $\quad 5x = 6x$
$x = -3$ $\quad 5x > 6x$

If $5x < 6x$, what must be true of x? $x > 0$

If $5x > 6x$, what must be true of x? $x < 0$

If $5x = 6x$, what must be true of x? $x = 0$

LESSON QUIZ

Solve and graph the solution.

1. $3x \leq 18$
   $x \leq 6$
2. $8x > 32$
   $x > 4$
3. $9z \geq -3$
   $z \geq -\frac{3}{9}$
4. $-6w < 36$
   $w > \frac{36}{-6}$

5. $-r \geq 14$
   $r \leq -14$
6. $-7q > -14$
   $q < 2$

Assignment Guide

Minimum: 1–33 e/o, MR

Regular: 1–42 e/o, 43, MR

Advanced: 1–42 m4, 43–45, MR, assign w. 4-2

ADDITIONAL ANSWERS

Try This

e. 

f. $-\frac{13}{5}$, -2, 0

g. 0, 5

h. 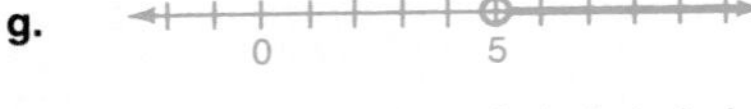

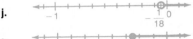

i. -1, $-\frac{1}{2}$, 0

j. -1, $-\frac{1}{18}$, 0

k. 

l. 

Exercises

1–15. See Teacher's Answer Section.
34. $x \le 0.9$
35. $y \ge \frac{9}{10}$
36. $x > -5.0625$
37. $x \le \frac{1}{6}$
38. $x < -3$
39. $y > 3$
40. $t < 0$
41. $n \le -\frac{1}{2}$
42. $m \le 4$

Mixed Review

46. a. No **b.** No **c.** Yes **d.** No **e.** Yes
47. $5m$
48. $11x + 5$
49. $33y$
50. $8x$
51. 26
52. −20

4-3 EXERCISES

A

Solve and graph the solution.

1. $5x < 35$ $x < 7$ **2.** $8x \ge 32$ $x \ge 4$ **3.** $9y \le 81$ $y \le 9$
4. $10x > 240$ $x > 24$ **5.** $6y > 72$ $y > 12$ **6.** $9x \le 63$ $x \le 7$
7. $7x < 13$ $x < \frac{13}{7}$ **8.** $8y < 17$ $y < \frac{17}{8}$ **9.** $4y \ge 15$ $y \ge \frac{15}{4}$
10. $3y \ge 19$ $y \ge \frac{19}{3}$ **11.** $6y \le 3$ $y \le \frac{1}{2}$ **12.** $14x \le 4$ $x \le \frac{2}{7}$
13. $7y \ge -21$ $y \ge -3$ **14.** $6x \ge -18$ $x \ge -3$ **15.** $12x < -36$ $x < -3$

Solve.

16. $16y < -64$ $y < -4$ **17.** $5y \ge -2$ $y \ge -\frac{2}{5}$ **18.** $7x \ge -4$ $x \ge -\frac{4}{7}$
19. $-2x \le 12$ $x \ge -6$ **20.** $-3y \le 15$ $y \ge -5$ **21.** $-4y \le 16$ $y \ge -4$
22. $-7y \le 21$ $y \ge -3$ **23.** $-6y > 360$ $y < -60$ **24.** $-9x > 540$ $x < -60$
25. $-12x < -24$ $x > 2$ **26.** $-14y < -70$ $y > 5$ **27.** $-18y \ge -36$ $y \le 2$
28. $-20x \ge -400$ $x \le 20$ **29.** $-2x < -17$ $x > \frac{17}{2}$ **30.** $-5y < -23$ $y > \frac{23}{5}$
31. $-8y \ge -31$ $y \le \frac{31}{8}$ **32.** $-7x \ge -43$ $x \le \frac{43}{7}$ **33.** $-3y < \frac{1}{7}$ $y > -\frac{1}{21}$

B

Solve.

34. $-7x \ge -6.3$ **35.** $-\frac{5}{6}y \le -\frac{3}{4}$ **36.** $-8x < 40.5$
37. $-\frac{3}{4}x \ge -\frac{1}{8}$ **38.** $5x + 6x < -33$ **39.** $-12 > 2y - 6y$
40. $0 > -5t + 10t$ **41.** $4 \le -9n + n$ **42.** $4m - 9m \ge -12 - 8$

43. ***Critical Thinking*** Solve $3x > 4x$. $x < 0$

Challenge

Determine whether the following statements are true or false.

44. $x^2 > y^2$ when $x > y$. False; $-2 > -3$ but $4 < 9$.

45. $\frac{x}{z} < \frac{y}{z}$ when $x < y$ and $z \ne 0$. False; $6 < 10$ but $\frac{6}{-2} > \frac{10}{-2}$.

Mixed Review

Determine whether the given number is a solution of the inequality.

46. $-4x > 9$; **a.** 10 **b.** 6 **c.** −8 **d.** 0 **e.** −5

Simplify. **47.** $4m + 2m - m$ **48.** $7x + 5 + 4x$

49. $6(y + 4y) + 3y$ **50.** $3(2x - 4) + 2x + 12$

Evaluate for $a = 2, b = 3, c = 4$. **51.** $a(b^2 + c)$ **52.** $c(2a - 3b)$

4-4 Using the Properties Together

Objective: Solve inequalities using the addition and multiplication properties.

We use the addition and multiplication properties together in solving inequalities in much the same way as for equations. We usually use the addition property first.

EXAMPLES Solve.

1.

$$6 + 5y > 21$$
$$-6 + 6 + 5y > -6 + 21 \quad \text{Using the addition property of inequalities}$$
$$5y > 15$$
$$\frac{1}{5} \cdot (5y) > \frac{1}{5} \cdot 15 \quad \text{Using the multiplication property of inequalities}$$
$$y > 3$$

Any number greater than 3 is a solution.

2.

$$7x + 4 \leq 4x + 16$$
$$-4x + 7x + 4 \leq -4x + 4x + 16 \quad \text{Using the addition property of inequalities}$$
$$3x + 4 \leq 16$$
$$3x + 4 + (-4) \leq 16 + (-4) \quad \text{Using the addition property of inequalities}$$
$$3x \leq 12$$
$$\frac{1}{3} \cdot 3x \leq \frac{1}{3} \cdot 12 \quad \text{Using the multiplication property of inequalities}$$
$$x \leq 4$$

Any number less than or equal to 4 is a solution.

3.

$$17 - 5y < 8y - 9$$
$$17 - 5y + (-8y) < 8y + (-8y) - 9 \quad \text{Using the addition property}$$
$$17 - 13y < -9$$
$$-17 + 17 - 13y < -17 - 9 \quad \text{Using the addition property}$$
$$-13y < -26$$
$$-\frac{1}{13} \cdot -13y > -\frac{1}{13}(-26) \quad \text{Using the multiplication property, reversing the inequality symbol}$$
$$y > 2$$

Any number greater than 2 is a solution.

Try This Solve.

a. $7 - 4x < -1$ $x > 2$

b. $13a + 5 \geq 12a + 4$ $a \geq -1$

c. $4m - 4 > 8 + 2m$ $m > 6$

d. $24 - 7n < 11n - 12$ $n > 2$

4-4

FIRST FIVE MINUTES

Solve.

1. $x + 11 < 18$
   $x < 7$
2. $z - 3 \geq 8$
   $z \geq 11$
3. $9x \geq 36$
   $x \geq 4$
4. $-6y < 30$
   $y > -5$
5. $-u \geq -2$
   $u \leq 2$

Point out that the solution to an inequality can have two different forms. For instance,

$$2y + 3 > 5y - 3$$

$-3y > -6$	$6 > 3y$
$y < 2$	$2 > y$

It is best to read both forms as "y is less than 2."

Key Question

- What properties are needed to solve the following inequality?
  $6 + 5y > 21$
  Both the addition and the multiplication properties

Chalkboard Examples

Solve.

1. $5x + 2 < 22$
   $5x + 2 - 2 < 22 - 2$
   $5x < 20$
   $\frac{1}{5}(5x) < \frac{1}{5} \cdot 20$
   $x < 4$
2. $5z + 3 \geq 3z + 13$
   $5z + 3 - 3 \geq 3z + 13 - 3$
   $5z \geq 3z + 10$
   $5z - 3z \geq 3z - 3z + 10$
   $2z \geq 10$
   $\frac{1}{2}(2z) \geq \frac{1}{2} \cdot 10$
   $z \geq 5$
3. $-6x + 7 - x + 1 < 2x + 4$
   $-7x + 8 < 2x + 4$
   $-7x + 8 - 8 < 2x + 4 - 8$
   $-7x < 2x - 4$
   $-7x - 2x < 2x - 2x - 4$
   $-9x < -4$
   $-\frac{1}{9}(-9x) > -\frac{1}{9}(-4)$
   $x > \frac{4}{9}$

LESSON QUIZ

Solve.

1. $7 + 2x > 19$
   $2x > 19 - 7$
   $2x > 12$
   $x > \frac{12}{2}$
   $x > 6$
2. $4z - 7 \geq 2z + 3$
   $4z \geq 2z + 3 + 7$
   $4z \geq 2z + 10$
   $4z - 2z \geq 2z - 2z + 10$
   $2z \geq 10$
   $z \geq \frac{10}{2}$
   $z \geq 5$
3. $-7w > 2w + 13$
   $-7w - 2w > 13$
   $-9w > 13$
   $w < \frac{13}{-9}$
   $w < -\frac{13}{9}$

Assignment Guide
Minimum: 1–34 e/o, MR

Regular: 1–58 e/o, 59, MR

Advanced: 1–58 m3, 59, 60–65 e/o, MR, assign w. Application

ADDITIONAL ANSWERS

Exercises

35. $t \leq 0$
36. $z < \frac{65}{16}$
37. $y < \frac{2.2}{7}$
38. $y > 1.8$
39. $x \leq 9$
40. $x > 2$
41. $y \leq -3$
42. $x \geq -25$
43. $x > \frac{8}{3}$
44. $x < \frac{30}{7}$
45. $1.8 \geq y$
46. $b \geq -4$
47. $a < -5$
48. $y \leq 10$
49. $2 \leq z$
50. $t \leq -\frac{19}{3}$

4-4 EXERCISES

A

Solve.

1. $4 + 3x < 28$ $x < 8$
2. $5 + 4y < 37$ $y < 8$
3. $6 + 5y \geq 36$ $y \geq 6$
4. $7 + 8x \geq 71$ $x \geq 8$
5. $3x - 5 \leq 13$ $x \leq 6$
6. $5y - 9 \leq 21$ $y \leq 6$
7. $10y - 9 > 31$ $y > 4$
8. $12y - 6 > 42$ $y > 4$
9. $13x - 7 < -46$ $x < -3$
10. $8y - 4 < -52$ $y < -6$
11. $5x + 3 \geq -7$ $x \geq -2$
12. $7y + 4 \geq -10$ $y \geq -2$
13. $4 - 3y > 13$ $y < -3$
14. $6 - 8x > 22$ $x < -2$
15. $3 - 9x < 30$ $x > -3$
16. $5 - 7y < 40$ $y > -5$
17. $3 - 6y > 23$ $y < -\frac{10}{3}$
18. $8 - 2y > 14$ $y < -3$
19. $4x + 2 - 3x \leq 9$ $x \leq 7$
20. $15x + 3 - 14x \leq 7$ $x \leq 4$
21. $8x + 7 - 7x > -3$ $x > -10$
22. $9x + 8 - 8x > -5$ $x > -13$
23. $6 - 4y > 4 - 3y$ $y < 2$
24. $7 - 8y > 5 - 7y$ $y < 2$
25. $5 - 9y \leq 2 - 8y$ $y \geq 3$
26. $6 - 13y \leq 4 - 12y$ $y \geq 2$
27. $19 - 7y - 3y < 39$ $y > -2$
28. $18 - 6y - 9y < 63$ $y > -3$
29. $21 - 8y < 6y + 49$ $y > -2$
30. $33 - 12x < 4x + 97$ $x > -4$
31. $14 - 5y - 2y \geq -19$ $y \leq \frac{33}{7}$
32. $17 - 6y - 7y \leq -13$ $y \geq \frac{30}{13}$
33. $27 - 11x > 14x - 18$ $x < \frac{9}{5}$
34. $42 - 13y > 15y - 19$ $y < \frac{61}{28}$

B

Solve.

35. $5(12 - 3t) \geq 15(t + 4)$
36. $6(z - 5) < 5(7 - 2z)$
37. $4(0.5 - y) + y > 4y - 0.2$
38. $3 + 3(0.6 + y) > 2y + 6.6$
39. $\frac{x}{3} - 2 \leq 1$
40. $\frac{2}{3} - \frac{x}{5} < \frac{4}{15}$
41. $\frac{y}{5} + 1 \leq \frac{2}{5}$
42. $\frac{3x}{5} \geq -15$
43. $\frac{-x}{4} - \frac{3x}{8} + 2 > 3 - x$
44. $11 - x > 5 + \frac{2x}{5}$
45. $0.2y + 2.1 \geq 1.2y + 0.3$
46. $0.3b + 5.4 \geq -b + 0.2$
47. $0.2(30 + a) < 5$
48. $0.3(10 + 2y) \leq 9$
49. $\frac{1}{5}(z + 6) \leq 0.4(2 + z)$
50. $\frac{1}{2}(t + 5) \leq 0.2(3 + t)$
51. $\frac{1}{2}(c + 3) - \frac{1}{3}(c - 2) > 0$
52. $\frac{3}{4}(2d + 1) + \frac{1}{3}(d - 3) < 0$
53. $0.3[4(x - 2) + x] < 0.3x$
54. $0.4[2(w + 3) - 5w] < 0.6$

Give a reason that justifies each step in the solution.

55. $8 + 3x - 7x \geq 32$

a. $8 - 4x \geq 32$ Simplifying

b. $-8 + 8 - 4x \geq 32 - 8$ Using the addition property

c. $-4x \geq 24$ Simplifying

d. $-\frac{1}{4}(-4x) \leq -\frac{1}{4} \cdot 24$ Using the multiplication property

e. $x \leq -6$ Simplifying

56. $11 - 6y < -34 + 9y$

a. $11 - 6y + 6y < -34 + 9y + 6y$ Using the addition property

b. $11 < -34 + 15y$ Simplifying

c. $34 + 11 < 34 - 34 + 15y$ Using the addition property

d. $45 < 15y$ Simplifying

e. $\frac{1}{15} \cdot 45 < \frac{1}{15} \cdot 15y$ Using the multiplication property

f. $3 < y$ Simplifying

57. $3(m - 8) \geq 4(m + 4)$

a. $3m - 24 \geq 4m + 16$ Using the distributive property

b. $3m - 24 + 24 \geq 4m + 16 + 24$ Using the addition property

c. $3m \geq 4m + 40$ Simplifying

d. $-4m + 3m \geq -4m + 4m + 40$ Using the addition property

e. $-m \geq 40$ Simplifying

f. $-1(-m) \leq -1 \cdot 40$ Using the multiplication property

g. $m \leq -40$ Simplifying

58. $\frac{x}{4} - \frac{1}{6} \leq \frac{2}{3}$

a. $12\left(\frac{x}{4} - \frac{1}{6}\right) \leq 12\left(\frac{2}{3}\right)$ Using the multiplication property

b. $12\left(\frac{x}{4}\right) - 12\left(\frac{1}{6}\right) \leq 12\left(\frac{2}{3}\right)$ Using the distributive property

c. $3x - 2 \leq 8$ Simplifying

d. $3x - 2 + 2 \leq 8 + 2$ Using the addition property

e. $3x \leq 10$ Simplifying

f. $\frac{1}{3}(3x) \leq \frac{1}{3}(10)$ Using the multiplication property

g. $x \leq \frac{10}{3}$ Simplifying

51. $c > -13$
52. $d < \frac{3}{22}$
53. $x < 2$
54. $w > 1.5$

59. $x < -15$. There are no positive solutions.
60. $x \le -4a$
61. $x > 7$
62. $x \ge \frac{3y}{2}$
63. $x > \frac{y-b}{a}$ if $a > 0$
$x < \frac{y-b}{a}$ if $a < 0$
64. $x \ge y$ and $x \le y$, so $x = y$
65. $x^2 < x$

Mixed Review

66. 48
67. 3
68. 18
69. 18
70. -7.5
71. $z < -3$
72. 4.4
73. 4
74. $\frac{3}{4}$, 75%
75. $\frac{9}{5}$, 180%
76. $\frac{5}{1}$, 500%
77. $\frac{3}{5}$, 60%
78. $\frac{9}{2}$, 450%
79. $M - 2$
80. $\frac{s}{4}$
81. $3L$

59. ***Critical Thinking*** Solve $\frac{1}{2}(5x + 5) < \frac{1}{3}(5x - 30)$ and describe its positive solutions.

Challenge

Solve for x.

60. $-(x + 5) \ge 4a - 5$ **61.** $\frac{1}{2}(2x + 2b) > \frac{1}{3}(21 + 3b)$

62. $-6(x + 3) \le -9(y + 2)$ **63.** $y < ax + b$

64. If $x \ge y$ and $-x \ge -y$, what can we conclude about x and y?

65. If $0 < x < 1$, then which of the following is true, $x^2 < x$ or $x < x^2$?

Mixed Review

Evaluate for $m = 6$. **66.** $m(m + 2)$ **67.** $0.5(m)$

68. $(m + 3)(m - 4)$ **69.** $m^2 - m - 12$

Solve. **70.** $9y = 3y - 45$ **71.** $3z + 45 < 36$

72. $-2.05n = -9.02$ **73.** $2x = 3x - 4$

Write each as a percent. **74.** $\frac{6}{8}$ **75.** $\frac{27}{15}$ **76.** $\frac{60}{12}$ **77.** $\frac{45}{75}$ **78.** $\frac{18}{4}$

79. Let M be Michele's age. Nicole is 2 years younger than Michele. Write an expression for Nicole's age.

80. Let s be the total amount Heidi spent for scarves. Each of the 4 scarves that she bought cost the same. Write an expression for the cost of each scarf.

81. Let L be the amount Lewis earns. Harry earns three times as much as Lewis. Write an expression for the amount Harry earns.

BIOGRAPHICAL NOTE: GEORGE PÓLYA

"A great discovery solves a great problem, but there is a grain of discovery in the solution of any problem."

George Pólya (1887–1985) was a mathematician who believed that problem solving was an art, like swimming or skiing or playing the piano, and that with practice it could be mastered. Born in Hungary, he first studied law, then literature and languages until his interest in discovery led him to the study of mathematics. In 1942 he came to Palo Alto, California, to teach at Stanford University.

Today his influence in the field of mathematics education is widespread. His studies in the methods and rules of discovery led to a specific problem-solving approach, which has become the model for problem-solving guidelines used in most mathematics curriculums. The four phases of problem solving that George Pólya outlines in his book *How to Solve It* are 1) Understand the problem, 2) Devise a plan, 3) Carry out the plan, and 4) Look back at the completed solution.

4-5 Problem Solving: Using Inequalities

Translating Phrases to Inequalities

Objective: Translate phrases to mathematical inequalities.

You have learned how to translate a problem to an equation and solve the equation to answer the problem. Some problems can be solved by translating to an inequality and solving the inequality to answer the problem.

EXAMPLES Translate to an inequality.

1. A number y is greater than 4.

   $y > 4$

2. A number x is less than or equal to $2\frac{1}{2}$.

   $x \leq 2\frac{1}{2}$

3. A number m is at least 3.

   $m \geq 3$ "At least 3" means the number could be 3 or greater.

4. A number p is at most $\frac{1}{3}$.

   $p \leq \frac{1}{3}$ "At most $\frac{1}{3}$" means the number could be $\frac{1}{3}$ or less.

5. 3 is greater than or equal to some number n.

   $3 \geq n$ We can also write this as $n \leq 3$.

6. 12 more than twice a number is less than 20.

   $2x + 12 < 20$ "12 more than twice a number" translates to $2x + 12$. "Is less than 20" translates to < 20.

Try This Translate to an inequality.

a. A number x is greater than or equal to 8. $x \geq 8$

b. A number t is less than 12. $t < 12$

c. A number x is at most $4\frac{1}{2}$. $x \leq 4\frac{1}{2}$

d. A number n is at least 0. $n \geq 0$

e. 3 less than a number is greater than 4. $n - 3 > 4$

4-5

FIRST FIVE MINUTES

Solve.

1. $9u + 1 < 19$
   $9u < 18$
   $u < \frac{18}{9}$
   $u < 2$
2. $5b + 2 - b > 8$
   $4b > 6$
   $b > \frac{6}{4}$
   $b > \frac{3}{2}$
3. $-7c \geq -14$
   $c \leq \frac{-14}{-7}$
   $c \leq 2$
4. $4x - 7x + 2 < x + 5$
   $-3x < x + 3$
   $-4x < 3$
   $x > \frac{3}{-4}$
   $x > -\frac{3}{4}$

Translating Phrases to Inequalities

You may wish to illustrate certain phrases with arithmetic examples to make sure students understand them. For instance,

"5 is at least 5" is true.
"5 is more than 5" is false.
"5 is as great as 5" is true.

Key Questions

- If a quantity is "at least 8," can it be greater than 8 or less than 8?
  Greater than 8
- If a quantity is "at most 10," can it be greater than 10 or less than 10?
  Less than 10

Chalkboard Examples

Translate to an inequality.

1. A number y is less than 4.
   $y < 4$
2. A number x is greater than $\frac{4}{3}$.
   $x > \frac{4}{3}$
3. 8 less than 3 times a number is more than 13.
   $3x - 8 > 13$

Solving Problems

Although the three main phases of problem solving remain unchanged, you may want to present the following guidelines for solving inequalities in the second phase of the problem-solving process.

Develop and carry out a PLAN
- Can I use a variable to represent an unknown number?
- Can I represent other conditions in terms of the variable?
- Can I find any relationships?
- Can I write and solve an inequality?

Key Questions

- In Example 7, what word indicates that a greater than or equal sign is to be used? exceeds
- In Example 8, what words indicate that a less than or equal sign is to be used? at most

Avoiding Common Errors

Students often see the words "more than" or "less than" and assume that they indicate inequalities. Remind students that "3 more than 10" is a specific number, 10 + 3 or 13. Point out that an inequality is implied if the question "Can there be more?" or "Can there be less?" can be answered as yes.

Chalkboard Examples

1. Thornton needs at least 500 milligrams of vitamin C each day. He gets his vitamin C by munching brussel sprouts. Each sprout furnishes 10 milligrams of vitamin C. Find the number of sprouts he must eat each day.
   Let s be the number of sprouts Thornton must eat each day. The amount of vitamin C is 10s. This must be at least 500.
   $10s \geq 500$
   $s \geq \frac{500}{10}$
   $s \geq 50$
   He must eat at least 50 sprouts.

Solving Problems

Objective: Solve problems by translating and solving inequalities.

PROBLEM-SOLVING GUIDELINES
■ UNDERSTAND the problem
■ Develop and carry out a PLAN
■ Find the ANSWER and CHECK

You can use the Problem-Solving Guidelines at the left to help you solve problems when your plan involves writing and solving an inequality.

EXAMPLE 7

Ruth Anne wants to enter her newborn black angus calf in the 4-H competition at the county fair. In order to qualify for the competition, her calf must weigh at least 200 pounds. Black angus calves weigh approximately 75 pounds at birth and gain around 2 pounds per day for the first few weeks. How many days will it take before the calf's weight exceeds 200 pounds?

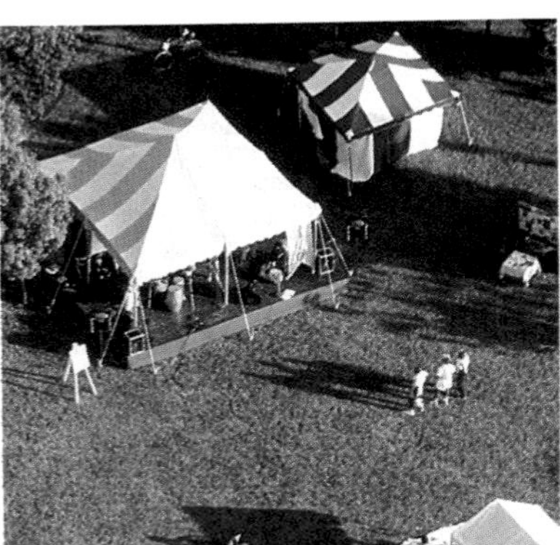

■ **UNDERSTAND the problem**

Question: How many days until the calf exceeds 200 pounds?
Data: Calf weighs 75 lb at birth; gains 2 lbs per day.

■ **Develop and carry out a PLAN**

Let d = the number of days until the calf exceeds 200 pounds.
$2d$ = the amount of weight gained in d days

$$75 + 2d > 200$$
$$2d > 125$$
$$d > 62.5$$

$75 + 2d$ is the total weight after d days. This amount must be greater than (>) 200.

■ **Find the ANSWER and CHECK**

On average, a calf should reach 200 pounds in about 63 days, or about 9 weeks. At 2 lb per day plus the birth weight, this answer seems reasonable.

EXAMPLE 8

The medium-size box of dog food weighs 1 lb more than the small size. The large-size weighs 2 lb more than the small size. If the total weight of the three boxes is at most 30 lb, what is the most a small box could weigh?

UNDERSTAND the problem

Question: What is the most the small box could weigh?

Data: Medium box weighs 1 lb more than the small; large box weighs 2 lb more than the small; total weight of the three boxes is at most 30 lb.

Develop and carry out a PLAN

Let s = the maximum weight of the small box.

$s + 1$ = the maximum weight of the medium box

$s + 2$ = the maximum weight of the large box

$s + (s + 1) + (s + 2) \leq 30$ — The total weight of the 3 boxes is 30 lb or less.

$3s + 3 \leq 30$ — Simplifying

$3s \leq 27$ — Adding -3 to both sides

$s \leq 9$ — Multiplying both sides by $\frac{1}{3}$

Find the ANSWER and CHECK

The small box can weigh at most 9 lb. We know that $3 \times 10 = 30$, so we can estimate that each box should weigh about 10 lb. The answer is reasonable.

Try This

f. Each student agreed to sell at least 50 seed packages for a school project. Yesterday one student sold 22 packages, and today this student sold 18. How many more packages does the student need to sell to reach the goal of 50 packages? $p \geq 10$; at least 10

g. In an algebra course you must get a total of at least 360 points on four tests for a grade of A. You get 85, 89, and 92 on the first three tests. What score on the last test will give you an A? $s \geq 94$; at least 94

h. The sum of two consecutive integers is less than 35. What is the greatest possible pair? 16, 17

2. Your test grades are 85, 74, and 91. What is the lowest grade you can get on the next test and have an average of at least 80?
Let s be your next test score. The average of the four tests must be greater than or equal to 80.

$$\frac{(85 + 74 + 91 + s)}{4} \geq 80$$

$$85 + 74 + 91 + s \geq 320$$

$$s \geq 70$$

You must score at least 70.

LESSON QUIZ

Write an expression for each statement.

1. x is greater than 3.
$x > 3$
2. There are at least as many x as y.
$x \geq y$
3. Twice the number n, plus 1, is greater than 7.
$2n + 1 > 7$

Solve.

4. The sum of two integers is greater than 20. The second number is three times as large as the first number. Find the range of the first number.
Let n be the first number. The second number is $3n$. The sum of the numbers is greater than 20.
$n + 3n > 20$
$4n > 20$
$n > 5$

Assignment Guide
Minimum: 1–22 e/o, MR

Regular: 1–25 e/o, 26, MR, assign w. Application
Advanced: 1–25 e/o, 26–28, MR, assign w. Connections

ADDITIONAL ANSWERS

Exercises

1. $y > 3$
2. $k < 5\frac{1}{2}$
3. $h \geq 4\frac{5}{6}$
4. $j \leq 2$
5. $x \geq 0$
6. $x - 7 < 5$
7. $x + 2 > 9$
8. $2x > 12$
9. $\frac{x}{2} \leq 6$
10. $\frac{x}{3} + 3 < 9$
11. $2x - 4 \leq 18$
12. $2x + 4 < -x$
13. $3x + 2 \leq 11$
14. $\frac{x}{3} - 5 \leq 15$

20. $b > 6$ cm; the base is longer than 6 cm.
21. $A > 12$, $D > 15$; Armando worked more than 12 hours, and Drew worked more than 15 hours.

4-5 EXERCISES

A

Translate to an inequality.

1. 3 is less than a number y.
2. $5\frac{1}{2}$ is greater than a number k.
3. A number h is at least $4\frac{5}{6}$.
4. A number j is at most 2.
5. A number is greater than or equal to 0.
6. 7 less than a number is less than 5.
7. 2 more than a number is greater than 9.
8. Twice a number is greater than 12.
9. Half a number is less than or equal to 6.
10. 3 more than one third of a number is less than 9.
11. 18 is greater than or equal to 4 less than twice a number.
12. 4 more than twice a number is less than the opposite of the number.
13. 2 more than 3 times a number is at most 11.
14. 5 less than a third of a number is at most 15.

Solve.

15. Your quiz grades are 73, 75, 89, and 91. What is the lowest grade you can obtain on the last quiz and still achieve an average of at least 85? 97
16. The sum of three consecutive odd integers is less than 100. What are the greatest possible values of these integers? 31, 33, 35
17. Find the greatest possible pair of integers such that one integer is twice the other and their sum is less than 30. 9, 18
18. The sum of two integers is greater than 12. One integer is ten less than twice the other. What are the least values of the integers? 8, 6
19. Find all sets of four consecutive even whole numbers whose sum is less than 35. 0, 2, 4, 6; 2, 4, 6, 8; 4, 6, 8, 10
20. Find the length of the base of a triangle when one side is 2 cm shorter than the base and the other side is 3 cm longer than the base. The perimeter is greater than 19 cm.
21. Armando and Drew do volunteer work at an animal shelter. Drew worked 3 more hours than Armando, and together they worked more than 27 hours. What is the least number of hours each worked?

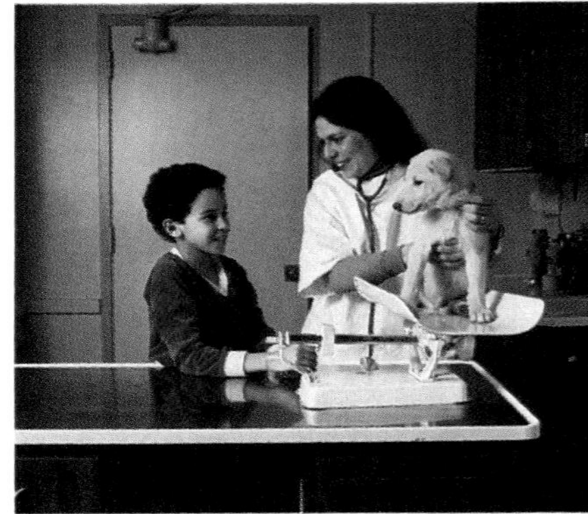

22. Mrs. Hays has promised her two teenagers that they may go to a concert if together they save more than \$25.00 of their spending money. The older teenager agrees to save twice as much as the younger. How much must each save? \$16.68; \$8.34

B

23. The length of a rectangle is 26 cm. What width will make the perimeter greater than 80 cm? $w > 14$ cm

24. The width of a rectangle is 8 cm. What length will make the area at least 150 cm^2? $l \geq 18.75$ cm

25. The height of a triangle is 20 cm. What length base will make the area greater than 40 cm^2? $b > 4$ cm

26. *Critical Thinking* A painter can be paid in two ways.

    Plan A: \$500 plus \$9 per hour
    Plan B: \$14 per hour

    Suppose the job takes n hours. For what values of n is Plan A better for the painter than Plan B? $n < 100$

Challenge

27. You have 5 sections of chain and each section has 3 links. The cost to have a link cut is 10¢. The cost to have a link welded is 20¢. How can you join the sections together for less than \$1?

28. The Wilsons are remodeling their bathroom. A new vanity and sink will cost \$291, the mirror and lights will cost \$239.75, and the vinyl behind the tub will cost \$191. The plumber will install everything and will charge a certain percent of the total cost of the material for his labor. What is the greatest percent the Wilsons can afford to pay to keep the total for material and labor less than \$1000?

Mixed Review

Evaluate for $n = \frac{2}{3}$. **29.** $n - \frac{3}{2}$ **30.** $\left(\frac{4}{5}\right)n$ **31.** $\frac{3}{5} - n$

Solve. **32.** $4(c + 3) = 14c - 3$ **33.** $9y + 16 = 3 - 4y$

34. $9 - 2x < -11$ **35.** $14a + 3 \leq 15a + 7$

Problem for Programmers

Write a program that will test possible solutions of the inequality $5 - 8y < 3$. Use the program to test 3.01, −4.14, and 0.25. The program should output the point being tested and indicate whether it is a solution or not.

27. Cut all three links of one section (30¢). Use each link to join the remaining 4 sections, requiring 3 welds (60¢). The total cost will be 90¢.
28. 38.55%

Mixed Review

29. $-\frac{5}{6}$
30. $\frac{8}{15}$
31. $-\frac{1}{15}$
32. $\frac{3}{2}$
33. -1
34. $x > 10$
35. $a \geq -4$

Problem for Programmers

This program can be written using any programming language (BASIC, PASCAL, LOGO, etc.).

Connections: Discrete Math

ANSWERS

1. If we can't play soccer, then it's raining. False
   Counterexample: It is a sunny day but we can't play soccer because no one can find the ball.
2. If a number is even, then it is divisible by 2. True
3. If a number is even, then it is divisible by 4. False
   Counterexample: 10 is even and is not divisible by 4.
4. If $x = 4$, then $5x + 4 = 24$. True
5. If $x < 10$, then $x < 5$. False
   Counterexample: 7 is less than 10 and is not less than 5.

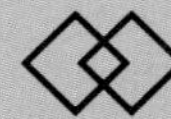

CONNECTIONS: DISCRETE MATH

If-Then Statements

One of the most common statements used in reasoning is a statement of the form if *A*, then *B*. Here are some examples:

If an animal is a cat, then it has four legs.
If a figure is a square, then it has four sides.
If $x = 1$, then $x + 1 = 2$.
If $x < 5$, then $x < 10$.
If the product of two numbers is 0, then at least one of the numbers must be 0.

A statement of this form is called a **conditional statement.** *If A, then B* means that if statement *A* is true, then statement *B* is true. In the statement *if A, then B, A* is called the **antecedent,** or **hypothesis,** and *B* is called the **consequent,** or **conclusion.**

The **converse** of a conditional statement can be found by interchanging the hypothesis and the conclusion. The converse of a true conditional statement may or may not be true.

EXAMPLE 1

Conditional: If the product of two numbers is 0, then at least one of the numbers must be 0.
Converse: If at least one of the numbers is 0, then the product of the two numbers is 0.

The converse is also a true statement.

EXAMPLE 2

Conditional: If a figure is a square, then it has four sides.
Converse: If it has four sides, then the figure is a square.

The converse is not necessarily true. A rectangle has four sides, but it is not a square. To show that a converse is not true, you need to give a **counterexample.** A rectangle is a counterexample for the statement above.

Exercises

Give the converse for each of the conditional statements below. Decide whether the converse is true. If not, give a counterexample.

1. If it's raining, then we can't play soccer.

2. If a number is divisible by 2, then it is an even number.

3. If a number is divisible by 4, then it is an even number.

4. If $5x + 4 = 24$, then $x = 4$.

5. If $x < 5$, then $x < 10$.

Problem Solving: Application

Reading Graphs

How do supermarket managers predict when customers will want to shop and what they'll want to buy? They can use graphs, such as **picture graphs** and **bar graphs**, to show data. Seeing the data graphically helps them make decisions about stock and staff.

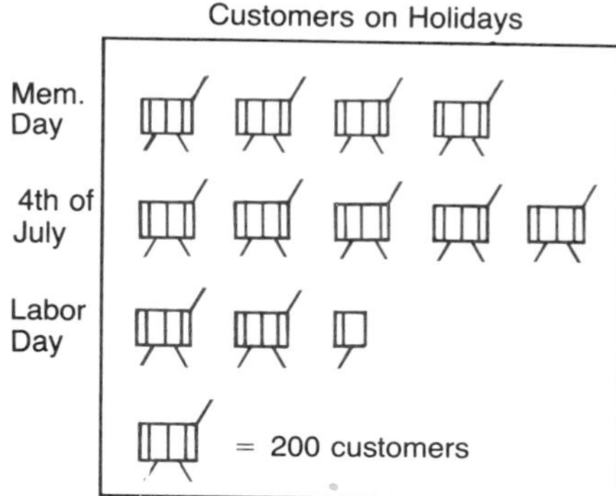

Problems

Use data from the graphs to solve.

1. How many customers visited the store on Memorial Day? How many on the Fourth of July? How many on Labor Day?
2. A manager's records show the average purchase on a holiday to be $12.50. At this rate, how much more was spent on the Fourth of July than on Labor Day?
3. In the past year, one out of every sixty checks cashed by the store has been returned by the bank. Assuming this rate, about how many checks did the bank return if half of the customers on Memorial Day paid by check?
4. What was the average number of customers per day for all three holidays?
5. What were the cheese sales in April? in May?
6. What was the increase or decrease during this period of the sale of ice cream? of cheese?
7. What was the average amount of ice cream sold per month for this period?

Ice Cream & Cheese Sales

Sales in 1000s of Dollars

35
25
15
5

March
April
May

Cheese
Ice Cream

Problem Solving: Application

You may want to review pictorial graphs and bar graphs with students. You may want to point out that in the pictorial graph, each grocery cart represents 200 customers.

ANSWERS

1. 800 customers on Memorial Day
   1000 customers on the Fourth of July
   500 customers on Labor Day
2. $6250 more was spent on the Fourth of July than on Labor Day.
3. About 7 checks were returned.
4. The average number of customers is about 767.
5. April cheese sales: $28,000
   May cheese sales: $22,000
6. From March to May the sale of ice cream increased $7000.
   Cheese sales decreased $9000.
7. The average amount of ice cream sold is $31,000.

4-6

FIRST FIVE MINUTES

1. What integer added to its reciprocal gives 5.2?
   5 (Guess, Check, Revise)
2. How many different ways are there to label the corners of a computer screen with the letters A, B, C, D?
   24 (Make an Organized List)

Use Logical Reasoning

Note that one must reason logically to solve any problem. The strategy called *Use Logical Reasoning* refers to a specific logical approach in which some information is given and "if-then" reasoning is used to make further conclusions, building up enough information to solve the problem.

Setting up information in a chart, as shown in the example, helps show the process of deductive logic. The given information is recorded and conclusions are drawn until all the possibilities except the solution are ruled out.

Key Questions

- In the example, what does the first headline tell you? **Neither Murata nor Holden is the new vice-president.**
- What does the second headline tell you? **Wells is the president.**
- What does the third headline tell you? **Holden is not the treasurer.**

Chalkboard Example

1. To celebrate getting their drivers' licenses, Liz, Ann, and Phil borrowed their parents' cars: a white sedan, a red sports car, and a red compact. (1) Phil's parents own only red cars. (2) Liz borrowed a red car, but her parents wouldn't let her drive their sports car. Who was driving which car?
   Make a chart like the one in the example. The number in the chart corresponds to the clue that ruled out that combination.

	Sports	Sedan	Compact
Liz	2	2	✓
Ann	×	✓	×
Phil	✓	1	×

Clue 2 means Liz was driving the compact. Then clue 1 means Phil was driving the sports car, so Ann was driving the sedan.

4-6 Problem Solving: Strategies

Use Logical Reasoning

Objective: Solve problems using the strategy *Use Logical Reasoning* and other strategies.

Some problems are solved by understanding the given relationships among the facts and using known facts and relationships to draw conclusions. This problem-solving strategy is called **Use Logical Reasoning.**

PROBLEM-SOLVING GUIDELINES
■ UNDERSTAND the problem
■ Develop and carry out a PLAN
■ Find the ANSWER and CHECK

You can use the Problem-Solving Guidelines at the left to help you solve problems when your plan involves the strategy *Use Logical Reasoning*.

EXAMPLE

A newspaper gave information about an election, but did not tell who was elected to which office. The offices were president, vice-president, secretary, and treasurer. Those elected, but not necessarily in the order of the offices above, were Mr. Berry, Ms. Wells, Mr. Murata, and Ms. Holden. Use these headlines from the paper to decide who was elected to which office.

(1) Murata and Holden Congratulate New Vice-President
(2) Wells—First Woman President
(3) Former Treasurer Holden Happy in New Office

You can solve this problem by recording the given information in a chart and making conclusions based on it. The charts below show the reasoning you might go through to solve this problem.

	B	W	M	H
P				
VP			no	no
S				
T				

Murata and Holden were not elected vice-president.

	B	W	M	H
P	no	yes	no	no
VP	yes	no	no	no
S	no	no		
T	no	no		

If Wells is president, no one else is president. Berry must be vice-president.

	B	W	M	H
P	no	yes	no	no
VP	yes	no	no	no
S	no	no	no	yes
T	no	no	yes	no

Since Holden was not treasurer, she has to be secretary. Murata must be treasurer.

Those elected were: president, Wells; vice-president, Berry; secretary, Holden; and treasurer, Murata.

Problem-Solving Strategies		
Draw a Diagram	Guess, Check, Revise	Write an Equation
Make an Organized List	Use Logical Reasoning	Make a Table
Look for a Pattern	Simplify the Problem	Work Backward

4-6 Problems

Solve using one or more strategies.

1. William, Carrie, Lester, and Rosa were hired as coaches at a high school. The coaching positions were for basketball, tennis, racquetball, and volleyball. William's sister was among those hired, and she was to be the tennis coach. Neither William nor Lester ever played basketball or knew how to coach it. Rosa had never learned to play tennis. Lester disliked all sports involving a racket. Who was hired to coach which sport?
2. A certain town can use the digits 0, 1, 2, 3, 7, and 9 for its telephone prefixes. How many 3-digit telephone prefixes are possible for this town if each digit can be used only once in a prefix and the first digit cannot be a 1 or a 0?
3. A student was hired by a city's maintenance department to paint house numbers on the curbs in a particular neighborhood. Each digit had to be painted separately, and the student was paid 10¢ per digit. He painted house numbers from 1 to 225. How much did he earn?
4. Two consultants were hired by a company. The total consultant fees were $12,500. If one consultant had earned $500 less, each consultant would have been paid the same. How much was each consultant paid?
5. Five tiles, each 1 foot square, were used to cover a spot on a floor. The tiles had to be placed so that the sides of any two tiles matched evenly. The perimeter of the spot that was covered was 10 feet. What are the possible shapes for the spot?
6. Five cars in a race all finished within 8 seconds of each other. Car 1 finished 1 second ahead of car 4, and car 4 was not last. Car 2 finished 6 seconds before car 5. Car 5 finished 3 seconds behind car 1. Car 1 finished 5 seconds behind car 3. In what order did the cars finish?
7. ***Write a convincing argument*** Solve the problem below. Then write an argument that would convince a classmate that your solution is correct.

   Meg, Scott, Nellie, and Jeff live in the towns Jackson, Springstown, Newton, and Mowetown. None lives in a town that has the same first letter as his or her name. Neither Jeff nor Nellie has ever been to Mowetown. Meg has spent all of her life in Springstown. Which person lives in which town?

Hints for Problems

1. Record the given information in a chart, and make conclusions to solve the problem.
2. Make an organized list of possible prefixes.
3. Make an organized list to find the number of digits painted. Find the number of houses with just one-digit house numbers.
4. Guess an amount for one consultant, find the fee for the other consultant, and check the total. Revise your guess.
5. Draw a diagram of possible placements of the 5 tiles.
6. Draw a diagram to show the order in which the cars finished.
7. Make a table similar to the one in the example.

ANSWERS

1. William coaches racquetball. Carrie coaches tennis. Lester coaches volleyball. Rosa coaches basketball.
2. There are 80 possible 3-digit telephone prefixes.
3. The student earned $56.70 for painting the house numbers.
4. Consultant A earned $6000, and consultant B earned $6500.
5. Answers may vary. Here are two ways the five tiles could be arranged.

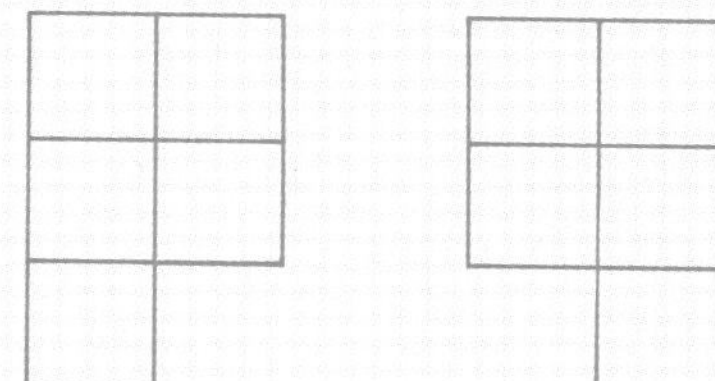

6. Car 3 finished first, followed by cars 2, 1, 4, and 5.
7. Nellie lives in Jackson, Meg lives in Springstown, Scott lives in Mowetown, and Jeff lives in Newton.

ANSWERS

1. a. Yes
   b. Yes
   c. Yes
   d. No
2. a. Yes
   b. No
   c. Yes
   d. Yes
3. 

4. 

5. 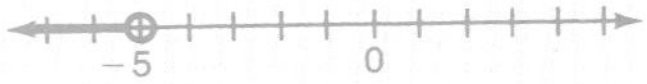

6. $y > -2$
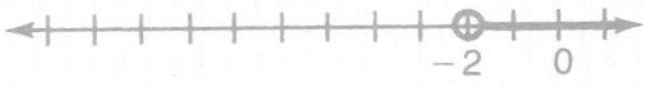

7. $b \geq \frac{9}{4}$
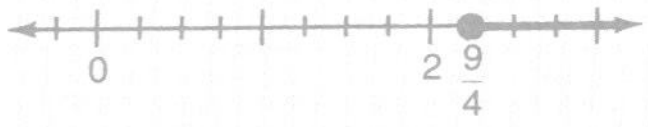

8. $a < 6$

9. $x > -4$
10. $a \leq \frac{1}{6}$
11. $y \leq 20$
12. $x < 5$

13. $b \leq -7$

14. $y < -\frac{3}{2}$
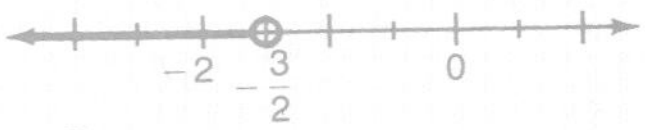

15. $y < 7$
16. $a \leq -\frac{13}{2}$
17. $y < 3$
18. $y < 3$
19. $x > -\frac{11}{7}$
20. $a \leq \frac{11}{3}$

Chapter 4 Summary and Review

4-1

A **solution** of an **inequality** is any number that makes the inequality true when that number is substituted for the variable.

Determine whether the given number is a solution of the inequality.

1. $y \leq 4$	**a.** 3	**b.** 0	**c.** −2	**d.** 8
2. $x > -12$	**a.** 6	**b.** −18	**c.** 0	**d.** 18

A graph of an inequality is a diagram of all its solutions on a number line. A closed circle indicates that the end point is part of the solution, and an open circle indicates that the end point is not part of the solution.

Graph on a number line.

3. $x > -1$ **4.** $x \leq 5$ **5.** $x < -5$

4-2

The **addition property of inequalities** states that if we add the same number to both sides of an inequality, we get another true inequality.

Solve and graph the solution.

6. $y + 5 > 3$ **7.** $b - \frac{1}{4} \geq 2$ **8.** $4a + 6 - 3a < 12$

Solve.

9. $4x + 6 - 3x > 2$ **10.** $a + \frac{2}{3} \leq \frac{5}{6}$ **11.** $-4y + 5y - 8 \leq 12$

4-3

The **multiplication property of inequalities** states that if we multiply both sides of an inequality by a positive number, we get another true inequality. If, however, we multiply both sides of an inequality by a negative number, we must reverse the inequality symbol.

Solve and graph the solution.

12. $5x < 25$ **13.** $-3b \geq 21$ **14.** $-2y > 3$

4-4

The addition and multiplication properties are often used together in solving inequalities. The addition property is usually used first.

Solve.

15. $3y + 4 < 25$ **16.** $4a + 9 \leq 2a - 4$
17. $7 - 6y > 3y - 20$ **18.** $6 - 5y > 3 - 4y$
19. $14 - 8x < 6x + 36$ **20.** $15a + 3 - 12a \leq 14$

4-5

Some problems can be solved by translating to an inequality and solving the inequality. Use the Problem-Solving Guidelines to help you.

Solve.

21. Alicia weighs 60 lb less than her father. Their combined weights total 300 lb at most. What is the most Alicia could weigh?

22. Heather received grades of 80, 75, and 86 on three algebra tests. What must her grade be on the next test if her average for the four tests is to be at least 82?

23. The sum of three consecutive even integers is less than or equal to 42. Find the largest set of these numbers.

24. Find all sets of four consecutive odd whole numbers whose sum is less than 38.

Chapter 4 Test

1. Determine whether each number is a solution of $b \geq -3$.

a. 0 **b.** -3 **c.** -5 **d.** 6

2. Determine whether each number is a solution of $x < 5$.

a. 3 **b.** -3 **c.** -8 **d.** 0

Graph on a number line.

3. $a \geq -5$ **4.** $c < -4$ **5.** $y \leq 6$

Solve.

6. $x - 2 > 5$

7. $9x + 2 - 4x > 17$

8. $x + \frac{1}{3} \geq -5$

9. $7y > -42$

10. $-6x \leq -24$

11. $5x \geq 8x - \frac{3}{2}$

12. $5a - 6 \geq 3a$

13. $2x - 15 > 5x$

14. $-5y - 34 \geq -19$

15. $7 - 6x < 2x + 87$

16. $5 - 8y \geq 23$

17. $9a - 16 < -52$

18. Kim is 3 years older than Bridget. The sum of their ages is less than 16. What is the oldest Bridget could be?

19. The sum of two consecutive even integers is less than or equal to 90. What is the greatest possible pair?

21. 120 lbs
22. $T \geq 87$
23. 12, 14, 16
24. 1, 3, 5, 7; 3, 5, 7, 9; 5, 7, 9, 11

ANSWERS

1. a. Yes
b. Yes
c. No
d. Yes
2. a. Yes
b. Yes
c. Yes
d. Yes

3. 

4. 

5. 

6. $x > 7$
7. $x > 3$
8. $x \geq -\frac{16}{3}$
9. $y > -6$
10. $x \geq 4$
11. $x \leq \frac{1}{2}$
12. $a \geq 3$
13. $x < -5$
14. $y \leq -3$
15. $x > -10$
16. $y \leq -\frac{9}{4}$
17. $a < -4$
18. $x < 6.5$; 6 years old
19. 44, 46

Test Item Analysis

Item	Lesson
1–5	4-1
6	4-2
7	4-4
8	4-2
9, 10	4-3
11–17	4-4
18, 19	4-5

ANSWERS

1. $\frac{3}{2}$
2. $\frac{15}{4}$
3. 8
4. 11
5. $y + 12$
6. $\frac{20}{24}$
7. $\frac{3x}{4z}$
8. $\frac{3}{2y}$
9. 16
10. 32
11. 10,000
12. 12
13. 1000
14. 261
15. $3 \cdot (y \cdot z)$
16. $(x + y) + 21$
17. $15x + 25y + 10z$
18. $16w + 32x + 24y$
19. $6(9y + 1)$
20. $6(7x + 6y + 2)$
21. $15b + 22y$
22. $9y + 10z$

Chapters 1–4 Cumulative Review

1-1

Evaluate.

1. $\frac{y - x}{4}$ for $y = 12$ and $x = 6$

2. $\frac{3x}{y}$ for $x = 5$ and $y = 4$

Simplify.

3. $16 \div (4 \cdot 2) + 9 - 3$

4. $(48 - 8) \div 5 + 3$

1-2

Write an equivalent expression using a commutative property or an identity property. Use $\frac{4}{4}$ for 1.

5. $12 + y$

6. $\frac{5}{6}$

Simplify.

7. $\frac{9xy}{12yz}$

8. $\frac{108}{72y}$

1-3

Evaluate each expression.

9. y^4 for $y = 2$

10. $x^3 + 5$ for $x = 3$

11. $(2a)^4$ for $a = 5$

12. $3a^2$ for $a = 2$

1-4

Calculate.

13. $(3 + 7)^3$

14. $5 + 4^4$

Use an associative property to write an equivalent expression.

15. $(3 \cdot y) \cdot z$

16. $x + (y + 21)$

1-5

Use the distributive property to write an equivalent expression.

17. $5(3x + 5y + 2z)$

18. $8(2w + 4x + 3y)$

Factor.

19. $54y + 6$

20. $42x + 36y + 12$

Collect like terms.

21. $9b + 18y + 6b + 4y$

22. $3y + 4z + 6z + 6y$

1-6

Write as an algebraic expression.

23. four less than twice w
24. three times the sum of x and y

1-7

Solve for the given replacement set.

25. $6y = 54$	$\{7, 8, 9\}$
26. $x^2 - x = 3$	$\{1, 3, 9\}$
27. $2.5y = 15$	$\{0.6, 6, 60\}$
28. $m - 18 = 56$	$\{38, 64, 74\}$

Each pair of equations is equivalent. What was done to the first equation to get the second one?

29. $\frac{4y}{7} = 3$
    $4y = 21$

30. $5x = 30$
    $5x - 4 = 26$

1-9

Evaluate.

31. Find the perimeter (p) of a rectangle with a length (l) of 12 m and a width (w) of 8.4 m using the formula $p = 2l + 2w$.
32. Find the area (A) of a rectangle with a length (l) of 12 m and a width (w) of 8.4 m using the formula $A = l \cdot w$.

2-1

Use > or < to write a true sentence.

33. $-4 \quad -6$
34. $-2 \quad 2$

Find the absolute values.

35. $|-14|$
36. $|65|$

2-2

Use > or < to write a true sentence.

37. $-2.5 \quad -4.25$
38. $-\frac{3}{4} \quad -\frac{3}{8}$

Graph each rational number on a number line.

39. -3.5
40. $\frac{5}{4}$

2-3

Add.

41. $5 + (-9) + 7$
42. $-3.5 + 7.2$

23. $2w - 4$
24. $3(x + y)$
25. $\{9\}$
26. No solution
27. $\{6\}$
28. $\{74\}$
29. Both sides were multiplied by 7.
30. 4 was subtracted from both sides.
31. $p = 40.8$ m
32. $A = 100.8$ m²
33. >
34. <
35. 14
36. 65
37. >
38. <
39. -3.5

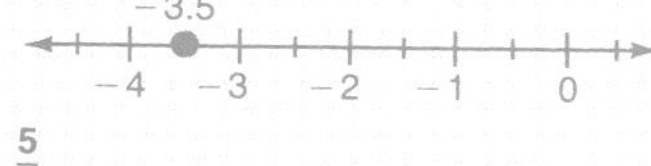

40. $\frac{5}{4}$

41. 3
42. 3.7

43. 1
44. $-\frac{17}{12}$
45. $3 - 10x$
46. $-1 + 3x$
47. 420
48. $\frac{5}{6}$
49. -105
50. -0.3
51. $-\frac{32}{125}$
52. $-\frac{9}{10}$
53. $-12x - 8$
54. $-12y + 24x$
55. $5x + 5$
56. $8(2y - 7)$
57. $-2(x + 4)$
58. $5(a - 3b + 5)$
59. $-9d - 3a + 1$
60. $-2.6x - 5.2y$
61. $-2x - y$
62. $-7x + 6$
63. $8x$
64. Reflexive property
65. Transitive property
66. 10.9
67. $3\frac{5}{6}$
68. -48
69. 12
70. -3
71. $-\frac{12}{5}$

2-4

Subtract.

43. $-7 - (-8)$

44. $-\frac{3}{4} - \frac{2}{3}$

Simplify.

45. $-2 - 4x - 6x + 5$

46. $7 - 2x - (-5x) - 8$

2-5

Multiply.

47. $5(-7)(3)(-4)$

48. $-\frac{5}{8}\left(-\frac{4}{3}\right)$

49. $(-7)(5)(-6)(-0.5)$

2-6

Divide.

50. $\frac{-10.8}{36}$

51. $\frac{-4}{5} \div \frac{25}{8}$

52. $\frac{81}{-90}$

2-7

Multiply.

53. $4(-3x - 2)$

54. $-6(2y - 4x)$

55. $-5(-x - 1)$

Factor.

56. $16y - 56$

57. $-2x - 8$

58. $5a - 15b + 25$

Collect like terms.

59. $-4d - 6a + 3a - 5d + 1$

60. $3.2x + 2.9y - 5.8x - 8.1y$

2-8

Remove parentheses and simplify.

61. $-3x - (-x + y)$

62. $-3(x - 2) - 4x$

63. $10 - 2(5 - 4x)$

2-10

Which properties of equality justify each statement?

64. $2a + 3b = 2a + 3b$

65. $60 = 45t$ and $60 = 35(t - 1)$. Therefore, $45t = 35(t - 1)$.

3-1 to 3-6

Solve.

66. $-2.6 + x = 8.3$

67. $4\frac{1}{2} + y = 8\frac{1}{3}$

68. $\frac{-3}{4}x = 36$

69. $-2.2y = -26.4$

70. $-4x + 3 = 15$

71. $-3x + 5 = -8x - 7$

72. $4y - 4 + y = 6y + 20 - 4y$

73. $-3(x - 2) = -15$

74. $\frac{1}{3}x - \frac{5}{6} = \frac{1}{2} + 2x$

75. $-3.7x + 6.2 = -7.3x - 5.8$

3-7

Solve.

76. $c = 10d + 5n$ for n

77. $L = 2rh$ for r

3-8

Solve.

78. $|y| = 7$

79. $|x| + 2 = 11$

80. $3|a| = 27$

3-9

Solve.

81. $\frac{x}{12} = \frac{16}{18}$

82. $\frac{16}{6} = \frac{x}{24}$

83. A car uses 32 L of gas to travel 450 km. How many liters would be required to drive 800 km (to the nearest tenth)?

3-10

Translate to an equation and solve.

84. What percent of 60 is 18?

85. Two is four percent of what number?

86. What is 16.5% of 80?

3-11

87. Money is invested in a savings account at 12% simple interest. After one year there is \$1680 in the account. How much was originally invested?

88. The sum of three consecutive integers is 114. Find the integers.

4-1

Determine whether each number is a solution of $a \geq -4$.

89. -6

90. 2

91. 0

92. -4

4-2 to 4-5

Solve and graph on a number line.

93. $x - \frac{1}{6} \geq \frac{2}{3}$

94. $-4x \geq 24$

95. $-3x < 30 + 2x$

96. $x + 3 \geq 6(x - 4) + 7$

97. Find the length and width of a rectangle when the width is 4 ft shorter than the length. The perimeter of the rectangle is greater than 72 ft.

72. 8
73. 7
74. $-\frac{4}{5}$
75. $-3\frac{1}{3}$ or $-3.3\overline{3}$
76. $n = \frac{c - 10d}{5}$
77. $r = \frac{L}{2h}$
78. 7, −7
79. 9, −9
80. 9, −9
81. $\frac{32}{3}$
82. 64
83. 56.9 L
84. 30%
85. 50
86. 13.2
87. \$1500
88. 37, 38, 39
89. No
90. Yes
91. Yes
92. Yes
93. $x \geq \frac{5}{6}$

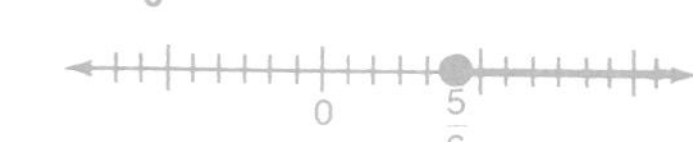

94. $x \leq -6$

95. $x > -6$

−6 0

96. $x \leq 4$

0 4

97. $l > 20$ ft, $w > 16$ ft

CHAPTER 5

Exponents and Polynomials

Chapter Overview

The rules for manipulating exponential expressions and the properties of polynomials are covered in this chapter. Monomial expressions are introduced, and multiplication and division of monomials are practiced. Scientific notation and the use of scientific notation on a calculator are discussed. Numbers expressed in scientific notation are multiplied, divided, and used in problem situations. The techniques of collecting like terms and arranging terms in ascending and descending order are practiced. Evaluation of polynomials for a given value is covered. Addition, subtraction, and multiplication of polynomials is modeled using algebra tiles. Patterns for the product of the sum and difference of two terms and for the square of a binomial are exhibited.

The problem-solving strategies *Make a Table* and *Look for a Pattern* are introduced to develop systematic methods to find solutions. Both strategies are often used with the strategy *Write an Equation* to solve problems.

Objectives

5-1 ▪ Multiply numbers in exponential form.
▪ Divide numbers in exponential form.
5-2 ▪ Find a power to a power.
▪ Find the power of a product or a quotient.
5-3 ▪ Multiply monomials.
▪ Divide monomials.
5-4 ▪ Write numbers using scientific notation.
5-5 ▪ Identify terms and their coefficients and the factors of a term.
▪ Simplify a polynomial by collecting like terms.
▪ Identify the degree of a polynomial.
5-6 ▪ Write polynomials in ascending and descending order.
▪ Evaluate polynomials.
5-7 ▪ Add polynomials.
5-8 ▪ Subtract polynomials.
5-9 ▪ Multiply a monomial and a polynomial.
▪ Multiply two binomials.
5-10 ▪ Multiply the sum and the difference of two expressions.
▪ Square a binomial.
5-11 ▪ Multiply any two polynomials.
5-12 ▪ Solve problems using the strategies *Make a Table* and *Look for a Pattern*.

TEACHING CHAPTER 5

Cooperative Learning Opportunities

The laws of exponents and multiplication of monomials require review and reinforcement until their application becomes automatic. Paired review can be helpful. As a homework assignment, have each student create 10 flash cards, each with a single short exercise of the kind taught in Lessons 5-1, 5-2, and 5-3.

Example: $a^2a^3 = ?$, $\left(\frac{x^2}{2}\right)^3 = ?$, $(-2x^2)(3x^3) = ?$
Answers should be placed on the reverse side.

Assign students to pairs. One student shows 5 of his or her cards, one by one. The other works each one out, orally or on paper, and then checks the answer. Then roles and process are reversed.

This activity, done for 5 minutes every other day for a few weeks will reinforce exponent skills. Assign different teams for each session to change the exercises.

Multicultural Note: *Hypatia*

Hypatia was a famous Egyptian mathematician and scientist who lived from 370 A.D. until 415 A.D. At the university at Alexandria, she taught scholars from all over Africa, Asia, and Europe. Hypatia was considered one of the great lecturers in this center of learning.

Hypatia researched conic sections, that is, the circle, ellipse, parabola, and hyperbola. Today, the conic sections are used to describe the orbits of planets, the paths of comets, and the motion of rockets. She also preserved and expanded the work of Diophantus, the "Father of Algebra." Historians believe that Hypatia's writings provide us with the only surviving copy of his algebra, and therefore deserves to be known as the "Mother of Algebra." Some believe that her death in 415 represents the end of ancient mathematics and science.

In algebra, Hypatia studied the number patterns arising from the numbers of points used to build nested geometric figures. Ask students to study the following patterns, see if they can continue them, draw the figures, and perhaps describe the patterns algebraically.

Triangular	1	3	6	10	**15,21,28**
Square	1	4	9	16	**25,36,49**
Pentagonal	1	5	12	22	**35,51,70**

Alternative Assessment and Communication Ideas

We have all had the experience of thinking that we had a solid grasp of a concept or process, but then we had trouble communicating it. Conversely, explaining something to others helps build our own understanding. These insights can be used to reinforce student learning. As often as possible have students do more than give a one-word answer. Have them explain things.

This process is particularly suited to the skills in Chapter 5. Have individual students prepare brief oral presentations to explain why scientific notation, exponents, or monomials work the way they do.

A student should not simply repeat, for example, that when you multiply a number raised to different powers, you add exponents. Rather, he or she should explain, using words and the chalkboard, how the law is derived from the basic meanings and definitions.

Investigations and Projects

Scientific notation will take on more meaning if students learn about real situations that name and use very small and very large numbers. Science has named some very small numbers to measure short time intervals like bursts of light from lasers, the decay of atomic particles, the speed of computer operations, and the speed of certain physiological reactions, especially in the brain.

Have students look up and write a report identifying the uses of these and other similar, very small time periods.

Name	Time
millisecond	0.001 sec (thousandth)
microsecond	0.000001 sec (millionth)
nanosecond	0.000000001 sec (billionth)
picosecond	0.000000000001 sec (trillionth)

MANAGING CHAPTER 5

Lesson	PACING CHART (DAYS) 2-Year* A for E	1-Year Minimum	1-Year Regular	1-Year Advanced	Opening Activity	Cooperative Activity	Seat or Group Work
5-1	3	1	1	1	First Five Minutes 5-1: ***FFMTM*** p. 16 or **TE** p. 204	✂ Manipulative Activity 5: ***Enrichment*** p. 38	Try This a–n
5-2	2	1	1	1	First Five Minutes 5-2: ***FFMTM*** p. 17 or **TE** p. 209	Suppose: **SE** p. 213	Try This a–o
5-3	2	1	1	1	First Five Minutes 5-3: ***FFMTM*** p. 17 or **TE** p. 214	Critical Thinking 5: ***Enrichment*** p. 22	Try This a–l
5-4	3	1	1	1	First Five Minutes 5-4: ***FFMTM*** p. 18 or **TE** p. 217; Application: **SE** p. 217	Calculator Worksheet 14: ***Technology*** p. 16	Try This a–j
5-5	2	1	1	1	First Five Minutes 5-5: ***FFMTM*** p. 18 or **TE** p. 221	Application: **SE** p. 221	Try This a–k
5-6	2	1	1	1	First Five Minutes 5-6: ***FFMTM*** p. 19 or **TE** p. 226	Problems 35–36: **SE** p. 229	Try This a–k
5-7	2	1	1	1	First Five Minutes 5-7: ***FFMTM*** p. 19 or **TE** p. 231	Problems 1–2: **SE** p. 233	Try This a–g
5-8	2	1	1	1	First Five Minutes 5-8: ***FFMTM*** p. 19 or **TE** p. 236	Problem 39: **SE** p. 239	Try This a–g
5-9	3	2	1	1	First Five Minutes 5-9: ***FFMTM*** p. 20 or **TE** p. 240; ***Overhead Transparencies*** T6	Lesson Enrichment: **TE** p. 241	Try This a–s
5-10	2	1	1	1	First Five Minutes 5-10: ***FFMTM*** p. 20 or **TE** p. 245	Problem 43: **SE** p. 247; Writing to Learn: **SE** p. 248	Try This a–j
5-11	2	2	1	1	First Five Minutes 5-11: ***FFMTM*** p. 20 or **TE** p. 249	Problem Solving: Application: **SE** p. 253	Try This a–l
5-12	2	1	1	0.5	First Five Minutes 5-12: **TE** p. 254	Problem 6: **SE** p. 255	Problem 1: **SE** p. 255
Review	2	1	1	0.5			
Test	1	1	1	1			

*2-Year Management Guide can be found in *Algebra for Everyone*. FFMTM: First Five Minutes Transparency Masters

Enrichment	Review/Assess	Reteach	Technology	Lesson
✂ Manipulative Activity 5: ***Enrichment*** p. 38	Lesson Quiz: **TE** p. 206		BASIC Computer Project 6: ***Technology*** p. 68	**5-1**
Suppose: **SE** p. 213	Lesson Quiz: **TE** p. 211		Evaluating Expressions: **SE** p. 209; Calculator Worksheet 13: ***Technology*** p. 15	**5-2**
Critical Thinking 5: ***Enrichment*** p. 22	Lesson Quiz: **TE** p. 215			**5-3**
Calculator Worksheet 14: ***Technology*** p. 16; Computer Exploration 3: **SE** p. 717	Mixed Review 9: ***SPMR*** p. 59; Lesson Quiz: **TE** p. 219; Quiz 9: ***Assessment*** p. 19	Skills Practice 12: ***SPMR*** p. 20	Calculating with Scientific Notation: **SE** p. 219; Computer Exploration 3: **SE** p. 717; Calculator Worksheet 14: ***Technology*** p. 16	**5-4**
Calculator Worksheet 15: ***Technology*** p. 17	Mixed Practice 9: **SE** p. 692; Lesson Quiz: **TE** p. 224		Calculator Worksheet 15: ***Technology*** p. 17	**5-5**
Evaluating Polynomials: **SE** p. 228	Lesson Quiz: **TE** p. 228		Evaluating Polynomials: **SE** p. 228	**5-6**
Problem for Programmers **SE** p. 235	Lesson Quiz: **TE** p. 233	Skills Practice 13: ***SPMR*** p. 21	Problem for Programmers **SE** p. 235	**5-7**
BASIC Computer Project 7: ***Technology*** p. 69	Lesson Quiz: **TE** p. 237		BASIC Computer Project 7: ***Technology*** p. 69	**5-8**
Lesson Enrichment: **TE** p. 241; Looking for Errors: **SE** p. 244	Mixed Review 10: ***SPMR*** p. 60; Lesson Quiz: **TE** p. 241; Quiz 10: ***Assessment*** p. 20			**5-9**
Writing to Learn: **SE** p. 248; Bonus Topic 5: ***Enrichment*** p. 6	Lesson Quiz: **TE** p. 246			**5-10**
Problem Solving: Application: **SE** p. 253	Lesson Quiz: **TE** p. 250	Skills Practice 14: ***SPMR*** p. 22	Spreadsheet Activity 3: ***Technology*** pp. 41–42	**5-11**
Looking for Errors 5: ***Enrichment*** p. 54	Mixed Practice 10: **SE** p. 693; Assessing Strategies 5: ***Assessment*** pp. 203–204	Strategy Problem Bank 5: ***Problem Bank*** p. 6	BASIC Computer Project 8: ***Technology*** p. 70	**5-12**
	Summary and Review: **SE** pp. 256–258; Test: **SE** p. 259			**Review**
	Chapter 5 Exam: ***A for E*** pp. 223–224; Chapter 5 Test: ***Assessment*** pp. 51–52 (min.), 95–100 (reg.), 171–172 (adv.)			**Test**

SPMR: Skills Practice Mixed Review

The solution to the problem posed on the facing page can be found on page 227.

Ready for Exponents and Polynomials?

1-3 Write using exponential notation.

1. $8 \cdot 8 \cdot 8 \cdot 8$ 8^4

2. $12 \cdot b \cdot b \cdot b$ $12b^3$

1-3 Evaluate each expression.

3. $m^4 - 5$ for $m = 2$ 11

4. $3b^2$ for $b = 4$ 48

1-5, 2-7 Multiply.

5. $3(s + t + w)$ $3s + 3t + 3w$

6. $-7(x + 4)$ $-7x - 28$

1-5 Collect like terms.

7. $2x + 8y + 7x + 5y$ $9x + 13y$

8. $7b^2 + 9b + 2b^2 + 8$ $9b^2 + 9b + 8$

2-5 Multiply.

9. $(-6)(-5)$ 30

10. $-\frac{1}{2} \cdot \frac{5}{8}$ $-\frac{5}{16}$

2-6 Divide.

11. $-\frac{16}{-2}$ 8

12. $-\frac{24}{16}$ $-\frac{3}{2}$

2-8 Rename the additive inverse without parentheses.

13. $-(4x - 7y + 2)$ $-4x + 7y - 2$

14. $-(12r + 7p - 9s)$ $-12r - 7p + 9s$

2-8 Simplify.

15. $5y - 8 - (9y - 6)$ $-4y - 2$

16. $5b - 4(6b - 2)$ $-19b + 8$

CHAPTER

Exponents and Polynomials

If the fuse is set to detonate a packet of spider design fireworks five seconds after launch, at what height will the fireworks explode?

5-1

FIRST FIVE MINUTES

1. $2 \cdot 2 \cdot 2 =$
   8
2. $3^2 =$
   9
3. $(2 \cdot 2 \cdot 2) \cdot (2 \cdot 2) =$
   32
4. $100 \cdot 1000 =$
   100,000

Rewrite without exponents.

5. x^3
   $x \cdot x \cdot x$
6. $\frac{1000}{100} =$
   10
7. $\frac{a^3}{a} =$
   a^2

Multiplying Using Exponents

Point out that we are not multiplying bases, but counting how many times we should multiply the base by itself.

Note that a^0 is discussed in the next subsection.

Key Questions

- Does $a^2 \cdot a^4 = a^3 \cdot a^3$?
  Yes
- Does $1^2 = 1^3$?
  Yes
- Does $a^3 \cdot a^2 = a^6$?
  No, $a^3 \cdot a^2 = a^5$.
- Does $a^2 \cdot b^2 = ab^4$?
  No, the bases are *not* the same.

Chalkboard Examples

Simplify. Express using exponents.

1. $2^3 \cdot 2^6$
   $2^{3+6} = 2^9$
   $(2 \cdot 2 \cdot 2)(2 \cdot 2 \cdot 2 \cdot 2 \cdot 2 \cdot 2) = 2^9$
2. $a^2 \cdot a^4$
   $a^{2+4} = a^6$
   $(a \cdot a)(a \cdot a \cdot a \cdot a) = a^6$
3. $z \cdot z^5 \cdot z^3$
   $z^{1+5+3} = z^9$
4. $(x^2y^3)(x^4y^5)$
   $(x^2x^4)(y^3y^5) = x^{2+4}y^{3+5} = x^6y^8$

5-1 Exponents

Recall that an exponent tells how many times we use a base as a factor. For example, $a^3 = a \cdot a \cdot a$. An expression written with exponents is written using **exponential notation.**

Multiplying Using Exponents

Objective: Multiply numbers in exponential form.

We can use the meaning of an exponent to develop a rule for multiplying powers with like bases.

$$8^3 \cdot 8^2 \text{ means } (8 \cdot 8 \cdot 8)(8 \cdot 8) = 8^5$$
$$5^2 \cdot 5^4 \text{ means } (5 \cdot 5)(5 \cdot 5 \cdot 5 \cdot 5) = 5^6$$
$$a^5 \cdot a \text{ means } (a \cdot a \cdot a \cdot a \cdot a)(a) = a^6$$

Notice we could have added the exponents to find the exponent of the product.

$$8^3 \cdot 8^2 = 8^{3+2} = 8^5$$
$$5^2 \cdot 5^4 = 5^{2+4} = 5^6$$
$$a^5 \cdot a = a^{5+1} = a^6 \qquad a = a^1$$

Multiplying Powers with Like Bases

For any rational number a, and for all whole numbers m and n,

$$a^m \cdot a^n = a^{m+n}$$

EXAMPLES Simplify. Express using exponents.

1. $8^4 \cdot 8^3 = 8^{4+3} = 8^7$ $\qquad (8 \cdot 8 \cdot 8 \cdot 8)(8 \cdot 8 \cdot 8) = 8^7$

2. $y \cdot y^2 \cdot y^5 = y^{1+2+5} = y^8$ $\qquad (y)(y \cdot y)(y \cdot y \cdot y \cdot y \cdot y) = y^8$

3. $(a^3b^2)(a^3b^5) = (a^3a^3)(b^2b^5) = a^{3+3}b^{2+5} = a^6b^7$

Try This Simplify. Express using exponents.

a. $5^2 \cdot 5^4$ 5^6 **b.** $a^5 \cdot a^3$ a^8 **c.** $y^3 \cdot y^2 \cdot y^5$ y^{10} **d.** $(mn^2)(m^4n^6)$ m^5n^8

Dividing Using Exponents

Objective: Divide numbers in exponential form.

The following suggests a rule for simplifying expressions in the form $\frac{a^m}{a^n}$.

$$\frac{3^5}{3^2} = \frac{3\cdot3\cdot3\cdot3\cdot3}{3\cdot3} = 3\cdot3\cdot3 = 3^3$$

Notice that we can subtract the exponents to find the exponent of the quotient.

Dividing Powers with Like Bases

For any rational number a except 0, and for all whole numbers m and n,

$$\frac{a^m}{a^n} = a^{m-n}$$

EXAMPLES Simplify. Express using exponents.

4. $\frac{4^5}{4^2} = 4^{5-2} = 4^3$ $\qquad \frac{4\cdot4\cdot4\cdot4\cdot4}{4\cdot4} = 4^3$

5. $\frac{x^6}{x^2} = x^{6-2} = x^4$ $\qquad \frac{x\cdot x\cdot x\cdot x\cdot x\cdot x}{x\cdot x} = x^4$

6. $\frac{p^5\cdot q^7}{p^2\cdot q^5} = p^{5-2}q^{7-5}$ $\qquad$ Think $\frac{p^5}{p^2}\cdot\frac{q^7}{q^5}$

$= p^3q^2$

Try This Simplify. Express using exponents.

e. $\frac{7^6}{7^2}$ 7^4 **f.** $\frac{a^7}{a^2}$ a^5 **g.** $\frac{m^4}{m^2}$ m^2 **h.** $\frac{x^4y^3}{x^2y^2}$ x^2y

You can use the meaning of an exponent to simplify $\frac{5^2}{5^5}$.

$$\frac{5^2}{5^5} = \frac{5\cdot5}{5\cdot5\cdot5\cdot5\cdot5} = \frac{1}{5^3}$$

You can also use the rule above to simplify the expression $\frac{5^2}{5^5}$.

$$\frac{5^2}{5^5} = 5^{2-5} = 5^{-3}$$

This suggests that $5^{-3} = \frac{1}{5^3}$.

Dividing Using Exponents

Note that the rule for dividing powers with like bases is given with the only restriction of $a \neq 0$. The definition of a negative exponent follows immediately. In the B-level exercises these two rules are combined to give an easy transition to dividing when the numerator is less than the denominator.

To help students understand negative exponents, show them this pattern.

$5^2 = 5\cdot5$

$5^1 = 5$

To continue the pattern for 0 and negative exponents, continue to divide by 5.

$5^0 = 1$

$5^{-1} = \frac{1}{5}$

$5^{-2} = \frac{1}{5\cdot5}$

You may wish to point out to students that 0^0 is undefined.

Avoiding Common Errors

Many students will mistakenly replace x^0 with 0 rather than 1. Remind students that *any number* (other than 0) to the zero power is 1.

Key Questions

- What is $54{,}321^0$? 1
- What is 1^{-1}? 1

Chalkboard Examples

Simplify. Express using exponents.

1. $\frac{7^5}{7^3}$

   $7^{5-3} = 7^2$

2. $\frac{y^8}{y^5}$

   $y^{8-5} = y^3$

3. $\frac{r^3s^4}{r^2s^2}$

   $r^{3-2}s^{4-2} = rs^2$

Simplify.

4. 6^{-1}

   $\frac{1}{6}$

5. 5^{-2}

   $\frac{1}{5^2}$

6. x^{-4}

   $\frac{1}{x^4}$

LESSON QUIZ

Simplify.

1. $5^6 \cdot 5^4$
   5^{10}
2. $m^4 \cdot m^5$
   m^9
3. $(a^2b^6)(a^4b^3)$
   a^6b^9

Express using positive exponents.

4. 7^{-1}
   $\frac{1}{7}$
5. 8^{-2}
   $\frac{1}{8^2}$
6. x^{-5}
   $\frac{1}{x^5}$

In general, we can state the following.

Definition

For any rational number a except 0, and for all whole numbers m,

$$a^{-m} = \frac{1}{a^m}$$

EXAMPLES Express using positive exponents.

7. $4^{-2} = \frac{1}{4^2}$

8. $m^{-3} = \frac{1}{m^3}$

9. $ab^{-1} = a \cdot \frac{1}{b} = \frac{a}{b}$ The exponent affects only b.

Try This Express using positive exponents.

i. 2^{-2} $\frac{1}{2^2}$ **j.** y^{-4} $\frac{1}{y^4}$ **k.** $3c^{-2}$ $\frac{3}{c^2}$

You know that any nonzero number divided by itself equals 1. For example, $\frac{a^2}{a^2} = 1$. Using the rule given above, we also find that $\frac{a^2}{a^2} = a^{2-2} = a^0$. We can state the following about zero as an exponent.

Definition

$a^0 = 1$ for any rational number a except 0.

EXAMPLES Simplify.

10. $3^{-2} = \frac{1}{3^2} = \frac{1}{9}$

11. $1^{-4} = \frac{1}{1^4} = 1$

12. $p^0 = 1$ Any number to the 0 power = 1.

Try This Simplify.

l. 4^{-2} $\frac{1}{16}$ **m.** 1^{-10} 1 **n.** 3^0 1

5-1 EXERCISES

A

Simplify. Express using exponents.

1. $2^4 \cdot 2^3$ 2^7 **2.** $3^5 \cdot 3^2$ 3^7 **3.** $8^5 \cdot 8^9$ 8^{14} **4.** $n^3 \cdot n^{20}$ n^{23}

5. $x^4 \cdot x^3$ x^7 **6.** $y^7 \cdot y^9$ y^{16} **7.** $n^3 \cdot n$ n^4 **8.** $z^7 \cdot z^7$ z^{14}

9. $x^3 \cdot x^1$ x^4 **10.** $a^6 \cdot a^8$ a^{14} **11.** $m^7 \cdot m^0$ m^7 **12.** $p \cdot p \cdot p$ p^3

13. $x^4 \cdot x^2 \cdot x$ **14.** $y^2 \cdot y^4 \cdot y^3$ **15.** $a^3 \cdot a^4 \cdot a \cdot a$ **16.** $b \cdot b^5 \cdot b^2 \cdot b^2$

17. $(a^3b^6)(a^5b)$ **18.** $(x^2y)(x^5y^2)$ **19.** $(p^2q^3r^2)(pqr^3)$

20. $(x^7y^4z^4)(x^2y^5z^8)$ **21.** $(5s^2t^3)(5s^2t)$ **22.** $(2xy^2)(2x^2y^2)$

23. $\frac{7^5}{7^2}$ 7^3 **24.** $\frac{4^7}{4^3}$ 4^4 **25.** $\frac{8^{12}}{8^6}$ 8^6 **26.** $\frac{9^{15}}{9^2}$ 9^{13}

27. $\frac{6^4}{6^4}$ 1 **28.** $\frac{2^7}{2^7}$ 1 **29.** $\frac{y^9}{y^5}$ y^4 **30.** $\frac{x^{12}}{x^{11}}$ x

31. $\frac{a^6}{a^4}$ a^2 **32.** $\frac{n^8}{n^4}$ n^4 **33.** $\frac{x^4}{x^2}$ x^2 **34.** $\frac{y^9}{y^6}$ y^3

35. $\frac{g^5}{g^5}$ 1 **36.** $\frac{h^4}{h}$ h^3 **37.** $\frac{m^8}{m^8}$ 1 **38.** $\frac{x^7}{x^5}$ x^2

39. $\frac{x^2y^5}{y^3}$ x^2y^2 **40.** $\frac{m^6n^4}{m^3}$ m^3n^4 **41.** $\frac{a^6b^9}{a^5b^5}$ ab^4 **42.** $\frac{p^5q^7}{pq^4}$ p^4q^3

43. $\frac{a^3b^4}{ab}$ a^2b^3 **44.** $\frac{x^8y}{x^7y}$ x **45.** $\frac{4^3x^3}{4^2x}$ $4x^2$ **46.** $\frac{6^4a^5b}{6^2a^2b}$ 6^2a^3

Express using positive exponents.

47. 3^{-2} $\frac{1}{3^2}$ **48.** 6^{-3} $\frac{1}{6^3}$ **49.** 2^{-4} $\frac{1}{2^4}$ **50.** 4^{-1} $\frac{1}{4}$

51. a^{-3} $\frac{1}{a^3}$ **52.** m^{-1} $\frac{1}{m}$ **53.** x^{-4} $\frac{1}{x^4}$ **54.** n^{-6} $\frac{1}{n^6}$

55. $3a^{-1}$ $\frac{3}{a}$ **56.** $(3x)^{-1}$ $\frac{1}{3x}$ **57.** $(2y)^{-1}$ $\frac{1}{2y}$ **58.** $4x^{-3}$ $\frac{4}{x^3}$

59. $5c^{-4}$ $\frac{5}{c^4}$ **60.** $8m^{-1}$ $\frac{8}{m}$ **61.** $(3a)^{-1}$ $\frac{1}{3a}$ **62.** cd^{-2} $\frac{c}{d^2}$

Simplify. Express without using exponents.

63. 4^{-2} $\frac{1}{16}$ **64.** 8^{-1} $\frac{1}{8}$ **65.** 7^{-1} $\frac{1}{7}$ **66.** 5^{-3} $\frac{1}{125}$

67. 1^{-4} 1 **68.** 5^0 1 **69.** 2^{-4} $\frac{1}{16}$ **70.** 1^{-3} 1

71. n^0 1 **72.** 6^{-2} $\frac{1}{36}$ **73.** 10^0 1 **74.** x^0 1

B

Simplify.

75. $(-2)^4(-2)^2$ **76.** $(-5)^2(-5)$ **77.** $\frac{(-3)^6}{(-3)^4}$ **78.** $\frac{(-10)^7}{(-10)^6}$

79. $\frac{4^3}{4^5}$ **80.** $\frac{3^4}{3^6}$ **81.** $\frac{(-2)^2}{(-2)^5}$ **82.** $\frac{(-5)^3}{(-5)^4}$

Assignment Guide
Minimum: 1–74 m3, MR

Regular: 1–74 m4, 75–98 e/o, 99, MR
Advanced: 1–74 m4, 75–98 e/o, 99, 100–107 e/o, MR

ADDITIONAL ANSWERS

Exercises

13. x^7
14. y^9
15. a^9
16. b^{10}
17. a^8b^7
18. x^7y^3
19. $p^3q^4r^5$
20. $x^9y^9z^{12}$
21. $5^2s^4t^4$
22. $2^2x^3y^4$

75. 64
76. −125
77. 9
78. −10
79. $\frac{1}{16}$
80. $\frac{1}{9}$
81. $-\frac{1}{8}$
82. $-\frac{1}{5}$

83. (a) x^{-4} (b) $\frac{1}{x^4}$

84. (a) y^{-3} (b) $\frac{1}{y^3}$

85. (a) a^{-4} (b) $\frac{1}{a^4}$

86. (a) m^{-5} (b) $\frac{1}{m^5}$

Mixed Review

108. $6(1 - t)$
109. $-(m + 3n)$
110. $-21a - 36a^2$
111. $12a^2 + 14a$
112. $w - 4$
113. $ac - 8$
114. $2(m + n)$
115. 369
116. -33
117. 5
118. -12
119. \$27 or less

Simplify. Express using (a) negative exponents; (b) positive exponents.

83. $\frac{x^3}{x^7}$ **84.** $\frac{y}{y^4}$ **85.** $\frac{a^2}{a^6}$ **86.** $\frac{m^5}{m^{10}}$

Evaluate each expression.

87. $x^5 \cdot x^3$ for $x = 2$ 256 **88.** $10^m \cdot 10^n$ for $m = 2$ and $n = 4$ 1,000,000

89. $a^3 \cdot a^2 \cdot a$ for $a = -2$ 64 **90.** $2^a \cdot 2^b \cdot 2^c$ for $a = 3, b = 2, c = 2$ 128

Simplify.

91. $\frac{4^2 \cdot 4^5}{4^3}$ 256 **92.** $\frac{2^5 \cdot 3^4}{2^2 \cdot 3^2}$ 72 **93.** $\frac{a^2 \cdot b^3}{a^2 \cdot b^5}$ b^{-2} or $\frac{1}{b^2}$ **94.** $\frac{m^5 \cdot n^6}{m^2 \cdot m^2}$ mn^6

95. $4^{-1} \cdot 4^5$ 256 **96.** $\frac{(-3)}{(-3)^{-4}}$ -243 **97.** $\frac{x^6 \cdot x^{-2}}{x^2}$ x^2 **98.** $\frac{a^{-2} \cdot b^{-3}}{a^4 \cdot b^{-1}}$ $\frac{1}{a^6b^2}$

99. ***Critical Thinking*** Is $(a + b)^m = a^m + b^m$ true for all numbers? If not, give a counterexample. No; let $a = 1$, $b = 2$, $m = 3$; $27 \neq 9$

Challenge

100. Write 16 as a power of 2. 2^4

101. Write 4^3 as a power of 2. 2^6

102. Write 8^2 as a power of 2. 2^6

103. Write $4^3 \cdot 8 \cdot 16$ as a power of 2. 2^{13}

104. Write $2^8 \cdot 16^3 \cdot 64$ as a power of 4. 4^{13}

105. Write $9 \cdot 27 \cdot 3 \cdot 81$ as a power of 3. 3^{10}

Simplify.

106. $\frac{\left(\frac{1}{c}\right)^4}{\left(\frac{1}{c}\right)^5}$ c **107.** $\frac{\left(\frac{a}{b}\right)^3}{\left(\frac{a}{b}\right)^6}$ $\frac{b^3}{a^3}$

Mixed Review

Simplify. **108.** $3[8 - 2(t + 3)]$ **109.** $(5m + 6n) - (6m + 9n)$

110. $6a - 9a(4a + 3)$ **111.** $7a(a + 2) + 3a^2 + 2a^2$

Write as an algebraic expression. **112.** the difference of w and 4

113. 8 less than the product of a and c **114.** twice the sum of m and n

Solve. **115.** $m - 422 = -53$ **116.** $21t = -693$

117. $6(m + 3) = 10m - 2$ **118.** $\frac{3}{4}c + 4 = \frac{1}{4}c - 2$

119. Frank needs a new shirt and sweater and wants to spend at most \$45. If he finds a shirt for \$18, how much can he spend on a sweater?

5-2 More with Exponents

Raising a Power to a Power

Objective: Find a power to a power.

We can use the meaning of an exponent to simplify an expression like $(3^2)^4$.

$$\begin{aligned}(3^2)^4 &= (3^2)(3^2)(3^2)(3^2)\\ &= 3^{2+2+2+2} \quad \text{Using the rule for multiplying powers with like bases}\\ &= 3^8\end{aligned}$$

Notice that we get the same result if we multiply the exponents.

$$(3^2)^4 = 3^{2\cdot 4} = 3^8$$

In general, we can state the following rule for raising a power to a power.

Raising a Power to a Power

For any rational number a, and for any whole numbers m and n,

$$(a^m)^n = a^{mn}$$

EXAMPLES Simplify.

1. $(3^5)^4 = 3^{5\cdot 4} = 3^{20}$ $\quad (3^5)(3^5)(3^5)(3^5) = 3^{5+5+5+5} = 3^{5\cdot 4}$
2. $((-2)^3)^2 = (-2)^{3\cdot 2} = (-2)^6$
3. $(y^5)^3 = y^{5\cdot 3} = y^{15}$ $\quad (y^5)(y^5)(y^5) = y^{5+5+5} = y^{5\cdot 3}$
4. $(m^2)^2 = m^{2\cdot 2} = m^4$

Try This Simplify.

a. $(5^4)^3$ 5^{12} **b.** $(2^2)^5$ 2^{10} **c.** $(a^6)^3$ a^{18} **d.** $(n^4)^4$ n^{16}

Evaluating Expressions

We can evaluate numbers expressed in exponential notation using a calculator. For example, evaluate $(3^2)^4$.

3  y^x 2  =  y^x 4  =  → 6561

For additional calculator practice, see Calculator Worksheet 13.

5-2

FIRST FIVE MINUTES

Write without exponents.

1. 2^3
   $2\cdot 2\cdot 2 = 8$
2. 2^{-1}
   $\frac{1}{2}$
3. 5^{-2}
   $\frac{1}{5^2} = \frac{1}{25}$

Simplify. Express using exponents.

4. $7^3\cdot 7^4\cdot 7^2$
   $7^{3+4+2} = 7^9$
5. $5^4\cdot 5^4\cdot 5^4$
   $5^{4+4+4} = 5^{12}$
6. $3^2\cdot 3^2\cdot 3^2\cdot 3^2\cdot 3^2\cdot 3^2$
   $3^{2\cdot 6} = 3^{12}$

Raising a Power to a Power

Emphasize that $(a^2)^3$ is short for $a^2\cdot a^2\cdot a^2 = a^{2+2+2} = a^6$. Since multiplication is short for repeated addition, we can multiply the powers to get the answer quickly.

Avoiding Common Errors

Students often confuse the rule for multiplying with exponents with the rule for taking a power to a power. They may incorrectly write $(a^3)^2 = a^5$.

Point out that $(a^3)^2$ is short for $(a^3)(a^3) = a^6$. Using the rule for raising a power to a power, $(a^3)^2 = a^{3\cdot 2} = a^6$.

Key Questions

- What does $(2^3)^2$ equal?
  $2^6 = 64$
- Does $(2^3)^2 = (2^2)^3$?
  Yes
- Does $(2^2)^3 = 2^2 2^3$?
  No

Chalkboard Examples

Simplify.

1. $(5^2)^3$
   $5^{2\cdot 3} = 5^6$
2. $(4^5)^6$
   $4^{5\cdot 6} = 4^{30}$
3. $(x^4)^7$
   $x^{4\cdot 7} = x^{28}$
4. $(t^2)^5$
   $t^{2\cdot 5} = t^{10}$

Raising a Product or a Quotient to a Power

You may wish to show that -1 raised to an even power is 1, while -1 raised to an odd power is -1.

Note that if $n = 0$ and either a or $b = 0$, then both sides of the equation $(ab)^n = a^n \cdot b^n$ are undefined. This is also true of $\left(\frac{a}{b}\right)^n = \frac{a^n}{b^n}$.

Key Questions

- Does $(2x)^3 = 2x^3$? No, $(2x)^3 = (2x)(2x)(2x) = 8x^3$.
- Does $(2a)^3 = 2^3 \cdot a^3$? Yes
- Does $\frac{2^3}{x} = \left(\frac{2}{x}\right)^3$? No

Chalkboard Examples

Simplify.

1. $(5x)^3$
   $(5x)(5x)(5x) = 5 \cdot 5 \cdot 5 \cdot x \cdot x \cdot x$
   $= 5^3x^3 = 125x^3$
2. $(3z)^2$
   $(3z)(3z) = 3^2z^2 = 9z^2$
3. $(2y)^4$
   $(2y)(2y)(2y)(2y)$
   $= 2^4y^4 = 16y^4$
4. $(2a^3)^2$
   $2^2(a^3)^2 = 4a^6$
5. $(4x^5y^2)^3$
   $4^3(x^5)^3(y^2)^3$
   $= 64x^{15}y^6$
6. $(-2x^5y^2)^7$
   $(-2)^7(x^5)^7(y^2)^7$
   $-128x^{35}y^{14}$
7. $[(-1)^3]^{11}$
   $(-1)^{3 \cdot 11} = (-1)^{33} = -1$
   The product of an odd number of (-1) equals -1.
8. $\left(\frac{b^3}{5}\right)^2$
   $\frac{(b^3)^2}{5^2} = \frac{b^6}{25}$
9. $\left(\frac{x^5}{y^3}\right)^4$
   $\frac{(x^5)^4}{(y^3)^4} = \frac{x^{20}}{y^{12}}$

Raising a Product or a Quotient to a Power

Objective: Find the power of a product or a quotient.

Recall from Chapter 1 that when an expression inside parentheses is raised to a power, everything inside the parentheses is the base. Compare $2n^3$ and $(2n)^3$.

$2n^3$ means $2 \cdot n \cdot n \cdot n$ (n is the base.)
$(2n)^3$ means $(2n)(2n)(2n)$ ($2n$ is the base.)

We can use the meaning of an exponent to write expressions like $(2n)^3$ without parentheses.

EXAMPLES Simplify.

5. $(2n)^3$ means $(2n)(2n)(2n) = 2 \cdot 2 \cdot 2 \cdot n \cdot n \cdot n$ Using the associative and commutative properties
$= 2^3n^3$
$= 8n^3$

6. $(4x)^2$ means $(4x)(4x) = 4 \cdot 4 \cdot x \cdot x$
$= 4^2x^2$
$= 16x^2$

7. $(3a^2)^3$ means $(3a^2)(3a^2)(3a^2) = 3 \cdot 3 \cdot 3 \cdot a^2 \cdot a^2 \cdot a^2$
$= 3^3 \cdot a^{2+2+2}$
$= 3^3a^{2 \cdot 3}$
$= 27a^6$

Try This Simplify.

e. $(3y)^2$ $9y^2$ **f.** $(6m)^4$ $1296m^4$ **g.** $(2a^3)^3$ $8a^9$ **h.** $(4x^3)^2$ $16x^6$

Note the following relationship in Example 7.

$$\begin{aligned}(3a^2)^3 &= (3^1a^2)^3 \\ &= 3^{1 \cdot 3}a^{2 \cdot 3} \\ &= 3^3 \cdot a^6\end{aligned}$$

Each factor inside parentheses is raised to the third power. We can use the following rule for raising a product to a power.

Raising a Product to a Power

For any rational numbers a and b, and for any whole number n,

$$(ab)^n = a^n \cdot b^n$$

EXAMPLES Simplify.

8. $(3x^2)^3 = 3^3(x^2)^3$
$= 3^3x^6$
$= 27x^6$

9. $(5x^3y^5z^2)^4 = 5^4(x^3)^4(y^5)^4(z^2)^4$
$= 625x^{12}y^{20}z^8$

10. $(-5x^4y^3)^3 = (-5)^3(x^4)^3(y^3)^3$
$= -125x^{12}y^9$

11. $[(-x)^{25}]^2 = (-x)^{50}$
$= (-1 \cdot x)^{50}$ Using the property of -1
$= (-1)^{50}x^{50}$
$= 1 \cdot x^{50}$ An even number of negative factors gives a positive product.
$= x^{50}$

Try This Simplify.

i. $(4y^3)^4$ **j.** $(3x^4y^7z^6)^5$ **k.** $(-7x^9y^6)^2$ **l.** $[(-y)^{15}]^3$

i. $256y^{12}$
j. $243x^{20}y^{35}z^{30}$
k. $49x^{18}y^{12}$
l. $-y^{45}$

The rule for raising a quotient to a power is similar to the rule for raising a product to a power.

Raising a Quotient to a Power

For any rational numbers a and b except $b = 0$, and for any whole number n,

$$\left(\frac{a}{b}\right)^n = \frac{a^n}{b^n}$$

EXAMPLES Simplify.

12. $\left(\frac{x^2}{4}\right)^3 = \frac{(x^2)^3}{(4)^3} = \frac{x^6}{64}$

13. $\left(\frac{a^4}{b^3}\right)^2 = \frac{a^8}{b^6}$

Try This Simplify.

m. $\left(\frac{y^3}{2}\right)^2$ $\frac{y^6}{4}$ **n.** $\left(\frac{a^5}{3}\right)^3$ $\frac{a^{15}}{27}$ **o.** $\left(\frac{x^2}{y^3}\right)^2$ $\frac{x^4}{y^6}$

LESSON QUIZ

Simplify.

1. $(7^6)^3$
7^{18}
2. $(w^4)^9$
w^{36}
3. $(6x)^3$
$6^3x^3 = 216x^3$
4. $(3y^3)^4$
$3^4y^{12} = 81y^{12}$
5. $(2a^2b^4)^5$
$2^5a^{10}b^{20} = 32a^{10}b^{20}$
6. $\left(\frac{x^3}{4}\right)^3$
$\frac{(x^3)^3}{4^3} = \frac{x^9}{4^3} = \frac{x^9}{64}$

> **Assignment Guide**
> Minimum: 1–40 e/o, MR
>
> Regular: 1–67 m3, 68, MR
>
> Advanced: 1–67 m4, 68, 69–80 e/o, MR

ADDITIONAL ANSWERS

Exercises

29. $4x^{16}y^6$ **30.** $27m^3n^{12}$
31. $-8x^6y^{12}$ **32.** $9m^8n^4$
33. $256x^8y^{12}z^4$ **34.** $8m^{15}n^{12}p^9$
35. $\frac{27}{a^6}$ **36.** $\frac{49}{x^{14}}$
37. $\frac{x^8}{256}$ **38.** $\frac{y^{10}}{9}$
39. $\frac{m^{12}}{n^6}$ **40.** $\frac{a^{24}}{b^{12}}$
41. $\frac{1728}{125}$ **42.** $\frac{6400}{9}$
43. $\frac{x^3y^6}{z^3}$ **44.** $\frac{a^3b^{12}}{c^3}$
45. $\frac{4x^4y^{12}}{25}$ **46.** $\frac{81x^{12}y^{12}}{16}$
47. $-\frac{64m^6n^{15}}{27}$ **48.** $-\frac{125p^{12}q^9}{8}$
49. x^{30} **50.** y^{36}
51. $-\frac{x^3}{27y^3}$ **52.** $\frac{16c^4}{y^4}$
53. $\frac{x^6y^3}{z^3}$ **54.** $\frac{m^3}{n^{12}p^3}$
55. $\frac{9a^4b^8}{16c^6}$ **56.** $\frac{8m^{15}n^{15}}{p^{12}}$

57. $54n^7$ **58.** $24x^6$
59. $19a^2$ **60.** 0
61. $8z^8$ **62.** $39c^2d^4$
63. $6z^7 - 25z^6$ **64.** $2a^6b^4$
65. $18c^9$ **66.** $16x^{11}y^{15}$
67. $-432a^{12}b^{14}$
68. Yes. We know $(a^m)^n = a^{mn}$. By the commutative property $mn = nm$, so $a^{mn} = a^{nm}$. Since $a^{nm} = (a^n)^m$, $(a^m)^n = (a^n)^m$.

5-2 EXERCISES

A

Simplify.

1. $(2^5)^2$ 2^{10} **2.** $(3^4)^3$ 3^{12} **3.** $(5^2)^3$ 5^6 **4.** $(6^8)^9$ 6^{72}

5. $(y^5)^9$ y^{45} **6.** $(x^3)^5$ x^{15} **7.** $(m^8)^4$ m^{32} **8.** $(n^5)^{12}$ n^{60}

9. $(a^6)^5$ a^{30} **10.** $(y^7)^7$ y^{49} **11.** $(p^{10})^{10}$ p^{100} **12.** $(w^{12})^7$ w^{84}

13. $(3y)^4$ $81y^4$ **14.** $(2t)^5$ $32t^5$ **15.** $(7y)^3$ $343y^3$ **16.** $(8x)^4$ $4096x^4$

17. $(5m)^2$ $25m^2$ **18.** $(4y)^5$ $1024y^5$ **19.** $(7x)^4$ $2401x^4$ **20.** $(12a)^3$ $1728a^3$

21. $(2m^2)^2$ $4m^4$ **22.** $(4n^3)^2$ $16n^6$ **23.** $(5y^4)^3$ $125y^{12}$ **24.** $(3x^5)^4$ $81x^{20}$

25. $(-6t^2)^3$ $-216t^6$ **26.** $(-10b^6)^2$ $100b^{12}$ **27.** $(8k^4)^3$ $512k^{12}$ **28.** $(7x^5)^3$ $343x^{15}$

29. $(2x^8y^3)^2$ **30.** $(3mn^4)^3$ **31.** $(-2x^2y^4)^3$ **32.** $(-3m^4n^2)^2$

33. $(4x^2y^3z)^4$ **34.** $(2m^5n^4p^3)^3$ **35.** $\left(\frac{3}{a^2}\right)^3$ **36.** $\left(\frac{7}{x^7}\right)^2$

37. $\left(\frac{x^2}{4}\right)^4$ **38.** $\left(\frac{y^5}{3}\right)^2$ **39.** $\left(\frac{m^4}{n^2}\right)^3$ **40.** $\left(\frac{a^8}{b^4}\right)^3$

B

Simplify.

41. $\left(\frac{3 \cdot 2^2}{5}\right)^3$ **42.** $\left(\frac{5 \cdot 2^4}{3}\right)^2$ **43.** $\left(\frac{xy^2}{z}\right)^3$

44. $\left(\frac{ab^4}{c}\right)^3$ **45.** $\left(\frac{-2x^2y^6}{5}\right)^2$ **46.** $\left(\frac{3x^3y^3}{2}\right)^4$

47. $\left(\frac{-4m^2n^5}{3}\right)^3$ **48.** $\left(\frac{-5p^4q^3}{2}\right)^3$ **49.** $[(-x^5)]^6$

50. $[(-y)^{18}]^2$ **51.** $\left(\frac{-x}{3y}\right)^3$ **52.** $\left(\frac{2c}{-y}\right)^4$

53. $\left(\frac{x^2y}{z}\right)^3$ **54.** $\left(\frac{m}{n^4p}\right)^3$ **55.** $\left(\frac{-3a^2b^4}{4c^3}\right)^2$

56. $\left(\frac{2m^5n^5}{p^4}\right)^3$ **57.** $(2n)^4\left(\frac{3}{2}n\right)^3$ **58.** $(4x^3)^2 + (2x^2)^3$

59. $(7a)(4a) - (3a)^2$ **60.** $(-2y^2)^3 + 4y(2y^5)$ **61.** $(-3z^4)^2 - (z^2)^4$

62. $(6cd^2)^2 + 3cd(cd^3)$ **63.** $3z^3(2z^4) - (-5z^3)^2$

64. $b^2(a^3b)^2 + a^2(a^2b^2)^2$ **65.** $(3c^4)^2(2c)$

66. $(-2x^2y^3)^4(xy)^3$ **67.** $(-3a^2b^4)^3(4a^3b)^2$

68. ***Critical Thinking*** Does $(a^m)^n = (a^n)^m$ for all rational numbers a and all natural numbers m and n? Explain.

Challenge

Simplify.

69. $x^{2a}x^4$

70. $x^{3a}x^{2b}$

71. $x^{a+4}x^3$

72. x^5x^{2a-4}

73. $(a^{n+1}b^{m+2})^3$

74. $(x^ay^{a-3})^3$

75. $(c^3d)^a(cd^7)^a$

76. $x^2(x^{a+2}y^3)$

Solve for a.

77. $x^{a+4} = x^4x^8$

78. $x^{a-3} = x^5x^3$

79. $x^{2a} = \frac{x^{12}}{x^9}$

80. $x^{3a} = x^4x^6$

Mixed Review

Simplify. **81.** $6c + (-9m) - 5c + m$ **82.** $21 - 8x - 9 - (-7x)$

Give the reciprocal. **83.** $\frac{x}{y}$ **84.** $\frac{5c}{8}$ **85.** $\frac{-5}{2a}$ **86.** $\frac{m}{2}$ **87.** $\frac{7}{t}$

Solve. **88.** $m + 4 = -3m$ **89.** $4x + 2x = 9x - 6$

SUPPOSE

1. Find the volume of a cube with sides of length $2x$.

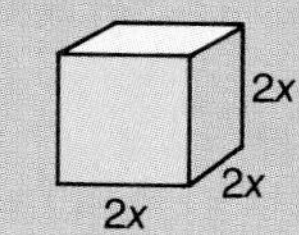

2. Suppose the cube has sides of length $4x$. What would its volume be?

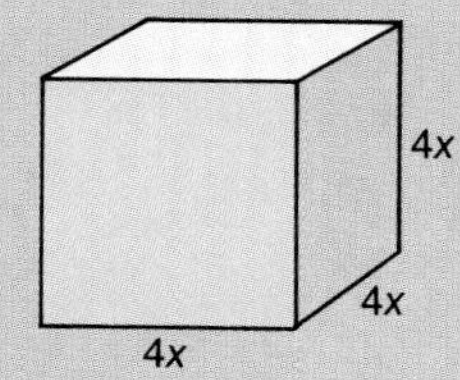

3. Suppose the cube has sides of length $8x$. What would its volume be?

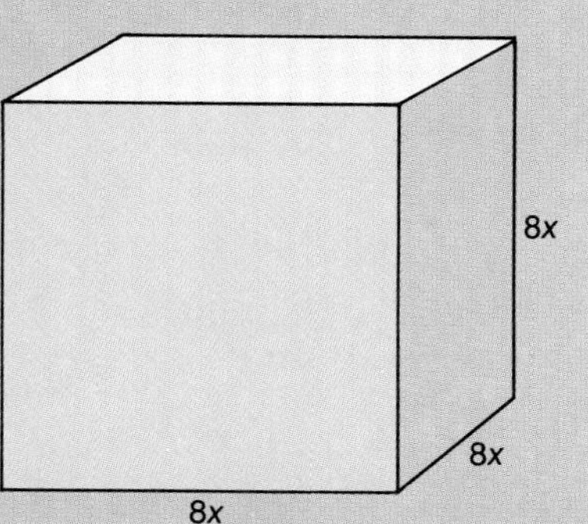

4. How do the volumes of each of the cubes above change as the dimension doubles?

69. x^{2a+4}
70. x^{3a+2b}
71. x^{a+7}
72. x^{2a+1}
73. $a^{3n+3}b^{3m+6}$
74. $x^{3a}y^{3a-9}$
75. $c^{4a}d^{8a}$
76. $x^{a+4}y^3$
77. $a = 8$
78. $a = 11$
79. $a = \frac{3}{2}$
80. $a = \frac{10}{3}$

Mixed Review

81. $c - 8m$
82. $12 - x$
83. $\frac{y}{x}$
84. $\frac{8}{5c}$
85. $-\frac{2a}{5}$
86. $\frac{2}{m}$
87. $\frac{t}{7}$
88. $m = -1$
89. $x = 2$

Suppose

1. $(2x)^3$ or $8x^3$
2. $(4x)^3$ or $64x^3$
3. $(8x)^3$ or $512x^3$
4. As the dimension doubles, the volume increases 8 times.

5-3

FIRST FIVE MINUTES

Simplify.

1. $3x + 2 + 4x$
   $7x + 2$
2. $x^5 \cdot x^9$
   x^{14}
3. $5a + 3b + 8a + 8b$
   $13a + 11b$
4. $a^4 \cdot a^{-7} \cdot a^2$
   a^{-1}
5. $3\left(-\frac{1}{6}\right)x^2$
   $-\frac{1}{2}x^2$
6. $(2x^3)^4$
   $16x^{12}$

Multiplying Monomials

Many students will start doing part of their solutions in their heads, rather than on paper. Point out that shortcuts often lead to errors, and that steps should be written out until the student is very comfortable with the material.

Key Questions

- Is $2xy$ a monomial?
  Yes
- Is $2x + y$ a monomial?
  No
- Is the product of two monomials always a monomial?
  Yes

Chalkboard Examples

Multiply.

1. $(7y)(2y)$
   $14y^2$
2. $(5a^3)(3a^2)$
   $(5 \cdot 3)(a^3a^2) = 15a^5$
3. $(-3x^3)(4xy^5)$
   $(-3 \cdot 4)(x^3x)y^5 = -12x^4y^5$
4. $(7r^3)(-2r^4)(3r^5)$
   $7 \cdot (-2) \cdot 3 \cdot (r^3r^4r^5) = -42r^{12}$

5-3 Multiplying and Dividing Monomials

Multiplying Monomials

Objective: Multiply monomials.

A **monomial** is an expression that is either a numeral, a variable, or a product of numerals and variables with whole number exponents. If the monomial is a numeral, we call it a **constant**.

These expressions are monomials.

$$4x^3 \qquad -7ab \qquad x \qquad \frac{1}{2}y^5 \qquad -8 \qquad 2x^2y$$

These expressions are not monomials.

$$\frac{1}{y} \qquad x^{1/2} \qquad x^2 + 4 \qquad y^2 + 2y - 4$$

We can multiply two monomials using the properties of rational numbers and the properties of exponents.

EXAMPLES Multiply.

1. $(3x)(4x) = (3 \cdot 4)(x \cdot x)$ — Using the associative and commutative properties
$= 12x^2$ — Multiplying

2. $(3x^2)(-x) = (3x^2)(-1x)$
$= (3 \cdot -1)(x^2 \cdot x)$
$= -3x^3$ — Multiplying $(x^2 \cdot x = x^{2+1})$

3. $(-7x^2y^5)(4xy^3) = (-7 \cdot 4)(x^2 \cdot x)(y^5 \cdot y^3)$
$= -28x^3y^8$ — Multiplying $(x^2 \cdot x = x^{2+1}, y^5 \cdot y^3 = y^{5+3})$

4. $(4m^2)(2m^3)(-m) = (4 \cdot 2 \cdot -1)(m^2 \cdot m^3 \cdot m)$
$= -8m^6$ — Multiplying $(m^2 \cdot m^3 \cdot m = m^{2+3+1})$

5. $(-3a)(4a^2)(-a^4) = (-3 \cdot 4 \cdot -1)(a \cdot a^2 \cdot a^4)$
$= 12a^7$

Try This Multiply.

a. $(3x)(-5)$ $-15x$ **b.** $(-m)m$ $-m^2$ **c.** $(-y)(-y)$ y^2

d. $(-x)^2x^3$ x^5 **e.** $(3p^5q^2)(4p^2q^3)$ $12p^7q^5$ **f.** $(4x^5y^5)(-2x^6y^4)$ $-8x^{11}y^9$

g. $(-7y^4)(-y)(2y^3)$ $14y^8$ **h.** $(7a^5)(3a^3)(-a^5)$ $-21a^{13}$

Dividing Monomials

Objective: Divide monomials.

We can also divide monomials using the properties of rational numbers and the properties of exponents.

EXAMPLES Divide.

6. $\frac{x^5}{x^2} = x^{5-2} = x^3$

7. $\frac{4x^2}{5x^7} = \frac{4}{5} \cdot x^{2-7} = \frac{4}{5}x^{-5} = \frac{4}{5x^5}$

8. $\frac{8x^5y^{12}}{-2x^3y^{10}} = \frac{8}{-2} \cdot x^{5-3}y^{12-10} = -4x^2y^2$

Try This Divide.

i. $\frac{x^8}{x^5}$ x^3 j. $\frac{12m^5}{8m^8}$ $\frac{3}{2m^3}$ k. $\frac{-5x^3y^4}{-5x^2y}$ xy^3 l. $\frac{-32x^{15}y^7}{8x^{14}y^6}$ $-4xy$

5-3 EXERCISES

A

Multiply.

1. $(6x^2)(7)$
2. $(5y^3)(-2)$
3. $(-x^3)(-x)$
4. $(-y^4)(y^2)$
5. $(-x^5)(x^3)$
6. $(-m^6)(-m^2)$
7. $(3a^4)(2a^2)$
8. $(5x^3)(4x^5)$
9. $(7t^5)(4t^3)$
10. $(-3b^3)(5b^5)$
11. $(3g^4)(-6g^3)$
12. $(b^5)(-7b^3)$
13. $(-6x^3)(x^8)$
14. $(-8m^7)(-4m^3)$
15. $(-5n^4)(-5n^4)$
16. $(-x^7)(5x^{12})$
17. $(x^3y^4)(x^4y^2)$
18. $(2m^3n^2)(-3m^6n^5)$
19. $(4a^4b^8)(2a^4b^2)$
20. $(-2x^3y)(-6x^9y^8)$
21. $(y^5)(2y)(3y^2)$
22. $(3x^4)(x^4)(5x^2)$
23. $(-4m^2)(5m^4)(-2m^3)$
24. $(9b^2)(2b^5)(-3b^7)$

Divide.

25. $\frac{x^6}{x^2}$ x^4
26. $\frac{a^7}{a}$ a^6
27. $\frac{4x^5}{2x^2}$ $2x^3$
28. $\frac{-6a^3}{6a}$ $-a^2$
29. $\frac{12m^4}{4m^4}$ 3
30. $\frac{-4x^6}{-2x^6}$ 2
31. $\frac{5a^3}{a^7}$ $\frac{5}{a^4}$
32. $\frac{15y^8}{3}$ $5y^8$
33. $\frac{-h^5}{2h^4}$ $-\frac{1}{2}h$
34. $\frac{k^3}{3k^8}$ $\frac{1}{3k^5}$
35. $\frac{2x^{10}}{8x^5}$ $\frac{1}{4}x^5$
36. $\frac{3m^5}{6m^7}$ $\frac{1}{2m^2}$

Dividing Monomials

You may want to illustrate the algebraic concept with an arithmetic example. For instance,

$$\frac{4^3}{4^2} = \frac{4 \cdot 4 \cdot 4}{4 \cdot 4} = \frac{64}{16} = 4$$

or

$$\frac{4^3}{4^2} = 4^{3-2} = 4^1 = 4$$

Key Question

- Is the quotient of two monomials always a monomial?
  No, the quotient may not have whole-number exponents. For example $x \div y = \frac{x}{y}$ or xy^{-1}. This is not a monomial.

Chalkboard Examples

Divide.

1. $\frac{y^7}{y^4}$
   $y^{7-4} = y^3$
2. $\frac{6a^9}{8a^4}$
   $\frac{6}{8}(a^{9-4}) = \frac{3}{4}a^5$
3. $\frac{9a^3b^5}{3a^2b^3}$
   $\frac{9}{3}a^{3-2}b^{5-3} = 3ab^2$

LESSON QUIZ

Multiply.

1. $(4x)(-5)$
   $-20x$
2. $(-3a^5)(4a^7)$
   $-12a^{12}$
3. $(x^3)(-6x^2)(4x^5)$
   $-24x^{10}$

Divide.

4. $\frac{y^9}{y^2}$
   y^7
5. $\frac{4x^7}{2x^3}$
   $2x^4$

Assignment Guide

Minimum: 1–48 e/o, MR

Regular: 1–48 m3, 49–68 e/o, 69, MR

Advanced: 1–68 m4, 69–77, MR

ADDITIONAL ANSWERS

Exercises

1. $42x^2$
2. $-10y^3$
3. x^4
4. $-y^6$
5. $-x^8$
6. m^8
7. $6a^6$
8. $20x^8$
9. $28t^8$
10. $-15b^8$
11. $-18g^7$
12. $-7h^8$
13. $-6x^{11}$
14. $32m^{10}$
15. $25n^8$
16. $-5x^{19}$
17. x^7y^6
18. $-6m^9n^7$
19. $8a^8b^{10}$
20. $12x^{12}y^9$
21. $6y^8$
22. $15x^{10}$
23. $40m^9$
24. $-54b^{14}$

37. -4
38. a^7
39. $3x$
40. $3m^4$
41. $5x^2y^3$
42. $-3m^5n^3$
43. $-4b^6$
44. $4x^5y^2$
45. $\frac{-3p^2}{r}$
46. $\frac{2x^8y^3}{3}$
47. $\frac{-5a^6}{7b^2}$
48. $\frac{x^8}{4y^3}$

49. x^{11}
50. p^{13}
51. a^{18}
52. m^{14}
53. $18x^8$
54. $75y^{12}$
55. $36x^{18}$
56. $256y^7$
57. $6x^6y^6$
58. $-12m^2n^6$
59. a^9b^{14}
60. m^9n^{17}
61. $4x$
62. $\frac{a^4}{2}$
63. y^2
64. 1
65. $\frac{a^2}{3b}$
66. $\frac{x^2}{4y^3}$
67. $\frac{1}{2mn^6}$
68. $\frac{1}{2ab}$

Mixed Review

78. 0.15
79. 0.0004
80. 1.25
81. $x < -7$
82. $x \leq -6$
83. $x > -1$
84. 403
85. $J - 14$

37. $\frac{16x^2}{-4x^2}$ 38. $\frac{-25a^7}{-25}$ 39. $\frac{45x^3}{15x^2}$ 40. $\frac{6m^6}{2m^2}$

41. $\frac{10x^5y^4}{2x^3y}$ 42. $\frac{-12m^7n^8}{4m^2n^5}$ 43. $\frac{24a^6b^9}{-6a^6b^3}$ 44. $\frac{48x^6y^7}{12xy^5}$

45. $\frac{-12p^8r^3}{4p^6r^4}$ 46. $\frac{2x^{12}y^5}{3x^4y^2}$ 47. $\frac{5a^{11}b^7}{-7a^5b^9}$ 48. $\frac{6x^{13}y^4}{24x^5y^7}$

B

Simplify.

49. $x^3(x^4)^2$ 50. $p(p^4)^3$ 51. $(a^3)^2(a^4)^3$
52. $(m^2)^4(m^3)^2$ 53. $(2x^2)(3x^3)^2$ 54. $(3y^4)(5y^4)^2$
55. $(3x^4)^2(2x^5)^2$ 56. $(4y)^3(-2y^2)^2$ 57. $(2x^2y)(3x^4y^5)$
58. $(-3mn^4)(4mn^2)$ 59. $(ab^2)^3(a^3b^4)^2$ 60. $(m^3n)^2(mn^5)^3$

61. $\frac{(-2x^2)^2}{x^3}$ 62. $\frac{(3a^3)^2}{18a^2}$ 63. $\frac{(4y^3)^2}{(4y^2)^2}$ 64. $\frac{(-5m)^4}{(-25m^2)^2}$

65. $\frac{a^4b^5}{3a^2b^6}$ 66. $\frac{2x^6y^4}{8x^4y^7}$ 67. $\frac{-2m^3}{-4m^4n^6}$ 68. $\frac{-4ab^3}{-8a^2b^4}$

69. ***Critical Thinking*** Whether a monomial is multiplied or divided by a second monomial, you get the same result. For this statement to be true, what must be true of the second monomial? It must be equal to one.

C

Challenge

Simplify.

70. $(5x^{-2})(2x^{-4})$ $\frac{10}{x^6}$
71. $(8m^{-3})(-4m^4)(m^{-4})$ $\frac{-32}{m^3}$
72. $\frac{25b^{16}}{5b^{-12}}$ $5b^{28}$
73. $\frac{12m^{-10}}{-4m^5}$ $-\frac{3}{m^{15}}$
74. $(3a^{-2}b^4)(-4a^6b^{-7})$ $-\frac{12a^4}{b^3}$
75. $(5x^6y^7)(3x^{-6}y^{-7})$ 15
76. $(5x^{-4}y^{-6}z^5)(-4x^5y^5z^{-3})(-4x^2yz^{-1})$ $80x^3z$
77. $(qrs)(-qrs^3)(-5q^{-3}r^4s^{-5})$ $\frac{5r^6}{qs}$

Mixed Review

Write each as a decimal. 78. 15% 79. 0.04% 80. 125%

Solve. 81. $8x + 4 - 6x < -10$ 82. $6x \leq -36$ 83. $3 - 6x < 9$

84. There were 407 books in the school library. The ninth grade returned 23 books and checked out 17; the tenth grade returned 15 books and checked out 29; the twelfth grade checked out 26 books and returned 30. How many books were left in the library?

85. Joachin scored J points on the math test. Max scored 14 fewer points than Joachin. Write an expression for Max's score.

5-4 Scientific Notation

Objective: Write numbers using scientific notation.

Application

The distance from Earth to the North Star is about 10,000,000,000,000,000,000 meters. The thickness of a soap bubble is about 0.0000001 meter. It is easy to make errors when working with numbers involving many zeros. If an extra zero is included, the resulting number is ten times larger or ten times smaller.

To prevent this type of error and to make it easier to work with very large and very small numbers, we can write these numbers in a form called **scientific notation.** Using scientific notation we can write a number as the product of a power of 10 and a number greater than or equal to 1, but less than 10. In scientific notation, the distance to the North Star is 1.0×10^{19} and the thickness of a soap bubble is about 1.0×10^{-6}. The numbers 10,000,000,000,000,000,000 and 0.0000001 are expressed using **standard notation.**

EXAMPLES

1. Write 4.58×10^4 using standard notation.

$4.58 \times 10^4 = 45{,}800$ — Multiplying 4.58 by 10^4, or 10,000, moves the decimal point 4 places to the right.

2. Write 3.4×10^{-2} using standard notation.

$$3.4 \times 10^{-2} = 3.4 \times \frac{1}{10^2} = \frac{3.4}{100} = 0.034$$

Multiplying by 10^{-2} is the same as dividing by 10^2, or 100, and moves the decimal point 2 places to the left.

Try This Write using standard notation.

a. 1.25×10^3 1250 **b.** 7×10^5 700,000 **c.** 4.8×10^{-3} 0.0048 **d.** 1.8×10^{-4} 0.00018

5-4

FIRST FIVE MINUTES

Calculate as a decimal number.

1. 10^6 1,000,000
2. 321×1000000 321,000,000
3. 0.0002×3000 0.6

Simplify. Express using exponents.

4. $10^5 \cdot 10^2$ 10^7
5. $10^7 \cdot 10^{-4} \cdot 10^2$ 10^5
6. 1,000,000,000,000 10^{12}
7. 0.1 10^{-1}

APPLICATION

The North Star is also known as the *Pole Star* (or *Polaris*) because it is almost directly over the North Pole. Navigators have used it for thousands of years. Because of slight changes in the rotation of the earth, it will be over the pole for only a few hundred more years. Then, after about 26,000 years, it will once again be the Pole Star.

A number is in standard notation if it is expressed as a single factor, such as 34.765. A number such as 12.3×10^2 is in neither standard notation nor scientific notation.

See Computer Exploration 3 on p. 717 for the use of Scientific Notation on a computer.

Math Point
The number 10^{100} is called a *googol.* It was named by a young nephew of the American mathematician Edward Kasner. The number 10 to the googol power is called a *googolplex* and can be written $10^{10^{100}}$

Key Questions

- Is 12.34×10^2 in scientific notation? No. 12.34 is not between 1 and 10.
- Is 0.237×10^3 in scientific notation? No. 0.237 is not between 1 and 10.
- Is 3.18×3^{10} in scientific notation? No. 3^{10} is not a power of ten.

Chalkboard Examples

Write using standard notation.

1. 1.76×10^1
   17.6
2. 1.76×10^2
   176
3. 1.76×10^4
   17,600

Write using scientific notation.

4. 32,100,000
   Move the decimal left 7 places.
   Multiply by 10^7 to bring it back.
   3.21×10^7

Multiply or divide. Express the result using scientific notation.

5. $(5.2 \times 10^9)(3.0 \times 10^{-3})$
   $= (5.2 \times 3.0)(10^9 \times 10^{-3})$
   $= 15.6 \times 10^6$
   $= 1.56 \times 10^7$
6. $\frac{2.7 \times 10^{16}}{9 \times 10^{-8}}$
   $= \frac{2.7}{9} \times \frac{10^{16}}{10^{-8}}$
   $= 0.3 \times 10^{24}$
   $= 3.0 \times 10^{23}$

Problems involving large numbers can also be done on calculators that do not have exponential notation. Students can write the numbers in scientific notation, peform the calculations on the decimal part, and use the laws of exponents to determine the magnitude of the answer.

EXAMPLES Write using scientific notation.

3. $12{,}450 = 1.2450 \times ?$ — Moving the decimal 4 places to the left, which is the same as dividing 12,450 by 10,000 or 10^4

   $= 1.245 \times 10^4$ — Multiplying by 10^4 to balance this division

4. $0.2362 = 2.362 \times ?$ — Moving the decimal 1 place to the right, which is the same as multiplying 0.2362×10

   $= 2.362 \times 10^{-1}$ — Multiplying by 10^{-1} to balance this multiplication

5. $0.00236 = 0\,002.36 \times ?$ — Moving the decimal 3 places to the right, which is the same as multiplying 0.00236 by 1000 or 10^3

   $= 2.36 \times 10^{-3}$ — Multiplying by 10^{-3} to balance this multiplication

Try This Write using scientific notation.

e. 3,200 3.2×10^3
f. 139,000 1.39×10^5
g. 0.0307 3.07×10^{-2}
h. 0.2004 2.004×10^{-1}

We can use the properties of exponents to multiply and divide numbers that are expressed in scientific notation.

EXAMPLES Multiply or divide. Express the result using scientific notation.

6. $(3.0 \times 10^5)(4.1 \times 10^{-3}) = (3.0 \times 4.1)(10^5 \times 10^{-3})$ — Applying the commutative and associative properties

   $= 12.3 \times 10^2$ — Adding exponents to multiply
   $= 1.23 \times 10^3$ — Converting to scientific notation

7. $\frac{2.5 \times 10^{-7}}{5.0 \times 10^6} = \frac{2.5}{5.0} \times \frac{10^{-7}}{10^6}$ — Factoring

   $= 0.5 \times 10^{-13}$ — Subtracting exponents to divide
   $= 5.0 \times 10^{-14}$ — Converting to scientific notation

Try This Multiply or divide. Express the result using scientific notation.

i. $(1.1 \times 10^{-8})(5 \times 10^{-7})$ 5.5×10^{-15}

j. $\frac{4.2 \times 10^5}{2.1 \times 10^2}$ 2.0×10^3

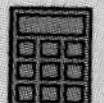

Calculating with Scientific Notation

Some calculators allow you to enter numbers in scientific notation. Using a scientific calculator, follow the example below. The EXP key tells the calculator that you are entering a power of ten. If the exponent is negative, enter the negative sign after you enter the exponent.

Problem in standard notation
(42,000,000)(250,000,000) = 10,500,000,000,000,000

Problem using scientific notation
$(4.2 \times 10^7)(2.5 \times 10^8) = (4.2)(2.5) \times (10^7)(10^8)$
$= 10.5 \times 10^{15} = 1.05 \times 10^{16}$

Using a calculator
4.2 EXP 7 × 2.5 EXP 8 = 1.05 16

Notice that the calculator display shows only the 16 rather than 10^{16}.

For additional calculator practice, see Calculator Worksheet 14.

5-4 EXERCISES

A

Write using standard notation.

1. 5.543×10^3 **2.** 3.29×10^2 **3.** 2.35×10^{-3}
4. 1.743×10^{-4} **5.** 5.7×10^4 **6.** 4.89×10^5
7. 3.4×10^{-5} **8.** 4×10^3 **9.** 6×10^{-4}
10. 1.206×10^2 **11.** 3.007×10^{-3} **12.** 8.04×10^{-5}

Write using scientific notation.

13. 425 **14.** 0.478 **15.** 12,400 **16.** 32,060
17. 0.045 **18.** 0.00003 **19.** 125,000 **20.** 12
21. 5,200,000 **22.** 12,400,000 **23.** 0.0000056 **24.** 0.000000032

Multiply or divide. Express your answer in scientific notation.

25. $(7 \times 10^4)(2 \times 10^2)$ **26.** $(2.2 \times 10^{-3})(3.0 \times 10^5)$
27. $(4.0 \times 10^7)(8.0 \times 10^3)$ **28.** $(6.1 \times 10^9)(2.5 \times 10^{-4})$
29. $(2.5 \times 10^{-3})(4.0 \times 10^{-8})$ **30.** $(5.4 \times 10^{-6})(5.1 \times 10^{-8})$

31. $\frac{(6.0 \times 10^7)}{(3.0 \times 10^2)}$ **32.** $\frac{(9.0 \times 10^8)}{(3.0 \times 10^2)}$ **33.** $\frac{(8.4 \times 10^6)}{(2.0 \times 10^8)}$

34. $\frac{(6.9 \times 10^4)}{(3.0 \times 10^8)}$ **35.** $\frac{(1.5 \times 10^{-2})}{(3 \times 10^{-4})}$ **36.** $\frac{(2.7 \times 10^{12})}{(9.0 \times 10^{12})}$

LESSON QUIZ

Write using standard notation.
1. 6.420×10^2
642
2. 1.357×10^5
135,700

Write using scientific notation.
3. 987654321
9.87654321×10^8

Multiply or divide. Express the result in scientific notation.
4. $(4.4 \times 10^{-5})(7.0 \times 10^{-5})$
3.08×10^{-9}
5. $\frac{8.1 \times 10^{-6}}{1.8 \times 10^9}$
4.5×10^{-15}

Assignment Guide
Minimum: 1–36, MR

Regular: 1–47 e/o, 48, MR

Advanced: 1–47 m3, 48–51, MR

ADDITIONAL ANSWERS

Exercises

1. 5543 **2.** 329
3. 0.00235 **4.** 0.0001743
5. 57,000 **6.** 489,000
7. 0.000034 **8.** 4000
9. 0.0006 **10.** 120.6
11. 0.003007 **12.** 0.0000804
13. 4.25×10^2 **14.** 4.78×10^{-1}
15. 1.24×10^4 **16.** 3.206×10^4
17. 4.5×10^{-2} **18.** 3×10^{-5}
19. 1.25×10^5 **20.** 1.2×10
21. 5.2×10^6 **22.** 1.24×10^7
23. 5.6×10^{-6} **24.** 3.2×10^{-8}
25. 1.4×10^7 **26.** 6.6×10^2
27. 3.2×10^{11} **28.** 1.525×10^6
29. 1.0×10^{-10} **30.** 2.754×10^{-13}
31. 2.0×10^5 **32.** 3.0×10^6
33. 4.2×10^{-2} **34.** 2.3×10^{-4}
35. 5.0×10^1 **36.** 3.0×10^{-1}

37. $4.08 \times 10^4 = 40{,}800$
38. $5.915 \times 10^{10} = 59{,}150{,}000{,}000$
39. $8.32 \times 10^{-8} = 0.0000000832$
40. $4.075 \times 10^{-9} = 0.000000004075$
Since all data are approximations, answers to Exercises 41–47 will be approximate. Students' answers may vary if they use a calculator.
41. 1.5×10^8 km = 150,000,000 km
42. 6.3072×10^{10} s = 63,072,000,000 s
43. Answers may vary.
44. 3.6×10^1 g = 36 g
45. 7.2917×10^2 days = 729.17 days
46. 5.8657×10^{12} mi = 5,865,700,000,000 mi
47. 1.5×10^4 = 15,000 s
48. $1.24 \times 10^{-3} = 0.00124$
49. 8×10^2
50. 3×10^{-2}
51. 2.5×10^{-1}

Mixed Review

52. $3(7 - 5t)$
53. $3(3a + 2)$
54. $15(2 + k)$
55. $4(3m - n)$
56. $3(a^2 + 2a + 3)$
57. $7x - 6$
58. $5y + 9$
59. $a - 15$
60. x

B

Divide. Express the result using scientific and standard notation.

37. $\dfrac{(3.4 \times 10^6)(6 \times 10^3)}{(5 \times 10^5)}$

38. $\dfrac{(4.55 \times 10^3)(2.6 \times 10^5)}{(2 \times 10^{-2})}$

39. $\dfrac{(5.2 \times 10^{-4})(4 \times 10^5)}{(2.5 \times 10^9)}$

40. $\dfrac{(5 \times 10^{-3})(3.26 \times 10^{-4})}{(4 \times 10^2)}$

41. Light traveling at about 3.0×10^5 km per second takes about 5.0×10^2 seconds to reach the earth. Approximately what is the distance, expressed in scientific notation, from the sun to the earth?

42. Approximately how many seconds are there in 2000 years? Assume 365 days per year.

43. About how many seconds have you been alive?

44. A certain molecule weighs 4.5×10^{-6} g. There are about 8×10^6 of these molecules in a cell. What is the approximate weight of these molecules?

45. It takes approximately 5 days for a spaceship to travel from the earth to the moon. At this rate, about how many days would it take to travel from Earth to Mars?

Distance from Earth*	
Moon	240,000 mi
Sun	93,000,000 mi
Mars	35,000,000 mi
Pluto	2,670,000,000 mi

*All distances are approximate.

46. Light travels 1.86×10^5 miles in 1 second. How far does light travel in one year (light year)?

47. Neptune is approximately 2,790,000,000 mi from the sun. About how many seconds does it take light from the sun to reach Neptune?

48. ***Critical Thinking*** Use the digits 1, 2, 3, and 4 and one negative sign to write a number in scientific notation that is close to 0.001.

Challenge

Solve for y.

49. $(8 \times 10^4)y = 6.4 \times 10^7$

50. $(3.1 \times 10^5)y = 9.3 \times 10^3$

Simplify.

51. $\dfrac{(3.6 \times 10^6)(4 \times 10^{-3})}{(4.8 \times 10^{-2})(1.2 \times 10^6)}$

Mixed Review

Factor. **52.** $21 - 15t$ **53.** $9a + 6$ **54.** $30 + 15k$

55. $12m - 4n$ **56.** $3a^2 + 6a + 9$

Simplify. **57.** $5x + (2x - 6)$ **58.** $(11y + 9) - 6y$

59. $4a - (3a + 15)$ **60.** $(4x - 7) - (3x - 7)$

5-5 Polynomials

Application

Mathematicians use expressions to model real-world situations. The expression

$$-0.346y + 914.31$$

is a mathematical model of the record for the mile race in any given year (y) after 1875.

The expression

$$-16t^2 + 96t$$

is a mathematical model of the height (in feet) after t seconds for a projectile with an initial vertical velocity of 96 feet per second.

Both expressions above are called polynomials. Polynomials are used in many areas of mathematics including mathematical applications.

Identifying Terms, Factors, and Coefficients

Objective: Identify terms and their coefficients and the factors of a term.

You have learned what a monomial is and how to simplify expressions by multiplying and dividing monomials. You will now be working with expressions like these.

$$5y + 3 \qquad 3x^2 + 2x - 5 \qquad -5a^3b^2 + \frac{1}{2}ab$$

Each of these expressions is a sum of monomials.

Definition

A **polynomial** is a monomial or a sum of monomials.

In a polynomial, each monomial can be called a term. Polynomials with exactly two terms are called **binomials.** Polynomials with exactly three terms are called **trinomials.**

5-5

FIRST FIVE MINUTES

Simplify.

1. $5x + 2 + 7x - 1$
   $12x + 1$
2. $3a + 2b - a - 2b$
   $2a$

Multiply.

3. $5(x + 4)$
   $5x + 20$
4. $3x(2x + 7)$
   $6x^2 + 21x$

APPLICATION

Have students use the model to predict the record for the mile race for several years. Their answers will be in seconds. For 1875, the model gives an answer of 265.6 seconds or 4:25.6. The actual record in 1875 was 4:24.5 or 264.5 seconds. The model gives a record of 229.2 seconds or 3:49.2 for 1980. The actual record in 1980 was 228.8 seconds or 3:48.8.

Identifying Terms, Factors, and Coefficients

Point out that monomials, trinomials and binomials are all polynomials.

Remind students that 9 in Example 3 can be thought of as $9x^0$.

Math Point
The prefix *poly* is a Greek word and means "many." The prefix *mono,* also Greek, means "one." The prefixes *bi* and *tri* are Latin words, and mean "two" and "three" respectively.

Key Questions

- Is 3 a trinomial?
  No
- Is 3 a polynomial?
  Yes
- Is 3 a monomial?
  Yes

Chalkboard Examples

Tell whether each expression is a polynomial. If it is a polynomial, identify it as a monomial, binomial, or trinomial.

1. $4x^2 + 9x + 4$
   The expression is the sum of three monomials, $4x^2$, $9x$, and 4. It is a trinomial because it has three terms.
2. $\frac{1}{2}xy^3 + a^5b^5$
   The expression is the sum of two monomials, $\frac{1}{2}xy^3$ and a^5b^5. It is a binomial because it has two terms.
3. $\frac{y}{x^2} - x^2$
   The expression is not a polynomial because $\frac{y}{x^2}$ is not a monomial.

Identify the terms. Give the coefficient of each term.

4. $4x^3y^2 - 3y^4z^2 + 5$
   The term $4x^3y^2$ has coefficient 4. The term $-3y^4z^2$ has coefficient -3. The term 5 has coefficient 5.

EXAMPLES Tell whether each expression is a polynomial. If it is a polynomial, identify it as a monomial, binomial, or trinomial.

1. $y^2 + y$

The expression $y^2 + y$ is a polynomial because it is the sum of the two monomials y^2 and y. It is a binomial since it has two terms.

2. $\frac{1}{x} + 2x^2 + \frac{1}{3}x^3$

The expression $\frac{1}{x} + 2x^2 + \frac{1}{3}x^3$ is not a polynomial because $\frac{1}{x}$ is not a monomial.

3. $5x^4 - 3x^2 + 9$

The expression $5x^4 - 3x^2 + 9$ can be rewritten as $5x^4 + (-3x^2) + 9$. Therefore, $5x^4 - 3x^2 + 9$ is a polynomial because it is the sum of the three monomials $5x^4$, $-3x^2$, and 9. It is a trinomial since it has three terms.

Try This Tell whether each expression is a polynomial. If it is a polynomial, identify it as a monomial, binomial, or trinomial.

a. $\frac{7}{n^2} + 4n + 3$ No **b.** $8xy^2 - 4$ Yes; binomial

Be careful not to confuse *terms* and *factors*. In a polynomial, terms are added and factors are multiplied. In the polynomial $2x^3 + 5x^4y^2$, the terms are $2x^3$ and $5x^4y^2$. In the term $2x^3$, 2 and x^3 are factors. In the term $5x^4y^2$, 5, x^4, and y^2 are factors.

The numeric factor of a term is called the **coefficient.** In the term $5x^4y^2$, 5 is the coefficient.

EXAMPLES Identify the terms. Give the coefficient of each term.

4. $4x^2 + 3x - 5$

The terms are $4x^2$, $3x$, and -5.
The coefficient of $4x^2$ is 4; the coefficient of $3x$ is 3; the coefficient of -5 is -5.

5. $2a^4b^3 - 3a^2b^3 - ab + 3$

The terms are $2a^4b^3$, $-3a^2b^3$, $-ab$, and 3.
The coefficient of $2a^4b^3$ is 2; the coefficient of $-3a^2b^3$ is -3; the coefficient of $-ab$ is -1; the coefficient of 3 is 3.

Try This Identify the terms. Give the coefficient of each term.

c. $5y^3 + 6y - 3$ **d.** $m^4 - 3m - 6$ **e.** $-3m^4n^2 - m^2n + 2n$

See Additional Answers.

Collecting Like Terms

Objective: Simplify a polynomial by collecting like terms.

We can often simplify polynomials by collecting like terms. Recall that terms like $3x^2y^3$ and $4x^2y^3$ whose variable factors are exactly the same are called **like terms.** The distributive property can be used as before to factor out the variable factors. The coefficients of the like terms can then be added to simplify the polynomial.

EXAMPLES Collect like terms.

6. $2m^3 - 6m^3 = (2 - 6)m^3$ Using the distributive property
$= -4m^3$

7. $3x^5y^4 - 6y^5 - x^5y^4 + 2y^5 = (3 - 1)x^5y^4 + (-6 + 2)y^5$
$= 2x^5y^4 + -4y^5$
$= 2x^5y^4 - 4y^5$

Recall that the coefficient of a term like x^3y is 1 and the coefficient of a term like $-x^3$ is -1.

8. $7x^3y + 3x^3 - x^3 + x^3y = (7 + 1)x^3y + (3 - 1)x^3$
$= 8x^3y + 2x^3$

Try This Collect like terms.

f. $2x - 4x^3 - 24 - 6x^3$ $2x - 10x^3 - 24$
g. $7m^2 - m - m^2 - 7$ $6m^2 - m - 7$
h. $8x^2y^2 - y^2 + y^3 - 1 - 4x^2y^2$ $4x^2y^2 - y^2 + y^3 - 1$
i. $4b^5 - 2ab^3 - 3b^5 + 7ab^3$ $b^5 + 5ab^3$

Degrees and Coefficients

Objective: Identify the degree of a polynomial.

The **degree of a term** is the sum of the exponents of the variables. The **degree of a polynomial** is the highest degree of its terms.

EXAMPLE 9

Identify the degree of each term of $8a^4b^2 + 3ab + 7$. Give the degree of the polynomial.

The degree of $8a^4b^2$ is $4 + 2 = 6$.
The degree of $3ab$ is $1 + 1 = 2$.
The degree of 7 is 0. Think of 7 as $7x^0$.
The degree of the polynomial $8a^4b^2 + 3ab + 7$ is 6.

The term with the highest degree is called the **leading term.** The coefficient of the leading term is called the **leading coefficient.**

Collecting Like Terms

Students may be able to collect like terms mentally without showing the use of the distributive property. It is important, however, that they understand that it is the distributive property that allows us to collect like terms.

Avoiding Common Errors

Students may try to combine terms such as xy and x^2y^2 and get x^3y^3 or $2x^2y^2$. When these types of errors occur, require students to show the use of the distributive property to collect like terms as shown in Examples 6–8.

Chalkboard Examples

Collect like terms.

1. $3ab + 7ab + 2ab$
   $(3 + 7 + 2)ab = 12ab$
2. $7xy + 3x^2y^3 + 4xy - x^2y^3$
   $11xy + 2x^2y^3$

Degrees and Coefficients

Emphasize that terminology is an important part of algebra, and that understanding the language will lead to an understanding of the concepts.

Key Questions

- What is the degree of 2?
  0
- What is the degree of x?
  1

Chalkboard Example

1. Identify the degree of each term of $5x^4y^3 - 2x^2y^4 + 3$. Give the degree of the polynomial.
   The degree of $5x^4y^3$ is 7.
   The degree of $-2x^2y^4$ is 6.
   The degree of 3 is 0.
   The degree of the polynomial is 7.

LESSON QUIZ

Determine whether each of the following is a polynomial.

1. $x^2 - y^2 + xy^2$ Yes
2. $a^2 - \frac{a^2}{5} + b^2$ Yes
3. Identify the terms. Give the coefficient of each term.
   $5x^2y^3 - 4y^2 - 3$
   The term $5x^2y^3$ has coefficient 5.
   The term $-4y^2$ has coefficient -4.
   The term -3 has coefficient -3.

Collect like terms.

4. $3 - 5x^4 + 7 + 8x^4 + x$
   $10 + x + 3x^4$
5. $4a^3b^6 + 2ab + 3a^3b^6 + 5ab$
   $7a^3b^6 + 7ab$
6. Identify the degree of each term and the degree of the polynomial.
   $3x^5 + 4x^3 + 1$
   $3x^5$ is of degree 5.
   $4x^3$ is of degree 3.
   1 is of degree 0.
   The degree of the polynomial is 5.

Assignment Guide

Minimum: 1–52 m3, MR

Regular: 1–52 m3, 53–58, MR

Advanced: 1–57 m3, 58–60, MR

ADDITIONAL ANSWERS

Try This

c. Terms: $5y^3, 6y, -3$
   Coefficients: $5, 6, -3$
d. Terms: $m^4, -3m, -6$
   Coefficients: $1, -3, -6$
e. Terms: $-3m^4n^2, -m^2n, 2n$
   Coefficients: $-3, -1, 2$

Exercises

15. Terms: $-4m^9, 6m, -1$
    Coefficients: $-4, 6, -1$
16. Terms: $a^5, 4a^3, -3a^2, a$
    Coefficients: $1, 4, -3, 1$
17. Terms: $2x^2y, 5xy^2, -6y^4$
    Coefficients: $2, 5, -6$
18. Terms: $m^4n^3, -3m^3n^2, 6m^2n^4$
    Coefficients: $1, -3, 6$
19. Terms: $8p^3, 2pq, -4$
    Coefficients: $8, 2, -4$
20. Terms: $a^4b^6, -2a^6b^4$
    Coefficients: $1, -2$
21. Terms: $-3n^6, 3n, -3$
    Coefficients: $-3, 3, -3$
22. Terms: $x^6, -2x^5, 3x^2, -2x, -4$
    Coefficients: $1, -2, 3, -2, -4$

Try This Identify the degree of each term. Give the degree of the polynomial.

j. $-6x^4 + 8x^2 - 2x + 9$ 4, 2, 1, 0; 4 **k.** $9x^6y^5 - 7x^4y^3 + 3x^3y^4 + 17x$ 11, 7, 7, 1; 11

5-5 EXERCISES

A

Tell whether each expression is a polynomial. If it is a polynomial, identify it as a monomial, binomial, or trinomial.

1. $\frac{1}{x}$ No
2. $5x^3 - 6x - 3$ Yes; trinomial
3. $7 + 6x^2$ Yes; binomial
4. $15p^2qr^5$ Yes; monomial
5. $-4m^5 + \frac{6}{m} - 1$ No
6. $a^2 + ab + b^3$ Yes; trinomial
7. $-12ab^7 - 12$ Yes; binomial
8. $4 + y$ Yes; binomial
9. -43 Yes; monomial
10. $y^3 - 3y^2 - 5$ Yes; trinomial
11. $-b^2 - 3b + 8$ Yes; trinomial
12. $5x^5y^3 + 5x^3y^2 + 6$ Yes; trinomial
13. $\frac{r^2}{7}$ Yes; monomial
14. $\frac{7}{r^2}$ No

Identify the terms. Give the coefficient of each term.

15. $-4m^9 + 6m - 1$
16. $a^5 + 4a^3 - 3a^2 + a$
17. $2x^2y + 5xy^2 - 6y^4$
18. $m^4n^3 - 3m^3n^2 + 6m^2n^4$
19. $8p^3 + 2pq - 4$
20. $a^4b^6 - 2a^6b^4$
21. $-3n^6 + 3n - 3$
22. $x^6 - 2x^5 + 3x^2 - 2x - 4$
23. $x^8y^6 - 2x^6y^6 + 8x^4y^7 - 4xy^8$
24. $12m^{12} - 8m^{11}n^{10} + 5m^5n^{11} - m^4n^{12} + n^{14}$

Collect like terms.

25. $2x - 5x$
26. $x - 9x$
27. $2x^2 + 8x^2$
28. $3x^2 - 4x^2$
29. $x^3 - 5x - 2x^3$
30. $5x^3 + 6x^3 + 4$
31. $6x^4 - 3x^4 + 7$
32. $6x^4 - 2x^4 + 5$
33. $5x^3 - 3 - 2x^3$
34. $-3x^4 - 6x^4 + 5$
35. $3a^4 - 2a + 2a + a^4$
36. $2x^2 - 6x + 3x + 4x^2$
37. $4xy^2 + 2x^2y - xy^2 + 3x^2y$
38. $-7m^2n^2 + 2mn - 2m^2n^2 - 4mn$
39. $2ab^2 + 3ab - 5a^2b + 4ab^2$
40. $6x^2 + 5xy^2 + 2x^2 - 3xy^2$

Identify the degree of each term and the degree of the polynomial.

41. $2x - 4$

42. $-3x + 6$

43. $3x^2 - 5x + 2$

44. $5x^2 + 3x + 3$

45. $-7x^3 + 6x^2 + 3x + 7$

46. $5x^4 + x^2 - x + 2$

47. $x^2 - 3x + x^6 - 9x^4$

48. $8x - 3x^2 + 9 - 8x^3$

49. $-7x^3y^3 + 6x^2y^2 + 3xy + 7$

50. $5x^4y - x^2y - x + 2$

51. $-5x^4y^5 + 6x^3y^6 - 3x^2y^2$

52. $7x^3y - 4x^2 - 4xy + 5$

B

Collect like terms.

53. $\frac{1}{4}x^5 - 5 + \frac{1}{2}x^5 - 2x$

54. $\frac{1}{3}x^3 + 2x - \frac{1}{6}x^3 + 4$

55. $\frac{1}{2}a^4 - 4a^2 + \frac{2}{3}a^4 - 3$

56. $\frac{2}{5}r^5 - \frac{1}{2}r^3 + \frac{7}{2}r^3$

57. Write a polynomial for the perimeter of these figures. Simplify the polynomial by collecting like terms.

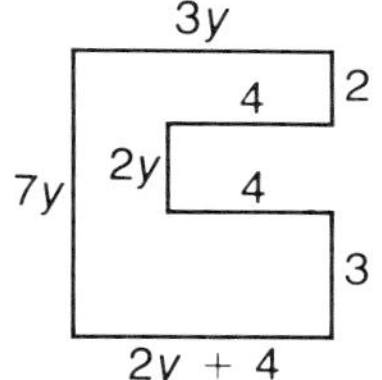

$14y + 17$

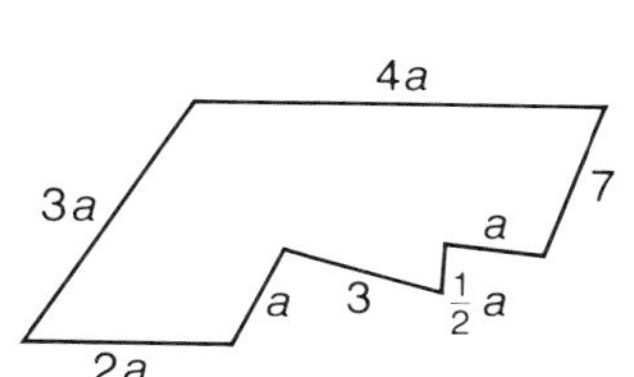

$11\frac{1}{2}a + 10$

58. ***Critical Thinking*** Tell why the following algebraic expressions are not polynomials.

$$\frac{1}{x} \qquad 7 + \frac{5}{y} \qquad x^2 - 5x + \sqrt{x} \qquad (y^2 + 3) \div y$$

Challenge

59. The sum of a number and 2 is multiplied by the number, and then 3 is subtracted from the result. Express the final result as a polynomial.

60. A polynomial in x has degree 3. The coefficient of x^2 is 3 less than the coefficient of x^3. The coefficient of x is 3 times the coefficient of x^2. The remaining coefficient is 2 more than the coefficient of x^3. The sum of the coefficients is -4. Find the polynomial.

Mixed Review

Simplify. **61.** $c^2 \cdot c^5 \cdot c^3$ **62.** $(3m^2)^3$ **63.** $(x^3y^2)(x^4y^9)$ **64.** $(-2ab)^3$ **65.** $(3c^{-2})^2$ **66.** $(3c)^{-2}$

Evaluate for $y = -\frac{1}{2}$. **67.** $y\left(y + \frac{2}{3}\right)$ **68.** y^4 **69.** $1 - \frac{3}{4}y$

Solve. **70.** $-6x \leq 12$ **71.** $2 + 9a \geq 29$ **72.** $9 - 6c = 3c + 54$

23. Terms: x^8y^6, $-2x^6y^6$, $8x^4y^7$, $-4xy^8$ Coefficients: 1, -2, 8, -4

24. Terms: $12m^{12}$, $-8m^{11}n^{10}$, $5m^5n^{11}$, $-m^4n^{12}$, n^{14} Coefficients: 12, -8, 5, -1, 1

25. $-3x$ **26.** $-8x$

27. $10x^2$ **28.** $-x^2$

29. $-x^3 - 5x$ **30.** $11x^3 + 4$

31. $3x^4 + 7$ **32.** $4x^4 + 5$

33. $3x^3 - 3$ **34.** $-9x^4 + 5$

35. $4a^4$ **36.** $6x^2 - 3x$

37. $3xy^2 + 5x^2y$

38. $-9m^2n^2 - 2mn$

39. $6ab^2 + 3ab - 5a^2b$

40. $8x^2 + 2xy^2$

41. 1, 0; 1

42. 1, 0; 1

43. 2, 1, 0; 2

44. 2, 1, 0; 2

45. 3, 2, 1, 0; 3

46. 4, 2, 1, 0; 4

47. 2, 1, 6, 4; 6

48. 1, 2, 0, 3; 3

49. 6, 4, 2, 0; 6

50. 5, 3, 1, 0; 5

51. 9, 9, 4; 9

52. 4, 2, 2, 0; 4

53. $\frac{3}{4}x^5 - 2x - 5$

54. $\frac{1}{6}x^3 + 2x + 4$

55. $\frac{7}{6}a^4 - 4a^2 - 3$

56. $3r^3 + \frac{2}{5}r^5$

58. Not a monomial; $\frac{5}{y}$ not a monomial; $\sqrt{x}$ not a monomial; $\frac{y^2 + 3}{y} = y + \frac{3}{y}$, $\frac{3}{y}$ not a monomial.

59. $n(n + 2) - 3 = n^2 + 2n - 3$

60. $x^3 - 2x^2 - 6x + 3$ is the polynomial.

Mixed Review

61. c^{10} **62.** $27m^6$

63. x^7y^{11} **64.** $-8a^3b^3$

65. $9c^{-4}$ or $\frac{9}{c^4}$ **66.** $\frac{1}{9c^2}$

67. $-\frac{1}{12}$ **68.** $\frac{1}{16}$

69. $\frac{11}{8}$ **70.** $x \geq -2$

71. $a \geq 3$ **72.** -5

5-6

FIRST FIVE MINUTES

Multiply.

1. $x^2(x^3 + y)$
   $x^5 + x^2y$
2. $3y^2(2x^3 + 6x + 2)$
   $6x^3y^2 + 18xy^2 + 6y^2$
3. Simplify. $5x^3 + 4x + 3x^3 + 2x$
   $8x^3 + 6x$
4. Find the degree of $15x^5 + 3x^7 + 18$.
   The degree is 7.

Ascending and Descending Order

Point out that polynomials are more often arranged in descending order than in ascending order.

Also, remind students that $x^0 = 1$ and that a nonzero constant has degree 0.

Key Questions

- Is $x + y$ in descending order with respect to y?
  No
- Is $y + x$ in ascending order with respect to x?
  Yes

Chalkboard Examples

Arrange each polynomial in descending order for the variable x.

1. $3x + 3 + 4x^7 - 4x^6$
   $4x^7 - 4x^6 + 3x + 3$
2. $7xy^2 + 5x^3y^3 - 3x^2y$
   $5x^3y^3 - 3x^2y + 7xy^2$

Collect like terms and arrange in descending order for the variable x.

3. $4xy^3 - 3x^5y^4 + 2xy^3 + 4$
   $-3x^5y^4 + 6xy^3 + 4$

5-6 More on Polynomials

Ascending and Descending Order

Objective: Write polynomials in ascending and descending order.

The polynomial $8x^4y^3 - 2x^3y^4 + 5x^2 - x + 3$ is written in **descending order** for the variable x. The term with the greatest exponent for x is first, the term with the next greatest exponent for x is second, and so on. The constant 3 can be written as $3x^0$. Thus the degree of the constant is 0.

The polynomial $5 - 3xy^3 + 4x^3y^4 - 3x^5y^3$ is written in **ascending order** for the variable x. The term with the least exponent for x is first, the term with the next larger exponent for x is second, and so on.

EXAMPLES Arrange each polynomial in descending order for the variable x.

1. $4x^4 + 4x^7 + x^2 + 2x^3 = 4x^7 + 4x^4 + 2x^3 + x^2$
2. $3y + 4x^5y^2 - 4x^2 + 5xy^4 + 3x^3 = 4x^5y^2 + 3x^3 - 4x^2 + 5xy^4 + 3y$

Try This Arrange each polynomial in descending order for the variable x.

a. $x + 3x^5 + 4x^3 + 5x^2 + 6x^7 - 2x^4$ $6x^7 + 3x^5 - 2x^4 + 4x^3 + 5x^2 + x$

b. $4x^2 - 3 + 7x^5 + 2x^3 - 5x^4$ $7x^5 - 5x^4 + 2x^3 + 4x^2 - 3$

c. $-14y + 7x^2y^3 - 10x^3y^2 - 14x^7$ $-14x^7 - 10x^3y^2 + 7x^2y^3 - 14y$

Sometimes we may need to collect like terms before arranging a polynomial.

EXAMPLE 3 Collect like terms and arrange in descending order for the variable x.

$$2x^2y^3 - 4x^3 + 3 - x^2y^3 - 2x^3 = x^2y^3 - 6x^3 + 3 \quad \text{Simplifying}$$
$$= -6x^3 + x^2y^3 + 3 \quad \text{Writing in descending order}$$

Try This Collect like terms and arrange in descending order for the variable m.

d. $3m^2 - 2m + 3 - 5m^2 - 1 - m$ $-2m^2 - 3m + 2$

e. $-4m^2y + my - 2m^2y - my + 3m^3y$ $3m^3y - 6m^2y$

Evaluating Polynomials

Objective: Evaluate polynomials.

When we replace the variable in a polynomial by a number and calculate, the result is a number. This process is called **evaluating the polynomial.**

EXAMPLES Evaluate each polynomial for the given value.

4. $3x + 5$ for $x = 6$

$$\begin{aligned} 3x + 5 &= 3 \cdot 6 + 5 \quad \text{Substituting} \\ &= 18 + 5 \\ &= 23 \end{aligned}$$

5. $2x^2 + 7x + 3$ for $x = 2$

$$\begin{aligned} 2x^2 + 7x + 3 &= 2 \cdot 2^2 + 7 \cdot 2 + 3 \\ &= 2 \cdot 4 + 14 + 3 \\ &= 8 + 14 + 3 \\ &= 25 \end{aligned}$$

Try This Evaluate each polynomial for the given value.

f. $-4x - 7$ for $x = 3$ −19 **g.** $-5x^2 + 7x + 10$ for $x = 3$ −14

h. $2x^2y + 5xy - 4$ for $x = -4$ and $y = 5$ 56

EXAMPLE 6

The height reached by a fireworks packet is given by the polynomial

$$-16t^2 + 140t$$

(height in ft, time (t) in sec).

If the fuse is set to detonate a packet of spider design fireworks five seconds after launch, at what height will the fireworks explode?

Evaluate the polynomial for $t = 5$ to find the height for the explosion of the fireworks.

$$\begin{aligned} -16t^2 + 140t &= -16(5)^2 + 140(5) \\ &= -16(25) + 700 \\ &= -400 + 700 \\ &= 300 \end{aligned}$$

The fireworks will explode at 300 feet.

Evaluating Polynomials

Point out that evaluating a polynomial is no different from evaluating any other expression.

Chalkboard Examples

1. Evaluate $x^2 + x + 1$ for $x = 3$.
   $3^2 + 3 + 1 = 9 + 3 + 1 = 13$
2. Evaluate $3x^3 + 2x^2 + 5$ for $x = 2$.
   $3 \cdot 2^3 + 2 \cdot 2^2 + 5$
   $= 24 + 8 + 5 = 37$
3. If a rock is thrown upward at a speed of 80 ft per second, the height it reaches in t seconds is $80t - 16t^2$. Find the height of the rock after
   a. 1 second
   $80(1) - 16(1^2)$
   $= 80 - 16(1)$
   $= 80 - 16$
   $= 64$ ft
   b. 2 seconds
   $80(2) - 16(2^2)$
   $= 160 - 16(4)$
   $= 160 - 64$
   $= 96$ ft
   c. 4 seconds
   $80(4) - 16(4^2)$
   $= 320 - 16(16)$
   $= 320 - 256$
   $= 64$ ft
   (It is on its way down.)

Some calculators use [M] and [MR] instead of [STO] and [RCL], and some use [x^y] instead of [y^x].

LESSON QUIZ

1. Arrange in descending order.
   $7 + 5x^2 + 3x^4 - 2x$
   $3x^4 + 5x^2 - 2x + 7$
2. Collect like terms and arrange in descending order.
   $4x^3 + 3x^2 + 5x^3 - 2x^2$
   $9x^3 + x^2$
3. Evaluate $3x^3 + x^2 + 1$
   a. for $x = 0$
   1
   b. for $x = 1$
   5
   c. for $x = 2$
   29
4. Evaluate $2xy + x^2y^2$ for $x = 2$, $y = 3$.
   $2 \cdot 2 \cdot 3 + 2^2 \cdot 3^2 = 48$

EXAMPLE 7

The cost of operating an automobile at speed s ($s > 0$), is approximated by the polynomial

$$0.005s^2 - 0.35s + 28$$

(cost in cents per mile, speed (s) in mi/h).

Evaluate the polynomial for $s = 50$ to find the cost of operating an automobile at 50 mi/h.

$$\begin{aligned} 0.005s^2 - 0.35s + 28 &= 0.005 \cdot 50^2 - 0.35 \cdot 50 + 28 \\ &= 0.005 \cdot 2500 - 17.5 + 28 \\ &= 12.5 - 17.5 + 28 \\ &= 23 \end{aligned}$$

The cost is approximately 23¢ per mile.

Try This

i. Evaluate the polynomial in Example 6 for $t = 7$ to find the height the fireworks will explode if set to detonate 7 seconds after launch. 196 ft

j. Evaluate the polynomial in Example 7 for $s = 55$ to find the cost of operating an automobile at 55 mi/h. ≈23.9¢ per mile

k. The lung capacity in liters for a woman can be estimated by the polynomial

$$0.041h - 0.018A - 2.69$$

(height (h) in centimeters, age (A) in years).

Find the lung capacity for a 25 year old woman who is 170 cm tall.
3.83 L

Evaluating Polynomials

We can evaluate polynomials using a calculator. We can use the memory key STO and the memory recall key RCL to save steps.

Evaluate $2x^3 + 4x^2 - 5$ for $x = 12$.

12 STO Storing the variable in the memory

2 × RCL y^x 3 + 4 × RCL y^x 2

− 5 = → 4027

For additional calculator practice, see Calculator Worksheet 15.

5-6 EXERCISES

A

Arrange each polynomial in descending order.

1. $x^5 + x + 6x^3 + 1 + 2x^2$ **2.** $3 + 2x^2 - 5x^6 - 2x^3 + 3x$

3. $5x^3 + 15x^9 + x - x^2 + 7x^8$ **4.** $9x - 5 + 6x^3 - 5x^4 + x^5$

5. $8y^3 - 7y^2 + 9y^6 - 5y^8 - y^7$ **6.** $p^8 - 4 + p + p^2 - 7p^4$

Collect like terms and then arrange in descending order for the variable m.

7. $3m^4 - 5m^6 - 2m^4 + 6m^6$

8. $-1 + 5m^3 - 3 - 7m^3 + m^4 + 5$

9. $-2m + 4m^3 - 7m + 9m^3 + 8$

10. $-6m^2 + m - 5m + 7m^2 + 1$

11. $3mp + 3mp + 3mp - m^2 - 4m^2$

12. $-2m - 2mp - 2m + m^3p^4 - 5m^3p^4$

13. $-m + \frac{3}{4} + 15m^4 - m - \frac{1}{2} - 3m^4$

14. $2m - \frac{5}{6} + 4m^3 + m + \frac{1}{3} - 2m$

Evaluate each polynomial for the given value.

15. $x^3 - 27$ for $x = 5$ 98 **16.** $x^5 + x$ for $x = -2$ −34

17. $x^4 - x$ for $x = 3$ 78 **18.** $5x^4 - 7x + 2$ for $x = -2$ 96

19. $2x^3 - 5x^2 + x - 3$ for $x = 3$ 9

20. $2x - 5 + 4x^3 + x + x^2 - 2x$ for $x = -4$ −249

21. $-4x^3 + 2x^2 + x - 3$ for $x = 5$ −448

22. $x^5 - x^4 + x^3 - x^2 + x - 1$ for $x = -1$ −6

Evaluate each polynomial for $x = 4$.

23. $-5x + 2$ −18 **24.** $-3x + 1$ −11 **25.** $2x^2 - 5x + 7$ 19

26. $3x^2 + x - 7$ 45 **27.** $x^3 - 5x^2 + x$ −12 **28.** $7 - x + 3x^2$ 51

Evaluate each polynomial for $a = -1$ and $b = 2$.

29. $3a + 5ab$ −13 **30.** $6 - 2ab$ 10

31. $a^2 - 2a + b$ 5 **32.** $5a - 6 + a^2b$ −9

33. $-3a^3 + 7a^2 - 3b - 2$ 2 **34.** $-2a^3 - 5a^2 + 4a + 3b$ −1

The daily number of automobile accidents involving drivers of age x ($x > 15$) is approximated by the polynomial $0.4x^2 - 40x + 1039$.

35. Evaluate the polynomial for $x = 18$ to find the number of daily accidents involving 18-year-old drivers. 448.6

36. Evaluate the polynomial for $x = 20$ to find the number of daily accidents involving 20-year-old drivers. 399

Assignment Guide

Minimum: 1–36 e/o, MR

Regular: 1–38 e/o, 39, MR

Advanced: 1–38 m3, 39–43, MR

ADDITIONAL ANSWERS

Exercises

1. $x^5 + 6x^3 + 2x^2 + x + 1$
2. $-5x^6 - 2x^3 + 2x^2 + 3x + 3$
3. $15x^9 + 7x^8 + 5x^3 - x^2 + x$
4. $x^5 - 5x^4 + 6x^3 + 9x - 5$
5. $-5y^8 - y^7 + 9y^6 + 8y^3 - 7y^2$
6. $p^8 - 7p^4 + p^2 + p - 4$
7. $m^6 + m^4$
8. $m^4 - 2m^3 + 1$
9. $13m^3 - 9m + 8$
10. $m^2 - 4m + 1$
11. $-5m^2 + 9mp$
12. $-4m^3p^4 - 2mp - 4m$
13. $12m^4 - 2m + \frac{1}{4}$
14. $4m^3 + m - \frac{1}{2}$

43. $a = 0.4, b = -40$
$2ax = -b$
$2(0.4)x = -(-40)$
$0.8x = 40$
$x = 50$
The age with the lowest daily accidents is age 50.

Mixed Review

44. xy^3

45. $\frac{x^9}{8}$

46. $4a^2$

47. $\frac{3c^3}{a^3}$

48. 16,030

49. 0.007662

50. $n + (n + 1) = 67$; 33, 34

B

37. A 4-ft by 4-ft sandbox is placed on a square lawn whose side is x ft long. Express the area left over as a polynomial. $x^2 - 16$

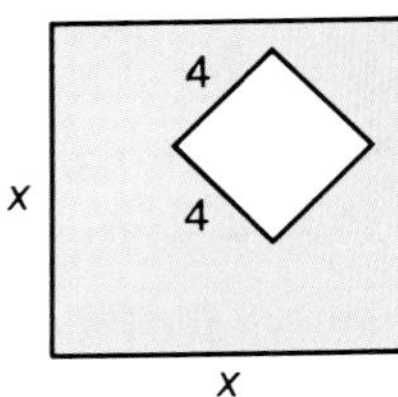

38. Express the shaded area in the figure below as a polynomial.

$\pi r^2 - 9\pi$ or $3.14\,r^2 - 28.26$

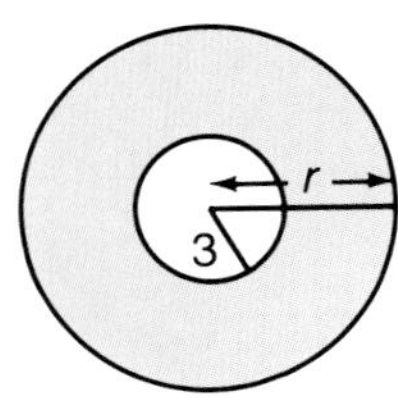

39. ***Critical Thinking*** The trinomial $ax^2 + 3x + 7$ is equal to 15 when x is 1, and the trinomial is equal to 33 when x is 2. What is the value of a? $a = 5$

C

Challenge

Evaluate each expression for the given value.

40. $(-5x^3 + 3x^2 + 6)(7x - 12)$ for $x = 3$ -918

41. $(2x^3 + 3x^2 - 4x + 8)(x^4 - x^2 + 5x)$ for $x = -2$ 24

42. $(4x^5 - 4x^3 + 5x^2 - 4x + 6)(-3x^3 + 6x^2 - x + 8)$ for $x = -1$ 270

43. For a polynomial of degree 2 of the form $ax^2 + bx + c$ where a, b, and c are coefficients, the extreme (highest or lowest) value of the polynomial is the value of x when $2ax = -b$. Find the age with the lowest daily accidents for the polynomial $0.4x^2 - 40x + 1039$, as given for Exercises 35 and 36.

Mixed Review

Simplify. **44.** $\frac{x^2y^4}{xy}$ **45.** $\left(\frac{x^3}{2}\right)^3$ **46.** $\frac{4a^9}{a^7}$ **47.** $\frac{21c^3}{7a^3}$

Write in standard notation. **48.** 1.603×10^4 **49.** 7.662×10^{-3}

Write an equation and solve. **50.** The sum of two consecutive integers is 67. Find the integers.

5-7 Addition of Polynomials

Objective: Add polynomials.

We can use algebra tiles to model polynomials and addition of polynomials.

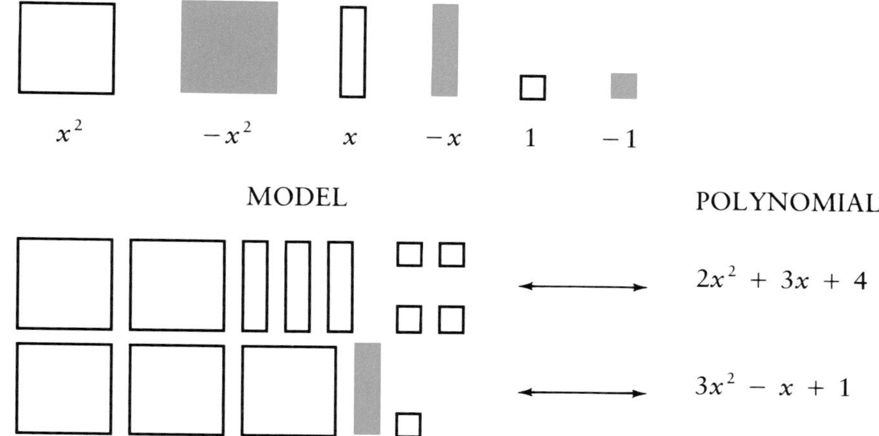

The sum of these two polynomials can be found by combining the algebra tiles and counting to find the total. Same size light and dark tiles are opposites and cancel each other.

MODEL | POLYNOMIAL

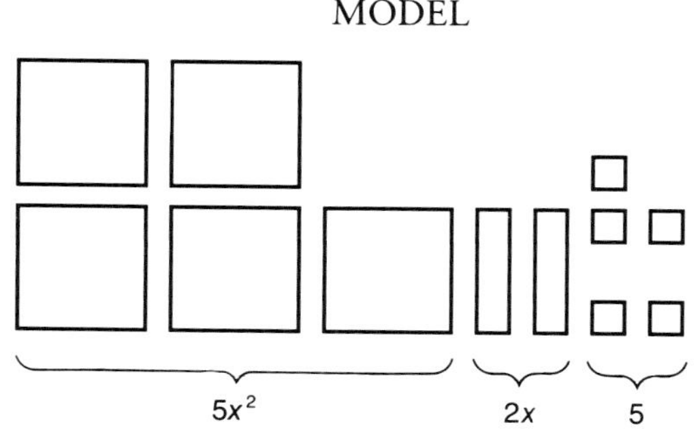

$$\begin{array}{r} 2x^2 + 3x + 4 \\ +3x^2 - x + 1 \\ \hline 5x^2 + 2x + 5 \end{array}$$

EXAMPLE 1 Write a polynomial for each model. Find the sum of the two polynomials.

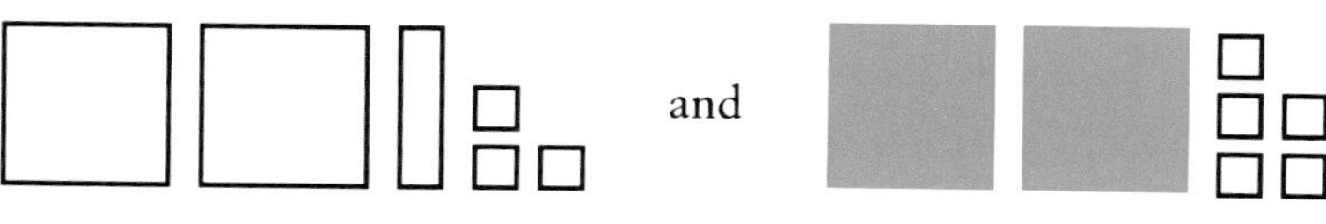

$(2x^2 + x + 3) + (-2x^2 + 5) = x + 8$

5-7

FIRST FIVE MINUTES

Collect like terms and arrange in descending order.

1. $4x^3 + 6x^4 - 2x^4 + 8x$
   $4x^4 + 4x^3 + 8x$
2. $3a - 5a^1 + 5 + 2a^0$
   $3a - 5a + 5 + 2 = -2a + 7$
3. Evaluate $4x^3 + x^2 - 2$
   a. for $x = 0$
      -2
   b. for $x = 1$
      3

Templates for making algebra tiles can be found in the supplement *Management and Teaching Aids*.

Point out to students the similarity between collecting like terms and adding polynomials. You may wish to have students do steps mentally if they have demonstrated that they understand the process.

If an expression has two or more variables, we usually arrange them with respect to the variable having the highest degree.

Key Questions

Write a polynomial for each model.

- x^2
- $-x$
- 2
- -4
- Can you add the polynomial $x + y$ to the polynomial $a + b$?
  Yes, $x + y + a + b$

Chalkboard Examples

1. Write a polynomial for each model. Find the sum of the two polynomials
Model 1:

Model 2:

Polynomial 1: $-3x^2 + 2x + 4$
Polynomial 2: $x^2 + 3x - 5$
Cancel out matching positive and negative numbers.

Add the remaining tiles.

Polynomial: $-2x^2 + 5x - 1$

2. $(5x^2 + 3x + 4) + (3x^2 + 5)$
$5x^2 + 3x^2 + 3x + 4 + 5$
$= 8x^2 + 3x + 9$
3. $(7a^2b^3 + ab) + (1 - 2a^2b^3)$
$7a^2b^3 - 2a^2b^3 + ab + 1$
$= 5a^2b^3 + ab + 1$

Add by writing like terms in columns.

4. $(2x^4 - 5x^2 + 4x + 5)$
$+ (5x^4 + 7x^3 - 2x^2 - 2x)$

$$\begin{array}{r} 2x^4 + 0x^3 - 5x^2 + 4x + 5 \\ 5x^4 + 7x^3 - 2x^2 - 2x + 0 \\ \hline 7x^4 + 7x^3 - 7x^2 + 2x + 5 \end{array}$$

Try This Write a polynomial for each model. Find the sum of the two polynomials.

a. [model] and [model]

$-x^2 + 5$ $\quad$ $2x^2 + 2x$
Sum: $x^2 + 2x + 5$

We can also add polynomials by adding the like terms. We usually arrange the terms of a polynomial in descending order for a particular variable.

EXAMPLES

2. $(3x^3 - 2x - 4) + (4x^3 - 3x^2 + 2)$
$= 3x^3 - 2x - 4 + 4x^3 - 3x^2 + 2$
$= 7x^3 - 3x^2 - 2x - 2$ $\quad$ Collecting like terms

3. $(4m^4n^3 + 3m^2n - 4n) + (2n - 5m^2n + 2m)$
$= 4m^4n^3 - 2m^2n + 2m - 2n.$

The answer in Example 3 was arranged in descending order for the variable m.

Try This Add.

b. $(3x^2 + 2x - 2) + (-2x^2 + 5x + 5)$
c. $(31m^4 + m^2 + 2m - 1) + (-7m^4 + 5m^3 - 2m + 2)$
d. $(4a^2b - 5a + 3) + (-2a^2b - 2a - 4)$
e. $(3n^3 - 3m^3n^2 - 5n - 3) + (5n^3 + 2m^3n^2 - 3m - 2n - 2)$

b. $x^2 + 7x + 3$
c. $24m^4 + 5m^3 + m^2 + 1$
d. $2a^2b - 7a - 1$
e. $8n^3 - m^3n^2 - 7n - 3m - 5$

We can also add polynomials by writing the polynomials in column form. Align the like terms so they can be easily added.

EXAMPLES Add by writing like terms in columns.

4. $(9m^5 - 2m^3 + 6m^2 + 3) + (5m^4 - 7m^2 + 6)$

$$\begin{array}{r} 9m^5 \qquad\qquad - 2m^3 + 6m^2 + 3 \\ 5m^4 \qquad\quad - 7m^2 + 6 \\ \hline 9m^5 + 5m^4 - 2m^3 - m^2 + 9 \end{array}$$

Aligning like terms

5. $(3x^3y + 6x^2y^3 - 4x + 3) + (2x^4y - 4x^3y + 6x - y)$

$$\begin{array}{r} 3x^3y + 6x^2y^3 - 4x \qquad + 3 \\ 2x^4y - 4x^3y \qquad\qquad + 6x - y \qquad \\ \hline 2x^4y - x^3y + 6x^2y^3 + 2x - y + 3 \end{array}$$

Aligning like terms

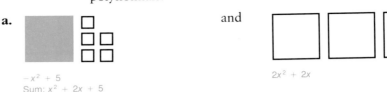

Try This Add using columns.

f. $m^4 - 2m^3 - 11m^2 + 5m - 14$
g. $-2x^4y^3 + x^2 - 3xy + 7$

f. $(-2m^3 - 5m^2 - 2m - 4) + (m^4 - 6m^2 + 7m - 10)$

g. $(-3x^4y^3 - 5xy + 2) + (x^4y^3 + x^2 + 2xy + 5)$

5-7 EXERCISES

A

Write a polynomial for each model. Find the sum of the two polynomials.

1. 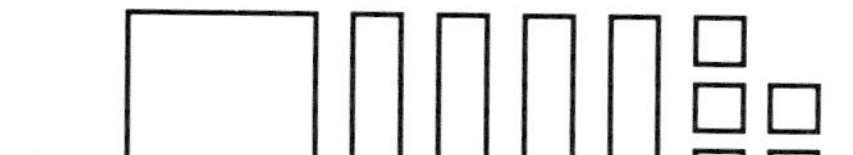 and 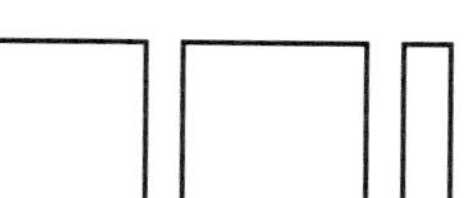

2. 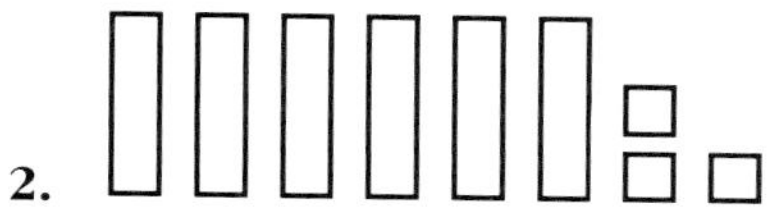 and 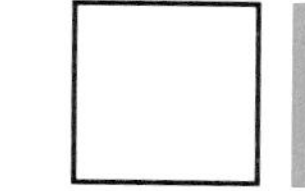 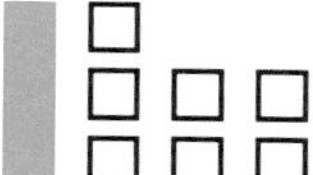

3. 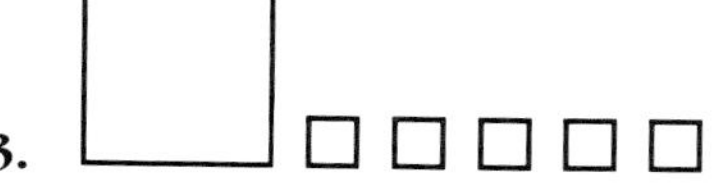 and

4.  and

Add.

5. $3x + 2$ and $-4x + 3$

6. $5x^2 + 6x + 1$ and $-7x + 2$

7. $-4x^4 + 6x^2 - 3x - 5$ and $6x^3 + 5x + 9$

8. $5x^3 + 6x^2 - 3x + 1$ and $5x^4 - 6x^3 + 2x - 5$

9. $(7x^3 + 6x^2 + 4x + 1) + (-7x^3 + 6x^2 - 4x + 5)$

10. $(3x^4 - 5x^2 - 6x + 5) + (-4x^3 + 6x^2 + 7x - 1)$

11. $5x^4 - 6x^3 - 7x^2 + x - 1$ and $4x^3 - 6x + 1$

12. $8x^5 - 6x^3 + 6x + 5$ and $-4x^4 + 3x^3 - 7x$

13. $9x^8 - 7x^4 + 2x^2 + 5$ and $8x^7 + 4x^4 - 2x$

14. $4x^5 - 6x^3 - 9x + 1$ and $6x^3 + 9x^2 + 9x$

15. $(-3cd^4 + 6d^2 + 2cd - 1) + (-3d^2 + 2cd + 1)$

LESSON QUIZ

1. Write a polynomial for each model. Find the sum of the two polynomials

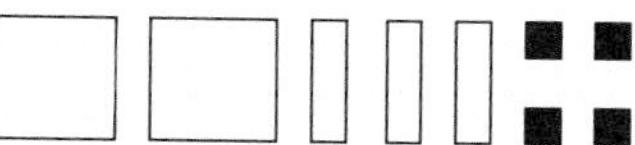

$2x^2 + 3x - 4$

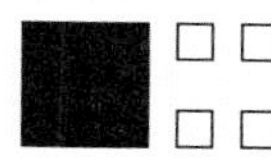

$-x^2 + 4$
Sum: $x^2 + 3x$

2. $4y + 7$ and $-6y - 2$
$-2y + 5$
3. $-4x^3 + 2x^2 + 5x - 6$ and $7x^3 + 5x + 4$
$3x^3 + 2x^2 + 10x - 2$
4. Add by writing like terms in columns.
$7x^4 - 3x^2 + 2x - 8$ and
$2x^4 + 4x^3 + 5x^2 - 6x + 9$
$9x^4 + 4x^3 + 2x^2 - 4x + 1$

Assignment Guide
Minimum: 1–32 e/o, MR
Regular: 1–32 m3, 33–40 e/o, 41, MR
Advanced: 1–40 m3, 41–45, MR

ADDITIONAL ANSWERS

Exercises

1. $x^2 + 4x + 5$; $2x^2 + x + 3$
Sum: $3x^2 + 5x + 8$
2. $6x + 3$; $x^2 - x + 7$
Sum: $x^2 + 5x + 10$
3. $x^2 + 5$; $x^2 + 4x$
Sum: $2x^2 + 4x + 5$
4. $2x^2 + 2x - 2$; $x^2 + 2x + 4$
Sum: $3x^2 + 4x + 2$
5. $-x + 5$
6. $5x^2 - x + 3$
7. $-4x^4 + 6x^3 + 6x^2 + 2x + 4$
8. $5x^4 - x^3 + 6x^2 - x - 4$
9. $12x^2 + 6$
10. $3x^4 - 4x^3 + x^2 + x + 4$
11. $5x^4 - 2x^3 - 7x^2 - 5x$
12. $8x^5 - 4x^4 - 3x^3 - x + 5$
13. $9x^8 + 8x^7 - 3x^4 + 2x^2 - 2x + 5$
14. $4x^5 + 9x^2 + 1$
15. $-3cd^4 + 3d^2 + 4cd$

16. $-4m^4n^3 + 4m^2n^2 + 6mn$
17. $3x^5y^5 - 3x^4y^3 + 4y - 3y^4$
18. $-3x^3y^2 + 2x^2 + 2x$
19. $-9x^2y^2 + 5xy + 5y^3 + 7$
20. $-4x^4 + 5x^3 - 2x^2y^4 + 2x$
21. $4m^4 + 3m^3 - 2m^2 + 2m - 3$
22. $5a^4 + 3a^3 - a^2 + 5a + 2$
23. $-3x^4 - 3x^2 + 4x + 1$
24. $-3t^4 + 8t^2 + 3t$
25. $7y^5 - y^3 + 6y^2 + 4$
26. $4n^5 + 3n^4 + 7n^3 + 3n^2 - 6$
27. $x^4 + x^3y^2 + 3x^2 + 3x + 7$
28. $-2h^3 - 2h^2k + 3hk + 4$
29. $5x^5 - 3x^4y^3 + 3x^3y^3 - 6x^2 + 1$
30. $12x^2y + 7xy^2 - 2xy + 5$
31. $9b^5c^3 + 4b^4c^4 + 5b^3c^5 + 4b^2c^6 - 4b$
32. $-2x^3y^4 + 4x^4y^3 - 4x^5 - 4x^4 - x^3$

Add.

16. $(-4m^4n^3 + 8m^2n^2 + 3mn - 2) + (-4m^2n^2 + 3mn + 2)$
17. $(3x^5y^5 - 6x^4y^3 + 3y) + (-3y^4 + 3x^4y^3 + y)$
18. $(4x^4 - 5x^3y^2 + 2x) + (-4x^4 + 2x^3y^2 + 2x^2)$
19. $(-3x^2y^2 + xy + 4) + (5y^3 - 6x^2y^2 + 4xy + 3)$
20. $(3x^3 - 4x^2y^4 + 2x) + (-4x^4 + 2x^3 + 2x^2y^4)$

Add using columns.

21. $(4m^4 - 3m^3 + 6m^2 + 5m - 4) + (6m^3 - 8m^2 - 3m + 1)$
22. $(5a^4 - 2a^3 + 4a^2 + 5a) + (5a^3 - 5a^2 + 2)$
23. $(3x^4 - 6x^2 + 7x) + (-6x^4 + 3x^2 - 3x + 1)$
24. $(5t^2 - 2t + 3) + (-3t^4 + 3t^2 + 5t - 3)$
25. $(7y^5 - 6y^4 + 3y^3 - 1) + (6y^4 - 4y^3 + 6y^2 + 5)$
26. $(4n^5 - 3n^4 + 2n^3 - 2) + (6n^4 + 5n^3 + 3n^2 - 4)$
27. $(-x^3y^2 + 6x^2 + 3x + 5) + (x^4 + 2x^3y^2 - 3x^2 + 2)$
28. $(-2h^3 + 3h^2k + 5hk + 3) + (-5h^2k - 2hk + 1)$
29. $(-3x^4y^3 + 6x^3y^3 - 6x^2 + 5xy^5 + 1) + (5x^5 - 3x^3y^3 - 5xy^5)$
30. $(4x^2y - 5xy + 7) + (8x^2y + 7xy^2 + 3xy - 2)$
31. $(9b^5c^3 - 3b^4c^4 + 4b^3c^5 - b) + (7b^4c^4 + b^3c^5 + 4b^2c^6 - 3b)$
32. $(4x^3y^4 + 7x^4y^3 - 4x^5 - 6x^4) + (-6x^3y^4 - 3x^4y^3 + 2x^4 - x^3)$

B

33. **a.** Express the sum of the areas of these rectangles as a polynomial.
$3x^2 + x^2 + x^2 + 4x = 5x^2 + 4x$

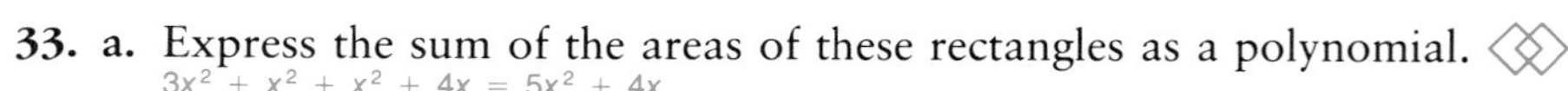

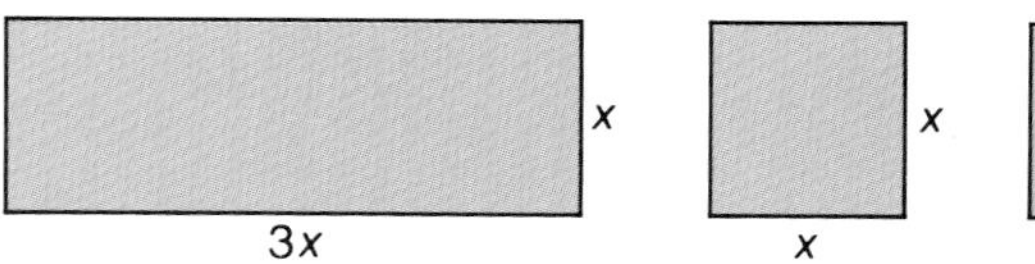

b. Find the sum of the areas when $x = 3$. 57

c. Find the sum of the areas when $x = 8$. 352

34. **a.** Express the sum of the areas of these circles as a polynomial (area $= \pi r^2$). $\pi r^2 + 9\pi + 4\pi = \pi r^2 + 13\pi$

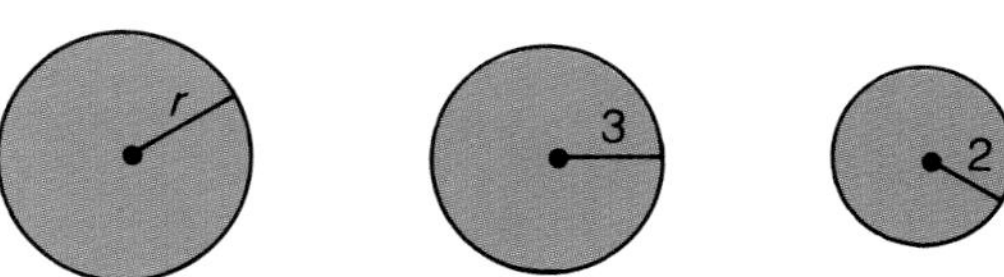

b. Find the sum of the areas when $r = 5$. 38π

c. Find the sum of the areas when $r = 11.3$. 140.69π

35. Three brothers have ages that are consecutive multiples of five. The sum of their ages two years ago was 69. Find their ages now. 20, 25, 30

36. Find four consecutive multiples of four where the sum of the first two is the fourth. $x + (x + 4) = x + 12$, $x = 8$, others are 12, 16, 20.

Draw a model to show each polynomial and the sum of the two polynomials.

37. $(2x^2 + x - 2) + (x^2 - 2x + 3)$ 38. $(x + 2) + (x^2 - x + 1)$

Express the perimeter of each figure as a polynomial.

39.

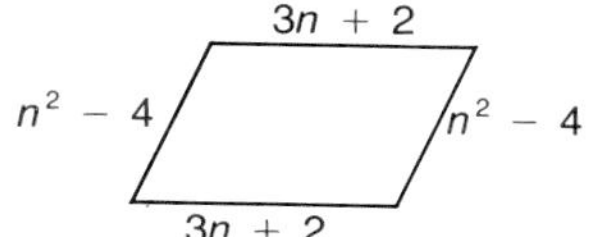

40.

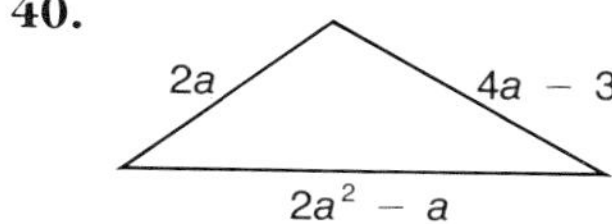

41. *Critical Thinking* Compare and contrast the column method for adding whole numbers and the column method for adding polynomials.

Challenge

42. The sum of two polynomials is $2x^2 + x + 8$. One polynomial is $x^2 + 3$. What is the other?

43. Addition of real numbers is commutative. That is, $a + b = b + a$ where a and b are any real numbers. Show that addition of binomials such as $(ax + b)$ and $(cx + d)$ is commutative.

44. Show that addition of trinomials such as $(ax^2 + bx + c)$ and $(dx^2 + ex + f)$ is commutative.

45. Show that addition of polynomials is commutative. Use $a_n x^n + a_{n-1}x^{n-1} + \ldots + a_1 x + a_0$ and $b_n x^n + b_{n-1}x^{n-1} + \ldots + b_1 x + b_0$

Mixed Review

Name the properties that guarantee that these statements are true.

46. $a(b + c) = ab + ac$ 47. $x + (-x) = 0$ 48. $y \cdot 1 = y$

49. $nm = mn$ 50. $a + 0 = a$ 51. $4 + 1 = 1 + 4$

Simplify. 52. $(2t^3)^5$ 53. $(3a^5)(6a^2)$ 54. $x^0 \cdot x^1$ 55. $(2m^2n)(6n)$

Factor. 56. $5ac + 12a$ 57. $xyz + 5y - 9yz$ 58. $a^2 + a + ab$

Problem for Programmers

Write a program that will find all pairs of integer factors of any input integer. For example, input 36; output 1 and 36, −1 and −36, 2 and 18, −2 and −18, 3 and 12, −3 and −12, 4 and 9, −4 and −9. Test your program using 36, 25, −50, and −32.

37.

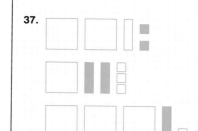

38.

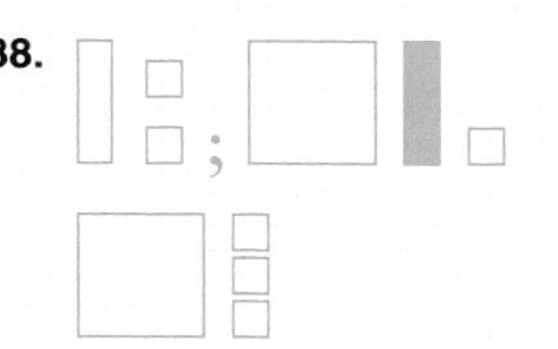

39. $2n^2 + 6n - 4$
40. $2a^2 + 5a - 3$
41. Answers may vary. Some differences are that coefficients of polynomials cannot be carried and that adding polynomials can involve adding negative coefficients.
42. $x^2 + x + 5$
43. $(ax + b) + (cx + d) = (a + c)x + (b + d)$
$(cx + d) + (ax + b) = (c + a)x + (d + b) = (a + c)x + (b + d)$
Addition of binomials is commutative.
44. See 43 above.
45. See 43 above.

Mixed Review

46. Distributive property of mult. over addition
47. Additive inverse
48. Multiplicative identity
49. Commutative property of multiplication
50. Additive identity
51. Commutative property of addition
52. $32t^{15}$ **53.** $18a^7$
54. x **55.** $12m^2n^2$
56. $a(5c + 12)$
57. $y(xz + 5 - 9z)$
58. $a(a + 1 + b)$

5-8

FIRST FIVE MINUTES

Multiply.

1. $3(4x^2 + 2x + 5)$
   $12x^2 + 6x + 15$
2. $-2(x^2 + 5)$
   $-2x^2 - 10$
3. $-1(5x^3 + 2x^2 + 3)$
   $-5x^3 - 2x^2 - 3$
4. $(-1)(-3x^2 + 4x - 7)$
   $3x^2 - 4x + 7$

Initially, you may want students to rewrite each polynomial as a sum to identify the coefficients before finding the additive inverse. In Example 1 we could rewrite $4x^5 - 7x - 8$ as $4x^5 + (-7x) + (-8)$.

You may wish to encourage students to subtract mentally if they can without making errors.

You can also use algebra tiles to demonstrate additive inverses. If the tiles are white on one side and black on the other, the inverse of a model is found by flipping over each tile. This is equivalent to changing the sign of each term. To subtract, add the inverse of the subtrahend.

Key Questions

- Is x^{-3} the additive inverse of x^3?
  No
- Is x^{-3} the additive inverse of $-x^3$?
  No
- Is x^{-3} the additive inverse of $-x^{-3}$?
  Yes

Chalkboard Examples

1. Find the additive inverse of $7x^4 - 3x + 5$.
   $-7x^4 + 3x - 5$

Subtract.

2. $(5x^2 + 3x - 2) - (2x^2 + 1)$
   $5x^2 + 3x - 2 - 2x^2 - 1$
   $= 3x^2 + 3x - 3$
3. $(2a^2b^2 + 3ab^3 - 4b^4) - (a^2b^2 - 5ab^3 + 3b - 2b^4)$
   $2a^2b^2 + 3ab^3 - 4b^4$
   $- a^2b^2 + 5ab^3 - 3b + 2b^4$
   $= a^2b^2 + 8ab^3 - 2b^4 - 3b$

5-8 Subtraction of Polynomials

Objective: Subtract polynomials.

We know that two numbers are additive inverses if their sum is zero. For example, 5 and -5 are additive inverses, since $5 + (-5) = 0$. The same definition holds for polynomials.

Definition

Two polynomials are **additive inverses** of each other if their sum is 0.

Consider the polynomial $8x^2 - 4x + 3$. The additive inverse of $8x^2 - 4x + 3$ is

$$-(8x^2 - 4x + 3)$$
$$= (-1)(8x^2 - 4x + 3) \quad \text{Using the property of } -1$$
$$= (-1)(8x^2) + (-1)(-4x) + (-1)(3) \quad \text{Using the distributive property}$$
$$= -8x^2 + 4x - 3$$

The additive inverse of a polynomial can be found by replacing each coefficient by its additive inverse.

EXAMPLE 1 Find the additive inverse of $4x^5 - 7x - 8$.

$-4x^5 + 7x + 8$ — Changing the sign of each coefficient gives the additive inverse of the polynomial.

Try This Find the additive inverse of each polynomial.

a. $12x^4 - 3x^2 + 4x$
$-12x^4 + 3x^2 - 4x$

b. $-13x^6y^4 + 2x^4y - 3x^2 + xy - \frac{5}{13}$
$13x^6y^4 - 2x^4y + 3x^2 - xy + \frac{5}{13}$

Recall that we can subtract a rational number by adding its additive inverse: $a - b = a + (-b)$. This rule also applies to polynomials.

EXAMPLE 2 Subtract.

$$(a^3 - 2a^2 + 4) - (a^4 - 4a^3 - 3a^2)$$
$$= (a^3 - 2a^2 + 4) + [-(a^4 - 4a^3 - 3a^2)] \quad \text{Adding the inverse}$$
$$= (a^3 - 2a^2 + 4) + (-a^4 + 4a^3 + 3a^2) \quad \text{Using the distributive property}$$
$$= -a^4 + 5a^3 + a^2 + 4 \quad \text{Collecting like terms}$$

EXAMPLE 3 Subtract.

$(4x^3y + 2x^2y^2 - 3xy + 6) - (x^3y - 2x^2y^2 - 2xy - 3)$
$= (4x^3y + 2x^2y^2 - 3xy + 6) + [-(x^3y - 2x^2y^2 - 2xy - 3)]$
$= (4x^3y + 2x^2y^2 - 3xy + 6) + (-x^3y + 2x^2y^2 + 2xy + 3)$
$= 3x^3y + 4x^2y^2 - xy + 9$

Try This Subtract.

c. $(5x^4 + 4) - (2x^2 - 1)$ $5x^4 - 2x^2 + 5$

d. $(-7m^3 + 2m + 4) - (-2m^3 - 4)$ $-5m^3 + 2m + 8$

e. $(-3a^2b^4 + 5ab - 4) - (-4a^3 + 11a^2b^4 - 2a - 6)$ $4a^3 - 14a^2b^4 + 5ab + 2a + 2$

We can also subtract polynomials by arranging like terms in columns.

EXAMPLES Subtract using columns.

4. $(5p^2 - 3p + 6) - (9p^2 - 5p - 3)$

(a) $\begin{array}{r} 5p^2 - 3p + 6 \\ \underline{-\ (9p^2 - 5p - 3)} \end{array}$ Writing like terms in columns

(b) $\begin{array}{r} 5p^2 - 3p + 6 \\ \underline{+\ (-9p^2 + 5p + 3)} \end{array}$ Changing subtraction to addition of the inverse

(c) $\begin{array}{r} 5p^2 - 3p + 6 \\ \underline{-9p^2 + 5p + 3} \\ -4p^2 + 2p + 9 \end{array}$ Adding

5. $(3x^3y^2 - 4xy + 1) - (-4x^3y^2 - 3x^2y^2 + 3xy - 5)$

(a) $\begin{array}{r} 3x^3y^2 \qquad\qquad - 4xy + 1 \\ \underline{-\ (-4x^3y^2 - 3x^2y^2 + 3xy - 5)} \end{array}$ Writing like terms in columns

(b) $\begin{array}{r} 3x^3y^2 \qquad\qquad - 4xy + 1 \\ \underline{+\ (4x^3y^2 + 3x^2y^2 - 3xy + 5)} \end{array}$ Changing signs to add

(c) $\begin{array}{r} 3x^3y^2 \qquad\qquad - 4xy + 1 \\ \underline{4x^3y^2 + 3x^2y^2 - 3xy + 5} \\ 7x^3y^2 + 3x^2y^2 - 7xy + 6 \end{array}$ Adding

Try This Subtract using columns.

f. $(4x^3 + 2x^2 - 2x - 3) - (2x^3 - 3x^2 + 2)$ $2x^3 + 5x^2 - 2x - 5$

g. $(-3ab^2 + 4ab - 7a) - (-2ab^2 - 3a + 4)$ $-ab^2 + 4ab - 4a - 4$

4. Use columns to subtract.
$8x^3 + 6x^2 - 3x + 5$ minus
$5x^3 - 3x^2 + 2x - 4$
$\begin{array}{r} 8x^3 + 6x^2 - 3x + 5 \\ \underline{-5x^3 + 3x^2 - 2x + 4} \\ 3x^3 + 9x^2 - 5x + 9 \end{array}$

5. $2a^4b + 5a^3b^2 - 4a^2b^3$ minus
$4a^4b + 2a^3b^2 - 4ab$
$\begin{array}{r} 2a^4b + 5a^3b^2 - 4a^2b^3 + 0ab \\ \underline{-4a^4b - 2a^3b^2 + 0a^2b^3 + 4ab} \\ -2a^4b + 3a^3b^2 - 4a^2b^3 + 4ab \end{array}$

LESSON QUIZ

1. Find the additive inverse of the polynomial $5x^4 - 2x^3 + x^2 - 6$.
$-5x^4 + 2x^3 - x^2 + 6$
2. Subtract.
$(7x^3 - 6x^2 + 3x)$
$-(5x^3 - 3x^2 - 5x + 4)$
$7x^3 - 6x^2 + 3x - 5x^3 + 3x^2 + 5x - 4 = 2x^3 - 3x^2 + 8x - 4$
3. Subtract using columns.
$(-4x^4 + 5x^2 + 3x + 5)$
$-(-6x^4 + 2x^3 - 3x^2 + 7)$
$2x^4 - 2x^3 + 8x^2 + 3x - 2$

Assignment Guide
Minimum: 1–30 e/o, MR

Regular: 1–41 e/o, 42, MR

Advanced: 1–41 m3, 42–44, MR

ADDITIONAL ANSWERS

Exercises

1. $5x$
2. $-x^2 + 3x$
3. $x^2 - 10x + 2$
4. $4x^3 + x^2 + x$
5. $-12x^4y + 3x^3 - 3$
6. $-4x^3 + 6x^2y^2 + 8xy - 1$
7. $2x^2 + 14$
8. $7a^3 - 9a^2 - 2a + 10$
9. $-2x^5 - 6x^4 + x + 2$
10. $-x^2 - 2x + 4$
11. $9b^2 + 9b - 8$
12. $7x^3 + 3x^2 + 2x - 1$
13. $7m^3 - 3m - 11$
14. $-5n^4 + 4n^3 + 3n^2 - 4$
15. $3y^4 + 8y^3 - 5y - 3$
16. $-6t^5 + 10t^4 - 2t^2 + t + 1$
17. $6v^4u + 9v^2 - 7$
18. $2m^3n^2 + 6m^2 - 4mn - 6$
19. $9mn^5 + n^4 + mn^4 - 3mn^3 + 3n^2 + 1$
20. $2x^6 + 6x^4y$

25. $11x^4 + 12x^3 - 9x^2 - 8x$
26. $5x^4 - 6x^3 - x^2 + 5x + 15$
27. $-4m^5 + 9m^4 + 6m^2 + 16m + 6$
28. $-4x^5 - 6x^3 + 8x^2 - 5x - 2$
29. $x^4y^2 + x^2y$
30. $-2x^3 + 2x^2y$

5-8 EXERCISES

A

Find the additive inverse of each polynomial.

1. $-5x$
2. $x^2 - 3x$
3. $-x^2 + 10x - 2$
4. $-4x^3 - x^2 - x$
5. $12x^4y - 3x^3 + 3$
6. $4x^3 - 6x^2y^2 - 8xy + 1$

Subtract.

7. $(5x^2 + 6) - (3x^2 - 8)$
8. $(7a^3 - 2a^2 + 6) - (7a^2 + 2a - 4)$
9. $(6x^5 - 3x^4 + x + 1) - (8x^5 + 3x^4 - 1)$
10. $\left(\frac{1}{2}x^2 - \frac{3}{2}x + 2\right) - \left(\frac{3}{2}x^2 + \frac{1}{2}x - 2\right)$
11. $(6b^2 + 2b) - (-3b^2 - 7b + 8)$
12. $7x^3 - (-3x^2 - 2x + 1)$
13. $(5m^3 - 3m - 6) - (-2m^3 + 5)$
14. $(-4n^4 + n^3 + 2n^2) - (n^4 - 3n^3 - n^2 + 4)$
15. $(6y^3 - 4y - 7) - (-3y^4 - 2y^3 + y - 4)$
16. $(7t^4 + 4t) - (6t^5 - 3t^4 + 2t^2 + 3t - 1)$
17. $(8v^4u + 6v^2 - 5) - (2v^4u - 3v^2 + 2)$
18. $(-3m^3n^2 + 2m^2 - mn - 4) - (-5m^3n^2 - 4m^2 + 3mn + 2)$
19. $(8mn^5 + n^4 - 3mn^3 + 2n^2) - (-mn^5 - mn^4 - n^2 - 1)$
20. $(3x^4y + 2x^3y - x^2 - 7) - (-2x^6 - 3x^4y + 2x^3y - x^2 - 7)$

Subtract.

21. $\begin{array}{r} x^2 + 5x + 6 \\ x^2 + 2x \phantom{{}+6} \\ \hline 3x + 6 \end{array}$

22. $\begin{array}{l} x^3 \phantom{{}+x^2} + 1 \\ x^3 + x^2 \\ \hline -x^2 + 1 \end{array}$

23. $\begin{array}{l} c^4 \phantom{{}-4c^3} - 3c^2 + c + 1 \\ c^4 - 4c^3 \\ \hline 4c^3 - 3c^2 + c + 1 \end{array}$

24. $\begin{array}{r} 3x^2 - 6x + 1 \\ 6x^2 + 8x - 3 \\ \hline -3x^2 - 14x + 4 \end{array}$

Subtract using columns.

25. $(5x^4 + 6x^3 - 9x^2) - (-6x^4 - 6x^3 + 8x)$
26. $(5x^4 + 6x^2 - 3x + 6) - (6x^3 + 7x^2 - 8x - 9)$
27. $(3m^4 + 6m^2 + 8m - 1) - (4m^5 - 6m^4 - 8m - 7)$
28. $(6x^5 + 3x^2 - 7x + 2) - (10x^5 + 6x^3 - 5x^2 - 2x + 4)$
29. $(x^5y^2 - x^3y^2 + xy - 1) - (x^5y^2 - x^4y^2 - x^3y^2 - x^2y + xy - 1)$
30. $(x^5 + x^4y^2 - x^3 + x^2y - xy + 2)$
$- (x^5 + x^4y^2 + x^3 - x^2y - xy + 2)$

B

Simplify.

31. $(y + 4) + (y - 5) - (y + 8)$

32. $(7y^2 - 5y + 6) - (3y^2 + 8y - 12) + (8y^2 - 10y + 3)$

33. $(4a^2 - 3a) + (7a^2 - 9a - 13) - (6a - 9)$

34. $(3x^2 - 4x + 6) - (-2x^2 + 4) + (-5x - 3)$

35. $(-8y^2 - 4) - (3y + 6) - (2y^2 - y)$

36. $(5x^3 - 4x^2 + 6) - (2x^3 + x^2 - x) + (x^3 - x)$

37. $(-xy^4 - 7y^3 + xy^2) + (-2xy^4 + 5y - 2) - (-6y^3 + xy^2)$

38. $(-4 + x^2y + 2x^3y) - (-6 - x + 3x^3) - (-x^2y - 5x^3y)$

Write a polynomial for each model. Find the difference of the two polynomials.

39. 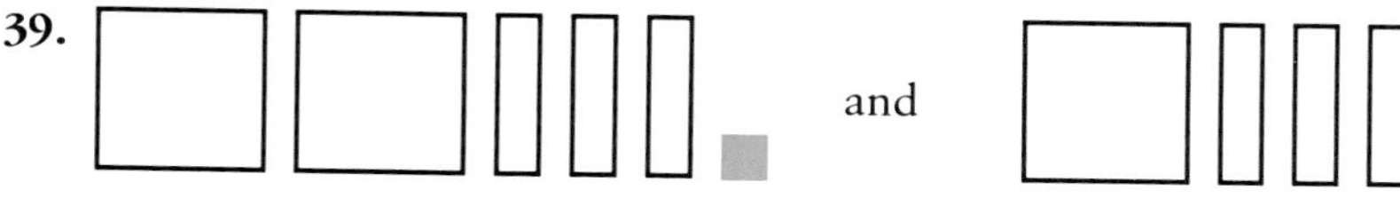

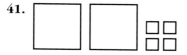

40. 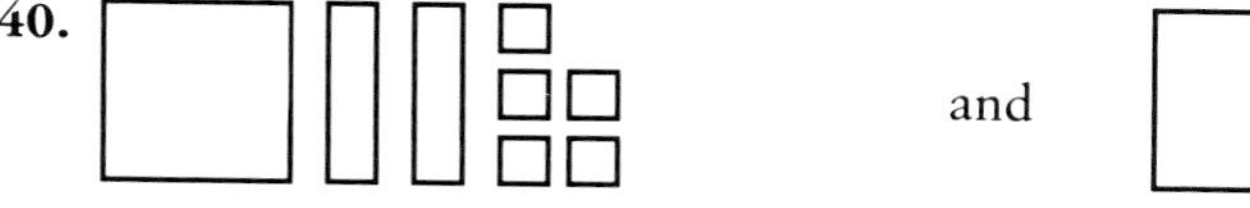

41. 

42. *Critical Thinking* The difference of two polynomials is $2x^2 + x + 4$. One polynomial is $3x^2 + x$. What is the other polynomial?

Challenge

43. Does replacing each occurrence of x with its additive inverse in the polynomial $5x^3 - 3x^2 + 2x$ result in the additive inverse of the polynomial? Explain.

44. What is the additive identity for addition of polynomials? Show that subtraction of binomials is not commutative. Is it associative? Justify your answer.

Mixed Review

Write using scientific notation. **45.** 1594 **46.** 0.772 **47.** 93,610

Identify the terms. Give the coefficient and factors of each term.

48. $5x^3 + 3x^2 - 2x + 1$ **49.** $5n^4m + 7n^2m^2 - 2m + 3$

Solve. **50.** $16 - 3a < 5a$ **51.** $21 + 4h = 11h$

31. $y - 9$
32. $12y^2 - 23y + 21$
33. $11a^2 - 18a - 4$
34. $5x^2 - 9x - 1$
35. $-10y^2 - 2y - 10$
36. $4x^3 - 5x^2 + 6$
37. $-3xy^4 - y^3 + 5y - 2$
38. $2 + x + 2x^2y - 3x^3 + 7x^3y$
39. $2x^2 + 3x - 1$, $x^2 + 3x$, $x^2 - 1$
40. $x^2 + 2x + 5$, $2x^2 + 2$, $-x^2 + 2x + 3$
41. $2x^2 + 4$, $x^2 - 2x + 5$, $x^2 + 2x - 1$
42. $x^2 - 4$ or $5x^2 + 2x + 4$
43. No, $-3(-x)^2 = -3x^2$
44.
a. A zero polynomial, or 0
b. $(ax + by) - (cx + dy)$
$= ax + by - cx - dy$
$= x(a - c) + y(b - d)$
$(cx + dy) - (ax + by)$
$= cx + dy - ax - by$
$= x(c - a) + y(d - b)$
Since the coefficients a, b, c, and d are rational numbers, and subtraction of rational numbers is not commutative, $(c - a) \neq (a - c)$ and $(b - d) \neq (d - b)$; thus, $(ax + by) - (cx + dy) \neq (cx + dy) - (ax + by)$, and subtraction of binomials is not commutative.
c. No, subtraction of binomials is not associative. Again, the coefficients are rational numbers, and rational numbers are not associative.

Mixed Review

45. 1.594×10^3
46. 7.72×10^{-1}
47. 9.361×10^4
48. Terms: $5x^3$, $3x^2$, $-2x$, 1
Coefficients: 5, 3, -2, 1
Factors: 5 and x^3; 3 and x^2; -2 and x; 1
49. Terms: $5n^4m$, $7n^2m^2$, $-2m$, 3
Coefficients: 5, 7, -2, 3
Factors: 5, n^4 and m; 7, n^2 and m^2; -2 and m; 3
50. $2 < a$
51. 3

5-9

FIRST FIVE MINUTES

Multiply.

1. $5(6x - 4)$ $30x - 20$
2. $a(b + c)$ $ab + ac$
3. $-x(y - z)$ $-xy + xz$
4. $(4a^2b)(-3b^3)$ $-12a^2b^4$
5. $p(qrp + p^2)$ $qrp^2 + p^3$

Multiplying a Polynomial by a Monomial

Remind students that negative signs should be distributed along with the monomials.

Key Question

- Does $-3(3 - x) = -9 - 3x$? No, $-3(3 - x) = -9 + 3x$.

Chalkboard Examples

Multiply.

1. $3a(6b + 7)$
   $(3a)(6b) + (3a)7$
   $= 18ab + 21a$
2. $2x(3x^2 + x + 4)$
   $(2x)(3x^2) + (2x)x + (2x)4$
   $= 6x^3 + 2x^2 + 8x$

Multiplying Two Binomials

Algebra tiles and the FOIL method are both useful tools for multiplying two binomials. Algebra tiles help students understand the multiplication process, and the FOIL method helps them remember how to calculate the product.

Point out that after like terms are collected, terms are usually arranged in descending order.

Key Question

- Will there always be like terms after multiplying binomials? No

5-9 Multiplication of Monomials and Binomials

Multiplying a Polynomial by a Monomial

Objective: Multiply a monomial and a polynomial.

We can use the rule for multiplying monomials and the distributive property to multiply a polynomial by a monomial.

EXAMPLES Multiply.

1. $2x(5x + 3) = (2x)(5x) + (2x)(3)$ Using the distributive property
   $= 10x^2 + 6x$

2. $8p(3q^4 - 2q^3p^2 + 2p) = (8p)(3q^4) + (8p)(-2q^3p^2) + (8p)(2p)$
   $= 24q^4p - 16q^3p^3 + 16p^2$

Try This Multiply.

a. $4x(2x + 4)$ $8x^2 + 16x$

b. $3a^2(-5a^3 + 2a - 7)$ $-15a^5 + 6a^3 - 21a^2$

c. $5s(8t^4 - 4s^2 - 9t - 11)$ $40st^4 - 20s^3 - 45st - 55s$

Multiplying Two Binomials

Objective: Multiply two binomials.

We can use algebra tiles to illustrate multiplication of two binomials.

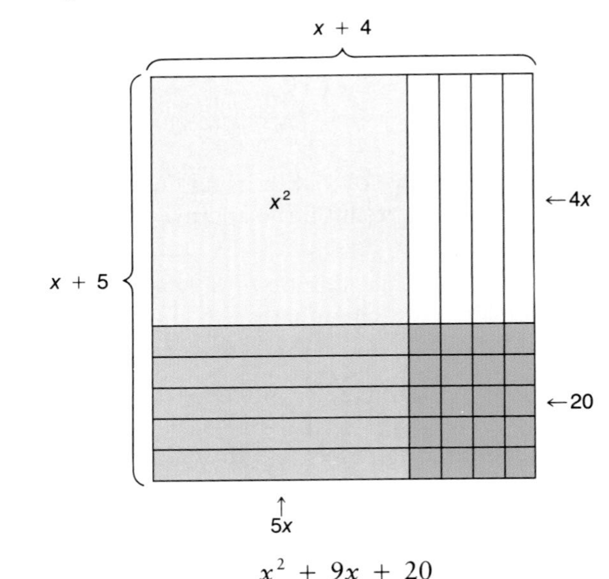

$x^2 + 9x + 20$

We can also use the distributive property twice to multiply two binomials. For example, $(x + 5)(x + 4)$.

(1) $(x + 4)(x + 5) = x(x + 5) + 4(x + 5)$		Using the distributive property
(2)	$= x \cdot x + x \cdot 5 + 4 \cdot x + 4 \cdot 5$	Using the distributive property again
(3)	$= x^2 + 5x + 4x + 20$	
(4)	$= x^2 + 9x + 20$	Collecting like terms

We can rewrite line (2) above to show a short way to find the product of two binomials.

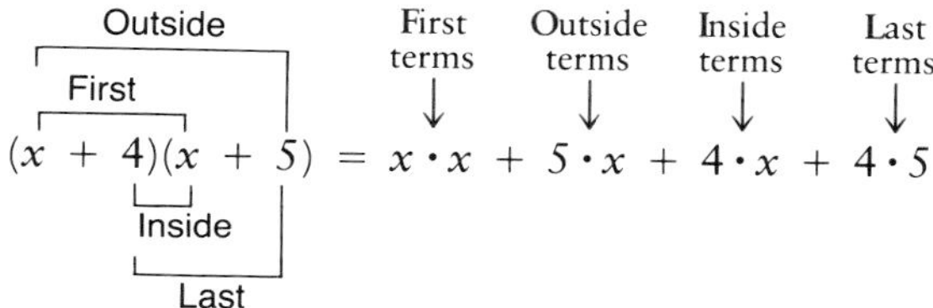

$$(x + 4)(x + 5) = x \cdot x + 5 \cdot x + 4 \cdot x + 4 \cdot 5$$

This is called the **FOIL** method for finding the product of two binomials.

EXAMPLES Multiply.

3. $(x + 6)(x - 6) = x^2 - 6x + 6x - 36$ Using FOIL
$= x^2 - 36$ Collecting like terms

4. $(x + 3)(x - 2) = x^2 - 2x + 3x - 6$
$= x^2 + x - 6$

5. $(x^3 + 5)(x^3 - 5) = x^6 - 5x^3 + 5x^3 - 25$
$= x^6 - 25$

6. $(4x^2 + 5)(3x^2 - 2) = 12x^4 - 8x^2 + 15x^2 - 10$
$= 12x^4 + 7x^2 - 10$

7. $(4m^2 + 5mn)(2mn - 4n) = 8m^3n - 16m^2n + 10m^2n^2 - 20mn^2$

Try This Multiply. See Additional Answers.

d. $(x + 3)(x + 4)$
e. $(x + 3)(x - 5)$
f. $(2x + 1)(x + 4)$
g. $(2x^2 - 3)(x - 2)$
h. $(6x^2 + 5)(2x^3 + 1)$
i. $(y^3 + 7)(y^3 - 7)$
j. $(2x^5 + x^2)(-x^3 + x)$
k. $(3a + b)(-2a - 4b)$
l. $(2xy + 4x)(-2y + y^2)$
m. $(3rs + 2r)(r^2 + 2rs^2)$

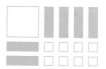

Chalkboard Examples (*T6*)

Multiply.

1. $(x - 4)(x + 2)$
$x^2 + 2x - 4x - 8$
$= x^2 - 2x - 8$
2. $(3x + 2)(x + 5)$
$3x^2 + 15x + 2x + 10$
$= 3x^2 + 17x + 10$
3. $(4ab + 3)(2a^2b + 1)$
$(4ab)(2a^2b) + (4ab)1 + 3(2a^2b) + 3 \cdot 1$
$= 8a^3b^2 + 4ab + 6a^2b + 3$

LESSON ENRICHMENT

Ask students to find the following products using algebra tiles.

1. $(2x - 2)(x + 1)$ $2x^2 - 2$

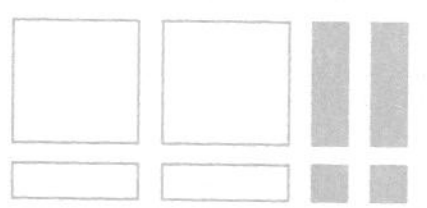

2. $(x - 4)(x - 2)$ $x^2 - 6x + 8$

3. $(x + 5)(2x)$ $2x^2 + 10x$

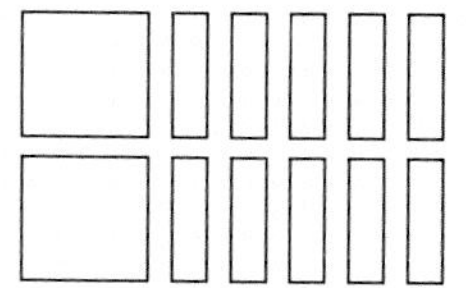

LESSON QUIZ

Multiply and collect like terms.

1. $5x^2(3x + 2)$
$15x^3 + 10x^2$
2. $(x + 7)(x + 2)$
$x^2 + 2x + 7x + 14$
$= x^2 + 9x + 14$
3. $(3x^2 + 4)(5x^3 + 1)$
$15x^5 + 3x^2 + 20x^3 + 4$
$= 15x^5 + 20x^3 + 3x^2 + 4$

Assignment Guide
Minimum: Day 1: 1–27 e/o, MR
Day 2: 28–54 e/o
Regular: 1–54 m3, 55–63, MR

Advanced: 1–62 m4, 63–71, MR

ADDITIONAL ANSWERS

Try This

d. $x^2 + 7x + 12$
e. $x^2 - 2x - 15$
f. $2x^2 + 9x + 4$
g. $2x^3 - 4x^2 - 3x + 6$
h. $12x^5 + 10x^3 + 6x^2 + 5$
i. $y^6 - 49$
j. $-2x^8 + 2x^6 - x^5 + x^3$
k. $-6a^2 - 14ab - 4b^2$
l. $2xy^3 - 8xy$
m. $3r^3s + 2r^3 + 6r^2s^3 + 4r^2s^2$

Exercises

1. $-3x^2 + 15x$
2. $8y^2 - 12y$
3. $12x^3 + 24x^2$
4. $-10a^3 + 5a^2$
5. $-6m^4 - 6m^2x$
6. $-4x^4 + 4x^3$
7. $3x^6 + 15x^3$
8. $15m^6 + 20m^3$
9. $18y^6 + 24y^5$
10. $4y^7 - 24y^6$
11. $6x^3 + 8x^2 - 6x$
12. $30x^4 + 6x^3 - 24x$
13. $15a^4 + 30a^3 - 35a^2$
14. $-24b^6 + 12b^4 - 16b^2$
15. $-8y^9 - 8y^8 + 4y^7 - 20y^6$
16. $-2x^9 - 4x^8 + 2x^7 + 2x^6 - 6x^5$
17. $-7h^4k^6 + 7h^4k^4 + 7h^4k^3 - 7h^4k$
18. $-x^3y^7 + x^3y^4 - x^3y^3 + x^3y^2 - x^3y$
19. $-10a^9b + 2a^3 - 24a^2b$
20. $-10xy^5 - 10x^2y^3 + 120x^2$
21. $x^3 + x^2 + 3x + 3$
22. $x^3 - x^2 - 3x + 3$
23. $x^4 + x^3 + 2x + 2$
24. $x^5 + 12x^4 + 2x + 24$
25. $a^2 - a - 6$
26. $x^2 + 4x + 4$
27. $9x^2 + 15x + 6$
28. $8x^2 + 10x + 2$

We can also use columns to multiply. We multiply each term on the top row by each term on the bottom. Then we add.

EXAMPLE 8

Multiply $4x - 3$ and $x - 2$.

$$\begin{array}{rrrl} 4x & -\ 3 & & \\ x & -\ 2 & & \\ \hline 4x^2 & -\ 3x & & \text{Multiplying the top row by } x \\ & -\ 8x & +\ 6 & \text{Multiplying the top row by } -2 \\ \hline 4x^2 & -\ 11x & +\ 6 & \text{Adding} \end{array}$$

Try This Multiply.

n. $(5x + 3)(x - 4)$ **o.** $(2y^2 - 3)(3y - 5)$
p. $(3a + b)(2a - b)$ **q.** $(6m^2 + n)(3m - n^2)$
r. $(4pq - p^2)(pq + p^2)$ **s.** $\left(\frac{1}{2}r^2s + s\right)\left(\frac{1}{2}r^2s - s\right)$

n. $5x^2 - 17x - 12$
o. $6y^3 - 10y^2 - 9y + 15$
p. $6a^2 - ab - b^2$
q. $18m^3 - 6m^2n^2 + 3mn - n^3$
r. $4p^2q^2 + 3p^3q - p^4$
s. $\frac{1}{4}r^4s^2 - s^2$

5-9 EXERCISES

A

Multiply.

1. $3x(-x + 5)$ **2.** $2y(4y - 6)$
3. $4x^2(3x + 6)$ **4.** $5a^2(-2a + 1)$
5. $-6m^2(m^2 + x)$ **6.** $-4x^2(x^2 - x)$
7. $3x^3(x^3 + 5)$ **8.** $-5m(-3m^5 - 4m^2)$
9. $3y^2(6y^4 + 8y^3)$ **10.** $4y^4(y^3 - 6y^2)$
11. $2x(3x^2 + 4x - 3)$ **12.** $-6x(-5x^3 - x^2 + 4)$
13. $-5a^2(-3a^2 - 6a + 7)$ **14.** $4b^2(-6b^4 + 3b^2 - 4)$
15. $4y^6(-2y^3 - 2y^2 + y - 5)$ **16.** $-2x^5(x^4 + 2x^3 - x^2 - x + 3)$
17. $-7h^4(k^6 - k^4 - k^3 + k)$ **18.** $x^3(-y^7 + y^4 - y^3 + y^2 - y)$
19. $2a(-5a^8b + a^2 - 12ab)$ **20.** $10x(-y^5 - xy^3 + 12x)$

Multiply.

21. $(x + 1)(x^2 + 3)$ **22.** $(x^2 - 3)(x - 1)$
23. $(x^3 + 2)(x + 1)$ **24.** $(x^4 + 2)(x + 12)$
25. $(a + 2)(a - 3)$ **26.** $(x + 2)(x + 2)$
27. $(3x + 2)(3x + 3)$ **28.** $(4x + 1)(2x + 2)$

Multiply.

29. $(5x - 6)(x + 2)$
30. $(x - 8)(x + 8)$
31. $(3x - 1)(3x + 1)$
32. $(2x + 3)(2x + 3)$
33. $(4x - 2y)(x - y)$
34. $(2x - y)(3x + y)$
35. $\left(x - \frac{1}{4}\right)\left(x + \frac{1}{4}\right)$
36. $\left(x + \frac{3}{4}\right)\left(x + \frac{3}{4}\right)$
37. $(x - 0.1)(x + 0.1)$
38. $(3x^2 + 1)(x + 1)$
39. $(2x^2 + 6)(x + 1)$
40. $(2b^2 + 3)(2b - 1)$
41. $(-2x + 1)(x - 6)$
42. $(3x + 4)(2x - 4)$
43. $(x + 7y)(x + 7y)$
44. $(2x + 5y)(2x + 5y)$
45. $(3x^5 + 2)(2x^2 + 6)$
46. $(1 - 2x)(1 + 3x^2)$
47. $(8x^3 + 1)(x^3 + 8)$
48. $(4 - 2x)(5 - 2x^2)$
49. $(4x^2 + 3)(x - 3)$
50. $(7x - 2)(2x - 7)$
51. $(4x^4 + x^2)(x^2 + x)$
52. $(5x^6 + 3x^3)(2x^6 + 2x^3)$
53. $(ab + 3b^2)(ab - 3b^2)$
54. $(m^2n - 5n)(m^2n + 5n)$

B

Multiply.

55. $(a + b)^2$
56. $(a - b)^2$
57. $(2x + 3)^2$
58. $(5y + 6)^2$

Find an expression for the area of the shaded regions.

59.

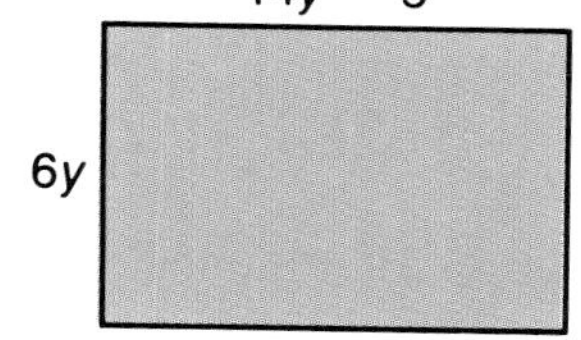

60.

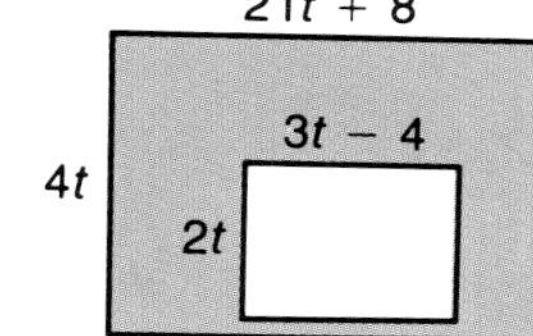

Find an expression for the area of the shaded portion of each square.

61.

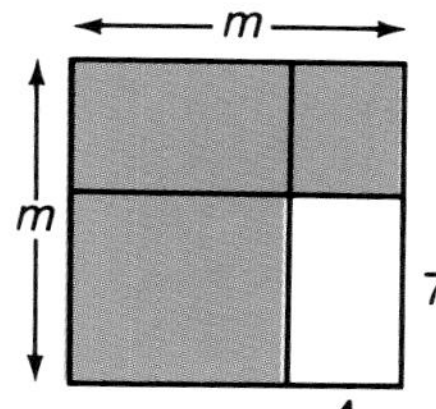

62.

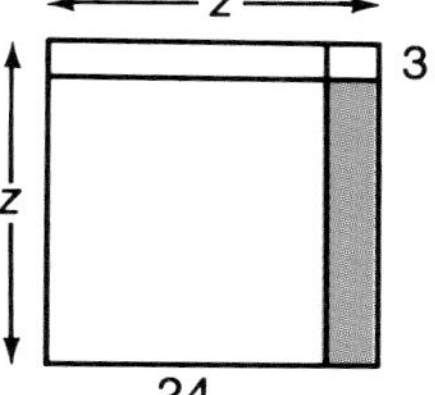

63. *Critical Thinking* The product of two binomials is $2x^2 + 5x + 2$. One of the binomials is $(x + 2)$. What is the other binomial?

29. $5x^2 + 4x - 12$
30. $x^2 - 64$
31. $9x^2 - 1$
32. $4x^2 + 12x + 9$
33. $4x^2 - 6xy + 2y^2$
34. $6x^2 - xy - y^2$
35. $x^2 - \frac{1}{16}$
36. $x^2 + \frac{3}{2}x + \frac{9}{16}$
37. $x^2 - 0.01$
38. $3x^3 + 3x^2 + x + 1$
39. $2x^3 + 2x^2 + 6x + 6$
40. $4b^3 - 2b^2 + 6b - 3$
41. $-2x^2 + 13x - 6$
42. $6x^2 - 4x - 16$
43. $x^2 + 14xy + 49y^2$
44. $4x^2 + 20xy + 25y^2$
45. $6x^7 + 18x^5 + 4x^2 + 12$
46. $1 - 2x + 3x^2 - 6x^3$
47. $8x^6 + 65x^3 + 8$
48. $20 - 10x - 8x^2 + 4x^3$
49. $4x^3 - 12x^2 + 3x - 9$
50. $14x^2 - 53x + 14$
51. $4x^6 + 4x^5 + x^4 + x^3$
52. $10x^{12} + 16x^9 + 6x^6$
53. $a^2b^2 - 9b^4$
54. $m^4n^2 - 25n^2$
55. $a^2 + 2ab + b^2$
56. $a^2 - 2ab + b^2$
57. $4x^2 + 12x + 9$
58. $25y^2 + 60y + 36$
59. $84y^2 - 30y$
60. $78t^2 + 40t$
61. $m^2 - 28$
62. $z^2 - 24(z - 3) - (24 \cdot 3) - 3(z - 24) = z^2 - 27z + 72$
63. $2x + 1$

64. Formulas are in Appendix.
$V = lwh$
$V = (12 - 2x)(12 - 2x)x$
$= (4x^2 - 48x + 144)x$
$= 4x^3 - 48x^2 + 144x$
$S =$ area of sides + area of base
$= 4x(12 - 2x) + (12 - 2x)^2$
$= -4x^2 + 144$

Mixed Review

72. $\frac{n + 3}{2}$
73. $6n + 9$
74. $3(7 - n)$
75. $n + (n + 1)$
76. 7
77. 10
78. −2
79. −4

Looking for Errors

1. The exponents were not added. The correct solution is $2x^4 - x^2y + 6x^2y^3 - 3y^4$.
2. Correct
3. The second term should be negative. The correct solution is $a^2b^2 - 4b^4$.
4. The exponents were multiplied instead of added. The correct solution is $-2x^5 - 6x^4 + 6x^3 - 4x^2$.

Challenge

64. A box with a square bottom is to be made from a 12 inch square piece of cardboard. Squares with side x are cut out of the corners, and the sides are folded up. Express the volume and the surface area of the outside of the box as polynomials.

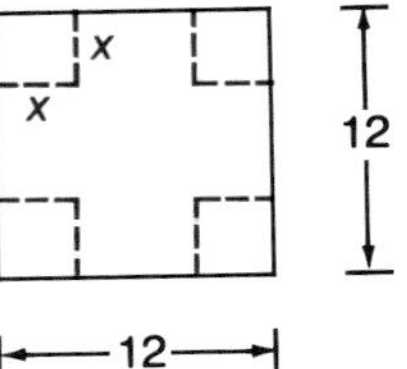

Compute.

65. a. $(x + 3)(x + 6) + (x + 3)(x + 6)$ $2x^2 + 18x + 36$
b. $(x + 4)(x + 5) - (x + 4)(x + 5)$ 0

66. a. $(x - 2)(x - 7) + (x - 2)(x - 7)$ $2x^2 - 18x + 28$
b. $(x - 6)(x - 2) - (x - 6)(x - 2)$ 0

67. a. $(x + 5)(x - 3) + (x + 5)(x - 3)$ $2x^2 + 4x - 30$
b. $(x + 9)(x - 4) - (x + 9)(x - 4)$ 0

68. a. $(x + 7)(x - 8) + (x - 7)(x + 8)$ $2x^2 - 112$
b. $(x + 2)(x - 5) - (x - 2)(x + 5)$ $-6x$

69. If a and b are positive, how many terms are there in $(x - a)(x - b) + (x - a)(x - b)$? 3

70. If a and b are positive, how many terms are there in $(x + a)(x - b) + (x - a)(x + b)$? 2

71. If a and b are positive, how many terms are there in $(x + a)(x - b) - (x + a)(x - b)$? 0

Mixed Review

Write as an algebraic expression. **72.** half of the sum of a number and 3 **73.** 9 more than the product of a number and 6 **74.** 3 times the difference of 7 and a number **75.** the sum of two consecutive integers

Solve. **76.** $15r = 3(r + 28)$ **77.** $25 = 4(m - 3) - 3$

78. $13k = 19k + 12$ **79.** $12x = 16(x - 2) + 48$

LOOKING FOR ERRORS

Study each of the products below. Which are correct and which are incorrect? For those that are incorrect, give the correct answer and state what error was made.

1. $(x^2 + 3y^3)(2x^2 - y) = 2x^2 - x^2y + 6x^2y^3 - 3y^3$
2. $(4m^3)(2m^2 - 2m + 1) = 8m^5 - 8m^4 + 4m^3$
3. $(ab + 2b^2)(ab - 2b^2) = a^2b^2 + 4b$
4. $-2x^2(x^3 + 3x^2 - 3x + 2) = -2x^6 - 6x^4 + 6x^2 - 4x^2$

5-10 Multiplying Binomials: Special Products

Multiplying the Sum and the Difference of Two Expressions

Objective: Multiply the sum and the difference of two expressions.

You have learned the FOIL method for multiplying two binomials. Here are some products found using the FOIL method.

$$(x + 2)(x - 2) = x^2 - 2x + 2x - 4 = x^2 - 4$$

$$(3x - 5)(3x + 5) = 9x^2 + 15x - 15x - 25 = 9x^2 - 25$$

$$(3 + x)(3 - x) = 9 - 3x + 3x - x^2 = 9 - x^2$$

In these examples, the first terms of the binomial are the same and the last terms differ only in sign. These examples suggest the following rule for multiplying the sum and the difference of the same terms.

Product of $(A + B)$ and $(A - B)$

The product of the sum and the difference of two terms is the square of the first expression minus the square of the second.

$$(A + B)(A - B) = A^2 - B^2$$

EXAMPLES Multiply.

1. $(x + 4)(x - 4) = x^2 - 4^2$ Squaring the first expression and subtracting the square of the second
   $= x^2 - 16$ Simplifying

2. $(2w + 5)(2w - 5) = (2w)^2 - 5^2 = 4w^2 - 25$

3. $(-4x - 10y)(-4x + 10y) = (-4x)^2 - (10y)^2 = 16x^2 - 100y^2$

Try This Multiply.

a. $(x + 2)(x - 2)$ $x^2 - 4$

b. $(x^2 + 7)(x^2 - 7)$ $x^4 - 49$

c. $(3t + 5)(3t - 5)$ $9t^2 - 25$

d. $(2x^3 + y)(2x^3 - y)$ $4x^6 - y^2$

5-10

FIRST FIVE MINUTES

1. Simplify.
   $4x^2 - 2x + 4 + 3x^2 + 4x - 1$
   $7x^2 + 2x + 3$

Multiply.

2. $(x + 7)(x - 2)$
   $x^2 - 2x + 7x - 14$
   $= x^2 + 5x - 14$
3. $(3x + 9)(7x - 1)$
   $21x^2 - 3x + 63x - 9$
   $= 21x^2 + 60x - 9$
4. $(x - 1)(x + 1)$
   $x^2 + x - x - 1$
   $= x^2 - 1$

Multiplying the Sum and the Difference of Two Expressions

Students may find it helpful to state the rule "the square of the first, minus the square of the second" as they do the multiplication.

Key Question

- When multiplying the sum and difference of two expressions, why does the product always have at most two terms?
  The other terms are additive inverses of each other, and therefore total zero.

Chalkboard Examples

Multiply.

1. $(r + 2)(r - 2)$
   $r^2 - 4$
2. $(2x + 3)(2x - 3)$
   $4x^2 - 9$
3. $(ab + c)(ab - c)$
   $a^2b^2 - c^2$
4. $(-3x + 4y)(-3x - 4y)$
   $9x^2 - 16y^2$

Squaring Binomials

Demonstrate that squaring a binomial with the FOIL method always leads to the combining of the outside and inside terms.

You may also wish to illustrate the squaring of a binomial with the following diagram.

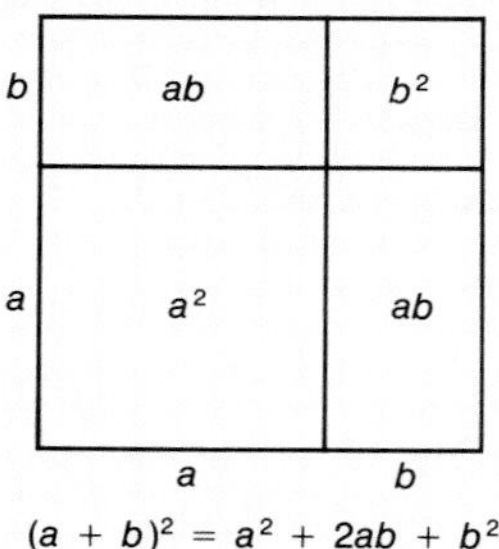

$(a + b)^2 = a^2 + 2ab + b^2$

Avoiding Common Errors

One of the most common errors made in a beginning algebra class is to give the square of a binomial such as $(x + 5)^2$ as $x^2 + 25$.

You can require that students who consistently make this error write $(x + 5)^2$ as $(x + 5)(x + 5)$ and use FOIL. You may want to show by substitution that

$(x + 5)^2 \neq x^2 + 25$. Let $x = 2$.
$(2 + 5)^2 \ ? \ 2^2 + 25$
$7^2 \ ? \ 4 + 25$
$49 \neq 29$

Chalkboard Examples

Multiply.

1. $(x + 5)^2$
   $x^2 + 2 \cdot x \cdot 5 + 25$
   $= x^2 + 10x + 25$
2. $(y - 3)^2$
   $y^2 - 2 \cdot y \cdot 3 + 9$
   $= y^2 - 6y + 9$
3. $(2a - 3b)^2$
   $(2a)^2 - 2 \cdot (2a)(3b) + (3b)^2$
   $= 4a^2 - 12ab + 9b^2$

LESSON QUIZ

Multiply.

1. $(x + 9)(x - 9)$
   $x^2 - 81$
2. $(2x - y)(2x + y)$
   $4x^2 - y^2$
3. $(x + 7)^2$
   $x^2 + 14x + 49$
4. $(x - 8)^2$
   $x^2 - 16x + 64$

Squaring Binomials

Objective: Square a binomial.

Multiplying a binomial by itself is called *squaring the binomial.* Look for a pattern.

$$\begin{aligned}(x + 2)^2 &= (x + 2)(x + 2)\\ &= x^2 + 2x + 2x + 4\\ &= x^2 + 4x + 4\end{aligned}$$

$$\begin{aligned}(x - 2)^2 &= (x - 2)(x - 2)\\ &= x^2 - 2x - 2x + 4\\ &= x^2 - 4x + 4\end{aligned}$$

$$\begin{aligned}(3x + 5)^2 &= (3x + 5)(3x + 5)\\ &= 9x^2 + 15x + 15x + 25\\ &= 9x^2 + 30x + 25\end{aligned}$$

$$\begin{aligned}(3x - 5y)^2 &= (3x - 5y)(3x - 5y)\\ &= 9x^2 - 15xy - 15xy + 25y^2\\ &= 9x^2 - 30xy + 25y^2\end{aligned}$$

There is a quick way to square a binomial.

Squaring Binomials

The square of a binomial is the square of the first term, plus or minus twice the product of the two terms, plus the square of the last term.

$$(A + B)^2 = A^2 + 2AB + B^2$$
$$(A - B)^2 = A^2 - 2AB + B^2$$

EXAMPLES Multiply.

4. $(x + 3)^2 = x^2 + 2 \cdot x \cdot 3 + 3^2$
   $= x^2 + 6x + 9$

5. $(t - 5)^2 = t^2 - 2 \cdot t \cdot 5 + 5^2$
   $= t^2 - 10t + 25$

6. $(2x + 7)^2 = (2x)^2 + 2 \cdot 2x \cdot 7 + 7^2$
   $= 4x^2 + 28x + 49$

7. $(3x - 5y)^2 = (3x)^2 - 2 \cdot 3x \cdot 5y + (5y)^2$
   $= 9x^2 - 30xy + 25y^2$

e. $x^2 + 4x + 4$
f. $y^2 - 18y + 81$
g. $16x^2 - 40x + 25$
h. $a^2 - 8a + 16$
i. $25x^4 + 40x^2 + 16$
j. $16x^4 - 24x^3 + 9x^2$

Try This Multiply.

e. $(x + 2)(x + 2)$ **f.** $(y - 9)(y - 9)$ **g.** $(4x - 5)^2$

h. $(a - 4)^2$ **i.** $(5x^2 + 4)(5x^2 + 4)$ **j.** $(4x^2 - 3x)^2$

5-10 EXERCISES

A

Multiply.

1. $(x + 4)(x - 4)$
2. $(a + 1)(a - 1)$
3. $(d - 6)(d + 6)$
4. $(y - 5)(y + 5)$
5. $(6 - m)(6 + m)$
6. $(8 + m)(8 - m)$
7. $(2x + 1)(2x - 1)$
8. $(3y - 1)(3y + 1)$
9. $(4a - 7)(4a + 7)$
10. $(5b - 2)(5b + 2)$
11. $(4x^2 - 3)(4x^2 + 3)$
12. $(2x^2 + 3)(2x^2 - 3)$
13. $(3x^4 + 2)(3x^4 - 2)$
14. $(6t^5 - 5)(6t^5 + 5)$
15. $(x^6 - x^2)(x^6 + x^2)$
16. $(3a - 4b)(3a + 4b)$
17. $(7c - 2d)(7c + 2d)$
18. $(-3m + 2n)(-3m - 2n)$
19. $(-6t + s)(-6t - s)$
20. $(x^2 + y^2)(x^2 - y^2)$

Multiply.

21. $(x + 2)^2$
22. $(a + 3)^2$
23. $(t - 3)^2$
24. $(r - 2)^2$
25. $(2x - 1)^2$
26. $(3c - 1)^2$
27. $(4a - 3b)^2$
28. $(7a - 2b)^2$
29. $(4s + 5t)^2$
30. $\left(x - \frac{1}{2}\right)^2$
31. $\left(x - \frac{1}{4}\right)^2$
32. $\left(a + \frac{2}{3}\right)^2$
33. $(2x + 7)(2x + 7)$
34. $(4x + 3)(4x + 3)$
35. $(3x - 2y)(3x + 2y)$
36. $(7x - 5y)(7x + 5y)$
37. $(5x^2 - 1)(5x^2 - 1)$
38. $(12 - 3x^2)(12 + 3x^2)$
39. $\left(2x - \frac{1}{5}\right)\left(2x - \frac{1}{5}\right)$
40. $\left(3x + \frac{3}{4}\right)\left(3x - \frac{3}{4}\right)$
41. $(2x^3 - 0.3)(2x^3 + 0.3)$
42. $(t^2 - 0.2)(t^2 + 0.2)$

B

43. a. Find the area of the 4 small rectangles. ac, ad, bc, bd

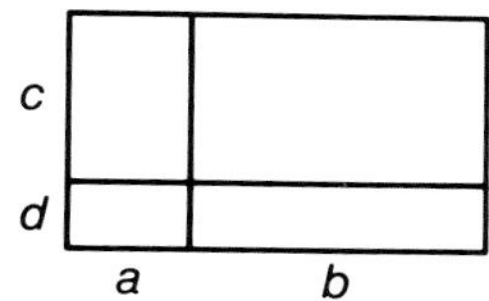

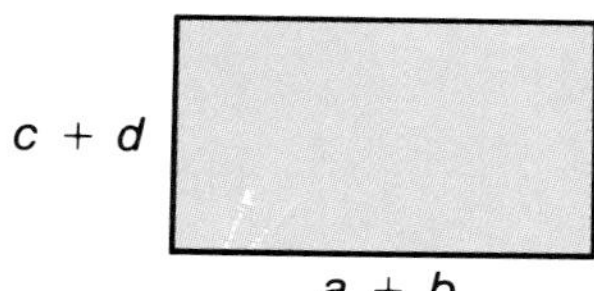

b. What is the sum of the areas? ac + ad + bc + bd

c. Find the area of the blue rectangle.
Compare your result with your answer to part b. ac + ad + bc + bd, equal

Assignment Guide
Minimum: 1–42 e/o, MR

Regular: 1–42 e/o, 43–45, MR

Advanced: 1–42 m3, 43–49, MR

ADDITIONAL ANSWERS

Exercises

1. $x^2 - 16$
2. $a^2 - 1$
3. $d^2 - 36$
4. $y^2 - 25$
5. $36 - m^2$
6. $64 - m^2$
7. $4x^2 - 1$
8. $9y^2 - 1$
9. $16a^2 - 49$
10. $25b^2 - 4$
11. $16x^4 - 9$
12. $4x^4 - 9$
13. $9x^8 - 4$
14. $36t^{10} - 25$
15. $x^{12} - x^4$
16. $9a^2 - 16b^2$
17. $49c^2 - 4d^2$
18. $9m^2 - 4n^2$
19. $36t^2 - s^2$
20. $x^4 - y^4$
21. $x^2 + 4x + 4$
22. $a^2 + 6a + 9$
23. $t^2 - 6t + 9$
24. $r^2 - 4r + 4$
25. $4x^2 - 4x + 1$
26. $9c^2 - 6c + 1$
27. $16a^2 - 24ab + 9b^2$
28. $49a^2 - 28ab + 4b^2$
29. $16s^2 + 40st + 25t^2$
30. $x^2 - x + \frac{1}{4}$
31. $x^2 - \frac{1}{2}x + \frac{1}{16}$
32. $a^2 + \frac{4}{3}a + \frac{4}{9}$
33. $4x^2 + 28x + 49$
34. $16x^2 + 24x + 9$
35. $9x^2 - 4y^2$
36. $49x^2 - 25y^2$
37. $25x^4 - 10x^2 + 1$
38. $144 - 9x^4$
39. $4x^2 - \frac{4}{5}x + \frac{1}{25}$
40. $9x^2 - \frac{9}{16}$
41. $4x^6 - 0.09$
42. $t^4 - 0.04$

45. 10, 11, 12
46. a. Additive inverses
b. Both $= x^2 - 2xy + y^2$
c. $a^2 = (-a)^2$ for any a
47. $100x^2 + 100x + 25$
$= 100(x^2 + x) + 25$
Add the first digit to its square, multiply by 100, add 25.
48. $(5a + 7)(5a - 7)$
49. a. $w(w + 1)(w + 2)$
$= w^3 + 3w^2 + 2w$
b. $l(l - 1)(l + 1) = l^3 - l$
c. $h(h - 1)(h - 2)$
$= h^3 - 3h^2 + 2h$

Mixed Review

50. $20x - 13$
51. $2y^3 + 5y^2 - 7y$
52. $27m^{15}$
53. $a^5b^6c^3$
54. $30y^7$
55. -73
56. 6
57. -11
58. 11
59. 0
60. 68
61. 60

44. Consider the rectangle at the right. The area of the shaded region is $(a + b)(a - b)$.
a. Find the area of the large rectangle. $a^2 + ab$
b. Find the area of the two small unshaded rectangles. $ab + b^2$
c. Find the difference of the areas in part a and part b. $a^2 + ab - (b^2 + ab) = a^2 - b^2$
d. Find the area of the shaded region and compare this result with part c.
$a(a - b) + b(a - b) = a^2 - b^2$, equal

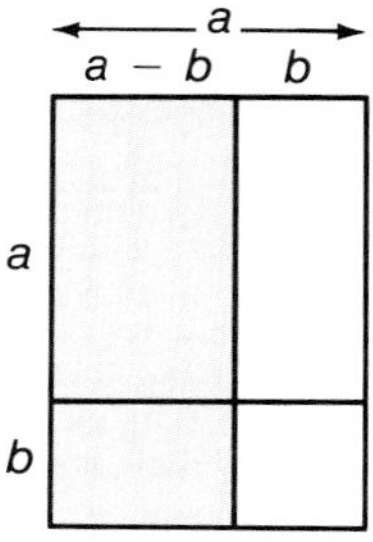

45. ***Critical Thinking*** Find three consecutive integers, the sum of whose squares is 65 more than three times the square of the smallest.

Challenge

46. a. What is the relationship between $x - y$ and $y - x$?
b. Find $(x - y)^2$ and $(y - x)^2$.
c. Explain your results.

47. Find $(10x + 5)^2$. Use your result to show how to mentally square any two digit number ending in 5.

48. The product of the sum and difference of two expressions is $25a^2 - 49$. What are the two expressions?

49. The height of a box is one more than its length, and the length is one more than its width.
a. Find the volume of the box in terms of the width (w).
b. Find the volume in terms of the length (l).
c. Find the volume in terms of the height (h).

Mixed Review

Simplify. **50.** $(9x - 7) + (11x - 6)$ **51.** $(4y^3 - 7y) - (2y^3 - 5y^2)$
52. $(3m^5)^3$ **53.** $(a^3b^2c)(a^2b^4c^2)$ **54.** $15(2y^2)(y^5)$
Evaluate for $a = 3$. **55.** $-9a^2 + 8$ **56.** $2a^2 - 9a + 15$
57. $7 - 9a + a^2$ **58.** $15a - 3a^2 - 7$ **59.** $5a^2 - 9a - 18$
60. 17 is 25% of what number? **61.** What number is 8% of 750?

WRITING TO LEARN

Suppose you are corresponding with a friend who asks what you are studying in algebra. Write your friend a letter that tells about polynomials. Use your own words to explain ideas like monomial, binomial, trinomial, term, degree, and factor. Your friend has not studied algebra yet, so do not assume these are familiar terms.

5-11 Multiplying Polynomials

Objective: Multiply any two polynomials.

To multiply two polynomials we can use the distributive property more than once.

EXAMPLES Multiply.

1. $(x^2 + 4)(x^2 + 2x - 3) = (x^2)(x^2 + 2x - 3) + (4)(x^2 + 2x - 3)$ ① ②

$$= (x^4 + 2x^3 - 3x^2) + (4x^2 + 8x - 12)$$
$$= x^4 + 2x^3 + x^2 + 8x - 12$$

2. $(a + 2b)(4a^2 - 2ab + 3b^2)$

$$= a(4a^2 - 2ab + 3b^2) + 2b(4a^2 - 2ab + 3b^2)$$
$$= 4a^3 - 2a^2b + 3ab^2 + 8a^2b - 4ab^2 + 6b^3$$
$$= 4a^3 + 6a^2b - ab^2 + 6b^3$$

Try This Multiply.

a. $(b^2 + 3b - 4)(b^2 + 5)$ $b^4 + 3b^3 + b^2 + 15b - 20$

b. $(2x - 3y + 5)(3x + 4y)$ $6x^2 - xy - 12y^2 + 15x + 20y$

Multiplying Polynomials

To multiply two polynomials, multiply each term of one polynomial by every term of the other. Then add the results.

We usually use columns for long multiplications. We multiply each term at the top by every term at the bottom and align like terms. Then we add.

EXAMPLE 3 Multiply $(2c^2 + 3c - 4)(2c^2 - c + 3)$.

$$\begin{array}{rrrrrl}
 & 2c^2 & + 3c & - 4 & & \\
 & 2c^2 & - c & + 3 & & \\
\hline
4c^4 & + 6c^3 & - 8c^2 & & & \text{Multiplying by } 2c^2 \\
 & - 2c^3 & - 3c^2 & + 4c & & \text{Multiplying by } -c \\
 & & 6c^2 & + 9c & - 12 & \text{Multiplying by } 3 \\
\hline
4c^4 & + 4c^3 & - 5c^2 & + 13c & - 12 &
\end{array}$$

5-11

FIRST FIVE MINUTES

Multiply.

1. $2x(3x^2 + 4x + 1)$
   $6x^3 + 8x^2 + 2x$
2. $(4x + 3) \cdot 2x$
   $8x^2 + 6x$
3. $(x + 1)(x - 7)$
   $x^2 - 6x - 7$
4. $(x + 10)^2$
   $x^2 + 20x + 100$
5. Simplify.
   $(x + 1)x^2 +$
   $(x + 1)x + (x + 1) \cdot 2$
   $x^3 + x^2 + x^2 + x + 2x + 2$
   $= x^3 + 2x^2 + 3x + 2$

You may want to point out that when two polynomials are multiplied, the number of terms in the product before adding like terms equals the number of terms in the first polynomial times the number of terms in the second polynomial. Students can use this rule as an informal check.

Key Questions

- If a binomial and a trinomial are multiplied, how many terms will the product have before like terms are combined?
  6
- If a trinomial and a monomial are multiplied, how many terms will the product have before like terms are combined?
  3

Chalkboard Examples

Multiply.

1. $(x + 1)(x^2 + x + 1)$
   $x(x^2 + x + 1) + 1(x^2 + x + 1)$
   $= x^3 + x^2 + x + x^2 + x + 1$
   $= x^3 + 2x^2 + 2x + 1$
2. $(2x + 3)(x^2 + 4x + 5)$
   $2x^3 + 8x^2 + 10x$
   $+ 3x^2 + 12x + 15$
   $= 2x^3 + 11x^2 + 22x + 15$

3. Multiply. Use columns.
$(5x^2 + 3x + 2)$ by
$(3x^2 + 2x - 1)$

$$\begin{array}{r} 15x^4 + 9x^3 + 6x^2 \\ 10x^3 + 6x^2 + 4x \\ - 5x^2 - 3x - 2 \\ \hline 15x^4 + 19x^3 + 7x^2 + x - 2 \end{array}$$

Multiply.

4. $(x + 10)(x - 10)$
$x^2 - 100$
5. $(r - 7)(r + 7)$
$r^2 - 49$
6. $(x + 11)^2$
$x^2 + 22x + 121$
7. $4x^2(5x^2 + 4x - 7)$
$20x^4 + 16x^3 - 28x^2$
8. $(5x^3 - 3x)^2$
$(5x^3)^2 - 2(5x^3)(3x) + (3x)^2$
$= 25x^6 - 30x^4 + 9x^2$
9. $\left(\frac{1}{2}x + \frac{2}{3}\right)^2$
$\frac{1}{4}x^2 + 2 \cdot \frac{1}{2} \cdot \frac{2}{3} \cdot x + \frac{4}{9}$
$= \frac{1}{4}x^2 + \frac{2}{3}x + \frac{4}{9}$

LESSON ENRICHMENT

Find the product.
$(x - 1)(x^{100} + x^{99} + \ldots + 1)$
$x^{101} - 1$

Find the product
$(x + 1)(x^{100} - x^{99} + \ldots + 1)$
where the odd powers have coefficient -1.
$x^{101} + 1$

LESSON QUIZ

Multiply.

1. $(x - 1)(x^2 + x + 1)$
$x^3 + x^2 + x - x^2 - x - 1$
$= x^3 - 1$
2. $(3x + 2)(4x^2 - 5x + 7)$
$12x^3 - 15x^2 + 21x + 8x^2 - 10x + 14 = 12x^3 - 7x^2 + 11x + 14$
3. $(x - 12)^2$
$x^2 - 24x + 144$
4. $(2x - 3)(2x + 3)$
$4x^2 - 9$

Try This Multiply.

c. $(3a^2 - 2a + 4)(a^2 + 5a + 1)$ $3a^4 + 13a^3 - 3a^2 + 18a + 4$

d. $(5x^2 + 4x + 2)(-4x^2 + x - 8)$ $-20x^4 - 11x^3 - 44x^2 - 30x - 16$

e. $(4n^3 - 6n - 5)(2n^2 + n - 2)$ $8n^5 + 4n^4 - 20n^3 - 16n^2 + 7n + 10$

f. $(3x^4y^2 - 4x^2 - 5)(x^3 + x^2y)$ $3x^7y^2 + 3x^6y^3 - 4x^5 - 4x^4y - 5x^3 - 5x^2y$

Here is a list of the rules you have learned for multiplying polynomials.

Rules for Multiplying Polynomials

A polynomial and a monomial:

(1) To find the product of a monomial and any polynomial, multiply each term of the polynomial by the monomial.

Two binomials:

(2) $(A + B)(A + B) = (A + B)^2 = A^2 + 2AB + B^2$
(3) $(A - B)(A - B) = (A - B)^2 = A^2 - 2AB + B^2$
(4) $(A + B)(A - B) = A^2 - B^2$

(5) To multiply any two binomials, find the sum of the products of the First terms, the Outside terms, the Inside terms, and the Last terms (FOIL).

Any two polynomials:

(6) To multiply any two polynomials, multiply each term of a polynomial by every term of the other polynomial.

Notice that the FOIL method will work for (2) through (4), but computation is quicker if you know these rules.

EXAMPLES Multiply.

4. $(x + 3)(x - 3) = x^2 - 9$ Using rule 4 (the product of a sum and difference)

5. $(t + 7)(t - 5) = t^2 + 2t - 35$ Using rule 5 (the product of two binomials)

6. $(x + 7)(x + 7) = x^2 + 14x + 49$ Using rule 2 (the square of a binomial sum)

7. $2y^3(9x^2 + x - 7) = 18x^2y^3 + 2xy^3 - 14y^3$ Using rule 1 (the product of a monomial and a polynomial)

8. $(3x^2 - 7x)^2 = 9x^4 - 42x^3 + 49x^2$ Using rule 3 (the square of a binomial difference)

9. $\left(3x + \frac{1}{4}\right)^2 = 9x^2 + 2(3x)\frac{1}{4} + \frac{1}{16}$

$= 9x^2 + \frac{3}{2}x + \frac{1}{16}$

Using rule 2 (the square of a binomial sum)

10. $(x^2 - 3x + 2)(2x - 4)$
$= 2x^3 - 6x^2 + 4x - 4x^2 + 12x - 8$
$= 2x^3 - 10x^2 + 16x - 8$

Using rule 6 (the product of any two polynomials)

Try This Multiply. See Additional Answers.

g. $(x + 5)(x + 6)$ **h.** $(x - 4)(x + 4)$ **i.** $4x^2(-2x^3 + 5x^2 + 10)$
j. $(9x^2 + 1)^2$ **k.** $(2x - 5)(2x + 8)$ **l.** $(x^2 - 4x - 3)(3x - 2)$

5-11 EXERCISES

A

Multiply.

1. $(x^2 + x + 1)(x - 1)$
2. $(n^2 - n + 2)(n + 2)$
3. $(2x^2 + 6x + 1)(2x + 1)$
4. $(4x^2 - 2x - 1)(3x - 1)$
5. $(3y^2 - 6y + 2)(y^2 - 3)$
6. $(y^2 + 6y + 1)(3y^2 - 3)$
7. $(x^3 + x^2 - x)(x^3 + x^2)$
8. $(x^3 - x^2 + x)(x^3 - x^2)$
9. $(a - b)(a^3 + a^2b + ab^2 + b^3)$
10. $(c + d)(c^3 - c^2d + cd^2 - d^3)$
11. $(x^2 + x + 1)(x^2 - x - 1)$
12. $(x^2 - x + 1)(x^2 - x + 1)$
13. $(2x^2 + 3x - 4)(2x^2 + x - 2)$
14. $(2x^2 - x - 3)(2x^2 - 5x - 2)$
15. $(2t^2 - t - 4)(3t^2 + 2t - 1)$
16. $(3a^2 - 5a + 2)(2a^2 - 3a + 4)$
17. $(2x^2 + x - 2)(-2x^2 + 4x - 5)$
18. $(3x^2 - 8x + 1)(-2x^2 - 4x + 2)$
19. $(x^5 - x^3 + x)(x^4 + x^2 - 1)$
20. $(3x^6 + 3x^4 + 3x^2)(x^5 - x^3 + x)$
21. $(b^3 + b^2 + b + 1)(b - 1)$
22. $(x^3 - x^2 + x - 2)(x - 2)$
23. $(x^3 + x^2 - x - 3)(xy - 3y)$
24. $(x^3 - x^2 - x + 4)(xy + 4y)$

Multiply.

25. $(x - 8)(x - 8)$
26. $(x + 7)(x + 7)$
27. $(x - 8)(x + 8)$
28. $(x + 7)(x - 7)$
29. $(x - 8)(x + 5)$
30. $(x + 7)(x - 4)$
31. $4x(x^2 + 6x - 3)$
32. $8x(-x^2 - 4x + 3)$
33. $\left(2x^2 - \frac{1}{2}\right)\left(2x^2 - \frac{1}{2}\right)$
34. $(1 - x^2)(1 - x^2)$

Assignment Guide
Minimum: Day 1: 1–24, assign w. Application
Day 2: 25–50, MR
Regular: 1–52 e/o, 53, MR, assign w. Application
Advanced: 1–52 e/o, 53–59, MR, assign w. Application

ADDITIONAL ANSWERS

Try This

g. $x^2 + 11x + 30$
h. $x^2 - 16$
i. $-8x^5 + 20x^4 + 40x^2$
j. $81x^4 + 18x^2 + 1$
k. $4x^2 + 6x - 40$
l. $3x^3 - 14x^2 - x + 6$

Exercises

1. $x^3 - 1$
2. $n^3 + n^2 + 4$
3. $4x^3 + 14x^2 + 8x + 1$
4. $12x^3 - 10x^2 - x + 1$
5. $3y^4 - 6y^3 - 7y^2 + 18y - 6$
6. $3y^4 + 18y^3 - 18y - 3$
7. $x^6 + 2x^5 - x^3$
8. $x^6 - 2x^5 + 2x^4 - x^3$
9. $a^4 - b^4$
10. $c^4 - d^4$
11. $x^4 - x^2 - 2x - 1$
12. $x^4 - 2x^3 + 3x^2 - 2x + 1$
13. $4x^4 + 8x^3 - 9x^2 - 10x + 8$
14. $4x^4 - 12x^3 - 5x^2 + 17x + 6$
15. $6t^4 + t^3 - 16t^2 - 7t + 4$
16. $6a^4 - 19a^3 + 31a^2 - 26a + 8$
17. $-4x^4 + 6x^3 - 2x^2 - 13x + 10$
18. $-6x^4 + 4x^3 + 36x^2 - 20x + 2$
19. $x^9 - x^5 + 2x^3 - x$
20. $3x^{11} + 3x^7 + 3x^3$
21. $b^4 - 1$
22. $x^4 - 3x^3 + 3x^2 - 4x + 4$
23. $x^4y - 2x^3y - 4x^2y + 9y$
24. $x^4y + 3x^3y - 5x^2y + 16y$
25. $x^2 - 16x + 64$
26. $x^2 + 14x + 49$
27. $x^2 - 64$
28. $x^2 - 49$
29. $x^2 - 3x - 40$
30. $x^2 + 3x - 28$
31. $4x^3 + 24x^2 - 12x$
32. $-8x^3 - 32x^2 + 24x$
33. $4x^4 - 2x^2 + \frac{1}{4}$
34. $x^4 - 2x^2 + 1$

35. $36a^6 - 1$
36. $6b^4 - 3b^2 - 63$
37. $-9x^2 + 4$
38. $-25x^2 + 16$
39. $36x^8 + 48x^4 + 16$
40. $36x^8 - 96x^4 + 64$
41. $-6x^5 - 48x^3 + 54x^2$
42. $-5x^5 + 10x^3 - 20x^2$
43. $12q^5 + 6q^3 - 2q^2 - 1$
44. $35p^4 - 36p^2 - 32$
45. $\frac{9}{16}x^2 + \frac{9}{4}x + 2$
46. $\frac{3}{25}x^4 + 4x^2 - 63$
47. $4x^3 + 13x^2 + 22x + 15$
48. $3x^4 + 10x^3 + 13x^2 + 10x$
49. $3x^5 - 14x^4 + 13x^3 - 20x^2$
50. $3x^5 - 14x^4 + 8x^3 + 15x^2 - 10x$

54. a. $x^3 - 1$
b. $x^3 + 2x^2 + 2x + 1$
c. $x^3 - 2x^2 + 2x - 1$
d. $x^3 + 1$
e. $-x^3 + 2x^2 - 2x + 1$
f. $-x^3 - 1$
g. $x^4 - 1$
h. $x^4 + 2x^3 + 2x^2 + 2x + 1$
i. $x^4 - 2x^3 + 2x^2 - 2x + 1$
j. $x^4 + 2x + 1$
k. $-x^4 + 2x^3 - 2x^2 + 2x - 1$
l. $-x^4 + 1$

59. Answers may vary. Ex. $(x^2 - x + 2)(x + 1)$

Mixed Review

60. $x^2 - 6x + 9$
61. $x^2 + 6x + 9$
62. $x^2 - 9$
63. $-7a$
64. $21n$
65. $-3y^2 + 9y - 1$
66. 0.000011
67. 21,000,000
68. 2, 1, 0; 2
69. 7, 3, 0; 7
70. 1, 0; 1
71. 9 ft

Multiply.

35. $(6a^3 - 1)(6a^3 + 1)$
36. $(2b^2 - 7)(3b^2 + 9)$
37. $(2 - 3x)(2 + 3x)$
38. $(4 + 5x)(4 - 5x)$
39. $(6x^4 + 4)^2$
40. $(8 - 6x^4)^2$
41. $-6x^2(x^3 + 8x - 9)$
42. $-5x^2(x^3 - 2x + 4)$
43. $(6q^3 - 1)(2q^2 + 1)$
44. $(7p^2 + 4)(5p^2 - 8)$
45. $\left(\frac{3}{4}x + 1\right)\left(\frac{3}{4}x + 2\right)$
46. $\left(\frac{1}{5}x^2 + 9\right)\left(\frac{3}{5}x^2 - 7\right)$
47. $(x^2 + 2x + 3)(4x + 5)$
48. $(x^2 + 2x)(3x^2 + 4x + 5)$
49. $(x^3 - 4x^2)(3x^2 - 2x + 5)$
50. $(x^3 - 4x^2 + 5)(3x^2 - 2x)$

B

51. Find $(x + y)^3$. $x^3 + 3x^2y + 3xy^2 + y^3$

52. Find $(x + y)^4$. $x^4 + 4x^3y + 6x^2y^2 + 4xy^3 + y^4$

53. *Critical Thinking* Study the pattern of your answers for Exercises 51 and 52. Without multiplying, find $(x + y)^5$.
$x^5 + 5x^4y + 10x^3y^2 + 10x^2y^3 + 5xy^4 + y^5$

Challenge

Multiply. Look for patterns.

54. **a.** $(x^2 + x + 1)(x - 1)$ **b.** $(x^2 + x + 1)(x + 1)$
c. $(x^2 - x + 1)(x - 1)$ **d.** $(x^2 - x + 1)(x + 1)$
e. $(-x^2 + x - 1)(x - 1)$ **f.** $(-x^2 + x - 1)(x + 1)$
g. $(x^3 + x^2 + x + 1)(x - 1)$ **h.** $(x^3 + x^2 + x + 1)(x + 1)$
i. $(x^3 - x^2 + x - 1)(x - 1)$ **j.** $(x^3 - x^2 + x + 1)(x + 1)$
k. $(-x^3 + x^2 - x + 1)(x - 1)$ **l.** $(-x^3 + x^2 - x + 1)(x + 1)$

55. What polynomial times $(x - 1)$ equals $x^5 - 1$? $x^4 + x^3 + x^2 + x + 1$

56. What polynomial times $(x + 1)$ equals $x^5 + 1$? $x^4 - x^3 + x^2 - x + 1$

57. What polynomial times $(x - 1)$ equals $x^6 - 1$? $x^5 + x^4 + x^3 + x^2 + x + 1$

58. Find $(x^2 + xy + y^2)^2$. $x^4 + 2x^3y + 3x^2y^2 + 2xy^3 + y^4$

59. Find a trinomial $ax^2 + bx + c$ and a binomial $dx + e$ so that when they are multiplied, the coefficient of the x term is 1.

Mixed Review

Multiply. **60.** $(x - 3)^2$ **61.** $(x + 3)^2$ **62.** $(x - 3)(x + 3)$

Give the additive inverse. **63.** $7a$ **64.** $-21n$ **65.** $3y^2 - 9y + 1$

Write in standard notation. **66.** 1.1×10^{-5} **67.** 2.1×10^7

Identify the degree of each term and the degree of the polynomial.

68. $3n^2 - 4n + 11$ **69.** $3x^3y^4 + 9x^2y - 24$ **70.** $9a + 6$

71. On a scale drawing of a certain building, 1 in. represents 2.5 ft. The length of one wall in the drawing is 3.6 in. What is the actual length of that wall?

Problem Solving: Application

Formulas in Health Care

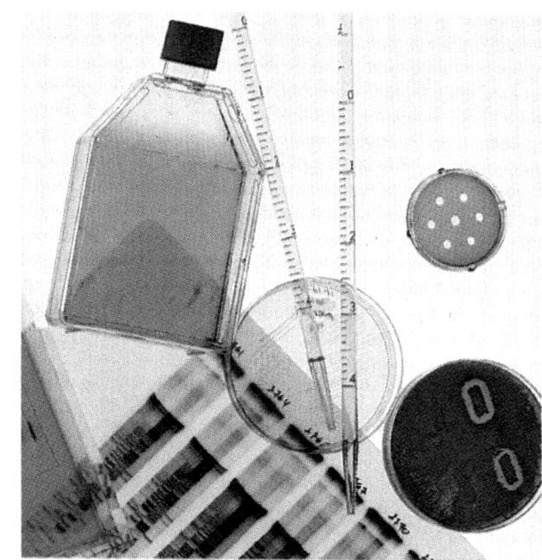

Doctors often use mathematics in evaluating health. For example, to determine whether a patient runs a higher-than-normal risk of heart problems, they can compare the graphs of the patient's pulse rate and blood pressure with graphs showing normal ranges for people of similar height, age, and weight.

Math is also used to determine body fat. Researchers have found that weight is not the best indicator of body fat. They have developed a formula that relates bone structure to actual fat in the body. The polynomial $0.49W + 0.45P - 6.36R + 8.7$, where W = waist circumference in centimeters, P = skinfold above the pectoral muscle in millimeters, and R = wrist diameter in centimeters, gives an estimate of the percent of body fat for a man.

EXAMPLE

Estimate the percent of body fat for a man with the measurements $W = 94.2$ cm, $P = 6.3$ mm, $R = 7.5$ cm.

$$0.49W + 0.45P - 6.36R + 8.7$$
$$= 0.49(94.2) + 0.45(6.3) - 6.36(7.5) + 8.7$$
$$= 9.993 \approx 10$$

The man has 10% body fat.

Problems

Solve.

1. Use the polynomial in the example to estimate the body fat of a young man with the measurements $W = 86.2$ cm, $P = 4.8$ mm, $R = 6.0$ cm.
2. Use the polynomial in the example to estimate the body fat of a man with the measurement $W = 95.8$ cm, $P = 5.1$ mm, $R = 7.2$ cm.
3. The polynomial $0.041h - 0.018A - 2.69$ gives an estimate of lung capacity in liters where h = height in cm and A = age in years. Find the lung capacity of a 29-year-old woman who is 138.7 cm tall.
4. Use the polynomial in Problem 3 to find the lung capacity of a person who is 18 years old and 125.5 cm tall.

Problem Solving: Application

Point out that the formula gives the answer directly as a percent. No conversion is necessary.

ANSWERS

1. 14.938% ≈ 15%
2. 12.145% ≈ 12%
3. 2.4747 Liters ≈ 2.5 Liters
4. 2.1315 Liters ≈ 2.1 Liters

5-12

FIRST FIVE MINUTES

1. What two numbers have a sum of 16 and a product of 48?
   4, 12
   (Guess, Check, Revise)

Determine a pattern and continue the sequence.

2. 2, 5, 8, 11, __, __, __, __
   14 17 20 23
3. 4, 8, 16, 32, __, __, __, __
   64 128 256 512
4. 72, 24, 8, __, __, __, __
   $\frac{8}{3}$ $\frac{8}{9}$ $\frac{8}{27}$ $\frac{8}{81}$

Make a Table, Look for a Pattern

Students have already had experience making a table in this chapter. You may want to point out that the table in the example can be completed by computing each entry, or, after the first three or four entries, can be completed by finding a pattern.

Point out that there is usually more than one strategy that can be used to solve a problem. You may want to ask students to solve the example using logical reasoning.

Possible Solution:
Since job A increases $3000 per year and job B increases $2000 per year, the difference in salaries between the two jobs will decrease by $1000 each year ($3000 − $2000). Since the initial difference in salaries is $7000, the two jobs will pay the same amount in the 8th year. The salaries for the next two years can then be found.

Key Questions

- Which job has a higher starting salary?
  Job B
- Which job offers higher raises?
  Job A
- Look at the table. What happens in the eighth year?
  Both jobs pay the same.
- Without continuing the table, can you tell which job will pay more in the fifteenth year?
  Job A
- Write an expression for the amount Job A will pay in the tenth year.
  18,000 + 9(3000)

5-12 Problem Solving: Strategies

Make a Table, Look for a Pattern

Objective: Solve problems using the strategies *Make a Table* and *Look for a Pattern.*

The problem-solving strategies called Make a Table and Look for a Pattern are helpful when you are solving problems involving numerical relationships. Recording data from a problem in a table organizes the data. When data are organized in a table, numerical patterns are easier to recognize.

EXAMPLE

A college graduate was offered two jobs. One job had a starting salary of $18,000 a year with a guaranteed $3000 a year raise for each of the next 10 years. The other job had a starting salary of $25,000 a year with a guaranteed $2000 a year raise for each of the next 10 years. After 10 years, both jobs offered a 10% raise each year thereafter. Which job would pay the most in the tenth year?

To find the amount of money earned in the tenth year, you can *make a table* showing the years and the amount earned each year for each job. *Look for a pattern* to extend the table to the tenth year.

JOB A

Year	1	2	3	4	5	6	7	8	9	10
Amount (in thousands)	18	21	24	27	30	33	36	39	42	45

The amount increases by $3000 each year for job A.

JOB B

Year	1	2	3	4	5	6	7	8	9	10
Amount (in thousands)	25	27	29	31	33	35	37	39	41	43

The amount increases by $2000 each year for job B.

You can see in the table that job A, the one with a starting salary of $18,000, will pay the most in the tenth year.

As we have seen, problems can be solved in more than one way. This problem could also have been solved using logical reasoning.

Problem-Solving Strategies		
Draw a Diagram	Guess, Check, Revise	Write an Equation
Make an Organized List	Use Logical Reasoning	Make a Table
Look for a Pattern	Simplify the Problem	Work Backward

5-12 PROBLEMS

Solve using one or more of the strategies.

1. In the example, in which job would this person have earned the most money altogether after 10 years?

2. A wealthy family donated money to a local university for a 10-year period. The first year they gave $1 million. The second year they gave $3 million. The third year they gave $5 million, and so on. They continued giving money in this manner. How much money did they give in all for these 10 years?

3. Members of a stamp-collecting club each bought one of the same kind of stamp at an auction. All stamps were sold at whole-dollar amounts. Each member paid the same amount, there was no tax, and no stamp at this auction sold for less than $10. The club paid a total of $203 for the stamps. How many people from the club bought the stamp?

4. The area of a square farm field was 25 acres. The field was divided into separate square lots of 1 acre. A fence was placed around the outside of the entire field. The base price for a lot was $1200. Lots on the edge, which had fences, cost $150 more for each side that had a fence. What were the different prices for the lots in this field, and how many of each price were there?

5. A company decides to increase its sales force. In the first week, each of the 25 original salespeople hires and trains 2 new salespeople. In week two, each of the new salespeople hires and trains two new salespeople. Again in week three, each of the most recently hired salespeople hires and trains 2 new salespeople. If the company continues this pattern, how large is the sales force after 3 months (12 weeks)?

6. *Write a Convincing Argument* Solve the problem below. Then write an argument that would convince a classmate that your solution is correct.

John was hired by a painter to paint doors. He was paid $10 for each door that he completed that did not need repainting by the painter. For each door that needed to be redone, he was fined $5. On a bad day, he painted 25 doors, but made a total of only $10. How many doors did he paint that did not need to be repainted?

Chalkboard Example

1. One car rental firm charges $37 per day and $0.10 per mile. Another charges $25 per day and $0.13 per mile. How far must you drive per day in order for the first firm to be more economical?
   Make a table showing total costs at 100 mile increments. Firm 1 charges $10 per hundred miles and Firm 2 charges $13 per hundred miles.

	0	100	200	300	400
1	$37	$47	$57	$67	$77
2	$25	$38	$51	$64	$77

At 400 miles, the cost is equal. Therefore Firm 1 will be more economical if you drive more than 400 miles per day.

Hints for Problems

1. Make a table similar to the sample problem. Add a row for total.
2. Make a table and look for a pattern.
3. Look for factors of 203.
4. Draw a diagram to help solve the problem.
5. Make a table. Look for a pattern.
6. Guess a number of good pieces, find the number of bad pieces, and total the amount earned. Revise your guess if necessary.

ANSWERS

1. Job B will pay more money for the 10-year period.
2. The family gave a total of $100 million for the 10-year period.
3. Seven people bought the stamp, each paying $29.
4. Nine lots with no fences were priced at $1200. Twelve lots, each with one fence, were priced at $1350. Four lots, each with two sides fenced, were priced at $1500.
5. The company would have 204,775 salespeople after 12 weeks.
6. The painter completed 9 doors that did not need repainting and 16 that did need repainting.

ANSWERS

1. 7^6
2. y^8
3. x^{11}
4. a^5b^5
5. x^8y^{10}
6. $l^3m^{13}n^6$
7. 7^2
8. a^5
9. x^7y^4
10. $\frac{1}{7^3}$
11. $\frac{1}{y^2}$
12. 1
13. 5^6
14. 3^{16}
15. x^{12}
16. a^9
17. $9a^2$
18. $8b^3$
19. $8x^9$
20. $64p^6$
21. $9x^4y^2z^8$
22. $-8x^{18}y^6$
23. n^{30}
24. $\frac{y^{12}}{81}$
25. $6a^2$
26. $-6x^3$
27. $-20b^3c^6$
28. $10y^8$
29. $15w^3z^7$
30. $32x^3y^4$
31. a^3
32. $-n^4$
33. $-3x^2y^3$
34. $4m^7n$
35. $-6b^7c^4$
36. $4x^2y^2$

Chapter 5 Summary and Review

5-1

To multiply powers with like bases, such as $x^2 \cdot x^5$, you add the exponents to get x^7. To divide powers with like bases, such as $\frac{y^6}{y^2}$, you subtract the exponents to get y^4. To divide $\frac{x^3}{x^5}$ where the larger exponent is in the denominator, you subtract the exponents to get x^{-2} or $\frac{1}{x^2}$.

Simplify.

1. $7^2 \cdot 7^4$ **2.** $y^3 \cdot y^5$ **3.** $x^7 \cdot x^3 \cdot x$

4. $(a^2b^4)(a^3b)$ **5.** $(x^4y^5)(x^4y^5)$ **6.** $(lm^7n^5)(l^2m^6n)$

Simplify.

7. $\frac{7^5}{7^3}$ **8.** $\frac{a^9}{a^4}$ **9.** $\frac{x^9y^7}{x^2y^3}$

Simplify. Express each using positive exponents.

10. 7^{-3} **11.** y^{-2} **12.** a^0

5-2

To raise a power to a power, such as $(a^2)^3$, you multiply the exponents to get a^6. To find the power of a product or quotient, everything inside the parentheses is raised to the power.

Simplify.

13. $(5^3)^2$ **14.** $(3^4)^4$ **15.** $(x^6)^2$ **16.** $(a^3)^3$

17. $(3a)^2$ **18.** $(2b)^3$ **19.** $(2x^3)^3$ **20.** $(4p^2)^3$

21. $(3x^2yz^4)^2$ **22.** $(-2x^6y^2)^3$ **23.** $[(-n)^{15}]^2$ **24.** $\left(\frac{y^3}{3}\right)^4$

5-3

To multiply two **monomials**, multiply the numerical factors and the variable factors. Use the properties of exponents to multiply the variables: $(-3x^2y)(-5xy^5) = 15x^3y^6$. To divide two monomials, divide the numerical factors and the variable factors: $\frac{15x^3y^4}{-5xy^2} = -3x^2y^2$

Multiply.

25. $(2a)(3a)$ **26.** $(-2x)(3x^2)$ **27.** $(5b^2c^3)(-4bc^3)$

28. $(5y^3)(-2y)(-y^4)$ **29.** $-(3wz^4)(-5w^2z^3)$ **30.** $(-4x^2y)(-8xy^3)$

Divide.

31. $\frac{a^6}{a^3}$ **32.** $\frac{15n^5}{-15n}$ **33.** $\frac{-15x^3y^6}{5xy^3}$

34. $\frac{-24m^{12}n^2}{-6m^5n}$ **35.** $\frac{18b^{14}c^6}{-3b^7c^2}$ **36.** $\frac{-28x^4y^8}{-7x^2y^6}$

5-4

The numbers 3.215×10^4 and 4.17×10^{-3} are expressed using **scientific notation**, and the numbers 32,150 and 0.00417 are expressed using **standard notation.**

Write using standard notation.

37. $3.25 \cdot 10^3$ **38.** $5.7 \cdot 10^{-3}$

Write using scientific notation.

39. 2,426,000 **40.** 0.000045

5-5

In a **polynomial**, each monomial can be called a **term**. In the term $3a^2b^3$, 3 is called the **coefficient**, and factors are 3, a^2, and b^3. To collect like terms, add or subtract the coefficients of the like terms. To find the **degree of a term**, add the exponents of the variables in that term. The **degree of a polynomial** is the highest degree of its terms.

Collect like terms.

41. $5x^3 - x^3 + 4$ **42.** $-2x^4 + 16 + 2x^4 + 9 - 3x^5$

Identify the degree of each term and the degree of the polynomial.

43. $3x^3y^2 + 7x^2y - 5$ **44.** $4y^2 + 7y + 2$

5-6

To write a polynomial in **descending order** for the variable x, write the term with the greatest exponent for x first, the next greatest exponent for x second, and so on. A constant term will always be last. To evaluate a polynomial, replace the variable with the given number and calculate the result.

Arrange each polynomial in descending order for the variable x.

45. $3x^2 - 2x^4 + 5 + 7x^5 - 2x$ **46.** $3y - 4x^5 - 2x^3y^2 + 7x^2y^3$

47. $-x^5 + 14x^4 - 7x - 1 - 4x^4$ **48.** $6y + 3x^3 - 7xy^2 + 8x^4y^3$

Evaluate each polynomial for $x = 5$.

49. $7x - 10$ **50.** $x^2 - 3x + 6$

5-7

To add polynomials collect like terms and arrange in descending order.

Add.

51. $(5x^3 - 2x^2 + 3x) + (2x^3 + 6x^2 + x)$

52. $(3x^4 - x^3 + x - 4) + (3x^4 - 5x^3 + 3x^2 - 5)$

53. $(3x^5 - 4x^4 + x^3 - 3) + (3x^4 - 5x^3 + 3x^2)$

54. $(a^3 + 7a^2b - ab^2 - 2b^3) + (2a^3 - 3ab^2 + 2b^3)$

37. 3250
38. 0.0057
39. 2.426×10^6
40. 4.5×10^{-5}
41. $4x^3 + 4$
42. $-3x^5 + 25$
43. 5, 3, 0; 5
44. 2, 1, 0; 2
45. $7x^5 - 2x^4 + 3x^2 - 2x + 5$
46. $-4x^5 - 2x^3y^2 + 7x^2y^3 + 3y$
47. $-x^5 + 10x^4 - 7x - 1$
48. $8x^4y^3 + 3x^3 - 7xy^2 + 6y$
49. 25
50. 16
51. $7x^3 + 4x^2 + 4x$
52. $6x^4 - 6x^3 + 3x^2 + x - 9$
53. $3x^5 - x^4 - 4x^3 + 3x^2 - 3$
54. $3a^3 + 7a^2b - 4ab^2$

55. $4y^3 + 14$
56. $2x^2 - 4x - 6$
57. $x^5 + 8x^4 - 3x^3 - 2x^2 + 8$
58. $-2y^2 - 2y + 11$
59. $-x^5 + x^4 - 5x^3 - 2x^2 + 2x$
60. $15x^2 + 18x$
61. $15x^6 - 40x^5 + 50x^4 + 10x^3$
62. $x^2 - 3x - 28$
63. $a^2 - 9$
64. $b^4 + 5b^2 + 6$
65. $6x^4 + 15x^3y - 6x^2 - 15xy$
66. $x^2 - 9$
67. $a^2 - 64$
68. $4y^2 - 9$
69. $9x^4 - 16$
70. $4y^2 - 49x^2$
71. $4 - 9y^2$
72. $a^2 + 8a + 16$
73. $9x^2 + 36x + 36$
74. $12x^3 - 23x^2 + 13x - 2$
75. $2a^4 + 3a^3 - 10a^2 - 12a + 8$
76. $4b^4 + 6b^3 - 14b^2 + 11b - 3$
77. $x^7 + x^5 - 3x^4 + 3x^3 - 2x^2 + 5x - 3$

5-8

When you find the **additive inverse of a polynomial,** you change the sign of each term in the polynomial. You can subtract a polynomial by adding its additive inverse.

Subtract.

55. $(7y^3 + 8) - (3y^3 - 6)$
56. $(5x^2 - 4x + 1) - (3x^2 + 7)$
57. $(3x^5 + 4x^4 + 2x^2 + 3) - (2x^5 - 4x^4 + 3x^3 + 4x^2 - 5)$

Use columns to subtract.

58. $(6y^2 - 5y + 3) - (8y^2 - 3y - 8)$
59. $(2x^5 - x^3 + x + 3) - (3x^5 - x^4 + 4x^3 + 2x^2 - x + 3)$

5-9

To multiply a polynomial by a monomial, multiply each term of the polynomial by the monomial. To multiply two binomials, use the **FOIL** method: multiply the First terms, the Outside terms, the Inside terms, and the Last terms. Then collect like terms.

Multiply.

60. $3x(5x + 6)$
61. $5x^3(3x^3 - 8x^2 + 10x + 2)$

Multiply and collect like terms.

62. $(x + 4)(x - 7)$
63. $(a - 3)(a + 3)$
64. $(b^2 + 3)(b^2 + 2)$
65. $(2x^2 + 5xy)(3x^2 - 3)$

5-10

Although FOIL can be used to multiply two binomials, the rules for the following special products can be used as shortcuts.

$$(A + B)(A - B) = A^2 - B^2$$
$$(A + B)^2 = A^2 + 2AB + B^2$$
$$(A - B)^2 = A^2 - 2AB + B^2$$

Multiply.

66. $(x - 3)(x + 3)$
67. $(a - 8)(a + 8)$
68. $(2y + 3)(2y - 3)$
69. $(3x^2 - 4)(3x^2 + 4)$
70. $(-2y + 7x)(-2y - 7x)$
71. $(2 + 3y)(2 - 3y)$
72. $(a + 4)^2$
73. $(3x + 6)^2$

5-11

To multiply a trinomial by a binomial, multiply the trinomial by each term of the binomial. To multiply two polynomials, multiply each term of one polynomial by every term of the other. It may help you to use columns for long multiplications.

74. $(4x^2 - 5x + 1)(3x - 2)$
75. $(2a^2 + 3a - 2)(a^2 - 4)$
76. $(2b^2 + 5b - 3)(2b^2 - 2b + 1)$
77. $(x^4 - 2x + 3)(x^3 + x - 1)$

Chapter 5 Test

Simplify. Express using exponents.

1. $6^2 \cdot 6^3$
2. $x^6 \cdot x^2$
3. $a^8 \cdot a^3$
4. $(r^2s^3)(rs^4)$
5. $\frac{3^5}{3^2}$
6. $\frac{a^4b^5}{ab^3}$

Simplify. Express using a positive exponent.

7. 6^{-2}
8. y^{-4}
9. 3^0

Simplify.

10. $(x^3)^2$
11. $(-3y^2)^3$
12. $\left(\frac{a^4}{3}\right)^3$

Multiply.

13. $(-2y^2)(4y)$
14. $(6x^2)(-2x^3)(-2x^5)$
15. $(-4n^3)(-4n^3)$

Divide.

16. $\frac{b^5}{b}$
17. $\frac{7a^4}{a^4}$
18. $\frac{4x^5}{12x^3}$

Write using standard notation.

19. $3.265 \cdot 10^5$
20. $2.07 \cdot 10^{-3}$

Write using scientific notation.

21. 246,000
22. 0.00385

Collect like terms.

23. $4a^2 - 6 + a^2$
24. $y^2 - 3y - y + 2y^2$

Collect like terms, and then arrange them in descending order.

25. $3 - x^2 + 2x + 5x^2 - 6x$

Evaluate the polynomial for $x = -2$.

26. $x^2 + 5x - 1$

Add.

27. $(5x^4 + 7x^3 - 8) + (3x^4 - 5x^3 + 6x^2)$

Subtract.

28. $(12x^2 - 3x - 8) - (4x^2 + 5)$

Multiply.

29. $-3x^2(4x^2 - 3x - 5)$
30. $(3b + 5)(b - 3)$
31. $(6a^2 - 2)(a^2 - 1)$
32. $(3p - 2)(3p + 2)$
33. $(3x^2 + 4)(3x^2 - 4)$
34. $(x - 9)^2$
35. $(4x^7 + 3)(4x^7 - 3)$
36. $(3x^2 - 2x)^2$
37. $(2x + 1)(3x^2 - 5x - 3)$
38. $(-2a^3 + 5a^2 - 3)(3a^2 + 1)$

ANSWERS

1. 6^5
2. x^8
3. a^{11}
4. r^3s^7
5. 3^3
6. a^3b^2
7. $\frac{1}{6^2}$
8. $\frac{1}{y^4}$
9. 1
10. x^6
11. $-27y^6$
12. $\frac{a^{12}}{27}$
13. $-8y^3$
14. $24x^{10}$
15. $16n^6$
16. b^4
17. 7
18. $\frac{x^2}{3}$
19. 326,500
20. 0.00207
21. 2.46×10^5
22. 3.85×10^{-3}
23. $5a^2 - 6$
24. $3y^2 - 4y$
25. $4x^2 - 4x + 3$
26. -7
27. $8x^4 + 2x^3 + 6x^2 - 8$
28. $8x^2 - 3x - 13$
29. $-12x^4 + 9x^3 + 15x^2$
30. $3b^2 - 4b - 15$
31. $6a^4 - 8a^2 + 2$
32. $9p^2 - 4$
33. $9x^4 - 16$
34. $x^2 - 18x + 81$
35. $16x^{14} - 9$
36. $9x^4 - 12x^3 + 4x^2$
37. $6x^3 - 7x^2 - 11x - 3$
38. $-6a^5 + 15a^4 - 2a^3 - 4a^2 - 3$

Test Item Analysis

Item	Lesson
1–9	5-1
10–12	5-2
13–18	5-3
19–22	5-4
23, 24	5-5
25, 26	5-6
27	5-7
28	5-8
29–32	5-9
33–36	5-10
37, 38	5-11

CHAPTER 6 Polynomials and Factoring

Chapter Overview

Techniques for factoring polynomial expressions are developed in this chapter. Monomials are factored, and common factors are factored from polynomials. Expressions that are the difference of two squares; expressions that are trinomial squares; and expressions that are the products of linear factors with simple integer coefficients are recognized and factored. A model for factoring $x^2 + bx + c$ is illustrated with algebra tiles. Factorization by grouping is covered, and a strategy for factoring is discussed.

Factorization and the principle of zero products are used to solve equations. Word problems involving second degree polynomials are translated to algebraic notation and solved. Binomial expansion is introduced in Connections: Discrete Math. Problem Solving: College Entrance Exams illustrates ways that skills learned can be adapted for specific types of problems that occur on college entrance exams.

Objectives

6-1 ■ Factor monomials.
■ Factor out common factors in the terms of a polynomial.
6-2 ■ Recognize a difference of two squares.
■ Factor a difference of two squares.
■ Factor a difference of two squares completely.
6-3 ■ Recognize a trinomial square.
■ Factor trinomial squares.
6-4 ■ Factor trinomials of the type $x^2 + bx + c$ where $c > 0$.
■ Factor trinomials of the type $x^2 + bx + c$ where $c < 0$.
6-5 ■ Factor trinomials of the type $ax^2 + bx + c$.
6-6 ■ Factor polynomials by grouping.
6-7 ■ Factor polynomials.
6-8 ■ Solve equations expressed as a product of factors equal to zero.
■ Factor and solve equations.
6-9 ■ Solve problems by writing and solving equations.

TEACHING CHAPTER 6

Cooperative Learning Opportunities

Tutoring is an effective form of paired cooperative learning. Most teachers find that some students catch on to factoring quickly while others just don't know what to look for. Repeatedly going over examples on the chalkboard might not serve either group very well. But a one-to-one review of exercises like those in Lessons 6-3 through 6-6 can be helpful. Pair students who could not do three or more homework problems with students who were able to do them. The tutors explain how they thought about the problem, what they tried, and how they checked their solutions. Their partners rate them on clarity of explanation.

The tutors probably will not say anything different from what you have said in class. But the one-to-one arrangement can sometimes make all the difference.

Alternative Assessment and Communication Ideas

In the film *Stand and Deliver*, Jaime Escalante, used a kind of calculus bee, like a spelling bee, for quick responses in basic knowledge. This approach can be used for some of the skills in Chapter 6 that should be at the tip of one's fingers.

Prepare a number of flash cards with exercises that you want students to solve in a few seconds. You can use the same polynomials several times asking different questions. For example,

Card Shown	Your Instruction
$x^2 + 7x$	Find the common factor.
$x^2 + 3x - 10$	Find the factors of 10 used in the factored form of this trinomial.
$x^2 - 7x$	Factor.

You can maintain interest in this activity by dividing the class into two teams, one on each side of the classroom. Students return to their seats after one (or 2) misses. Last one up wins for his or her team. You may wish to permit group coaching to promote team spirit.

Multicultural Note: *Chu Shih-Chieh*

The derivation of Pascal's Triangle from the binomial expansion is shown on page 285. This apparently simple device, which has far-reaching applications, was discovered several times—in widely separated times and places. It is usually attributed to Blaise Pascal, the French mathematician who lived from 1623 to 1662. However, Pascal's Triangle was discovered some 500 years before he was born.

In 1303, the Chinese mathematician Chu Shih-Chieh displayed the famous triangle in his book, *Precious Mirror of the Four Elements*. He did not take credit but referred to it as the *ku-fa* ("old method") for finding binomial coefficients. He was the last mathematician of the golden age of Chinese mathematics during the Sung Dynasty, and some describe him as the greatest mathematician of all time. His book deals with simultaneous equations and the solution of equations with exponents as high as fourteen.

A form of Pascal's Triangle appears even earlier. The Persian mathematician Omar Khayyam (1050–1122) also displayed the method.

For more information, see page 45 of **Multiculturalism in Mathematics, Science, and Technology**.

Investigations and Projects

Recent research in the learning of mathematics has found that the casual exploration of future topics, when undertaken within the scope of students' knowledge and ability, can lead to more solid and integrated learning. Making connections among the topics of factoring polynomials, solving equations, and graphing can enhance the understanding of each of these areas.

Ask students to construct tables showing the numbers that appear in the following tables.

x	−3	−2	−1	0	1	2	3
x^2	**9**	**4**	**1**	**0**	**1**	**4**	**9**
$x+3$	**0**	**1**	**2**	**3**	**4**	**5**	**6**
x^2+x+3	**9**	**5**	**3**	**3**	**5**	**9**	**15**

Ask students to describe and discuss the patterns that they see in each line of the tables. This activity will give students a fresh look at polynomials and a preview of some characteristics of graphs. You can use other polynomials according to time and interest.

Lesson	PACING CHART (DAYS) 2-Year* A for E	1-Year Minimum	1-Year Regular	1-Year Advanced	Opening Activity	Cooperative Activity	Seat or Group Work
6-1	3	1	1	1	First Five Minutes 6-1: ***FFMTM*** p. 21 or **TE** p. 262	Explore: **SE** p. 262; Connections: Geometry: **SE** p. 265	Try This a–i
6-2	2	1	1	1	First Five Minutes 6-2: ***FFMTM*** p. 21 or **TE** p. 266	Critical Thinking 6: ***Enrichment*** p. 23	Try This a–r
6-3	2	1	1	1	First Five Minutes 6-3: ***FFMTM*** p. 21 or **TE** p. 270	Lesson Enrichment: **TE** p. 271	Try This a–j
6-4	3	1.5	1	1	First Five Minutes 6-4: ***FFMTM*** p. 22 or **TE** p. 273	✂ Manipulative Activity 6: ***Enrichment*** p. 39	Try This a–l
6-5	3	1.5	1	1	First Five Minutes 6-5: ***FFMTM*** p. 22 or **TE** p. 278	Suppose: **SE** p. 277	Try This a–i
6-6	2	1	1	1	First Five Minutes 6-6: ***FFMTM*** p. 22 or **TE** p. 281	Problem 29: **SE** p. 282	Try This a–d
6-7	2	2	1	1	First Five Minutes 6-7: ***FFMTM*** p. 22 or **TE** p. 283	Connections: Discrete Math: **SE** p. 285	Try This a–f
6-8	3	1.5	1	1	First Five Minutes 6-8: ***FFMTM*** p. 23 or **TE** p. 286	Lesson Enrichmen: **TE** p. 288	Try This a–j
6-9	2	1.5	2	1.5	First Five Minutes 6-9: ***FFMTM*** p. 23 or **TE** p. 291; ***Overhead Transparencies*** T7	Problem 26: **SE** p. 295	Try This a–g
Review	2	1	1	0.5			
Test	1	1	1	1			
Cum. Review	0	2	0	0			
Mid-Year Test	0	1	0	0			

*2-Year Management Guide can be found in *Algebra for Everyone*. FFMTM: First Five Minutes Transparency Masters

Enrichment	Review/Assess	Reteach	Technology	Lesson
Bonus Topic 6: ***Enrichment*** p. 7 Connections: Geometry: **SE** p. 265	Lesson Quiz: **TE** p. 263		BASIC Computer Project 9: ***Technology*** p. 71	**6-1**
Critical Thinking 6: ***Enrichment*** p. 23	Mixed Review 11: ***SPMR*** p. 61; Lesson Quiz: **TE** p. 268		BASIC Computer Project 10: ***Technology*** p. 72	**6-2**
Lesson Enrichment: **TE** p. 271	Lesson Quiz: **TE** p. 271; Quiz 11: ***Assessment*** p. 21	Skills Practice 15: ***SPMR*** p. 23		**6-3**
✂ Manipulative Activity 6: ***Enrichment*** p. 39	Lesson Quiz: **TE** p. 275		Calculator Worksheet 16: ***Technology*** p. 18	**6-4**
Suppose: **SE** p. 277	Mixed Practice 11: **SE** p. 694; Lesson Quiz: **TE** p. 279			**6-5**
Writing to Learn: **SE** p. 280	Lesson Quiz: **TE** p. 281; Quiz 12: ***Assessment*** p. 22	Skills Practice 16: ***SPMR*** p. 24		**6-6**
Looking for Errors 6: ***Enrichment*** p. 55; Connections: Discrete Math: **SE** p. 285	Lesson Quiz: **TE** p. 283			**6-7**
Lesson Enrichment: **TE** p. 288; Problem for Programmers: **SE** p. 290	Mixed Review 12: ***SPMR*** p. 62; Lesson Quiz: **TE** p. 288		Calculator Worksheet 17: ***Technology*** p. 19; Problem for Programmers: **SE** p. 290	**6-8**
Biographical Note: Thomas Harriot: **SE** p. 296; Problem Solving: College Entrance Exams: **SE** pp. 297–298	Mixed Practice 12: **SE** p. 695; Lesson Quiz: **TE** p. 293	Skills Practice 17: ***SPMR*** p. 25; Problem Bank 12: ***Problem Bank*** p. 29		**6-9**
	Summary and Review: **SE** pp. 299–301; Test: **SE** p. 301	Strategy Problem Bank 6: ***Problem Bank*** p. 7		**Review**
	Chapter 6 Exam: ***A for E*** pp. 263–264; Chapter 6 Test: ***Assessment*** pp. 53–54 (min.), 101–106 (reg.), 173–174 (adv.)			**Test**
	Cumulative Review: **SE** pp. 351–355			**Cum. Review**
	Mid-Year Test: ***Assessment*** pp. 213–216 (min.)			**Mid-Year Test**

SPMR: Skills Practice Mixed Review

The solution to the problem posed on the facing page can be found on pages 292–293.

Ready for Polynomials and Factoring?

1-5 Factor.

1. $6x + 6y$ $6(x + y)$ **2.** $24w + 24z$ $24(w + z)$ **3.** $4y + 28 + 12z$ $4(y + 7 + 3z)$

3-4 Write as an algebraic expression.

4. 10 more than twice the number $2n + 10$

5. 2 times the sum of a number and 6 $2(n + 6)$

3-5 Solve.

6. $6y + 4 = 2y + 8$ 1 **7.** $3(2a + 4) = 20$ $\frac{4}{3}$

3-11

8. The perimeter of a rectangle is 280 cm. The length is 20 cm more than the width. Find the dimensions. 80 cm, 60 cm

5-3 Multiply.

9. $(-6x^8)(2x^5)$ $-12x^{13}$ **10.** $(-6x^2y^2)(4xy^4)$ $-24x^3y^6$

5-9 Multiply.

11. $9x(4x + 7)$ $36x^2 + 63x$ **12.** $3s(6t^4 - 2s^2 - 3t - 6)$ $18st^4 - 6s^3 - 9s$

13. $(3x + 8)(x - 7)$ $3x^2 - 13x - 56$ **14.** $(x + 3)(5x - 7)$ $5x^2 + 8x - 21$

15. $8x(2x^2 - 6x + 1)$ $16x^3 - 48x^2 + 8x$ **16.** $(x + 6)(x - 4)$ $x^2 + 2x - 24$

17. $(y - 8)(y + 3)$ $y^2 - 5y - 24$ **18.** $(7w + 6)(4w - 1)$ $28w^2 + 17w - 6$

5-10 Multiply.

19. $(x - 9)^2$ $x^2 - 18x + 81$ **20.** $(5x + 3)^2$ $25x^2 + 30x + 9$

21. $(a - 7)(a + 7)$ $a^2 - 49$ **22.** $(2 - 5y)(2 + 5y)$ $4 - 25y^2$

CHAPTER

6 Polynomials and Factoring

The area of the foresail on a 12-meter racing yacht is 93.75 square meters. The sail's height is 8.75 meters greater than its base. Find its base and height.

6-1

FIRST FIVE MINUTES

Multiply.

1. $(3x)(4x)$ $12x^2$
2. $-5x(2x)$ $-10x^2$
3. $-2x(-4x)$ $8x^2$
4. $4(x + 3)$ $4x + 12$
5. $3x(2x^2 - 4)$ $6x^3 - 12x$

EXPLORE

Some examples are $8x$ and $2x^3$, 4 and $4x^4$, x^2 and $16x^2$, $4x^2$ and $4x^2$, $8x^3$ and $2x$, $16x$ and x^3, and others.

Factoring Monomials

You may want to review factoring numbers before you begin factoring monomials.

The strategy *Make an Organized List* is useful for finding all factorizations of monomials.

Avoiding Common Errors

Students may list $(2x)(3)$ and $3(2x)$ as two different factors. Point out that since multiplication is commutative, these are the same factors. If students list the factors in an organized fashion (see *Make an Organized List*), they will not be as likely to have this kind of duplication.

Key Questions

- Are 8 and 2 factors of 18? No
- Are 7 and 5 factors of 105? Yes

Chalkboard Examples

1. Find factorizations of $6x^2$.
   Possible factorizations are
   $(1)(6x^2)$, $(2)(3x^2)$, $(3)(2x^2)$, $(6)(x^2)$, $(1x)(6x)$, $(2x)(3x)$, $(-1)(-6x^2)$, $(-2)(-3x^2)$, $(-3)(-2x^2)$, $(-6)(-x^2)$, $(-1x)(-6x)$, $(-2x)(-3x)$
2. Find factorizations of $6c^2d$.
   Possible factorizations are
   $(1)(6c^2d)$, $(c)(6cd)$, $(c^2)(6d)$, $(c^2d)(6)$, $(2)(3c^2d)$, $(2c)(3cd)$, $(2c^2)(3d)$, $(2c^2d)(3)$

6-1 Factoring Polynomials

Explore

How many pairs of monomials can you find whose product is $16x^4$. *Make an organized list* showing the pairs you find.

Factoring Monomials

Objective: Factor monomials.

Factoring is the reverse of multiplying. To factor an expression means to write an equivalent expression that is a product of two or more expressions.

To factor a monomial, we find two monomials whose product is that monomial. Compare.

Multiplying	**Factoring**
$(4x)(5x) = 20x^2$	$20x^2 = (4x)(5x)$
$(2x)(10x) = 20x^2$	$20x^2 = (2x)(10x)$
$(-4x)(-5x) = 20x^2$	$20x^2 = (-4x)(-5x)$
$(x)(20x) = 20x^2$	$20x^2 = (x)(20x)$
$(2)(10x^2) = 20x^2$	$20x^2 = (2)(10x^2)$

There are still other ways to factor $20x^2$. Each is called a **factorization** of $20x^2$.

EXAMPLE 1 Find factorizations of $15x^3$.

Factors of $15x^3$ are $1, -1, 3, -3, 5, -5, 15, -15, x, x^2, x^3$. Some possible factorizations are

$(15x)(1x^2)$ $(5x)(3x^2)$ $(3)(5x^3)$
$(1x)(15x^2)$ $(3x)(5x^2)$ $(5)(3x^3)$

Since $(-1)(-1) = 1$, we could also have the following.

$(-15x)(-1x^2)$ $(-5x)(-3x^2)$ $(-3)(-5x^3)$
$(-1x)(-15x^2)$ $(-3x)(-5x^2)$ $(-5)(-3x^3)$

There are still other ways to factor $15x^3$.

Try This Find three factorizations of each monomial.

a. $8x^4$ **b.** $6m^5$ **c.** $12a^2b^2$

Answers may vary.
a. $(4x^2)(2x^2)$, $(4x)(2x^3)$, $(8x)(x^3)$
b. $(2m)(3m^4)$, $(m^2)(6m^3)$, $(2m^3)(3m^2)$
c. $(6ab)(2ab)$, $(6a^2)(2b^2)$, $(12)(a^2b^2)$

Factoring When Terms Have a Common Factor

Objective: Factor out common factors in the terms of a polynomial.

To multiply a monomial and a polynomial, we use the distributive property to multiply each term of the polynomial by the monomial. To factor, we do the reverse and *factor out* a common factor. We use the factor common to each term with the greatest possible coefficient and the variable to the greatest power.

Compare.

Multiply	Factor
$5(x + 3) = 5 \cdot x + 5 \cdot 3$	$5x + 15 = 5 \cdot x + 5 \cdot 3$
$= 5x + 15$	$= 5(x + 3)$
$3a(b^2 + 2) = 3a(b^2) + 3a(2)$	$3ab^2 + 6a = 3a(b^2) + 3a(2)$
$= 3ab^2 + 6a$	$= 3a(b^2 + 2)$

We say we have "factored out" the common factor.

EXAMPLES Factor.

2. $3x^2 + 3 = 3(x^2) + 3(1)$
   $= 3(x^2 + 1)$ Factoring out the common factor, 3

3. $5y^4 - 20y^3 = 5y^3(y) - 5y^3(4)$
   $= 5y^3(y - 4)$ Factoring out the common factor, $5y^3$

4. $16a^2b^2 + 20a^2 = 4a^2(4b^2) + 4a^2(5)$
   $= 4a^2(4b^2 + 5)$ Factoring out the common factor, $4a^2$

5. $15x^5 - 12x^4 + 27x^3 - 3x^2$
   $= 3x^2(5x^3) - 3x^2(4x^2) + 3x^2(9x) - 3x^2(1)$
   $= 3x^2(5x^3 - 4x^2 + 9x - 1)$ Factoring out the common factor, $3x^2$

6. $4m^2n^3 + 2m^2n^2 + 6m^2n = 2m^2n(2n^2) + 2m^2n(n) + 2m^2n(3)$
   $= 2m^2n(2n^2 + n + 3)$

Try This Factor.

d. $x^2 + 3x$ $x(x + 3)$

e. $a^2b + 2ab$ $ab(a + 2)$

f. $3x^6 - 5x^3 + 2x^2$ $x^2(3x^4 - 5x + 2)$

g. $9x^4 - 15x^3 + 3x^2$ $3x^2(3x^2 - 5x + 1)$

h. $2p^3q^2 + p^2q + pq$ $pq(2p^2q + p + 1)$

i. $12m^4n^4 + 3m^3n^2 + 6m^2n^2$ $3m^2n^2(4m^2n^2 + m + 2)$

Factoring When Terms Have a Common Factor

Students can learn to factor expressions mentally by scanning. For example, suppose we want to factor the expression $4x^3y^2 + 6x^2y^3 + 8x^4y$.

First, scan the coefficients of the terms to find the greatest common factor, 2.

Next, scan the terms for the greatest common power of the first variable x, in this case x^2. The factor so far is $2x^2$.

Finally, scan the terms for the greatest common power of y, in this case y. The greatest common factor is $2x^2y$. Factor out this common factor.
$2x^2y(2xy + 3y^2 + 4x^2)$

Chalkboard Examples

Factor.

1. $5x^3 + 10$
   $5(x^3) + 5(2) = 5(x^3 + 2)$
2. $6x^3 + 12x^2$
   $6x^2(x) + 6x^2(2) = 6x^2(x + 2)$
3. $12u^3v^2 + 16uv^4$
   $4uv^2(3u^2) + 4uv^2(4v^2)$
   $= 4uv^2(3u^2 + 4v^2)$
4. $18y^4 - 6y^3 + 12y^2$
   $6y^2(3y^2) - 6y^2(y) + 6y^2(2)$
   $= (6y^2)(3y^2 - y + 2)$
5. $8x^4y^3 - 6x^2y^4$
   $2x^2y^3(4x^2) - 2x^2y^3(3y)$
   $= 2x^2y^3(4x^2 - 3y)$
6. $5x^3y^4 + 7x^2z^3 + 3y^2z$
   There is no common factor in this case.

LESSON QUIZ

Factor.

1. $6y^3 + 4y$
   $2y(3y^2 + 2)$
2. $9x^3 + 6x^2 + 12x$
   $3x(3x^2 + 2x + 4)$
3. $15x^3y^5 - 10x^2y^6 + 20x^5y^3$
   $5x^2y^3(3xy^2 - 2y^3 + 4x^3)$

Assignment Guide
Minimum: 1–41 e/o, MR

Regular: 1–54 e/o, 55, MR

Advanced: 1–41 m3, 42–54 e/o, 55–59, MR

ADDITIONAL ANSWERS

Exercises

10. $x(x - 4)$
11. $y(y + 8)$
12. $2a(a + 3)$
13. $3p(p - 1)$
14. $3(y^4 + 2y^2 + 2)$
15. $5(x^2 + 2x + 6)$
16. $2m(7m^3 - 6)$
17. $7y^2(4 + 3y^2)$
18. $x^4(32x - 17)$
19. $x^3(9 + 25x^4)$
20. a^2
21. $18y^4$
22. $2(x^2 + x - 4)$
23. $3(2x^2 + x - 5)$
24. $x^2y(x + 6)$
25. $a^2b(4a^2b + 1)$
26. $8x^2y(x^2y - 3)$
27. $5m^3(m^2n + 2)$
28. $3m^3n(4m^2n + 3m + 2n)$
29. $2xy^2(x^2 + 3y + 4)$
30. $17x(x^4 + 2x^2 + 3)$
31. $16x(x^5 - 2x^4 - 3)$
32. $x^2(6x^2 - 10x + 3)$
33. $x(5x^4 + 10x - 8)$
34. $x^2(x^3 + x^2 + x - 1)$
35. $x^3(x^6 - x^4 + x + 1)$
36. $2x^3(x^4 - x^3 - 32x^2 + 2)$
37. $5(2x^3 + 5x^2 + 3x - 4)$
38. $2a^2(2a^2b^4 - ab^2 + 3)$
39. $5pq^2(p^2 + 2p - 4)$
40. $x^2(2xy - 4y + 1)$
41. $m^2n^2(6mn + 3m + 1)$

6-1 EXERCISES

A

Find three factorizations for each monomial. Answers may vary.

1. $6x^3$ **2.** $9y^4$ **3.** $-9a^5$
4. $-12x^6$ **5.** $24x^4y^2$ **6.** $15m^5n$
7. $-18p^3q^2$ **8.** $10r^2s^6$ **9.** $12a^3b^4$

Factor.

10. $x^2 - 4x$
11. $y^2 + 8y$
12. $2a^2 + 6a$
13. $3p^2 - 3p$
14. $3y^4 + 6y^2 + 6$
15. $5x^2 + 10x + 30$
16. $14m^4 - 12m$
17. $28y^2 + 21y^4$
18. $32x^5 - 17x^4$
19. $9x^3 + 25x^7$
20. $6a^2 - 5a^2$
21. $11y^4 + 7y^4$
22. $2x^2 + 2x - 8$
23. $6x^2 + 3x - 15$
24. $x^3y + 6x^2y$
25. $4a^4b^2 + a^2b$
26. $8x^4y^2 - 24x^2y$
27. $5m^5n + 10m^3$
28. $12m^5n^2 + 9m^4n + 6m^3n^2$
29. $2x^3y^2 + 6xy^3 + 8xy^2$
30. $17x^5 + 34x^3 + 51x$
31. $16x^6 - 32x^5 - 48x$
32. $6x^4 - 10x^3 + 3x^2$
33. $5x^5 + 10x^2 - 8x$
34. $x^5 + x^4 + x^3 - x^2$
35. $x^9 - x^7 + x^4 + x^3$
36. $2x^7 - 2x^6 - 64x^5 + 4x^3$
37. $10x^3 + 25x^2 + 15x - 20$
38. $4a^4b^4 - 2a^3b^2 + 6a^2$
39. $5p^3q^2 + 10p^2q^2 - 20pq^2$
40. $2x^3y - 4x^2y + x^2$
41. $6m^3n^3 + 3m^3n^2 + m^2n^2$

B

Two polynomials are relatively prime if they have no common factors other than constants. Tell which pairs are relatively prime.

42. $5x, x^2$ No
43. $3x, ax - 3$ Yes
44. $x + x^2, 3x^3$ No
45. $y - 6, y$ Yes
46. $7a, a$ No
47. $2p^2 + 2, 2p$ Yes
48. $t^2 - 4t, t^2 - 4$ Yes
49. $3a^2 - a, a^3 - 2a$ No
50. $2x + 4, 2x^2 - 4$ Yes
51. $m^2 + 4mn, 3mn + 2m$ No
52. $4x^5 + 8x^3 - 6x, 8x^3 + 12x^2 + 24x - 16$ Yes
53. $6x^2y + 4xy + 2x, 2x^3 + 8x^2y + 14x$ No
54. $a^3 + a^2b + ab^2 + b^3, a^2 - ab^2$ Yes

55. *Critical Thinking* Represent the area (A) of the shaded region using an expression in factored form. (Formulas for area can be found in Table 3 in the appendix.) $r^2(4 - \pi)$

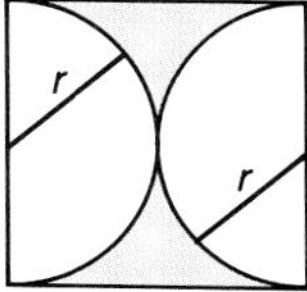

Challenge

Find the common factor, if one exists.

56. $6t^3 + 30t^2, 9t^3 + 27t^2 + 9t$ $3t$

57. $12t^4 - 15t^3 + 6t + 18, 16t^4 + 24t^3 - 48t^2 - 32t$ No common factor

58. $192t^6 - 480t^4, 144t^8 + 72t^2$ $24t^2$

59. $27x^5 - 81x^2 + 9x, 8x^4 - 16x + 4$ No common factor

Mixed Review

Simplify. **60.** $x^7 \cdot x^5 \cdot x$ **61.** $(3m^2n^3)^2$ **62.** $(9t^2)(-2t^5)$

Write using scientific notation. **63.** 0.00437 **64.** 307.5 **65.** 5613

Collect like terms and then arrange in descending order for the variable m.

66. $12 - 9m^3 + 6m^2 + 4m^3 - 8m^2$ **67.** $5m^2 + 116 - 4m^2 + 3$

Mixed Review
60. x^{13}
61. $9m^4n^6$
62. $-18t^7$
63. 4.37×10^{-3}
64. 3.075×10^2
65. 5.613×10^3
66. $-5m^3 - 2m^2 + 12$
67. $m^2 + 119$

CONNECTIONS: GEOMETRY

Recall that the perimeter of a polygon is the sum of the lengths of its sides. Use the idea of perimeter to complete each of the following.

1. The perimeter of the parallelogram below is $8x + 4y$. What are the lengths of the missing sides?

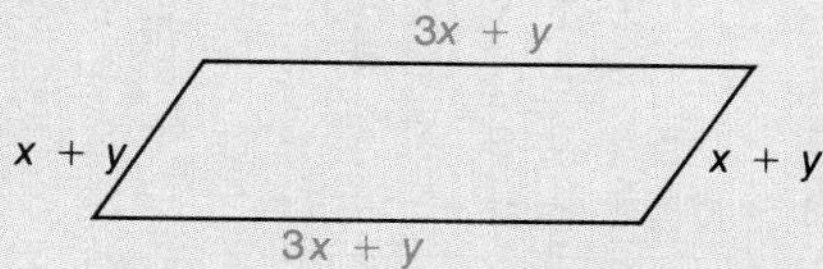

2. The perimeter of the trapezoid below is $16x + 3$. The base of the trapezoid is 1 more than twice the length of the opposite side. What are the lengths of the missing sides?

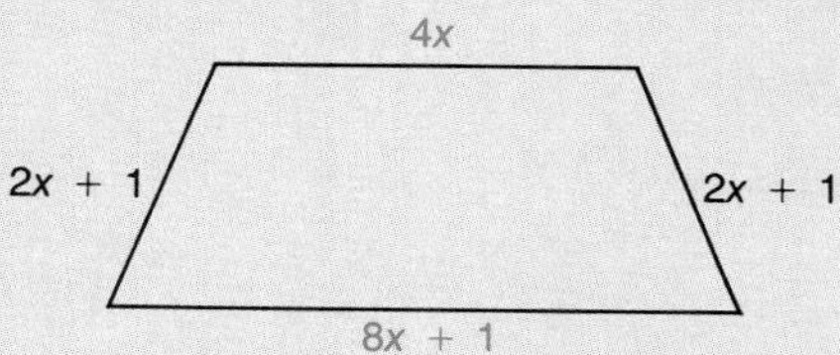

6-2

FIRST FIVE MINUTES

1. Factor $3x^2 + 9x$.
   $3x(x + 3)$
2. Multiply $2x^2(3x + 4)$.
   $6x^3 + 8x^2$
3. Multiply $(x + 3)(x - 3)$.
   $x^2 - 9$
4. Multiply $(x - 5)(x + 5)$.
   $x^2 - 25$

Recognizing Differences of Two Squares

Recognizing the difference of two squares leads naturally into the next section, factoring the difference of two squares. You may wish to point out that the only binomials that can be factored to the product of two binomials are differences of two squares.

Key Questions

Is the polynomial the difference of two squares?

- $u^2 - v^2$
  Yes
- $x^2 - y^3$
  No
- $x^2 + y^2$
  No
- $x^2 - 1$
  Yes

Chalkboard Examples

Rewrite as a difference of two squares.

1. $4x^2 - 16y^2$
   $(2x)^2 - (4y)^2$
2. $9a^2 + 6ab + b^2 - 1$
   $(3a + b)^2 - (1)^2$

Factoring Differences of Two Squares

Only a few special polynomial forms can be factored. In order to factor some polynomials, students should recognize those special forms. Emphasize that students must memorize the special forms to do the problems.

Students can make the following model out of paper. By cutting along the lines, discarding the square with sides b, and fitting the remaining two pieces together, they can show concretely that $a^2 - b^2 = (a + b)(a - b)$.

6-2 Differences of Two Squares

Recognizing Differences of Two Squares

Objective: Recognize a difference of two squares.

For a binomial to be a **difference of two squares,** two conditions must hold.

(A) There must be two terms, both squares. Examples are $4x^2$ and $9x^4$, 16 and y^2.

(B) There must be a minus sign between the two terms.

EXAMPLES

1. Is $9x^2 - 36$ a difference of two squares?
The first term is a square. $9x^2 = (3x)^2$
The second term is a square. $36 = 6^2$
There is a minus sign between them.
Thus we have a difference of two squares.

2. Is $-4x^2 + 16$ a difference of two squares?
$-4x^2 + 16 = 16 - 4x^2$ — Rewriting as a difference
$16 = 4^2$ and $4x^2 = (2x)^2$ — The first and last terms are squares.
Since there is a minus sign between 16 and $4x^2$, we have a difference of two squares.

Try This State whether each expression is a difference of two squares.

a. $x^2 - 25$ Yes **b.** $x^2 - 24$ No **c.** $-36 - x^2$ No
d. $4x^2 - 15$ No **e.** $-49 + 16a^2$ Yes **f.** $-1 + 9m^6$ Yes

Factoring Differences of Two Squares

Objective: Factor a difference of two squares.

Here is one of the special products you learned in Chapter 5.

$$(A + B)(A - B) = A^2 - B^2$$

We can use this relationship to factor differences of two squares.

$$A^2 - B^2 = (A + B)(A - B)$$

EXAMPLE 3 Factor.

$$\begin{array}{ccccccccc} x^2 - 4 & = & x^2 & - & 2^2 & = & (x + 2)(x - 2) \\ & & \uparrow & & \uparrow & & \uparrow\ \ \uparrow\ \uparrow\ \ \uparrow \\ & & A^2 & - & B^2 & = & (A + B)(A - B) \end{array}$$

Try This Factor.

g. $x^2 - 9$ $(x + 3)(x - 3)$ **h.** $y^2 - 64$ $(y + 8)(y - 8)$

EXAMPLES Factor.

4. $4x^2 - 25 = (2x)^2 - (5)^2 = (2x + 5)(2x - 5)$

$$A^2 - B^2 = (A + B)(A - B)$$

5. $m^6 - 16n^2 = (m^3)^2 - (4n)^2 = (m^3 + 4n)(m^3 - 4n)$

$$A^2 - B^2 = (A + B)(A - B)$$

6. $36x^2 - 25y^6 = (6x)^2 - (5y^3)^2$ Writing as a difference of squares

$= (6x - 5y^3)(6x + 5y^3)$

7. $9a^8b^4 - 49 = (3a^4b^2)^2 - (7)^2 = (3a^4b^2 + 7)(3a^4b^2 - 7)$

Try This Factor.

i. $4y^2 - 49$ **j.** $16x^2 - 25y^2$

k. $a^8b^4 - 4$ **l.** $25a^{10} - 36b^8$

i. $(2y + 7)(2y - 7)$
j. $(4x - 5y)(4x + 5y)$
k. $(a^4b^2 - 2)(a^4b^2 + 2)$
l. $(5a^5 - 6b^4)(5a^5 + 6b^4)$

If the terms of a binomial have a common factor, first factor out the common factor. Then continue factoring.

EXAMPLES Factor.

8. $49x^4 - 9x^6 = x^4(49 - 9x^2)$ Factoring out the common factor, x^4

$= x^4[(7)^2 - (3x)^2]$

$= x^4(7 + 3x)(7 - 3x)$ Factoring a difference of two squares

9. $18a^2b^2 - 50a^6 = 2a^2(9b^2 - 25a^4)$ Factoring out the common factor, $2a^2$

$= 2a^2[(3b)^2 - (5a^2)^2]$

$= 2a^2(3b + 5a^2)(3b - 5a^2)$ Factoring a difference of two squares

Try This Factor.

m. $32y^2 - 8y^6$ **n.** $5 - 20y^6$

o. $a^3b - 4ab^3$ **p.** $64x^4y^4 - 25x^6y^8$

m. $8y^2(2 + y^2)(2 - y^2)$
n. $5(1 + 2y^3)(1 - 2y^3)$
o. $ab(a + 2b)(a - 2b)$
p. $x^4y^4(8 - 5xy^2)(8 + 5xy^2)$

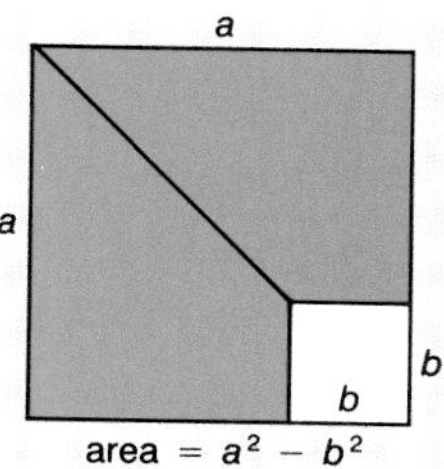

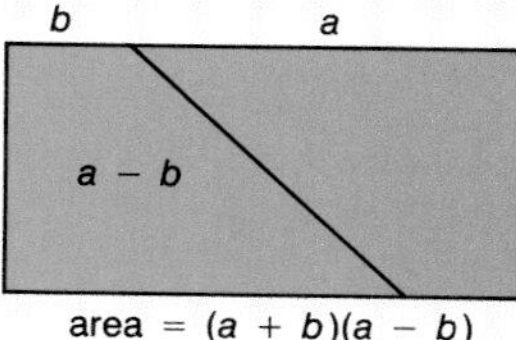

Avoiding Common Errors

Many students make the mistake of factoring $a^2 + b^2$ as $(a + b)(a + b)$. Show by multiplying that $(a + b)(a + b)$ equals $a^2 + 2ab + b^2$ and that $a^2 + b^2$ cannot be factored.

You may want to show that the product of two binomials has four terms, which can often be simplified to three terms and in special cases to two terms.

$(x + y)(w + u)$
$= xw + xu + yw + yu$

$(x + y)(x + y) = x^2 + xy + xy + y^2$
$= x^2 + 2xy + y^2$

$(x + y)(x - y) = x^2 - xy + xy - y^2$
$= x^2 - y^2$

Key Questions

- Can $16 + y^2$ be factored? No
- Can $16 - x^2$ be factored? Yes

Chalkboard Examples

Factor.

1. $y^2 - 16$
   $(y + 4)(y - 4)$
2. $25x^2 - 4$
   $(5x)^2 - 2^2 = (5x + 2)(5x - 2)$
3. $25x^4 - 64y^2$
   $(5x^2)^2 - (8y)^2$
   $= (5x^2 + 8y)(5x^2 - 8y)$
4. $32x^2 - 50y^2$
   $2(16x^2 - 25y^2)$
   $= 2[(4x)^2 - (5y)^2]$
   $= 2(4x + 5y)(4x - 5y)$

Factoring Completely

Show that factoring is the opposite of multiplication by factoring an expression and then multiplying the factors to return to the original expression.

Chalkboard Example

1. Factor.
   $a^4 - b^4$
   $(a^2)^2 - (b^2)^2$
   $= (a^2 + b^2)(a^2 - b^2)$
   $= (a^2 + b^2)(a + b)(a - b)$
   Note that $a^2 + b^2$ cannot be factored.

LESSON QUIZ

Factor.

1. $a^2 - 16$
   $(a + 4)(a - 4)$
2. $25x^2 - 16$
   $(5x + 4)(5x - 4)$
3. $x^4 - 1$
   $(x^2 + 1)(x^2 - 1)$
   $= (x^2 + 1)(x + 1)(x - 1)$

Assignment Guide

Minimum: 1–46 e/o, MR

Regular: 1–76 m3, 77, MR

Advanced: 1–76 m4, 77, 78–82 e/o, MR

ADDITIONAL ANSWERS

Exercises

9. $(x + 2)(x - 2)$
10. $(x + 6)(x - 6)$
11. $(x + 3y)(x - 3y)$
12. $(m + y)(m - y)$
13. $(4a + 3)(4a - 3)$
14. $(5x + 2)(5x - 2)$
15. $(2x + 5)(2x - 5)$
16. $(3a + 4)(3a - 4)$
17. $(5m + 7)(5m - 7)$
18. $(10x + 5)(10x - 5)$
19. $(x^2 + 3)(x^2 - 3)$
20. $(y^3 + 2)(y^3 - 2)$
21. $(m^8 + 5)(m^8 - 5)$
22. $(a^6 + 4)(a^6 - 4)$
23. $(2x^2 + 4)(2x^2 - 4)$
24. $(4x^3 + 5)(4x^3 - 5)$
25. $(8y^2 + 9)(8y^2 - 9)$
26. $(2x^5 + 5)(2x^5 - 5)$
27. $(6x^6 + 7)(6x^6 - 7)$
28. $(4y + 5)(4y - 5)$
29. $x(6 + 7x)(6 - 7x)$

Factoring Completely

Objective: Factor a difference of two squares completely.

After you factor a difference of two squares, you can sometimes continue factoring. **Factoring completely** means to factor until factoring is no longer possible (other than for a common factor of 1).

EXAMPLE 10 Factor.

$$\begin{aligned} 1 - 16x^{12} &= (1)^2 - (4x^6)^2 \\ &= (1 - 4x^6)(1 + 4x^6) \\ &= [(1)^2 - (2x^3)^2](1 + 4x^6) \\ &= (1 + 2x^3)(1 - 2x^3)(1 + 4x^6) \end{aligned}$$

Factoring the first binomial as a difference of squares

Try This Factor.

q. $81x^4 - 1$ **r.** $16m^4 - n^8$

q. $(3x + 1)(3x - 1)(9x^2 + 1)$
r. $(4m^2 + n^4)(2m - n^2)(2m + n^2)$

6-2 EXERCISES

A

State whether each expression is a difference of two squares.

1. $x^2 - 4$ Yes **2.** $x^2 - 36$ Yes **3.** $x^2 + 36$ No **4.** $x^2 + 4$ No
5. $x^2 - 35$ No **6.** $x^2 - 50$ No **7.** $-25 + 16x^2$ Yes **8.** $-1 + 36x^2$ Yes

Factor.

9. $x^2 - 4$ **10.** $x^2 - 36$ **11.** $x^2 - 9y^2$
12. $m^2 - y^2$ **13.** $16a^2 - 9$ **14.** $25x^2 - 4$
15. $4x^2 - 25$ **16.** $9a^2 - 16$ **17.** $25m^2 - 49$
18. $100x^2 - 25$ **19.** $x^4 - 9$ **20.** $y^6 - 4$
21. $m^{16} - 25$ **22.** $-16 + a^{12}$ **23.** $-16 + 4x^4$
24. $16x^6 - 25$ **25.** $64y^4 - 81$ **26.** $4x^{10} - 25$
27. $36x^{12} - 49$ **28.** $16y^2 - 25$ **29.** $36x - 49x^3$
30. $121a^8 - 100$ **31.** $81y^6 - 25y^2$ **32.** $100y^6 - 49y^4$
33. $8x^2 - 98y^2$ **34.** $-54y^4 + 24x^2$ **35.** $-50y^2 + 32x^2$
36. $27y^2 - 48y^4$ **37.** $75m^6n^2 - 147$ **38.** $50a^{10}b^4 - 72$
39. $x^4 - 1$ **40.** $x^4 - 16$ **41.** $4x^4 - 64$ **42.** $5x^4 - 80$
43. $16 - y^4$ **44.** $25 - x^4$ **45.** $625 - m^4$ **46.** $4 - 9y^2$

B

Factor.

47. $16x - 81x^3$
48. $1 - y^8$
49. $b^8 - a^4$
50. $16x^2 - 25x^4$
51. $x^{16} - 9x^2$
52. $-16 + x^6$
53. $-81 + 49a^4$
54. $-64 + c^{14}$
55. $x^{12} - 16$
56. $x^8 - 1$
57. $a^{12} - 4a^2$
58. $16p^8 - t^4$
59. $-9 + 25a^4$
60. $x^8 - 81$
61. $-49 + 9c^8$
62. $4x^4 - 4x^2$
63. $3x^5 - 12x^3$
64. $3x^2 - \frac{1}{3}$
65. $18x^3 - \frac{8}{25}x$
66. $x^2 - 2.25$
67. $x^3 - \frac{x}{16}$
68. $3.24x^2 - 0.81$
69. $0.64x^2 - 1.21$
70. $1.28x^2 - 2$
71. $(x + 3)^2 - 9$
72. $(y - 5)^2 - 36$
73. $(3a + 4)^2 - 49$
74. $(2y - 7)^2 - 1$
75. $y^8 - 256$
76. $x^{16} - 1$
77. ***Critical Thinking*** Can you find a rational nonzero value for b that allows you to factor $x^2 + b^2$? Explain.

Challenge

78. Find 2 polynomials, each with three factors, where the only common factor is $(x + 2)$.
79. Find a polynomial with 2 factors where one factor is $(x^2 - 2)$.
80. Find a third-degree polynomial where one factor is $(x + 5)$ and the other 2 factors are binomials.
81. Find a third-degree polynomial where there are three binomial factors and one factor is $(a + 2b)$.
82. Find a fourth-degree polynomial where there are three factors and one factor is $x^2 - 5$.

Mixed Review

Multiply. **83.** $(x + 7)(x + 7)$ **84.** $(2a - 3)(2a - 3)$

Identify the degree of each term and the degree of the polynomial.

85. $12c + 1$ **86.** $6y^3 - 25y^2 - 8y + 15$ **87.** $9a^2c^3 + 45ac - 7$

Write each as a decimal. **88.** 20% **89.** 8% **90.** 430% **91.** 6.5%

Solve. **92.** $26 - 3c = 10c$ **93.** $4t - 12 = t + 3$

94. Ana has saved \$68 to buy a new bicycle. The total cost of the bike is \$105. How much more money does Ana need?
95. Find the length of the base of a triangle if one side is 3 cm longer than the base, and the other side is 5 cm shorter than the base. The perimeter of the triangle is 52 cm.

30. $(11a^4 + 10)(11a^4 - 10)$
31. $y^2(9y^2 + 5)(9y^2 - 5)$
32. $y^4(10y + 7)(10y - 7)$
33. $2(2x + 7y)(2x - 7y)$
34. $6(2x + 3y^2)(2x - 3y^2)$
35. $2(4x + 5y)(4x - 5y)$
36. $3y^2(3 + 4y)(3 - 4y)$
37. $3(5m^3n + 7)(5m^3n - 7)$
38. $2(5a^5b^2 + 6)(5a^5b^2 - 6)$
39. $(x^2 + 1)(x + 1)(x - 1)$
40. $(x^2 + 4)(x + 2)(x - 2)$
41. $4(x^2 + 4)(x + 2)(x - 2)$
42. $5(x^2 + 4)(x + 2)(x - 2)$
43. $(4 + y^2)(2 + y)(2 - y)$
44. $(5 + x^2)(5 - x^2)$
45. $(25 + m^2)(5 + m)(5 - m)$
46. $(2 + 3y)(2 - 3y)$
47. $x(4 + 9x)(4 - 9x)$
48. $(1 + y^4)(1 + y^2)(1 + y)(1 - y)$
49. $(b^4 + a^2)(b^2 + a)(b^2 - a)$
50. $x^2(4 + 5x)(4 - 5x)$
51. $x^2(x^7 + 3)(x^7 - 3)$
52. $(x^3 + 4)(x^3 - 4)$
53. $(7a^2 + 9)(7a^2 - 9)$
54. $(c^7 + 8)(c^7 - 8)$
55. $(x^6 + 4)(x^3 + 2)(x^3 - 2)$
56. $(x^4 + 1)(x^2 + 1)(x + 1)(x - 1)$
57. $a^2(a^5 + 2)(a^5 - 2)$
58. $(4p^4 + t^2)(2p^2 + t)(2p^2 - t)$
59. $(5a^2 + 3)(5a^2 - 3)$
60. $(x^4 + 9)(x^2 + 3)(x^2 - 3)$
61. $(3c^4 + 7)(3c^4 - 7)$
62. $4x^2(x + 1)(x - 1)$
63. $3x^3(x + 2)(x - 2)$
64. $3\left(x + \frac{1}{3}\right)\left(x - \frac{1}{3}\right)$
65. $2x\left(3x + \frac{2}{5}\right)\left(3x - \frac{2}{5}\right)$
66. $(x + 1.5)(x - 1.5)$
67. $x\left(x + \frac{1}{4}\right)\left(x - \frac{1}{4}\right)$
68. $(1.8x + 0.9)(1.8x - 0.9)$
69. $(0.8x + 1.1)(0.8x - 1.1)$
70. $2(0.8x + 1)(0.8x - 1)$
71. $x(x + 6)$
72. $(y + 1)(y - 11)$
73. $3(a - 1)(3a + 11)$
74. $4(y - 4)(y - 3)$
75. $(y^4 + 16)(y^2 + 4)(y + 2)(y - 2)$
76. $(x^8 + 1)(x^4 + 1)(x^2 + 1)(x + 1)(x - 1)$
77–82. See Teacher's Answer Section.

Mixed Review

83. $x^2 + 14x + 49$
84. $4a^2 - 12a + 9$
85. 1, 0; 1
86. 3, 2, 1, 0; 3
87. 5, 2, 0; 5
88. 0.2
89. 0.08
90. 4.3
91. 0.065
92. 2
93. 5
94. \$37
95. The base is 18 cm.

6-3

FIRST FIVE MINUTES

1. Factor $x^2 - 49$.
   $(x + 7)(x - 7)$
2. Factor $8y^2 - 18$.
   $2(4y^2 - 9) = 2(2y + 3)(2y - 3)$
3. Multiply $(x + 3)^2$.
   $x^2 + 6x + 9$
4. Multiply $(x - 5)^2$.
   $x^2 - 10x + 25$

Recognizing Trinomial Squares

You may want to compare products of binomials such as those in the First Five Minutes and discuss any patterns students may notice about those products that result from squaring a binomial.

Key Questions

Why is each of the following *not* a trinomial square?

- $a^3 + 2a + 1$
  The first term is not a square.
- $x^2 + 5xy + 1$
  The middle term is not 2 · any
- $a^2 + 2a - 1$
  The last term is negative.

Chalkboard Examples

Which of the following are trinomial squares?

1. $x^2 + 2x + 1$
   Yes, $x^2 + 2x(1) + (1)^2$
2. $x^2 + 3xy + y^2$
   No, the middle term is not $2xy$
3. $81x^2 + 36xy + 4y^2$
   Yes, $(9x)^2 + 2(9x)(2y) + (2y)^2$

6-3 Trinomial Squares

Recognizing Trinomial Squares

Objective: Recognize a trinomial square.

From the study of special products we know that the square of a binomial is a trinomial. Such trinomials are often called trinomial squares.

$$(x + 3)^2 = x^2 + 6x + 9$$
$$(x - 3)^2 = x^2 - 6x + 9$$

The trinomial $x^2 + 6x + 9$ and $x^2 - 6x + 9$ are trinomial squares, as each are squares of a binomial.

Use the following to help recognize a trinomial square.

A. Two of the terms must be squares, A^2 and B^2.
B. There must be no minus sign before A^2 or B^2.
C. If we multiply A and B and double the result, we get the third term, $2AB$, or its additive inverse, $-2AB$.

EXAMPLE 1 Is $x^2 + 6x + 9$ a trinomial square?

A. $x^2 = (x)^2$ and $9 = (3)^2$
B. There is no minus sign before x^2 or 9.
C. If we multiply x and 3 and double the result, we get the third term, $2 \cdot 3 \cdot x$, or $6x$.

Thus $x^2 + 6x + 9$ is the square of the binomial $(x + 3)$.

EXAMPLE 2 Is $x^2 + 6x + 11$ a trinomial square?

The answer is no because only one term is a square.

EXAMPLE 3 Is $16a^2 - 56ab + 49b^2$ a trinomial square?

A. $16a^2 = (4a)^2$ and $49b^2 = (7b)^2$
B. There is no minus sign before $16a^2$ or $49b^2$.
C. If we multiply $4a$ and $7b$ and double the result, we get the additive inverse of the third term, $2 \cdot 4a \cdot 7b = 56ab$.

Thus $16a^2 - 56ab + 49b^2$ is the square of $(4a - 7b)$.

Try This Which of the following are trinomial squares?

a. $x^2 + 8x + 16$ Yes **b.** $x^2 - 10x + 25$ Yes **c.** $x^2 - 12x + 4$ No
d. $4x^2 + 20x + 25$ Yes **e.** $9x^2 - 14x + 16$ No **f.** $16x^2 + 40xy + 25y^2$ Yes

Factoring Trinomial Squares

Objective: Factor trinomial squares.

To factor trinomial squares, you can use the following relationships.

$$A^2 + 2AB + B^2 = (A + B)^2$$
$$A^2 - 2AB + B^2 = (A - B)^2$$

Remember to factor out a common factor first, if possible.

EXAMPLES Factor.

4. $x^2 + 6x + 9 = x^2 + 2 \cdot x \cdot 3 + 3^2 = (x + 3)^2$ — The sign of the middle term is positive.

5. $x^2 - 14x + 49 = x^2 - 2 \cdot x \cdot 7 + 7^2 = (x - 7)^2$ — The sign of the middle term is negative.

6. $16a^2 - 40ab + 25b^2 = (4a - 5b)^2$

7. $27m^2 + 72mn + 48n^2 = 3(9m^2 + 24mn + 16n^2) = 3(3m + 4n)^2$ — Factoring out the common factor, 3

Try This Factor.

g. $x^2 + 2x + 1$ $(x + 1)^2$

h. $x^2 - 2x + 1$ $(x - 1)^2$

i. $25x^2 - 70x + 49$ $(5x - 7)^2$

j. $48m^2 + 120mn + 75n^2$ $3(4m + 5n)^2$

6-3 EXERCISES

A

Which of the following are trinomial squares?

1. $x^2 - 14x + 49$ Yes

2. $x^2 - 16x + 64$ Yes

3. $x^2 + 16x - 64$ No

4. $x^2 - 14x - 49$ No

5. $x^2 - 6x + 9$ Yes

6. $x^2 + 2x + 4$ No

7. $8x^2 + 40x + 25$ No

8. $9x^2 + 18xy + 9y^2$ Yes

9. $36m^2 - 24m + 16n^2$ No

10. $16x^2 - 56xy + 49y^2$ Yes

Factor. Remember to look first for a common factor.

11. $x^2 - 14x + 49$ $(x - 7)^2$

12. $x^2 - 16x + 64$ $(x - 8)^2$

13. $x^2 + 16x + 64$ $(x + 8)^2$

14. $x^2 + 14x + 49$ $(x + 7)^2$

15. $x^2 - 2x + 1$ $(x - 1)^2$

16. $x^2 + 2x + 1$ $(x + 1)^2$

17. $x^2 + 4xy + 4y^2$ $(x + 2y)^2$

18. $x^2 - 4xy + 4y^2$ $(x - 2y)^2$

19. $y^2 - 6xy + 9x^2$ $(y - 3x)^2$

20. $y^2 + 6xy + 9x^2$ $(y + 3x)^2$

Factoring Trinomial Squares

Remind students that the following model illustrates that $(a + b)^2 = a^2 + 2ab + b^2$

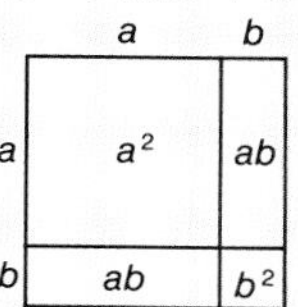

Have students substitute $-b$ into the equation
$(a + (-b))^2 = a^2 + 2a(-b) + (-b)^2 = a^2 - 2ab + b^2$
Then have them multiply $(a - b)(a - b)$ to get the same result. Remind students to check their factorization using multiplication.

Chalkboard Examples

Factor.

1. $x^2 + 10x + 25$
   $x^2 + 2 \cdot x \cdot 5 + 5^2 = (x + 5)^2$
2. $y^2 - 8y + 16$
   $y^2 - 2 \cdot y \cdot 4 + 4^2 = (y - 4)^2$
3. $4x^2 + 12x + 9$
   $(2x)^2 + 2 \cdot 2x \cdot 3 + 3^2 = (2x + 3)^2$
4. $2x^2 + 12x + 18$
   $2(x^2 + 6x + 9) = 2(x + 3)^2$

LESSON ENRICHMENT

The expressions

$x^3 + 9x^2 + 27x + 27$ $(x + 3)^3$
$x^3 + 12x^2 + 28x + 64$ $(x + 4)^3$
$x^3 + 15x^2 + 75x + 125$ $(x + 5)^3$

are all cubes of binomials. Determine what each binomial is. Determine a pattern for recognizing cubes of binomials.

LESSON QUIZ

Factor.

1. $x^2 + 20x + 100$ $(x + 10)^2$
2. $y^2 - 4y + 4$ $(y - 2)^2$
3. $4a^2 + 12ab + 9b^2$ $(2a + 3b)^2$
4. $7x^3 + 14x^2 + 7x$
   $7x(x^2 + 2x + 1) = 7x(x + 1)^2$

Assignment Guide

Minimum: 1–38 e/o, MR

Regular: 1–38 m3, 39–56 e/o, 57, MR

Advanced: 1–56 m4, 57–64, MR

ADDITIONAL ANSWERS

Exercises

21. $2(x - 1)^2$
22. $2(x - 10)^2$
23. $x(x - 9)^2$
24. $x(x + 12)^2$
25. $5(2x + 5)^2$
26. $3(2x + 3y)^2$
27. $(7y - 3x)^2$
28. $(8y - 7x)^2$
29. $5(y^2 + 1)^2$
30. $(a^2 + 7)^2$
31. $(y^3 + 13)^2$
32. $(y^3 - 8)^2$
33. $(4x^5 - 1)^2$
34. $(3x^5 + 2)^2$
35. $(2x^2 + 1)^2$
36. $(a^3 - 1)^2$ or $(1 - a^3)^2$
37. $(9x^3 + 4y)^2$
38. $(3a^4 - 5b)^2$
39. Not possible
40. $x(27x^2 - 13)$
41. $(x + 11)^2$
42. Not possible
43. Not possible
44. $2x(3x + 1)^2$
45. $7(9x - 4)$
46. $2x(81x - 41)$
47. $y^4(x^2 - 3)(x^2 + 3)$
48. $x(81x - 64)$
49. $(x^4 + 16)(x^2 + 4)(x + 2)(x - 2)$
50. $(9 + x^2)(3 + x)(3 - x)$
51. $(y + 4)^2$
52. $(a + 3)^2$
53. $(2a + 15)^2$
54. $(7x + 4)^2$
55. $(x + 5)^2$
56. $(a + 1)^2$
57. $a = 2$
58. $(3x^9 + 8)^2$
59. $(x^n + 5)^2$
60. $(a + 1)^2 - 3^2 = (a + 4)(a - 2)$
61. $(y + 3)^2 - (x + 4)^2$
$= (y + x + 7)(y - x - 1)$

Mixed Review

65. $-2x^3 - x^2 + 18x + 9$
66. $y^6 + y^5 - 4y^3 - 4y^2$
67. $3x(2x - 3)$
68. $12a(2a - 1)$
69. $3y(3y^2 + 1)$
70. 0.001667
71. 359,400

21. $2x^2 - 4x + 2$
22. $2x^2 - 40x + 200$
23. $x^3 - 18x^2 + 81x$
24. $x^3 + 24x^2 + 144x$
25. $20x^2 + 100x + 125$
26. $12x^2 + 36xy + 27y^2$
27. $49y^2 - 42xy + 9x^2$
28. $64y^2 - 112xy + 49x^2$
29. $5y^4 + 10y^2 + 5$
30. $a^4 + 14a^2 + 49$
31. $y^6 + 26y^3 + 169$
32. $y^6 - 16y^3 + 64$
33. $16x^{10} - 8x^5 + 1$
34. $9x^{10} + 12x^5 + 4$
35. $4x^4 + 4x^2 + 1$
36. $1 - 2a^3 + a^6$
37. $81x^6 + 72x^3y + 16y^2$
38. $9a^8 - 30a^4b + 25b^2$

B

Factor, if possible.

39. $49x^2 - 216$
40. $27x^3 - 13x$
41. $x^2 + 22x + 121$
42. $4x^2 + 9$
43. $x^2 - 5x + 25$
44. $18x^3 + 12x^2 + 2x$
45. $63x - 28$
46. $162x^2 - 82x$
47. $x^4y^4 - 9y^4$
48. $81x^2 - 64x$
49. $x^8 - 2^8$
50. $3^4 - x^4$

Factor.

51. $(y + 3)^2 + 2(y + 3) + 1$
52. $(a + 4)^2 - 2(a + 4) + 1$
53. $4(a + 5)^2 + 20(a + 5) + 25$
54. $49(x + 1)^2 - 42(x + 1) + 9$
55. $(x + 7)^2 - 4x - 24$
56. $(a + 4)^2 - 6a - 15$

57. ***Critical Thinking*** Suppose $x^2 + a^2x + a^2$ factors into $(x + a)^2$. Find the value of a.

Challenge

Factor.

58. $9x^{18} + 48x^9 + 64$
59. $x^{2n} + 10x^n + 25$

Factor as the square of a binomial, then as a difference of two squares.

60. $a^2 + 2a + 1 - 9$
61. $y^2 + 6y + 9 - x^2 - 8x - 16$

Find c so that the polynomial will be the square of a binomial.

62. $cy^2 + 6y + 1$ 9
63. $cy^2 - 24y + 9$ 16

64. Show that the difference of the squares of two consecutive integers is the sum of the integers. (Hint: Use x for the smaller number.) $(x + 1)^2 - x^2 = 2x + 1$

Mixed Review

Multiply. **65.** $(9 - x^2)(1 + 2x)$ **66.** $(y^3 + y^2)(y^3 - 4)$

Factor. **67.** $6x^2 - 9x$ **68.** $24a^2 - 12a$ **69.** $9y^3 + 3y$

Write using standard notation. **70.** 1.667×10^{-3} **71.** 3.594×10^5

6-4 Factoring $x^2 + bx + c$

Constant Term Positive

Objective: Factor trinomials of the type $x^2 + bx + c$ where $c > 0$.

In the polynomial $x^2 + bx + c$, recall that c is called the constant term or just the constant. If the constant of a polynomial in the form $x^2 + bx + c$ is not a perfect square, the trinomial cannot be factored into a square of a binomial. It may, however, be possible to factor it as the product of two different binomials.

In Chapter 5, we used models to illustrate products of two binomials. We can use these models when factoring the trinomial $x^2 + 7x + 10$. Since $1 \cdot 10 = 10$ and $2 \cdot 5 = 10$, there are two possible arrangements to try.

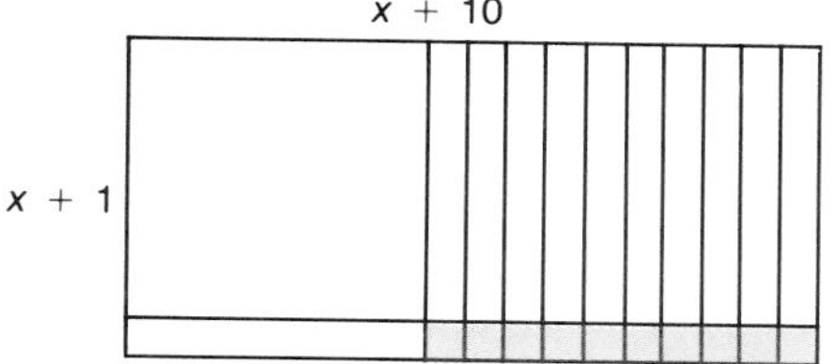

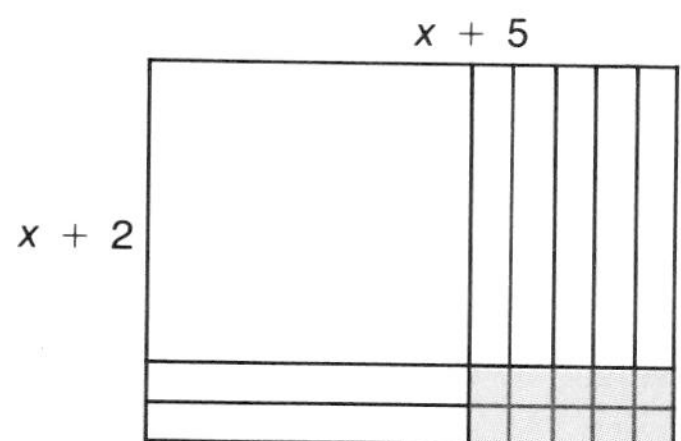

When we complete the rectangle in each model, we see that the model on the right shows the correct factorization: $x^2 + 7x + 10 = (x + 2)(x + 5)$.

Recall the FOIL method. It is useful when factoring polynomials such as $x^2 + 7x + 10$.

$$(x+2)(x+5) = \overset{F}{x^2} + \underbrace{\overset{O}{5x} + \overset{I}{2x}} + \overset{L}{10}$$
$$= x^2 \quad + 7x \quad + 10$$

To factor $x^2 + 7x + 10$, think of FOIL in reverse. The first term, x^2, is the result of x times x. Thus the first term of each binomial factor is x.

$$(x + \_)(x + \_)$$

The coefficient of the middle term and the last term of the trinomial are two numbers whose product is 10 and whose sum is 7. Those numbers are 2 and 5. Thus the factorization is

$$(x + 2)(x + 5)$$

6-4

FIRST FIVE MINUTES

1. Factor $x^2 - 4$.
   $(x + 2)(x - 2)$
2. Factor $x^2 + 8x + 16$.
   $(x + 4)^2$
3. Multiply $(x + 3)(x + 5)$.
   $x^2 + 8x + 15$
4. Multiply $(x - 2)(x - 7)$.
   $x^2 - 9x + 14$

Constant Term Positive

Emphasize that to factor a trinomial of the form $x^2 + bx + c$, we try to find two numbers with a product of c and a sum or difference of b. You may want to point out that if the sign of the third term, c, is positive, the two numbers must have the same sign.

The technique used in this lesson to factor polynomials is a form of the *Guess, Check, Revise* problem-solving strategy. We first *guess* which factors of c will have a sum or difference of b. We must remember to *check* these factors, and then *revise* if the factors do not yield the correct sum or difference. As students practice this procedure, their first guesses will improve.

Key Questions

- What two numbers have a sum of 5 and a product of 6?
  2, 3
- What two numbers have a sum of 8 and a product of 12?
  2, 6
- What two numbers have a sum of -8 and a product of 7?
  $-7, -1$
- What two numbers have a sum of 18 and a product of 0?
  18, 0

Chalkboard Examples

1. Factor $x^2 + 8x + 12$.
   The factorizations of 12 are $1 \cdot 12$, $2 \cdot 6$, $3 \cdot 4$, $-1 \cdot (-12)$, $-2 \cdot (-6)$, $-3 \cdot (-4)$. The numbers 2 and 6 are the only pair with the sum 8. The factorization is $(x + 2)(x + 6)$.
2. Factor $x^2 - 10x + 16$.
   The factorizations of 16 are $1 \cdot 16$, $2 \cdot 8$, $4 \cdot 4$, $-1 \cdot (-16)$, $-2 \cdot (-8)$, $-4 \cdot (-4)$. The factors -2, -8 have sum -10. The factorization is $(x - 2)(x - 8)$.
3. Factor $p^2 - 3pq + 2q^2$.
   The factorizations of 2 are $1 \cdot 2$ and $-1 \cdot (-2)$. The factors -1 and -2 have sum -3. The required factorization is $(p - 1q)(p - 2q)$.

When factoring, it can be helpful to *make a table.*

EXAMPLE 1 Factor $x^2 + 5x + 6$.

The first term of each factor is x.

$$(x + \_)(x + \_)$$

Look for two numbers whose product is 6 and whose sum is 5.

Product of 6	Sum
1, 6	7
2, 3	5 ← The numbers we need are 2 and 3.

$x^2 + 5x + 6 = (x + 2)(x + 3)$

Try This Factor.

a. $x^2 + 7x + 12$ $(x + 4)(x + 3)$

b. $x^2 + 13x + 36$ $(x + 9)(x + 4)$

Consider this multiplication.

$$(x - 3)(x - 4) = \overset{F}{x^2} \overset{O}{- 4x} \overset{I}{- 3x} \overset{L}{+ 12}$$
$$= x^2 - 7x + 12$$

When the constant term of a trinomial is positive, we look for two numbers with the same sign. The sign is that of the middle term.

$$(x^2 - 7x + 12) = (x - 3)(x - 4)$$

EXAMPLE 2 Factor $x^2 - 8x + 12$.

Since the coefficient of the middle term is negative, we need two negative numbers whose product is 12 and whose sum is -8.

Product of 12	Sum
-1, -12	-13
-2, -6	-8 ← The numbers we need are -2 and -6.
-3, -4	-7

$x^2 - 8x + 12 = (x - 2)(x - 6)$

Try This Factor.

c. $x^2 - 8x + 15$ $(x - 5)(x - 3)$

d. $x^2 - 9x + 20$ $(x - 4)(x - 5)$

e. $x^2 - 7x + 12$ $(x - 3)(x - 4)$

EXAMPLE 3 Factor $a^2 + 7ab + 10b^2$.

Since a^2 is the product of a times a, and b^2 is the product of b times b, we are looking for binomials of the form

$$(a + \_b)(a + \_b)$$

Find two numbers whose sum is 7 and whose product is 10.

Product of 10	Sum
1, 10	11
2, 5	7 ← The numbers we need are 2 and 5.

$$a^2 + 7ab + 10b^2 = (a + 2b)(a + 5b)$$

Try This Factor.

f. $m^2 + 8mn + 15n^2$ $(m + 3n)(m + 5n)$ **g.** $a^2 + 5ab + 6b^2$ $(a + 3b)(a + 2b)$ **h.** $p^2 + 6pq + 8q^2$ $(p + 4q)(p + 2q)$

Constant Term Negative

Objective: Factor trinomials of the type $x^2 + bx + c$ where $c < 0$.

Sometimes the constant term of a trinomial is negative. In this case, the middle term may be positive or negative. Consider these multiplications.

$$\begin{aligned}(x - 5)(x + 2) &= \overset{F}{x^2} + \underbrace{\overset{O}{2x} - \overset{I}{5x}} - \overset{L}{10}\\ &= x^2 \quad - 3x \quad - 10\end{aligned}$$

$$\begin{aligned}(x + 5)(x - 2) &= \overset{F}{x^2} - \underbrace{\overset{O}{2x} + \overset{I}{5x}} - \overset{L}{10}\\ &= x^2 \quad + 3x \quad - 10\end{aligned}$$

Since the product is negative, one factor is positive and the other negative. Their sum is still the coefficient of the middle term.

EXAMPLE 4 Factor $x^2 - 8x - 20$.

Find two numbers whose sum is -8 and whose product is -20.

Product of -20	Sum
-1, 20	19
1, -20	-19
-2, 10	8
2, -10	-8 ← The numbers we need are 2 and -10.
4, -5	-1
-4, 5	1

$$x^2 - 8x - 20 = (x + 2)(x - 10)$$

Constant Term Negative

Emphasize that checking the factoring by multiplication is important. Students often have the factors correct except for the signs.

Key Questions

- What two numbers have a sum of -6 and a product of -7? $-7, 1$
- What two numbers have a sum of 2 and a product of -8? $4, -2$
- What two numbers have a sum of -1 and a product of -2? $-2, 1$

Chalkboard Examples

1. Factor $u^2 - 3uv - 10v^2$.
   The factorizations of -10 are $-1 \cdot 10$, $-2 \cdot 5$, $1 \cdot (-10)$, $2 \cdot (-5)$. The pair 2, -5 has sum -3. The required factorization is $(u + 2v)(u - 5v)$.
2. Factor $x^2 + 3x - 4$.
   The factorizations of -4 are $1 \cdot (-4)$, $-1 \cdot 4$, $2 \cdot (-2)$. The pair -1, 4 has sum 3. The required factorization is $(x - 1)(x + 4)$.
3. Factor $y^2 - 12yz - 28z^2$.
   The factorizations of -28 are $-1 \cdot 28$, $-2 \cdot 14$, $-4 \cdot 7$, $1 \cdot (-28)$, $2 \cdot (-14)$, $4 \cdot (-7)$. The pair 2, -14 has sum -12. The required factorization is $(y + 2z)(y - 14z)$.

LESSON QUIZ

Factor.

1. $x^2 + 8x + 7$
   $(x + 1)(x + 7)$
2. $a^2 - 8a + 15$
   $(a - 3)(a - 5)$
3. $x^2 - 5xy - 14y^2$
   $(x + 2y)(x - 7y)$

Assignment Guide
Minimum: Day 1: 1–21 e/o, MR
Day 2: 22–36 e/o
assign w. 6-5
Regular: 1–36 m3, 37–50 e/o, 51, MR
Advanced: 1–50 m3, 51–55, MR

ADDITIONAL ANSWERS

Exercises

1. $(x + 5)(x + 3)$
2. $(x + 3)(x + 2)$
3. $(x + 4)(x + 3)$
4. $(x + 8)(x + 1)$
5. $(x - 3)^2$
6. $(y + 7)(y + 4)$
7. $(x + 7)(x + 2)$
8. $(a + 6)(a + 5)$
9. $(b + 4)(b + 1)$
10. $(x - 7)(x - 4)$
11. $(a - 8)(a - 6)$
12. $(z - 1)(z - 7)$
13. $(m + 7)(m + 3)$
14. $(a - 9)(a - 5)$
15. $(z - 4)(z - 6)$
16. $(t + 6p)^2$
17. $(a - 5b)(a - 4b)$
18. $(x - 4y)(x - y)$
19. $(c - 5d)(c - 2d)$
20. $(x - 5y)(x - 3y)$
21. $(y - 10z)(y - z)$
22. $(x - 5)(x + 3)$
23. $(x + 7)(x - 6)$
24. $(x + 5)(x - 3)$
25. $(x - 9)(x + 2)$
26. $(y - 7)(y + 4)$
27. $(x - 8)(x + 2)$
28. $(x - 7)(x + 6)$
29. $(y - 9)(y + 5)$
30. $(x - 12)(x + 5)$
31. $(x - 11y)(x + 9y)$
32. $(x + 12y)(x - 6y)$
33. $(c + 8d)(c - 7d)$
34. $(b + 8c)(b - 3c)$
35. $(a + 7b)(a - 5b)$
36. $(y + x)(y - 2x)$

EXAMPLE 5 Factor $a^2 + ab - 6b^2$.

We are looking for binomials of the form $(a \_\_ b)(a \_\_ b)$. Find two numbers whose sum is 1 and whose product is -6.

Product of -6	Sum
$1, \ -6$	-5
$-1, \ 6$	5
$2, \ -3$	-1
$-2, \ 3$	1 ← The numbers we need are -2 and 3.

$$a^2 + ab - 6b^2 = (a - 2b)(a + 3b)$$

Try This Factor.

i. $x^2 + 4x - 12$
j. $x^2 - 4x - 12$
k. $a^2 + 5ab - 14b^2$
l. $x^2 - xy - 30y^2$

i. $(x + 6)(x - 2)$
j. $(x - 6)(x + 2)$
k. $(a + 7b)(a - 2b)$
l. $(x - 6y)(x + 5y)$

6-4 EXERCISES

A

Factor.

1. $x^2 + 8x + 15$
2. $x^2 + 5x + 6$
3. $x^2 + 7x + 12$
4. $x^2 + 9x + 8$
5. $x^2 - 6x + 9$
6. $y^2 + 11y + 28$
7. $x^2 + 9x + 14$
8. $a^2 + 11a + 30$
9. $b^2 + 5b + 4$
10. $x^2 - 11x + 28$
11. $a^2 - 14a + 48$
12. $z^2 - 8z + 7$
13. $m^2 + 10m + 21$
14. $a^2 - 14a + 45$
15. $z^2 - 10z + 24$
16. $t^2 + 12tp + 36p^2$
17. $a^2 - 9ab + 20b^2$
18. $x^2 - 5xy + 4y^2$
19. $c^2 - 7cd + 10d^2$
20. $x^2 - 8xy + 15y^2$
21. $y^2 - 11yz + 10z^2$
22. $x^2 - 2x - 15$
23. $x^2 + x - 42$
24. $x^2 + 2x - 15$
25. $x^2 - 7x - 18$
26. $y^2 - 3y - 28$
27. $x^2 - 6x - 16$
28. $x^2 - x - 42$
29. $y^2 - 4y - 45$
30. $x^2 - 7x - 60$
31. $x^2 - 2xy - 99y^2$
32. $x^2 + 6xy - 72y^2$
33. $c^2 + cd - 56d^2$
34. $b^2 + 5bc - 24c^2$
35. $a^2 + 2ab - 35b^2$
36. $y^2 - xy - 2x^2$

B

Factor.

37. $x^2 + 20x + 100$ $(x + 10)^2$

38. $x^2 + 20x + 99$ $(x + 11)(x + 9)$

39. $x^2 - 21x - 100$ $(x - 25)(x + 4)$

40. $x^2 - 20x + 96$ $(x - 12)(x - 8)$

41. $x^2 - 21x - 72$ $(x - 24)(x + 3)$

42. $4x^2 + 40x + 100$ $4(x + 5)^2$

43. $x^2 - 25x + 144$ $(x - 16)(x - 9)$

44. $y^2 - 21y + 108$ $(y - 12)(y - 9)$

45. $a^2 + a - 132$ $(a + 12)(a - 11)$

46. $a^2 + 9a - 90$ $(a + 15)(a - 6)$

47. $120y^2 - 23xy + x^2$ $(15y - x)(8y - x)$

48. $96e^2 + 22de + d^2$ $(16e + d)(6e + d)$

49. $108y^2 - 3xy - x^2$ $(12y + x)(9y - x)$

50. $112z^2 + 9yz - y^2$ $(7z + y)(16z - y)$

51. *Critical Thinking* A hot air balloon flies at a speed of $(n + 8)$ miles per hour. At this rate, how long will it take to fly $(n^2 + 5n - 24)$ miles? $(n - 3)$ hours

Challenge

52. Find all integers m for which $y^2 + my + 50$ can be factored.

53. Find all integers b for which $a^2 + ba - 50$ can be factored.

Factor completely.

54. $x^3 - x^2 - 6x$

55. $-x^3 + 22x^2 + 23x$

Mixed Review

Find three factorizations for each monomial. 56. $12x^3$ 57. $8y^3$

Simplify. 58. $(3m + 14) - (m + 9)$ 59. $\frac{a^6b^3}{a^2b^2}$ 60. $\frac{6m^6}{3m^6}$

61. $(4y^2 - 3) + (y^2 + 11)$ 62. $\frac{5t^3}{11t}$ 63. $\frac{4c^3}{4c^2}$

Solve. 64. $|x| + 3 = 7$ 65. $3|c| - 2 = 4$ 66. $4 - |m| = -2$

SUPPOSE

1. Let $x^2 - 3x - 10 = (x + a)(x + b)$.
   a. What do you know about the signs of a and b?
   b. Suppose $|a| > |b|$. Which number, a or b, is a negative integer? How do you know?
2. Let $x^2 + 3x - 10 = (x + a)(x + b)$.
   a. What do you know about the signs of a and b?
   b. Suppose $|a| > |b|$. Which number, a or b, is a negative integer? How do you know?

52. $-51, -27, -15, 15, 27, 51$
53. $-49, -23, -5, 5, 23, 49$
54. $x(x - 3)(x + 2)$
55. $-x(x - 23)(x + 1)$

Mixed Review

Answers may vary for 56 and 57.

56. $(12x)(x^2)$, $(6x^2)(2x)$, $(4x)(3x^2)$, etc.
57. $8y(y^2)$, $(4y^2)(2y)$, $(2y^2)(4y)$, etc.
58. $2m + 5$
59. a^4b
60. 2
61. $5y^2 + 8$
62. $\frac{5t^2}{11}$
63. c
64. $4, -4$
65. $2, -2$
66. $6, -6$

Suppose

1. a. The signs of a and b must be opposite.
   b. Since the middle term is negative, the number with the larger absolute value must be negative. Therefore, a must be a negative integer.
2. a. The signs of a and b must be opposite.
   b. Since the middle term is positive, the number with the larger absolute value must be positive. Therefore, b is a negative integer.

6-5

FIRST FIVE MINUTES

1. Factor $x^2 + 3x + 2$.
   $(x + 1)(x + 2)$
2. Multiply $(2x + 3)(5x + 7)$.
   $10x^2 + 29x + 21$
3. Multiply $(x + 2)(3x + 5)$.
   $3x^2 + 11x + 10$

This section extends the trial-and-error method of the last section to include coefficients of the first term other than 1.

In Example 1, the pair $-1, -3$ was not used, as it is simpler to use positive coefficients for the first terms. However, it should be noted that other factorizations are possible; for example, $(-3x - 2)(-x - 1)$.

Key Questions

What number goes in the blank?

- $(\_x + 2)(3x + 5) = 21x^2 + 41x + 10$
  7
- $(3x + 1)(\_x + 2) = 15x^2 + 11x + 2$
  5
- $(\_x + 2)(\_x + 5) = 12x^2 + 23x + 10$
  3, 4

Chalkboard Examples

1. Factor $21x^2 + 13x + 2$.
   There are no common factors. Here are a few of the possible trial factorizations of the polynomial.
   $(1x + 1)(21x + 2)$
   $(3x + 2)(7x + 1)$
   $(3x + 1)(7x + 2)$
   The third possibility checks. The required factorization is $(3x + 1)(7x + 2)$.
2. Factor $8x^2 + 14x + 3$.
   Here are a few possibilities.
   $(1x + 1)(8x + 3)$
   $(2x + 1)(4x + 3)$
   $(2x + 3)(4x + 1)$
   The third trial factorization has the proper middle term. The required factorization is $(2x + 3)(4x + 1)$.
3. Factor $18x^2 + 36x - 14$.
   Factor out the common factor 2.
   $2(9x^2 + 18x - 7)$
   This factors into $2(3x - 1)(3x + 7)$.

6-5 Factoring $ax^2 + bx + c$

Objective: Factor trinomials of type $ax^2 + bx + c$.

Suppose the leading coefficient of a trinomial is not 1. Consider this multiplication.

$$(2x + 5)(3x + 4) = \overset{F}{6x^2} + \overset{O}{8x} + \overset{I}{15x} + \overset{L}{20}$$

$$= 6x^2 + 23x + 20$$

Factoring Trinomials

To factor $ax^2 + bx + c$, we look for binomials

$$(\_x + \_)(\_x + \_)$$

where products of numbers in the blanks are as follows.

1. The numbers in the *first* blanks of each binomial have product a.
2. The numbers in the *last* blanks of each binomial have product c.
3. The *outside* product and the *inside* product have a sum of b.

EXAMPLE 1 Factor $3x^2 + 5x + 2$.

First look for a factor common to all terms. There is none. Next look for two numbers whose product is 3.

$1, 3 \qquad -1, -3$

Now look for numbers whose product is 2.

$1, 2 \qquad -1, -2$

Since the last term of the trinomial is positive, the signs of the second terms must be the same. Here are some possible factorizations.

$(x + 1)(3x + 2) \qquad (x + 2)(3x + 1)$
$(x - 1)(3x - 2) \qquad (x - 2)(3x - 1)$

When we multiply, the first term will be $3x^2$ and the last term will be 2 in each case. Only the first multiplication gives a middle term of $5x$.

$$3x^2 + 5x + 2 = (x + 1)(3x + 2)$$

Try This Factor.

a. $6x^2 + 7x + 2$ $(3x + 2)(2x + 1)$ **b.** $8x^2 + 10x - 3$ $(4x - 1)(2x + 3)$ **c.** $6x^2 - 41x - 7$ $(6x + 1)(x - 7)$

EXAMPLES

2. Factor $2x^2 + 5x - 12$.

First terms: Find two numbers whose product is 2.
Last terms: Find two numbers whose product is -12.

$(2x + 3)(x - 4)$ $(2x - 2)(x + 6)$ $(2x - 1)(x + 12)$
$(2x - 3)(x + 4)$ $(2x + 2)(x - 6)$ $(2x - 12)(x + 1)$ Possible factorizations

The outside product plus the inside product must equal $5x$.

$$2x^2 + 5x - 12 = (2x - 3)(x + 4)$$

3. Factor $8m^2 + 8m - 6$.

$8m^2 + 8m - 6 = 2(4m^2 + 4m - 3)$ Factoring out the common factor, 2

First terms: Find two numbers whose product is 4.
Last terms: Find two numbers whose product is -3.

$(4m + 3)(m - 1)$ $(4m - 3)(m + 1)$ $(2m + 3)(2m - 1)$
$(4m - 1)(m + 3)$ $(4m + 1)(m - 3)$ $(2m - 3)(2m + 1)$ Possible factorizations

The outside product plus the inside product must equal $4m$.

$$8m^2 + 8m - 6 = 2(4m^2 + 4m - 3) = 2(2m + 3)(2m - 1)$$

Try This Factor. See Additional Answers.

d. $3x^2 - 21x + 36$ **e.** $8x^2 - 2$ **f.** $9a^2 - 15a - 6$
g. $2x^2 + 4x - 6$ **h.** $4a^2 + 2a - 6$ **i.** $6m^2 + 15mn - 9n^2$

6-5 EXERCISES

A

Factor.

1. $2x^2 - 7x - 4$ **2.** $3x^2 - x - 4$ **3.** $5x^2 + x - 18$
4. $3x^2 - 4x - 15$ **5.** $6x^2 + 23x + 7$ **6.** $6x^2 + 13x + 6$
7. $3x^2 + 4x + 1$ **8.** $7x^2 + 15x + 2$ **9.** $4x^2 + 4x - 15$
10. $9a^2 + 6a - 8$ **11.** $2x^2 - x - 1$ **12.** $15n^2 - 19n - 10$
13. $9x^2 + 18x - 16$ **14.** $2y^2 + 5y + 2$ **15.** $3x^2 - 5x - 2$
16. $18c^2 - 3c - 10$ **17.** $12x^2 + 31x + 20$ **18.** $15x^2 + 19x - 10$
19. $14x^2 + 19x - 3$ **20.** $35x^2 + 34x + 8$ **21.** $9p^2 + 18p + 8$
22. $6 - 13x + 6x^2$ **23.** $49 - 42b + 9b^2$ **24.** $15x^2 - 19x + 6$
25. $24x^2 + 47x - 2$ **26.** $16a^2 + 78a + 27$ **27.** $35x^2 - 57x - 44$
28. $9a^2 + 12a - 5$ **29.** $20 + 6x - 2x^2$ **30.** $15 + x - 2x^2$

LESSON QUIZ

1. Factor $2x^2 + 7x + 3$.
   $(2x + 1)(x + 3)$
2. Factor $6x^2 + 17x + 5$.
   $(3x + 1)(2x + 5)$

Assignment Guide
Minimum: Day 1: 1–30 e/o, assign w. 6-4
Day 2: 31–46, MR
Regular: 1–46 m3, 47–62 e/o, 63, MR
Advanced: 1–62 m4, 63–68, MR

ADDITIONAL ANSWERS

Try This

d. $3(x - 3)(x - 4)$
e. $2(2x + 1)(2x - 1)$
f. $3(3a + 1)(a - 2)$
g. $2(x + 3)(x - 1)$
h. $2(2a + 3)(a - 1)$
i. $3(2m - n)(m + 3n)$

Exercises

1. $(2x + 1)(x - 4)$
2. $(3x - 4)(x + 1)$
3. $(5x - 9)(x + 2)$
4. $(3x + 5)(x - 3)$
5. $(2x + 7)(3x + 1)$
6. $(2x + 3)(3x + 2)$
7. $(3x + 1)(x + 1)$
8. $(7x + 1)(x + 2)$
9. $(2x + 5)(2x - 3)$
10. $(3a - 2)(3a + 4)$
11. $(2x + 1)(x - 1)$
12. $(3n - 5)(5n + 2)$
13. $(3x + 8)(3x - 2)$
14. $(2y + 1)(y + 2)$
15. $(3x + 1)(x - 2)$
16. $(6c - 5)(3c + 2)$
17. $(3x + 4)(4x + 5)$
18. $(3x + 5)(5x - 2)$
19. $(7x - 1)(2x + 3)$
20. $(7x + 4)(5x + 2)$
21. $(3p + 4)(3p + 2)$
22. $(2 - 3x)(3 - 2x)$
23. $(7 - 3b)^2$
24. $(3x - 2)(5x - 3)$
25. $(x + 2)(24x - 1)$
26. $(8a + 3)(2a + 9)$
27. $(7x + 4)(5x - 11)$
28. $(3a - 1)(3a + 5)$
29. $2(5 - x)(2 + x)$
30. $(5 + 2x)(3 - x)$

31. $4(3x - 2)(x + 3)$
32. $3(2c - 1)(c - 5)$
33. $6(5x - 9)(x + 1)$
34. $5(4x - 1)(x - 1)$
35. $2(3x + 5)(x - 1)$
36. $3(2y - 3)(3y + 1)$
37. $(3a - 1)(a - 1)$
38. $(2x + 3)(3x + 2)$
39. $4(3x + 2)(x - 3)$
40. $3(2x + 1)(x + 5)$
41. $(2x - 1)(x + 1)$
42. $(5s + 3)(3s + 2)$
43. $(3b - 8)(3b + 2)$
44. $7(2x + 1)(x + 2)$
45. $5(3x + 1)(x - 2)$
46. $(6b - 5)(5b + 4)$
47. $(6x + 5y)(3x - 2y)$
48. $(3a - 4b)(4a - 5b)$
49. $(5m + 2n)(3m - 5n)$
50. $(7p + q)(2p - 3q)$
51. $(5x - 2y)(7x - 4y)$
52. $(8a - b)(7a - b)$
53. $(3x^2 + 2)(3x^2 + 4)$
54. $(3 - 2y)(2 - 3y)$
55. $(3x - 7)^2$
56. $(5x^2 - 3)(3x^2 - 2)$
57. $2a(3a + 5)(a - 1)$
58. $3x(2x - 3)(3x + 1)$
59. Not factorable
60. Not factorable
61. $x(x^2 + 3)(x^2 - 2)$
62. $x(x^2 - 5)(x + 1)(x - 1)$
63. $a = 4, c = 9$
64. $(10x^n + 3)(2x^n + 1)$
65. $(-3x^m + 4)(5x^m - 2)$
66. $(x^{3a} - 1)(3x^{3a} + 1)$
67. $x(x^n - 1)^2$
68. $-2(a + 1)^n(a + 3)^2(a + 6)$

Mixed Review

69. $mn + 11$
70. $\frac{a + b}{2}$
71. $(x - y)^2$
72. $\frac{r}{s + t}$
73. $y > -1$
74. $t < -3$
75. $y \geq 2$

Writing to Learn

Answers may vary, but students should recognize that Bobbi should have factored 4 out of the polynomial.
$(2y + 10)(2y + 8)$
$= 2(y + 5) \cdot 2(y + 4)$
$= 4(y + 5)(y + 4)$

Factor.

31. $12x^2 + 28x - 24$
32. $6c^2 - 33c + 15$
33. $30x^2 - 24x - 54$
34. $20x^2 - 25x + 5$
35. $6x^2 + 4x - 10$
36. $18y^2 - 21y - 9$
37. $3a^2 - 4a + 1$
38. $6x^2 + 13x + 6$
39. $12x^2 - 28x - 24$
40. $6x^2 + 33x + 15$
41. $2x^2 + x - 1$
42. $15s^2 + 19s + 6$
43. $9b^2 - 18b - 16$
44. $14x^2 + 35x + 14$
45. $15x^2 - 25x - 10$
46. $30b^2 - b - 20$

B

Factor, if possible.

47. $18x^2 + 3xy - 10y^2$
48. $12a^2 - 31ab + 20b^2$
49. $15m^2 - 19mn - 10n^2$
50. $14p^2 - 19pq - 3q^2$
51. $35x^2 - 34xy + 8y^2$
52. $56a^2 - 15ab + b^2$
53. $9x^4 + 18x^2 + 8$
54. $6y^2 - 13y + 6$
55. $9x^2 - 42x + 49$
56. $15x^4 - 19x^2 + 6$
57. $6a^3 + 4a^2 - 10a$
58. $18x^3 - 21x^2 - 9x$
59. $x^2 + 3x - 7$
60. $b^2 + 13b - 12$
61. $x^5 + x^3 - 6x$
62. $x^5 - 6x^3 + 5x$
63. ***Critical Thinking*** What are the values of a and c in the trinomial square $ax^2 + 12x + c$ if $a \neq 1$ and $c > a$?

Challenge

Factor.

64. $20x^{2n} + 16x^n + 3$
65. $-15x^{2m} + 26x^m - 8$
66. $3x^{6a} - 2x^{3a} - 1$
67. $x^{2n+1} - 2x^{n+1} + x$
68. $3(a + 1)^{n+1}(a + 3)^2 - 5(a + 1)^n(a + 3)^3$

Mixed Review

Write as an algebraic expression. **69.** 11 more than the product of m and n **70.** the sum of a and b, divided by 2 **71.** the square of the difference between x and y **72.** r divided by the sum of s and t

Solve. **73.** $3 - 4y < 7$ **74.** $6t > 9 + 9t$ **75.** $8 - 3y \leq 2$

WRITING TO LEARN

Bobbi factored $4y^2 + 36y + 80$ as $2(y + 5)(y + 4)$. She argued that using the distributive property, $2(y + 5) = 2y + 10$ and $2(y + 4) = 2y + 8$. We know that $(2y + 10)(2y + 8) = 4y^2 + 36y + 80$. Thus $2(y + 5)(y + 4) = 4y^2 + 36y + 80$. Write a paragraph evaluating Bobbi's argument.

6-6 Factoring by Grouping

Objective: Factor polynomials by grouping.

The distributive property can be used to factor some polynomials with four terms. Consider $x^3 + x^2 + 2x + 2$.

There is no factor common to all terms other than 1. We can, however, factor $x^3 + x^2$ and $2x + 2$ separately.

$$x^3 + x^2 = x^2(x + 1) \qquad 2x + 2 = 2(x + 1)$$

Therefore, $x^3 + x^2 + 2x + 2 = x^2(x + 1) + 2(x + 1)$. We can use the distributive property again and factor out the common factor, $x + 1$.

$$x^2(x + 1) + 2(x + 1) = (x + 1)(x^2 + 2)$$

This method is called **factoring by grouping.** Not all expressions with four terms can be factored by this method.

EXAMPLES Factor.

1. $6x^3 - 9x^2 + 4x - 6 = (6x^3 - 9x^2) + (4x - 6)$
   $= 3x^2(2x - 3) + 2(2x - 3)$ — Factoring each binomial
   $= (2x - 3)(3x^2 + 2)$ — Factoring out the common factor, $2x - 3$

2. $x^3 + x^2 + x + 1 = (x^3 + x^2) + (x + 1)$
   $= x^2(x + 1) + 1(x + 1)$ — Factoring each binomial
   $= (x + 1)(x^2 + 1)$ — Factoring out the common factor, $x + 1$

3. $x^3 + 2x^2 - x - 2 = (x^3 + 2x^2) + (-x - 2)$
   $= x^2(x + 2) + 1(-x - 2)$
   $= x^2(x + 2) - 1(x + 2)$ — Using $ab = (-a)(-b)$
   $= (x + 2)(x^2 - 1)$
   $= (x + 2)(x + 1)(x - 1)$ — Factoring completely

4. $x^2y^2 + ay^2 + ab + bx^2 = y^2(x^2 + a) + b(x^2 + a)$
   $= (x^2 + a)(y^2 + b)$

5. $x^3 + x^2 + 2x - 2 = x^2(x + 1) + 2(x - 1)$

   This cannot be factored by grouping.

Try This Factor.

a. $8x^3 + 2x^2 + 12x + 3$ **b.** $4x^3 - 6x^2 - 6x + 9$

c. $x^3 + x^2 - x - 1$ **d.** $3a - 6b + 5a^2 - 10ab$

a. $(4x + 1)(2x^2 + 3)$
b. $(2x - 3)(2x^2 - 3)$
c. $(x + 1)(x + 1)(x - 1)$
d. $(a - 2b)(3 + 5a)$

6-6

FIRST FIVE MINUTES

1. Factor.
   $3x^2 + 5x + 2$
   $(3x + 2)(x + 1)$
2. Simplify.
   $x(x^2 + x) + 2(x + 1)$
   $x^3 + x^2 + 2x + 2$

You may want to show that the grouping can be done in more than one way. For example, an alternative way to work Example 4 would be to factor x^2 in the first and fourth terms and a in the second and third terms.

$x^2y^2 + ay^2 + ab + bx^2$
$= x^2(y^2 + b) + a(y^2 + b)$
$= (x^2 + a)(y^2 + b)$

The final factorization is the same.

Point out that $(a + b) = -(-a - b)$ and that $(a - b) = -(-a + b) = -(b - a)$.

Key Questions

- Does $(7 - x) = -(x - 7)$?
  Yes
- Does $(y - 2) = -(2 + y)$?
  No

Chalkboard Examples

Factor.

1. $2x^3 + 6x^2 + x + 3$
   $2x^2(x + 3) + 1(x + 3)$
   $= (2x^2 + 1)(x + 3)$
2. $4a^3 + 10a^2 + 6a + 15$
   $2a^2(2a + 5) + 3(2a + 5)$
   $= (2a^2 + 3)(2a + 5)$
3. $5x^4 - 5x^3 - x + 1$
   $5x^3(x - 1) - 1(x - 1)$
   $= (5x^3 - 1)(x - 1)$
4. $2x^3 + 2x^2 - 8x - 8$
   $2(x^3 + x^2 - 4x - 4)$
   $= 2(x^3 - 4x + x^2 - 4)$
   $= 2[x(x^2 - 4) + 1(x^2 - 4)]$
   $= 2(x + 1)(x^2 - 4)$
   $= 2(x + 1)(x + 2)(x - 2)$
5. $4x^3 + 3x^2 + 2x + 1$
   $x^2(4x + 3) + 2x + 1$
   The method doesn't work in this case.

LESSON QUIZ

Factor.

1. $x^3 + x^2 + x + 1$
   $x^2(x + 1) + (x + 1)$
   $= (x^2 + 1)(x + 1)$
2. $3x^3 + 6x^2 + 2x + 4$
   $3x^2(x + 2) + 2(x + 2)$
   $= (3x^2 + 2)(x + 2)$

Assignment Guide
Minimum: 1–20, MR

Regular: 1–28 e/o, 29, MR

Advanced: 1–28 e/o, 29–32, MR

ADDITIONAL ANSWERS

Exercises

1. $(x + 3)(x^2 + 2)$
2. $(2z + 1)(3z^2 + 1)$
3. $(y + 3)(2y^2 + 1)$
4. $(3x + 2)(x^2 + 1)$
5. $(2a - 3)(4a^2 + 3)$
6. $(2p - 5)(5p^2 + 2)$
7. $(3x - 4)(4x^2 + 1)$
8. $(6c - 7)(3c^2 + 5)$
9. $(b + 8)(b^2 - 3)$
10. $(x + 6)(2x^2 - 5)$
11. Not factorable
12. $(8x + 9)(3x^2 - 1)$
13. $(x - 4)(2x^2 - 9)$
14. $(5g - 1)(4g^2 - 5)$
15. $(a - b)(x + y)$
16. $(b + c)(x + 2)$
17. $(n + p)(n + 2)$
18. $(2x + z)(x - 2)$
19. $(a + y)(a - 3)$
20. $(3y + p)(2y - 1)$
21. $(2x^2 + 3)(2x^3 + 3)$
22. $y^2(2y + 3)(2y^2 + 3)$
23. $(c^2 + 1)(c + 1)(c + 1)(c - 1)(c - 1)$
24. $(x^7 + 1)(x^6 + 1)$
25. $(x - y + z)(x - y - z)$
26. $(2 + 2a + 3b)(2 - 2a - 3b)$
27. $(a + b + 1)(a + b - 1)$
28. $(c - 3d + 2)(c - 3d - 2)$
29. $D = abc$

Mixed Review

33. $m^2 + 2mn + n^2$
34. $m^2 - 2mn + n^2$
35. $m^2 - n^2$
36. $(x + 4)(x - 4)$
37. $(y + 3)(y + 3)$ or $(y + 3)^2$
38. $3(a - 1)(a - 1)$ or $3(a - 1)^2$
39. $(c + 9)(c - 10)$
40. $(n - 6)(n - 9)$
41. $(5 - x)(4 - y)$
42. $(x + 1)(x + 2)$
43. $(3a^2 + b)(3a^2 - b)$
44. $(5 - 4a)^2$

6-6 EXERCISES

A

Factor.

1. $x^3 + 3x^2 + 2x + 6$
2. $6z^3 + 3z^2 + 2z + 1$
3. $2y^3 + 6y^2 + y + 3$
4. $3x^3 + 2x^2 + 3x + 2$
5. $8a^3 - 12a^2 + 6a - 9$
6. $10p^3 - 25p^2 + 4p - 10$
7. $12x^3 - 16x^2 + 3x - 4$
8. $18c^3 - 21c^2 + 30c - 35$
9. $b^3 + 8b^2 - 3b - 24$
10. $2x^3 + 12x^2 - 5x - 30$
11. $14x^3 + 18x^2 - 21x + 27$
12. $24x^3 + 27x^2 - 8x - 9$
13. $2x^3 - 8x^2 - 9x + 36$
14. $20g^3 - 4g^2 - 25g + 5$
15. $ax - bx + ay - by$
16. $bx + 2b + cx + 2c$
17. $n^2 + 2n + np + 2p$
18. $2x^2 - 4x + xz - 2z$
19. $a^2 - 3a + ay - 3y$
20. $6y^2 - 3y + 2py - p$

B

Factor.

21. $4x^5 + 6x^3 + 6x^2 + 9$
22. $4y^5 + 6y^4 + 6y^3 + 9y^2$
23. $c^6 - c^4 - c^2 + 1$
24. $x^{13} + x^7 + x^6 + 1$

Factor each as a difference of two squares.

25. $(x - y)^2 - z^2$
26. $4 - (2a + 3b)^2$
27. $a^2 + 2ab + b^2 - 1$
28. $c^2 - 6cd + 9d^2 - 4$

29. ***Critical Thinking*** What is the relationship between the value of D in the polynomial and the values of a, b, and c in the binomials?

$$Ax^3 + Bx^2 + Cx + D = (x + a)(x + b)(x + c)$$

Challenge

30. Factor $acx^{m+n} + adx^n + bcx^m + bd$ into two factors. Assume a, b, c, and d are constants. $(ax^n + b)(cx^m + d)$

31. Find $ax^3 + bx^2 + cx + d$ so that a, b, c, and d are integers, $\frac{a}{c} = \frac{b}{d} = 4$, and $\frac{a}{b} = \frac{7}{5}$. Factor the result by grouping. $28x^3 + 20x^2 + 7x + 5$, $(7x + 5)(4x^2 + 1)$

32. Subtract $(x^2 + 1)^2$ from $x^2(x + 1)^2$ and factor the result. $x^2(x + 1)^2 - (x^2 + 1)^2 = x^4 + 2x^3 + x^2 - (x^4 + 2x^2 + 1) = 2x^3 - 2x^2 + x^2 - 1 = 2x^2(x - 1) + (x + 1)(x - 1) = (2x^2 + x + 1)(x - 1)$

Mixed Review

Multiply. **33.** $(m + n)^2$ **34.** $(m - n)^2$ **35.** $(m + n)(m - n)$

Factor. **36.** $x^2 - 16$ **37.** $y^2 + 6y + 9$ **38.** $3a^2 - 6a + 3$ **39.** $c^2 - c - 90$ **40.** $n^2 - 15n + 54$ **41.** $20 - 4x - 5y + xy$ **42.** $x^2 + 3x + 2$ **43.** $9a^4 - b^2$ **44.** $25 - 40a + 16a^2$

6-7 Factoring: A General Strategy

Objective: Factor polynomials.

Here is a general strategy for factoring.

Factoring Polynomials

A. Always look first for a common factor.
B. Then look at the number of terms.
Two terms: Determine whether you have a difference of squares.
Three terms: Determine whether the trinomial is a square of a binomial. If not, test the factors of the terms.
Four terms: Try factoring by grouping.
C. Always factor completely.

EXAMPLES Factor.

1. $10x^3 - 40x$

A. Look first for a common factor.
$10x^3 - 40x = 10x(x^2 - 4)$ — Factoring out the greatest common factor

B. Factor a difference of two squares.
$10x(x + 2)(x - 2)$ — Factoring $x^2 - 4$

C. Have we factored completely? Yes, because no factor can be factored further.

2. $t^4 - 16 = (t^2 + 4)(t^2 - 4)$ — Factoring a difference of two squares
$= (t^2 + 4)(t + 2)(t - 2)$ — Factoring a difference of two squares again

3. $2a^3 + 10a^2 + a + 5 = (2a^3 + 10a^2) + (a + 5)$
$= 2a^2(a + 5) + 1(a + 5)$ — Factoring each binomial
$= (2a^2 + 1)(a + 5)$ — Using the distributive property

4. $x^4 - 10x^2 + 25 = (x^2)^2 - 10x^2 + 25$ — Writing an equivalent expression
$= (x^2 - 5)^2$ — Factoring a trinomial square

Try This Factor. See Additional Answers.

a. $3m^4 - 3$ **b.** $x^6 + 8x^3 + 16$ **c.** $2x^4 + 8x^3 + 6x^2$
d. $3x^3 + 12x^2 - 2x - 8$ **e.** $8x^3 - 200x$ **f.** $y^5 - 2y^4 - 35y^3$

6-7

FIRST FIVE MINUTES

Factor.
1. $3x^3 + 6x^2$
$3x^2(x + 2)$
2. $x^2 - 64$
$(x - 8)(x + 8)$
3. $x^2 + 2x + 1$
$(x + 1)^2$
4. $x^2 + 4x + 3$
$(x + 1)(x + 3)$

Emphasize that a factorization can be easily checked by multiplication.

Key Questions

Are these products correct?
- $(x + 3)(x - 3) = x^2 - 3$
No, $x^2 - 9$
- $(x + 6)^2 = x^2 + 8x + 36$
No, $x^2 + 12x + 36$
- $(x + 3)(x + 5) = x^2 + 8x + 15$
Yes

Chalkboard Examples

Factor.
1. $14a^4 - 14a^2$
$14a^2(a^2 - 1)$
$= 14a^2(a + 1)(a - 1)$
2. $x^8 - 1$
$(x^4)^2 - 1$
$= (x^4 + 1)(x^4 - 1)$
$= (x^4 + 1)(x^2 + 1)(x^2 - 1)$
$= (x^4 + 1)(x^2 + 1)(x + 1)(x - 1)$
3. $12x^3 - 21x^2 + 8x - 14$
Factor by grouping, since there are four terms.
$3x^2(4x - 7) + 2(4x - 7)$
$= (3x^2 + 2)(4x - 7)$
4. $3x^4 + 30x^3 + 75x^2$
$= 3x^2(x^2 + 10x + 25)$
This is a binomial square.
$3x^2(x + 5)^2$
5. $2a^4 + 14a^3 + 24a^2$
$2a^2(a^2 + 7a + 12)$
$= 2a^2(a + 3)(a + 4)$

LESSON QUIZ

Factor.
1. $3x^3 - 27x$
$3x(x^2 - 9) = 3x(x + 3)(x - 3)$
2. $x^3 + 12x^2 + 36x$
$x(x^2 + 12x + 36) = x(x + 6)^2$
3. $2a^3 + 7a^2 + 3a$
$a(2a^2 + 7a + 3)$
$= a(2a + 1)(a + 3)$

Assignment Guide
Minimum: Day 1: 1–14
Day 2: 15–28, MR
Regular: 1–28 m3, 29–40 e/o, 41, MR, assign w. Connections
Advanced: 1–40 m3, 41–43, MR, assign w. Connections

ADDITIONAL ANSWERS

Try This

a. $3(m^2 + 1)(m + 1)(m - 1)$
b. $(x^3 + 4)^2$
c. $2x^2(x + 3)(x + 1)$
d. $(x + 4)(3x^2 - 2)$
e. $8x(x + 5)(x - 5)$
f. $y^3(y - 7)(y + 5)$

Exercises

9. $(x - 2)(x + 2)(x + 3)$
10. $(x - 5)^2(x + 5)$
11. $6(2x + 3)(2x - 3)$
12. $2(2x + 7)(2x - 7)$
13. $4x(x - 2)(5x + 9)$
14. $3x(x + 3)(3x - 5)$
15. Not factorable
16. Not factorable
17. $x(x - 3)(x^2 + 7)$
18. $m(m^2 + 8)(m + 8)$
19. $x^3(x - 7)^2$
20. $2x^4(x + 2)^2$
21. Not factorable
22. Not factorable
23. $4(x^2 + 4)(x + 2)(x - 2)$
24. $5x(x^2 + 4)(x + 2)(x - 2)$
25. $(y^4 + 1)(y^2 + 1)(y + 1)(1 - y)$
26. $(t^4 + 1)(t^2 + 1)(t + 1)(t - 1)$
27. $x^3(x - 3)(x - 1)$
28. $x^4(x^2 - 2x + 7)$
29. $(a + 1)(a + 1)(a - 1)(a - 1)$
30. Not factorable
31. $-2(x - 2)(x + 5)$ or $2(2 - x)(5 + x)$
32. $-3(2x - 5)(x + 3)$ or $3(5 - 2x)(3 + x)$
33. $(y - 2)(y + 3)(y - 3)$
34. $-1(x^2 + 2)(x + 3)(x - 3)$
35. $(a + 4)(a^2 + 1)$
36. $(x + 2)(x - 2)(x + 1)$
37. $2ab(2ab - 1)(3a + 1)$
38. $a(a - 7b)(a + 2b)$
39. $x^2y(x + 1)(3x - 2y)$
40. $n^2(m + 5n)(m + 2n)$

Mixed Review

44. $\frac{1}{m^2}$ **45.** $\frac{1}{x}$ **46.** $\frac{3}{c^2}$

6-7 EXERCISES

A

Factor.

1. $2x^2 - 128$ $2(x + 8)(x - 8)$
2. $3t^2 - 27$ $3(t + 3)(t - 3)$
3. $a^2 + 25 - 10a$ $(a - 5)^2$
4. $y^2 + 49 + 14y$ $(y + 7)^2$
5. $2x^2 - 11x + 12$ $(2x - 3)(x - 4)$
6. $8y^2 - 18y - 5$ $(2y - 5)(4y + 1)$
7. $x^3 + 24x^2 + 144x$ $x(x + 12)^2$
8. $x^3 - 18x^2 + 81x$ $x(x - 9)^2$
9. $x^3 + 3x^2 - 4x - 12$
10. $x^3 - 5x^2 - 25x + 125$
11. $24x^2 - 54$
12. $8x^2 - 98$
13. $20x^3 - 4x^2 - 72x$
14. $9x^3 + 12x^2 - 45x$
15. $x^2 + 4$
16. $t^2 + 25$
17. $x^4 + 7x^2 - 3x^3 - 21x$
18. $m^4 + 8m^3 + 8m^2 + 64m$
19. $x^5 - 14x^4 + 49x^3$
20. $2x^6 + 8x^5 + 8x^4$
21. $x^2 + 3x + 1$
22. $x^2 + 5x + 2$
23. $4x^4 - 64$
24. $5x^5 - 80x$
25. $1 - y^8$
26. $t^8 - 1$
27. $x^5 - 4x^4 + 3x^3$
28. $x^6 - 2x^5 + 7x^4$

B

Factor completely.

29. $a^4 - 2a^2 + 1$
30. $x^4 + 9$
31. $20 - 6x - 2x^2$
32. $45 - 3x - 6x^2$
33. $18 + y^3 - 9y - 2y^2$
34. $-(x^4 - 7x^2 - 18)$
35. $a^3 + 4a^2 + a + 4$
36. $x^3 + x^2 - (4x + 4)$
37. $12a^3b^2 - 6a^2b + 4a^2b^2 - 2ab$
38. $a^3 - 5a^2b - 14ab^2$
39. $3x^3y - 2x^2y^2 + 3x^4y - 2x^3y^2$
40. $m^2n^2 + 7mn^3 + 10n^4$
41. ***Critical Thinking*** polynomials $x^4 + 3x^2 - 28$ and $x^2 + 7x + 10$ have a common binomial factor. What is it? $x + 2$

Challenge

42. Factor $64a^4 + 1$. (Hint: Write it as $64a^4 + 16a^2 + 1 - 16a^2$.) $(8a^2 - 4a + 1)(8a^2 + 4a + 1)$
43. Factor $x^{2h} - 2^{2h}$ when $h = 4$. $(x^4 + 16)(x^2 + 4)(x + 2)(x - 2)$

Mixed Review

Express using positive exponents. **44.** m^{-2} **45.** x^{-1} **46.** $3c^{-2}$
Subtract. **47.** $(8a^5 + a^3 - 1) - (2a^5 + 4a^3 - 1)$ $6a^5 - 3a^3$
48. $(-3a^2b + 7ab - 4a) - (-2a^2b - 4a + 3ab)$ $-a^2b + 4ab$

CONNECTIONS: DISCRETE MATH

Binomial Expansion

The distributive property can be used as many times as needed to expand binomials to powers.

$$\begin{aligned}(x + 2)^3 = (x + 2)(x + 2)(x + 2) &= (x + 2)(x^2 + 4x + 4)\\ &= x^3 + 4x^2 + 4x + 2x^2 + 8x + 8\\ &= x^3 + 6x^2 + 12x + 8\end{aligned}$$

Consider the following expansions of $(a + b)^n$ for $n = 0, 1, 2, 3, 4$, and 5. Look for patterns.

$$\begin{aligned}(a+b)^0 &= 1\\ (a+b)^1 &= a + b\\ (a+b)^2 &= a^2 + 2ab + b^2\\ (a+b)^3 &= a^3 + 3a^2b + 3ab^2 + b^3\\ (a+b)^4 &= a^4 + 4a^3b + 6a^2b^2 + 4ab^3 + b^4\\ (a+b)^5 &= a^5 + 5a^4b + 10a^3b^2 + 10a^2b^3 + 5ab^4 + b^5\end{aligned}$$

Compare the above expansions with *Pascal's Triangle.*

```
              1
            1   1
          1   2   1
        1   3   3   1
      1   4   6   4   1
    1   5  10  10   5   1
```

We can use Pascal's Triangle and the patterns in the above expansions to find powers of binomials.

EXAMPLE Expand $(x + 3)^4$.

We can use the pattern shown above.

$$(a + b)^4 = a^4 + 4a^3b + 6a^2b^2 + 4ab^3 + b^4$$

We substitute x for a and 3 for b.

$$\begin{aligned}(x + 3)^4 &= x^4 + 4\cdot x^3\cdot 3 + 6\cdot x^2\cdot 3^2 + 4\cdot x\cdot 3^3 + 3^4\\ &= x^4 + 4\cdot x^3\cdot 3 + 6\cdot x^2\cdot 9 + 4\cdot x\cdot 27 + 81\\ &= x^4 + 12x^3 + 54x^2 + 108x + 81\end{aligned}$$

Problems

Use the patterns above to expand the binomials.

1. $(m + n)^5$
2. $(x + 1)^3$
3. $(a + 4)^4$
4. Write the next row of numbers in Pascal's Triangle.
5. Use Pascal's Triangle to find $(a + b)^6$.

Connections: Discrete Math

Math Point
The binomial expansion pattern known as Pascal's Triangle has a history stretching back centuries before Blaise Pascal was born in 1623. References indicate that it was known to the Persian poet and mathematician Omar Khayyam, who lived in the early 12th century, and that it was also known in China at this time. When Chu Shih-Chieh published the triangle in 1303 in China, he referred to it as an "old" method.

Answers

1. $m^5 + 5m^4n + 10m^3n^2 + 10m^2n^3 + 5mn^4 + n^5$
2. $x^3 + 3x^2 + 3x + 1$
3. $a^4 + 16a^3 + 96a^2 + 256a + 256$
4. 1 6 15 20 15 6 1
5. $a^6 + 6a^5b + 15a^4b^2 + 20a^3b^3 + 15a^2b^4 + 6ab^5 + b^6$

6-8

FIRST FIVE MINUTES

Factor.

1. $x^2 + 12x + 35$
   $(x + 5)(x + 7)$

Solve.

2. $3x = 0$ $x = 0$
3. $5(x - 1) = 0$ $x = 1$
4. $x^2 = 0$ $x = 0$
5. $x^2 = 1$ $x = 1$ or $x = -1$

The Principle of Zero Products

The principle of zero products can be rephrased as follows. For any rational numbers a and b, $ab = 0$ if and only if $a = 0$ or $b = 0$.

The phrase "if and only if" is sometimes abbreviated "iff."

Avoiding Common Errors

Students may want to multiply the factors first. Emphasize that there is nothing wrong with their result, but it does not bring them closer to their goal, the solution for x.

Key Questions

- If $3a = 0$, does $a = 0$?
  Yes, since 3 is not 0, a must equal 0.
- If $3a = 9$, can $a = 0$?
  No, $a = 3$.
- If $cd = 0$, does $c = 0$?
  It could be 0 or d could be 0. They do not both need to equal 0.
- If $cd = 18$, can $c = 0$?
  No, it must be a factor of 18.

Chalkboard Examples

1. Solve.
   $(x - 2)(x - 3) = 0$
   $x - 2 = 0$ or $x - 3 = 0$
   $x = 2$ or $x = 3$
2. Solve.
   $3(x - 5)x = 0$
   $x - 5 = 0$ or $x = 0$
   $x = 5$ or $x = 0$
3. Solve.
   $(x - 2)(x - 3)(x - 4) = 0$
   $x - 2 = 0$ or $x - 3 = 0$ or $x - 4 = 0$
   Hence
   $x = 2$ or $x = 3$ or $x = 4$

6-8 Solving Equations By Factoring

The Principle of Zero Products

Objective: Solve equations expressed as a product of factors equal to zero.

The product of two or more numbers is 0 if any of the factors is 0. Also, if a product is 0, at least one of the factors must be 0. In general, we can state the following rule.

The Principle of Zero Products

For any rational numbers a and b, if $ab = 0$, then $a = 0$ or $b = 0$, and if $a = 0$ or $b = 0$, then $ab = 0$.

If we have an equation with 0 on one side and a factorization on the other, we can solve the equation by finding the values that make the factors 0.

EXAMPLE 1 Solve.

$$(5x + 1)(x - 7) = 0$$

$$5x + 1 = 0 \quad \text{or} \quad x - 7 = 0 \qquad \text{Using the principle of zero products}$$

$$5x = -1 \quad \text{or} \quad x = 7$$

$$x = -\frac{1}{5} \quad \text{or} \quad x = 7 \qquad \text{Solving the two equations separately}$$

Check to see whether $-\frac{1}{5}$ and 7 are both solutions of the equation.

Check: for $-\frac{1}{5}$

$(5x + 1)(x - 7)$	$= 0$
$\left(5\left(-\frac{1}{5}\right) + 1\right)\left(-\frac{1}{5} - 7\right)$	0
$(-1 + 1)\left(-7\frac{1}{5}\right)$	0
$0\left(-7\frac{1}{5}\right)$	0
0	0 ✓

Check: for 7

$(5x + 1)(x - 7)$	$= 0$
$(5 \cdot 7 + 1)(7 - 7)$	0
$(35 + 1)0$	0
0	0 ✓

The solutions are $-\frac{1}{5}$ and 7.

EXAMPLE 2 Solve.

$$x(2x - 9) = 0$$
$$x = 0 \text{ or } 2x - 9 = 0 \quad \text{Using the principle of zero products}$$
$$x = 0 \text{ or } 2x = 9$$
$$x = 0 \text{ or } x = \frac{9}{2}$$

Check: for 0

$x(2x - 9)$	$= 0$
$0(2 \cdot 0 - 9)$	0
$0(-9)$	0
0	0 ✓

Check: for $\frac{9}{2}$

$x(2x - 9)$	$= 0$
$\frac{9}{2}\left(2 \cdot \frac{9}{2} - 9\right)$	0
$\frac{9}{2}(0)$	0
0	0 ✓

The solutions are 0 and $\frac{9}{2}$.

Try This Solve using the principle of zero products.

a. $(x - 3)(x + 4) = 0$ 3, −4
b. $(x - 7)(x - 3) = 0$ 7, 3
c. $y(3y - 17) = 0$ 0, $\frac{17}{3}$
d. $(4t + 1)(3t - 2) = 0$ $-\frac{1}{4}, \frac{2}{3}$

Factoring and Solving

Objective: Factor and solve equations.

You can use the following steps to solve equations using the principle of zero products.

A. Get zero on one side of the equation using the addition property.
B. Factor the expression on the other side of the equation.
C. Set each factor equal to zero.
D. Solve each equation.

EXAMPLE 3 Solve. $x^2 + 5x = -6$

$$x^2 + 5x + 6 = 0 \quad \text{Adding 6 to get 0 on one side}$$
$$(x + 2)(x + 3) = 0 \quad \text{Factoring}$$
$$x + 2 = 0 \text{ or } x + 3 = 0 \quad \text{Using the principle of zero products}$$
$$x = -2 \text{ or } x = -3$$

Check:

$x^2 + 5x$	$= -6$
$(-2)^2 + 5(-2)$	-6
$4 + (-10)$	-6
-6	-6 ✓

$x^2 + 5x$	$= -6$
$(-3)^2 + 5(-3)$	-6
$9 + (-15)$	-6
-6	-6 ✓

The solutions are -2 and -3.

Factoring and Solving

Remind students that they must set the polynomial equal to zero before applying the principle of zero products.

Avoiding Common Errors

Students may incorrectly apply the principle of zero products to products other than zero. Remind students that if the product of two factors is 12, for example, there are many pairs of numbers whose product is 12.

$3 \times 4 = 12$, $2 \times 6 = 12$, $\frac{1}{2} \times 24 = 12$, $\frac{1}{4} \times 48 = 12$, and so on.

Chalkboard Examples

1. Solve $x^2 + 7x + 12 = 0$.
   Factor.
   $(x + 3)(x + 4) = 0$
   $x + 3 = 0$ or $x + 4 = 0$
   $x = -3$ or $x = -4$
2. Solve $x^2 = -3x - 2$.
   $x^2 + 3x + 2 = 0$
   Factor.
   $(x + 1)(x + 2) = 0$
   $x + 1 = 0$ or $x + 2 = 0$
   $x = -1$ or $x = -2$
3. Solve $x^2 + 10x + 25 = 0$.
   Factor.
   $(x + 5)^2 = 0$
   $x + 5 = 0$ or $x + 5 = 0$
   $x = -5$ or $x = -5$
   There is only one solution in this case, -5.
4. Solve $9x^2 - 4 = 0$.
   $(3x + 2)(3x - 2) = 0$
   $3x + 2 = 0$ or $3x - 2 = 0$
   $3x = -2$ or $3x = 2$
   $x = -\frac{2}{3}$ or $x = \frac{2}{3}$

LESSON ENRICHMENT

Here is a nonstandard method for finding the solution to a second-degree equation. Solve $x^2 - x - 1 = 0$. Rewrite the equation as

$$x^2 = x + 1$$

Divide both sides by x, if x is not 0.

$$x = 1 + \frac{1}{x}$$

We have solved for x in terms of x. Substitute for x in the denominator.

$$x = 1 + \cfrac{1}{1 + \cfrac{1}{x}}$$

We can substitute again, and again.

$$x = 1 + \cfrac{1}{1 + \cfrac{1}{1 + \cfrac{1}{1 + \dots}}}$$

Calculate the expression shown above. Does it give an approximate solution to the equation? **Yes**

LESSON QUIZ

Solve.

1. $(x - 3)(x + 5) = 0$ $x = 3$ or $x = -5$
2. $(2x - 1)x = 0$ $x = \frac{1}{2}$ or $x = 0$
3. $x^2 + 4x + 3 = 0$ $x = -1$ or $x = -3$
4. $x^2 + 6x + 9 = 0$ $x = -3$

Try This Solve.

e. $x^2 - x - 6 = 0$ 3, −2 **f.** $m^2 - m = 56$ 8, −7 **g.** $x^2 - 3x = 28$ 7, −4

EXAMPLES Solve.

4. $x^2 - 8x + 16 = 0$

$(x - 4)(x - 4) = 0$ Factoring the square of a binomial

$x - 4 = 0$ or $x - 4 = 0$

$x = 4$ or $x = 4$

Check:

$x^2 - 8x + 16$	$= 0$
$4^2 - 8 \cdot 4 + 16$	0
$16 - 32 + 16$	0
0	0 ✓

There is only one solution, 4.

5. $x^2 = 5x$

$x^2 - 5x = 0$ Getting 0 on one side

$x(x - 5) = 0$ Factoring

$x = 0$ or $x - 5 = 0$

$x = 0$ or $x = 5$

Check:

x^2	$= 5x$
0^2	$5 \cdot 0$
0	0 ✓

x^2	$= 5x$
5^2	$5 \cdot 5$
25	25 ✓

The solutions are 0 and 5.

6. $4x^2 = 25$

$4x^2 - 25 = 0$

$(2x - 5)(2x + 5) = 0$ Factoring a difference of two squares

$2x - 5 = 0$ or $2x + 5 = 0$

$2x = 5$ or $2x = -5$

$x = \frac{5}{2}$ or $x = -\frac{5}{2}$

Check:

$4x^2$	$= 25$
$4\left(\frac{5}{2}\right)^2$	25
$4 \cdot \frac{25}{4}$	25
25	25 ✓

$4x^2$	$= 25$
$4\left(-\frac{5}{2}\right)^2$	25
$4 \cdot \frac{25}{4}$	25
25	25 ✓

The solutions are $\frac{5}{2}$ and $-\frac{5}{2}$.

Try This Solve.

h. $x^2 + 9 = 6x$ 3 **i.** $x^2 = 4x$ 0, 4 **j.** $25x^2 = 16$ $\frac{4}{5}, -\frac{4}{5}$

6-8 EXERCISES

A

Solve.

1. $(x + 8)(x + 6) = 0$

2. $(c + 3)(c + 2) = 0$

3. $(a - 3)(a + 5) = 0$

4. $(x + 9)(x - 3) = 0$

5. $(x + 12)(x - 11) = 0$

6. $(x - 13)(x + 53) = 0$

7. $x(x + 5) = 0$

8. $y(y + 7) = 0$

9. $y(y - 13) = 0$

10. $v(v - 4) = 0$

11. $0 = y(y + 10)$

12. $0 = x(x - 21)$

13. $(7x - 28)(28x - 7) = 0$

14. $(12x - 11)(8x - 5) = 0$

15. $2x(3x - 2) = 0$

16. $75x(8x - 9) = 0$

17. $\frac{1}{2}x\left(\frac{2}{3}x - 12\right) = 0$

18. $\frac{5}{7}d\left(\frac{3}{4}d - 6\right) = 0$

19. $\left(\frac{1}{3} - 3x\right)\left(\frac{1}{5} - 2x\right) = 0$

20. $\left(\frac{1}{5} + 2x\right)\left(\frac{1}{9} - 3x\right) = 0$

21. $\left(\frac{1}{3}y - \frac{2}{3}\right)\left(\frac{1}{4}y - \frac{3}{2}\right) = 0$

22. $\left(\frac{7}{4}x - \frac{1}{12}\right)\left(\frac{2}{3}x - \frac{12}{11}\right) = 0$

23. $(0.3x - 0.1)(0.05x - 1) = 0$

24. $(0.1x - 0.3)(0.4x - 20) = 0$

25. $9x(3x - 2)(2x - 1) = 0$

26. $(x - 5)(x + 55)(5x - 1) = 0$

27. $x^2 + 6x + 5 = 0$ $-5, -1$

28. $d^2 + 7d + 6 = 0$ $-6, -1$

29. $x^2 + 7x - 18 = 0$ $2, -9$

30. $x^2 + 4x - 21 = 0$ $-7, 3$

31. $b^2 - 8b + 15 = 0$ $5, 3$

32. $x^2 - 9x + 14 = 0$ $7, 2$

33. $x^2 - 8x = 0$ $0, 8$

34. $x^2 - 3x = 0$ $0, 3$

35. $x^2 + 19x = 0$ $0, -19$

36. $x^2 + 12x = 0$ $0, -12$

37. $c^2 - 16 = 0$ $4, -4$

38. $x^2 - 100 = 0$ $10, -10$

39. $9x^2 - 4 = 0$ $\frac{2}{3}, -\frac{2}{3}$

40. $4a^2 - 9 = 0$ $\frac{3}{2}, -\frac{3}{2}$

41. $x^2 + 6x + 9 = 0$ -3

42. $x^2 + 10x + 25 = 0$ -5

43. $12y^2 - 5y = 2$ $\frac{2}{3}, -\frac{1}{4}$

44. $2y^2 + 12y = -10$ $-5, -1$

45. $x(x - 5) = 14$ $7, -2$

46. $t(3t + 1) = 2$ $\frac{2}{3}, -1$

47. $64m^2 = 81$ $\frac{9}{8}, -\frac{9}{8}$

48. $100t^2 = 49$ $\frac{7}{10}, -\frac{7}{10}$

49. $(4x + 9)(14x - 7) = 0$

50. $(3w - 1)(w + 2) = 0$

51. $5x^2 = 6x$

52. $3x^2 - 7x = 20$

53. $(5x + 1)(4x - 12) = 0$

54. $x^2 - 2x + 1 = 0$

55. $(3x - 9)(x + 3) = 0$

56. $7x^2 = 8x$

57. $6x^2 - 4x = 10$

58. $(2x + 5)(x + 4) = 0$

59. $(2x + 9)(x + 8) = 0$

60. $v^2 - 6v - 16 = 0$

Assignment Guide

Minimum: Day 1: 1–30 e/o, MR
Day 2: 31–60 e/o, assign w. 6–9

Regular: 1–68 m3, 69, MR

Advanced: 1–68 m4, 69–71, MR

ADDITIONAL ANSWERS

Exercises

1.	$-8, -6$	**2.**	$-3, -2$
3.	$3, -5$	**4.**	$-9, 3$
5.	$-12, 11$	**6.**	$13, -53$
7.	$0, -5$	**8.**	$0, -7$
9.	$0, 13$	**10.**	$0, 4$
11.	$0, -10$	**12.**	$0, 21$
13.	$4, \frac{1}{4}$	**14.**	$\frac{11}{12}, \frac{5}{8}$
15.	$0, \frac{2}{3}$	**16.**	$0, \frac{9}{8}$
17.	$0, 18$	**18.**	$0, 8$
19.	$\frac{1}{9}, \frac{1}{10}$	**20.**	$-\frac{1}{10}, \frac{1}{27}$
21.	$2, 6$	**22.**	$\frac{1}{21}, \frac{18}{11}$
23.	$\frac{1}{3}, 20$	**24.**	$3, 50$
25.	$0, \frac{2}{3}, \frac{1}{2}$	**26.**	$5, -55, \frac{1}{5}$
49.	$-\frac{9}{4}, \frac{1}{2}$	**50.**	$\frac{1}{3}, -2$
51.	$0, \frac{6}{5}$	**52.**	$4, -\frac{5}{3}$
53.	$3, -\frac{1}{5}$	**54.**	1
55.	$3, -3$	**56.**	$0, \frac{8}{7}$
57.	$\frac{5}{3}, -1$	**58.**	$-\frac{5}{2}, -4$
59.	$-\frac{9}{2}, -8$	**60.**	$8, -2$

69. $x^2 - 16$, $x^2 - 15x - 16$, $x^2 + 15x - 16$, $x^2 - 6x - 16$, $x^2 + 6x - 16$

70. a. $x^2 + 2x - 3 = 0$
b. $x^2 - 2x - 3 = 0$
c. $x^2 - 4x + 4 = 0$
d. $x^2 - 7x + 12 = 0$
e. $x^2 + x - 12 = 0$
f. $x^2 - x - 12 = 0$
g. $x^2 + 7x + 12 = 0$
h. $x^2 - x + \frac{1}{4}$ or $4x^2 - 4x + 1 = 0$
i. $x^2 - 25 = 0$
j. $x^3 - \frac{14}{40}x^2 + \frac{1}{40}x$ or $40x^3 - 14x^2 + x = 0$

71. a. (3)
b. (5)
c. (1)
d. (2)
e. (4)
f. (6)

Mixed Review

72. $3n + 8$ 73. $3(n + 8)$
74. $\frac{n - 15}{2}$ 75. $(a + b)^2$
76. $a^2 + b^2$ 77. $a^2 - b^2$
78. $2(2y - 1)(y + 3)$
79. $(2x - y)(2x + y)$
80. $(2y - 3)(3y + 2)$

Problem for Programmers

This program can be written using any programming language (BASIC, PASCAL, LOGO, etc.)

B

Solve.

61. $b(b + 9) = 4(5 + 2b)$ 4, −5
62. $y(y + 8) = 16(y - 1)$ 4
63. $(t - 3)^2 = 36$ 9, −3
64. $(t - 5)^2 = 2(5 - t)$ 5, 3
65. $x^2 - \frac{1}{64} = 0$ $\frac{1}{8}, \frac{-1}{8}$
66. $x^2 - \frac{25}{36} = 0$ $\frac{5}{6}, \frac{-5}{6}$
67. $\frac{5}{16}x^2 = 5$ 4, −4
68. $\frac{27}{25}x^2 = \frac{1}{3}$ $\frac{5}{9}, \frac{-5}{9}$
69. ***Critical Thinking*** Write all factorable second-degree trinomials whose first term is x^2 and whose last term is -16.

Challenge

70. Find an equation that has the given numbers as solutions. For example, 3 and -2 are solutions to $x^2 - x - 6 = 0$.
a. 1, −3 **b.** 3, −1 **c.** 2, 2 **d.** 3, 4 **e.** 3, −4
f. −3, 4 **g.** −3, −4 **h.** $\frac{1}{2}, \frac{1}{2}$ **i.** 5, −5 **j.** 0, 0.1, $\frac{1}{4}$

71. For each equation in the left-hand column, find an equation in the right-hand column that has the same two solutions.

a. $3x^2 - 4x + 8 = 0$	**(1)** $4x^2 + 8x + 36 = 0$
b. $(x - 6)(x + 3) = 0$	**(2)** $(2x + 8)(2x - 5) = 0$
c. $x^2 + 2x + 9 = 0$	**(3)** $9x^2 - 12x + 24 = 0$
d. $(2x - 5)(x + 4) = 0$	**(4)** $(x + 1)(5x - 5) = 0$
e. $5x^2 - 5 = 0$	**(5)** $x^2 - 3x - 18 = 0$
f. $x^2 + 10x - 2 = 0$	**(6)** $2x^2 + 20x - 4 = 0$

Mixed Review

Write as an algebraic expression. **72.** 3 times a number plus 8 **73.** 3 times the sum of a number and 8 **74.** half of the difference of a number and 15 **75.** the square of the sum of a and b **76.** the sum of the squares of a and b **77.** the difference of the squares of a and b
Factor. **78.** $4y^2 + 10y - 6$ **79.** $4x^2 - y^2$ **80.** $6y^2 - 5y - 6$

Problem for Programmers

Write a program to help you factor a polynomial in the form $x^2 + bx + c$. The program should input b, and c, find pairs of factors of c (see Problem for Programmers in Chapter 5), and add them until the sum equals b. Output the factors whose sum equals b.

Challenge: Write a program to help you factor a polynomial in the form $ax^2 + bx + c$.

6-9 Problem Solving: Using Equations

Objective: Solve problems by writing and solving equations.

You can use the Problem-Solving Guidelines below to help you solve problems when your plan involves writing and solving an equation.

PROBLEM-SOLVING GUIDELINES

- **Phase 1: UNDERSTAND the problem**
  What am I trying to find?
  What data am I given?
  Have I ever solved a similar problem?
- **Phase 2: Develop and carry out a PLAN**
  What strategies might I use to solve the problem?
  How can I correctly carry out the strategies I selected?
- **Phase 3: Find the ANSWER and CHECK**
  Does the proposed solution check?
  What is the answer to the problem?
  Does the answer seem reasonable?
  Have I stated the answer clearly?

EXAMPLE 1 Translate to an equation and solve.

The product of one more than a number and one less than the number is 8. Find the number.

Let x = the number.

$\underbrace{\text{One more than a number}}_{(x+1)}$ $\underset{\cdot}{\text{times}}$ $\underbrace{\text{one less than the number}}_{(x-1)}$ $\underset{=}{\text{is}}$ $\underset{8}{8.}$

$(x + 1) \cdot (x - 1) = 8$ Translating

$$(x + 1)(x - 1) = 8 \quad \text{Multiplying}$$
$$x^2 - 1 = 8$$
$$x^2 - 1 - 8 = 0$$
$$x^2 - 9 = 0$$
$$(x - 3)(x + 3) = 0 \quad \text{Factoring}$$
$$x - 3 = 0 \quad \text{or} \quad x + 3 = 0 \quad \text{Using the principle of zero products}$$
$$x = 3 \quad \text{or} \quad x = -3$$

6-9

FIRST FIVE MINUTES

1. Solve $x^2 = 3x$.
   $x^2 - 3x = 0$
   $x(x - 3) = 0$
   $x = 0$ or $x = 3$
2. Solve $x^2 + 2x + 1 = 0$.
   $(x + 1)^2 = 0$
   $x = -1$
3. Solve $x^2 + 11x + 30 = 0$.
   $(x + 5)(x + 6) = 0$
   $x = -5$ or $x = -6$

Point out that a solution to an equation may or may not be the solution to the problem. For example, suppose we are trying to find a distance (d) and the solutions are 3 or -2. Since a distance cannot be negative, only the number 3 is a solution to the problem.

Key Questions

- Is it possible for a problem to have more than one solution?
  Yes. See Examples 1 and 2.
- If the equation used to solve a problem is correct, will all solutions to the equation satisfy the problem?
  No. See Example 3.

Chalkboard Examples (T7)

1. The sum of a number and its square is 6. Find the number.
   Let x = the number.
   $x + x^2 = 6$
   $x^2 + x - 6 = 0$
   $(x - 2)(x + 3) = 0$
   $x - 2 = 0$ or $x + 3 = 0$
   $x = 2$ or $x = -3$
   There are two numbers, 2 and -3.
   The sum of 2 and its square, 4, is 6.
   The sum of -3 and its square, 9, is 6.
   Both answers check.
2. A rectangular area is such that one side is 4 ft longer than the other, and the area is 5 ft^2. Find the length and width of the area.
   Let w = width.
   $w + 4$ = length
   $w(w + 4)$ = area
   $w(w + 4) = 5$
   $w^2 + 4w - 5 = 0$
   $(w - 1)(w + 5) = 0$
   $w - 1 = 0$ or $w + 5 = 0$
   $w = 1$ or $w = -5$
   Since the width cannot be negative, the width is 1 ft. The length is $w + 4 = 1 + 4 = 5$ ft. The area is $1(5) = 5$ square ft. The answer checks.
   The area is $1(5) = 5$ ft^2.
3. A triangular banner has an area of 5 ft^2. The length is 3 ft more than the base. Find the base and the length.
   Let b = base of the banner.
   Then $b + 3$ = the length.
   Area $= \frac{1}{2}b(b + 3)$
   $\frac{1}{2}b(b + 3) = 5$
   $\frac{1}{2}(b^2 + 3b) = 5$
   $b^2 + 3b = 10$
   $b^2 + 3b - 10 = 0$
   $(b + 5)(b - 2) = 0$
   $b + 5 = 0$ or $b - 2 = 0$
   $b = -5$ or $b = 2$
   Since the base cannot be negative, the base is 2 ft. The length is $2 + 3 = 5$ ft.

Check for 3: $3 + 1 = 4$; $3 - 1 = 2$; and the product, $4 \cdot 2$, is 8.
Check for -3: $-3 + 1 = -2$; $-3 - 1 = -4$; and the product, $-2(-4)$, is 8.

Both 3 and -3 check. They are both solutions.

EXAMPLE 2 Translate to an equation and solve.

The square of a number minus twice the number is 48. Find the number.
Let x = the number.

$$\underbrace{\text{The square of a number}}_{x^2}\ \underset{-}{\text{minus}}\ \underbrace{\text{twice the number}}_{2x}\ \underset{=}{\text{is}}\ \underset{48}{48.} \qquad \text{Translating}$$

$$x^2 - 2x = 48$$
$$x^2 - 2x - 48 = 0$$
$$(x - 8)(x + 6) = 0$$

$$x - 8 = 0 \quad \text{or} \quad x + 6 = 0 \qquad \text{Using the principle of zero products}$$
$$x = 8 \quad \text{or} \quad x = -6$$

Check for 8: $8^2 - 2(8) = 64 - 16 = 48$.
Check for -6: $(-6)^2 - 2(-6) = 36 + 12 = 48$.

Both 8 and -6 check. They are both solutions.

Try This Translate to an equation and solve.

a. Seven less than a number times eight less than the number is 0. 7, 8
b. A number times one less than the number is zero. 0, 1
c. One more than a number times one less than the number is 24. 5, -5
d. The square of a number minus the number is 20. 5, -4
e. Twice the square of a number plus one is 73. 6, -6

Sometimes it helps to reword before translating.

EXAMPLE 3 Translate to an equation and solve.

The area of the foresail on a 12-meter racing yacht is 93.75 square meters. The sail's height is 8.75 meters greater than its base. Find its base and height.

$$\text{Area} = \frac{1}{2} \times \text{base} \times \text{height}$$

Let h = the sail's height and $h - 8.75$ = the length of the sail's base.

$\frac{1}{2}$ times the base times the height is 93.75. Rewording

$$\frac{1}{2} \cdot (h - 8.75) \cdot h = 93.75 \quad \text{Translating}$$

$$\frac{1}{2}(h - 8.75)h = 93.75$$

$$(h - 8.75)h = 187.5 \quad \text{Multiplying both sides by 2}$$

$$h^2 - 8.75h = 187.5 \quad \text{Using the distributive property}$$

$$h^2 - 8.75h - 187.5 = 0 \quad \text{Adding } -187.5 \text{ to both sides to get 0 on one side}$$

$$(h - 18.75)(h + 10) = 0 \quad \text{Factoring}$$

$$h - 18.75 = 0 \quad \text{or} \quad h + 10 = 0 \quad \text{Using the principle of zero products}$$

$$h = 18.75 \quad \text{or} \quad h = -10$$

The solutions of the equation are 18.75 and -10. The height of the sail cannot have a negative value, so the height must be 18.75 meters. The length of the base is then 8.75 meters shorter, or 10 meters.

EXAMPLE 4 Translate to an equation and solve.

The product of two consecutive integers is 156. Find the integers. (Consecutive integers differ by 1, such as 49 and 50, or -6 and -5.)

Let x represent the first integer. Then $x + 1$ represents the second integer.

First integer times second integer is 156. Rewording

$$x \cdot (x + 1) = 156 \quad \text{Translating}$$

$$x(x + 1) = 156$$

$$x^2 + x = 156$$

$$x^2 + x - 156 = 0$$

$$(x - 12)(x + 13) = 0$$

$$x - 12 = 0 \quad \text{or} \quad x + 13 = 0 \quad \text{Using the principle of zero products}$$

$$x = 12 \quad \text{or} \quad x = -13$$

When $x = 12$, $x + 1 = 13$, and $12(13) = 156$.
When $x = -13$, $x + 1 = -12$, and $-12(-13) = 156$.

We have two pairs of solutions, 12 and 13, and -12 and -13. Both are pairs of consecutive integers whose product is 156.

Try This Translate to an equation and solve.

f. The width of a rectangular card is 2 cm less than the length. The area is 15 cm^2. Find the length and width. 5 cm, 3 cm

g. The product of two consecutive integers is 462. Find the integers. 21, 22; -21, -22

LESSON QUIZ

Translate into an equation and solve.

1. The square of a certain number is 12 greater than the number. Find the number.
   Let x be the number.
   $x^2 = x + 12$
   $x^2 - x - 12 = 0$
   $(x + 3)(x - 4) = 0$
   $x = -3$ or $x = 4$
2. The product of two consecutive, positive even integers is 24. Find the integers.
   Let x be the smaller number. The larger number is $x + 2$.
   $x(x + 2) = 24$
   $x^2 + 2x = 24$
   $x^2 + 2x - 24 = 0$
   $(x - 4)(x + 6) = 0$
   $x = 4$ or $x = -6$
   The positive solution $x = 4$ is the one required. Hence the two numbers are 4 and 6.

Assignment Guide
Minimum: Day 1: 1–4, assign w. 6-8
Day 2: 5–20 e/o, MR
Regular: 1–26 e/o, 27, MR

Advanced: 1–26 m3, 27–31, MR

ADDITIONAL ANSWERS

Exercises

1. $\frac{-3}{4}$ or 1
2. −5 or 5
3. 2 or 4
4. 3 or 5
5. 13 and 14, −13 and −14
6. 7 and 8, −7 and −8
7. 12 and 14, −12 and −14
8. 14 and 16, −14 and −16
9. 15 and 17, −15 and −17
10. 11 and 13, −11 and −13
11. 12 m, 8 m
12. 12 cm, 7 cm
13. 5 ft
14. 1 in. or 3 in.
15. 4 cm, 14 cm
16. 2 m, 10 m
17. 6 m
18. 4 in.
19. 5 and 7
20. 7 and 9
21. $7x + 1 = (x + 1)^2$, $x = 5$
22. $6x + 1 = (x - 1)^2$, $x = 8$
23. $x^3 = 2x^2$, $x = 0$ or $x = 2$

6-9 EXERCISES

A

Translate to an equation and solve.

1. If you subtract a number from four times its square, the result is three.
2. If seven is added to the square of a number, the result is 32.
3. Eight more than the square of a number is six times the number.
4. Fifteen more than the square of a number is eight times the number.
5. The product of two consecutive integers is 182.
6. The product of two consecutive integers is 56.
7. The product of two consecutive even integers is 168.
8. The product of two consecutive even integers is 224.
9. The product of two consecutive odd integers is 255.
10. The product of two consecutive odd integers is 143.
11. The length of a rectangle is 4 m greater than the width. The area of the rectangle is 96 m^2. Find the length and width.
12. The length of a rectangle is 5 cm greater than the width. The area of the rectangle is 84 cm^2. Find the length and width.
13. The area of a square is 5 ft more than the perimeter. Find the length of a side.
14. The perimeter of a square is 3 in. more than the area. Find the length of a side.
15. The base of a triangle is 10 cm greater than the height. The area is 28 cm^2. Find the height and base.
16. The height of a triangle is 8 m less than the base. The area is 10 m^2. Find the height and base.
17. If the sides of a square are lengthened by 3 m, the area becomes 81 m^2. Find the length of a side of the original square.
18. If the sides of a square are lengthened by 7 in., the area becomes 121 in^2. Find the length of a side of the original square.
19. The sum of the squares of two consecutive odd positive integers is 74.
20. The sum of the squares of two consecutive odd positive integers is 130.

B

21. The sum of 7 times a positive number and 1 is the same as the square of 1 more than the number.
22. The sum of 6 times a positive number and 1 is the same as the square of 1 less than the number.
23. The cube of a number is the same as twice the square of the number.

24. Mark launched a model rocket using an engine that will generate a speed of 180 ft per second. After how many seconds will Mark's rocket reach a height of 464 ft?

a. The formula $h = rt - 16t^2$ gives the height of an object projected upward at a rate of r feet per second after t seconds. Rewrite this equation substituting the data you are given.

b. Solve the equation and answer the problem.

c. After how many seconds will it be at that height again?

25. When distance is measured in meters and the speed of the object is measured in meters per second, the formula in Exercise 24 becomes $h = rt - 4.9t^2$. A baseball is thrown upward with speed of 19.6 m per second.

a. After how many seconds will the ball reach a height of 14.7 m?

b. After how many seconds will the ball hit the ground?

26. A cement walk of constant width is built around a 20 ft × 40 ft rectangular pool. The total area of the pool and walk is 1500 ft². Find the width of the walk.

Let w be the width of the walkway.

a. Copy and complete the diagram below showing all of the data you are given and the unknown dimensions.

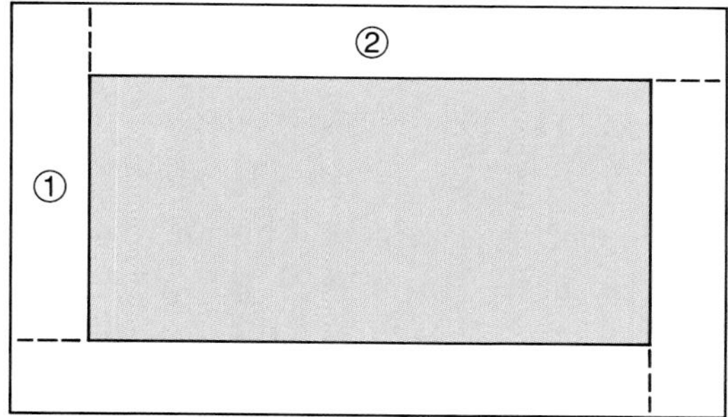

b. What is the total area of the walkway?

c. Write an expression for the area of section 1.

d. Write an expression for the area of section 2.

e. Write an expression that represents the total area of the walkway.

f. Solve the equation and answer the problem.

27. ***Write a Convincing Argument*** Solve the problem below. Then write an argument that would convince a classmate that your solution is correct.

The total surface area of a box is 350 in.² The box is 9 in. high and has a square base. Find the length of the side of the base.

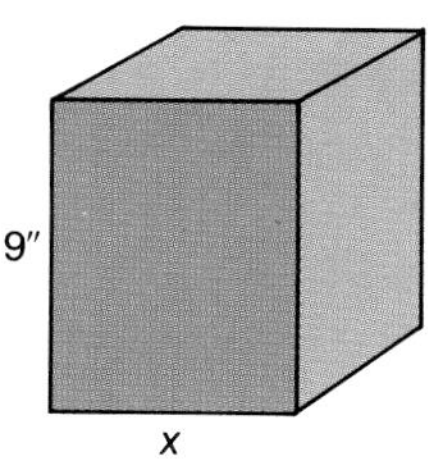

24. a. $464 = 180t - 16t^2$
b. 4 s
c. $7\frac{1}{4}$ s

25. a. 1 second (on the way up)
3 seconds (on the way back down)
b. 4 seconds

26. a.

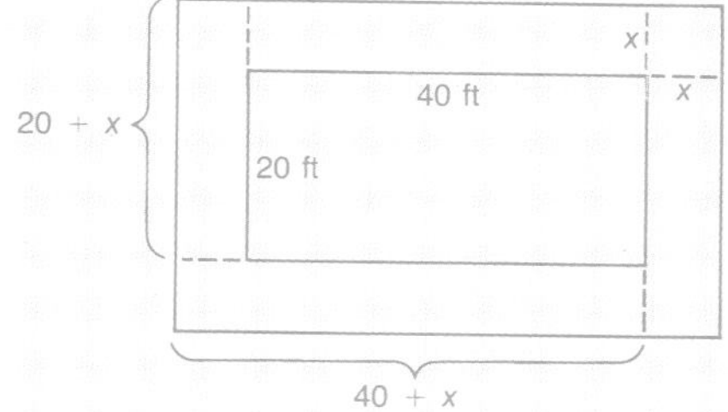

b. $1500 - (40 \cdot 20) = 700$ ft²
c. $x(x + 20)$
d. $x(x + 40)$
e. $2[x(x + 20) + x(x + 40)]$
f. The width of the walkway is 5 ft.

27. 7 in.

Mixed Review

32. 1.17203×10^5
33. 5.59×10^{-3}
34. $10{,}000m^8$
35. $80x^8$
36. $-15a^4b^5$
37. 24
38. 680
39. $(a - 4)^2$
40. $3(2c + 1)(c - 3)$
41. $x^2(x - 1)(x + 1)$
42. $(2m^2 - 1)(m - 2)$
43. $9(4y^4 - 7)$
44. $5(x + 7)^2$

Challenge

28. Find two consecutive positive numbers such that the product of the sum and difference of the numbers plus eight is the sum of their squares. 2, 3

29. The pages of a book are 15 cm by 20 cm. Margins of equal width surround the printing on each page and comprise one half the area of the page. Find the width of the margins. $2\frac{1}{2}$ cm

30. A rectangular piece of cardboard is twice as long as it is wide. A 4 cm square is cut out of each corner, and the sides are turned up to make a box. The volume of the box is 616 cm³. Find the original dimensions of the cardboard. ◇
30 cm by 15 cm

31. An open rectangular gutter is made by turning up the sides of a piece of metal 20 in. wide. The area of the cross section of the gutter is 50 in.² Find the depth of the gutter. ◇
5 in.

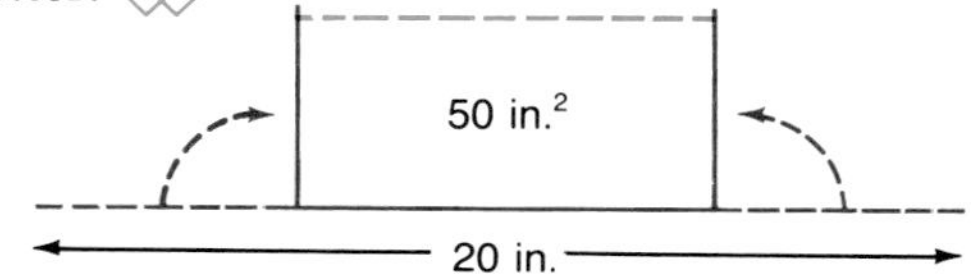

Mixed Review

Write using scientific notation. **32.** 117,203 **33.** 0.00559

Simplify. **34.** $(10m^2)^4$ **35.** $(5x^5)(x^2)(16x)$ **36.** $(3a^3b^2)(-5ab^3)$

Solve. **37.** What number is 80% of 30? **38.** 34 is 5% of what number?

Factor. **39.** $a^2 - 8a + 16$ **40.** $6c^2 - 15c - 9$ **41.** $x^4 - x^2$

42. $2m^3 - 4m^2 - m + 2$ **43.** $36y^4 - 63$ **44.** $5x^2 + 70x + 245$

BIOGRAPHICAL NOTE: THOMAS HARRIOT

One of the important mathematicians in the seventeenth century was the Englishman Thomas Harriot. Like other mathematicians of his time he was not interested only in math. He had been sent by Sir Walter Raleigh as a surveyor on an expedition to the New World in 1585 and was the first well-known mathematician to set foot in North America. On his return he published a book about his travels.

Harriot was among the first to use some of the symbols of algebra we use today. In a book published in 1631, ten years after his death, he used the inequality symbols $<$ and $>$ for the first time. He wrote the cube of a number A as AAA—a great improvement over the Latin phrase *A cubus.* In other writing he found methods of factoring higher degree polynomials and of determining the areas of spherical triangles.

Problem Solving: College Entrance Exams

Factoring

The special products that you learned in this chapter can be very useful on college entrance exams.

$$(a - b)(a + b) = a^2 - b^2$$
$$(a + b)^2 = a^2 + 2ab + b^2$$
$$(a - b)^2 = a^2 - 2ab + b^2$$

Although the instructions may not tell you to factor, you can often solve problems more efficiently by factoring an expression first.

EXAMPLE 1

If $x^2 - 4 = (14)(18)$, then x could be
(A) 12 (B) 14 (C) 16 (D) 18 (E) 20

Here we can factor, $x^2 - 4 = (x - 2)(x + 2)$. If we write the factors under $(14)(18)$, we can see that x must be 16.

$$x^2 - 4 = \underset{(x-2)}{(14)} \cdot \underset{(x+2)}{(18)}$$

EXAMPLE 2

$0.74^2 - 0.73^2 =$
(A) 0.00147 (B) 0.0147 (C) 0.147 (D) 14.70 (E) 147.0

If we factor, we can do the arithmetic mentally.

$$\begin{aligned} 0.74^2 - 0.73^2 &= (0.74 + 0.73)(0.74 - 0.73) \\ &= (1.47)(0.01) \\ &= 0.0147 \end{aligned}$$

Factoring in Example 2 makes the computation much simpler.

Example 3 also illustrates the value of looking for a simpler way to solve a problem rather than doing the computation in its present form.

EXAMPLE 3

$(43)^2 + 2(43)(57) + (57)^2 =$
(A) 3,467 (B) 7,842 (C) 8,900 (D) 10,000 (E) 14,959

We recognize that this problem is in the form $a^2 + 2ab + b^2$ and can be simplified to $(a + b)^2$.

$$a^2 + 2ab + b^2 = (a + b)^2$$
$$(43)^2 + 2(43)(57) + (57)^2 = (43 + 57)^2 = 100^2 = 10{,}000$$

Problem Solving: College Entrance Exams

All of the strategies for solving problems are useful on pre-college tests. The strategies for college entrance exams are extensions of the other strategies presented throughout the text.

These questions are posed in the format that is found on many standardized tests. It is important that students be familiar with this format prior to taking a standardized test so they can be relaxed and perform at their best level.

ANSWERS

1. (C)
2. (D)
3. (B)
4. (E)
5. (C)
6. (C)
7. (B)
8. (D)
9. (D)
10. (C)

EXAMPLE 4

If $x = 8.000001$, then $\frac{x^2 + 2x}{x}$ rounded to the nearest whole number is

(A) 4 (B) 6 (C) 8 (D) 10 (E) 12

We factor before substituting for x.

$$\frac{x^2 + 2x}{x} = \frac{x(x+2)}{x} = \frac{8.000001(8.000001 + 2)}{8.000001} = 8.000001 + 2$$
$$\approx 10$$

Problems

1. If $x + y = 4$ and $x - y = 6$, then $x^2 - y^2 =$
   (A) 2 (B) 10 (C) 24 (D) 34 (E) 99

2. If $(r + 2)\left(\frac{1}{r}\right) = 0$, what is r?
   (A) 2 (B) 1 (C) -1 (D) -2 (E) any integer

3. $0.53^2 - 0.52^2 =$
   (A) 0.00105 (B) 0.0105 (C) 0.105 (D) 10.50 (E) 105.0

4. If $x + 3x$ is 7 more than $y + 3y$, then $x - y =$
   (A) 0 (B) $\frac{3}{7}$ (C) $\frac{4}{7}$ (D) $\frac{7}{3}$ (E) $\frac{7}{4}$

5. If $x^2 - 16 = (8)(16)$, then x could be
   (A) 8 (B) 10 (C) 12 (D) 14 (E) 16

6. $(23)^2 - 2(23)(13) + (13)^2 =$
   (A) 34 (B) 46 (C) 100 (D) 438 (E) 1,296

7. If $ab = 2$, $(a + b)^2 = 10$, then $a^2 + b^2 =$
   (A) 4 (B) 6 (C) 8 (D) 10 (E) 12

8. If $xy - 2y + 7x - 14 = 12$, and $x - 2 = 4$, then $y + 7 =$
   (A) 0 (B) 1 (C) 2 (D) 3 (E) 4

9. If $x + y = m$ and $x - y = \frac{1}{m}$, then when $m \neq 0$, $x^2 - y^2 =$
   (A) $\frac{1}{m}$ (B) m^2 (C) m (D) 1 (E) 2

10. If $m = 11$, then $\frac{m^2 + 3m}{m} =$
    (A) 9 (B) 11 (C) 14 (D) 44 (E) 124

Chapter 6 Summary and Review

6-1

Factoring is the reverse of multiplying. Some of the possible **factorizations** for $12a^2b$ are $(12a)(ab)$, $(6a^2)(2b)$, $(3a)(4ab)$, $12(a^2b)$. To factor a polynomial, factor out the greatest common factor of each term.

$$6a^2b - 12ab^2 = (6ab)a - (6ab)(2b) = 6ab(a - 2b)$$

Find three factorizations for each monomial.

1. $-10x^2$

2. $36x^5$

Factor.

3. $x^2 - 3x$

4. $6y^3 + 12y^2 + 3y$

5. $8x^6 - 32x^5 + 4x^4$

6. $6a^4b^4 - 2a^3b + 8a^2$

6-2

A binomial is a **difference of two squares** if both terms of the binomial are squares, and there is a minus sign between the two terms. The difference of two squares, $A^2 - B^2$, factors as two binomials $(A - B)(A + B)$.

Which of the following are differences of squares?

7. $4x^2 - 8y^2$

8. $-25 + 81a^2$

Factor.

9. $9x^2 - 4$

10. $4x^2 - 25$

11. $2x^2 - 50$

12. $3x^2 - 27$

13. $x^4 - 81$

14. $16x^4 - 1$

6-3

A **trinomial square** has three terms and is the square of a binomial.

$$A^2 + 2AB + B^2 = (A + B)^2$$
$$A^2 - 2AB + B^2 = (A - B)^2$$

Which of the following are trinomial squares?

15. $y^2 + 3y + 9$

16. $49a^2 - 112a + 16$

17. $c^2 + 12c + 36$

18. $4c^2 - 4c - 1$

Factor.

19. $x^2 - 6x + 9$

20. $x^2 + 14x + 49$

21. $9x^2 - 30x + 25$

22. $25x^2 - 20x + 4$

23. $18x^2 - 12x + 2$

24. $12x^2 + 60x + 75$

ANSWERS

1., **2.** Answers may vary.
3. $x(x - 3)$
4. $3y(2y^2 + 4y + 1)$
5. $4x^4(2x^2 - 8x + 1)$
6. $2a^2(3a^2b^4 - ab + 4)$
7. No
8. Yes
9. $(3x - 2)(3x + 2)$
10. $(2x - 5)(2x + 5)$
11. $2(x - 5)(x + 5)$
12. $3(x - 3)(x + 3)$
13. $(x^2 + 9)(x - 3)(x + 3)$
14. $(4x^2 + 1)(2x - 1)(2x + 1)$
15. No
16. No
17. Yes
18. No
19. $(x - 3)^2$
20. $(x + 7)^2$
21. $(3x - 5)^2$
22. $(5x - 2)^2$
23. $2(3x - 1)^2$
24. $3(2x + 5)^2$

25. $(x - 5)(x - 3)$
26. $(x + 6)(x - 2)$
27. $(y + 4)(y + 5)$
28. $(b - 6)(b + 3)$
29. $(m + 7)(m + 8)$
30. $(p - 8)(p + 1)$
31. $(2x + 1)(x - 4)$
32. $(2y - 1)(3y - 1)$
33. $2(a - 6)(3a + 4)$
34. $(x^2 + 3)(x + 1)$
35. $(x^3 - 2)(x + 4)$
36. $(x - 1)(x + 1)(x + 3)$
37. $(3x + 2)(2x^2 + 1)$
38. $7(x - 1)(x + 1)$
39. $-3x(5x - 2)^2$
40. $(a - 7)(a + 3)$
41. $(x + 15)(x - 13)$
42. $(x + 4)(x^2 - 3)$
43. $(1 + a^4)(1 + a^2)(1 + a)(1 - a)$
44. $1, -3$
45. $0, \frac{3}{2}$
46. $-7, 5$
47. $-4, 3$
48. $-\frac{1}{3}, 2$
49. $\frac{4}{3}, -\frac{4}{3}$

6-4

To factor a trinomial of the type $x^2 + bx + c$, think of FOIL in reverse. Look for factors of the constant term whose sum is the coefficient of the middle term.

Factor.

25. $x^2 - 8x + 15$ **26.** $x^2 + 4x - 12$ **27.** $y^2 + 9y + 20$

28. $b^2 - 3b - 18$ **29.** $m^2 + 15m + 56$ **30.** $p^2 - 7p - 8$

6-5

To factor a trinomial of the type $ax^2 + bx + c$, first check for common factors. Then test factors of the first and last terms to find the correct combination, using FOIL to test possible factorizations.

Factor.

31. $2x^2 - 7x - 4$ **32.** $6y^2 - 5y + 1$ **33.** $6a^2 - 28a - 48$

6-6

A polynomial with four terms can sometimes be factored by grouping and using the distributive property twice.

$$a^3 + 2a^2 + 3a + 6 = (a^3 + 2a^2) + (3a + 6) = a^2(a + 2) + 3(a + 2)$$
$$= (a + 2)(a^2 + 3)$$

Factor by grouping.

34. $x^3 + x^2 + 3x + 3$ **35.** $x^4 + 4x^3 - 2x - 8$

36. $x^3 + 3x^2 - x - 3$ **37.** $6x^3 + 4x^2 + 3x + 2$

6-7

When you factor a polynomial, first look for a common factor. Then check the number of terms and look for special cases (difference of squares or trinomial squares). Always factor completely.

38. $7x^2 - 7$ **39.** $-75x^3 + 60x^2 - 12x$

40. $a^2 - 4a - 21$ **41.** $x^2 + 2x - 195$

42. $x^3 - 3x + 4x^2 - 12$ **43.** $1 - a^8$

6-8

To solve an equation using the **principle of zero products,** use the addition principle to get zero on one side of the equation and a factorization on the other side. Set each of the factors equal to 0 and solve separately. Check all solutions.

Solve.

44. $(x - 1)(x + 3) = 0$ **45.** $y(4y - 6) = 0$

46. $x^2 + 2x - 35 = 0$ **47.** $x^2 + x - 12 = 0$

48. $3x^2 - 2 = 5x$ **49.** $9x^2 = 16$

6-9

You can use the Problem-Solving Guidelines to help you translate a problem into an equation and solve it. After you have solved the problem, check to see if your answer is reasonable.

Translate into an equation and find all solutions.

50. The square of a number is six more than the number. Find the number.

51. The product of two consecutive even integers is 288. Find the integers.

52. The product of two consecutive odd integers is 323. Find the integers.

53. Twice the square of a number is 10 more than the number. Find the number.

54. If the sides of a square picture frame are increased by 5 cm, the area becomes 289 cm^2. Find the length of a side of the original picture frame.

Chapter 6 Test

Factor.

1. $x^2 - 5x$	**2.** $6x^3 + 9x^2 - 3x$
3. $4y^4 - 8y^3 + 6y^2$	**4.** $4x^2 - 9$
5. $3x^2 - 75$	**6.** $3x^4 - 48$
7. $x^2 - 10x + 25$	**8.** $49x^2 - 84x + 36$
9. $45x^2 + 60x + 20$	**10.** $x^2 - 7x + 10$
11. $x^2 - x - 12$	**12.** $x^3 + 2x^2 - 3x$
13. $4x^2 - 4x - 15$	**14.** $5x^2 - 26x + 5$
15. $10x^2 + 28x - 48$	**16.** $x^3 + x^2 + 2x + 2$
17. $x^4 + 2x^3 - 3x - 6$	**18.** $6x^3 + 9x^2 - 15x$
19. $80 - 5x^4$	**20.** $y^5 - 8y^4 + 15y^3$

Solve.

21. $x^2 - x - 20 = 0$	**22.** $2x^2 + 7x = 15$
23. $4a^2 = 25$	**24.** $x(x - 3) = 28$

Translate to an equation and find all solutions.

25. Find the number whose square is 24 more than five times the number.

26. The length of a rectangle is 6 m more than the width. The area of the rectangle is 40 m^2. Find the length and the width.

27. The product of two consecutive even integers is 288. Find the integers.

50. 3 or -2
51. $-18, -16$ or 16, 18
52. $-19, -17$ or 17, 19
53. $\frac{5}{2}$ or -2
54. 12 cm

ANSWERS

1. $x(x - 5)$
2. $3x(2x^2 + 3x - 1)$
3. $2y^2(2y^2 - 4y + 3)$
4. $(2x + 3)(2x - 3)$
5. $3(x + 5)(x - 5)$
6. $3(x^2 + 4)(x + 2)(x - 2)$
7. $(x - 5)^2$
8. $(7x - 6)^2$
9. $5(3x + 2)^2$
10. $(x - 2)(x - 5)$
11. $(x + 3)(x - 4)$
12. $x(x - 1)(x + 3)$
13. $(2x - 5)(2x + 3)$
14. $(x - 5)(5x - 1)$
15. $2(x + 4)(5x - 6)$
16. $(x^2 + 2)(x + 1)$
17. $(x^3 - 3)(x + 2)$
18. $3x(x - 1)(2x + 5)$
19. $5(4 + x^2)(2 + x)(2 - x)$
20. $y^3(y - 3)(y - 5)$
21. $-4, 5$
22. $\frac{3}{2}, -5$
23. $\frac{5}{2}, -\frac{5}{2}$
24. $7, -4$
25. $8, -3$
26. 10 m, 4 m
27. $-18, -16$, or 16, 18

Test Item Analysis

Item	Lesson
1–3	6-1
4–6	6-2
7–9	6-3
10–12	6-4
13–15	6-5
16, 17	6-6
18–20	6-7
21–24	6-8
25–27	6-9

CHAPTER 7

Graphs and Linear Equations

Chapter Overview

Understanding and graphing linear equations in two variables is the major goal of this chapter. Through explorations, the concepts of and relationships between slope and linear equations are investigated. The slope of a line is defined and determined from two points on the line as well as from the equation of the line. The graph of a line is determined using substitution, using intercepts, and using the slope and y-intercept. The equation of a line is obtained from the slope and y-intercept, from the slope and one point, and from two points. Techniques for determining when lines are parallel or perpendicular are discussed. An optional section on proofs gives examples of algebraic arguments to prove some facts about slope.

A problem-solving section discusses techniques for fitting a straight line to empirical data. The problem-solving strategy *Simplify the Problem* is introduced, and problems are presented that use one or more of the previously presented strategies.

Objectives

7-1
- Plot points on the coordinate system.
- Identify the quadrant associated with a point.
- Identify the coordinates of a point.

7-2
- Determine whether an ordered pair is a solution of an equation.
- Graph equations in two variables.

7-3
- Graph linear equations in two variables.
- Graph linear equations using intercepts.
- Graph linear equations that graph as horizontal and vertical lines.

7-4
- Find the slope of a line given two points on the line.
- Give the slope of horizontal and vertical lines.

7-5
- Find the slope of a line from an equation.
- Find the slope and y-intercept of a line from an equation.
- Graph lines using the slope-intercept equation.

7-6
- Write an equation of a line using the slope-intercept equation.
- Write an equation of a line using the point-slope equation.

7-7
- Find an equation of a line that models given data.

7-8
- Determine whether the graphs of two equations are parallel.
- Determine whether the graphs of two equations are perpendicular.

7-9
- Prove theorems related to slope.

7-10
- Solve problems using the strategy *Simplify the Problem* and other strategies.

Cooperative Learning Opportunities

After students become comfortable with cooperative learning, you can try groups of 3 or 4. The following is an exploratory activity for groups of 3. Three different group activities are suggested. If you have 8 groups, for example, assign each group activity to 2 or 3 different groups.

Each group explores a particular set of graphs. Place role cards with the numbers 1, 2, and 3 face down for each group. Each student selects a card that assigns the role: (1) on the same set of axes, draw the graphs of the given equations; (2) watch and check several points of each graph for accuracy; (3) present the graphs to the class.

Group 1: Graph $y = x$, $y = 3x$, $y = 3x + 2$

Group 2: Graph $y = -x$; $y = -3x$; $y = -3x + 2$

Group 3: Graph $y = x$; $y = \frac{1}{2}x$; $y = \frac{1}{4}x + 5$

The students in each group are to discuss their graphs and come to conclusions. The **Suppose** activity on page 327 provides a good follow-up cooperative activity using the same roles.

Multicultural Note: *Egyptian Coordinates*

The coordinate system that we use originated in the work of Descartes, but even the ancient Egyptians had a coordinate system.

This drawing is a reproduction of a piece of limestone that gives the coordinates for a curved structure. The writing between the vertical lines is a series of pictures, in ancient Egyptian script, that gives a vertical coordinate.

Consider the leftmost writing. The bent line at the top represents an elbow and the three lines under it mean "3 elbows." The next horizontal dash represents a palm. So there are 3 palms. The bottom curved lines represent fingers. So the coordinate has a measure of "3 elbows, 3 palms, and 2 fingers." Find the measures of the other coordinates.

For more information, see page 60 of **Multiculturalism in Mathematics, Science, and Technology**.

Alternative Assessment and Communication Ideas

Finding a best–fit equation is introduced in Lesson 7-7, but the process of working from table to equation can be used earlier in the chapter as a means of alternative assessment.

To assess mastery of the concepts in Lessons 7-2 and 7-3, ask students to find the equation that corresponds to each of the tables below. It doesn't matter whether students collaborate as long as they understand the connection between the table and graph. The **Guess-Check-Revise** strategy can be used to find the equations and students can take turns explaining their approaches.

Ans. $\boldsymbol{y = x; y = x + 2; y = -x + 1.}$

x	−1	−2	1	2	5
y	−1	−2	1	2	5

x	−4	−2	0	2	4
y	−2	0	2	4	6

x	−4	−2	0	2	4	6
y	5	3	1	−1	−3	−5

Investigations and Projects

Battleship is a popular game that uses coordinates to find hidden ships. Two students play against each other. On a coordinate system (−10, 10) by (−10, 10) each student draws a battleship and two destroyers but does not show them to the opponent. The battleship goes through four points: vertical, horizontal, or diagonal (slope of 1 or −1). Each destroyer uses three dots. Players take turns guessing the locations of the other's ships. This game develops familiarity with the coordinate system.

The project is for students to invent a similar game. The game should involve searching for defined objects on the coordinate system. Students can work individually or in small groups to develop the games.

MANAGING CHAPTER 7

Lesson	PACING CHART (DAYS) 2-Year* A for E	1-Year Minimum	1-Year Regular	1-Year Advanced	Opening Activity	Cooperative Activity	Seat or Group Work
7-1	2	1	1	1	First Five Minutes 7-1: ***FFMTM*** p. 23 or **TE** p. 304; ***Overhead Transparencies*** T8	Problems 29–30: **SE** p. 308	Try This a–n
7-2	2	1	1	1	First Five Minutes 7-2: ***FFMTM*** p. 23 or **TE** p. 309; ***Overhead Transparencies*** T9	Calculator Worksheet 18: ***Technology*** p. 20	Try This a–e
7-3	3	1	1	1	First Five Minutes 7-3: ***FFMTM*** p. 24 or **TE** p. 313; ***Overhead Transparencies*** T10	Explore: **SE** p. 313; Bonus Topic 7: ***Enrichment*** p. 8	Try This a–k
7-4	2	1	1	1	First Five Minutes 7-4: ***FFMTM*** p. 24 or **TE** p. 318; ***Overhead Transparencies*** T11; Application: **SE** p. 318	Problem 35: **SE** p. 322	Try This a–i
7-5	2	1.5	1	1	First Five Minutes 7-5: ***FFMTM*** p. 24 or **TE** p. 323	Explore: **SE** p. 323; Suppose: **SE** p. 327	Try This a–k
7-6	2	1.5	1	1	First Five Minutes 7-6: ***FFMTM*** p. 24 or **TE** p. 328; ***Overhead Transparencies*** T12	Problem 34: **SE** p. 332	Try This a–h
7-7	2	1	1	0.5	First Five Minutes 7-7: ***FFMTM*** p. 25 or **TE** p. 333; ***Overhead Transparencies*** T13	✂ Manipulative Activity 7: ***Enrichment*** p. 40	Try This a–b
7-8	2	1	1	0.5	First Five Minutes 7-8: ***FFMTM*** p. 25 or **TE** p. 338; ***Overhead Transparencies*** T14	Explore: **SE** p. 338	Try This a–d
7-9	0	0	0	0.5	First Five Minutes 7-9: ***FFMTM*** p. 25 or **TE** p. 342		Try This a–b
7-10	1	2	1	1	First Five Minutes 7-10: ***FFMTM*** p. 26 or **TE** p. 344	Problem 2: **SE** p. 345; Problem Solving: Application: **SE** p. 346	Problem 1: **SE** p. 345
Review	2	1	1	0.5			
Test	1	1	1	1			
Cum. Review	2	0	1	0			
Mid-Year Test	1	0	1	0			

*2-Year Management Guide can be found in *Algebra for Everyone.*

FFMTM: First Five Minutes Transparency Masters

Enrichment	Review/Assess	Reteach	Technology	Lesson
BASIC Computer Project 11: ***Technology*** p. 73	Lesson Quiz: **TE** p. 307		BASIC Computer Project 11: ***Technology*** p. 73	7-1
Calculator Worksheet 18: ***Technology*** p. 20	Lesson Quiz: **TE** p. 310	Skills Practice 18: ***SPMR*** p. 26	Calculator Worksheet 18: ***Technology*** p. 20	7-2
Spatial Relations: **SE** p. 317; Bonus Topic 7: ***Enrichment*** p. 8	Mixed Review 13: ***SPMR*** p. 63; Lesson Quiz: **TE** p. 315; Quiz 13: ***Assessment*** p. 23		BASIC Computer Project 12: ***Technology*** p. 74; Worksheet 1: ***TI-81 Activities*** pp. 5–6; Computer Exploration 4: **SE** p. 718	7-3
Writing to Learn: **SE** p. 322; Teacher Demonstration Lesson 1: ***Master Grapher*** pp. 7–8, 63–64, or 118–119	Mixed Practice 13: **SE** p. 696; Lesson Quiz: **TE** p. 320	Skills Practice 19: ***SPMR*** p. 27	Worksheets 1, 2: ***Master Grapher*** pp. 15–19, 71–75, or 126–130; Worksheet 2: ***TI-81 Activities*** pp. 7–9; TI-81 Investigation 1: **SE** pp. 724–725	7-4
Suppose: **SE** p. 327	Lesson Quiz: **TE** p. 325		Worksheet 3: ***Master Grapher*** pp. 20–23, 76–79, or 131–134; Worksheet 3: ***TI-81 Activities*** pp. 11–14; Computer Exploration 5: **SE** p. 718	7-5
Looking for Errors 7: ***Enrichment*** p. 56	Lesson Quiz: **TE** p. 330; Quiz 14: ***Assessment*** p. 24		Worksheet 4: ***Master Grapher*** pp. 24–26, 80–82, or 135–137; Worksheet 4: ***TI-81 Activities*** pp. 15–17	7-6
✂ Manipulative Activity 7: ***Enrichment*** p. 40	Lesson Quiz: **TE** p. 335	Problem Bank 13: ***Problem Bank*** p. 30	Spreadsheet Activity 4: ***Technology*** pp. 43–44; Computer Exploration 6: **SE** p. 719	7-7
Critical Thinking 7: ***Enrichment*** p. 24; Problem for Programmers: **SE** p. 341	Mixed Review 14: ***SPMR*** p. 64; Lesson Quiz: **TE** p. 339	Skills Practice 20: ***SPMR*** p. 28	Worksheet 5: ***Master Grapher*** pp. 27–29, 83–85, or 138–140; Worksheet 5: ***TI-81 Activities*** pp. 19–21; Computer Exploration 7: **SE** p. 720	7-8
College Entrance Exam 2: ***Problem Bank*** pp. 52–56	Mixed Practice 14: **SE** p. 697; Lesson Quiz: **TE** p. 342			7-9
Problem Solving: Application: **SE** p. 346	Assessing Strategies 6: ***Assessment*** pp. 205–206	Strategy Problem Bank 7: ***Problem Bank*** p. 8		7-10
	Summary and Review: **SE** pp. 347–349; Test: **SE** pp. 350			Review
	Chapter 7 Exam: ***A for E*** pp. 305–306; Chapter 7 Test: ***Assessment*** pp. 55–56 (min.), 107–112 (reg.), 175–176 (adv.)			Test
	Cumulative Review: **SE** pp. 351–355			Cum. Review
	Cumulative Exam: ***A for E*** pp. T63–T66; Mid-Year Test: ***Assessment*** pp. 217–228 (reg.)			Mid-Year Test

SPMR: Skills Practice Mixed Review

The solution to the problem posed on the facing page can be found on page 334.

Ready for Graphs and Linear Equations?

1-1 Evaluate.

1. $3x + y$ for $x = 4$ and $y = 3$ 15

2. $\frac{3m + 1}{2n}$ for $m = 5$ and $n = 2$ 4

1-3 Evaluate each expression.

3. $y^2 + 2$ for $y = 6$ 38

4. $m^2 + 7$ for $m = 7$ 56

2-1 Make true sentences using > or <.

5. $-3 < 2$

6. $-2 > -6$

7. $0 > -8$

8. $5 > -2$

3-1 to 3-3 Solve and check.

9. $\frac{5}{2} - y = \frac{1}{3}$ $\frac{13}{6}$

10. $w + 8 = -3$ -11

11. $-4 + x = 8$ 12

12. $6x = -12$ -2

13. $\frac{7}{8}w = -\frac{2}{3}$ $-\frac{16}{21}$

14. $\frac{2}{3}t = \frac{1}{8}$ $\frac{3}{16}$

15. $5x + 8 = 43$ 7

16. $-2x + 9 = -11$ 10

17. $-8x + 3x = 25$ -5

3-5 Solve and check.

18. $5x + 6 = -2x - 8$ -2

19. $6(x - 6) = 3(x - 4)$ 8

3-8 Solve for the indicated letter.

20. $d = \frac{5k}{s}$, for k $k = \frac{ds}{5}$

21. $S = \frac{Mp^2}{mv}$, for v $v = \frac{Mp^2}{mS}$

CHAPTER 7

Graphs and Linear Equations

Using the winning times for the men's 1500-meter run at the 1952 through 1988 Olympics, predict the winning times for the next Olympic 1500-meter race.

7-1

FIRST FIVE MINUTES

1. Given that $x = 2$, find y where $y = 5x + 4$.
   $y = 5(2) + 4 = 14$
2. Given that $x = 1$, find y where $2x + 3y = 8$.
   $2(1) + 3y = 8$
   $3y = 6$
   $y = 2$
3. Given that $y = 3$, find x where $5y^2 = 3x$.
   $5(3)^2 = 3x$
   $45 = 3x$
   $15 = x$

MATH HISTORY

If students wish to see how the Cartesian coordinate system fits into the development of mathematics, have them refer to Milestones in Mathematics on page 725.

Plotting Points

The concepts in this chapter blend algebra and geometry. Graphing concepts can be applied to many algebraic ideas. In this course, graphing concepts appear again with linear systems of equations (Lesson 9-1), linear inequalities (Lesson 9-5), and quadratic functions (Lesson 12-4). Students should use graph paper for all exercises that involve graphing.

Avoiding Common Errors

Students will often plot the point (4, 3) as (3, 4) or (0, 2) as (2, 0).

Emphasize that the coordinates are an *ordered pair,* with the first coordinate indicating the direction on the x-axis and the second coordinate indicating the direction on the y-axis.

Point out that if one of the coordinates is 0, then the point is on one of the axes.

Key Questions

- Is the point (3, 4) the same as the point (4, 3)?
  No
- Which axis is the point (2, 0) on?
  x-axis

7-1 Graphing Ordered Pairs

Math History

In this lesson you will learn a system for graphing and naming points in a plane. This system is called the **Cartesian coordinate system** and is named after René Descartes (1596–1650), a French mathematician and philosopher. Before Descartes, algebra and geometry were separate areas of mathematics. Algebra dealt with numbers; geometry was the study of points, lines, and curves. Technological advances in fields such as navigation and optics made it necessary to define curves mathematically. People needed to know how much to curve lenses in microscopes and telescopes and how to plot the course of ships traveling on the curved surface of the world. Descartes's coordinate system enabled mathematicians to represent lines and curves with algebraic equations.

Plotting Points

Objective: Plot points using the coordinate system.

On a number line, each point is the graph of a number. On a plane, each point is the graph of an **ordered pair.** We use two perpendicular number lines called **axes,** which divide the plane into four regions. The horizontal axis is called the **x-axis** and the vertical axis is called the **y-axis.** The axes cross at a point called the **origin.** The arrows show the positive direction for each number line. The plane is often called a **coordinate plane,** and the axes are called **coordinate axes.**

The numbers in an ordered pair are called **coordinates.** In the ordered pair (4, 3) the first number, 4, is the **x-coordinate** (or the **abscissa**) and the second number, 3, is the **y-coordinate** (or the **ordinate**). The x-coordinate tells the distance right (positive) or left (negative) from the y-axis. The y-coordinate tells the distance up (positive) or down (negative) from the x-axis.

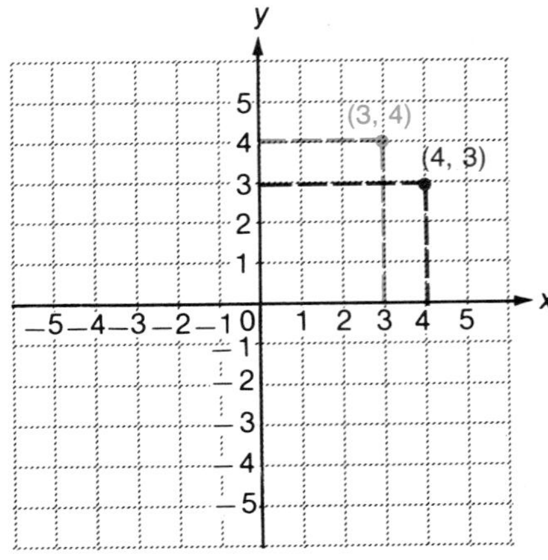

EXAMPLE 1 Plot the points $(-3, 4)$, $(2, -5)$, and $(-4, -4)$.

The coordinates of the first point $(-3, 4)$ tell us that the point is located 3 units to the left of the y-axis and 4 units up from the x-axis. The graphs of the other points are shown.

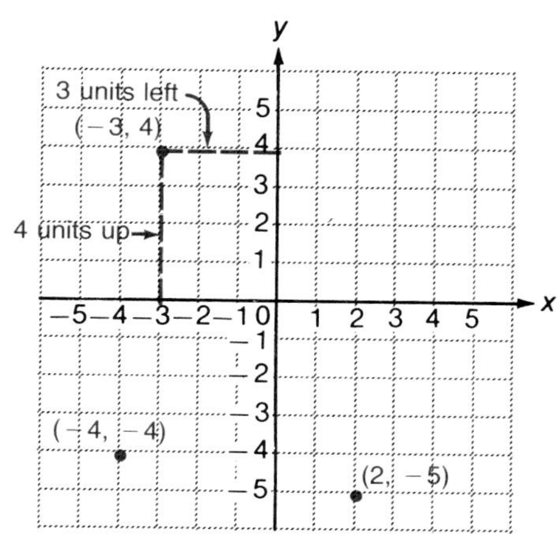

Try This Plot these points on the same graph. Write the ordered pair next to each point. See Additional Answers.

a. $(4, 6)$ **b.** $(6, 4)$ **c.** $(-2, 5)$
d. $(-3, -3)$ **e.** $(5, -3)$

When one coordinate is 0, the point is on one of the axes. The origin has coordinates $(0, 0)$.

EXAMPLE 2 Plot the points $(0, -3)$ and $(-2, 0)$.

For the point $(0, -3)$, move 0 units left or right and 3 units down. The point $(0, -3)$ is on the y-axis.

For the point $(-2, 0)$, move 2 units left and 0 units up or down. The point $(-2, 0)$ is on the x-axis.

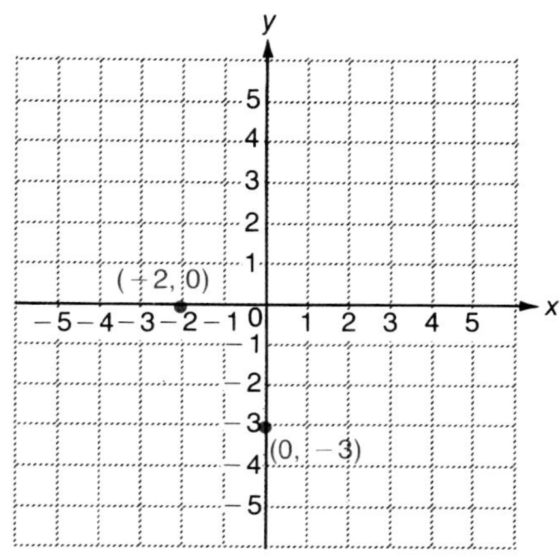

Try This Plot the following points.

f. $(0, 7)$ **g.** $(5, 0)$ **h.** $(0, 0)$ **i.** $(0, -5)$ See Additional Answers.

Chalkboard Examples (*T8*)

1. Plot the points $(3, 5)$, $(-4, 1)$, $(-3, -4)$, and $(4, -2)$.

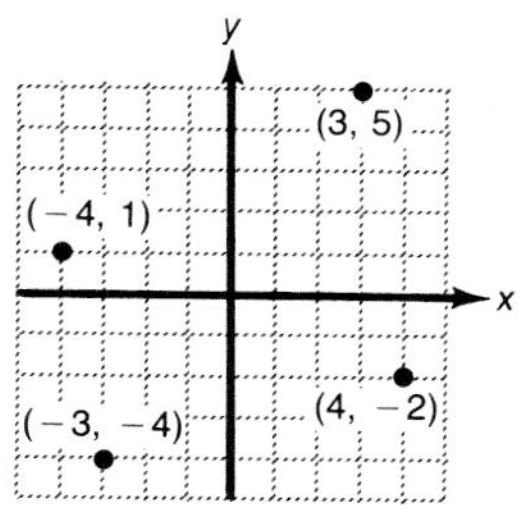

2. Plot the points $(0, 1)$, $(1, 0)$, $(0, -1)$, $(-1, 0)$.

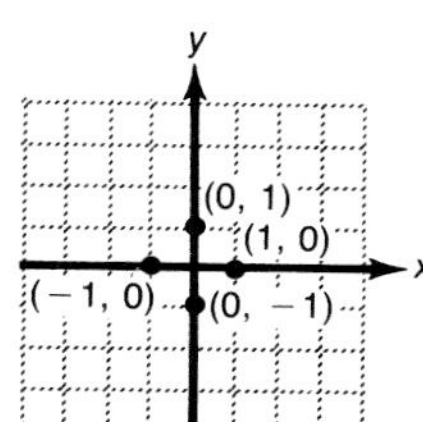

Quadrants

Point out that the points on the axes are not in a quadrant.

Note that the quadrants are numbered in a counterclockwise direction.

You may want to use the following diagram to point out that the signs of the coordinates are the same in each quadrant.

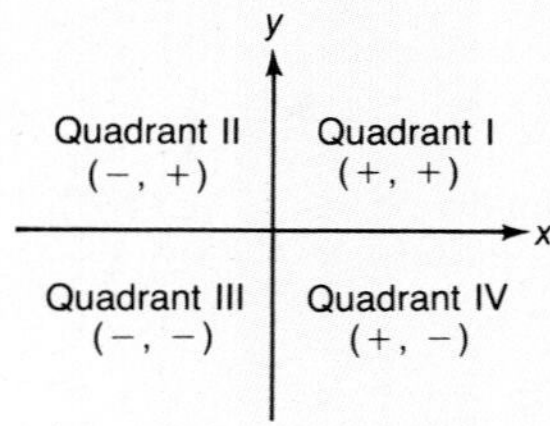

Key Questions

- What is the sign of all x-coordinates in Quadrant I?
Positive
- What is the sign of all y-coordinates in Quadrant II?
Positive
- In which quadrant are both coordinates negative?
Quadrant III

Chalkboard Example

1. In which quadrant is each point located? (−1, −1), (1, −1), (1, 1), (−1, 1)
III, IV, I, II

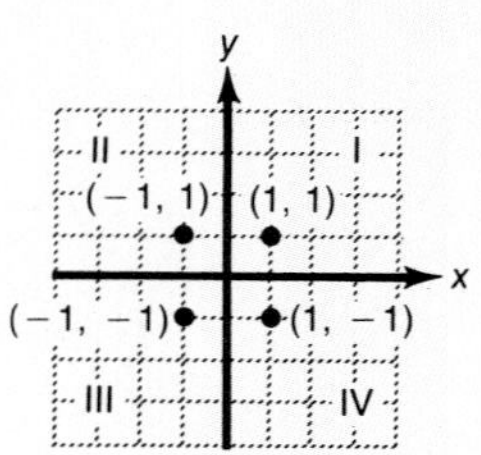

Quadrants

Objective: Identify the quadrant associated with a point.

The coordinate plane is divided into four regions called **quadrants**, as shown at the right. The quadrants are numbered counterclockwise starting at the upper right. The graph also shows some points and their coordinates.

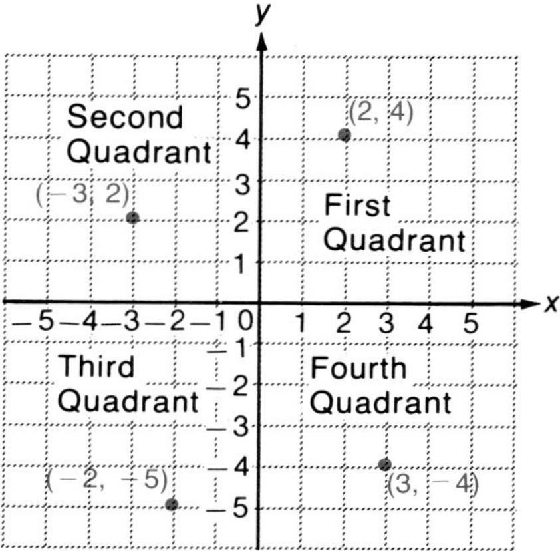

The point (−3, 2) is located in the second quadrant.

The point (3, −4) is located in the fourth quadrant.

The axes are not a part of any quadrant. A point on the x- or y-axis is not in a quadrant since it is on the boundary between quadrants.

The quadrants are traditionally denoted by Roman numerals.

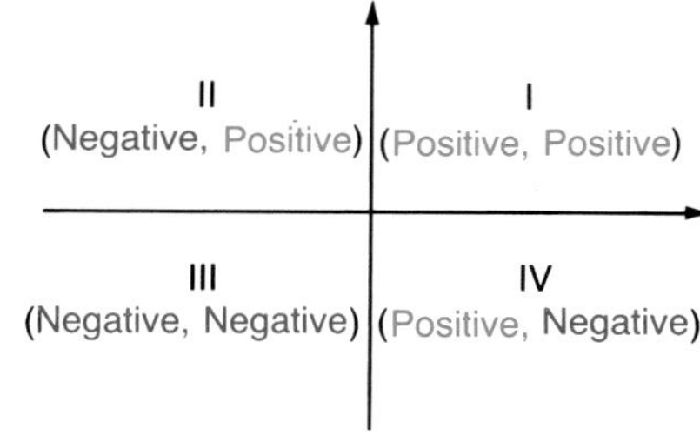

EXAMPLE 3 In which quadrant is each point located?

(4, −5)	Quadrant IV
(2, 2)	Quadrant I
(−1, −3)	Quadrant III
(−6, 1)	Quadrant II
(−4, 0)	Not in a quadrant

Try This In which quadrant is each point located?

j. (5, 3) I **k.** (−6, −4) III **l.** (10, −14) IV **m.** (−13, 4) II

Finding Coordinates

Objective: Identify the coordinates of a point.

We can count the number of units a point is to the left or right of the y-axis and the number of units up or down from the x-axis to find the coordinates of the point.

EXAMPLE 4 Find the coordinates of point B.

Point B is 3 units to the left and 5 units up. Its coordinates are $(-3, 5)$.

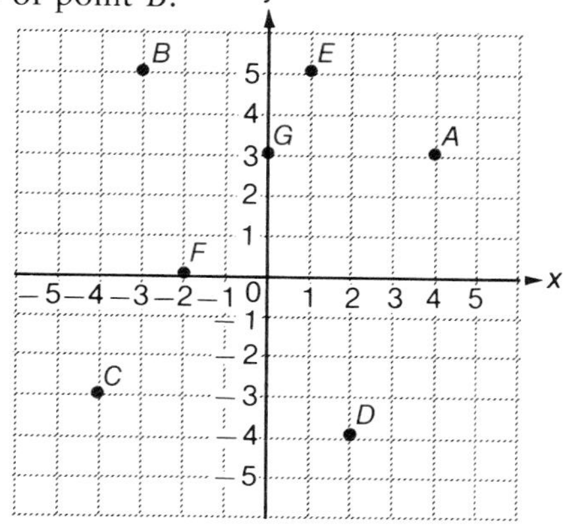

Try This

n. Find the coordinates of points A, C, D, E, F, and G in the graph of Example 4. (4, 3), (−4, −3), (2, −4), (1, 5), (−2, 0), (0, 3)

7-1 EXERCISES

A

Plot these points. Write the ordered pair close to each point.

1. (2, 5) **2.** (4, 6) **3.** (−1, 3) **4.** (−2, 4)
5. (3, −2) **6.** (5, −3) **7.** (−2, −4) **8.** (−5, −7)
9. (0, 4) **10.** (0, 6) **11.** (0, −5) **12.** (0, −7)
13. (5, 0) **14.** (6, 0) **15.** (−7, 0) **16.** (−8, 0)

In which quadrant is each point located?

17. (−5, 3) II **18.** (−12, −1) III **19.** (100, −1) IV **20.** (35.6, −2.5) IV
21. (−6, −29) III **22.** (−3.6, 10.9) II **23.** (3.8, 9.2) I **24.** (1895, 1492) I

25. In the second quadrant, x-coordinates are always ___ and y-coordinates are always ___. Negative, positive

26. In the fourth quadrant, _x_ coordinates are always positive and _y_ coordinates are always negative.

Finding Coordinates

Chalkboard Example

1. Find the coordinates of the points A, B, C, D, E, F, G, H.

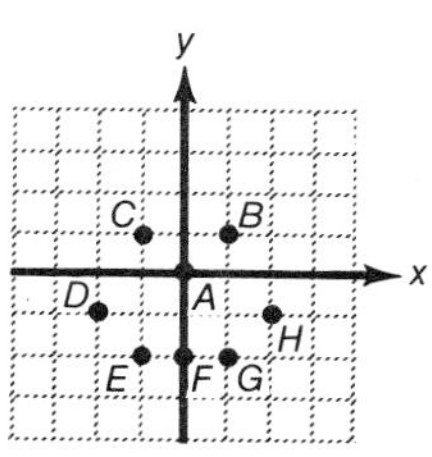

A: (0, 0), B: (1, 1), C: (−1, 1), D: (−2, −1), E: (−1, −2), F: (0, −2), G: (1, −2), H: (2, −1)

LESSON QUIZ

1. Draw an x-axis and a y-axis on graph paper and plot these points. (2, 3), (−2, 3), (0, −3), (2, 0)

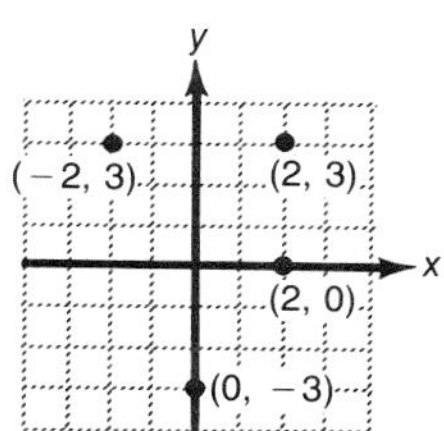

2. In which quadrant is the point (2, −3)? IV
3. Find the coordinates of points A, B, C.

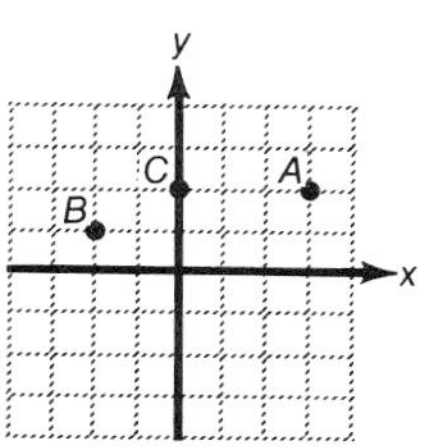

A: (3, 2), B: (−2, 1), C: (0, 2)

Assignment Guide
Minimum: 1–28 e/o, MR

Regular: 1–32 e/o, 33, MR

Advanced: 1–32 m3, 33, 34–37 e/o, MR

ADDITIONAL ANSWERS

Try This

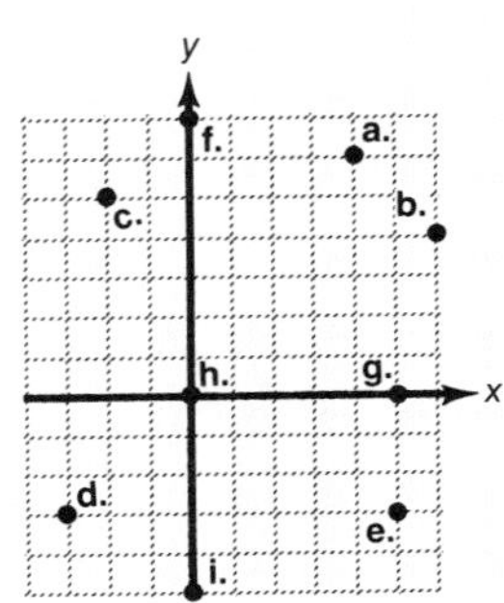

Exercises

1–15 Odd

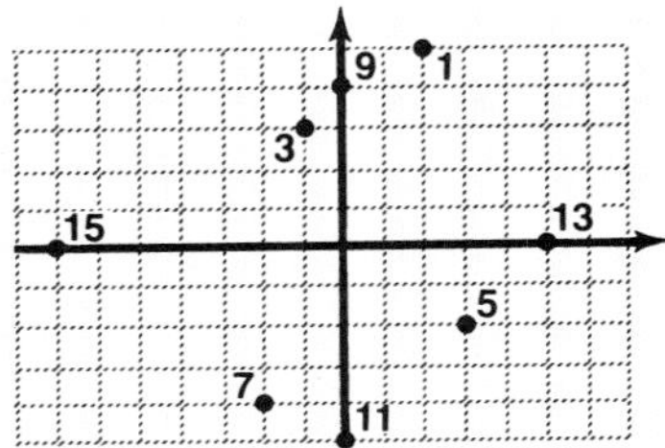

2–16 Even

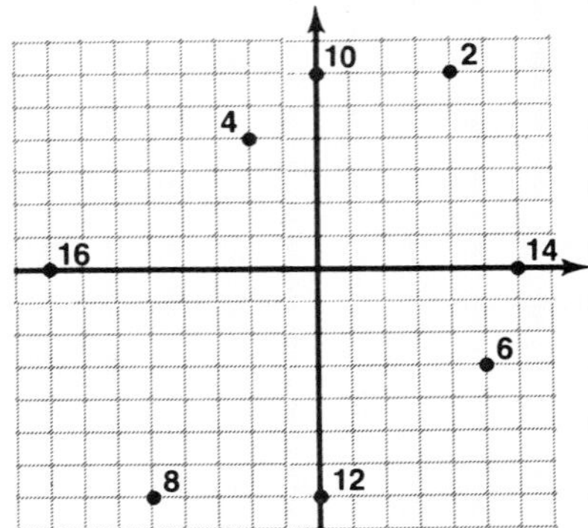

29–35. See Teacher's Answer Section.

Mixed Review

38. $6(3m - 2n)(3m + 2n)$
39. $(x^2 + 2)(x - 5)$
40. $xy + 2yz$
41. $4ab - 3bc$
42. $-xy + 8yz$
43. $-4mn - 3pq$

Find the coordinates of points A, B, C, D, and E.

27.

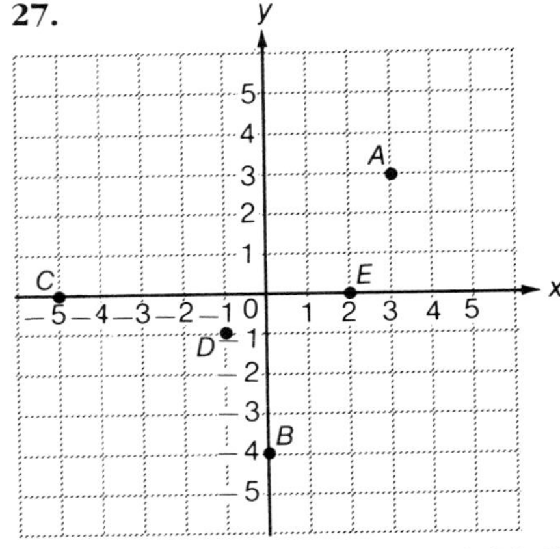

$A(3, 3)$, $B(0, -4)$, $C(-5, 0)$, $D(-1, -1)$, $E(2, 0)$

28.

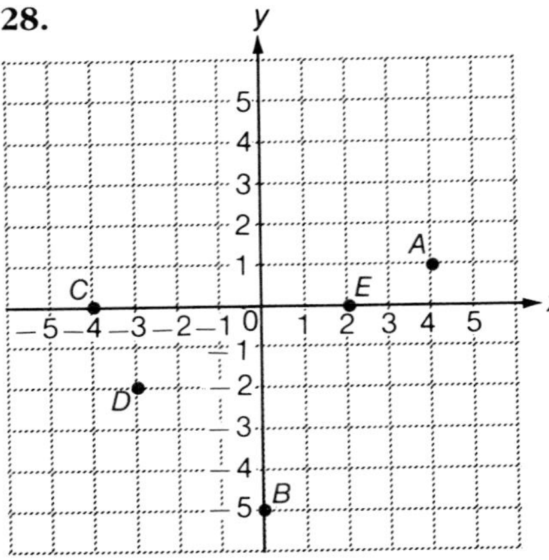

$A(4, 1)$, $B(0, -5)$, $C(-4, 0)$, $D(-3, -2)$, $E(2, 0)$

B

Find three points that satisfy the following conditions.

29. The absolute values of the x-coordinate and the y-coordinate are equal.

30. The x-coordinate and the y-coordinate are additive inverses of each other.

31. The x-coordinate is the square of the y-coordinate.

32. Graph 12 points where the difference between the x- and y-coordinates of each point is 1.

33. ***Critical Thinking*** Graph the following pairs of points: $(1, -1)$, $(-1, 1)$; $(2, 5)$, $(5, 2)$; $(-3, -4)$, $(-4, -3)$; $(3, -1)$, $(-1, 3)$; and $(1, 4)$, $(4, 1)$. Make a conclusion about the graphs of the points (q, r) and (r, q) from the pattern formed.

Challenge

34. Find three points such that the product of the coordinates is 2.

35. Find three points such that the sum of the x- and y-coordinates is 5.

36. Find the perimeter of a rectangle whose vertices have coordinates $(5, 3)$, $(5, -2)$, $(-3, -2)$, and $(-3, 3)$. 26

37. Find the area of a triangle whose vertices have coordinates $(0, 9)$, $(0, -4)$, and $(5, -4)$. 32.5

Mixed Review

Factor. **38.** $54m^2 - 24n^2$ **39.** $x^3 - 5x^2 + 2x - 10$

Simplify. **40.** $(xy - 4yz) + 6yz$ **41.** $(ab - bc) + (3ab - 2bc)$

42. $(xy + 3yz) - (2xy - 5yz)$ **43.** $(mn - pq) - (2pq + 5mn)$

7-2 Graphing Equations

Solutions of Equations in Two Variables

Objective: Determine whether an ordered pair is a solution of an equation.

An equation such as $3x + 2 = 8$ has one number, 2, as its solution. An equation with two variables, such as $y = 2x + 1$, has many solutions, which we write as ordered pairs of numbers. We usually consider variables in alphabetical order. For an equation such as $y = 2x + 1$, we write an ordered pair in the form (x, y).

EXAMPLE 1

Determine whether (3, 7) is a solution of $y = 2x + 1$.

$$y = 2x + 1$$
$$7 = 2 \cdot 3 + 1 \quad \text{Substituting 3 for } x \text{ and 7 for } y$$
$$7 = 7$$

The equation is *true*. The ordered pair (3, 7) is a solution.

EXAMPLE 2

Determine whether (−2, 3) is a solution of $2y = 4x - 8$.

$$2y = 4x - 8$$
$$2 \cdot 3 = 4(-2) - 8$$
$$6 = -16$$

The equation is *false*. The ordered pair (−2, 3) is *not* a solution.

Try This

a. Determine whether (2, 3) is a solution of $y = 2x + 3$. No

b. Determine whether (−2, 4) is a solution of $4y - 3x = 22$. Yes

We can find solutions of equations in two variables by choosing a value for one variable, substituting, and computing to find the value of the other variable.

EXAMPLE 3

Find three solutions of $y - 3x = -2$.

Solving for y first makes it easier to substitute for x and compute.

$$y = 3x - 2$$

7-2

FIRST FIVE MINUTES

1. Graph the pairs (−1, −1), (0, 0), (1, 1), (2, 2).

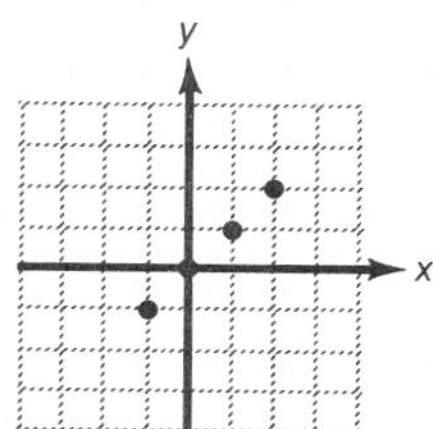

Solutions of Equations in Two Variables

Emphasize that the order in which the variables appear in the equation does not change the ordered pair. In the equation $y = 2x + 1$ of Example 1, for instance, y appears before x, but the ordered pair is still (x, y).

Key Questions

- How many ordered pairs are solutions of the equation $y = 2x$? Infinitely many
- Give one point that will make the equation $y = 2x$ false. Answers may vary.

Chalkboard Examples

1. Determine whether (2, 4) is a solution of $y = 3x - 2$.
   $(4) = 3(2) - 2$
   The equation is true.
   (2, 4) is a solution.
2. Determine whether (3, −2) is a solution of $5y = 4x - 22$.
   $5(-2) = 4(3) - 22$
   The equation is true.
   (3, −2) is a solution.
3. Find three solutions of the equation $y = 2x + 11$.
   If $x = 1$, then $y = 2(1) + 11 = 13$. The ordered pair is (1, 13). If $x = 2$, then $y = 2(2) + 11 = 15$. The ordered pair is (2, 15). If $x = 3$, then $y = 2(3) + 11 = 17$. The ordered pair is (3, 17).

Graphing Equations

Emphasize that it is easy to generate solutions to many equations if we first solve for one variable, say y, in terms of the other, x. Then each time we pick a value for x, we can calculate a corresponding value for y.

Avoiding Common Errors

Some students will plot the points but not connect them. Emphasize that there are infinite solutions to equations in two variables and that we must connect the points to complete the graph.

Chalkboard Example *(T9)*

1. Graph the equation $6x + 2y = 4$.
   Solve for y.
   $2y = 4 - 6x$
   $y = 2 - 3x$
   Make a table of solutions.

x	-1	0	1	2
y	5	2	-1	-4

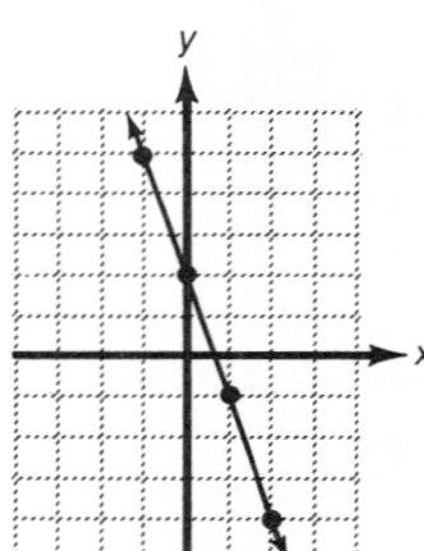

LESSON QUIZ

1. Determine whether the point (3, 5) is a solution of the equation $4x - 2y = 2$.
   (3, 5) is a solution.
2. Graph the equation $y = 2x - 1$.

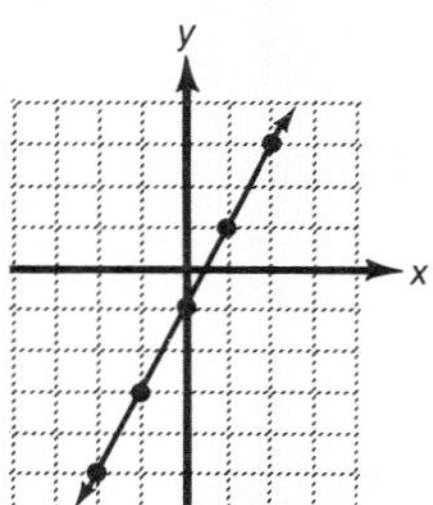

We can substitute values for x and find corresponding values for y. We choose any value for x. The easiest is 0.

$y = 3x - 2$
$y = 3 \cdot 0 - 2$ Substituting 0 for x
$y = -2$

The ordered pair $(0, -2)$ is a solution. We choose another number for x.

$y = 3 \cdot 2 - 2$ Substituting 2 for x
$y = 4$

A second solution is (2, 4). Now try -2 for x.

$y = 3(-2) - 2$ Substituting -2 for x
$y = -8$

A third solution is $(-2, -8)$.

We can record the ordered pairs in a table to show the solutions at a glance.

x	y
0	-2
2	4
-2	-8

Try This

c. Find three solutions of $y - 2x = 3$. Answers may vary. Ex. (0, 3), (1, 5), $(-1, 1)$, $(-2, -1)$

Graphing Equations

Objective: Graph equations in two variables.

We know that a solution of an equation with two variables is an ordered pair of numbers, which can be plotted on a coordinate plane. A **graph** of an equation is a drawing that represents its solutions.

EXAMPLE 4 Graph the equation $y - x = 1$.

Solve for y and find several solutions by substituting values for x.

$y - x = 1$
$y = 1 + x$

If $x = 0$, $y = 1 + 0 = 1$
If $x = -1$, $y = 1 + -1 = 0$
If $x = -5$, $y = 1 + -5 = -4$
If $x = 1$, $y = 1 + 1 = 2$
If $x = 3$, $y = 1 + 3 = 4$

x	y
0	1
-1	0
-5	-4
1	2
3	4

Making a table to record ordered pairs

Plot the points (0, 1), (−1, 0), (−5, −4), (1, 2), and (3, 4).

The points all lie on a straight line. We can see that if we could plot all solutions, the graph would be a line. Thus we connect the points to draw the line. The arrows show that the line continues endlessly.

The line is the graph of the equation $y - x = 1$. Every point on the line is a solution of this equation.

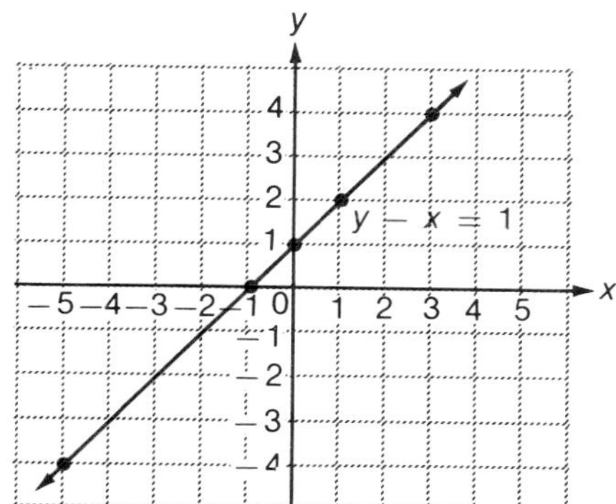

Try This Graph each equation.

d. $y - x = 3$ **e.** $y = x$ For graphs, see Additional Answers.

Assignment Guide

Minimum: 1–27 e/o, MR

Regular: 1–30 e/o, 31, MR

Advanced: 1–30 e/o, 31–33, MR

ADDITIONAL ANSWERS

Try This

d.

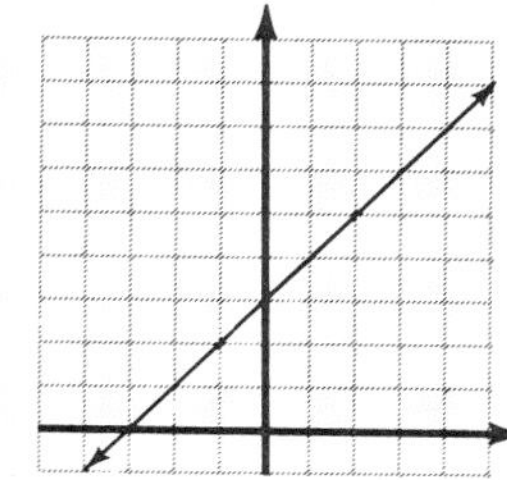

e.

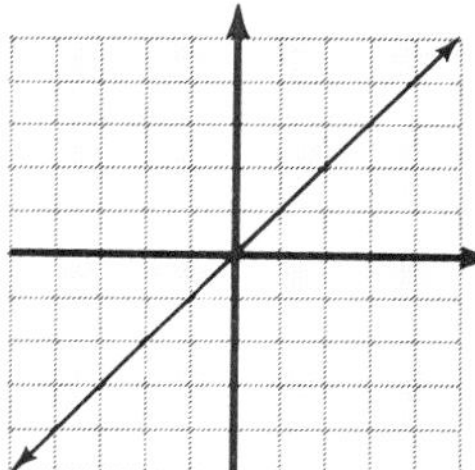

Exercises

16–27. See Teacher's Answer Section.

28.

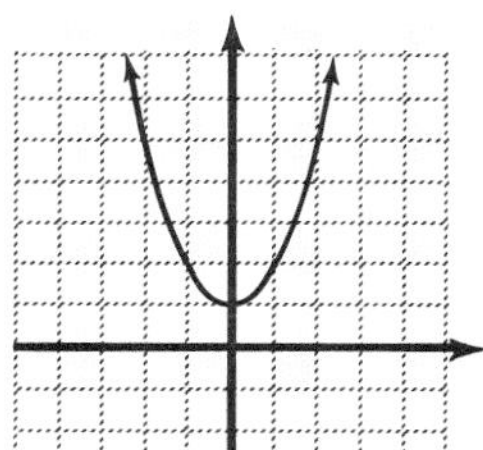

7-2 EXERCISES

A

Determine whether the given point is a solution of the equation.

1. (2, 5), $y = 3x - 1$ Yes **2.** (1, 7), $y = 2x + 5$ Yes

3. (2, −3), $3x - y = 3$ No **4.** (−1, 4), $2x + y = 2$ Yes

5. (−2, −1), $2x + 3y = -7$ Yes **6.** (0, −4), $4x + 2y = 8$ No

Find three solutions of each equation. Answers may vary.

7. $y = 2x + 1$ **8.** $y = 3x + 2$ **9.** $x + y = 6$

10. $x + y = 8$ **11.** $2x + y = 10$ **12.** $3x - y = 11$

13. $4x + 3y = 14$ **14.** $5x + 7y = 19$ **15.** $6x - 5y = 23$

Make a table of solutions and graph each equation.

16. $y = x$ **17.** $y = -x$ **18.** $y = -2x$

19. $y = 2x$ **20.** $y = x + 1$ **21.** $y = x - 1$

22. $y = 2x + 1$ **23.** $y = 3x - 1$ **24.** $y = -3x + 2$

25. $y = -4x + 1$ **26.** $2x + y = 3$ **27.** $5x + y = 7$

B

28. Complete the table for $y = x^2 + 1$. Plot the points on graph paper and draw the graph.

x	0	−1	1	−2	2	−3	3
y	1	2	2	5	5	10	10

29.

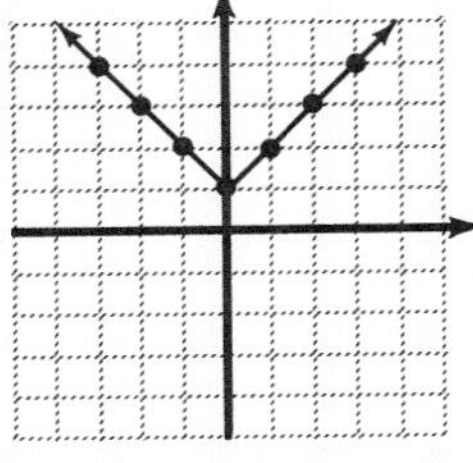

30.

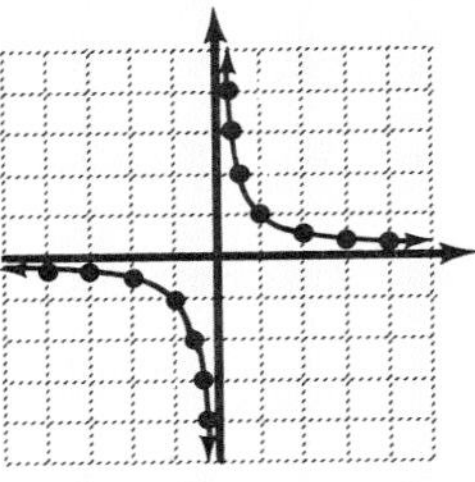

32. a. $4x + 6y$
b. 2 h on Friday and 5 h on Saturday or 5 h on Friday and 3 h on Saturday or 8 h on Friday and 1 h on Saturday

33. $68x + 76y = 864$, let $x = y$, 6 h each machine

Mixed Review

34. $\frac{1}{64}$
35. 1
36. y^6
37. $x(7x^3 + 1)$
38. $-3, -\frac{3}{2}$
39. 0
40. $\frac{5}{3}, \frac{-5}{3}$
41. $-6, 3$
42. $0, \frac{7}{5}$
43. $-1, -3$
44. $4(4 - 3c)$
45. $(mn^2)(mn + 2)$
46. $9(a^2 + b^2)(a + b)(a - b)$
47. $(x + 3y)^2$
48. $(x + 9)(x - 2)$
49. $(3x - 2)(2x - 1)$
50. $C = \frac{5}{9}(F - 32)$
51. $r = \frac{A - P}{Pt}$
52. $b_2 = \frac{2A - hb_1}{h}$

29. Copy and complete the table for $y = |x| + 1$. Plot the points on graph paper and draw the graph.

x	-4	-3	-2	-1	0	1	2	3	4
y	5	4	3	2	1	2	3	4	5

30. Copy and complete the table for $y = \frac{1}{x}$. Plot the points on graph paper and draw the graph.

x	4	3	2	1	$\frac{1}{2}$	$\frac{1}{3}$	$\frac{1}{4}$	$\frac{1}{5}$	0	$-\frac{1}{4}$	$-\frac{1}{3}$	$-\frac{1}{2}$	-1	-2	-3	-4
y	$\frac{1}{4}$	$\frac{1}{3}$	$\frac{1}{2}$	1	2	3	4	5	No sol.	-4	-3	-2	-1	$-\frac{1}{2}$	$-\frac{1}{3}$	$-\frac{1}{4}$

31. ***Critical Thinking*** Looking at the graphs of the equations in Exercises 1–30, which of the equations below would you expect to graph as a straight line?

$y = 3x - 1$ Yes $x^2 + y^2 = 3$ No $y = \frac{3}{xy}$ No $y = |x - 1|$ No

Challenge

32. Joan earns \$4 an hour on her new job. If she works on Saturdays, she earns \$6 an hour. Joan worked x hours on Friday and y hours on Saturday.

a. Write an expression showing Joan's total earnings for the two days.

b. Suppose Joan earned a total of \$38 on the two days. If x and y are whole numbers, find all of the possibilities for the number of hours she worked each day.

33. Two machines, X and Y, produce rivets. Machine X produces 68 rivets per hour, and machine Y produces 76 rivets per hour. Let x represent the number of hours machine X runs, and let y represent the number of hours machine Y runs. Write an equation giving the combined production of machine X and machine Y on a given day as 864. Find a solution to the equation. Explain your solution.

Mixed Review

Simplify. **34.** 4^{-3} **35.** m^0 **36.** $(y^2)^3$ **37.** $8x^4 - (x^4 + 2x) + 3x$

Solve. **38.** $(2y + 3)(y + 3) = 0$ **39.** $36c^2 = 0$ **40.** $9x^2 = 25$

41. $y^2 + 3y - 18 = 0$ **42.** $5x^2 = 7x$ **43.** $3x^2 + 14x + 9 = 2x$

Factor. **44.** $16 - 12c$ **45.** $m^2n^3 + 2mn^2$ **46.** $9a^4 - 9b^4$

47. $x^2 + 6xy + 9y^2$ **48.** $x^2 + 7x - 18$ **49.** $6x^2 - 7x + 2$

Solve for the indicated letter. **50.** $\frac{9}{5}C + 32 = F$ for C

51. $A = P(1 + rt)$ for r **52.** $A = \frac{1}{2}h(b_1 + b_2)$ for b_2

7-3 Linear Equations and Their Graphs

Master Grapher Worksheet 1 can be used with this lesson.

Explore

Determine which of the following equations has a straight line for the graph of its solutions.

$xy = 4$ No $\quad y = 3x - 4$ Yes $\quad y - 4x = 2$ Yes

$2x - 3y = 0$ Yes $\quad y = 2x^2$ No $\quad y = \frac{3}{x}$ No

Linear Equations

Objective: Graph linear equations in two variables.

Equations whose graphs are straight lines are called **linear equations.** An equation is linear if the variables occur to the first power only, there are no products of variables, and no variable appears in a denominator.

Linear Equations	$y = 2x + 1$	$y - 3x = -2$	$5y = -4$	$9x - 15y = 7$
Nonlinear Equations	$y = x^2 - 4$	$x^2 + y^2 = 16$	$y = \frac{2}{x}$	$xy = 3$

Since two points determine a line, plotting two points is sufficient for linear equations. We should, however, use a third point as a check.

EXAMPLE 1 Graph the equation $2y - 4 = 4x$.

Solve for y and find three solutions.

$$y = 2x + 2$$

If $x = 1$, $y = 2(1) + 2 = 4$
If $x = -2$, $y = 2(-2) + 2 = -2$
If $x = 3$, $y = 2(3) + 2 = 8$

x	y
1	4
−2	−2
3	8

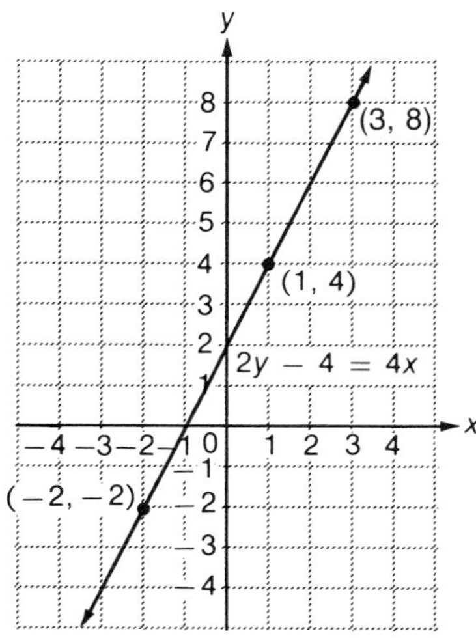

Plot the points (1, 4), (−2, −2), and (3, 8) and draw the line containing the points.

7-3

FIRST FIVE MINUTES

1. Determine whether the point (0, 3) is a solution to $y = 5x + 3$. Yes
2. Graph $y = -2x + 1$.

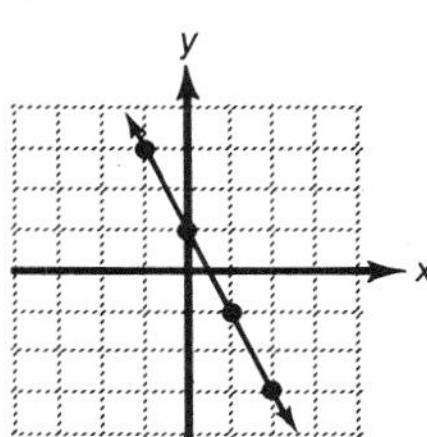

EXPLORE

Some students will have developed an intuitive understanding of linear equations from Lesson 7-2. Others will need to see the graphs in order to determine whether they are linear. You may wish to graph these equations using a computer or graphing calculator.

See Computer Exploration 4 on p. 718 for further exploration on determining linear equations.

Linear Equations

Stress that every point on the line is a solution to the linear equation, and that the line can be determined by any 2 solutions.

Key Questions

- Is $2x + 3y = 7$ a linear equation? Yes
- Is $xy = 1$ a linear equation? No
- Is $y = \frac{1}{x}$ a linear equation? No

Chalkboard Example

1. Graph the equation $2y + 6x = 4$.
   Solve for y and find 3 solutions.
   $y = -3x + 2$
   If $x = 0$, $y = -3(0) + 2 = 2$
   If $x = 2$, $y = -3(2) + 2 = -4$
   If $x = -1$, $y = -3(-1) + 2 = 5$

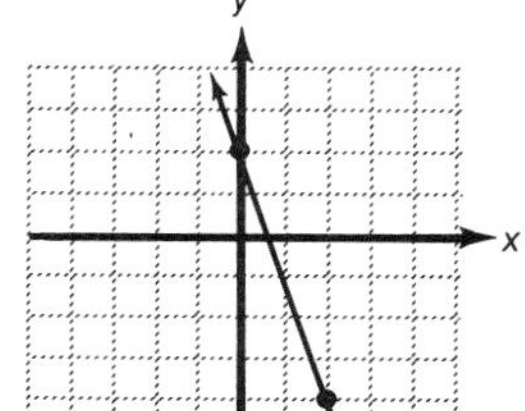

Graphing Using Intercepts

Remind students that only two points are necessary to determine a straight line. The x-intercept a and the y-intercept b give us the points $(a, 0)$ and $(0, b)$, and are often the easiest points both to find and to plot.

Key Questions

- What is the y-intercept of $y = 77777x + 99999$? 99999
- What is the x-intercept of $989898y + x = 767676$? 767676

Chalkboard Example (*T10*)

1. Graph $2x + 5y = 10$.
   Let $x = 0$, then
   $5y = 10$
   $y = 2$
   We can plot $(0, 2)$.
   Let $y = 0$, then
   $2x = 10$
   $x = 5$
   We can plot $(5, 0)$.

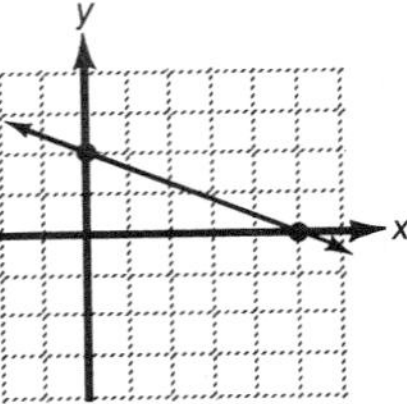

Try This Graph these linear equations using three points.

a. $3y - 12 = 9x$ **b.** $4y + 8 = -16x$ **c.** $6x - 2y = -2$
d. $-10x - 2y = 8$ For graphs, see Additional Answers.

Graphing Using Intercepts 

Objective: Graph linear equations using intercepts.

We can graph a linear equation by finding any two points that belong to the graph. Often the easiest points to find are the points where the graph crosses the axes.

The line shown at the right crosses the x-axis at $(-2, 0)$ and the y-axis at $(0, 3)$.

We say that the **x-intercept** is -2 and that the **y-intercept** is 3.

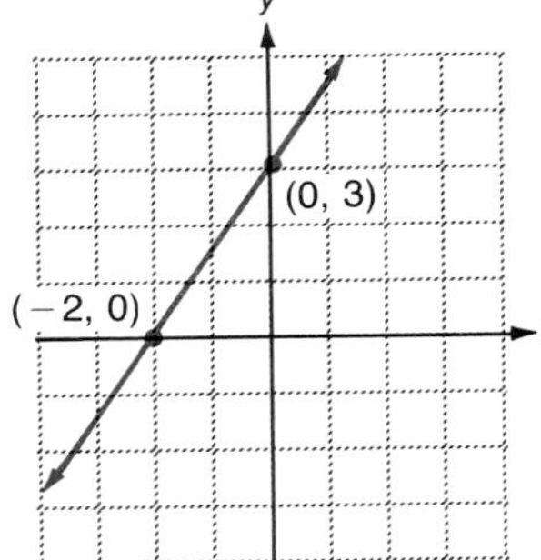

Definition

The **x-intercept** of a line is the x-coordinate of the point where the line intercepts the x-axis.

The **y-intercept** of a line is the y-coordinate of the point where the line intercepts the y-axis.

EXAMPLE 2 Graph $4x + 3y = 12$ using intercepts.

To find the x-intercept, let $y = 0$ and solve for x.

$$4x + 3 \cdot 0 = 12$$
$$4x = 12$$
$$x = 3$$

The x-intercept is 3. We plot the point $(3, 0)$.

To find the y-intercept, let $x = 0$ and solve for y.

$$4 \cdot 0 + 3y = 12$$
$$3y = 12$$
$$y = 4$$

The y-intercept is 4. We plot the point $(0, 4)$ and draw the line.

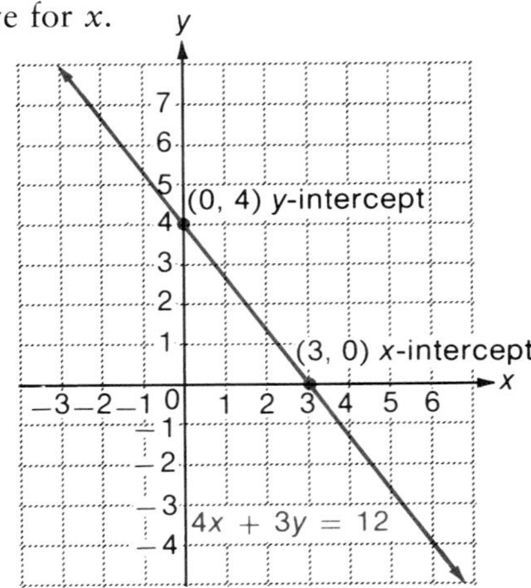

Try This Graph using intercepts. See Teacher's Answer Section.

e. $2y = 3x - 6$ **f.** $5x + 7y = 35$ **g.** $8x + 2y = 24$

Graphing Horizontal and Vertical Lines

Objective: Graph linear equations that graph as horizontal and vertical lines.

The **standard form** of a linear equation is $Ax + By = C$, where A, B, and C are constants and A and B are not both 0.

EXAMPLE 3 Graph $y = 3$.

Write the equation in standard form.

$$0 \cdot x + 1 \cdot y = 3$$

You can see that for any value of x, $y = 3$. Thus any ordered pair $(x, 3)$, such as $(0, 3)$, $(4, 3)$, or $(-1, 3)$, is a solution. The line is parallel to the x-axis with y-intercept 3.

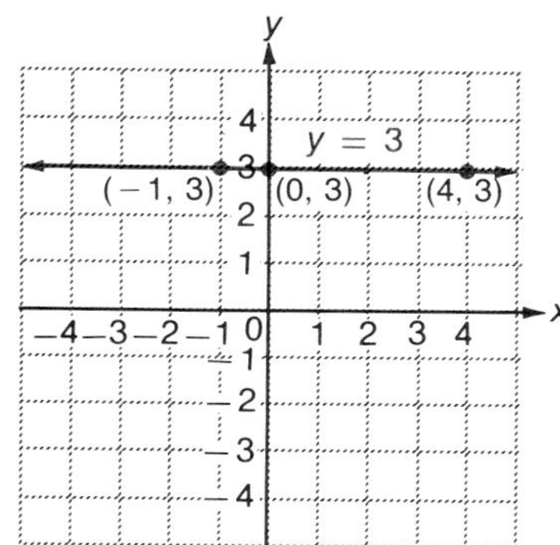

EXAMPLE 4 Graph $x = -4$.

Write this equation in standard form.

$$1 \cdot x + 0 \cdot y = -4$$

You can see that for any value of y, $x = -4$. Thus any ordered pair $(-4, y)$, such as $(-4, 3)$, $(-4, 1)$, or $(-4, -1)$, is a solution. The line is parallel to the y-axis with x-intercept -4.

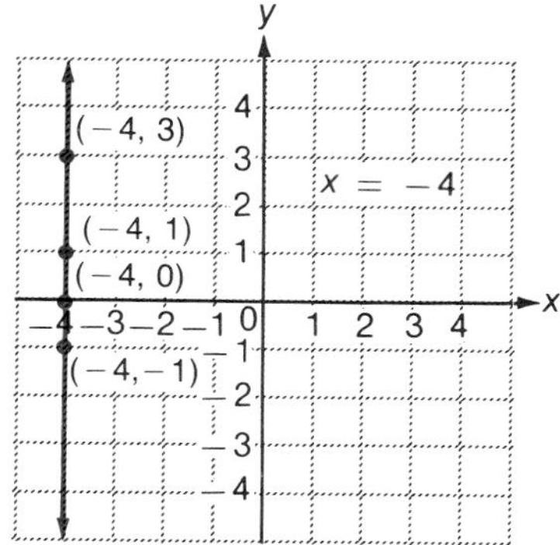

Horizontal and Vertical Lines

For constants a and b,

- the graph of $y = b$ is the x-axis or a line parallel to the x-axis with y-intercept b.
- the graph of $x = a$ is the y-axis or a line parallel to the y-axis with x-intercept a.

Try This Graph these equations.

h. $x = 5$ **i.** $y = -2$ **j.** $x = 0$ **k.** $x = -6$ See Teacher's Answer Section.

Graphing Horizontal and Vertical Lines

When one of the coefficients of a linear equation is zero, students may not immediately recognize the equation as the equation of a line. Point out that such equations can be written in standard form as in Example 3.

Chalkboard Examples

1. Graph $y = -2$.
   Any pair of the form $(x, -2)$ is a solution. There is no restriction on the x value. The line is parallel to the x-axis with y-intercept -2.

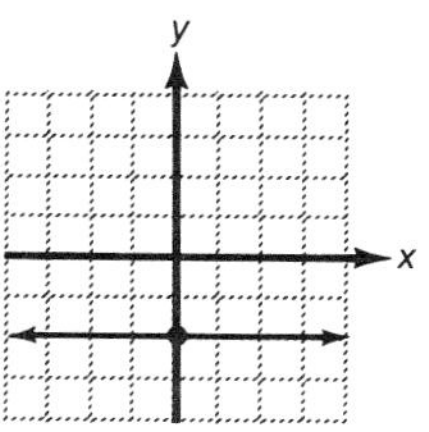

2. Graph $x = 3$.
   Any ordered pair of the form $(3, y)$ is a solution. There is no restriction on the y value. The line is parallel to the y-axis with x-intercept 3.

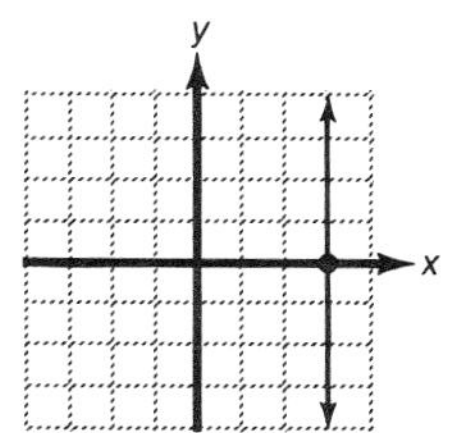

LESSON QUIZ

Graph. See Teacher's Answer Section.

1. $6x - 3y = 6$
   The intercepts are $(0, -2)$ and $(1, 0)$.
2. $y = 1$
   This is a line parallel to the x-axis with y-intercept 1.
3. $x = -2$
   This is a line parallel to the y-axis with x-intercept -2.

Assignment Guide
Minimum: 1–41 e/o, MR

Regular: 1–41 m3, 42–51 e/o, 52, MR
Advanced: 1–41 m4, 42–51 e/o, 52–54, MR

ADDITIONAL ANSWERS

Try This

a.

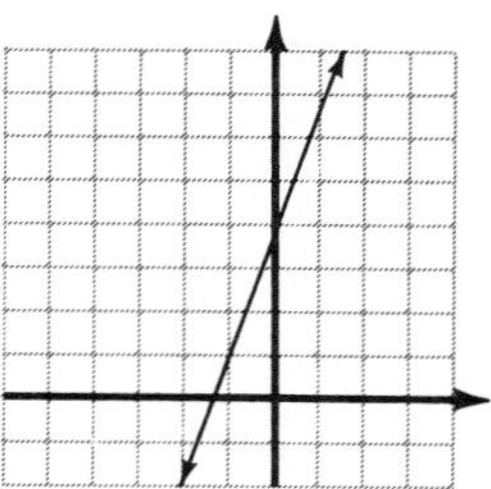

b.

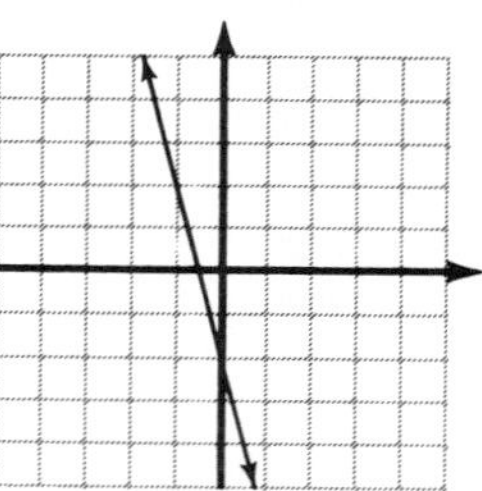

c.

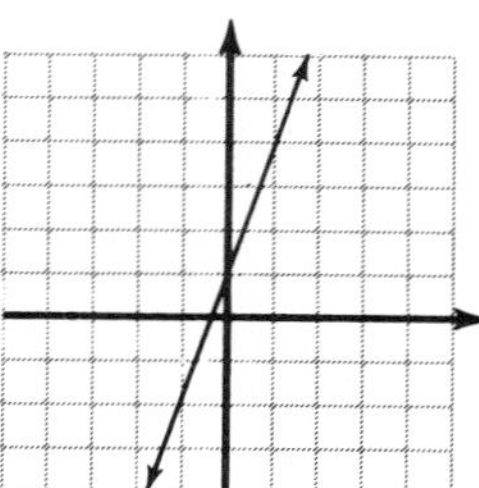

d.

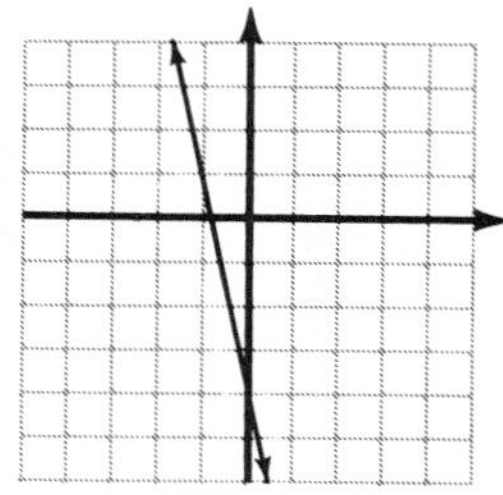

Exercises

1–41. See Teacher's Answer Section.

7-3 EXERCISES

A

Graph these linear equations using three points.

1. $x + 3y = 6$ **2.** $x + 2y = 8$ **3.** $-x + 2y = 4$
4. $-x + 3y = 9$ **5.** $3x + y = 9$ **6.** $2x + y = 6$
7. $2y - 2 = 6x$ **8.** $3y - 6 = 9x$ **9.** $2x - 5y = 10$
10. $4x + 5y = 20$ **11.** $2x + 6y = 12$ **12.** $2x + 3y = 8$
13. $3x - 4y = 12$ **14.** $y = \frac{1}{2}x + 1$ **15.** $y = \frac{1}{3}x - 1$

Graph using intercepts.

16. $x - 1 = y$ **17.** $x - 3 = y$ **18.** $2x - 1 = y$
19. $3x - 2 = y$ **20.** $4x - 3y = 12$ **21.** $6x - 2y = 18$
22. $7x + 2y = 6$ **23.** $3x + 4y = 5$ **24.** $y = -4 - 4x$
25. $y = -3 - 3x$ **26.** $-3x = 6y - 2$ **27.** $-4x = 8y - 5$
28. $3x - 6y = 12$ **29.** $-5x + y = 3$ **30.** $3x - 4y = -12$
31. $8y + 5x = 24$ **32.** $y = -6 + 2x$ **33.** $3y = 2x - 7$

Graph.

34. $x = -4$ **35.** $x = -3$ **36.** $y = -7$ **37.** $y = -9$
38. $x = 5$ **39.** $x = 7$ **40.** $y = 0$ **41.** $y = -2$

B

Match each equation with its corresponding graph at the right.

42. $y = \frac{1}{2}x$ c

43. $y = \frac{1}{2}x + 1$ b

44. $y = \frac{1}{2}x - 1$ d

45. $y = \frac{1}{2}x + 2$ a

46. $y = \frac{1}{2}x - 2$ e

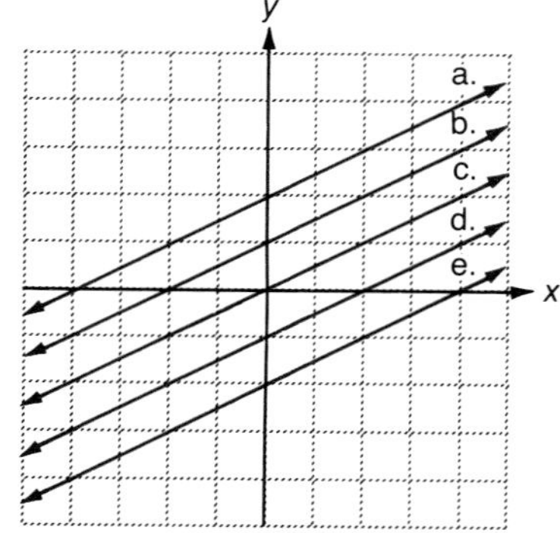

47. Write an equation whose graph is the y-axis. $x = 0$

48. Find the coordinates of the point of intersection of the graphs of the equations $x = -3$ and $y = 6$. $(-3, 6)$

49. Write an equation of a line that is parallel to the x-axis and 5 units below it. $y = -5$

50. Write an equation of a line that is parallel to the y-axis and 13 units to the right of it. $x = 13$

51. Write an equation of a line that is parallel to the x-axis and intersecting the y-axis at (0, 2.8). $y = 2.8$

52. ***Critical Thinking*** In Exercises 42–46, what effect does changing the constant in an equation have on the graph of the equation?

Challenge

53. Plot the points (10, 10), (10, −10), (−10, −10), and (−10, 10). Connect the points to form a square. Then graph the following equations, but draw only the part of each line that is inside the square.

a. $y = x - 7$ **b.** $y = x - 5$ **c.** $y = 5$ **d.** $y = 2x$

e. $y = -x$ **f.** $y = -x + 7$ **g.** $y = -x + 5$ **h.** $2y = x$

54. The part of each line that is inside the square is called a **line segment.** Which of the eight line segments is the longest? Which pairs of line segments have the same length? e; b and g, a and f, d and h

Mixed Review

Determine whether the following are squares of binomials.

55. $x^2 + 24x + 144$ **56.** $m^2 - 24m - 144$ **57.** $a^2 - 2ac + c^2$

Factor. **58.** $a^2c - ac^2$ **59.** $x^2y^2 - 2xy - 8$ **60.** $a^2 - 3ab - 4b^2$

Solve for the indicated letter. **61.** $a = \frac{v^2}{r}$ for r **62.** $K = \frac{1}{2}Iw^2$ for I

63. A secretary types 65 words per minute. At that rate, how long will it take him to complete a 2500-word document?

SPATIAL RELATIONS

The 6 diagrams below all show the same cube from a different angle.

Give the letter that is on the opposite side of the cube for each of the following sides.

1. A D **2.** B C **3.** E F **4.** C B

52. Changing the constant raises or lowers the graph.
53. See Teacher's Answer Section.

Mixed Review

55. Yes
56. No
57. Yes
58. $ac(a - c)$
59. $(xy + 2)(xy - 4)$
60. $(a - 4b)(a + b)$
61. $r = \frac{v^2}{a}$
62. $I = \frac{2K}{w^2}$
63. About 38.5 minutes

7-4

FIRST FIVE MINUTES

Graph.

1. $5x - 4y = 20$

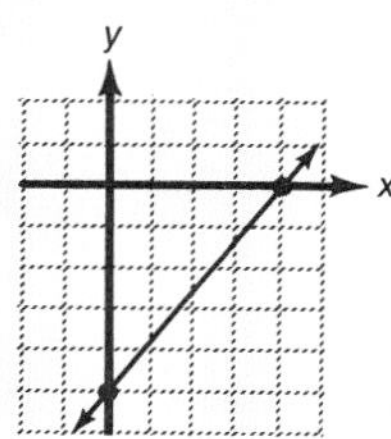

2. $x = 4$

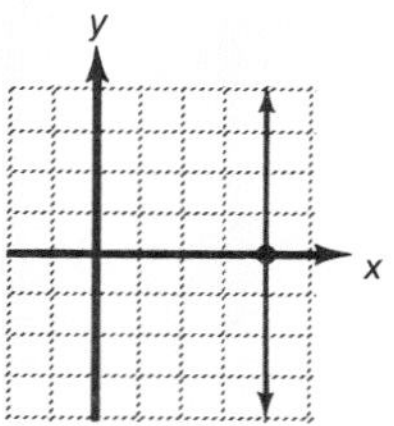

3. $y = 5$

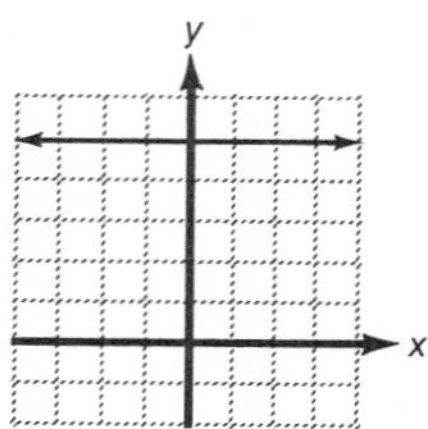

APPLICATION

Point out that the ordered pair here is (year, number of people in attendance). Students should recognize that the steeper slope of the line representing women's basketball means that the number of people attending is growing faster than for men's basketball. Point out that when the lines cross, attendance will be equal.

Meaning of Slope

Use the word "slope" informally before introducing the formal definition. Students may have experience with the slopes of roads, ski slopes, or staircases.

Emphasize that the slope is the same between any two points on the line. In the example in the text use (0, 0) and (2, 1) to show that the slope is again 2.

7-4 Slope

Master Grapher Worksheet 2 can be used with this lesson.

TI-81 Investigation 1 (page 724) can be used with this lesson.

Application

Attendance at men's and women's basketball games at a large university has been increasing for the past 6 years. The lines on the graph at the right approximate the growth patterns. We see that the line for women's basketball is steeper than the line for men's basketball. We can define a ratio that describes the steepness and direction of a line. This ratio is called the **slope.**

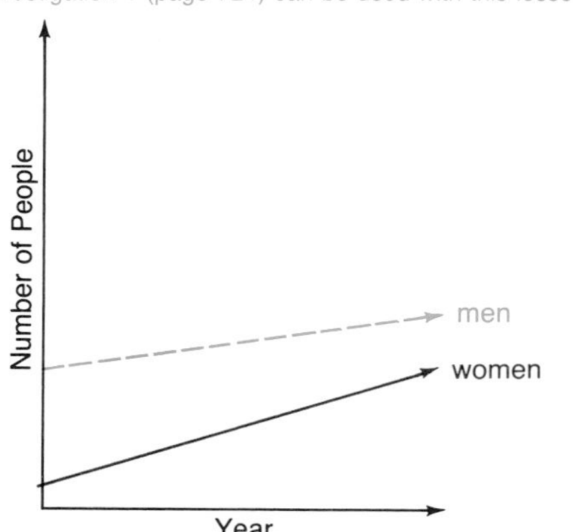

Meaning of Slope

Objective: Find the slope of a line given two points on the line.

In the graph at the right, as we move from P to Q, the change in the x-coordinates is $6 - 2$, or 4 units. We call the change in the x-coordinates the **run.** The change in the y-coordinates is $3 - 1$, or 2 units. We call the change in the y-coordinates the **rise.** For the line at the right, the ratio of the rise to the run is 2 to 4. That is $\frac{\text{rise}}{\text{run}} = \frac{2}{4}$, or $\frac{1}{2}$. This ratio is the slope of the line.

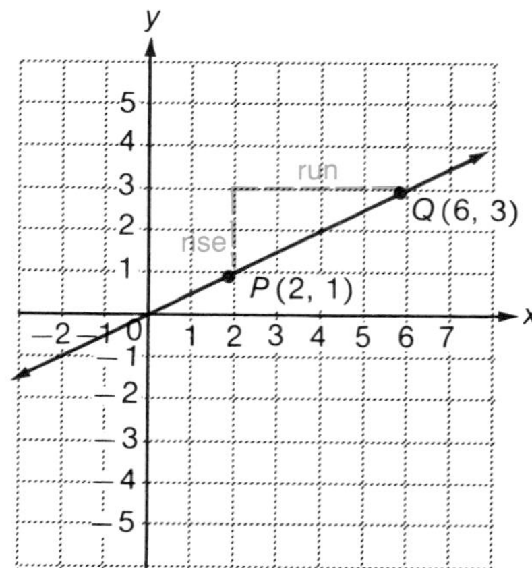

Definition

$$\text{Slope} = \frac{\text{rise}}{\text{run}} = \frac{\text{change in the } y\text{-coordinates}}{\text{change in the } x\text{-coordinates}}$$

$$= \frac{\text{difference of } y\text{-coordinates}}{\text{difference of } x\text{-coordinates}}$$

EXAMPLE 1

Graph the line containing points $(-4, 2)$ and $(2, -3)$ and find the slope.

We plot the points $(-4, 2)$ and $(2, -3)$ and draw the line containing these points. We can use the definition of slope to find the slope of the line.

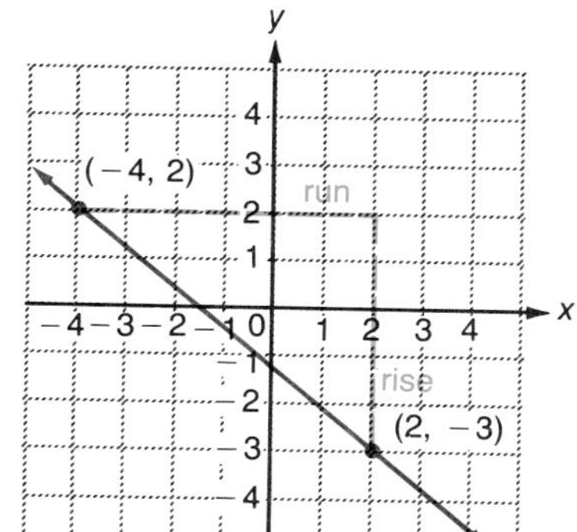

We know that the points $(-4, 2)$ and $(2, -3)$ are on the line.

$$\text{Slope} = \frac{\text{rise}}{\text{run}} = \frac{\text{change in } y}{\text{change in } x} = \frac{2 - (-3)}{-4 - 2} = \frac{5}{-6} = -\frac{5}{6}$$

The slope is $-\frac{5}{6}$.

Try This Graph the lines containing these points and find their slopes. See Additional Answers.

a. $(-2, 3)$ $(3, 5)$ Slope $= \frac{2}{5}$ **b.** $(0, -3)$ $(-3, 2)$ Slope $= -\frac{5}{3}$

In Example 1 we found the change in y by subtracting the y-coordinates, and we found the change in x by subtracting the x-coordinates. We can also find the slope by subtracting the coordinates in reverse order.

$$\text{slope} = \frac{\text{change in } y}{\text{change in } x} = \frac{-3 - 2}{2 - (-4)} = \frac{-5}{6} = -\frac{5}{6}$$

The slope is the same. In general, the slope of a line can be found using any two points (x_1, y_1) and (x_2, y_2) and this formula.

$$m = \frac{y_2 - y_1}{x_2 - x_1}$$

The letter m is commonly used for slope.

EXAMPLE 2

Find the slope of the line containing $(1, 1)$ and $(3, 5)$.

$$m = \frac{y_2 - y_1}{x_2 - x_1} = \frac{5 - 1}{3 - 1} = \frac{4}{2} = 2$$

Try This Find the slopes of the lines containing these points.

c. $(2, 2)$ $(8, 9)$ $\frac{7}{6}$ **d.** $(-4, -6)$ $(3, -2)$ $\frac{4}{7}$

e. $(-2, 3)$ $(2, 1)$ $-\frac{1}{2}$ **f.** $(5, -11)$ $(-9, 4)$ $-\frac{15}{14}$

Avoiding Common Errors

Students may reverse the order of subtraction when calculating the slope. For example, in calculating the slope between (1, 2) and (3, 4), a student may incorrectly calculate $\frac{4-2}{1-3}$. Emphasize that the coordinates must be subtracted in the same order.

Chalkboard Examples (*T11*)

1. Graph the line containing points (2, 1) and (4, 3) and find the slope.

$$\text{slope} = \frac{\text{rise}}{\text{run}} = \frac{\text{change in } y}{\text{change in } x} = \frac{3-1}{4-2} = \frac{2}{2} = 1$$

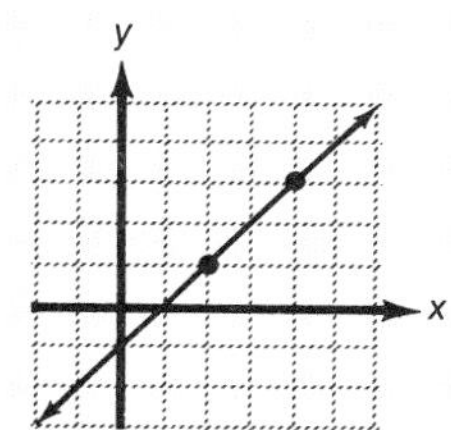

2. Find the slope of the line containing the points (7, 3) and (2, 1).

$$m = \frac{3-1}{7-2} = \frac{2}{5}$$

Horizontal and Vertical Lines

Emphasize that $x = 0$ is the y-axis and $y = 0$ is the x-axis.

Math Point
Why is m commonly used to represent slope?
It may have derived from the French word *monter,* which means "to mount, to climb, to slope up." This explanation seems credible, as René Descartes, the creator of the coordinate system, was French.

Key Questions

- Slope is rise divided by run. How much does a horizontal line rise?
  It doesn't rise.
- What is the slope of a horizontal line?
  0

Chalkboard Examples

1. Find the slope of the line $y = -2$.
   0
2. Find the slope of $x = 2$.
   This line has no slope.

LESSON QUIZ

1. Graph the line and find the slope of the line containing the points (4, 3) and (2, −1).
   The slope equals 2.

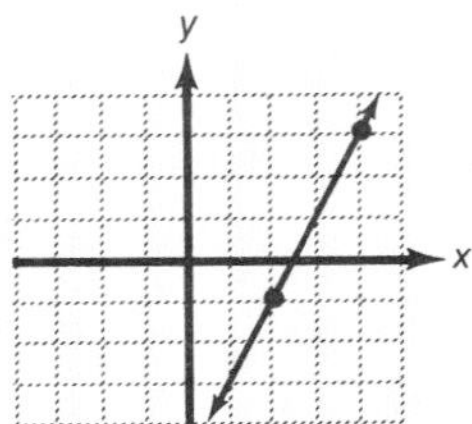

Find the slope, if possible, of the lines containing these points.

2. (−6, 3), (4, −9)
   $-\frac{6}{5}$
3. (3, 4), (5, 4)
   0
4. (5, 7), (5, −3)
   Not possible

Horizontal and Vertical Lines 

Objective: Give the slope of horizontal and vertical lines.

What about the slope of a horizontal or vertical line?

EXAMPLE 3 Find the slope of the line $y = 4$.

$$m = \frac{\text{change in } y}{\text{change in } x} = \frac{4 - 4}{-3 - 2} = \frac{0}{-5} = 0$$

Any two points on a horizontal line have the same y-coordinate. Thus the change in y is 0, so the slope is 0.

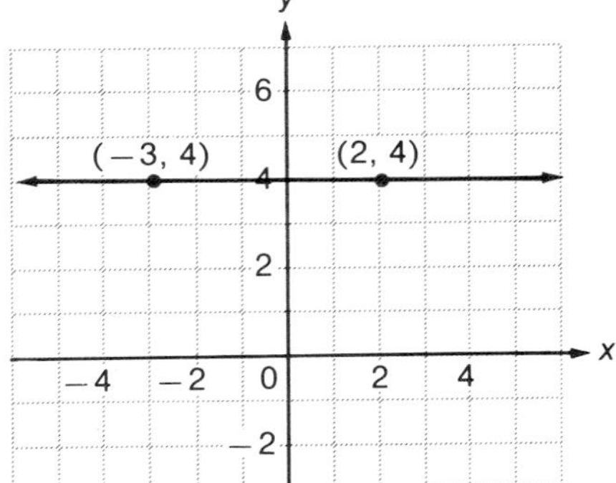

EXAMPLE 4 Find the slope of the line $x = -3$.

$$m = \frac{\text{change in } y}{\text{change in } x} = \frac{3 - (-2)}{-3 - (-3)} = \frac{5}{0}$$

Since division by 0 is not defined, this line has no slope.

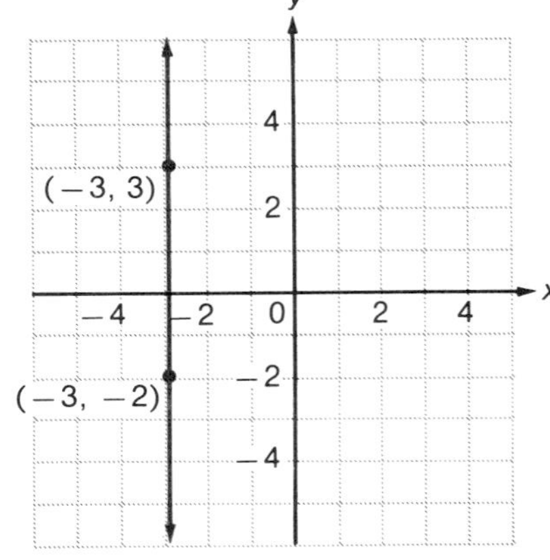

Definition

Slope of Horizontal and Vertical Lines

A horizontal line has slope 0.
A vertical line has no slope.

Try This Find the slopes, if they exist, of the lines containing these points.

g. (9, 7) (3, 7) 0 **h.** (4, −6) (4, 0) No slope **i.** (2, 4) (−1, 5) $-\frac{1}{3}$

7-4 EXERCISES

A

Find the slope of each line.

1.

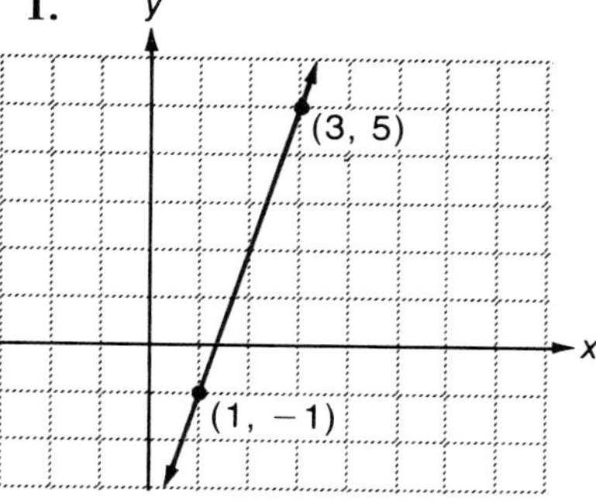

$m = 3$

2.

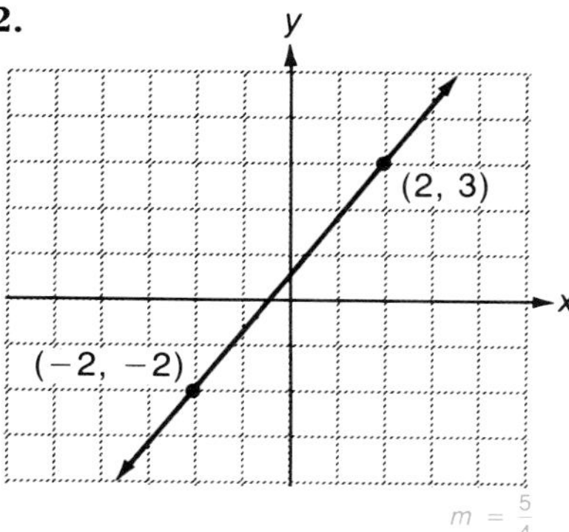

$m = \frac{5}{4}$

3.

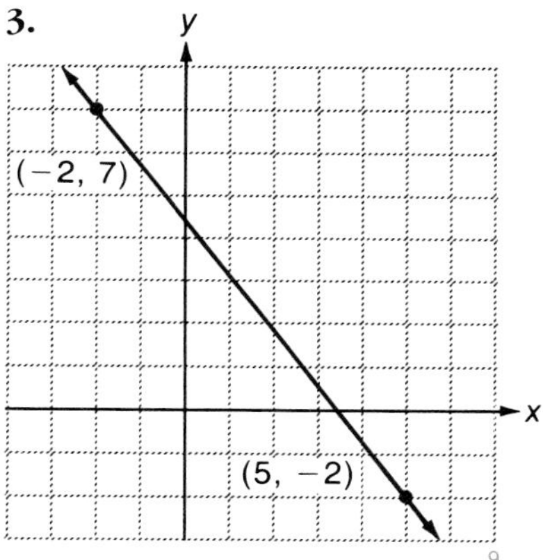

$m = -\frac{9}{7}$

4.

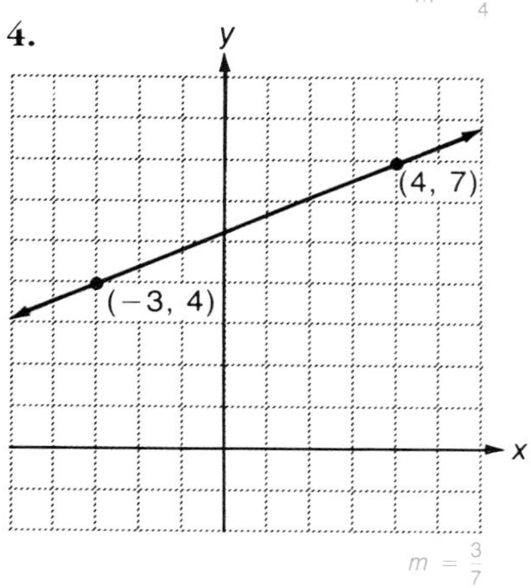

$m = \frac{3}{7}$

Graph the lines containing these points and find their slopes.

5. $(-4, 2)$ $(2, -3)$ **6.** $(4, 1)$ $(-2, -3)$ **7.** $(-2, 4)$ $(3, 0)$

8. $(3, 2)$ $(-1, 2)$ **9.** $(0, 5)$ $(-4, -3)$ **10.** $(1, 6)$ $(-2, -4)$

Find the slopes of the lines containing these points.

11. $(4, 0)$ $(5, 7)$ 7 **12.** $(3, 0)$ $(6, 2)$ $\frac{2}{3}$

13. $(0, 8)$ $(-3, 10)$ $-\frac{2}{3}$ **14.** $(0, 9)$ $(4, 7)$ $-\frac{1}{2}$

15. $(3, -2)$ $(5, -6)$ -2 **16.** $(-2, 4)$ $(6, -7)$ $-\frac{11}{8}$

17. $(0, 0)$ $(-3, -9)$ 3 **18.** $(0, 0)$ $(-4, -8)$ 2

19. $\left(\frac{3}{4}, \frac{1}{2}\right)$ $\left(\frac{1}{4}, -\frac{1}{2}\right)$ 2 **20.** $\left(\frac{1}{4}, \frac{1}{8}\right)$ $\left(\frac{1}{2}, \frac{3}{4}\right)$ $\frac{5}{2}$

Find the slope, if it exists, of each of these lines.

21. $x = -8$ **22.** $x = -4$ **23.** $y = 2$ **24.** $y = 17$

25. $x = 9$ **26.** $x = 6$ **27.** $y = -9$ **28.** $y = -4$

Assignment Guide

Minimum: 1–28 e/o, MR

Regular: 1–34 e/o, 35, MR

Advanced: 1–34 m3, 35–37, MR

ADDITIONAL ANSWERS

Try This

a.

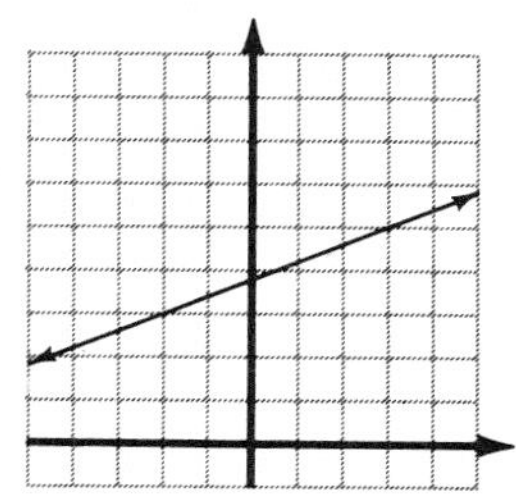

b.

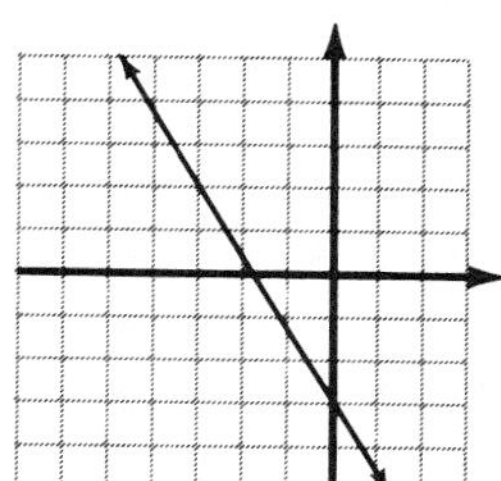

Exercises

5. $m = -\frac{5}{6}$

6. $m = \frac{2}{3}$

7. $m = -\frac{4}{5}$

8. $m = 0$

9. $m = 2$

10. $m = \frac{10}{3}$

21. No slope
22. No slope
23. Zero slope
24. Zero slope
25. No slope
26. No slope
27. Zero slope
28. Zero slope

34. $XY: m = -\frac{2}{3}$

$XZ: m = -2$

YZ: no slope

35. Yes. A line can be determined by a point and a slope. The slope between $(-1, 3)$ and $(1, 1)$ equals -1, and the slope between $(1, 1)$ and $(10, -8)$ also equals -1. Since both lines have slope -1 and contain the point $(1, 1)$, they must be the same line, and all 3 points are on a line.

Mixed Review

38. $(3m^2n + 4)(3m^2n - 4)$
39. $(ab + 2)(ab - 1)$
40. $(3x - y)(x + y)$
41. Yes
42. No
43. 0.002575
44. 100,400
45. $-2, 9$
46. $-5, 2$
47. -2

Writing to Learn

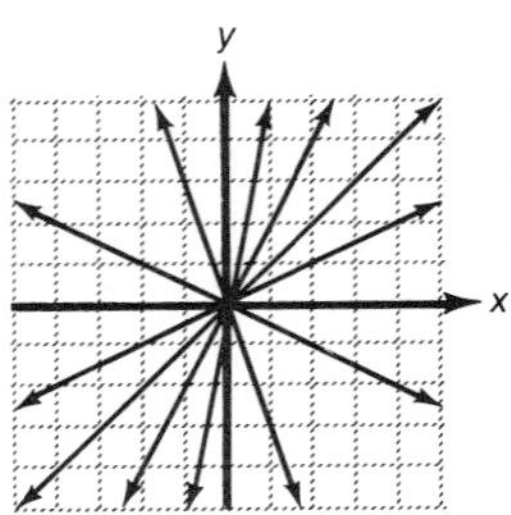

Answers may vary but students should notice that as the absolute value of the coefficient of x increases, the line becomes steeper, and that if the coefficient is positive, the line slopes upward to the right, while if it is negative, the line slopes upward to the left.

B

29. A line contains $(4, 3)$ and $(x, 7)$. It has slope 2. Find x. 6
30. A line contains $(9, y)$ and $(-6, 3)$. It has slope $\frac{2}{3}$. Find y. 13
31. A line contains $(-4, y)$ and $(2, 4y)$. It has slope 6. Find y. 12
32. The grade of a road is its slope expressed as percent. What is the slope of a road with a 7% grade? $\frac{7}{100}$
33. Suppose a plane climbs 11.7 ft for every 30 ft it moves horizontally. Express the slope as a percent. 39%
34. The vertices of a triangle are $X(-1, 4)$, $Y(2, 2)$, and $Z(2, -2)$. Find the slope of each side of the triangle.
35. *Critical Thinking* Use the definition of slope to determine whether $(-1, 3)$, $(1, 1)$, and $(10, -8)$ are on the same line. Explain your answer.

Challenge

36. A line contains points $\left(p, \frac{p}{q}\right)$ and $\left(q, \frac{q}{p}\right)$ where p and q are not 0. Find the slope. $\frac{p+q}{pq}$
37. In the chessboard drawing, the knight may move to any of the eight squares shown. If the beginning and end squares of any move determine a line, what slopes are possible?

$2, \frac{1}{2}, -\frac{1}{2}, -2$

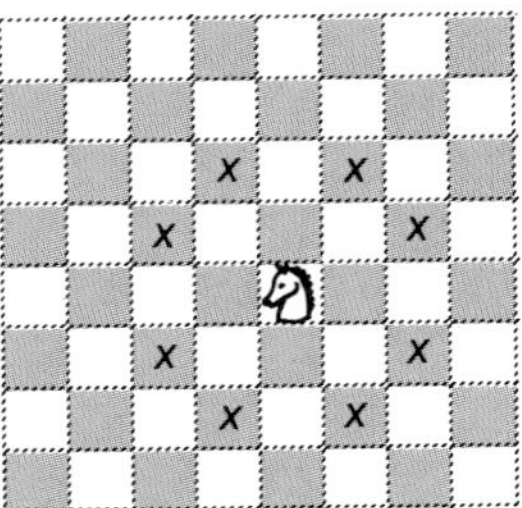

Mixed Review

Factor. **38.** $9m^4n^2 - 16$ **39.** $a^2b^2 + ab - 2$ **40.** $3x^2 + 2xy - y^2$

Determine whether the given point is a solution of the equation.

41. $(0, -2)$, $3x - y = 2$ **42.** $(2, 3)$, $3x - 2y = 2$

Write in standard notation. **43.** 2.575×10^{-3} **44.** 1.004×10^5

Solve. **45.** $y^2 - 7y = 18$ **46.** $m^2 + 3m = 10$ **47.** $a^2 + 4a = -4$

WRITING TO LEARN

Graph the following equations using the same set of axes.

$$y = x \quad y = 2x \quad y = 5x \quad y = -3x \quad y = \frac{1}{2}x \quad y = -\frac{1}{2}x$$

Write a paragraph explaining how the slopes of these lines change as the coefficient of x changes.

7-5 Equations and Slope

Master Grapher Worksheet 3 can be used with this lesson.

Explore

Determine the slope of each line.

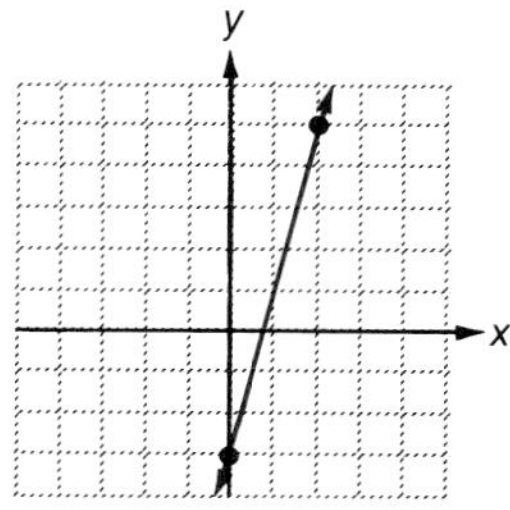

$y = 4x - 3$

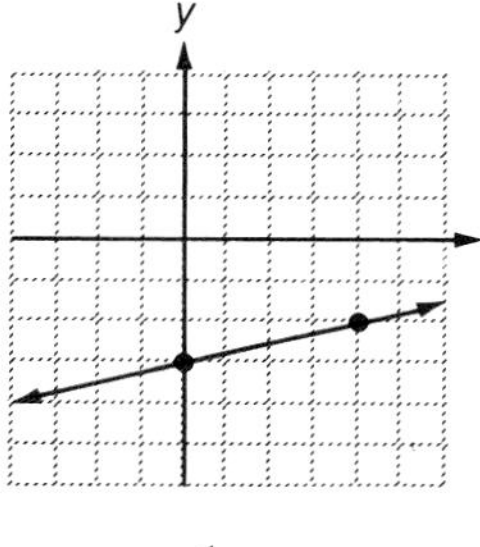

$y = \frac{1}{4}x - 3$

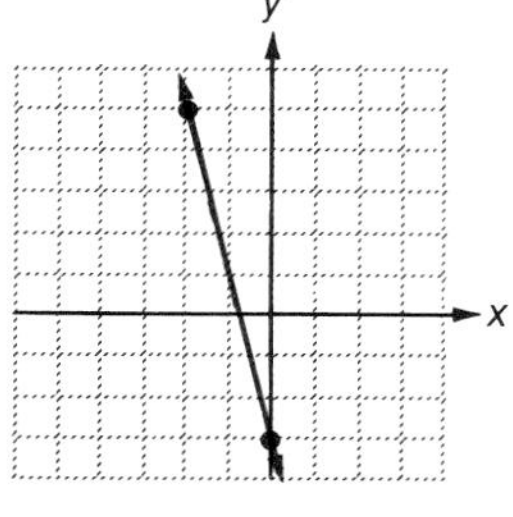

$y = -4x - 3$

What is the relationship between the slope and the equation of each line?

Finding Slope From an Equation

Objective: Find the slope of a line from an equation.

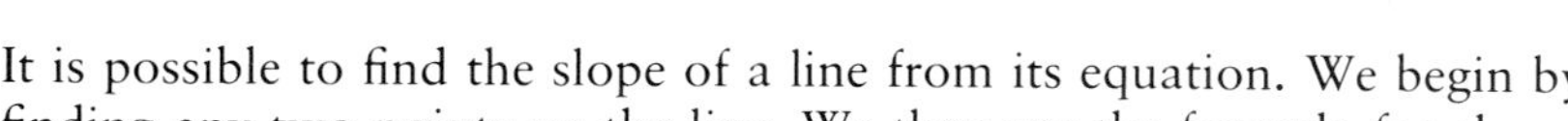

It is possible to find the slope of a line from its equation. We begin by finding any two points on the line. We then use the formula for slope.

EXAMPLE 1 Find the slope of the line $y = 2x + 3$.

We choose the points (0, 3) and (1, 5).

$$m = \frac{\text{change in } y}{\text{change in } x} = \frac{5 - 3}{1 - 0}$$
$$= \frac{2}{1}$$
$$= 2$$

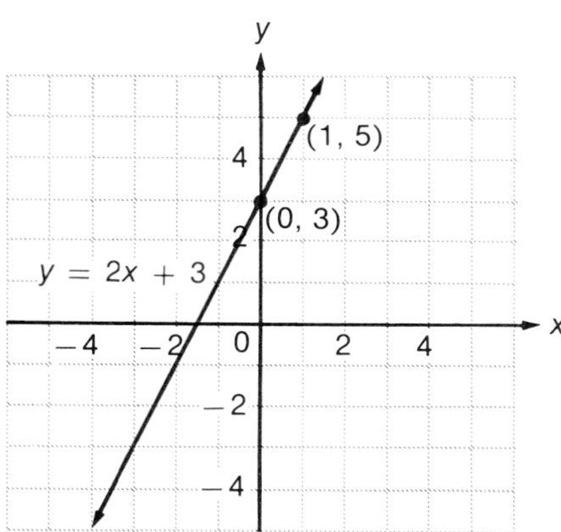

The slope is 2.

Notice that the slope, 2, is also the coefficient of the x-term in the equation $y = 2x + 3$. We can always find m, the slope of a line, if its equation is written in the form, $y = mx + b$. The coefficient of the x-term, m, is the slope.

7-5

FIRST FIVE MINUTES

Graph. Then find the slope and the y-intercept.

1. $y = \frac{1}{2}x + 2$

   $m = \frac{1}{2}$

   The y-intercept is 2.
2. $y = -x - 2$

   $m = -1$

   The y-intercept is -2.

EXPLORE

Students should recognize that the coefficient of x is equal to the slope.

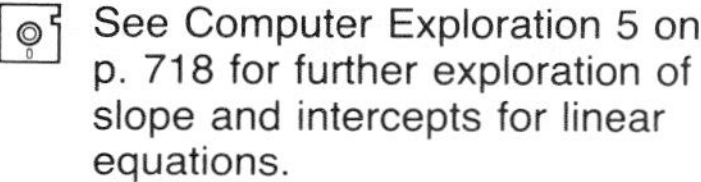

See Computer Exploration 5 on p. 718 for further exploration of slope and intercepts for linear equations.

Finding Slope From an Equation

Emphasize that all the information about a line is contained in its equation. In particular, the slope of a line can be determined from its equation.

Chalkboard Examples

1. Find the slope of the line $y = 3x + 1$.

   We choose the points (0, 1) and (1, 4). The slope is

   $\frac{4 - 1}{1 - 0} = 3$

   Note that this is the same as the coefficient of x.
2. Find the slope of the line $3x + 5y = 7$.

   We solve for y.

   $5y = -3x + 7$

   $y = -\frac{3}{5}x + \frac{7}{5}$

   The slope is $-\frac{3}{5}$.

Slope-Intercept Equation of a Line

Note that a linear equation can be written in many forms. In Lesson 7-3 we discussed standard form $Ax + By = C$, and in this lesson we cover the slope-intercept form $y = mx + b$. Each form has specific uses. The slope-intercept form, as its name suggests, makes the slope and y-intercept of the line obvious, which is useful for graphing the equation.

You may want to point out that although the y-intercept is defined to be b, the point on the graph where the line intercepts the y-axis is $(0, b)$.

Chalkboard Examples

1. Find the slope and y-intercept of $y = 5x + 7$.
   The slope is 5.
   The y-intercept is 7.
2. Find the slope and y-intercept of $4x + 7y = 8$.
   $7y = -4x + 8$
   $y = -\frac{4}{7}x + \frac{8}{7}$
   The slope is $-\frac{4}{7}$.
   The y-intercept is $\frac{8}{7}$.

EXAMPLE 2 Find the slope of $2x + 3y = 7$.

Solve for y.

$$2x + 3y = 7$$
$$3y = -2x + 7$$
$$y = \frac{-2}{3}x + \frac{7}{3}$$

The slope is $-\frac{2}{3}$.

Try This Find the slope of each line by solving for y.

a. $4x + 5y = 7$ $-\frac{4}{5}$ **b.** $3x + 8y = 9$ $-\frac{3}{8}$
c. $x + 5y = 7$ $-\frac{1}{5}$ **d.** $5x - 4y = 8$ $\frac{5}{4}$

Slope-Intercept Equation of a Line

Objective: Find the slope and y-intercept of a line from an equation.

In the equation $y = mx + b$, m is the slope. If $x = 0$, then $y = m(0) + b$ or $y = b$. Thus the graph crosses the y-axis at the point $(0, b)$, and b is the y-intercept. In the graph at the right, the line $y = 2x - 3$ has slope 2 and y-intercept -3.

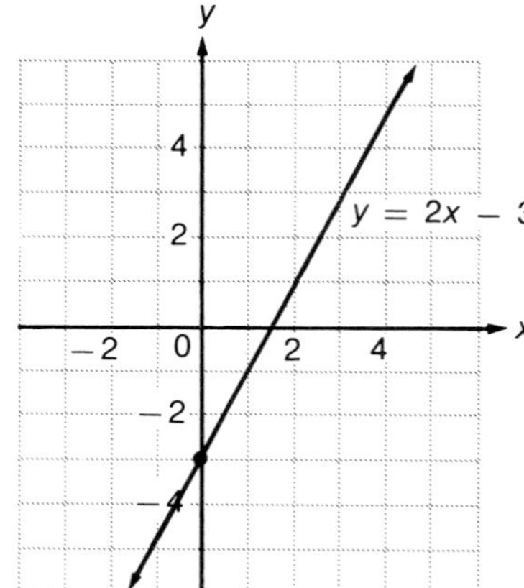

Definition

An equation $y = mx + b$ is called the **slope-intercept equation** of a line. The slope is m and the y-intercept is b.

EXAMPLE 3 Find the slope and y-intercept of $y = 3x - 4$.

$y = 3x - 4$

slope: 3 y-intercept: -4

The slope is 3. The y-intercept is -4.

EXAMPLE 4 Find the slope and y-intercept of $2x + 3y = 6$.

First solve for y.

$$2x + 3y = 6$$

$$y = -\frac{2}{3}x + 2$$

The slope is $-\frac{2}{3}$. The y-intercept is 2.

Try This Find the slope and y-intercept.

e. $y = 5x$ 5, 0 **f.** $y = -\frac{3}{2}x - 6$ $-\frac{3}{2}$, -6

g. $3x + 4y = 16$ $-\frac{3}{4}$, 4 **h.** $-7x - 5y = 25$ $-\frac{7}{5}$, -5

Graphing Using the Slope-Intercept Equation

Objective: Graph lines using the slope-intercept equation.

We can graph lines using the slope-intercept form of an equation.

EXAMPLE 5 Graph $y = -2x + 3$ using y-intercept and slope.

From the equation $y = -2x + 3$, we know that the slope is -2 and that the y-intercept is 3.

First we plot (0, 3). We can think of the slope as $\frac{-2}{1}$. Using the slope, we find another point by moving 2 units down (negative) and 1 unit right (positive). The point is (1, 1). We connect the points to graph the line.

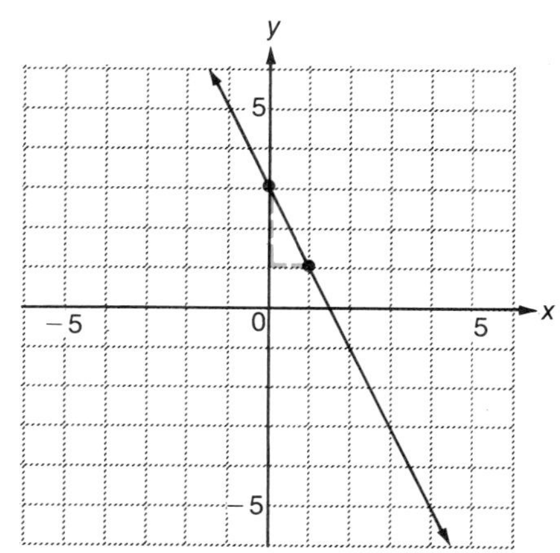

Try This Graph each equation using y-intercept and slope.

i. $y = 3x - 4$ **j.** $y = -\frac{1}{3}x + 4$

k. $y = -\frac{3}{4}x + 2$

See Teacher's Answer Section.

Graphing Using the Slope-Intercept Equation

Chalkboard Example

1. Graph the equation $y = \frac{2}{3}x + 2$.

   The slope is $\frac{2}{3}$ and the y-intercept is 2. First plot the y-intercept (0, 2). Next, find a second point by "running" 3 to the right and "rising" 2. The point is (3, 4). Connect the points to graph the line.

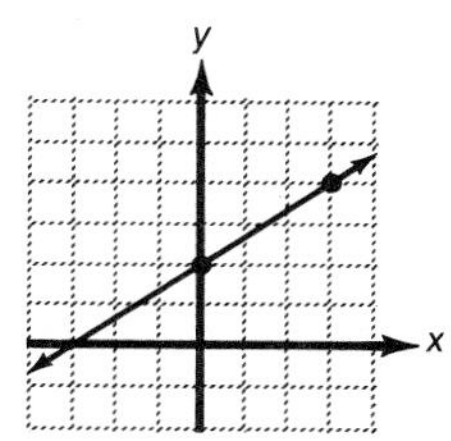

LESSON QUIZ

1. Determine the slope and y-intercept of the line $y = 7x + 6$.
   The slope is 7.
   The y-intercept is 6.
2. Determine the slope and y-intercept of the line $7x - 4y = 3$.
   The slope is $\frac{7}{4}$.
   The y-intercept is $-\frac{3}{4}$.
3. Graph $y = \frac{1}{2}x - 2$ using y-intercept and slope.

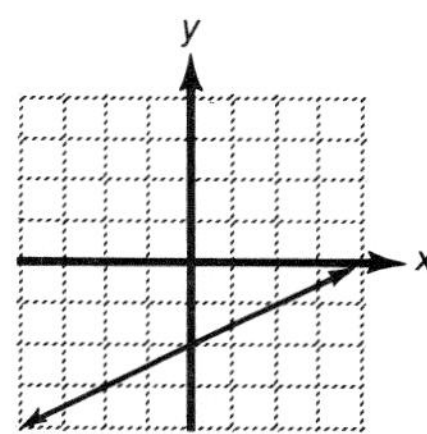

Assignment Guide
Minimum: Day 1: 1–27 e/o, MR
Day 2: 28–39,
assign w. 7-6
Regular: 1–39 m3, 40–55 e/o, 56, MR
Advanced: 1–55 m4, 56–58, MR

ADDITIONAL ANSWERS

Exercises

19. $m = -4, b = -9$
20. $m = -3, b = -5$
21. $m = -\frac{2}{3}, b = 3$
22. $m = -\frac{5}{4}, b = 3$
23. $m = -\frac{8}{7}, b = -3$
24. $m = -\frac{2}{9}, b = -\frac{13}{9}$
25. $m = 3, b = -\frac{5}{3}$
26. $m = \frac{4}{9}, b = -\frac{7}{9}$
27. $m = -\frac{3}{2}, b = -\frac{1}{2}$
28–45. See Teacher's Answer Section.
48. $y = 3x - 2$
49. $y = 8x$
50. $y = -5$
51. $y = -7x + 4$
52. $y = \frac{1}{2}x + 1$
53. $y = -6x + \frac{3}{4}$

7-5 EXERCISES

A

Find the slope of each line by solving for y.

1. $3x + 2y = 6$ $-\frac{3}{2}$
2. $4x - y = 5$ 4
3. $x + 4y = 8$ $-\frac{1}{4}$
4. $x + 3y = 6$ $-\frac{1}{3}$
5. $-2x + y = 4$ 2
6. $-5x + y = 5$ 5
7. $4x - 3y = -12$ $\frac{4}{3}$
8. $3x - 4y = -12$ $\frac{3}{4}$
9. $x - 2y = 9$ $\frac{1}{2}$
10. $x - 3y = -2$ $\frac{1}{3}$
11. $-2x + 4y = 8$ $\frac{1}{2}$
12. $-5x + 7y = 2$ $\frac{5}{7}$
13. $-7x + 5y = 16$ $\frac{7}{5}$
14. $-3x + 2y = 9$ $\frac{3}{2}$
15. $-6x - 9y = 13$ $-\frac{2}{3}$
16. $-8x - 5y = 18$ $-\frac{8}{5}$
17. $8x + 9y = 10$ $-\frac{8}{9}$
18. $7x + 4y = 13$ $-\frac{7}{4}$

Find the slope and y-intercept.

19. $y = -4x - 9$
20. $y = -3x - 5$
21. $2x + 3y = 9$
22. $5x + 4y = 12$
23. $-8x - 7y = 21$
24. $-2x - 9y = 13$
25. $9x = 3y + 5$
26. $4x = 9y + 7$
27. $-6x = 4y + 2$

Graph each line using the y-intercept and slope.

28. $y = 2x + 3$
29. $y = -3x + 4$
30. $y = -x + 7$
31. $y = \frac{2}{3}x - 3$
32. $y = \frac{3}{4}x - 3$
33. $y = \frac{1}{2}x + 2$
34. $y + \frac{1}{3}x = 2$
35. $y - \frac{2}{3}x = 0$
36. $y + \frac{3}{5}x = -3$
37. $y - 5x = -4$
38. $y - 7 = -3x$
39. $y + 4 = -2x$

B

Graph each line using the slope and y-intercept.

40. $2y - 6x = -8$
41. $4y + 2x = 12$
42. $2x - 5y = 15$
43. $6x + 3y = -12$
44. $8x - 3y = 15$
45. $-2x = -4y + 16$

46. Write the equation of a line that has the same slope as $y = \frac{2}{3}x + 5$ with a y-intercept of -8. $y = \frac{2}{3}x - 8$

47. Consider the equation $ky + 2x = 7$. For what value of k will the slope be 1? -2

Write an equation for each line given the slope and y-intercept. Express the equation in slope-intercept form.

48. $m = 3, b = -2$
49. $m = 8, b = 0$
50. $m = 0, b = -5$
51. $m = -7, b = 4$
52. $m = \frac{1}{2}, b = 1$
53. $m = -6, b = \frac{3}{4}$

Find the slope and y-intercept. Do not graph.

54. $3(x + 4) = y - 8x + 3$ $m = 11, b = 9$

55. $2y + 4x = 3(y - x) + 8$ $m = 7, b = -8$

56. *Critical Thinking* The x- and y-intercepts of a line are $(a, 0)$ and $(0, b)$. What is the equation of the line? $y = -\frac{b}{a}x + b$

Challenge

57. A linear equation of the form $Ax + By = C$ where A and B are not both 0 is in standard form. Find the slope and y-intercept in terms of A, B, and C. $m = -\frac{A}{B}, b = \frac{C}{B}$

58. Graph $y = 3|x| + 5$. Your graph should look like an angle. Give the slope of each ray of the angle. Slopes: $-3, 3$

Mixed Review

In which quadrant is each point located? **59.** $(1, -5)$ **60.** $(-1, 3)$ **61.** $(2, 3)$ **62.** $(-4, -1)$ **63.** $(2, -6)$ **64.** $(-3, 2)$

Find three solutions of each equation. **65.** $x + 2y = 5$ **66.** $2x - 4y = 0$ **67.** $3x + y = 2$ **68.** $2x - 2y = 4$

Factor. **69.** $25b^2 - 16a^2$ **70.** $a^4 + 4a^3b + 4a^2b^2$ **71.** $mn + 5m + 3n + 15$ **72.** $6x^2 + 14x + 8$

Solve. **73.** $12y^2 = 108$ **74.** $a^2 - 3a = 10$ **75.** $x^2 - 25 = 0$

76. The Correction Company produces erasers and packages them in boxes of 144. On Tuesday, the Correction Company produced and packed 31 boxes, with 4 erasers left over. How many erasers were produced that day?

SUPPOSE

The graph of the equation $y = 3x - 4$ is shown at the right.

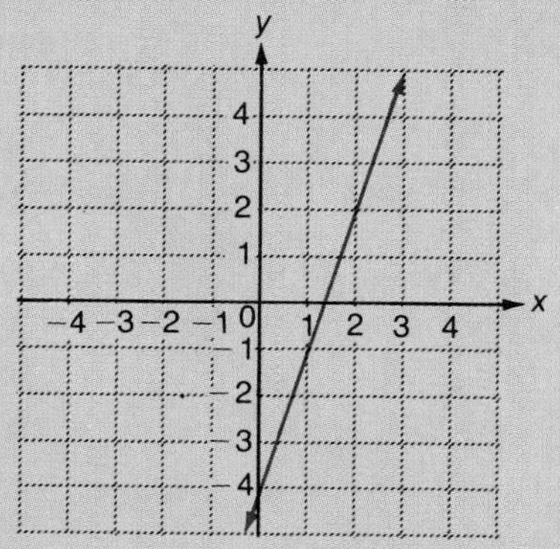

Suppose you graphed each of the following equations on the same coordinate axes. How would the graph of each equation be related to the graph at the right?

a. $y = 3x + 6$ **b.** $y = 6x - 4$

c. $2y = 6x - 8$ **d.** $4 = 3x - y$

e. $y = \frac{-x}{3} - 4$ **f.** $-y = -3x + 4$

Mixed Review

59. IV
60. II
61. I
62. III
63. IV
64. II

Answers may vary for 65–68.

65. Ex: $(-1, 3), (1, 2), \left(2, \frac{3}{2}\right)$
66. Ex: $(-2, -1), (2, 1), (4, 2)$
67. Ex: $(0, 2), (1, -1), (-1, 5)$
68. Ex: $(2, 0), (0, -2), (1, -1)$
69. $(5b + 4a)(5b - 4a)$
70. $a^2(a + 2b)^2$
71. $(m + 3)(n + 5)$
72. $2(x + 1)(3x + 4)$
73. $-3, 3$
74. $-2, 5$
75. $-5, 5$
76. 4468 erasers

Suppose

a. Same slope, but $b = 6$
b. Same y-intercept, but $m = 6$
c. Same line
d. Same line
e. Same y-intercept, but $m = -\frac{1}{3}$
f. Same line

7-6

FIRST FIVE MINUTES

1. Find the slope of the line containing the points $(-3, 4)$ and $(2, -7)$.
   $\frac{-7-4}{2-(-3)} = -\frac{11}{5}$
2. Find the slope of the line $y = -5x + 9$.
   The slope is -5.
3. Find the slope of the line $5x + 4y = 3$.
   $4y = -5x + 3$
   $y = -\frac{5}{4}x + \frac{3}{4}$
   The slope is $-\frac{5}{4}$.

The Slope-Intercept Equation

You may want to introduce this lesson by asking students to write an equation for a line given the slope and y-intercept. For example:

$m = 4, b = 3; y = 4x + 3$
$m = 2, b = -1; y = 2x - 1$
$m = -1, b = 4; y = -x + 4$

Key Questions

- Can we draw a line if we are given one point on it and its slope?
  Yes
- If a line contains the point $(2, 3)$ and has slope 5, and (x, y) is some other point on the line, what is the value of $\frac{y-3}{x-2}$?
  5

Chalkboard Examples

1. Write the equation for a line with slope 8 and y-intercept 6.
   $y = 8x + 6$
2. Write an equation for the line containing the points $(2, -2)$ and $(6, 0)$.
   $m = \frac{0-(-2)}{6-2} = \frac{2}{4} = \frac{1}{2}$
   $y = \frac{1}{2}x + b$
   $-2 = \frac{1}{2}(2) + b$
   $-2 = 1 + b$
   $-3 = b$
   $y = \frac{1}{2}x - 3$

7-6 Finding the Equation of a Line

Master Grapher Worksheet 4 can be used with this lesson.

The Slope-Intercept Equation

Objective: Write an equation of a line using the slope-intercept equation.

If we can determine the slope and y-intercept of a line, we can use the slope-intercept equation, $y = mx + b$, to write an equation of the line.

EXAMPLE 1 Write an equation for the line with slope 2 that contains the point $(3, 1)$.

Use the given point $(3, 1)$ and substitute 3 for x and 1 for y in $y = mx + b$, the slope-intercept equation. Substitute 2 for m, the slope. Then solve for b.

$y = mx + b$
$1 = 2(3) + b$ Substituting
$-5 = b$ Solving for b, the y-intercept

We can substitute 2 for m and -5 for b in $y = mx + b$.

$y = mx + b$
$y = 2x - 5$

Try This Write an equation for the line that contains the given point and has the given slope.

a. $(4, 2)$, $m = 5$ $y = 5x - 18$ **b.** $(-2, 1)$, $m = -3$ $y = -3x - 5$

EXAMPLE 2 Write an equation for the line containing $(1, 3)$ and $(-2, -3)$.

$$m = \frac{\text{change in } y}{\text{change in } x} = \frac{-3-3}{-2-1} = \frac{-6}{-3} = 2$$

Choose either point and substitute for x and y in $y = mx + b$. Also substitute 2 for m, the slope. Then solve for b.

$y = mx + b$
$3 = 2(1) + b$ Substituting $(1, 3)$ for (x, y) and 2 for m
$1 = b$ Solving for b, the y-intercept

Substitute 2 for m and 1 for b in $y = mx + b$.

$y = mx + b$
$y = 2x + 1$

Try This Write an equation for the line that contains the given two points.

c. (8, 2) (2, 6) $y = -\frac{2}{3}x + \frac{22}{3}$ **d.** (− 1, 4) (−3, −5) $y = \frac{9}{2}x + \frac{17}{2}$

The Point-Slope Equation

Objective: Write an equation of a line using the point-slope equation.

Consider Example 2 again. We know that the line contains the point (1, 3). Let (x, y) represent any other point on this line. We can use the definition of slope to write the following.

$$m = \frac{\text{difference of } y\text{-coordinates}}{\text{difference of } x\text{-coordinates}} = \frac{y - 3}{x - 1}$$

We know the slope is 2. Thus we can write

$$2 = \frac{y - 3}{x - 1} \quad \text{or} \quad \frac{y - 3}{x - 1} = 2$$

If we multiply both sides by $(x - 1)$, we have

$$y - 3 = 2(x - 1) \quad \text{or} \quad y = 2x + 1$$

This last equation is satisfied by every point on the line and is the equation for the line.

Recall that we started with a line with slope 2 and containing the point (1, 3). For the point (1, 3) and slope 2, we develop the equation above.

$$\underset{y\text{-coordinate}}{y - 3} = \underset{\text{slope}}{2} \cdot \underset{x\text{-coordinate}}{(x - 1)}$$

We can state this relationship in general.

The Point-Slope Equation

A nonvertical line with slope m and containing a point (x_1, y_1) has an equation

$$y - y_1 = m(x - x_1)$$

EXAMPLE 3 Write an equation for the line with slope 3 that contains the point (5, 2). Express the equation in slope-intercept form.

$y - y_1 = m(x - x_1)$

$y - 2 = 3(x - 5)$ Substituting 3 for m and (5, 2) for (x_1, y_1)

$y - 2 = 3x - 15$ Using the distributive property

$y = 3x - 13$ Simplifying

The Point-Slope Equation

Note that the point-slope equation is derived from the slope-intercept equation. You may want students to learn one or both methods for determining the equation for a line. The direction lines do not specify which form to use.

Point out that $y - 3 = 2(x - 1)$ can be written as $-2x + y = 1$ or $2x - y = -1$.

In Example 4, emphasize that either of the two points could have been substituted.

Math Point

Any nonvertical line containing the points (x_1, y_1) and (x_2, y_2) has an equation

$$y - y_1 = \frac{y_2 - y_1}{x_2 - x_1}(x - x_1)$$

Chalkboard Examples (*T12*)

1. Write an equation for the line with slope 7 that contains the point (3, 4).
   $y - 4 = 7(x - 3)$, or
   $y - 4 = 7x - 21$
   $y = 7x - 17$
2. Write an equation for the line containing (5, 7) and (2, 6).
   First find the slope.
   $m = \frac{7 - 6}{5 - 2} = \frac{1}{3}$
   The equation is
   $y - 7 = \frac{1}{3}(x - 5)$
   $y - 7 = \frac{1}{3}x - \frac{5}{3}$
   $y = \frac{1}{3}x + \frac{16}{3}$

3. Find the slope-intercept equation of the line shown in the graph.

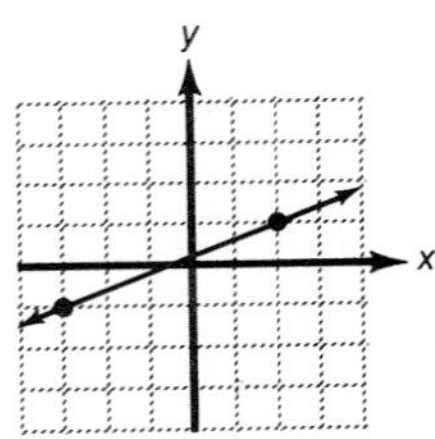

First, find any two points on the line. The points $(-3, -1)$ and $(2, 1)$ appear to lie on the line. Find the slope.

$m = \frac{2}{5}$

We next use the slope and the point $(2, 1)$ in the point-slope equation.

$y - 1 = \frac{2}{5}(x - 2)$

$y - 1 = \frac{2}{5}x - \frac{4}{5}$

$y = \frac{2}{5}x + \frac{1}{5}$

Check by noting that the slope is $\frac{2}{5}$ and the y-intercept appears to be $\frac{1}{5}$.

LESSON QUIZ

1. Write the equation of the line with slope 6 and y-intercept -5.
   $y = 6x - 5$
2. Write the slope-intercept form of the line with slope 5, containing the point $(2, 7)$.
   $y = 5x - 3$
3. Write the slope-intercept form for the line containing the points $(8, 3)$ and $(4, 1)$.
   $y = \frac{1}{2}x - 1$

Try This Write an equation for each line with the given point and slope. Express the equation in slope-intercept form.

e. $(3, 5)$, $m = 6$ $y = 6x - 13$ **f.** $(1, 4)$, $m = -\frac{2}{3}$ $y = -\frac{2}{3}x + \frac{14}{3}$

We can also use the point-slope equation to find the equation of a line if we know any two points on the line.

EXAMPLE 4 Write an equation for the line shown in the graph. Express the equation in slope-intercept form.

We first find any two points on the line. Use $(1, 1)$ and $(2, 3)$. We next find the slope.

$$m = \frac{3 - 1}{2 - 1} = \frac{2}{1} = 2$$

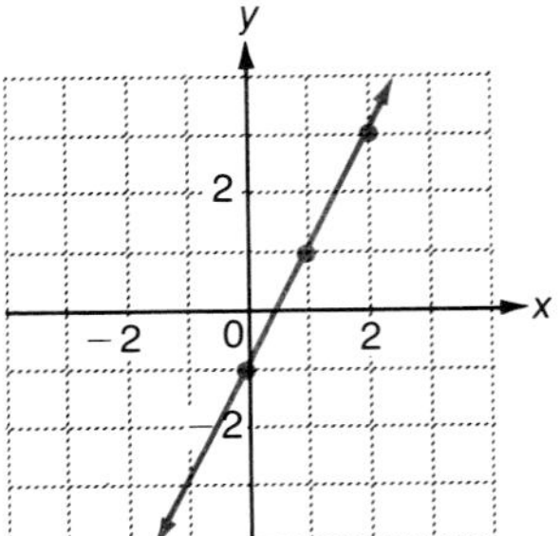

We can now use the point-slope equation to find the equation for the line. We can use either point. Using $(1, 1)$ may make the computation easier.

$$y - y_1 = m(x - x_1)$$
$$y - 1 = 2(x - 1)$$
$$y - 1 = 2x - 2$$
$$y = 2x - 1$$

Try This Write an equation for each line in slope-intercept form.

g.

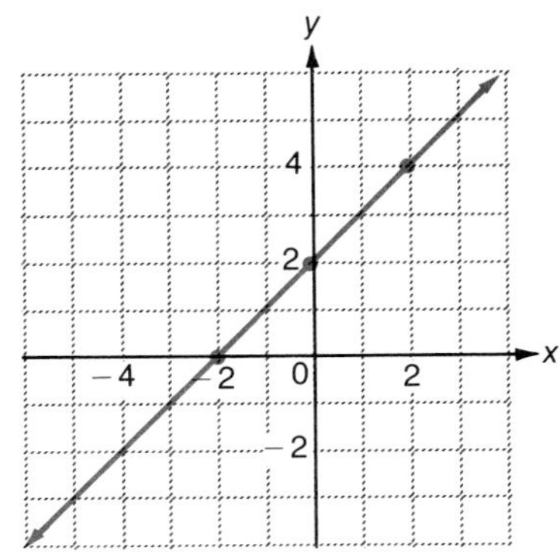

$y = x + 2$

h.

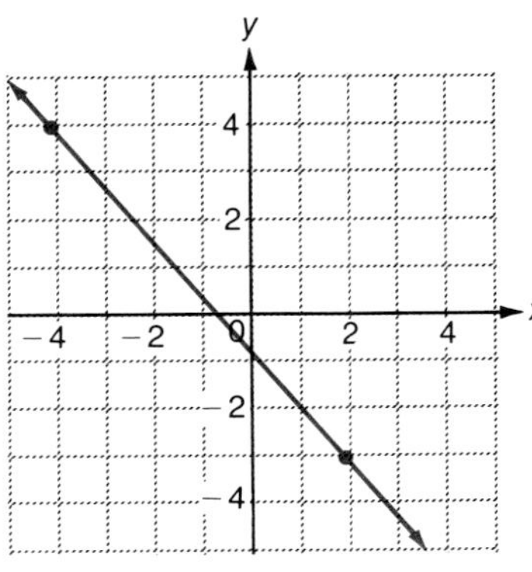

$y = -\frac{7}{6}x - \frac{2}{3}$

7-6 EXERCISES

A

Write an equation for each line with the given point and slope. Express the equation in slope-intercept form.

1. $(2, 5)$, $m = 5$
2. $(-3, 0)$, $m = -2$
3. $(2, 4)$, $m = \frac{3}{4}$
4. $\left(\frac{1}{2}, 2\right)$, $m = -1$
5. $(2, -6)$, $m = 1$
6. $(4, -2)$, $m = 6$
7. $(-3, 0)$, $m = -3$
8. $(0, 3)$, $m = -3$
9. $(4, 3)$, $m = \frac{3}{4}$
10. $(5, 6)$, $m = \frac{2}{3}$
11. $(2, 7)$, $m = \frac{5}{6}$
12. $(-2, 1)$, $m = \frac{1}{2}$
13. $(-3, -5)$, $m = -\frac{3}{5}$
14. $(-6, -2)$, $m = \frac{5}{2}$
15. $\left(-\frac{1}{2}, 0\right)$, $m = 3$

Write an equation for each line that contains the given pair of points.

16. $(-6, 1)$ $(2, 3)$
17. $(12, 16)$ $(1, 5)$
18. $(0, 4)$ $(4, 2)$
19. $(0, 0)$ $(4, 2)$
20. $(3, 2)$ $(1, 5)$
21. $(-4, 1)$ $(-1, 4)$
22. $(5, 0)$ $(0, -2)$
23. $(-2, -2)$ $(1, 3)$
24. $(-2, -4)$ $(2, -1)$
25. $(-3, 5)$ $(-1, -3)$

Write an equation for each line in slope-intercept form.

26.

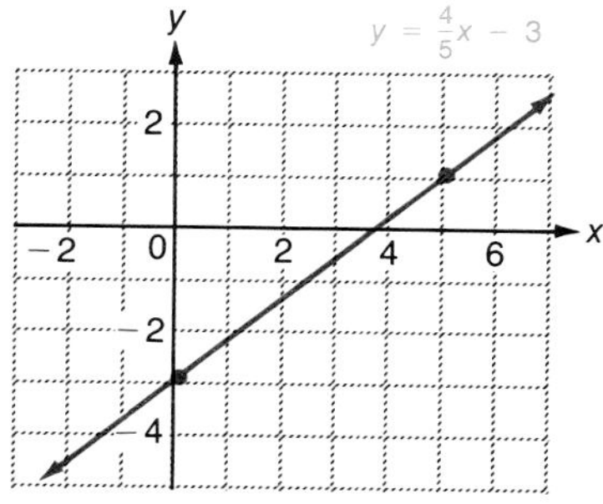

27.

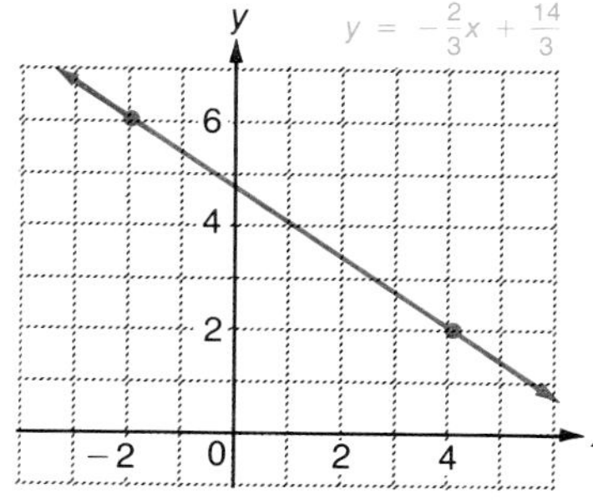

28.

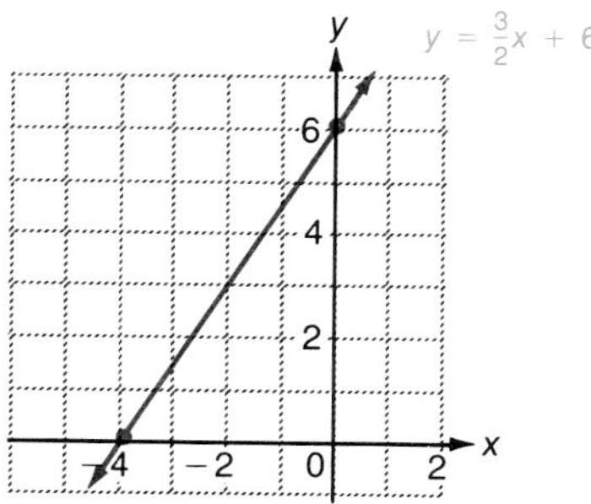

29.

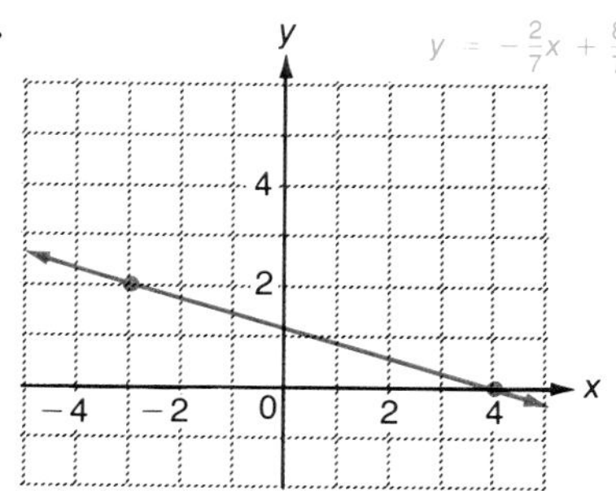

Assignment Guide

Minimum: Day 1: 1–15, e/o, assign w. 7-5
Day 2: 16–29, MR

Regular: 1–29 m3, 30–34, MR

Advanced: 1–33 m3, 34–37, MR

ADDITIONAL ANSWERS

Exercises

1. $y = 5x - 5$
2. $y = -2x - 6$
3. $y = \frac{3}{4}x + \frac{5}{2}$
4. $y = -x + \frac{5}{2}$
5. $y = x - 8$
6. $y = 6x - 26$
7. $y = -3x - 9$
8. $y = -3x + 3$
9. $y = \frac{3}{4}x$
10. $y = \frac{2}{3}x + \frac{8}{3}$
11. $y = \frac{5}{6}x + \frac{16}{3}$
12. $y = \frac{1}{2}x + 2$
13. $y = -\frac{3}{5}x - \frac{34}{5}$
14. $y = \frac{5}{2}x + 13$
15. $y = 3x + \frac{3}{2}$
16. $y = \frac{1}{4}x + \frac{5}{2}$
17. $y = x + 4$
18. $y = -\frac{1}{2}x + 4$
19. $y = \frac{1}{2}x$
20. $y = -\frac{3}{2}x + \frac{13}{2}$
21. $y = x + 5$
22. $y = \frac{2}{5}x - 2$
23. $y = \frac{5}{3}x + \frac{4}{3}$
24. $y = \frac{3}{4}x - \frac{5}{2}$
25. $y = -4x - 7$

Mixed Review

38. 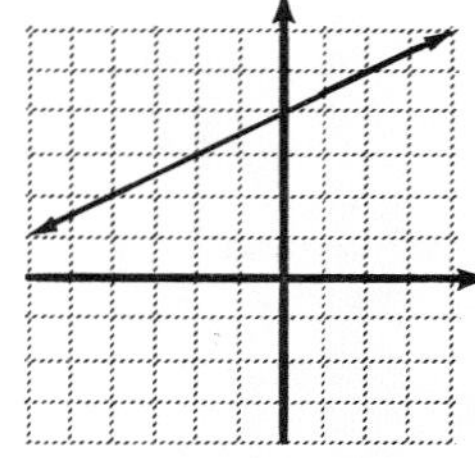

39. 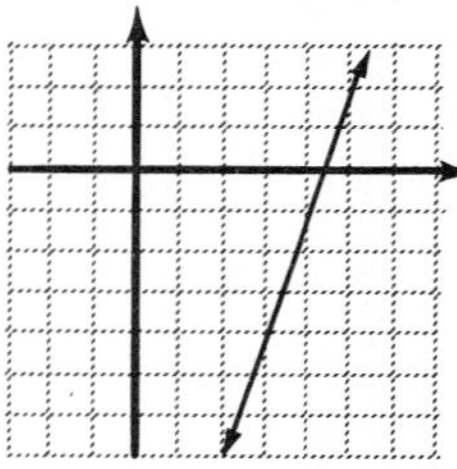

40. 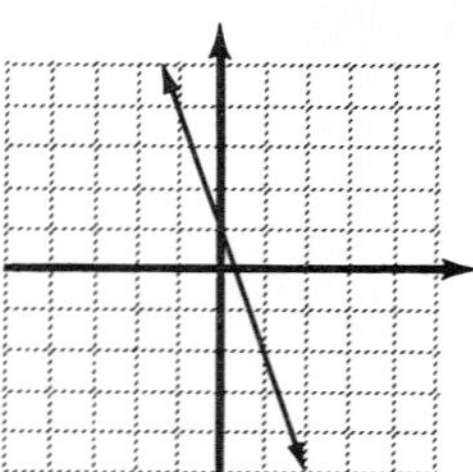

41. 163.2
42. 450
43. $-7, 7$
44. $-2, 3$
45. $-9, 4$
46. $0, -7$
47. $9, -\frac{5}{3}$
48. $\frac{4}{9}, -\frac{4}{9}$
49. $4(m-4)(m-5)$
50. $x^3(x+2)^2$
51. $(3c^2-1)(3c-1)$
52. $y(y-4)(y+2)$
53. $(xy-z)(xy+z)$
54. 4^3
55. p^2
56. 5^{12}
57. 50 million

B

30. Write an equation for the line that has the same slope as the line described by $3x - y + 4 = 0$ and contains the point $(2, -3)$. $y = 3x - 9$

31. Write an equation for the line that has the same y-intercept as the line described by $x - 3y = 6$ and contains the point $(5, -1)$. $y = \frac{1}{5}x - 2$

32. Write an equation with the same slope as $3x - 2y = 8$ and the same y-intercept as $2y + 3x = -4$. $y = \frac{3}{2}x - 2$

33. Write an equation for a line with the same slope as $2x = 3y - 1$ and containing the point $(8, -5)$. $y = \frac{2}{3}x - \frac{31}{3}$

34. ***Critical Thinking*** A line contains the points (12, 8) and (14, 9). Write an argument that would convince a classmate that the line intercepts the y-axis at the point (0, 2). Answers may vary.

Challenge

35. If the endpoints of a line segment are (x_1, y_1) and (x_2, y_2), then the coordinates of the **midpoint of the segment** are

$$\left(\frac{x_1 + x_2}{2}, \frac{y_1 + y_2}{2}\right)$$

Use this formula to find the midpoints of the segments with these endpoints.

a. $(-4, 3)$ and $(6, -9)$ $(1, -3)$ **b.** $(-4, 0)$ and $(4, 0)$ $(0, 0)$

c. $(-2, 1)$ and $(4, 3)$ $(1, 2)$ **d.** $(-4, 3)$ and $(4, -3)$ $(0, 0)$

36. Consider the triangle with vertices at (1, 4), (5, 10), and (9, 2). Form a second triangle by connecting the midpoints of the sides of the original triangle. Repeat this process to get a third triangle. What is the relationship of the slopes of the sides of the third triangle to the slopes of the sides of the original triangle? Corresponding sides have the same slope.

37. Find the y-intercept of the line containing the point (2, 5) and the midpoint of the segment with endpoints (3, 6) and $(10, -2)$. $\left(0, \frac{19}{3}\right)$

Mixed Review

Graph each line using the given information. **38.** $(-6, 1)$ and $(4, 6)$ are on the line. **39.** $m = 3$ and $(4, -1)$ is on the line.

40. slope $= -2$, y-intercept is 1 **41.** What number is 68% of 240?

42. 54 is 12% of what number?

Solve. **43.** $x^2 - 49 = 0$ **44.** $a^2 - a = 6$ **45.** $m^2 + 5m = 36$

46. $c(c + 7) = 0$ **47.** $(x - 9)(3x + 5) = 0$ **48.** $81x^2 = 16$

Factor. **49.** $4m^2 - 36m + 80$ **50.** $x^5 + 4x^4 + 4x^3$

51. $9c^3 - 3c^2 - 3c + 1$ **52.** $y^3 - 2y^2 - 8y$ **53.** $x^2y^2 - z^2$

Simplify. **54.** $\frac{4^7}{4^4}$ **55.** $\frac{p^{18}}{p^{16}}$ **56.** $(5^3)^4$

57. The population of the United States in 1980 was 225 million. This was a 350% increase over the population in 1880. What was the population in 1880?

7-7 Problem Solving: Fitting Equations to Data

Objective: Find an equation of a line that models given data.

The mathematical relationship between two variables is of interest in many real-world situations. The relationship between two variables can often be expressed as a linear equation, which is called a **model** of the situation.

EXAMPLE 1

To produce 50 copies of a school newspaper, the cost per paper is 26¢. To produce 200 newspapers, the cost per paper is 20¢. Let n be the number of copies of a school newspaper, and let c be the cost per paper. Assume that a linear relationship fits these data with ordered pairs (n, c).

(1) Find the linear equation that fits these data.

(2) Use the linear equation to predict what it would cost per paper to produce 300 copies.

■ UNDERSTAND the problem

Question: How much would it cost per paper to produce 300 copies?
Data: 50 copies cost 26¢ each; 200 copies cost 20¢ each.

Develop and carry out a PLAN

(1) Use the ordered pairs (50, 26¢) and (200, 20¢) to find the linear equation.

$$m = \frac{26 - 20}{50 - 200} = \frac{6}{-150} = -\frac{1}{25} \quad \text{Finding the slope}$$

$$c - 26 = -\frac{1}{25}(n - 50) \quad \text{Using the point-slope equation}$$

$$c - 26 = -\frac{1}{25}n + 2$$

$$c = -\frac{1}{25}n + 28$$

(2) To find the cost per paper for 300 papers, substitute 300 for n and solve for c.

$$c = -\frac{1}{25}n + 28$$

$$c = -\frac{1}{25}(300) + 28$$

$$c = -12 + 28 = 16$$

■ Find the ANSWER and CHECK

The cost to produce 300 papers is 16¢ per paper. The answer seems reasonable, since the cost decreases as the number produced increases.

7-7

FIRST FIVE MINUTES

1. Write the equation of the line with slope -2 and y-intercept 6.
   $y = -2x + 6$
2. Write the slope-intercept form of the equation for the line with slope 7 containing the point (3, 8).
   $y - 8 = 7(x - 3)$
   $y = 7x - 13$
3. Write the slope-intercept form of the equation for the line containing the points (9, 2) and (3, 5).
   The slope is $-\frac{1}{2}$.
   $y - 2 = -\frac{1}{2}(x - 9)$
   $y = -\frac{1}{2}x + \frac{13}{2}$

In real-life situations the data points will often not be collinear. We say that a linear relation exists, however, if the points tend to cluster about a straight line. Point out that there is often more than one line that approximates the fit of data.

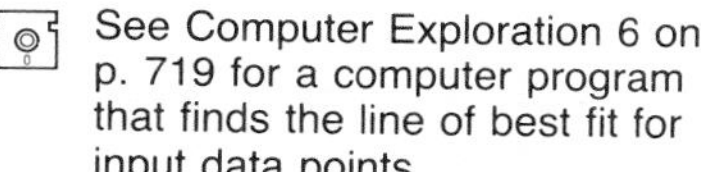
See Computer Exploration 6 on p. 719 for a computer program that finds the line of best fit for input data points.

Key Questions

What linear equation will give these values?

■

x	0	1	2	3
y	1	2	3	4

$y = x + 1$

■

x	0	1	2	3
y	0	2	4	6

$y = 2x$

Chalkboard Examples (*T13*)

1. The cost c, in dollars, of heating fuel is linearly related to the amount a delivered, in gallons. An amount of 20 gallons costs \$4. An amount of 80 gallons costs \$10. Find a linear equation that fits this data.
   The pairs of the relation will be of the form (a, c) where a is the amount and c is the corresponding cost. We know two pairs on the line, (20, 4) and (80, 10). The slope of the line is $\frac{1}{10}$. The point-slope equation is $c - 4 = \frac{1}{10}(a - 20)$. Solving for c yields

   $$c - 4 = \frac{1}{10}a - 2$$
   $$c = \frac{1}{10}a + 2$$

2. Graph the pairs (x, y). Estimate and draw the line of best fit. Find the equation of the line.

x	0	1	2	3	4	5
y	1	3	3	4	4	6

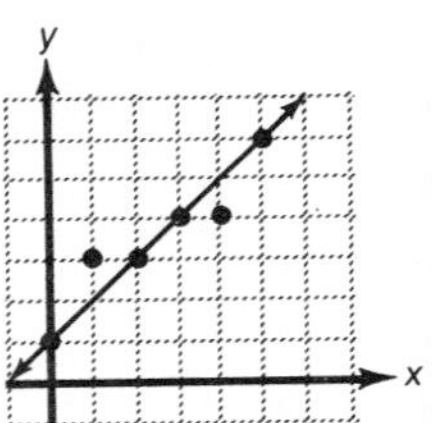

There may be variations in the students' "best" lines. The line $y = x + 1$ is one reasonable choice.

EXAMPLE 2

The chart below shows the winning times for the men's 1500-meter run at the 1952 through 1988 Olympic Games. Let o be the Olympic Game and t be the winning time in seconds.

1500-Meter Run

1952	Joseph Barthel, Luxemburg	3m. 45.2s
1956	Ron Delany, Ireland	3m. 41.2s
1960	Herb Elliott, Australia	3m. 35.6s
1964	Peter Snell, New Zealand	3m. 38.1s
1968	Kipchoge Keino, Kenya	3m. 34.9s
1972	Pekka Vasala, Finland	3m. 36.3s
1976	John Walker, New Zealand	3m. 39.17s
1980	Sebastian Coe, Great Britain	3m. 38.4s
1984	Sebastian Coe, Great Britain	3m. 32.53s
1988	Peter Rono, Kenya	3m.35.96s

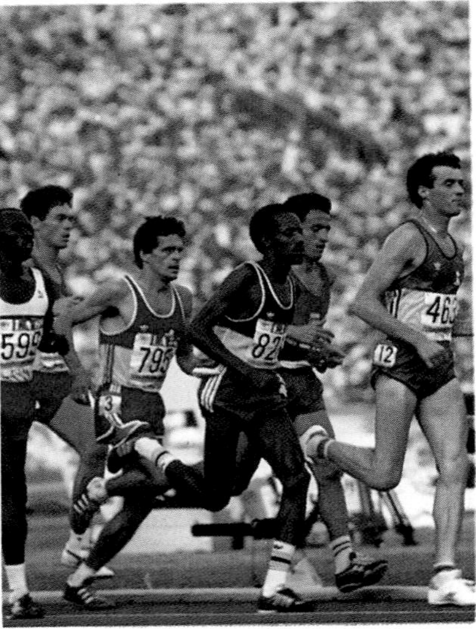

Graph the ordered pairs (o, t). Draw a line of best fit and find the equation of the line. Use the line to predict the winning times for the 1992 Olympic 1500-meter race. Check your answer against the actual results.

Olympics (o)	1	2	3	4	5	6	7	8	9	10
Time (t)	225	221	216	218	215	216	219	218	213	216

We will number the Olympic Games from 1 to 10, with 1952 being number 1. We can change the winning times to seconds in order to make plotting the points easier. 3:45.2 becomes 225 s rounded to the nearest second, and so on. When all the times are converted to seconds, we plot each ordered pair (o, t) and draw a line so that there are about the same number of points above and below the line. This is called the **line of best fit.**

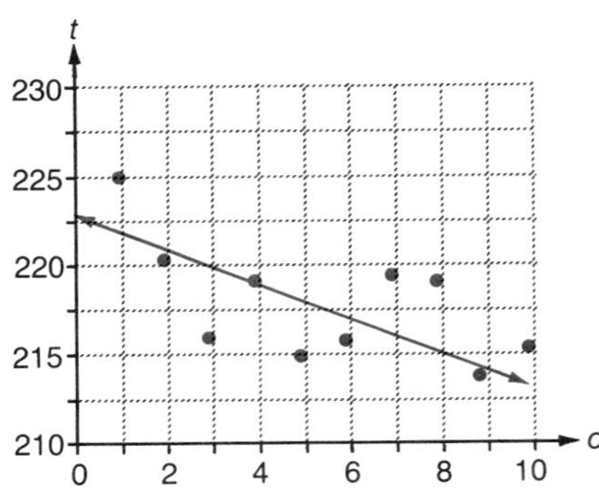

The points (4, 218) and (6, 216) are close to the line. We use these points to approximate the line.

$$m = \frac{216 - 218}{6 - 4} = -1, \text{ or a drop of 1 second per Olympics}$$

$$t - 216 = -1(o - 6)$$
$$t - 216 = -o + 6$$
$$t = -o + 222$$

Since the 1992 Olympics will be the eleventh Olympics in our set of data, we evaluate the equation for $o = 11$.

$$t = -11 + 222$$
$$t = 211$$

We can expect a winning time of about 211 seconds or 3:31 in the 1992 Olympic 1500-meter run.

Try This

a. A college record in the 100-m dash in 1950 (t) was 10.5 seconds (r). In 1980 the new record was 10.2 seconds. Assume a linear relationship fits these data with ordered pairs (t, r).
(1) Find a linear equation to fit the data points. $r = -0.01t + 30$
(2) Use the linear equation to predict the record in 1990. 10.1 s

b. Graph the ordered pairs (d, c). Draw the line of best fit and find the equation of the line. See Additional Answers.

Distance (d) in miles	10	15	20	25	30	40	50	60
Cost (c)	10	15	20	22	24	35	42	50

7-7 EXERCISES

A

Solve. Assume a linear relationship fits each set of data.

1. A long-distance telephone company advertised the following rates: "5 minutes (m) for just 85¢ (p) and 10 minutes for just \$1.10." Use the ordered pairs (m, p).
a. Find a linear equation for these data points.
b. Use this linear equation to find the cost of a 20-minute phone call.

2. A temperature of 0°C is the same as 32°F. A temperature of 10°C is the same as 50°F. Use the ordered pairs (C, F).
a. Find a linear equation for these data points.
b. Use this linear equation to find the temperature Fahrenheit when the temperature is 30°C.

3. For a ground temperature of 15°C, the air temperature (t) at an altitude of 500 m (h) is 10°C. At 2000 m, the air temperature is −5°C. Use the ordered pairs (h, t).
a. Find a linear equation for these data points. $t = -\frac{1}{100}h + 15$
b. Use this linear equation to find the air temperature at 1500 m. 0°C

LESSON QUIZ

1. A wholesale poster company sells 20 posters for \$12 and 30 posters for \$15. The relationship between the number of posters and the cost is linear. Find an equation giving cost (c) in terms of the number (n) of posters.
Let the pairs of the relation be of the form (n, c), where n is the number of posters sold and c is the cost of the posters in dollars. The pairs (20, 12) and (30, 15) satisfy the relation.
The slope of the line is $\frac{3}{10}$. The point slope equation is

$$c - 12 = \frac{3}{10}(n - 20)$$
$$c - 12 = \frac{3}{10}n - 6$$
$$c = \frac{3}{10}n + 6$$

Assignment Guide
Minimum: 1–10 e/o, MR
Regular: 1–12 e/o, 13, MR
Advanced: 1–12 e/o, 13–15, MR, assign w. Application

ADDITIONAL ANSWERS

Try This

b. Answers may vary; $c = \frac{5}{6}d$

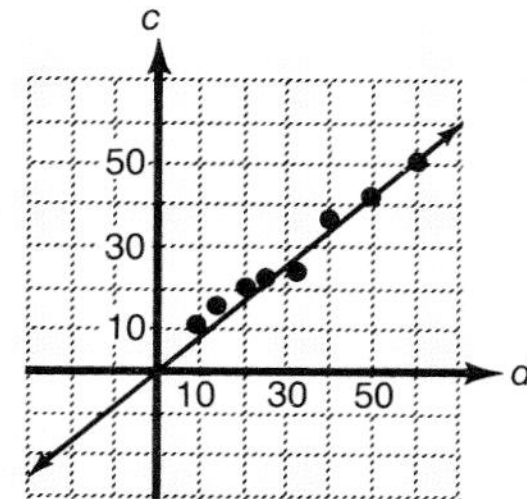

Exercises

1. a. $p = 0.05\,m + \$0.60$
b. \$1.60

2. a. $F = \frac{9}{5}C + 32$
b. 86°F

7. Answers may vary; using (10, 5) and (40, 20), $y = \frac{1}{2}d$.

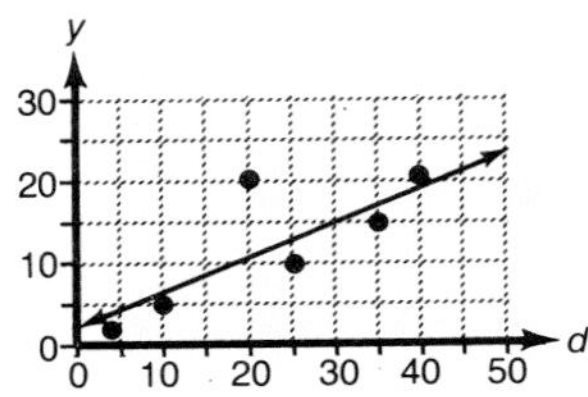

8. Answers may vary; using (2, 4) and (20, 31), $c = \frac{3}{2}m + 1$.

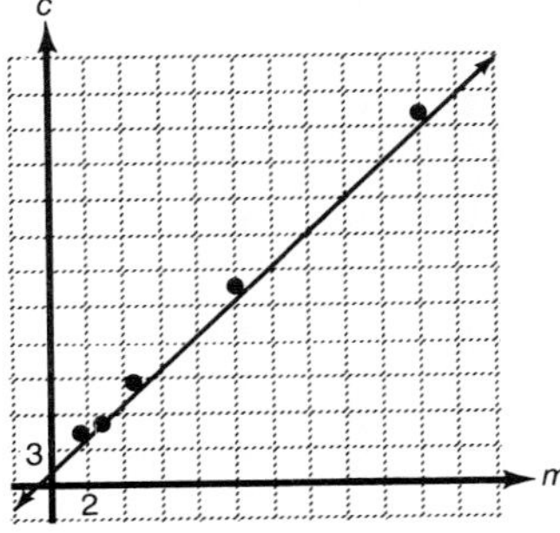

9. Answers may vary; using (3, 60) and (6, 35), $c = -\frac{25}{3}d + 85$.

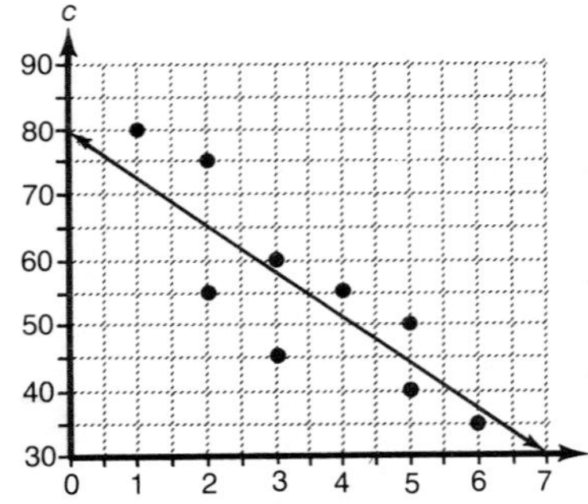

4. Scores on an achievement test (a) are related linearly to scores on another test (b). Here are two students' scores: $a = 500$, $b = 100$ and $a = 680$, $b = 127$. Use the ordered pairs (a, b).

a. Find a linear equation for these data points. $b = \frac{3}{20}a + 25$

b. Use this linear equation to predict the score on the b test for a student with a score of 700 on the a test. 130

5. A school record in a certain race in 1960 (t) was 3.8 minutes (r). In 1980 the school record was 3.65 minutes. Use the ordered pairs (t, r).

a. Find a linear equation for these data points. $r = -0.0075t + 18.5$

b. Use this linear equation to predict the school's record in 1990. 3.575

6. The total length (l) of a certain species of snake is related linearly to the tail length (t) of this snake. Here are the measurements for two snakes of this species. Snake 1: $l = 150$ mm and $t = 19$ mm; Snake 2: $l = 300$ mm and $t = 40$ mm. Use the ordered pairs (l, t).

a. Find a linear equation for these data points. $t = \frac{7}{50}l - 2$

b. Use this linear equation to predict the tail length of a snake with a total length of 200 mm. 26 mm

c. Use this linear equation to predict the tail length of a snake with a total length of 350 mm. 47 mm

7. Graph the ordered pairs (d, y). Draw the line of best fit and find an equation of the line.

Diameter of tree trunk in inches (d)	4	10	40	35	25	35	20
Age (y)	1	5	20	15	10	15	20

8. Graph the ordered pairs (m, c). Draw the line of best fit and find an equation of the line.

Miles (m)	2	3	5	10	20
Cost of a taxi (c)	\$4.00	\$5.25	\$8.50	\$16.25	\$31.00

9. A hotel owners' association compared the prices of hotel rooms in a large city. Each ordered pair represents the distance in miles a hotel is from the center of the city (d) and the cost of a hotel room for one person (c). Graph the ordered pairs (d, c). Draw the line of best fit and find an equation of the line.

Distance (d) in miles	1	2	2	3	3	4	5	5	6
Cost (c)	\$80	\$75	\$55	\$60	\$45	\$55	\$40	\$50	\$35

10. Below are some world records for the fastest speed attained on land, in miles per hour. The speed (s) is linearly related to the year. Graph the ordered pairs (y, s). Draw the line of best fit and find the equation of the line. Use the equation to estimate the record for the year 2000.

Speed	39	105	132	204	301	394	537
Year	1898	1904	1910	1927	1935	1947	1964

B

11. Solve, assuming a linear equation fits the situation. The value of a computer is \$3500. After 2 years, the value of this computer is \$2200. Find the value of the computer after 5 years. \$250

12. Solve, assuming a linear equation fits the situation. The value of a new car is \$10,000. Two years later, its value is \$7500. What will the value of this car be after 5 years? \$3750

13. ***Write a Convincing Argument*** Solve the problem below. Then write an argument to convince a classmate that your solution is correct. Solve, assuming a linear equation fits the situation. At the age of 8 years, a saguaro cactus is 7 ft high. After 20 years, the cactus is 10 ft high. Find the height of the saguaro after 200 years. 55 ft

Challenge

14. An elevator has a total capacity of 1000 kg. Suppose an average child weighs 34 kg and an average adult weighs 75 kg. Find 3 combinations of adults and children that would exceed the weight limit of this elevator.

15. The formula below gives an approximate value for the stopping distance (d) of a car traveling at speed (s), given in miles per hour.

$$d = s + \frac{s^2}{20}$$

Find 6 ordered pairs that satisfy this relationship. Graph these ordered pairs. Is the relationship linear?

Mixed Review

Find the slope of each line. **16.** $2y - 6x = 5$ **17.** $4x + y = 7$

Multiply. **18.** $(x^3 - 2)(x^2 + 2)$ **19.** $3y^3(y^2 - 2y)$ **20.** $(a^2 - 2a)^2$

Factor. **21.** $50y^4 - 72y^2$ **22.** $16 - 9m^2$ **23.** $ab + 3a - 6b - 18$

Write an equation and solve.

24. One less than the square of a number is 143.

25. The product of two consecutive integers is 110.

26. Three times the difference of the square of a number and 1 is 72.

10. Answers may vary. Using the points (1898, 39) and (1910, 132) $s = \frac{93}{12}y - \frac{176514}{12}$ Using this equation, when $y = 2000$, $s = \frac{9954}{12} = 829.5$

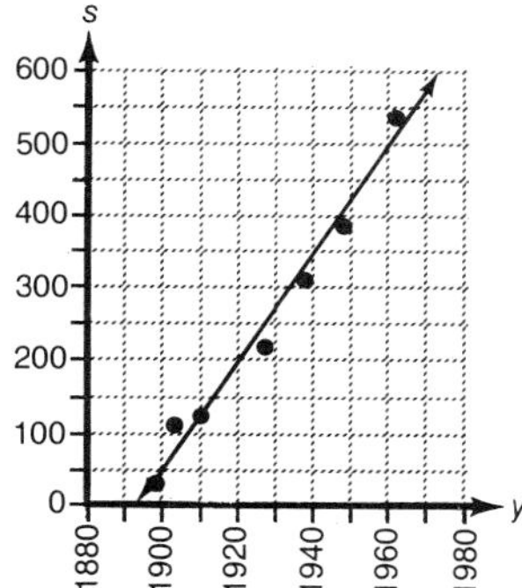

14. 8 children, 10 adults
10 children, 9 adults
4 children, 12 adults

15. $(0, 0), \left(1, \frac{21}{20}\right), \left(2, \frac{11}{5}\right), \left(3, \frac{69}{20}\right), \left(4, \frac{24}{5}\right), \left(5, \frac{25}{4}\right)$; No

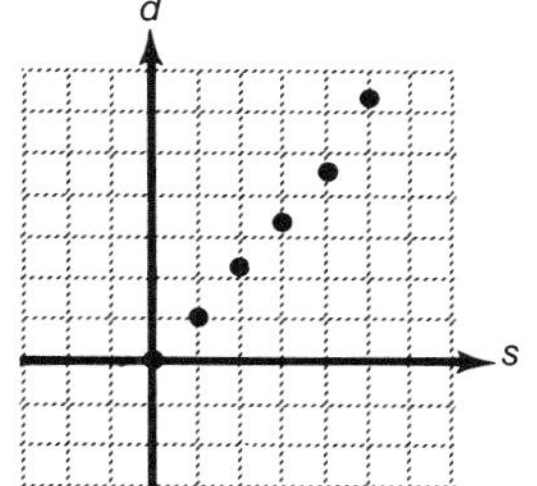

Mixed Review

16. $m = 3$
17. $m = -4$
18. $x^5 + 2x^3 - 2x^2 - 4$
19. $3y^5 - 6y^4$
20. $a^4 - 4a^3 + 4a^2$
21. $2y^2(5y + 6)(5y - 6)$
22. $(4 + 3m)(4 - 3m)$
23. $(a - 6)(b + 3)$
24. $n^2 - 1 = 143; -12, 12$
25. $n(n + 1) = 110$; 10, 11 or −11, −10
26. $3(n^2 - 1) = 72; -5, 5$

7-8

FIRST FIVE MINUTES

1. What is the slope of the line $y - 5 = \frac{1}{2}(x - 12)$? $\frac{1}{2}$
2. Write the equation of the line with slope 7 and y-intercept 8. $y = 7x + 8$
3. Write the equation of the line with slope $-\frac{1}{7}$ and y-intercept 8. $y = -\frac{1}{7}x + 8$

EXPLORE

You may want to have students graph these equations using a computer or graphing calculator.

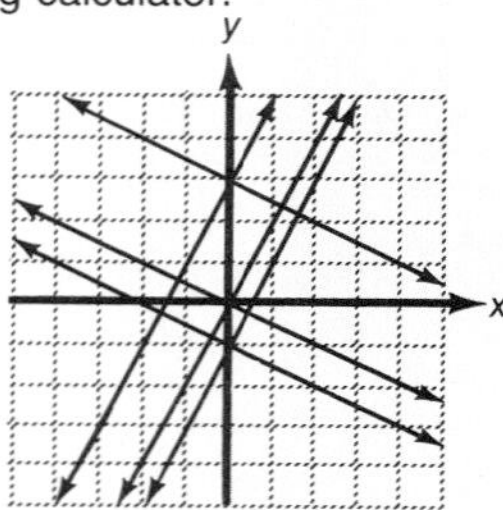

Students should have an intuitive understanding of the words *parallel* and *perpendicular* and should recognize their presence in the graph.

See Computer Exploration 7 on p. 720 for further exploration of parallel and perpendicular lines.

Parallel Lines (*T*14)

Key Question

- What are some common examples of parallel lines? The dividing lines on a freeway, train tracks, opposite edges of a rectangular table, etc.

Chalkboard Example

1. Determine whether these lines are parallel or not. $y - 2 = 5x + 4$ and $-15x + 3y = 9$
   The first line may be rewritten $y = 5x + 6$
   The second line may be rewritten $3y = 15x + 9$
   $y = 5x + 3$
   The two lines both have slope 5, and they have different y-intercepts. They are parallel.

7-8 Parallel and Perpendicular Lines

Master Grapher Worksheet 5 can be used with this lesson.

Explore

Graph the following equations on the same set of axes.

$y = 2x$ $\quad$ $y = 2x + 3$ $\quad$ $y = 2x - 1$

$y = -\frac{1}{2}x$ $\quad$ $y = -\frac{1}{2}x + 3$ $\quad$ $y = -\frac{1}{2}x - 1$

What patterns do you see?

Parallel Lines

Objective: Determine whether the graphs of two equations are parallel.

Parallel lines are lines in the same plane that never intersect. Nonvertical lines are *parallel* if they have the same slope and different y-intercepts.

The graphs at the right are for the linear equations $y = 2x + 5$ and $y = 2x - 3$. The slope of each line is 2. The coordinates of the y-intercepts are 5 and -3. The lines are parallel.

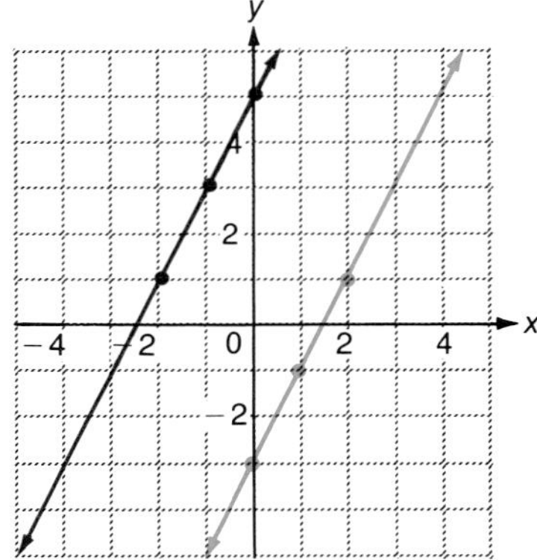

EXAMPLE 1 Determine whether the graphs of $y = -3x + 4$ and $6x + 2y = -10$ are parallel lines.

We first solve each equation for y.

$$y = -3x + 4 \qquad 6x + 2y = -10$$
$$2y = -6x - 10$$
$$y = -3x - 5$$

The graphs of these lines have the same slope and different y-intercepts. Thus the lines are parallel.

Try This Determine whether the graphs are parallel lines.

a. $3x - y = -5$ and $5y - 15x = 10$ Yes

b. $4y = -12x + 16$ and $y = 3x + 4$ No

Perpendicular Lines

Objective: Determine whether the graphs of two equations are perpendicular.

Perpendicular lines are lines in the same plane that intersect to form a 90° angle (a right angle).

> **Perpendicular Lines**
>
> Two lines are perpendicular if the product of their slopes is -1.

In the graphs of the linear equations at the right, the slopes are 2 and $-\frac{1}{2}$. The product of the slopes is -1. The lines are perpendicular.

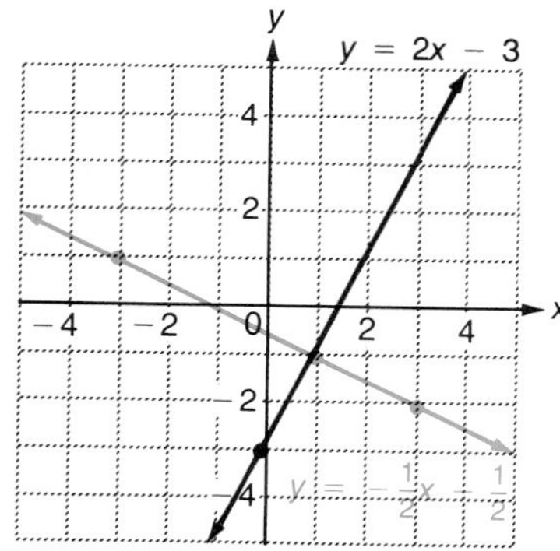

EXAMPLE 2 Determine whether the graphs of $3y = 9x + 3$ and $6y + 2x = 6$ are perpendicular lines.

We first solve for y in each equation to find the slopes.

$$3y = 9x + 3 \qquad 6y + 2x = 6$$
$$y = 3x + 1 \qquad 6y = -2x + 6$$
$$y = -\frac{1}{3}x + 1$$

The slopes are 3 and $-\frac{1}{3}$.

$$3\left(-\frac{1}{3}\right) = -1$$

The product of the slopes of these lines is -1. Thus the lines are perpendicular.

Try This Determine whether the graphs of the equations are perpendicular lines.

c. $2y - x = 2$ and $y = -2x + 4$ Yes

d. $4y = 3x + 12$ and $-3x + 4y - 2 = 0$ No

Perpendicular Lines (*T*14)

Use "perpendicular" informally before introducing the formal definition. You may want to review angle measure before this lesson.

Key Questions

- How many degrees in a right angle? 90 degrees
- What are some common examples of perpendicular lines? Adjacent edges of a table, the floor line at a corner, the edges of a piece of paper, etc.

Chalkboard Example (*T14*)

1. Determine whether the graphs of these lines are perpendicular or not.

   $y = \frac{1}{3}x + 7$ and

   $y = -3x - 7$

   The lines are perpendicular since the product of $\frac{1}{3}$ and -3 equals -1.

LESSON QUIZ

Determine whether the following pairs of lines are parallel, perpendicular, or neither.

1. $y - 2 = 4x + 6$
   $2y = 8(x + 1)$
   The lines are parallel.
2. $y = 3x - 9$
   $x + y = 7$
   The lines are neither parallel nor perpendicular.
3. $y = 4x + 2$
   $4y = -x + 12$
   The lines are perpendicular.

Assignment Guide
Minimum: 1–25 e/o, MR

Regular: 1–29 e/o, 30, MR

Advanced: 1–29 m4, 30–37, MR, assign w. 7-9

ADDITIONAL ANSWERS

Exercises

30. $ax + by = d$; $-bx + ay = c$

7-8 EXERCISES

A

Determine whether the graphs of the equations are parallel lines.

1. $x + 4 = y$
$y - x = -3$ Yes

2. $3x - 4 = y$
$y - 3x = 8$ Yes

3. $y + 3 = 6x$
$-6x - y = 2$ No

4. $y = -4x + 2$
$-5 = -2y + 8x$ No

5. $y = 2x + 7$
$5y + 10x = 20$ No

6. $y = -7x - 5$
$2y = -7x - 10$ No

7. $3x - y = -9$
$2y - 6x = -2$ Yes

8. $y - 6 = -6x$
$-2x + y = 5$ No

9. $-3x + y = 4$
$3x - y = -6$ Yes

10. $-4 = y + 2x$
$6x + 3y = 4$ Yes

11. $8x - 4y = 16$
$5y - 10x = 3$ Yes

12. $-4x = 3y + 5$
$8x + 6y = -1$ Yes

Determine whether the graphs of the equations are perpendicular lines.

13. $y = -4x + 3$
$4y + x = -1$ No

14. $y = -\frac{2}{3}x + 4$
$3x + 2y = 1$ No

15. $x + y = 6$
$4y - 4x = 12$ Yes

16. $2x - 5y = -3$
$5x + 2y = 6$ Yes

17. $y = -x + 8$
$x - y = -1$ Yes

18. $2x + 6y = -3$
$12y = 4x + 20$ No

19. $6x + y = -4$
$6x - y = 4$ No

20. $4y = x + 5$
$9y + 3x = 2$ No

21. $6y - x = -12$
$\frac{1}{6}x + y = 3$ No

22. $\frac{2}{3}x + y = 6$
$8y - 12x - 12 = 0$ Yes

23. $\frac{2}{5}x - \frac{1}{10}y = 20$
$5x + 10y = -5$ No

24. $\frac{1}{2}x + \frac{3}{4}y = 6$
$-\frac{3}{2}x + y = 4$ Yes

25. $\frac{3}{8}x - \frac{y}{2} = 1$
$\frac{4}{3}x - y + 1 = 0$ No

B

26. Write an equation of the line containing the point (0, 6) and parallel to the line $y - 3x = 4$. $y = 3x + 6$

27. Write an equation of the line containing the point (−2, 4) and parallel to the line $y = 2x - 3$. $y = 2x + 8$

28. Write an equation of the line containing the point (0, 2) and perpendicular to the line $3y - x = 0$. $y = -3x + 2$

29. Write an equation of the line containing the point (1, 0) and perpendicular to the line $2x + y = -4$. $y = \frac{1}{2}x - \frac{1}{2}$

30. ***Critical Thinking*** Write an equation of a line parallel to $ax + by = c$ and an equation of a line perpendicular to $ax + by = c$.

Challenge

Answers may vary.

31. Graph two lines that are parallel. Give the equations of these lines.

32. Graph two lines that are perpendicular. Give the equations of these lines. Answers may vary.

33. Graph the line $y = 4x + 2$. Give the equations of three other lines that together with the line $y = 4x + 2$ would form a rectangle. Graph your rectangle. Answers may vary.

34. Find the value of k so that the graphs of $4y = kx - 6$ and $5x + 20y = 12$ are parallel. -1

35. Using the same equations as in Exercise 34, find the value of k so that the graphs are perpendicular. 16

Assume each pair of lines is perpendicular. Find the equation for each line.

36.

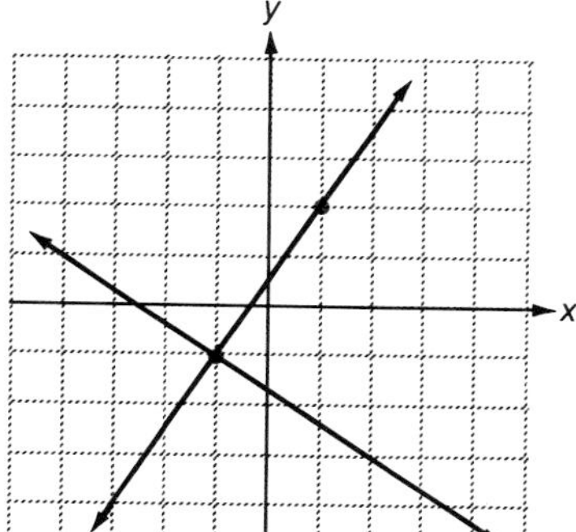

37.

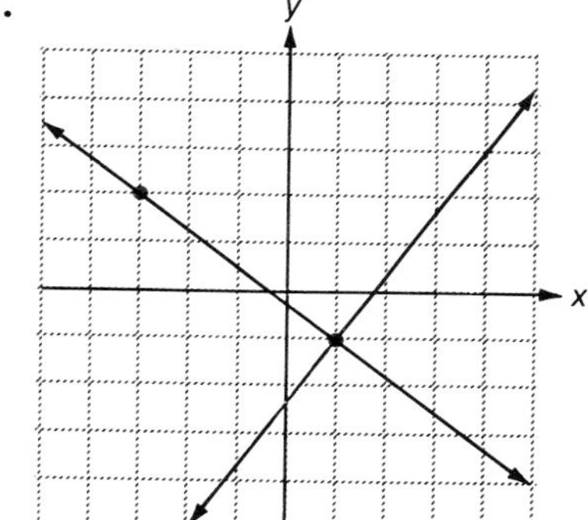

Mixed Review

Find the slope and y-intercept of each line. **38.** $y = 3x + 5$

39. $2x + 4y = 5$ **40.** $6x = 2y + 3$ **41.** $6x = 3y - 2$

42. $5y - 3x = 15$ **43.** $2x = 3y + 4$ **44.** $3x + 4y = 8$

Write an equation in slope-intercept form for each line with the given slope and point. **45.** $(1, 3)$, $m = -2$ **46.** $(-1, 4)$, $m = 9$

Factor. **47.** $9a^2 - 49b^2$ **48.** $5x^2 + 70x + 245$

49. $2m^3 + 3m^2 - 18m - 27$ **50.** $3x^2 - 3x - 90$

Simplify. **51.** $(3t^3)^2$ **52.** $(4ab^2c)(3abc^3)$ **53.** $(2x^2yz)(3x^3yz^2)$

54. $(y + 11)(y - 11) + 121$ **55.** $(2x + y)(3x + 3y)$

Problem for Programmers

Write a program that will find the slope of a line that contains any two given pairs of points, (x_1, y_1) and (x_2, y_2). Use the exercises in this lesson to test your program.

36. $2y - 3x = 1$
$3y + 2x = -5$

37. $4y + 3x = -1$
$3y - 4x = -7$

Mixed Review

38. $m = 3, b = 5$

39. $m = -\frac{1}{2}, b = \frac{5}{4}$

40. $m = 3, b = -\frac{3}{2}$

41. $m = 2, b = \frac{2}{3}$

42. $m = \frac{3}{5}, b = 3$

43. $m = \frac{2}{3}, b = -\frac{4}{3}$

44. $m = -\frac{3}{4}, b = 2$

45. $y = -2x + 5$

46. $y = 9x + 13$

47. $(3a - 7b)(3a + 7b)$

48. $5(x + 7)^2$

49. $(2m + 3)(m + 3)(m - 3)$

50. $3(x - 6)(x + 5)$

51. $9t^6$

52. $12a^2b^3c^4$

53. $6x^5y^2z^3$

54. y^2

55. $6x^2 + 9xy + 3y^2$

Problem For Programmers

This program can be written using any programming language (BASIC, PASCAL, LOGO, etc.).

This program can also be written on a spreadsheet where each coordinate is input in a separate column and the slope is computed in another column.

7-9

FIRST FIVE MINUTES

Find the slope and y-intercept of the graph of each equation.

1. $2x - 3y = 6$ $m = \frac{2}{3}, b = -2$
2. $2x - y = 1$ $m = 2, b = -1$
3. $4y = 2x + 9$ $m = \frac{1}{2}, b = \frac{9}{4}$

Note that constructing a proof is somewhat like putting together a jigsaw puzzle. It always helps to have the completed picture in front of you as a goal.

Key Questions

In the point-slope equation $y - y_1 = m(x - x_1)$,

- what does m represent? Slope of the graph of the equation
- what do x_1 and y_1 represent? They are the first and second coordinates of any point on the graph of the equation.

Chalkboard Example

1. Prove that the graph of an equation of the form $\frac{x}{a} + \frac{y}{b} = 1$ crosses the x-axis at $(a, 0)$ and crosses the y-axis at $(0, b)$.
   Solve for y.
   $$\frac{x}{a} + \frac{y}{b} = 1$$
   $$bx + ay = ab$$
   $$ay = -bx + ab$$
   $$y = \frac{-b}{a}x + b$$
   The y-intercept is b; therefore, the line crosses the y-axis at the point $(0, b)$.
   Set $y = 0$, $x = a$. The line crosses the x-axis at $(a, 0)$.

LESSON QUIZ

1. Prove that the slope of the line $Ax + By = C$, $B \neq 0$, is $-\frac{A}{B}$.
   Solve for y.
   $$By = -Ax + C$$
   $$y = -\frac{A}{B}x + \frac{C}{B}$$
   This is the slope-intercept equation of the line, so $m = -\frac{A}{B}$, where $B \neq 0$.

7-9 Proofs

(Optional)

Objective: Prove theorems related to slope.

A proof is a convincing argument that a statement is true. Before beginning to write a proof, we must organize our ideas and see exactly what we want to prove.

We have stated that in the equation $y = mx + b$, m is the slope. Before writing a proof of this statement, we must think about what it means to prove that m is the slope. We know the definition of slope.

$$\text{slope} = \frac{\text{change in } y}{\text{change in } x}$$

We must show that the m-value in $y = mx + b$ is also $\frac{\text{change in } y}{\text{change in } x}$.

Proof

Consider any linear equation $y = mx + b$. Suppose that (x_1, y_1) and (x_2, y_2) are any two points on the line. Then, since each of these points must satisfy the equation, we have the two equations

$$y_2 = mx_2 + b \quad \text{and} \quad y_1 = mx_1 + b$$

(Our strategy will be to work with these two equations and to try to show $m = \frac{(y_2 - y_1)}{(x_2 - x_1)}$.)

From the second equation we know that y_1 and $mx_1 + b$ are the same number. Thus $-y_1$ and $-(mx_1 + b)$ are also the same number. We add this number to both sides of the first equation.

$$y_2 - y_1 = (mx_2 + b) - (mx_1 + b)$$
$$y_2 - y_1 = mx_2 - mx_1 \quad \text{Simplifying}$$
$$y_2 - y_1 = m(x_2 - x_1) \quad \text{Factoring out } m$$
$$\frac{y_2 - y_1}{x_2 - x_1} = m \quad \text{Solving for } m$$

Since $\frac{y_2 - y_1}{x_2 - x_1}$ is the $\frac{\text{change in } y}{\text{change in } x}$ for the given two points, then the m-value in $y = mx + b$ is the slope.

Try This

a. Write a proof to show that in the equation $y = mx + b$, b is the y-intercept. (Hint: Think about what is true of a y-intercept.)
See Additional Answers.

We have also stated that a horizontal line has slope 0. Before we begin to write the proof, we think about horizontal lines. On any horizontal line, each point has the same y-coordinate. This is the key to the proof.

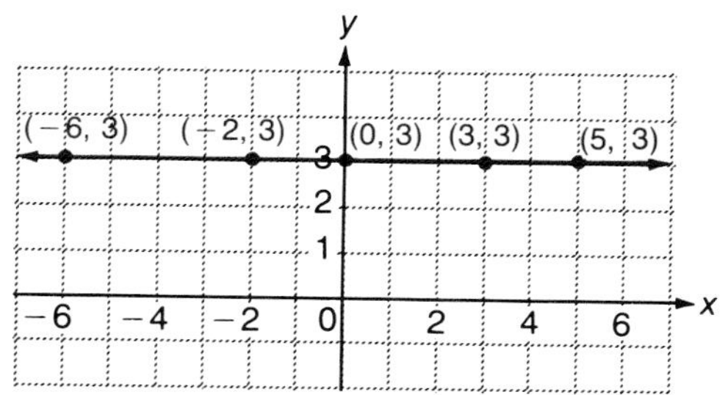

Proof

Consider any horizontal line. Suppose that (x_1, y_1) and (x_2, y_2) are any two points on the line. Then the slope of the line is

$$\frac{y_2 - y_1}{x_2 - x_1}$$

Since the y-coordinates are the same,

$$\frac{y_2 - y_1}{x_2 - x_1} = \frac{0}{x_2 - x_1} = 0$$

Try This

b. Prove that a vertical line has no slope. (Hint: Think about the coordinates of the points on a vertical line and division by 0.) See Additional Answers.

7-9 EXERCISES

A

1. Prove the point-slope equation theorem. (Hint: Suppose (x, y) is any other point on the line. Then the slope of the line is $\frac{y - y_1}{x - x_1}$.)
2. Prove that if a line has slope m and y-intercept b, then an equation of the line is $y = mx + b$. (Hint: Use the point-slope equation theorem.)

Mixed Review

Identify the degree of each term and the degree of the polynomial.
3. $c^2 - 25$ **4.** $3a^4b^2 + 21b^4 - 11a$ **5.** $a^3b^2c - 4c^3$

Give the additive inverse. **6.** $ax^2 + bx + c$ **7.** $35 - 8c$ **8.** $y - 9$

Find three factorizations for each monomial. **9.** $3a^3$ **10.** $15a^2b$

Find three solutions of the equation. **11.** $4y - x = 1$

Factor. **12.** $4a^2b + 2a$ **13.** $4y^2 - 9$ **14.** $10c^2 + 28c - 6$

Assignment Guide
Minimum: Omit

Regular: Omit

Advanced: 1, 2, MR, assign w. 7-8

ADDITIONAL ANSWERS

Try This

a. The y-intercept of a line is the point where the line crosses the y-axis. Thus, the x-coordinate of the point is zero. Let $x = 0$ in the equation $y = mx + b$. $y = m \cdot 0 + b, y = 0 + b, y = b$ Thus, b is the y-intercept.

b. Suppose that (x_1, y_1) and (x_2, y_2) are any two points on a vertical line. The slope of the line is $\frac{y_2 - y_1}{x_2 - x_1}$. Since the line is vertical, the x-coordinates are the same, so the slope is $\frac{y_2 - y_1}{0}$. Division by 0 is not allowed, so the line has no slope.

Exercises

For Exercises 1 and 2, see Teacher's Answer Section.

Mixed Review

3. 2, 0; 2 **4.** 6, 4, 1; 6
5. 6, 3; 6
6. $-ax^2 - bx - c$
7. $-35 + 8c$ **8.** $-y + 9$
9. Answers may vary. $3(a^3)$, $(3a)(a^2)$, $(3a^2)(a)$, etc.
10. Answers may vary. $(3)(5a)(ab)$, $(5a^2)(3b)$, $(a^2)(15b)$, etc.
11. Answers may vary. $\left(-4, -\frac{3}{4}\right)$, $(3, 1)$, $\left(4, \frac{5}{4}\right)$, etc.
12. $2a(2ab + 1)$
13. $(2y + 3)(2y - 3)$
14. $2(c + 3)(5c - 1)$

7-10

FIRST FIVE MINUTES

1. Finish the list.
   $1^3 = 1$
   $2^3 = 3 + 5$
   $3^3 = 7 + 9 +$ ___
   $4^3 = 13 +$ ___ $+$ ___ $+$ ___
   11, 15, 17, 19
   (Look for a Pattern)
2. What whole number squared is closest to 300?
   17
   (Guess, Check, Revise)

Simplify the Problem

Emphasize that complicated problems are very often solved by looking at simpler problems first. Engineers and mathematicians solve very complex problems by this procedure. Devising a simple problem that relates directly to the complex one is crucial, and so is the organization of steps going from the simple to the complex.

Show students that in problems like the example, once they see a *pattern* in the simple problems, they can use it to devise a formula for solving the complex problem. Instead of filling out the table for every number of buildings up to 10, they can use the formula to "jump ahead" to a solution.

Key Question

- If you know how many lines it takes to connect n buildings, how would you find how many lines it takes to connect $n + 1$ buildings?
  Add n to the number of lines it takes to connect n buildings.

7-10 Problem Solving: Strategies

Simplify the Problem

Objective: Solve problems using the strategy *Simplify the Problem* and other strategies.

A problem that may seem difficult because of the large numbers involved can be solved more easily using a strategy called **Simplify the Problem.** A problem can be *simplified* by substituting smaller numbers. You may need to solve a series of simpler problems, each one with progressively larger numbers. Organizing the information in a *table* can help you find a pattern and the solution to the original problem.

EXAMPLE

How many phone lines are needed to connect the 10 buildings at the right? A separate line must be used to connect each pair of buildings.

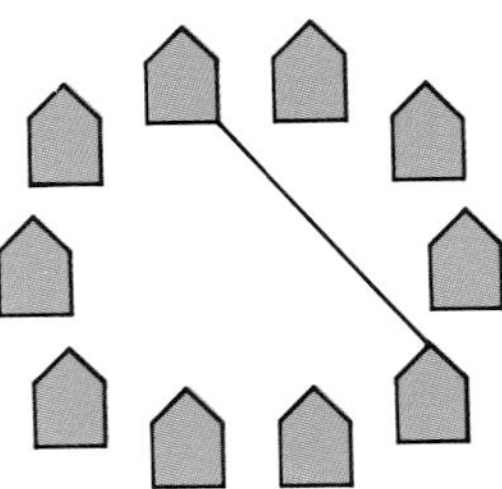

Simplify the problem by determining how many lines are needed to connect 2 buildings, then 3 buildings, and so on. *Drawing a diagram, making a table,* and *looking for a pattern* are other strategies used.

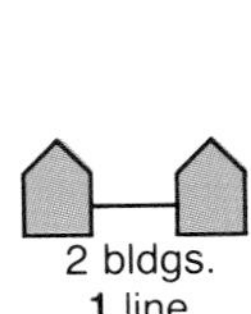

2 bldgs.
1 line

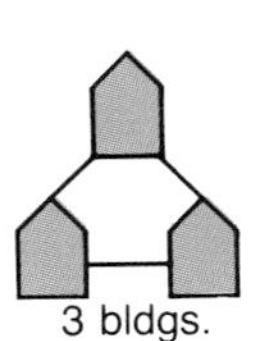

3 bldgs.
3 lines

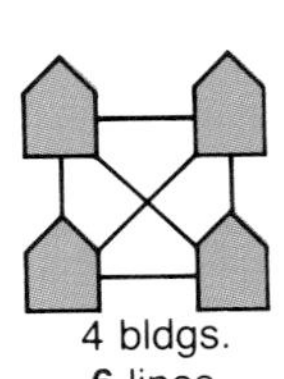

4 bldgs.
6 lines

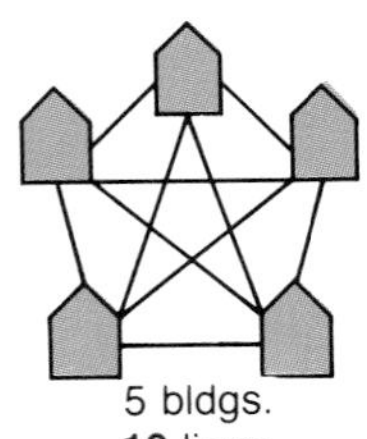

5 bldgs.
10 lines

Number of buildings	Number of lines
2	1
3	$3 = 1 + 2$
4	$6 = 1 + 2 + 3$
5	$10 = 1 + 2 + 3 + 4$

Organizing the data in the table helps you see a *pattern.* For n buildings, there will be a total of $1 + 2 + 3 + \ldots + (n - 1)$ lines. Thus for 10 buildings there will be a total of $1 + 2 + 3 + \ldots + 9 = 45$ lines.

Problem-Solving Strategies		
Draw a Diagram	Guess, Check, Revise	Write an Equation
Make an Organized List	Use Logical Reasoning	Make a Table
Look for a Pattern	Simplify the Problem	Work Backward

7-10 PROBLEMS

Solve using one or more of the strategies.

1. The figure at the right was made with 4 triangles. An architect made a figure like this using 70 triangles. Each side of each triangle is 1 meter long. What is the perimeter of the figure made with 70 triangles?

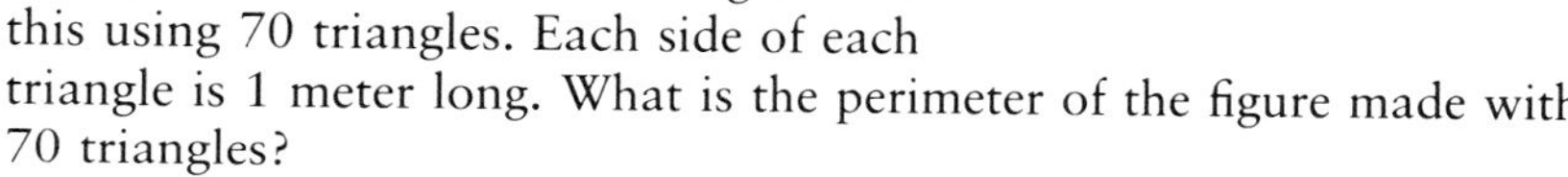

2. There were 12 teams in a soccer tournament. When a team lost, it was eliminated from the tournament and it played no more games. How many games were needed to determine a champion?
3. Three men and three women signed up for a mixed-doubles tennis tournament. In mixed doubles a team consists of 1 man and 1 woman. How many different matches could be made with different mixed-doubles teams?
4. A bank has checkbook covers that are either pocket or desk size. The covers can be orange, black, red, or tan. The customer's name will be stamped on the cover in gold or silver. How many different choices are available for checkbook covers?
5. Half of all baseball fans in a survey are also soccer fans. Half of all football fans in this survey are also baseball fans. No football fan is a soccer fan. All soccer fans are also baseball fans. There are 20 soccer fans and 30 football fans in this survey. How many baseball fans are neither soccer fans nor football fans?
6. The Windsville Park District used a pneumatic pump to fill a reservoir from a nearby river. Each day the pump raised the water level 2 m, but at night the water leaked back into the river and the level of the reservoir dropped 50 cm. At this rate, how many days did it take the pump to fill the reservoir to a height of 15 m?
7. ***Write a Convincing Argument*** Solve the problem below. Then write an argument that would convince a classmate that your solution is correct.

   How many different squares are there in a 7-by-7 grid?

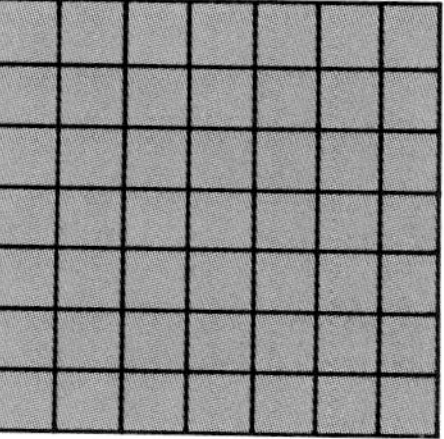

Chalkboard Example

1. Suppose you are stacking pennies in a pyramid with a triangular base. How many pennies would you need to make a pyramid that is 10 levels tall?

   Simplify the problem by finding how many pennies you need for a smaller pyramid. Then look for a pattern.

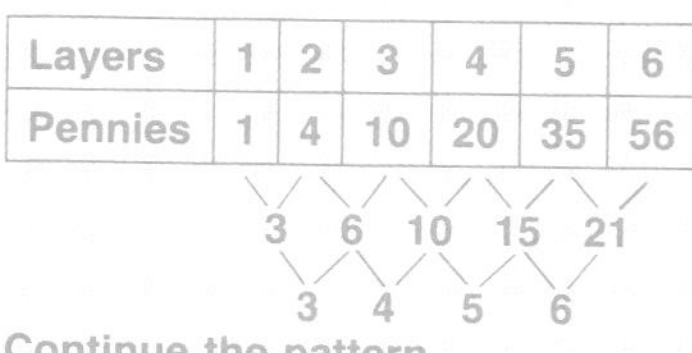

Layers	1	2	3	4	5	6
Pennies	1	4	10	20	35	56

3 6 10 15 21

3 4 5 6

Continue the pattern.

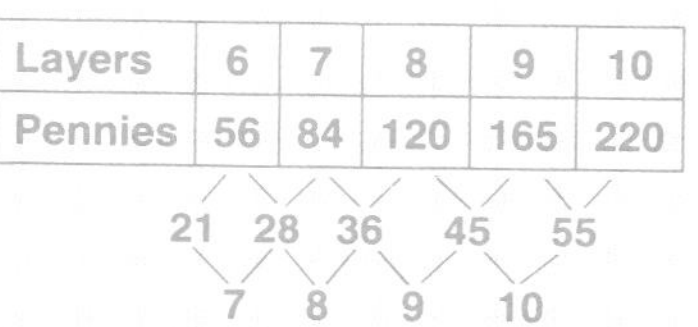

Layers	6	7	8	9	10
Pennies	56	84	120	165	220

21 28 36 45 55

7 8 9 10

A pyramid with 10 layers needs 220 pennies.

Hints for Problems

1. Simplify the problem. What would the perimeter be using 1 triangle? 2 triangles? Look for a pattern.
2. Simplify the problem. How many games would be needed if there were 1 team? 2 teams? 3 teams?
3. Make an organized list of couple combinations and an organized list of match combinations.
4. Make an organized list of different choices.
5. Draw a diagram to represent the number of people in each club. (A Venn diagram might help.)
6. Simplify the problem by finding how much the level changes each day.
7. Simplify the problem. How many squares in a 1 × 1 grid? a 2 × 2 grid? a 3 × 3 grid?

ANSWERS

1. The perimeter would be 72.
2. 11 games are needed.
3. 18 different matches could be played.
4. There are 16 possible checkbook covers.
5. Five baseball fans are neither soccer fans nor football fans.
6. The pump takes 10 days to raise the water level to 15 m.
7. There are 140 different squares.

Problem Solving: Application

For this computation, students will need to use calculators with power keys (usually x^y). Note that their answers will vary slightly because of differences in rounding and display capabilities on various calculators. Emphasize the importance of keeping as many digits as possible when doing calculations with large powers.

The answers to the problems can be the basis of an interesting discussion. Note that the greater the frequency of compounding, the greater the total becomes; but the increases get smaller and smaller. As you increase the number of compounding periods, the amount gets closer and closer to an amount found by *continuous compounding,* in this case $12,460.77.

Most banks advertise *nominal interest rates* that are compounded daily, then give the *effective annual yield* or *annual percentage rate,* a rate that can be used to find the annual yield by a simple interest formula (compounding once a year). The Problem Solving: Application lesson in Chapter 13 includes a formula for determining the effective annual yield, given interest rate and frequency of compounding.

ANSWERS

Answers may vary—see notes above.

a. $10{,}000\left(1 + \frac{0.11}{1}\right)^{2 \cdot 1} = \$12{,}321$

b. $10{,}000\left(1 + \frac{0.11}{2}\right)^{2 \cdot 2} = \$12{,}388.25$

c. $10{,}000\left(1 + \frac{0.11}{4}\right)^{2 \cdot 4} = \$12{,}423.81$

d. $10{,}000\left(1 + \frac{0.11}{12}\right)^{2 \cdot 12} = \$12{,}448.29$

e. $10{,}000\left(1 + \frac{0.11}{365}\right)^{2 \cdot 365} = \$12{,}460.35$

f. $10{,}000\left(1 + \frac{0.11}{24 \cdot 365}\right)^{2 \cdot 24 \cdot 365}$ $\approx \$12{,}460.72$

Problem Solving: Application

Compound Interest

Interest is a charge for the use of money. When you borrow money, either by taking out a loan or by making purchases on a credit card or installment plan, you pay interest to the lender. When you put money in a savings account, the bank pays you interest for the use of your money. The amount invested or loaned is called the **principal.** The **interest rate** is given as a percent. Simple interest is interest computed on the principal alone. Today, we deal mostly with **compound interest,** or interest figured on both the principal and previously accumulated interest. Compound interest is found by the following formula.

$$A = P\left(1 + \frac{r}{n}\right)^{nt}$$

where principal P is invested at interest rate r compounded n times per year; in t years it will grow to amount A. The number nt is the total number of payment periods.

Suppose you invest $1000 at 8% interest. How much will be in the account at the end of 3 years if interest is compounded

a. annually? **b.** quarterly? **c.** daily?

a. $$A = P\left(1 + \frac{r}{n}\right)^{nt} = \$1000\left(1 + \frac{0.08}{1}\right)^{3}$$
$$= \$1000(1.08)^3 = \$1000(1.259712)$$
$$\approx \$1259.71$$

b. $$A = P\left(1 + \frac{r}{n}\right)^{nt} = \$1000\left(1 + \frac{0.08}{4}\right)^{4 \times 3}$$
$$= \$1000(1 + 0.02)^{12}$$
$$= \$1000(1.02)^{12} = \$1000(1.268242)$$
$$\approx \$1268.24$$

c. $$A = P\left(1 + \frac{r}{n}\right)^{nt} = \$1000\left(1 + \frac{0.08}{365}\right)^{365 \times 3}$$
$$= \$1000(1 + 0.000219)^{1095}$$
$$= \$1000(1.000219)^{1095} = \$1000(1.270967)$$
$$\approx \$1270.97$$

Problem

Suppose you invest $10,000 for 2 years at an interest rate of 11%. How much will be in the account if interest is compounded:

a. annually? **b.** semiannually? **c.** quarterly?

d. monthly? **e.** daily? **f.** hourly?

Chapter 7 Summary and Review

7-1

On a plane, each point is the graph of an **ordered pair.** The numbers in the ordered pair are called **coordinates.** The first number in the pair, the ***x*-coordinate,** tells the distance right or left from the *y*-axis. The second number, the ***y*-coordinate,** tells the distance up or down from the *x*-axis.

Plot these points on graph paper.

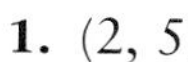

1. (2, 5) **2.** (0, −3)
3. (−4, −2) **4.** (5, 0)
5. (4, −3) **6.** (−4, 3)

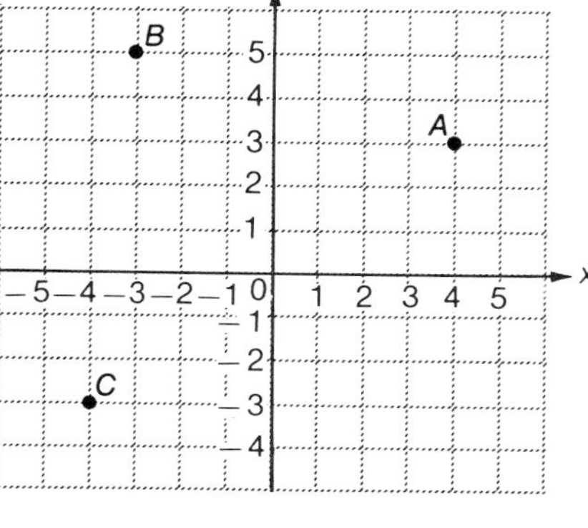

In which quadrant is each point located?

7. (3, −8) **8.** (−20, −14)
9. (4.9, 1.3) **10.** (−1, 12)

Find the coordinates of each point.

11. *A* **12.** *B* **13.** *C*

7-2

An ordered pair of numbers is a solution of an equation if the numbers make the equation true when the numbers are substituted for the variables.

Determine whether the given point is a solution of $3x + y = 4$.

14. (0, 4) **15.** (1, −1)

Make a table of solutions and graph the equations.

16. $2x - y = 1$ **17.** $y - 5 = 2x$

7-3

An equation whose graph is a straight line is called a **linear equation.** To graph a linear equation, plot two points (ordered pairs) and draw the line that contains the two points. Use a third point to check.
The ***x*-intercept** of a line is the *x*-coordinate of the point where the line crosses the *x*-axis. To find the *x*-intercept, let $y = 0$ and solve for x. The ***y*-intercept** of a line is the *y*-coordinate of the point where the line crosses the *y*-axis. To find the *y*-intercept, let $x = 0$ and solve for y.

Graph using intercepts.

18. $2x - 7y = 14$ **19.** $3x - 2y = -6$

Graph.

20. $y = -4$ **21.** $x = 7$

ANSWERS

1–6.

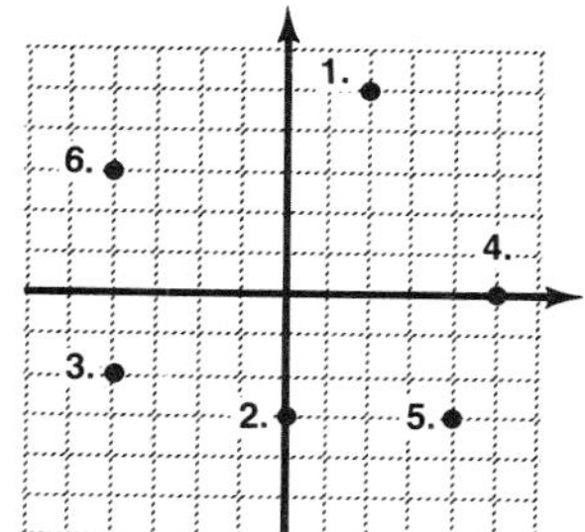

7. IV
8. III
9. I
10. II
11. (4, 3)
12. (−3, 5)
13. (−4, −3)
14. Yes
15. No

16.

x	y
0	−1
1	1
2	3

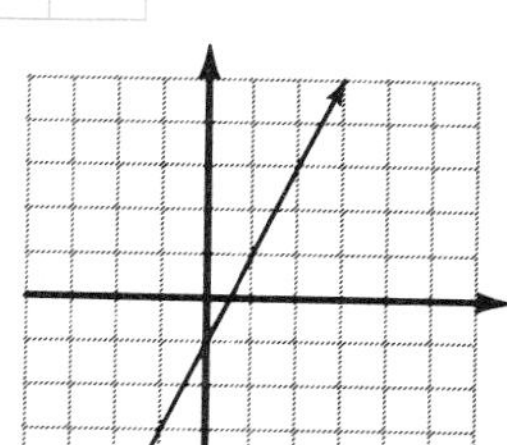

17.

x	y
0	5
1	7
2	9

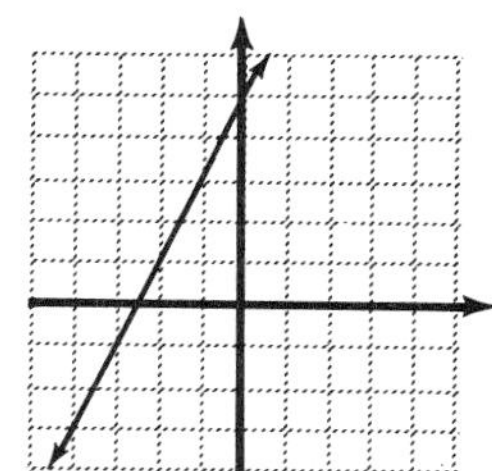

18.

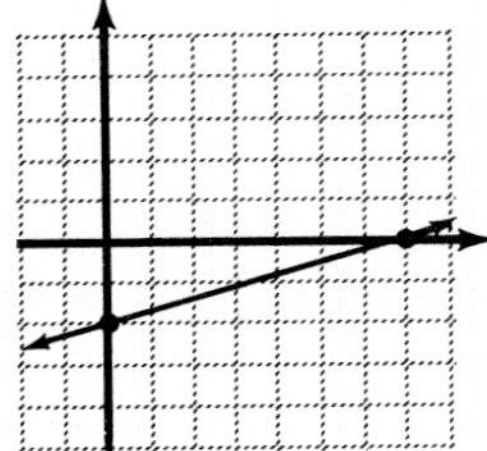

19.

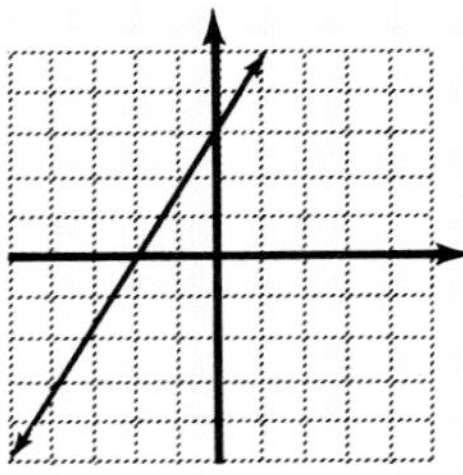

20.

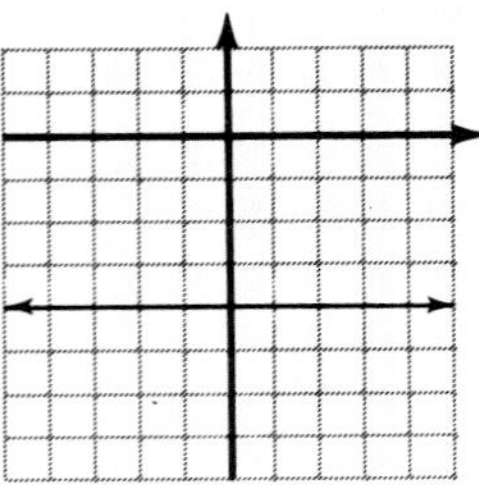

21.

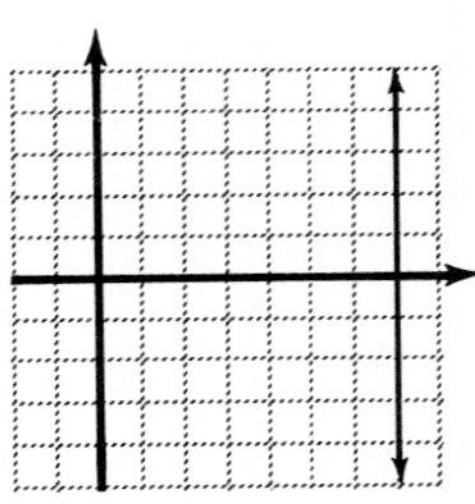

7-4

The **slope** of a line is a ratio that describes which way the line slants and how steep it is.

$$m = \text{slope} = \frac{\text{rise}}{\text{run}} = \frac{y_2 - y_1}{x_2 - x_1}$$

A horizontal line has a slope of 0 and a vertical line has no slope.

Find the slopes, if they exist, of the lines containing these points.

22. $(6, 8)\ (-2, -4)$ $\frac{3}{2}$

23. $(5, 1)\ (-1, 1)$ 0

24. $(-3, 0)\ (-3, 5)$ No slope

25. $(3, 4)\ (5, -8)$ -6

7-5

To find the slope and the y-intercept of a line from its equation, solve the equation for y to get the form $y = mx + b$. This is called the **slope-intercept equation.** The coefficient of the x-term, m, is the slope, and b is the y-intercept.

Find the slope of each line by solving for y.

26. $3x - 2y = -6$ $\frac{3}{2}$

27. $5x + 3y = 4$ $-\frac{5}{3}$

Find the slope and y-intercept of each line.

28. $3x - 5y = 4$ $\frac{3}{5}, -\frac{4}{5}$

29. $2x = 6y + 12$ $\frac{1}{3}, -2$

Graph each line using the y-intercept and slope.

30. $y = -x + 5$

31. $y = \frac{3}{5}x - 2$

32. $y - \frac{3}{4}x = 0$

7-6

If you know the slope, m, and the y-intercept, b, of a line, you can use the slope-intercept equation for the line, $y = mx + b$, to find the equation of the line. If you know the slope, m, and a point on the line, (x_1, y_1), you can use the **point-slope equation,** $y - y_1 = m(x - x_1)$, to find the equation of the line. If you know two points on the line, first find the slope and then use the point-slope equation.

Write an equation for each line with the given slope and y-intercept.

33. $m = 3$, y-intercept $= -4$

34. $m = 5$, y-intercept $= 0$

Write an equation for each line with the given slope and point.

35. $(1, 2)$, $m = 3$

36. $(0, 4)$, $m = -2$

37. $(-2, 4)$, $m = -\frac{1}{2}$

Write an equation for each line that contains the given pair of points.

38. $(5, 7)\ (-1, 1)$

39. $(2, 0)\ (-4, -3)$

Write an equation for each line in slope-intercept form.

40.

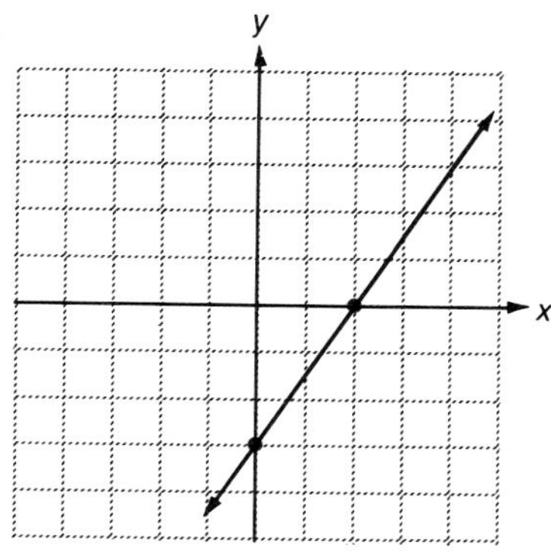

41.

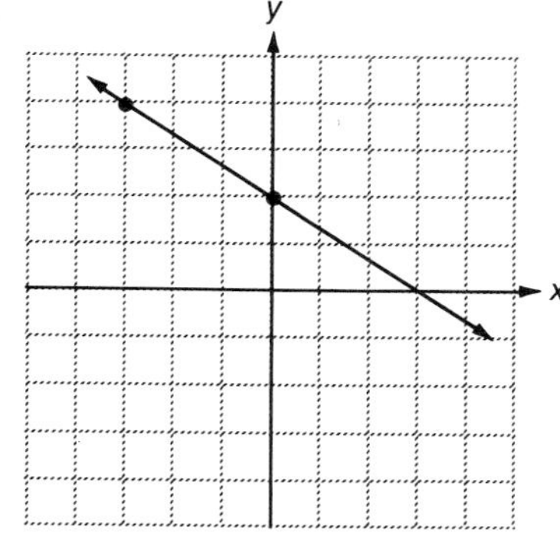

7-7

In real-world situations, the relationship between two variables can sometimes be expressed as a linear equation. You can then use the linear equation to solve problems involving a prediction between two variables.

Solve.
A temperature of 59°F equals 15°C. A temperature of 68°F equals 20°C.

42. Find the linear equation with ordered pairs (F, C) for these data points.

43. Use this linear equation to find the Celsius temperature when it is 77°F.

7-8

Two non-vertical lines are **parallel** if they have the same slope and different y-intercepts. Two lines are **perpendicular** if the product of their slopes is -1.

Determine whether the graphs of the equations are parallel.

44. $y - 5 = -2x$
$y + 2x = -3$ Yes

45. $y = 3x - 4$
$y + 3x = 2$ No

Determine whether the graphs of the equations are perpendicular.

46. $y = \frac{2}{3}x$
$2y = -3x + 8$ Yes

47. $6y = -x + 18$
$y = -6x - 4$ No

Determine whether the graphs of the equations are parallel, perpendicular, or neither.

48. $4x + y = 6$
$4x + y = 8$ Parallel

49. $2x + y = 10$
$y = \frac{1}{2}x - 4$ Perpendicular

50. $x + 4y = 8$
$x = -4y - 10$ Parallel

51. $3x - y = 6$
$3x + y = 8$ Neither

30.

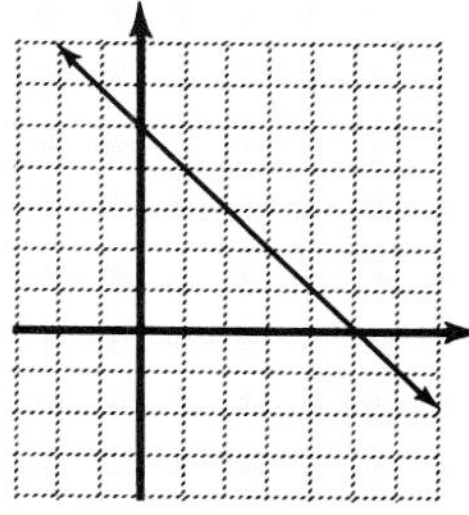

31.

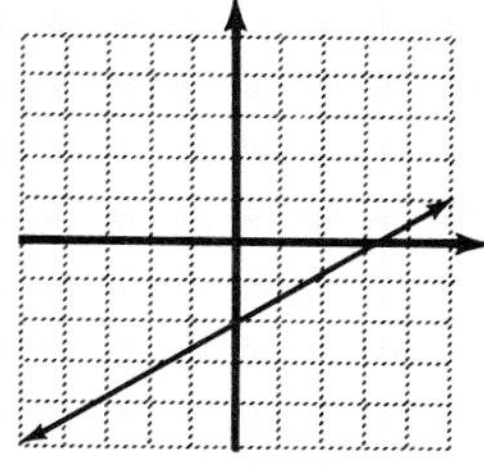

32.

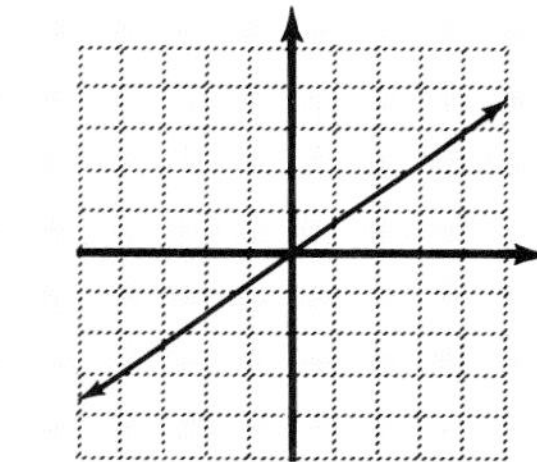

33. $y = 3x - 4$
34. $y = 5x$
35. $y = 3x - 1$
36. $y = -2x + 4$
37. $y = -\frac{1}{2}x + 3$
38. $y = x + 2$
39. $y = \frac{1}{2}x - 1$
40. $y = \frac{3}{2}x - 3$
41. $y = -\frac{2}{3}x + 2$
42. $C = \frac{5}{9}F - \frac{160}{9} = \frac{5}{9}(F - 32)$
43. 25°C

ANSWERS

1–2.

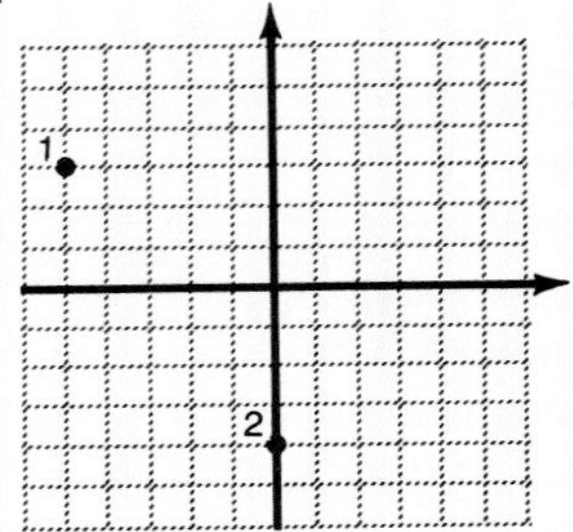

3. III
4. II
5. (3, 3)
6. (0, −4)
7. (−5, 0)
8. (−1, 1)
9. No
10. Yes

11.

x	y
1	7
2	4
3	1

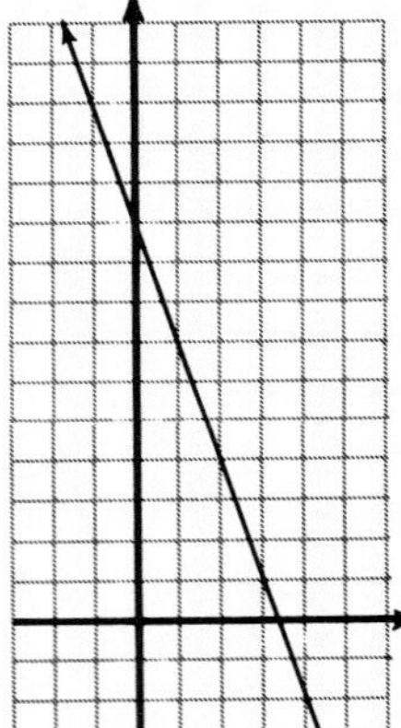

12.

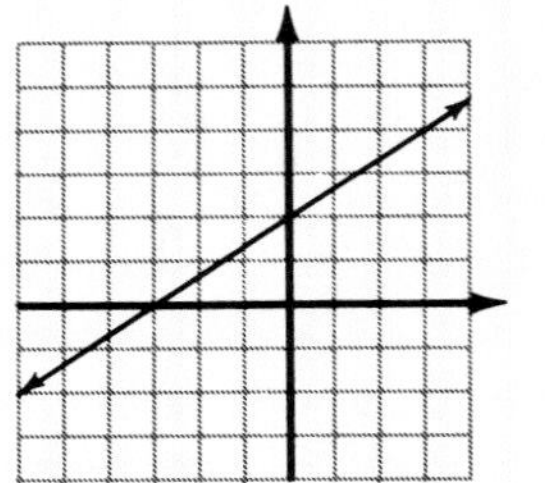

For answers to items 13, 14, and 18, see margin p. 351.

Test Item Analysis

Item	Lesson
1–8	7-1
9–11	7-2
12–14	7-3
15, 16	7-4
17, 18	7-5
19–22	7-6
23, 24	7-7
25–27	7-8

Chapter 7 Test

Use graph paper to plot these points.

1. $(-5, 3)$
2. $(0, -4)$

In which quadrant is each point located?

3. $(-1, -4)$
4. $(-1, 8)$

Find the coordinates of each point.

5. A 6. B 7. C 8. D

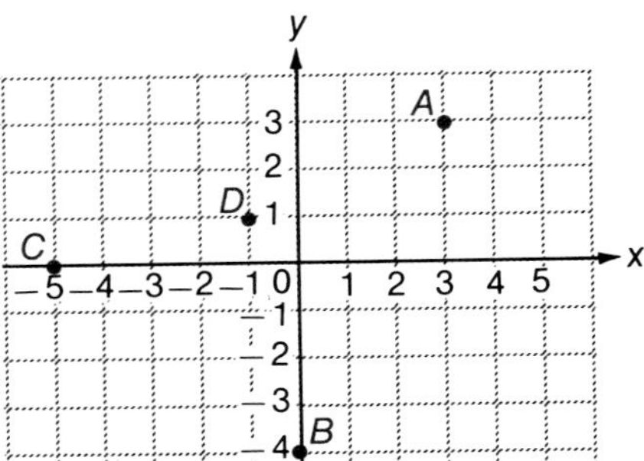

Determine whether the given point is a solution of $2x + 3y = 12$.

9. $(2, 3)$
10. $(3, 2)$
11. Make a table of solutions and graph $3x + y = 10$.
12. Use intercepts to graph $2x - 3y = -6$.

Graph.

13. $x = 8$
14. $y = -2$

Find the slopes, if they exist, of the lines containing these points.

15. $(9, 2)\ (-3, -5)$ $\frac{7}{12}$
16. $(4, 7)\ (4, -1)$ No slope

Use the equation $-4x + 3y = -6$.

17. Find the slope and y-intercept. $\frac{4}{3}$, -2
18. Graph the equation.

Write an equation for the line containing the given point and having the given slope.

19. $(3, 5)$ $m = 1$ $y = x + 2$
20. $(-2, 0)$ $m = -3$ $y = -3x - 6$

Write an equation for the line containing the two given points.

21. $(1, 1)\ (2, -2)$ $y = -3x + 4$
22. $(4, -1)\ (-4, -3)$ $y = \frac{1}{4}x - 2$

When an electronics company produces 1000 chips, it makes a profit of \$10 per unit. When it produces 5000 chips, the company makes a profit of \$30 per unit. Assume that a linear relationship fits this data.

23. Find the linear equation that fits this data. $p = \frac{1}{200}n + 5$
24. Use the linear equation to predict the profit per unit if the company produced 10,000 chips. 55

Determine whether the graphs of the equations are parallel, perpendicular, or neither.

25. $2x + y = 8$
    $2x + y = 4$
    Parallel
26. $2x + 5y = 2$
    $y = 2x + 4$
    Neither
27. $x + 2y = 8$
    $-2x + y = 8$
    Perpendicular

Chapters 1 – 7 Cumulative Review

1-1 Evaluate.

1. $y + 6 + y$ for $y = 8$ 22

2. $\frac{x}{18}$ for $x = 24$ $\frac{4}{3}$

1-2

3. Use a commutative property to write three equivalent expressions for $4x + 3y$. Answers may vary. Ex. $4x + y \cdot 3$, $x \cdot 4 + 3y$, $3y + 4x$

Simplify.

4. $\frac{16}{48}$ $\frac{1}{3}$

5. $\frac{q}{12pq}$ $\frac{1}{12p}$

6. $\frac{51s}{3st}$ $\frac{17}{t}$

1-3, 1-4 Evaluate.

7. $x^2 - 5$ for $x = 3$

8. $(4y)^3$ for $y = 3$

9. $(y - 1)^2$ for $y = 6$

1-5 Multiply.

10. $3(2x + y)$

11. $4(3x + 4y + z)$

Collect like terms.

12. $7a + 7b + a + 7c$

13. $6x^2 + 2y + 2z + 3x^2$

1-6 Write as an algebraic expression.

14. 7 less than twice y

15. the difference of x and three times y

16. Let s be Shawn's age 5 years ago. Write an expression for Shawn's age now.

1-7 State whether each sentence is true, false, or open.

17. a. $15x + 325 = 90$ b. $9 \cdot 8 - 5 = 27$ c. $12x - 5x = 7$

Solve for the given solution set.

18. $x + 2.7 = 8.5$ {5.4, 5.8, 6.2}

19. $112t = 4256$ {35, 37}

1-9 Evaluate.

20. $D = rt$ for $r = 55$ mi/h and $t = 270$ min

21. $F = \frac{9}{5}C + 32$ for $C = 15°$

ADDITIONAL ANSWERS FOR CHAPTER 7 TEST

13.

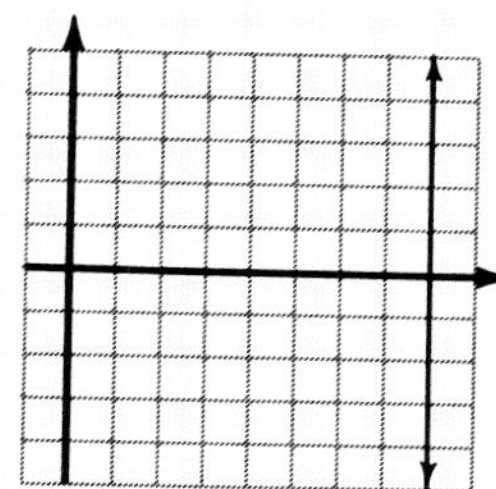

14.

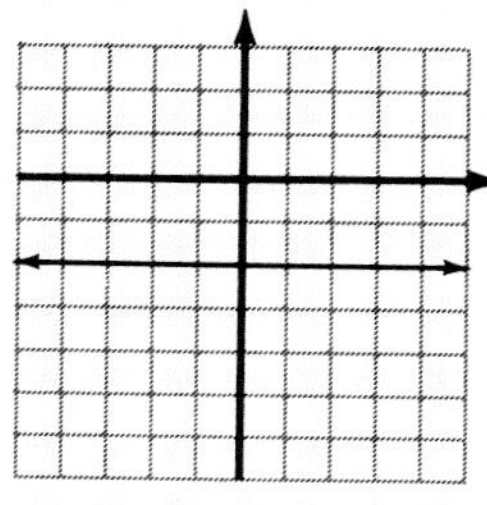

18.

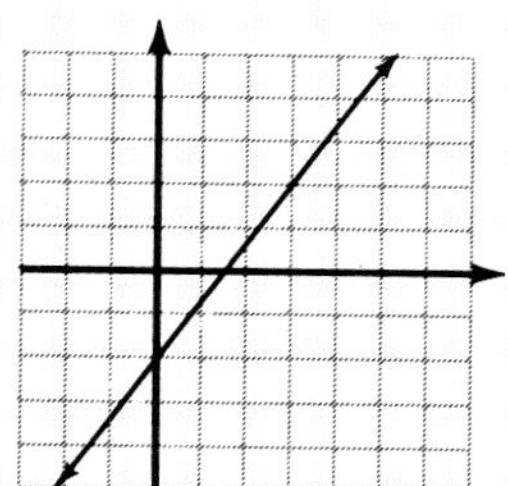

ANSWERS

7. 4
8. 1728
9. 25
10. $6x + 3y$
11. $12x + 16y + 4z$
12. $8a + 7b + 7c$
13. $9x^2 + 2y + 2z$
14. $2y - 7$
15. $x - 3y$
16. $s + 5$
17. a. Open
    b. False
    c. Open
18. {5.8}
19. No solution
20. 247.5 mi
21. 59°F

30. $-\frac{43}{8}$
31. -15
32. 3.6
33. $-\frac{2}{3}$
34. $-\frac{4}{5}$
35. 1
36. -42
37. 6
38. -6.2
39. 1
40. $11(11x - 5)$
41. $-2(3 + x + 6y)$ or $2(-3 - x - 6y)$
42. $-4x - 9$
43. $-5y - 6$
44. Additive inverse property
45. Distributive property
46. $\frac{7}{8}$
47. 2.6
48. 0
49. $\frac{9}{2}$
50. 48
51. $-\frac{1}{2}$
52. -3
53. 10
54. -1
55. $12d = 9$; \$0.75
56. $b + 2b + 1 = 19$; 6 boys

2-1 Use >, <, or = to write a true sentence.

22. $-10 > -14$ **23.** $-3.1 > -3.15$ **24.** $0.01 < 0.1$

Find the absolute value.

25. $|-18|$ 18 **26.** $|25|$ 25

Use >, <, or = to write a true sentence.

27. $-\frac{2}{3} > -\frac{3}{4}$ **28.** $\frac{7}{8} < \frac{8}{9}$ **29.** $\frac{-4}{10} < \frac{5}{7}$

2-3, 2-4 Add or subtract.

30. $-\frac{1}{2} + \frac{3}{8} + (-6) + \frac{3}{4}$ **31.** $-2.6 + (-7.5) + 2.6 + (-7.5)$

32. $-6.1 - (-3.1) + 7.9 - 3.1 + 1.8$ **33.** $-\frac{5}{9} - \frac{2}{18}$

2-5 Multiply.

34. $\left(-\frac{2}{3}\right)\left(\frac{18}{15}\right)$ **35.** $\frac{3}{5}\left(-\frac{3}{5}\right)\left(-\frac{25}{9}\right)$ **36.** $-2(-7)(-3)$

2-6 Divide.

37. $-\frac{4}{3} \div \frac{-2}{9}$ **38.** $-6.262 \div 1.01$ **39.** $-\frac{72}{108} \div -\frac{2}{3}$

2-7 Factor.

40. $121x - 55$ **41.** $-6 - 2x - 12y$

2-8 Simplify.

42. $-8x - (9 - 4x)$ **43.** $-2(y + 3) - 3y$

2-10 Name the following properties.

44. $a + (-a) = 0$ **45.** $a(b + c) = ab + ac$

3-1 to 3-3 Solve.

46. $x - \frac{3}{8} = \frac{1}{2}$ **47.** $-3.2 = y - 5.8$ **48.** $-\frac{2}{3} = x - \frac{8}{12}$

49. $-4x = -18$ **50.** $-\frac{x}{3} = -16$ **51.** $-\frac{5}{6} = x - \frac{1}{3}$

52. $6y + 3 = -15$ **53.** $3(x - 2) = 24$ **54.** $-2(x - 4) = 10$

3-4, 3-11 Write an equation and solve.

55. Twelve computer disks cost \$9. How much does one disk cost?

56. The number of girls in the band is one more than twice the number of boys. There are 19 students in the band. How many are boys?

3-5, 3-6 Solve.

57. $9(t + 2) = 5(t - 3)$

58. $4 + 3x - 2 = 5x + 8 - x$

59. $\frac{5}{3} + \frac{2}{3}x = \frac{13}{12} + \frac{5}{4}x + \frac{3}{4}$

60. $\frac{1}{3}x - \frac{2}{9} = \frac{2}{3} + \frac{4}{9}x$

3-7 Solve.

61. $C = 2\pi r$ for r $r = \frac{C}{2\pi}$

3-8 Solve.

62. $4|x| = 28$ 7, −7

63. $|x| - 16 = 45$ 61, −61

3-9 Solve these proportions.

64. $\frac{24}{x} = \frac{8}{3}$ 9

65. $\frac{12}{15} = \frac{t}{35}$ 28

3-10 Translate to an equation and solve.

66. What is the interest on \$300 at 6% for one year?

67. A football quarterback completes 21 passes out of a total of 35. What percent does he complete?

4-1 Determine whether the given number is a solution of the inequality $x \geq -5$.

68. **(a)** -2 Yes **(b)** 0 Yes **(c)** -8 No

4-2 to 4-5 Solve and graph the solution.

69. $4y + 4 - 2y \leq 12$ $y \leq 4$

70. $4x + 3 - 3x > 2$ $x > -1$

71. $-2y > 3$ $y < -\frac{3}{2}$

72. $6 - 5y > 8 - 4y$ $y < -2$

73. The sum of three consecutive odd integers is less than 100. Find the largest set of these numbers. 31, 33, 35

5-1 Simplify.

74. $x^8 \cdot x^2$ x^{10}

75. $\frac{z^4}{z^7}$ $\frac{1}{z^3}$

5-2 Simplify.

76. $(4y^3)^2$ $16y^6$

77. $(3x^2y)^3$ $27x^6y^3$

5-3 Multiply.

78. $(-2x)(4x^3)$ $-8x^4$

79. $(3b^2c^3)(-4bc^4)(-2b^2)$ $24b^5c^7$

57. $-\frac{33}{4}$
58. -6
59. $-\frac{2}{7}$
60. -8

66. \$18
67. 60%

69.
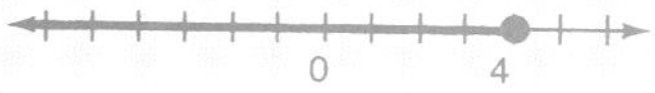

70.

71.

72.
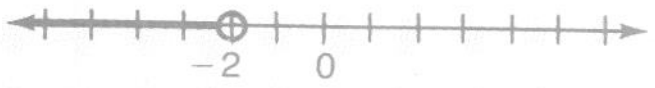

82. $-\frac{12b^5}{a^2}$
83. $\frac{1}{3p^3r^5}$
84. 2.48×10^5
85. 3.75×10^{-5}
86. $-5x^3 - 9x^2 + x + 2$
87. $-4x^3 - x^2 - 2$
88. 0
89. $x^4 + 2x^3 - 9x^2 - 7$
90. $6a^4b^2 + 3a^2b - 5b^3$
91. $-y^3 - 2y^2 - 2y + 7$
92. $6v^3u + 10u^2 - 8v^2$
93. $8x^5 - 4x^4 + 28x^3$
94. $6x^2 - 7x - 20$
95. $x^2y^2 - 49y^4$
96. $-3m^8 + 12m^3n + 9mn^3$
97. $4a^2 - 20ab + 25b^2$
98. $4x^2 + 19xy - 30y^2$
99. $2 - 10x^2 + 12x^4$
100. $6x^7 - 12x^5 + 9x^2 - 18$
101. $4x^6 - 1$
102. $64x^2 + 48x + 9$
103. $36x^2 - 60x + 25$
104. $4x^4 - 4x^3 - x^2 + 2x - 1$
105. $x(x - 4)$
106. $3x^2(2x^3 - 12x + 3)$
107. $4x(3 - x - 12x^3)$
108. $(3x + 1)(3x - 1)$
109. $2(x - 2)(x + 2)$
110. $(4x^2 + 9)(2x + 3)(2x - 3)$
111. $(x - 7)^2$
112. $(4x + 5)^2$
113. $(x - 4y)^2$
114. $(c - 6d)(c - d)$
115. $2(3x - 4)^2$
116. $(x - 6)(x - 4)$
117. $(x - 7)(x + 5)$
118. $x(x - 7)(x + 3)$
119. $(2x + 1)(4x + 3)$
120. $(3x - 2)(x + 4)$
121. $2(3x - 2)(x - 4)$
122. $(x^2 + 2)(x + 1)$
123. $(x^3 - 3)(x + 2)$
124. $3(1 + 2x^3)(1 - 2x^3)$
125. $(x + 5)(x + y)$
126. $(m + n)(a - b)$
127. $2, -6$
128. $\frac{1}{2}, -4$
129. $14, 16$ or $-16, -14$

Divide.

80. $\frac{-25n^6}{-5n^3}$ $5n^3$

81. $\frac{-48m^6n^8}{8m^4n^8}$ $-6m^2$

82. $\frac{36a^4b^7}{-3a^6b^2}$

83. $\frac{4p^2r^4}{12p^5r^9}$

5-4 Write in scientific notation.

84. 248,000

85. 0.0000375

5-5, 5-6 Collect like terms and arrange in descending order for the variable x.

86. $-3x^2 + 4x - 5x^3 - 6x^2 + 2 - 3x$

87. $2x^3 - 7 + 3x^2 - 6x^3 - 4x^2 + 5$

Evaluate.

88. $x^2 - 6x + 8$ for $x = 4$

5-7 Add.

89. $(3x^4 + 2x^3 - 6x^2) + (-2x^4 - 3x^2 - 7)$

90. $(a^4b^2 - 3a^2b + 4b^3) + (5a^4b^2 + 6a^2b - 9b^3)$

5-8 Subtract.

91. $(-8y^2 - y + 2) - (y^3 - 6y^2 + y - 5)$

92. $(14v^3u + 4u^2 - 3v^2) - (8v^3u - 6u^2 + 5v^2)$

5-9 to 5-11 Multiply.

93. $4x^3(2x^2 - x + 7)$

94. $(2x - 5)(3x + 4)$

95. $(xy - 7y^2)(xy + 7y^2)$

96. $3m(-m^7 + 4m^2n + 3n^3)$

97. $(2a - 5b)^2$

98. $(4x - 5y)(x + 6y)$

99. $(1 - 3x^2)(2 - 4x^2)$

100. $(2x^5 + 3)(3x^2 - 6)$

101. $(2x^3 + 1)(2x^3 - 1)$

102. $(8x + 3)^2$

103. $(6x - 5)^2$

104. $(4x^3 - x + 1)(x - 1)$

6-1 to 6-7 Factor.

105. $x^2 - 4x$

106. $6x^5 - 36x^3 + 9x^2$

107. $12x - 4x^2 - 48x^4$

108. $9x^2 - 1$

109. $2x^2 - 8$

110. $16x^4 - 81$

111. $x^2 - 14x + 49$

112. $16x^2 + 40x + 25$

113. $x^2 - 8xy + 16y^2$

114. $c^2 - 7cd + 6d^2$

115. $18x^2 - 48x + 32$

116. $x^2 - 10x + 24$

117. $x^2 - 2x - 35$

118. $x^3 - 4x^2 - 21x$

119. $8x^2 + 10x + 3$

120. $3x^2 + 10x - 8$

Factor.

121. $6x^2 - 28x + 16$

122. $x^3 + x^2 + 2x + 2$

123. $x^4 + 2x^3 - 3x - 6$

124. $3 - 12x^6$

125. $x^2 + 5x + xy + 5y$

126. $am + an - bm - bn$

6-8 Solve for x.

127. $x^2 + 4x - 12 = 0$

128. $2x^2 + 7x - 4 = 0$

6-9 Solve.

129. The product of two consecutive even integers is 224. Find the integers.

7-1 In which quadrant is each point located?

130. (4, 3) I

131. (−2, 7) II

132. (4, −9) IV

7-2 Graph the equations. Make a table of solutions.

133. $3x - y = 2$

134. $y - 4 = 3x$

7-3 Graph the equations. Use intercepts.

135. $3y = x + 6$

136. $2x = 3y + 9$

7-4 Find the slopes of the lines containing these points.

137. (0, −3) and (4, 0)

138. (2, 2) and (−1, 8)

7-5 Find the slope and y-intercept of each line.

139. $2y = -4x + 8$

140. $4x = 9y - 7$

7-6 Write an equation for each line.

141. $m = -1$, y-intercept $= 3$

142. $m = 5$, passes through (5, 2)

143. $m = \frac{2}{3}$, passes through (2, 5)

144. contains points (6, 4) and (−2, 0)

7-8 Determine whether the graphs of the equations are parallel or perpendicular lines.

145. $y = -\frac{1}{2}x - \frac{1}{2}$, $-2y = x + 6$

146. $6x + y = -4$, $6y = x + 8$

133.

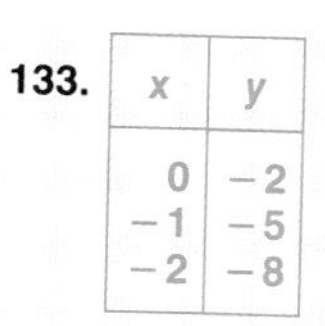

x	y
0	−2
−1	−5
−2	−8

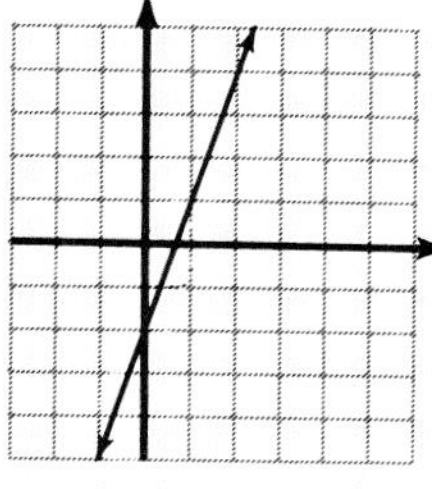

134.

x	y
0	4
1	7
2	10

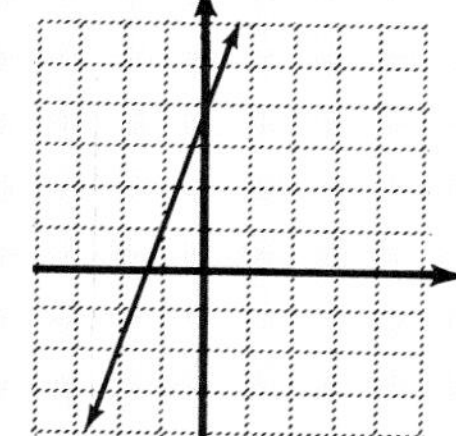

135.

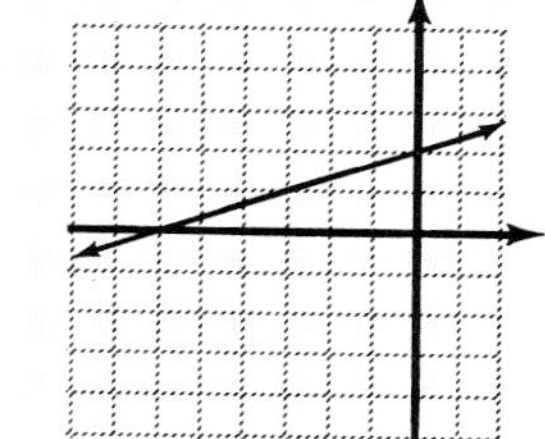

136.

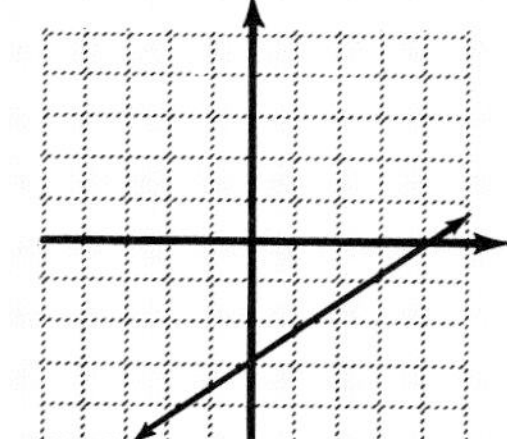

137. $\frac{3}{4}$

138. -2

139. $m = -2$, $b = 4$

140. $m = \frac{4}{9}$, $b = \frac{7}{9}$

141. $y = -x + 3$

142. $y = 5x - 23$

143. $y = \frac{2}{3}x + \frac{11}{3}$

144. $y = \frac{1}{2}x + 1$

145. Parallel

146. Perpendicular

CHAPTER 8 Systems of Equations

Chapter Overview

The methods used to graph linear equations in Chapter 7 are extended to solving systems of two equations graphically. Techniques to solve a system of equations using the substitution and the addition methods are then covered.

Word problems that can be easily solved using two variables are introduced. These problems include digit and coin problems and problems involving uniform motion. Problems involving systems of equations on college entrance exams are discussed in the Problem Solving: College Entrance Exams section.

Objectives

8-1 ■ Determine whether an ordered pair is a solution of a system of equations.
■ Find the solution of a system of equations by graphing.

8-2 ■ Solve a system of equations by substituting for a variable.
■ Solve problems using systems of equations.

8-3 ■ Solve a system of equations using the addition method.
■ Solve a system of equations by using the multiplication and addition properties.
■ Solve problems using the addition method.

8-4 ■ Solve problems using systems of equations.

8-5 ■ Solve problems involving uniform motion.

8-6 ■ Use systems of equations to solve digit and coin problems.

Cooperative Learning Opportunities

In Lesson 8-4, Example 4 on page 376 can form the basis for a paired co-operative–learning activity. Go over the example and then display the graph (**Teacher's Edition**, 375). Then have students, in pairs, do Exercises 9, 10, and 19 and draw the graphs. One student is the writer, the other the plotter. As a follow-up that works back from the graph you can use this graph and these questions.

1. Which video store charges a membership fee? **Sights & Sounds**

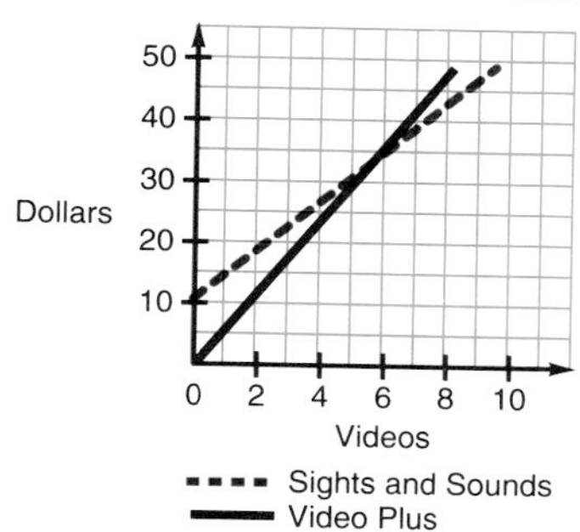

2. How much is the membership fee? **$10.00**
3. What is the approximate cost per video at Sights & Sounds? **$4.00**
4. Describe the meaning of the point (5, 30) at which the graphs intersect. **If you rent 5 videos, the cost at each store is $30.00.**
5. Write equations for the cost of the videos at each store. **Video Plus: $c = 6v$; Sights & Sounds: $c = 4v + 10$**

Multicultural Note: *Seki Kowa*

Many of the mathematical problems that eventually led to new discoveries in Western mathematics had, for centuries, also stimulated Oriental mathematicians, who found new solutions and methods independently.

Seki Kowa was born in Japan in 1642. At an early age, he displayed a remarkable aptitude for mathematics. He studied the work of an earlier mathematician, Kazuyuki Sawaguchi, who had proposed 15 "unsolvable" problems based on the work of Chu Shih-Chieh (discussed in the **Multicultural Note** for Chapter 6.)

Seki Kowa solved all 15 of the proposed problems and his solutions went so far beyond what was then known that no one could understand them. Among his many achievements, Seki Kowa improved upon the Chinese methods for solving higher–degree equations, developed the use of determinants to solve systems of linear equations, and invented a form of the calculus to find the area of a circle.

For more information, see page 151 of **Multiculturalism in Mathematics, Science, and Technology**.

Alternative Assessment and Communication Ideas

The **Write a convincing argument** exercise in Lesson 8-4 offers an opportunity to review the understanding of instructions, reasoning, and verbal expression used by students. The instructions do not say to take someone through the entire reasoning process, which is best handled with simultaneous equations. Rather, the student is told "to convince a classmate that your solution is correct." What this really calls for is a check, in verbal form, showing that the answers satisfy the given conditions.

Instructions for the **Write a convincing argument** exercise in Lesson 8-5 also suggest that the writing is to be done after the solution is found. But it could be used as an assessment of mathematical reasoning. Tell students that, even if they are not able to solve the problem, they should write an approach to a solution. What they write will help you correct errors in students' understanding and logic, and help move them toward a solution.

Investigations and Projects

Show these graphs. Ask students what they think the axes stand for and how they might interpret each graph. The first might show a drive home at an even speed, with one stop. The second, relating speed to time, might represent a car in traffic.

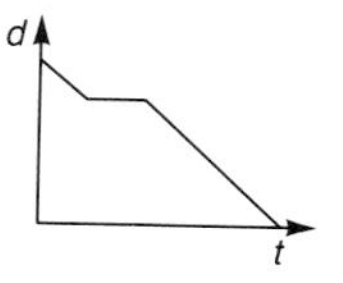

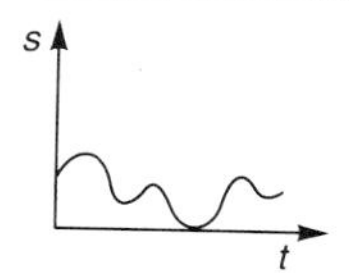

Project: Individually or in groups, students devise 3 graphs that relate common experiences. The graphs and stories should be different from those shown above. Students show their graphs to the class and explain what they represent.

MANAGING CHAPTER 8

Lesson	PACING CHART (DAYS) 2-Year* A for E	1-Year Minimum	1-Year Regular	1-Year Advanced	Opening Activity	Cooperative Activity	Seat or Group Work
8-1	2	2	2	1	First Five Minutes 8-1: ***FFMTM*** p. 26 or **TE** p. 358; ***Overhead Transparencies*** T15	Explore: **SE** p. 358	Try This a–f
8-2	2	1	1	1	First Five Minutes 8-2: ***FFMTM*** p. 26 or **TE** p. 362	Critical Thinking 8: ***Enrichment*** p. 25	Try This a–h
8-3	3	2	2	1	First Five Minutes 8-3: ***FFMTM*** p. 27 or **TE** p. 367	✂ Manipulative Activity 8: ***Enrichment*** p. 41	Try This a–j
8-4	3	1	1	1	First Five Minutes 8-4: ***FFMTM*** p. 27 or **TE** p. 373	Lesson Enrichment: **TE** p. 375	Try This a–f
8-5	2	2	2	1	First Five Minutes 8-5: ***FFMTM*** p. 27 or **TE** p. 380	Problem Solving: Application **SE** p. 394	Try This a–d
8-6	3	2	2	1	First Five Minutes 8-6: ***FFMTM*** p. 28 or **TE** p. 387	Problem 18: **SE** p. 391	Try This a–e
Review	2	1	1	1			
Test	1	1	1	1			
Cum. Review	0	0	0	1			
Mid-Year Test	0	0	0	1			

*2-Year Management Guide can be found in *Algebra for Everyone*.

FFMTM: First Five Minutes Transparency Masters

MANAGING CHAPTER 8

Enrichment	Review/Assess	Reteach	Technology	Lesson
Bonus Topic 8: ***Enrichment*** p. 9	Lesson Quiz: **TE** p. 360		Spreadsheet Activity 5: ***Technology*** pp. 45–46; Worksheet 6: ***Master Grapher*** pp. 30–31, 86–87, or 141–142; Worksheet 6: ***TI-81 Activities*** pp. 23–24; TI-81 Investigation 2: **SE** pp. 726–727	**8-1**
Critical Thinking 8: ***Enrichment*** p. 25	Lesson Quiz: **TE** p. 364	Skills Practice 21: ***SPMR*** p. 29; Problem Bank 14: ***Problem Bank*** p. 31	Problem for Programmers **SE** p. 366; Worksheet 7: ***Master Grapher*** pp. 32–34, 88–90, or 143–145; Worksheet 7: ***TI-81 Activities*** pp. 25–27	**8-2**
✂ Manipulative Activity 8: ***Enrichment*** p. 41; Looking for Errors 8: ***Enrichment*** p. 57	Mixed Practice 15: **SE** p. 698; Lesson Quiz: **TE** p. 370; Quiz 15: ***Assessment*** p. 25	Problem Bank 15: ***Problem Bank*** p. 32	Calculator Worksheet 19: ***Technology*** p. 21	**8-3**
Lesson Enrichment: **TE** p. 375	Mixed Review 15: ***SPMR*** p. 65; Lesson Quiz: **TE** p. 376	Skills Practice 22: ***SPMR*** p. 30; Problem Bank 16: ***Problem Bank*** p. 33		**8-4**
Problem Solving: Application: **SE** p. 394; Looking for Errors: **SE** p. 386	Mixed Review 16: ***SPMR*** p. 66; Lesson Quiz: **TE** p. 383; Quiz 16: ***Assessment*** p. 26	Problem Bank 17: ***Problem Bank*** p. 34	BASIC Computer Project 13: ***Technology*** p. 75	**8-5**
Problem Solving: College Entrance Exams: **SE** pp. 392–393	Mixed Practice 16: **SE** p. 699; Lesson Quiz: **TE** p. 389	Skills Practice 23: ***SPMR*** p. 31; Problem Bank 18: ***Problem Bank*** p. 34		**8-6**
	Summary and Review: **SE** pp. 395–396; Test: **SE** p. 397	Strategy Problem Bank 8: ***Problem Bank*** p. 9		**Review**
	Chapter 8 Exam: ***A for E*** pp. 333–334; Chapter 8 Test: ***Assessment*** pp. 57–58 (min.), 113–118 (reg.), 177–178 (adv.)			**Test**
	Cumulative Review: **SE** pp. 351–355			**Cum. Review**
	Mid-Year Test: ***Assessment*** pp. 229–233 (adv.)			**Mid-Year Test**

SPMR: Skills Practice Mixed Review

The solution to the problem posed on the facing page can be found on page 376.

Ready for Systems of Equations?

3-1 to 3-3 Solve.

1. $y + 3 = -2$ -5

2. $9y = 2$ $\frac{2}{9}$

3. $-3x + 2 = -10$ 4

4. $3x + 4 = 19$ 5

5. $6x + 2x = 45$ $\frac{45}{8}$

6. $-7y - 8y = -30$ 2

3-4 Write as an algebraic expression.

7. 8 more than twice a number $2n + 8$

8. the value of x dimes plus the value of y nickels $10x + 5y$

3-5 Solve.

9. $6x + 5 = 2x + 13$ 2

10. $9(t + 2) = 6(t - 2)$ -10

5-6 Evaluate each polynomial for $w = -2$.

11. $3 + 4w$ -5

12. $-7w - 8$ 6

13. $w^2 - 2w + 3$ 11

7-2

14. Determine whether $(3, -2)$ is a solution of $y = 4x - 14$. Yes

15. Determine whether $(-1, 5)$ is a solution of $y = -3x - 2$. No

Find three solutions of each equation. Answers may vary.

16. $y = 3x - 1$

17. $2w + 4x = -7$

18. $-4y - 2z = 10$

7-3, 7-5 Graph the following equations. See Teacher's Answer Section.

19. $2x - 4y = 1$

20. $-x + 3y = 5$

21. $y = -2$

22. $x = 5$

CHAPTER

8 Systems of Equations

Badger Rent-A-Car rents compact cars at a daily rate of \$23.95 plus 20¢ per mile. Cactus Rent-A-Car rents compact cars at a daily rate of \$22.95 plus 22¢ per mile. For what mileage is the cost the same?

8-1 Solving Systems of Equations by Graphing

Master Grapher Worksheet 6 can be used with this lesson.

TI-81 Investigation 2 (page 726) can be used with this lesson.

Explore

Graph each set of equations on separate coordinate axes. For each set, how many solutions do the two equations have in common?

Set 1: $2x + 3y = 12$, $x - 4y = -5$ **Set 2:** $x = 2y + 1$, $3x - 6y = 9$ **Set 3:** $2x = 4 - y$, $6x + 3y = 12$

Identifying Solutions

Objective: Determine whether an ordered pair is a solution of a system of equations.

A set of equations for which a common solution is sought is called a **system of equations.** A **solution** of a system of two equations in two variables is an ordered pair that makes both equations true. Since the solution of a system satisfies both equations simultaneously, we say that we have a **system of simultaneous equations.** When we find all the solutions of a system, we say that we have solved the system.

EXAMPLES

1. Determine whether (1, 2) is a solution of the system.

$$y = x + 1$$
$$2x + y = 4$$

y	$= x + 1$
2	$1 + 1$
2	2 ✓

$2x + y$	$= 4$
$2(1) + 2$	4
$2 + 2$	4
4	4 ✓

(1, 2) is a solution of the system.

2. Determine whether $(-3, 2)$ is a solution of the system.

$$a + b = -1$$
$$b + 3a = 4$$

$a + b$	$= -1$
$-3 + 2$	-1
-1	-1 ✓

$b + 3a$	$= 4$
$2 + 3(-3)$	4
$2 - 9$	4
-7	4

Since $(-3, 2)$ is not a solution of $b + 3a = 4$, it is not a solution of the system.

8-1

FIRST FIVE MINUTES

1. Write an equation for a line with slope 2 passing through the point (5, 7).
   $y = 2x - 3$
2. Write an equation for a line with slope 3 passing through the point (5, 7).
   $y = 3x - 8$

EXPLORE

Remind students that the graph is a representation of all of the solutions of the equation. Thus, two equations have a common solution wherever their graphs intersect.

The first set of equations has one solution in common, the second set has no solutions in common, and the third set has an infinite number of solutions in common (they are equivalent equations).

Identifying Solutions

Stress that for an ordered pair to be a solution of a system of equations, the ordered pair must satisfy all equations in the system. Students must check the ordered pair in all equations.

Remind students that the variables of an ordered pair are written alphabetically.

Key Questions

- How do you write the solution to a system of two equations in two variables?
  As an ordered pair
- Does a system of equations have only one solution?
  No, it may have no solution or an infinite number of solutions.

Chalkboard Examples

1. Determine whether (3, 5) is a solution of the system.
   $y = 4x - 7$
   $x + y = 8$

y	$= 4x - 7$
5	$4(3) - 7$
5	$12 - 7$
5	5 ✓

$x + y$	$= 8$
$3 + 5$	8
8	8 ✓

(3, 5) is a solution.

Try This Determine whether the given ordered pair is a solution of the system.

a. $(2, -3)$; $x = 2y + 8$ $\quad 2x + y = 1$ Yes

b. $(20, 40)$; $a = \frac{1}{4}b + 10$ $\quad b - a = -20$ No

Finding Solutions by Graphing

Objective: Find the solution of a system of equations by graphing.

One way to solve a system of equations is to graph the equations and find the coordinates of the point(s) of intersection. Since the point, or points, of intersection are on both lines, these ordered pairs are the solutions of the system.

EXAMPLE 3 Solve by graphing.

$$x + 2y = 7$$
$$x = y + 4$$

We graph the equations using any of the methods learned in Chapter 7. Point P appears to have coordinates (5, 1).

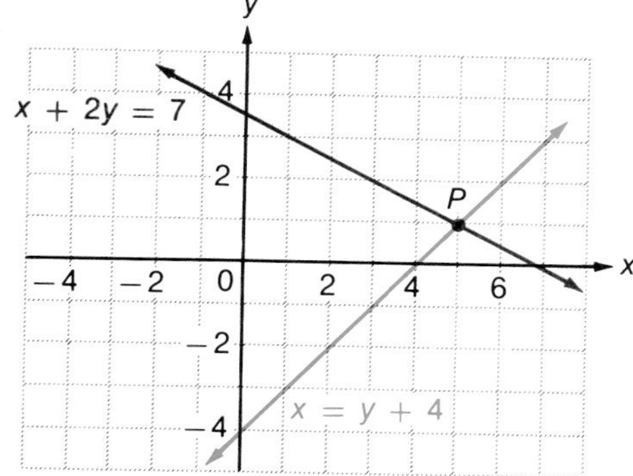

Check $x = 5$ and $y = 1$ in *both* equations.

$x + 2y = 7$	
$5 + 2(1)$	7
7	7 ✓

$x = y + 4$	
5	$1 + 4$
5	5 ✓

(5, 1) is the solution of the system.

When we graph a system of two linear equations, one of three things may happen.

1. The lines have one point of intersection. The point of intersection is the *only solution* of the system.
2. The lines are parallel. If this is so, there is no point that satisfies both equations. The system has *no solution.*
3. The lines coincide. Thus the equations have the same graph, and every solution of one equation is a solution of the other. There is an *infinite number of solutions.*

2. Determine whether $(-2, 1)$ is a solution of the system.
$2x - y = -5$
$3x + 2y = 3$

$2x - y = -5$	
$2(-2) - 1$	-5
$-4 - 1$	-5
-5	-5 ✓

$3x + 2y = 3$	
$3(-2) + 2(1)$	3
$-6 + 2$	3
-4	3

$(-2, 1)$ is not a solution of the system as it does not satisfy the second equation.

Finding Solutions by Graphing

Emphasize that accuracy is especially important with graphical solutions. Students should always check the apparent point of intersection to see if it is correct.

Note that the terms consistent, inconsistent, and dependent are introduced in Exercises 29, 30, and 31. If you choose to introduce these terms, point out that they correspond to the three possible graphs of two lines.

Chalkboard Example (*T15*)

1. Solve the following system by graphing.
$x + y = 2$
$x = y$

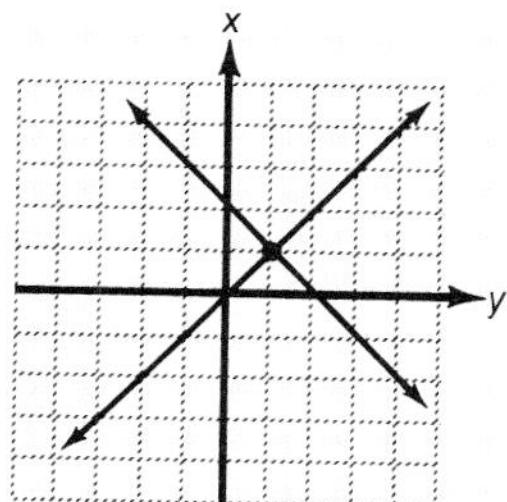

The point of intersection seems to be at (1, 1). This point checks in the system.

LESSON QUIZ

1. Determine whether the ordered pair (5, 1) is a solution of the system.
$5x - 2y = 23$
$4x + y = 21$
Yes
2. Determine whether the ordered pair (−1, 6) is a solution of the system.
$-x + y = 7$
$2x - 3y = 4$
No
3. Solve by graphing.
$y = x + 4$
$y = -2x - 2$

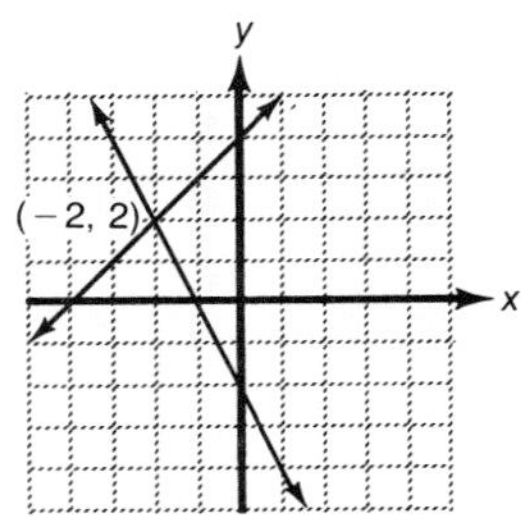

Assignment Guide
Minimum: Day 1: 1–10, MR
Day 2: 11–22
Regular: Day 1: 1–16, MR
Day 2: 17–33
Advanced: 1–32 m3, 33–36, MR

ADDITIONAL ANSWERS

Exercises

11. (2, 1)
12. (4, 2)
13. (−12, 11)
14. (−8, −7)
15. (4, 3)
16. (3, 2)
17. (−3, −3)
18. (−6, −2)
19. No solution
20. Infinitely many solutions
21. (2, 2)
22. (1, −3)
23. (5, 3)
24. (4, 3)
25. $\left(\frac{1}{3}, 1\right)$
26. Infinitely many solutions
27. No solution
28. No solution

Try This Solve by graphing.

c. $x + 4y = -6$, $2x - 3y = -1$ (−2, −1)
d. $y + 2x = 5$, $2y - 5x = 10$ (0, 5)
e. $y - 2x = 7$, $y = 2x + 8$ No solution
f. $3y - 2x = 6$, $4x - 6y = -12$ Infinitely many solutions

8-1 EXERCISES

A

Determine whether the given ordered pair is a solution of the system of equations.

1. (3, 2); $2x + 3y = 12$, $x - 4y = -5$ Yes
2. (1, 5); $5x - 2y = -5$, $3x - 7y = -32$ Yes
3. (3, 2); $3t - 2s = 0$, $t + 2s = 15$ No
4. (2, −2); $b + 2a = 2$, $b - a = -4$ Yes
5. (15, 20); $3x - 2y = 5$, $6x - 5y = -10$ Yes
6. (−1, −3); $3r + s = -6$, $2r = 1 + s$ Yes
7. (−1, 1); $x = -1$, $x - y = -2$ Yes
8. (−3, 4); $2x = -y - 2$, $y = -4$ No
9. (12, 3); $y = \frac{1}{4}x$, $3x - y = 33$ Yes
10. (−3, 1); $y = -\frac{1}{3}x$, $3y = -5x - 12$ Yes

Solve by graphing.

11. $x + y = 3$, $x - y = 1$
12. $x - y = 2$, $x + y = 6$
13. $x + 2y = 10$, $3x + 4y = 8$
14. $x - 2y = 6$, $2x - 3y = 5$
15. $8x - y = 29$, $2x + y = 11$
16. $4x - y = 10$, $3x + 5y = 19$
17. $x = y$, $4x = 2y - 6$
18. $x = 3y$, $3y - 6 = 2x$
19. $x = -y$, $x + y = 4$
20. $-3x = 5 - y$, $2y = 6x + 10$
21. $a = \frac{1}{2}b + 1$, $a - 2b = -2$
22. $x = \frac{1}{3}y + 2$, $-2x - y = 1$

B

Solve these systems graphically.

23. $y = 3$, $x = 5$
24. $x = 4$, $3y - 2x = 1$
25. $y = 3x$, $y = -3x + 2$
26. $x + y = 9$, $3x + 3y = 27$
27. $x + y = 4$, $x + y = -4$
28. $y = 2x - 1$, $y - 2x = 3$

29. A system of equations that has one or more solutions is called **consistent.** Which systems of equations in Exercises 11–28 are consistent? All except 19, 27, and 28

30. A system of equations that has infinitely many solutions is called consistent and **dependent.** Which systems of equations in Exercises 11–28 are dependent? Exercises 20 and 26

31. A system of equations that has no solution is called **inconsistent.** Which systems of equations in Exercises 11–28 are inconsistent? Ex 19, 27, and 28

32. Estimate the solutions to the system of equations below by studying the graph at the right. Check your solutions using substitution in both equations. (0, 1), (2, 1)

$$y = -2x^2 + 4x + 1$$
$$y = x^2 - 2x + 1$$

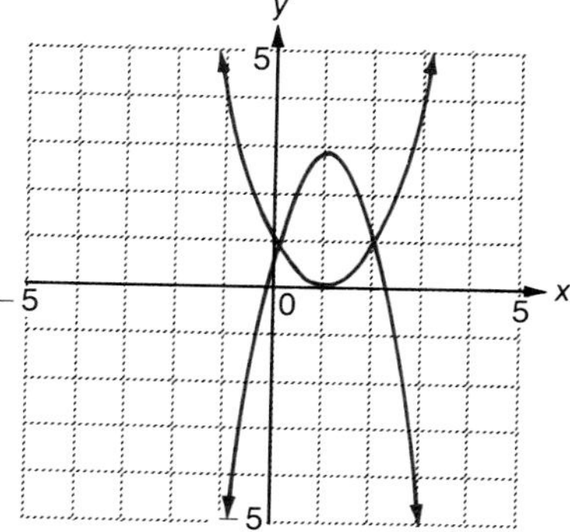

33. *Critical Thinking* The solution of the following system is $(2, -3)$. Find A and B. $A = 2, B = 2$

$$Ax - 3y = 13$$
$$x - By = 8$$

Challenge

34. Solve this system by graphing. What happens when you check your possible solution? Noninteger solutions are difficult to approximate from graphs. Other methods are needed. $\left(\frac{2}{3}, \frac{3}{7}\right)$

$$3x + 7y = 5$$
$$6x - 7y = 1$$

35. Find a system of equations with $(2, -4)$ as the solution. Answers may vary.

36. Find an equation to go with $5x + 2y = 11$ so that the solution to the system of equations is $(3, -2)$. Answers may vary.

Mixed Review

Find the slope and y-intercept. **37.** $x - y = 3$ **38.** $2x = y + 1$
Write an equation in slope-intercept form **39.** for the line with $m = -3$, y-intercept $= 2$ **40.** for the line that contains $(2, 4)$ and $(0, -2)$
Factor. **41.** $4a^2 - 14a - 18$ **42.** $y^3 + 2y^2 + 5y$ **43.** $16m^4 - 1$
Solve. **44.** $m^2 + 5m - 14 = 0$ **45.** $2x^2 - 9x - 5 = 0$

46. The difference of the squares of two consecutive odd positive integers is 40. Find the integers.

Mixed Review

37. $m = 1, b = -3$
38. $m = 2, b = -1$
39. $y = -3x + 2$
40. $y = 3x - 2$
41. $2(a + 1)(2a - 9)$
42. $y(y^2 + 2y + 5)$
43. $(4m^2 + 1)(2m + 1)(2m - 1)$
44. $2, -7$
45. $5, -\frac{1}{2}$
46. 9 and 11

8-2

FIRST FIVE MINUTES

1. Determine whether $(-1, 7)$ is a solution of the system.
$3x - y = -10$
$-x + y = 8$
Yes
2. Solve for x where $5x + 3(2x - 1) = 5$.
$5x + 6x - 3 = 5$
$11x = 8$
$x = \frac{8}{11}$

Substituting for A Variable

In this chapter, students learn several techniques for solving systems of equations. Emphasize that all methods should be learned in order to solve systems of equations efficiently. Finding solutions by graphing is difficult if the points of intersection are noninteger solutions or are far from the origin. Substitution is particularly useful when the coefficient of one of the variables is 1 or -1.

Remind students again of the need to check the solutions in both equations.

Key Questions

- If x equals 6 and $y = 3x + 2$, what is y?
20
- If x equals y and $2y + x = 6$, what is y?
2

8-2 The Substitution Method

Master Grapher Worksheet 7 can be used with this lesson.

Solving systems of equations by graphing is often not accurate if the solutions are not integers. There are several methods for solving systems of equations without graphing. One of these is called the **substitution method.**

Substituting for a Variable

Objective: Solve a system of equations by substituting for a variable.

If a variable in one equation of a system of equations is alone on one side of the equation, you can substitute for that variable in the other equation.

EXAMPLE 1 Solve using the substitution method.

$$x + y = 6$$
$$x = y + 2$$

The second equation states that x and $y + 2$ are equivalent expressions. Thus in the first equation, we can substitute $y + 2$ for x.

$$x + y = 6$$
$$y + 2 + y = 6 \quad \text{Substituting } y + 2 \text{ for } x \text{ in the first equation}$$

Since this equation now has only one variable, we can solve for y.

$$2y + 2 = 6 \quad \text{Collecting like terms}$$
$$2y = 4$$
$$y = 2$$

Next substitute 2 for y in either of the original equations.

$$x + y = 6$$
$$x + 2 = 6 \quad \text{Substituting 2 for } y$$
$$x = 4$$

We check $x = 4$ and $y = 2$ in *both* equations.

Check:

$x + y$	$= 6$
$4 + 2$	6
6	6 ✓

x	$= y + 2$
4	$2 + 2$
4	4 ✓

The solution of the system is (4, 2).

Try This Solve using the substitution method.

a. $x + y = 5$
$x = y + 1$ (3, 2)

b. $a - b = 4$
$b = 2 - 5a$ (1, −3)

c. $y = x + 2$
$y = 2x - 1$ (3, 5)

Sometimes neither equation has a variable alone on one side. We can solve one equation for one of the variables and proceed as before.

EXAMPLE 2 Solve using the substitution method.

$$x - 2y = 6$$
$$3x + 2y = 4$$

Solve the first equation for x.

$$x = 6 + 2y$$

Substitute $6 + 2y$ for x in the second equation.

$$3(6 + 2y) + 2y = 4$$
$$18 + 6y + 2y = 4$$
$$18 + 8y = 4$$
$$8y = -14$$
$$y = -\frac{7}{4}$$

We go back to either of the original equations and substitute $-\frac{7}{4}$ for y. It will be easier to solve for x in the first equation.

$$x - 2\left(-\frac{7}{4}\right) = 6$$
$$x + \frac{7}{2} = 6$$
$$x = \frac{5}{2}$$

We check $\left(\frac{5}{2}, -\frac{7}{4}\right)$ in both equations.

$x - 2y = 6$	
$\frac{5}{2} - 2\left(-\frac{7}{4}\right)$	6
$\frac{5}{2} + \frac{7}{2}$	6
6	6 ✓

$3x + 2y = 4$	
$3 \cdot \frac{5}{2} + 2\left(-\frac{7}{4}\right)$	4
$\frac{15}{2} - \frac{7}{2}$	4
4	4 ✓

The solution of the system is $\left(\frac{5}{2}, -\frac{7}{4}\right)$.

Try This Solve using the substitution method.

d. $x - 2y = 8$
$2x + y = 8$ $\left(\frac{24}{5}, \frac{-8}{5}\right)$

e. $4x - y = 5$
$2x + y = 10$ $\left(\frac{5}{2}, 5\right)$

f. $y = x + 5$
$2x + y = 8$ (1, 6)

g. $3x + 4y = 2$
$2x - y = 5$ (2, −1)

Chalkboard Examples

1. Solve.
$y = 3x$ (1)
$2x + 4y = 28$ (2)
Use (1) to substitute for y in (2).
$2x + 4(3x) = 28$
$2x + 12x = 28$
$14x = 28$
$x = 2$
Substitution in (1) yields
$y = 3(2) = 6$.
The solution (2, 6) checks.

2. Solve.
$2x + y = 13$ (1)
$4x - 3y = 11$ (2)
Solve (1) for y in terms of x.
$y = -2x + 13$
Substitute in (2).
$4x - 3(-2x + 13) = 11$
$4x + 6x - 39 = 11$
$10x = 50$
$x = 5$
Substitution in (1) yields
$y = -2(5) + 13 = 3$.
The solution (5, 3) checks.

Problem Solving

Translating to a system of two equations is often easier than trying to fit all the information into one equation. Point out that if two variables are used, however, then two equations must be written in order to have a unique solution.

Chalkboard Example

1. Translate into a system of linear equations and solve. The sum of a number and twice another number is 13. The first number is 4 larger than the second number. What are the numbers?
   Let x be the first number.
   Let y be the second number.
   $x + 2y = 13$ (1)
   $x = y + 4$ (2)
   Use (2) to substitute for x in (1).
   $(y + 4) + 2y = 13$
   $3y = 9$
   $y = 3$
   Substitute in (2).
   $x = 3 + 4 = 7$
   The solution (7, 3) checks.

LESSON QUIZ

Solve by substitution.

1. $y = 2x + 7$
   $2y - 5x = 11$
   (3, 13)
2. $-3x + y = 5$
   $5x + 2y = 21$
   (1, 8)

Problem Solving

Objective: Solve problems using systems of equations.

PROBLEM-SOLVING GUIDELINES
■ UNDERSTAND the problem
■ Develop and carry out a PLAN
■ Find the ANSWER and CHECK

We can solve many problems by translating to a system of equations and using the Problem-Solving Guidelines as always.

EXAMPLE 3 Translate to a system of equations and solve.

The sum of two numbers is 82. One number is twelve more than the other. Find the larger number.

Let x = one number and y = the other number. There are two statements in this problem.

The sum of two numbers is 82.

$$\underbrace{x + y}_{\text{The sum of two numbers}} \; \underset{\text{is}}{=} \; \underset{82}{82}$$

One number is twelve more than the other number.

$$\underbrace{x}_{\text{One number}} \; \underset{\text{is}}{=} \; \underset{\text{twelve}}{12} \; \underbrace{+}_{\text{more than}} \; \underbrace{y}_{\text{the other number}}$$

Now we have a system of equations.

$$x + y = 82$$
$$x = 12 + y$$

We solve, substituting $12 + y$ for x in the first equation.

$$12 + y + y = 82 \quad \text{Substituting } 12 + y \text{ for } x$$
$$12 + 2y = 82$$
$$2y = 70$$
$$y = 35$$

Next we solve for x by substituting 35 for y in the second equation.

$$x = 12 + 35$$
$$x = 47$$

The two numbers are 47 and 35. We check in the original problem. The sum of 35 and 47 is 82, and 47 is 12 more than 35. The larger number is 47.

Try This Translate to a system of equations and solve.

h. The sum of two numbers is 84. One number is three times the other. Find the numbers. 63, 21

8-2 EXERCISES

A

Solve using the substitution method.

1. $x + y = 4$
   $y = 2x + 1$
2. $x + y = 10$
   $y = x + 8$
3. $x = y - 1$
   $y = 4 - 2x$
4. $x = y + 6$
   $y = -2 - x$
5. $y = 2x - 5$
   $3y - x = 5$
6. $y = 2x + 1$
   $x + y = -2$
7. $x = -2y$
   $x = 2 - 4y$
8. $r = -3s$
   $r = 10 - 4s$
9. $x = 3y - 4$
   $2x - y = 7$
10. $s + t = -4$
    $s - t = 2$
11. $x - y = 6$
    $x + y = -2$
12. $y - 2x = -6$
    $2y - x = 5$
13. $x - y = 5$
    $x + 2y = 7$
14. $2x + 3y = -2$
    $2x - y = 9$
15. $x + 2y = 10$
    $3x + 4y = 8$
16. $x - y = -3$
    $2x + 3y = -6$
17. $3b + 2a = 2$
    $-2b + a = 8$
18. $r - 2s = 0$
    $4r - 3s = 15$
19. $y - 2x = 0$
    $3x + 7y = 17$
20. $x - 3y = 7$
    $-3x + 16y = 28$
21. $8x + 4y = 6$
    $4x = 3 - y$

Translate to a system of equations and solve.

22. The sum of two numbers is 27. One number is 3 more than the other. Find the numbers. 15, 12
23. The sum of two numbers is 36. One number is 2 more than the other. Find the numbers. 19, 17
24. Find two numbers whose sum is 58 and whose difference is 16. 37, 21
25. Find two numbers whose sum is 66 and whose difference is 8. 37, 29
26. The difference between two numbers is 16. Three times the larger number is seven times the smaller. What are the numbers? 28, 12
27. The difference between two numbers is 18. Twice the smaller number plus three times the larger is 74. What are the numbers? 22, 4

B

Solve each system of equations by using the substitution method and by graphing. Explain your results.

28. $3y + 3x = 14$
    $y = -x + 4$
29. $y = x + 5$
    $-3x + 3y = 15$
30. Determine whether $(2, -3)$ is a solution of this system of equations. No

$$x + 3y = -7 \qquad -x + y = -5 \qquad 2x - y = 1$$

Assignment Guide
Minimum: 1–27 e/o, MR

Regular: 1–30 e/o, 31, MR

Advanced: 1–30 m3, 31–34, MR

ADDITIONAL ANSWERS

Exercises

1. (1, 3)
2. (1, 9)
3. (1, 2)
4. (2, −4)
5. (4, 3)
6. (−1, −1)
7. (−2, 1)
8. (−30, 10)
9. (5, 3)
10. (−1, −3)
11. (2, −4)
12. $\left(\frac{17}{3}, \frac{16}{3}\right)$
13. $\left(\frac{17}{3}, \frac{2}{3}\right)$
14. $\left(\frac{25}{8}, \frac{-11}{4}\right)$
15. (−12, 11)
16. (−3, 0)
17. (4, −2)
18. (6, 3)
19. (1, 2)
20. (28, 7)
21. $\left(\frac{3}{4}, 0\right)$

28. Substitution yields 12 = 14. Since this equation is false for all values of x, there are no solutions.

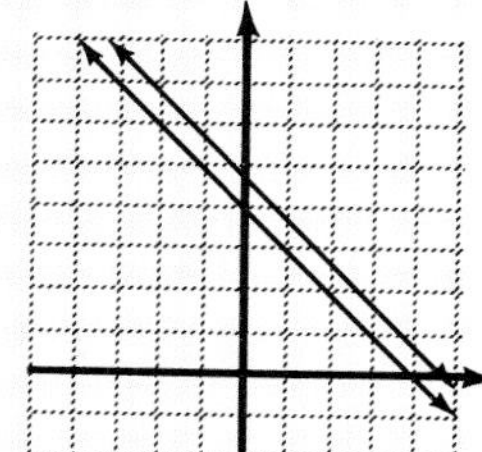

29. Substitution yields 15 = 15. Since this equation is true for all values of x, there are infinitely many solutions.

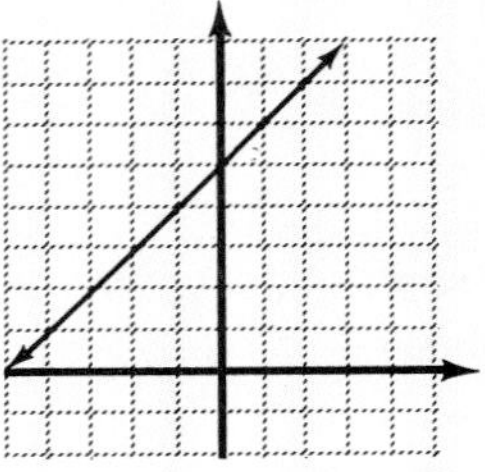

32. (2, −1, 3)
33. (30, 50, 100)
34. Answers may vary. For example: $x = 10 - z$ and $y = 10 - z$, so $(10 - z) + (10 - z) + z = 10$ or $z = 10$. $x = 10 - z$, so $x = 0$, and $y = 10 - z$, so $y = 0$. Then $x + y = 0$, but we know $x + y = 10$, so there is no solution.

Mixed Review

35. Yes
36. Yes
37. No
38. $(3a - b)^2$
39. $y^2(6y - 5)(6y + 5)$
40. $(x - 2yz^2)^2$
41. $(3x + 2z^3)^2$
42. −5
43. 5
44. 5, −5
45. $\frac{7}{2}, -\frac{7}{2}$
46. 95 cm, 80 cm
47. 5 in.

Problem for Programmers

This program can be written using any programming language (BASIC, PASCAL, LOGO, etc.).

This program can also be written on a spreadsheet where the values of *a*, *b*, and *c* are each input in a separate column, and the ordered pair in two more columns. The evaluation can be calculated in another column and compared with the value of *c*.

31. ***Critical Thinking*** Here are two equivalent systems of equations. Find the values of A and B. $A = 6, B = 4$

$$x + 2y = 2 \qquad Ax + 5y = -9$$
$$5x - 3y = -29 \qquad x + By = 8$$

Challenge

Here are systems of three equations in three variables. Use the substitution method to solve.

32. $x + y + z = 4$, $x - 2y - z = 1$, $y = -1$

33. $x + y + z = 180$, $x = z - 70$, $2y - z = 0$

34. Why is there no solution to the following system? (Hint: Use substitution more than once.)

$$x + y = 10$$
$$y + z = 10$$
$$x + z = 10$$
$$x + y + z = 10$$

Mixed Review

Determine whether the graphs of the equations are parallel.

35. $y = 2x - 9$, $y - 2x = 11$ **36.** $6y - 21x = 3$, $8y - 5 = 28x$ **37.** $4y + 9 = x$, $5 - 2y = 8x$

Factor. **38.** $9a^2 - 6ab + b^2$ **39.** $36y^4 - 25y^2$

40. $x^2 - 4xyz^2 + 4y^2z^4$ **41.** $9x^2 + 12xz^3 + 4z^6$

Solve. **42.** $n^2 + 10n + 25 = 0$ **43.** $n^2 - 10n + 25 = 0$

44. $n^2 - 25 = 0$ **45.** $4n^2 - 49 = 0$

46. The perimeter of a rectangle is 350 cm. The width is 15 cm shorter than the length. What are the length and the width of this rectangle?

47. If the sides of a square are lengthened by 8 in., the area becomes 169 in^2. Find the length of a side of the original square.

Problem for Programmers

Write a program that will check any ordered pair to see if it is a solution of the equation $4x + 5y = 1$. Test your program using the ordered pairs (1, 1), (−1, 1), (1, −1), and (4.5, −3.4).

Challenge: Extend this program so that it will check any ordered pair to see if it is a solution of any equation of the form $ax + by = c$ where the ordered pair is input as well as a, b, and c.

8-3 The Addition Method

Using the Addition Method

Objective: Solve a system of equations using the addition method.

Another method for solving systems of equations is called the **addition method.** It is especially useful when both equations are written in standard form, $Ax + By = C$.

EXAMPLE 1 Solve using the addition method.

$$x + y = 5$$
$$x - y = 1$$

According to the second equation, $x - y$ and 1 are equivalent expressions. The addition property for equations states that we can add the same number or expression to both sides of an equation and still have a true equation. Thus we can add $x - y$ to the left side and 1 to the right side of the first equation.

$$\begin{aligned} x + y &= 5 \\ x - y &= 1 \\ \hline 2x + 0y &= 6 && \text{Using the addition property} \\ 2x &= 6 \\ x &= 3 && \text{Solving for } x \end{aligned}$$

Next substitute 3 for x in either of the original equations.

$$\begin{aligned} x + y &= 5 \\ 3 + y &= 5 && \text{Substituting 3 for } x \text{ in the first equation} \\ y &= 2 && \text{Solving for } y \end{aligned}$$

Check $x = 3$ and $y = 2$ in both equations.

Check:

$x + y$	$= 5$
$3 + 2$	5
5	5 ✓

$x - y$	$= 1$
$3 - 2$	1
1	1 ✓

The solution of the system is (3, 2).

Try This Solve using the addition method.

a. $x + y = 5$
$2x - y = 4$ (3, 2)

b. $3x - 3y = 6$
$3x + 3y = 0$ (1, −1)

8-3

FIRST FIVE MINUTES

1. Solve.
$y = 5x - 30$
$2x - 2y = 4$
The solution is (7, 5).
2. Solve.
$6x + y = 18$
$3x + 2y = 18$
The solution is (2, 6).

Using the Addition Method

Remind students of the addition property of equality. If the same number is added to both sides of a true equation, then the result is a true equation.

Emphasize that any system of equations may be solved by either the substitution method or the addition method. However, one is usually easier than the other, depending on the system of equations. Students should learn to recognize and use the appropriate method.

Key Questions

- If $a = b$ and $c = d$, what does $a + c$ equal?
$b + d$
- If $a + b = 0$ and $a - b = 0$, what does a equal?
0

Chalkboard Example

1. Solve.
$2x + 3y = 11$ (1)
$-2x + 9y = 1$ (2)
Add (1) and (2) to get
$0 + 12y = 12$
$y = 1$
Substitute in (1).
$2x + 3(1) = 11$
Solve for x.
$2x = 8$
$x = 4$
The solution (4, 1) checks.

Using the Multiplication Property First

Remind students of the multiplication property of equality. If both sides of a true equation are multiplied by the same number, then the result is a true equation.

Avoiding Common Errors

Students commonly forget to multiply both sides of an equation by a constant. Remind students that the multiplication property requires that all terms on both sides be multiplied to preserve equality.

> **Math Point**
> A constant multiple of one equation added to a constant multiple of a second equation results in a linear combination of the two equations. Its graph will intersect the graphs of the original two equations only where the graphs of the original two equations also intersect.

Key Questions

- If $a = b$, what does ac equal?
  bc
- When using the multiplication method, does the solution satisfy the original equations or the modified equations?
  Both

Chalkboard Examples

1. Solve.
   $5x + 3y = 22$ (1)
   $5x + 6y = 34$ (2)
   Multiply (2) by -1.
   $-5x - 6y = -34$
   Add to equation (1).
   $0 - 3y = -12$
   $y = 4$
   Substitute in (1).
   $5x + 3(4) = 22$
   $5x = 10$
   $x = 2$
   The solution (2, 4) checks.

Using the Multiplication Property First

Objective: Solve a system of equations by using the multiplication and addition properties.

The multiplication property for equations states that we can multiply each side of an equation by the same number and still have a true equation. Sometimes we may need to multiply both sides of an equation by a number before using the addition method.

EXAMPLE 2 Solve using the addition method.

$$\begin{aligned} 2x + 3y &= 8 \\ x + 3y &= 7 \end{aligned}$$

If we add the equations, no variables will be eliminated. If the $3y$ in the second equation were $-3y$, the y-terms would be additive inverses and would be eliminated when added. We use the multiplication property to multiply both sides of the second equation by -1 and add the two equations. This new equation is called a **linear combination** of the original equations.

$$\begin{aligned} 2x + 3y &= 8 &\longrightarrow\quad 2x + 3y &= 8 \\ -1(x + 3y) &= -1(7) &\longrightarrow\quad \underline{-x - 3y} &\underline{= -7} \\ & & x &= 1 \quad \text{Adding} \end{aligned}$$

Substitute 1 for x in either of the original equations.

$$\begin{aligned} x + 3y &= 7 \\ 1 + 3y &= 7 \quad \text{Substituting 1 for } x \text{ in the second equation} \\ 3y &= 6 \\ y &= 2 \quad \text{Solving for } y \end{aligned}$$

Substitution will show that (1, 2) checks in both equations. The solution of the system is (1, 2).

Try This Solve using the addition method.

c. $5x + 3y = 17$
$5x - 2y = -3$ (1, 4)

d. $8x + 11y = 37$
$-2x + 11y = 7$ $\left(3, \frac{13}{11}\right)$

In Example 2, we used the multiplication property for equations, multiplying by -1. We often need to multiply by some number other than -1.

EXAMPLE 3 Solve.

$$\begin{aligned} 3x + 6y &= -6 \\ 5x - 2y &= 14 \end{aligned}$$

If the y-term of the second equation were $-6y$, the y-terms would be additive inverses and could be eliminated by using the addition property.

We can multiply the second equation by 3 to get $-6y$.

$$\begin{aligned} 3x + 6y &= -6 &\longrightarrow\quad 3x + 6y &= -6 \\ 3(5x - 2y) &= 3(14) &\longrightarrow\quad 15x - 6y &= 42 \\ & & 18x \qquad &= 36 \quad \text{Adding} \\ & & x &= 2 \end{aligned}$$

Substitute 2 for x in either of the original equations.

$$\begin{aligned} 3(2) + 6y &= -6 && \text{Substituting 2 for } x \text{ in the first equation} \\ 6 + 6y &= -6 \\ 6y &= -12 \\ y &= -2 && \text{Solving for } y \end{aligned}$$

Substitution will show that $(2, -2)$ checks in both equations. The solution of the system is $(2, -2)$.

Try This Solve.

e. $4a + 7b = 11$
$4a + 6b = 10$ (1, 1)

f. $7x - 5y = 76$
$4x + y = 55$ (13, 3)

g. $5b + 10c = 15$
$3b - 2c = -7$ (−1, 2)

When we use the addition method for solving systems of equations, we sometimes need to use the multiplication property more than once.

EXAMPLE 4 Solve.

$$\begin{aligned} 3x + 5y &= 30 \\ 5x + 8y &= 49 \end{aligned}$$

We can multiply the first equation by 5 and the second by -3 to make the x-terms additive inverses.

$$\begin{aligned} 5(3x + 5y) &= 5(30) &\longrightarrow\quad 15x + 25y &= 150 \\ -3(5x + 8y) &= -3(49) &\longrightarrow\quad -15x - 24y &= -147 \\ & & y &= 3 \quad \text{Adding} \end{aligned}$$

Substitute 3 for y in one of the original equations.

$$\begin{aligned} 3x + 5y &= 30 && \text{Choosing the first equation} \\ 3x + 5(3) &= 30 && \text{Substituting 3 for } y \\ 3x &= 15 \\ x &= 5 \end{aligned}$$

Substitution will show that $(5, 3)$ checks in both equations. The solution of the system is $(5, 3)$.

Try This Solve.

h. $5x + 3y = 2$
$3x + 5y = -2$ (1, −1)

i. $6x + 2y = 4$
$10x + 7y = -8$ (2, −4)

---

2. Solve.
$-6x + 5y = 4$ (1)
$3x + 4y = 11$ (2)
Multiply (2) by 2 to get
$6x + 8y = 22$
Now add this to (1).
$0 + 13y = 26$
$y = 2$
Substitute in (1).
$-6x + 5(2) = 4$
$-6x = -6$
$x = 1$
The solution (1, 2) checks.

3. Solve.
$2x + 3y = 23$ (1)
$3x + 5y = 37$ (2)
Multiply equation (1) by 3, and equation (2) by -2 to get
$6x + 9y = 69$ (1)
$-6x - 10y = -74$ (2)
Add.
$0 - y = -5$
$y = 5$
Substitute in (1).
$2x + 3(5) = 23$
$2x = 8$
$x = 4$
The solution (4, 5) checks.

Problem Solving

Chalkboard Example

1. Four times a certain number is three more than twice another number. The sum of the first number and twice the second number is 5. Find the numbers.

Let x be the first number.
Let y be the second number.

$4x = 2y + 3$ (1)
$x + 2y = 5$ (2)

When the first equation is written in standard form the system becomes

$4x - 2y = 3$ (1)
$x + 2y = 5$ (2)

Add.

$5x = 8$

$x = \frac{8}{5}$

Substitute in (2).

$\left(\frac{8}{5}\right) + 2y = 5$

Solve for y.

$2y = \frac{17}{5}$

$y = \frac{17}{10}$

The solution is $\left(\frac{8}{5}, \frac{17}{10}\right)$.

LESSON QUIZ

1. Solve using the addition method.
$3x - 4y = 7$ (1)
$2x + 4y = 8$ (2)
$\left(3, \frac{1}{2}\right)$

2. Solve using the addition method.
$4x - 3y = 3$ (1)
$8x + 5y = 50$ (2)
$\left(\frac{15}{4}, 4\right)$

Problem Solving

Objective: Solve problems using the addition method.

PROBLEM-SOLVING GUIDELINES
■ UNDERSTAND the problem
■ Develop and carry out a PLAN
■ Find the ANSWER and CHECK

Once we have translated a problem to a system of equations, we can use the addition method to solve.

EXAMPLE 5 Translate to a system of equations and solve.

The sum of two numbers is 56. One third of the first number plus one fourth of the second number is 16. Find the numbers.

Let x = the first number and y = the second number. We translate to a system of equations.

$$x + y = 56$$
$$\frac{1}{3}x + \frac{1}{4}y = 16$$

First we clear the second equation of fractions.

$$x + y = 56 \longrightarrow x + y = 56$$
$$12\left(\frac{1}{3}x + \frac{1}{4}y\right) = 12(16) \longrightarrow 4x + 3y = 192$$

Next we multiply both sides of the first equation by -4.

$$-4(x + y) = -4(56) \longrightarrow -4x - 4y = -224$$
$$4x + 3y = 192 \longrightarrow 4x + 3y = 192$$
$$-y = -32$$
$$y = 32$$

Substitute for y in either of the first equations.

$x + 32 = 56$ Substituting 32 for y in the first equation
$x = 24$

The two numbers are 24 and 32.

Their sum, $24 + 32$, is 56. One third of 24 is 8. One fourth of 32 is 8, and the sum, $8 + 8$, is 16. The answer checks.

Try This Translate to a system of equations and solve.

j. The difference between two numbers is 36. One sixth of the larger number minus one ninth of the smaller number is 11. Find the numbers.
126, 90

8-3 EXERCISES

A

Solve using the addition method.

1. $x + y = 10$
$x - y = 8$

2. $x - y = 7$
$x + y = 3$

3. $x + y = 8$
$-x + 2y = 7$

4. $x + y = 6$
$-x + 3y = -2$

5. $3x - y = 9$
$2x + y = 6$

6. $4x - y = 1$
$3x + y = 13$

7. $4a + 3b = 7$
$-4a + b = 5$

8. $7c + 5d = 18$
$c - 5d = -2$

9. $8x - 5y = -9$
$3x + 5y = -2$

10. $3a - 3b = -15$
$-3a - 3b = -3$

11. $4x - 5y = 7$
$-4x + 5y = 7$

12. $2x + 3y = 4$
$-2x - 3y = -4$

Solve.

13. $-x - y = 8$
$2x - y = -1$

14. $x + y = -7$
$3x + y = -9$

15. $x + 3y = 19$
$x - y = -1$

16. $3x - y = 8$
$x + 2y = 5$

17. $x + y = 5$
$5x - 3y = 17$

18. $x - y = 7$
$4x - 5y = 25$

19. $2w + 3z = 17$
$3w + 4z = 24$

20. $7p + 5q = 2$
$8p - 9q = 17$

21. $2a + 3b = -1$
$3a + 5b = -2$

22. $3x - 4y = 16$
$5x + 6y = 14$

23. $x - 3y = 0$
$5x - y = -14$

24. $5a - 2b = 0$
$2a - 3b = -11$

25. $3x - 2y = 10$
$5x + 3y = 4$

26. $2p + 5q = 9$
$3p - 2q = 4$

27. $3x - 8y = 11$
$x + 6y - 8 = 0$

28. $m - n = 32$
$3m - 8n - 6 = 0$

29. $a + b = 12$
$\frac{1}{2}a + \frac{1}{4}b = 4$

30. $2p - q = 8$
$\frac{1}{3}p + \frac{1}{4}q = 3$

Translate to a system of equations and solve.

31. The sum of two numbers is 115. The difference is 21. Find the numbers. 68, 47

32. The sum of two numbers is 26.4. One is five times the other. Find the numbers. 22, 4.4

33. The sum of two numbers is 92. One eighth of the first number plus one third of the second number is 19. Find the numbers. 56, 36

34. The difference of two numbers is 49. One half of the larger number plus one seventh of the smaller number is 56. Find the numbers. 98, 49

35. The sum of the length and width of a rectangle is 19 in. The length is one less than twice the width. Find the length and width of the rectangle. $\frac{37}{3}$ in., $\frac{20}{3}$ in.

36. The perimeter of a rectangle is 48 m. The width of the rectangle is 2 more than half the length. Find the length and the width. $\frac{44}{3}$ m, $\frac{28}{3}$ m

Assignment Guide

Minimum: Day 1: 1–21 e/o, MR
Day 2: 22–38 e/o

Regular: Day 1: 1–30 e/o
Day 2: 31–43 e/o, 44, MR

Advanced: 1–38 m4, 39–49, MR

ADDITIONAL ANSWERS

Exercises

1. (9, 1)
2. (5, −2)
3. (3, 5)
4. (5, 1)
5. (3, 0)
6. (2, 7)
7. $\left(\frac{-1}{2}, 3\right)$
8. $\left(2, \frac{4}{5}\right)$
9. $\left(-1, \frac{1}{5}\right)$
10. (−2, 3)
11. No solution
12. Infinitely many solutions
13. (−3, −5)
14. (−1, −6)
15. (4, 5)
16. (3, 1)
17. (4, 1)
18. (10, 3)
19. (4, 3)
20. (1, −1)
21. (1, −1)
22. (4, −1)
23. (−3, −1)
24. (2, 5)
25. (2, −2)
26. (2, 1)
27. $\left(5, \frac{1}{2}\right)$
28. (50, 18)
29. (4, 8)
30. (6, 4)

Mixed Review

50. No
51. Yes
52. Yes
53. (5, 2)
54. (−4, 2)
55. $(2m^2 - 1)(m - 2)$
56. $3(y + 2)(y - 2)$
57. $xz(x - z)$
58. $-2a^2b + ab^2$
59. $y^2 + 4xy + 3x$

37. Two angles are complementary. Their difference is 34°. Find the angles. (Complementary angles are angles whose sum is 90°.) 62°, 28°

38. Two angles are complementary. One angle is 42° more than one half the other. Find the angles. 58°, 32°

B

Solve each system.

39. $3(x - y) = 9$
$x + y = 7$ (5, 2)

40. $5(a - b) = 10$
$a + b = 2$ (2, 0)

41. $2(x - y) = 3 + x$
$x = 3y + 4$ (1, −1)

42. $2(5a - 5b) = 10$
$-5(6a + 2b) = 10$ (0, −1)

43. $1.5x + 0.85y = 1637.5$
$0.01(x + y) = 15.25$ (525, 1000)

44. ***Critical Thinking*** Suppose we can get a system into the form

$$ax + by = c$$
$$dx + ey = f$$

where a, b, c, d, e, and f are any positive or negative rational numbers. Solve the system for x and y. $x = \frac{ce - bf}{ae - bd}$, $y = \frac{af - cd}{ae - bd}$

Challenge

Solve each system.

45. $y = ax + b$
$y = x + c$ $\left(\frac{b - c}{1 - a}, \frac{b - ac}{1 - a}\right)$

46. $ax + by + c = 0$
$ax + cy + b = 0$ $\left(\frac{-b - c}{a}, 1\right)$

47. $3(7 - a) - 2(1 + 2b) + 5 = 0$
$3a + 2b - 18 = 0$ (4, 3)

48. $\frac{2}{x} - \frac{3}{y} = -\frac{1}{2}$, and $\frac{1}{x} + \frac{2}{y} = \frac{11}{12}$ (4, 3)

49. Use the pattern of your solution in Exercise 44 to solve the following system.

$$14x - 10y = 2600$$
$$24x + 20y = 520$$ (110, −106)

Mixed Review

Determine whether the graphs of the equations are perpendicular.

50. $8y - 3x = 10$
$-6y - 3x = 4$

51. $3x + 2y = 1$
$2x - 3y = 4$

52. $8x + y = 10$
$x - 8y = 0$

Solve by graphing.

53. $x + 2y = 9$
$3y - x = 1$

54. $3x + 5y = -2$
$2y - 7x = 32$

Factor. 55. $2m^3 - 4m^2 - m + 2$ 56. $3y^2 - 12$ 57. $x^2z - xz^2$

Simplify. 58. $(a^2b + 2ab^2) - (3a^2b + ab^2)$

59. $(3y^2 - xy + 2x) + (5xy - 2y^2 + x)$

8-4 Problem Solving: Using Systems of Equations

Objective: Solve problems using systems of equations.

Systems of two equations with two variables are often used to solve problems. When you use two variables, you must remember to write two equations in order to have one solution.

After a problem is translated to a system of equations, you must decide whether to use the substitution or addition method.

PROBLEM-SOLVING GUIDELINES
■ UNDERSTAND the problem
■ Develop and carry out a PLAN
■ Find the ANSWER and CHECK

We can use the Problem-Solving Guidelines to solve problems involving systems of equations.

EXAMPLE 1

A baseball team played 162 games. They won 44 more games than they lost. How many games did they lose?

■ **UNDERSTAND the problem**

Question: How many games did the team lose?
Data: Total games played = 162; 44 more games were won than lost.

■ **Develop and carry out a PLAN**

Let x = the number of games won and y = the number of games lost. There are two statements in this problem.

The number of games won plus the number of games lost is 162

$$x + y = 162$$

The number of games won minus the number of games lost is 44

$$x - y = 44$$

We solve the system of equations by the addition method.

$$\begin{aligned} x + y &= 162 \\ x - y &= 44 \\ \hline 2x \quad &= 206 && \text{Adding} \\ x &= 103 && \text{Number of games won} \end{aligned}$$

$$\begin{aligned} x + y &= 162 && \text{Choosing the first equation} \\ 103 + y &= 162 && \text{Substituting 103 for } x \\ y &= 59 && \text{Number of games lost} \end{aligned}$$

8-4

FIRST FIVE MINUTES

1. Solve.
$$y = 3x - 2 \quad (1)$$
$$2x + 5y = 7 \quad (2)$$
Substitute for y in (2).
$$2x + 5(3x - 2) = 7$$
$$17x = 17$$
$$x = 1$$
Substitute in (1).
$$y = 3(1) - 2 = 1$$
The solution is (1, 1).
2. Solve.
$$5x - 2y = 4 \quad (1)$$
$$2x + 4y = 16 \quad (2)$$
Multiply (1) by 2 to get
$$10x - 4y = 8 \quad (1)$$
Add to (2) to get
$$12x + 0 = 24$$
$$x = 2$$
Substitute in (2).
$$2(2) + 4y = 16$$
$$4y = 12$$
$$y = 3$$
The solution is (2, 3).

Emphasize that several methods can be used to get a correct answer. Ask the class for different methods. Praise the odd or unexpected approach; it may show some intellectual courage.

Chalkboard Examples

1. Translate into a system of equations and solve. The Acme Transportation company owns three times as many mini-buses as regular buses. There are 60 more mini-buses than regular buses. How many of each does Acme own?
Let m be the number of mini-buses.
Let r be the number of regular buses.
$m = 3r$
$m = r + 60$
Substitute $3r$ for m in the second equation.
$3r = r + 60$
$2r = 60$
$r = 30$
$m = 3r$
$m = 90$
Acme owns 90 mini-buses and 30 regular buses.

2. Bob is 6 years older than Fred. Fred is half as old as Bob. How old are they?
Let b be the age of Bob.
Let f be the age of Fred.
$b = f + 6$ (1)
$f = \frac{1}{2}b$ (2)
Substitute for f in (1).
$b = \left(\frac{1}{2}b\right) + 6$
Solve for b.
$\frac{1}{2}b = 6$
$b = 12$
Substitute in (2).
$f = \frac{1}{2}(12)$
$f = 6$
Bob is 12.
Fred is 6.

3. Computer Information Inc. charges $10 per month plus $7 per minute for computer access to its information. Data Access Corporation charges $20 per month plus $5 per minute. For what number of minutes are the charges the same?
Let c be the cost in dollars. Let t be the time used, in minutes. For CII the cost is
$c = 10 + 7t$
For DAC the cost is
$c = 20 + 5t$
Substituting $10 + 7t$ for c,
$10 + 7t = 20 + 5t$
Solve for t.
$2t = 10$
$t = 5$
The companies charge the same amount for five minutes.

■ **Find the ANSWER and CHECK**

The team lost 59 games. They won 103 games, which is 44 more than they lost, and played a total of 162 games. The answer checks.

Try This Translate to a system of equations and solve.

a. An automobile dealer sold 180 vans and trucks at a sale. He sold 40 more vans than trucks. How many of each did he sell? 70 trucks, 110 vans

EXAMPLE 2

Ramon sells cars and trucks. He has room on his lot for 510 vehicles. From experience he knows that his profits will be greatest if he has 190 more cars than trucks. How many of each vehicle should he have?

Let x = the number of cars and y = the number of trucks.

Number of cars plus number of trucks is 510 — Rewording

$x + y = 510$ — Translating

Number of cars is 190 plus number of trucks — Rewording

$x = 190 + y$ — Translating

We now have a system of equations.

$$x + y = 510$$
$$x = 190 + y$$

We use the substitution method to solve this system. — Substituting $190 + y$ for x in the first equation

$$(190 + y) + y = 510$$
$$190 + 2y = 510$$
$$2y = 320$$
$$y = 160 \quad \text{Number of trucks}$$

Substituting 160 for y in the second equation, we have

$$x = 190 + 160$$
$$x = 350$$

The solution of this system is (350, 160).
Ramon should have 350 cars and 160 trucks in his lot.

The number of cars, 350, plus 160 trucks is 510 vehicles. Also, 350 is 190 more than 160. The answer checks.

Try This Translate to a system of equations and solve.

b. A family went camping at a place 45 km from town. They drove 13 km more than they walked to get to the campsite. How far did they walk? 16 km

EXAMPLE 3

Shirley is 21 years older than Laura. In six years, Shirley will be twice as old as Laura. How old are they now?
Let x = Shirley's age and y = Laura's age.

	Age now	Age in 6 years
Shirley	x	$x + 6$
Laura	y	$y + 6$

Recording the data in a *table* helps you write equations.

Shirley's age now is 21 more than Laura's age now.

$$x = 21 + y$$

Shirley's age in 6 years will be twice Laura's age in 6 years.

$$x + 6 = 2(y + 6)$$

We have a system of equations.

$$x = 21 + y$$
$$x + 6 = 2(y + 6)$$

Simplifying the second equation gives $x = 2y + 6$.

$$x = 21 + y$$
$$x = 2y + 6$$

Next we use the substitution method.

$2y + 6 = 21 + y$ Substituting $2y + 6$ for x in the first equation

$y = 15$ Laura's age now

We substitute 15 for y in $x = 21 + y$.

$x = 21 + 15$

$x = 36$ Shirley's age now

Shirley is 36 and Laura is 15.

Shirley's age, 36, is 21 more than Laura's age, 15. In six years, Shirley will be 42 and Laura will be 21. The answers check.

Try This Translate to a system of equations and solve.

c. Wilma is 13 years older than Bev. In nine years, Wilma will be twice as old as Bev. How old is Bev? 4

d. Stan is two thirds as old as Adam. In 7 years, Stan will be three fourths as old as Adam. How old are they now? 14, 21

e. Four pencils and two pens cost $0.74. Six pencils and five pens cost $1.53. Find the cost of a pencil and a pen. $0.08, $0.21

LESSON ENRICHMENT

Although the problems in this lesson are more efficiently solved using the substitution or addition methods, graphic solutions can be very useful. The graph for Example 4 follows.

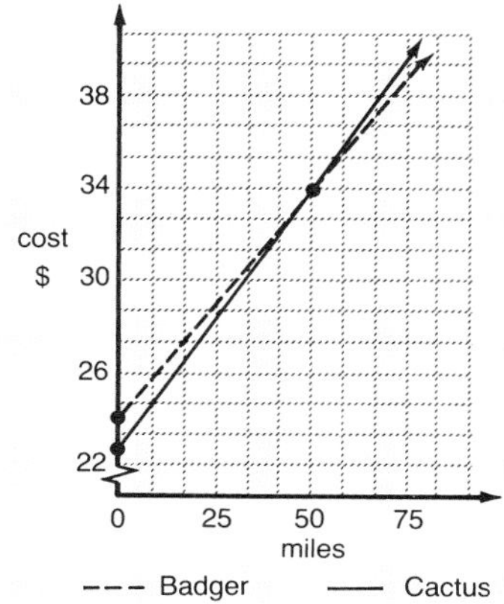

From this graph students can estimate which rent-a-car company would be better for various mileages.

Ask students to give graphic solutions for Exercises 9, 10, and 19. Then ask them to expand their answers (e.g., under what circumstances would each company be preferred?).

LESSON QUIZ

1. A class has 31 students. There are 5 more boys than girls. How many girls are there?
   13
2. Together Lucas and Beverly have \$52. Beverly has \$1 more than twice as much as Lucas has. How much money does Beverly have?
   \$35

EXAMPLE 4

Badger Rent-a-Car rents compact cars at a daily rate of \$23.95 plus 20¢ per mile. Cactus Rent-a-Car rents compact cars at a daily rate of \$22.95 plus 22¢ per mile. For what mileage is the cost the same?

Let m represent the mileage.

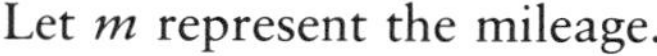

Let c represent the cost.

	Charge per mile (\$)	Charge for m miles (\$)	Daily Rate (\$)
Badger	0.20	$0.20m$	23.95
Cactus	0.22	$0.22m$	22.95

We write the cost for Badger. $23.95 + 0.20m$

We write the cost for Cactus. $22.95 + 0.22m$

We want the cost for both to be the same, so both can equal c.

We have a system of equations.

$$\begin{aligned} 23.95 + 0.20m &= c \\ 22.95 + 0.22m &= c \end{aligned}$$

Clear the system of decimals and multiply the second equation by -1. Then we use the addition method to solve the system.

$$\begin{array}{r} 2395 + 20m = 100c \\ -2295 - 22m = -100c \\ \hline 100 - 2m = 0 \\ 100 = 2m \\ 50 = m \quad \text{mileage} \end{array}$$

If the cars are driven 50 miles, the cost will be the same.

We can substitute for m in both equations to see if the cost is the same.

$$\begin{aligned} c &= 23.95 + 0.20(50) = \$33.95 \\ c &= 22.95 + 0.22(50) = \$33.95 \end{aligned}$$

The cost is the same. The answer checks.

Try This Translate to a system of equations and solve.

f. Acme rents a station wagon at a daily rate of \$21.95 plus 23¢ per mile. Speedo Rentzit rents a wagon for \$24.95 plus 19¢ per mile. For what mileage is the cost the same? 75 miles

8-4 EXERCISES

A

Translate to a system of equations and solve.

1. Marco has 150 coins, all nickels and dimes. He has 12 more dimes than nickels. How many nickels and how many dimes does he have?

a. Let n be the number of nickels and d be the number of dimes. Write an equation that shows that the sum of the number of nickels and the number of dimes is 150. $n + d = 150$

b. Which equation shows that there are 12 more dimes than nickels: $n + 12 = d$ or $d + 12 = n$? $n + 12 = d$

c. Show the system of equations that can be used to solve this problem. $n + d = 150, n + 12 = d$

d. Solve the system of equations and answer the problem. 69 nickels, 81 dimes

2. Use the sales receipts at the right to find the cost of a taco and a glass of milk.

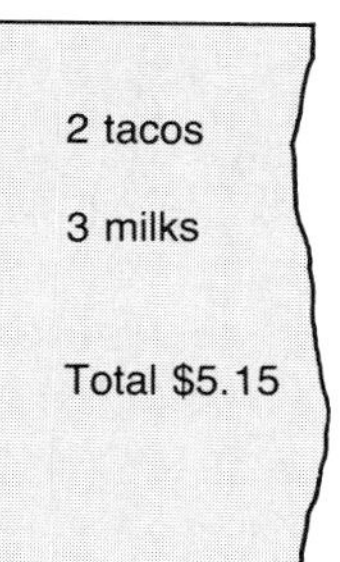

a. Let t be the cost of a taco and m be the cost of a glass of milk. Write an expression that shows that the sum is $2.10. $t + m = \$2.10$

b. Write an expression for the cost of two tacos. $2t$

c. Write an expression for the cost of three glasses of milk. $3m$

d. Write an equation that shows that the total cost for two tacos and three glasses of milk is $5.15. $2t + 3m = \$5.15$

e. Show the system of equations you can use to solve this problem. $t + m = 2.1, 2t + 3m = 5.15$

f. Solve the system of equations and answer the problem. milk $.95, taco $1.15

3. Four oranges and five apples cost $2.00. Three oranges and four apples cost $1.56. Find the cost of an orange and the cost of an apple. 20¢, 24¢

4. Zelma is eighteen years older than her son. She was three times as old as he was one year ago. How old are they now? 28, 10

5. Tyrone is twice as old as his daughter. In six years Tyrone's age will be three times what his daughter's age was six years ago. How old are they at present? 48, 24

6. Frederique is two years older than her brother. Twelve years ago she was twice as old as he was. How old are they now? 16, 14

7. The perimeter of a rectangle is 160 ft. One fourth the length is the same as twice the width. Find the dimensions of the rectangle. $71\frac{1}{9}$ ft, $8\frac{8}{9}$ ft

Assignment Guide
Minimum: 1–16 e/o, MR

Regular: 1–19 e/o, 20, MR

Advanced: 1–19 m3, 20–23, MR

8. On a fishing trip, Mariko caught twenty-four fish. She caught some rockfish averaging 2.5 lb. and some bluefish averaging 8 lb. The total weight of the fish was 137 lb. How many of each kind of fish did she catch? 10 rock, 14 blue

9. Safety Rent-a-Car rents an intermediate-size car at a daily rate of $21.95 plus 19¢ per mile. City Rentals rents an intermediate-size car for $18.95 plus 21¢ per mile. For what mileage is the cost the same? 150 mi

10. Sunshine Car Rentals rents a basic car at a daily rate of $17.99 plus 18¢ per mile. City Rentals rents a basic car at $18.95 plus 16¢ per mile. For what mileage is the cost the same? 48 mi

11. Six apples and three oranges cost $1.77. Two apples and five oranges cost $1.27. Find the cost of an apple and the cost of an orange. $0.21, $0.17

12. Susan wants to have business cards printed. One style will cost $25 plus 2 cents per card. Another style will cost $10 plus 5 cents per card. For how many cards will the cost be the same for both styles? 500 cards

13. The Booster Club voted on where they would go for their annual trip. A majority of the club voted to go to a baseball game. They bought 29 tickets. Some of the tickets cost $7 each and some cost $9 each. All of the tickets cost $225. How many tickets of each price did they buy? 18 $7 tickets, 11 $9 tickets

TICKET INFORMATION	
Lower Box................	$10.00
Upper Box................	$ 9.00
Lower Reserved...........	$ 8.00
Upper Reserved...........	$ 7.00
General Admission	$ 2.50
General Admission .... (Fans 14 and under, except Opening Night, Sundays, Holidays and Concert dates. Must be accompanied by an adult.)	$ 1.00

14. Jermaine was in charge of buying milk for a class picnic for 32 students. Milk is sold in half-gallon cartons and gallon cartons at a neighborhood grocery store. The half-gallon carton costs $1 and the gallon carton costs $1.70. When he got to the store, there was not much milk left. Jermaine bought all 21 cartons they had and paid a total of $29.40. How many cartons of each size did he buy? $9\frac{1}{2}$ - gal, 12 gal

15. Lorena bought 10 packs of styrofoam cups for the graduation dance. A pack of fifty 12-oz cups costs $1.80 and a pack of fifty 16-oz cups costs $2.40. Lorena paid a total of $21.60 excluding tax. How many packs of each size cup did she buy? 4 12-oz, 6 16-oz

16. The Taylor family reunion had a record turnout of 38 people last year. For a change of pace, they decided to go ice skating instead of having a picnic. Admission for the group cost $153.50 (including skates). How many adults and how many children were at the reunion? 22 adults, 16 children

ICELAND SKATING RINK	
Admission:	
ADULTS	$2.75
CHILDREN	$1.50
Admission and skate rental:	
ADULTS	$4.25
CHILDREN	$3.75

B

17. In Lewis Carroll's *Through the Looking Glass,* Tweedledum says to Tweedledee, "The sum of your weight and twice mine is 361 pounds." Then Tweedledee says to Tweedledum, "Contrariwise, the sum of your weight and twice mine is 362 pounds." Find the weight of Tweedledum and Tweedledee.

18. During a publicity campaign, a cycle shop gave away 5000 miniature cycles and bumper stickers. The cycles cost 21¢ each and the bumper stickers cost 14¢ each. The cycle shop spent $826 on the gifts. How many of each gift did they buy?

19. Fenton Rent-a-Car charges $22.85 plus 19¢ per mile for a certain car. Classic Auto Rents charges $21.95 plus 18¢ per mile for the same car. For what mileage is the cost the same?

20. ***Write a Convincing Argument*** Solve the problem below. Then write an argument that would convince a classmate that your solution is correct.

Several ancient Chinese books include problems that can be solved by translating to systems of equations. *Arithmetical Rules in Nine Sections* was compiled by Chang Tsang, a Chinese mathematician who died in 152 B.C. One of the problems is: Suppose there are a number of rabbits and pheasants confined in a cage. In all there are 35 heads and 94 feet. How many rabbits and how many pheasants are there?

Challenge

21. Daniel earned $288 on his investments. He invested $1100 at one yearly rate and $1800 at a rate that was 1.5% higher. Find the two rates of interest. $1100x + 1800(x + 0.015) = 288$; 9%, 10.5%

22. The sum of the digits of a three-digit number is 9. If the digits are reversed, the number increases by 495. The sum of the tens digit and the hundreds digit is half the units digit. Find the number. 126

23. Together, a bat, a ball, and a glove cost $99.00. The bat costs $9.95 more than the ball, and the glove costs $65.45 more than the bat. How much does each cost? glove $79.95, bat $14.50, ball $4.55

Mixed Review

Graph the lines containing these points and find their slope.

24. $(2, 5), (-3, 10)$ **25.** $(-1, -1), (2, 5)$ **26.** $(4, -7), (2, 3)$

27. Write an equation for the line that contains $(-2, 2)$ and $(3, 7)$.

28. Write an equation for the line with $m = 6$, y-intercept $= 7$.

Simplify. **29.** $\frac{x^6}{x^2}$ **30.** $\frac{t^9}{t^8}$ **31.** $\frac{n^4}{n^4}$ **32.** $\frac{x^3y^5}{x^3y^4}$

Factor. **33.** $7m^4n^2 - 7m^2n^4$ **34.** $81x^2 - 126xy + 49y^2$

ADDITIONAL ANSWERS

Exercises

17. 120, 121
18. 3200 bumper stickers, 1800 cycles
19. No solution
20. 12 rabbits, 23 pheasants

Mixed Review

24. -1
25. 2
26. -5
27. $y = x + 4$
28. $y = 6x + 7$
29. x^4
30. t
31. 1
32. y
33. $7m^2n^2(m + n)(m - n)$
34. $(9x - 7y)^2$

8-5

FIRST FIVE MINUTES

1. Morgan is 9 years older than Emma. The sum of their ages is 43. How old are they?
   Let m be the age of Morgan, in years.
   Let e be the age of Emma, in years.
   $m = e + 9$ (1)
   $m + e = 43$ (2)
   Substitute for m in (2).
   $(e + 9) + e = 43$
   $2e = 34$
   $e = 17$
   $m = e + 9$
   $m = 26$
   Morgan is 26. Emma is 17.

Discuss types of units commonly used for distance (miles, meters, kilometers, etc.), for time, (hours, minutes, seconds, etc.), and for rate (miles/hour, meters/second, etc.) Point out the similarity between units for rate and the formula for rate, $r = \frac{d}{t}$.

Key Questions

- How far will you go if you travel at 60 miles per hour for 5 hours?
  300 miles
- If you walked 6 miles in 3 hours, what was your walking speed?
  2 miles per hour
- How long will it take to walk 12 miles if you walk 3 miles per hour?
  4 hours

8-5 Problem Solving: Motion Problems

Objective: Solve problems involving uniform motion.

PROBLEM-SOLVING GUIDELINES
■ UNDERSTAND the problem
■ Develop and carry out a PLAN
■ Find the ANSWER and CHECK

The three strategies *Write an Equation, Draw a Diagram,* and *Make a Table* will be particularly helpful for the problems in this section.

The formula $d = r \cdot t$ shows the relationship between distance (d), rate (r), and time (t). We use this formula in the following examples.

EXAMPLE 1

A train leaves Slaton traveling east at 80 kilometers per hour. An hour later, another train leaves Slaton on a parallel track at 120 km/h. How far from Slaton will the trains meet?

■ **UNDERSTAND the problem**

Question: At what distance from Slaton will the trains meet?
Data: The rate of the slow train is 80 km/h. The rate of the fast train is 120 km/h. The fast train leaves 1 hour after the slow train.

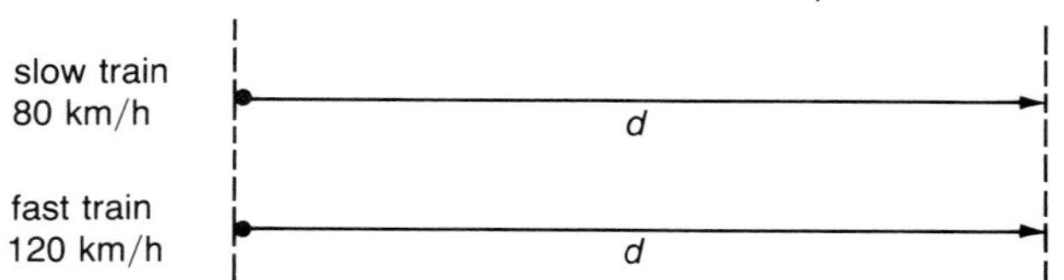

■ **Develop and carry out a PLAN**

Let d = distance traveled when the trains meet.
Let t = time for the faster train.

$t + 1$ = time for the slower train

	Distance	Rate	Time
Slow train	d	80	$t + 1$
Fast train	d	120	t

Recording the data in a *table* helps you write equations.

For each row in the chart we can *write an equation* in the form $d = r \cdot t$.

$d = 80(t + 1)$ and $d = 120t$

Thus we have a system of equations. We solve the system by the substitution method, since both distances are the same.

$$120t = 80(t + 1) \quad \text{Substituting } 120t \text{ for } d \text{ in the first equation}$$
$$120t = 80t + 80$$
$$40t = 80$$
$$t = 2 \quad \text{Time (hours)}$$

Solve for d using either equation.

$$d = 120t$$
$$d = 120(2) \quad \text{Substituting 2 for } t$$
$$d = 240 \quad \text{Distance (kilometers)}$$

■ **Find the ANSWER and CHECK**

The problem asks us to find how far from Slaton the trains meet. The trains meet 240 km from Slaton.

The time for the fast train is 2 h; 2 × 120 = 240 km. The time for the slow train is 2 + 1 or 3 h; 3 × 80 = 240 km. The answer checks.

Try This Solve.

a. A car leaves Hartford traveling north at 56 km/h. Another car leaves Hartford one hour later traveling north on the same road at 84 km/h. How far from Hartford will the second car overtake the first? (Hint: The cars travel the same distance.) 168 km

---

EXAMPLE 2

A motorboat took 3 hours to make a downstream trip with a current of 6 km/h. The return trip against the same current took 5 hours. Find the speed of the boat in still water.

Let r represent the speed of the boat in still water. Then, when traveling downstream, the speed of the boat is $r + 6$ (the current helps the boat along). When traveling upstream the speed of the boat is $r - 6$ (the current holds the boat back). We can organize the information in a table.

	Distance	Rate	Time
Downstream	d	$r + 6$	3
Upstream	d	$r - 6$	5

From each row of the table, we write an equation of the form distance = rate × time.

$$d = (r + 6)3$$
$$d = (r - 6)5$$

Thus we have a system of equations.

Chalkboard Examples

1. Bud takes a leisurely stroll. He walks at a constant rate of two miles per hour. Carrie starts out for a brisk walk one hour later. She walks at a constant rate of 3 miles per hour. How long will it take for Carrie to catch up with Bud?
   Let t be the time in hours that Carrie walks.
   Let d be the distance in miles that they each walked.

	Distance	Rate	Time
Bud	d	2	$t + 1$
Carrie	d	3	t

$d = 2(t + 1)$
$d = 3t$
Substituting,
$2(t + 1) = 3t$
$2t + 2 = 3t$
$2 = t$
They meet after Carrie walks for 2 hours.

2. Antonio is riding on a train. He gets up from his seat and walks forward. As he walks, he travels 1.1 miles in two minutes. As he walks back to his seat, he travels 0.9 miles in 2 minutes. How fast was the train moving, and how fast did Antonio walk inside the train?
   Let s be Antonio's walking speed inside the train, in miles per minute.
   Let t be the speed of the train, in miles per minute.

	Distance	Rate	Time
Forward	1.1	$t + s$	2
Backward	0.9	$t - s$	2

$2(t + s) = 1.1$ (1)
$2(t - s) = 0.9$ (2)
$2t + 2s = 1.1$ (1)
$2t - 2s = 0.9$ (2)
Add.
$4t = 2.0$
$t = 0.5$ miles per minute
Subtract (2) from (1).
$4s = 0.2$
$s = 0.05$
Antonio walks 0.05 miles per minute.

3. Alan has challenged Sam to a duel with water pistols at 50 feet. They start walking in opposite directions. Alan walks at 2 feet per second. Sam runs at 6 feet per second. How long will it take them to be 50 feet apart?
Let t be the time, in seconds, for them to be 50 feet apart. Let d be the distance between them, which is 50 feet.

$$rt = d$$
$$(2 + 6)t = 50$$
$$8t = 50$$
$$t = \frac{50}{8}$$
$$t = 6\frac{1}{4}$$

They are 50 feet apart in $6\frac{1}{4}$ seconds.

Since the distance upstream or downstream is the same, we solve the system by the substitution method.

$$(r + 6)3 = (r - 6)5 \quad \text{Substituting } (r + 6)3 \text{ for } d \text{ in the second equation}$$
$$3r + 18 = 5r - 30$$
$$-2r = -48$$
$$r = 24 \quad \text{Rate, or speed}$$

The speed in still water is 24 km/h.

We check in the original problem. When $r = 24$, $r + 6 = 30$ and the distance is $30 \cdot 3$, or 90. When $r = 24$, $r - 6 = 18$ and the distance is $18 \cdot 5$, or 90. In both cases we get a distance of 90 km.

Try This Solve.

b. An airplane flew for 5 hours with a tail wind of 25 km/h. The return flight against the same wind took 6 hours. Find the speed of the airplane in still air. (Hint: The distance is the same both ways.) 275 km/h

---

EXAMPLE 3

Two cars leave town at the same time going in opposite directions. One of them travels 60 mi/h and the other 30 mi/h. In how many hours will they be 150 miles apart?

We first make a diagram.

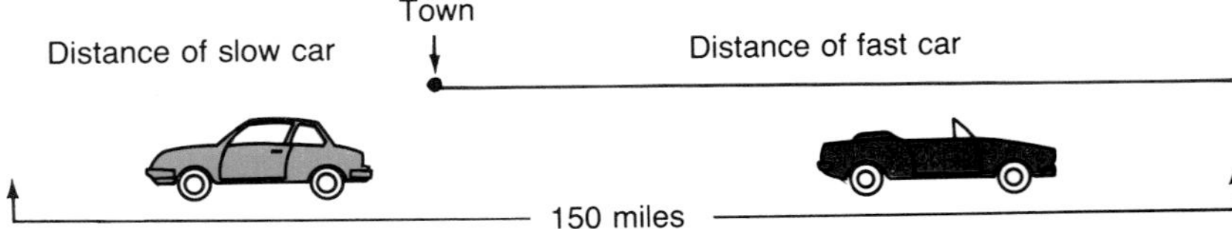

From the diagram and the wording of the problem, we see that the distances are *not* the same. We also see that the distance of the slow car plus the distance of the fast car is 150 mi. Both cars travel for the same amount of time, so we use t for both times. We organize the information in a chart.

	Distance	Rate	Time
Slow car	distance of slow car	30	t
Fast car	distance of fast car	60	t

Using the chart, we translate this information.

$$\underbrace{\text{Distance of slow car}}_{30t} \ \underset{+}{\text{plus}} \ \underbrace{\text{distance of fast car}}_{60t} \ \underset{=}{\text{is}} \ \underset{150}{150.}$$

We solve this equation for t.

$$30t + 60t = 150$$
$$90t = 150$$
$$t = \frac{5}{3}, \text{ or } 1\frac{2}{3} \text{ hours}$$

In $1\frac{2}{3}$ hours the cars will be 150 miles apart.

Try This Solve.

c. Two cars leave town at the same time in opposite directions. One travels 35 km/h and the other 40 km/h. In how many hours will they be 200 km apart? $35t + 40t = 200, t = 2\frac{2}{3}$ h

d. Two cars leave town at the same time in the same direction. One travels 35 mi/h and the other 40 mi/h. In how many hours will they be 15 miles apart? $d = 35t, d + 15 = 40t, t = 3$ h

8-5 EXERCISES

A

Solve.

1. Two cars leave town at the same time going in opposite directions. One travels 55 mi/h and the other travels 48 mi/h. In how many hours will they be 206 miles apart?
   a. Draw a diagram that represents the situation. Label your diagram using data from the problem.
   b. Copy and complete the missing information in the table below.

	Distance	Rate	Time
Slow car	distance of slow car	48	t
Fast car	distance of fast car	55	t

   c. Use the data in your table to write an equation.
   d. Solve the equation and answer the question.

2. Two cars leave town at the same time going in the same direction on the same road. One travels 30 mi/h and the other travels 46 mi/h. In how many hours will they be 72 miles apart?
   a. Draw a diagram that represents the situation. Label your diagram using data from the problem.

LESSON QUIZ

1. Two cars leave town, traveling in opposite directions. The first car travels at 50 miles per hour and the second car travels at 60 miles per hour. How long will it take them to be 100 miles apart?
   $\frac{10}{11}$ hours
2. You have a choice of two typing services. The Type-Fast Company will type research papers for $10 plus 85¢ per page. The Type-It-Well Company will type research papers for $12 plus 75¢ per page. For how many pages is the cost the same?
   20 pages

Assignment Guide
Minimum: Day 1: 1–8, assign w. Application
Day 2: 9–14, MR
Regular: Day 1: 1–14 e/o, assign w. Application
Day 2: 15–19, MR
Advanced: 1–14 m3, 15–18 e/o, 19–21, MR

1. a.

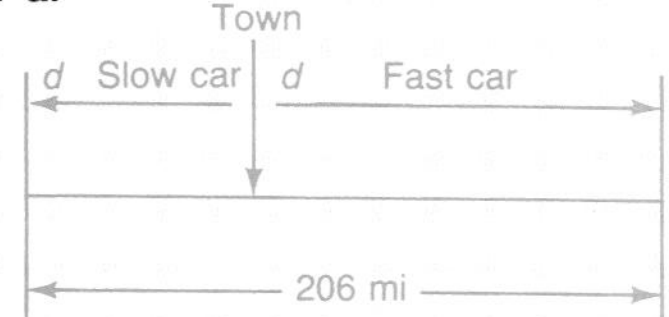

c. $48t + 55t = 206$
d. $t = 2$; in 2 hours they will be 206 miles apart.

2. a.

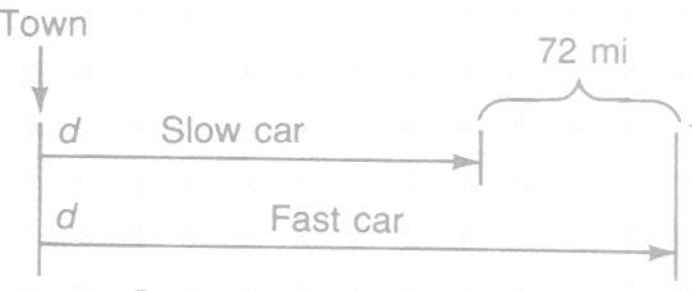

c. $d = 30t$
$d + 72 = 46t$
d. $t = 4.5$; in 4.5 hours they will be 72 miles apart.

3. a.

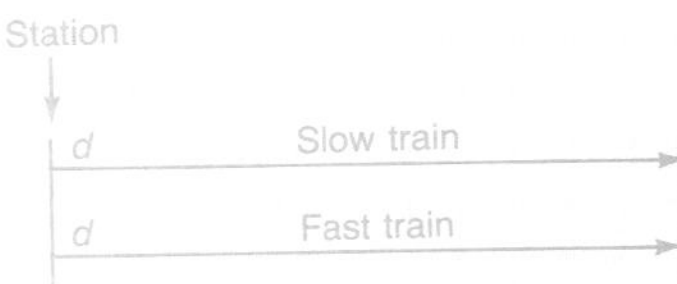

c. $d = 72(t + 3)$
$d = 120t$

d. $t = 4.5$; 4.5 hours after the second train leaves, the second train will overtake the first train.

b. Copy and complete the missing information in the table below.

	Distance	Rate	Time
Slow car	d	30	t
Fast car	$d + 72$	46	t

c. Use the data in your table to write a system of equations.

d. Solve the system of equations and answer the question.

3. A train leaves a station and travels east at 72 km/h. Three hours later a second train leaves on a parallel track and travels east at 120 km/h. When will it overtake the first train?

a. Draw a diagram that represents the situation. Label your diagram using data from the problem.

b. Copy and complete the missing information in the table below.

	Distance	Rate	Time
1st train	d	72	$t + 3$
2nd train	d	120	t

c. Use the data in your table to write a system of equations.

d. Solve the system of equations and answer the question.

4. Two cars leave town at the same time going in opposite directions. One travels 44 mi/h and the other travels 55 mi/h. In how many hours will they be 297 miles apart? 3 h

5. Two cars leave town at the same time going in the same direction on the same road. One travels 32 mi/h and the other travels 47 mi/h. In how many hours will they be 69 miles apart? 4.6 h

6. A private airplane leaves an airport and flies due south at 192 km/h. Two hours later a jet leaves the same airport and flies due south at 960 km/h. When will the jet overtake the plane? $\frac{1}{2}$ hour after jet leaves

7. A canoeist paddled for 4 hours with a 6-km/h current to reach a campsite. The return trip against the same current took 10 hours. Find the speed of the canoe in still water. 14 km/h

8. An airplane flew for 4 hours with a 20-km/h tail wind. The return flight against the same wind took 5 hours. Find the speed of the plane in still air. 180 km/h

9. It takes a passenger train 2 hours less time than it takes a freight train to make the trip from Central City to Clear Creek. The passenger train averages 96 km/h while the freight train averages 64 km/h. How far is it from Central City to Clear Creek? 384 km

10. It takes a small jet plane 4 hours less time than it takes a propeller-driven plane to travel from Glen Rock to Oakville. The jet plane averages 637 km/h while the propeller plane averages 273 km/h. How far is it from Glen Rock to Oakville? 1911 km

11. An airplane took 2 hours to fly 600 km against a head wind. The return trip with the wind took $1\frac{2}{3}$ hours. Find the speed of the plane in still air. 330 km/h

12. It took 3 hours to row a boat 18 km against the current. The return trip with the current took $1\frac{1}{2}$ hours. Find the speed of the rowboat in still water. 9 km/h

13. A motorcycle breaks down and the rider has to walk the rest of the way to work. The motorcycle was traveling at 45 mi/h, and the rider walks at a speed of 6 mi/h. The distance from home to work is 25 miles, and the total time for the trip was 2 hours. How far did the motorcycle go before it broke down? 15 mi

14. A student walks and jogs to college each day. The student averages 5 km/h walking and 9 km/h jogging. The distance from home to college is 8 km, and the student makes the trip in 1 hour. How far does the student jog? $6\frac{3}{4}$ km

B

15. An airplane flew for 4.23 hours with a 25.5-km/h tail wind. The return flight against the same wind took 4.97 hours. Find the speed of the plane in still air. ≈317.03 km/h

16. An airplane took 2.5 hours to fly 625 miles with the wind. It took 4 hours and 10 minutes to make the return trip against the same wind. Find the wind speed and the speed of the plane in still air. 50 mi/h, 200 mi/h

17. To deliver a package, a messenger must travel at a speed of 60 mi/h on land and then use a motorboat whose speed is 20 mi/h in still water. The messenger goes by land to a dock and then travels on a river against a current of 4 mi/h. He reaches the destination in 4.5 hours and then returns to the starting point in 3.5 hours. How far did the messenger travel by land and how far by water? 90 mi, 48 mi

18. Against a head wind, Jeff computes his flight time for a trip of 2900 miles at 5 hours. The flight would take 4 hours and 50 minutes if the head wind were half as much. Find the head wind and the plane's air speed. 40 mi/h, 620 mi/h

19. ***Write a Convincing Argument*** Solve the problem below. Then write an argument that would convince a classmate that your solution is correct.

A truck and a car leave a service station at the same time and travel on the same road in the same direction. The truck travels at 55 mi/h and th car at 40 mi/h. They can maintain CB radio contact within a range of 10 miles. When will they lose contact? After 40 min

Mixed Review

22. No
23. Yes
24. 4, -1
25. 9, -2
26. x^3y^4
27. a^5b^6
28. q^6s^9
29. $x^9y^2z^2$

Challenge

20. In 1927 Charles Lindbergh flew the *Spirit of St. Louis* from New York to Paris at an average speed of 107.4 mi/h. Eleven years later, Howard Hughes flew the same route, averaged 217.1 mi/h, and took 16 hours, 57 minutes less time. Find the length of their route. ≈3603 mi

21. During normal traffic it takes Ingrid 24 minutes to travel the 18 miles from her house to the train station. However, during rush hour (5:30–8:30 a.m.) Ingrid can only travel 12 miles in the same length of time. It then takes at least 5 minutes to get onto a train, 30 minutes to get to her destination, and 5 minutes to get to her office. If trains leave every 15 minutes starting at 6:00 a.m., when does Ingrid have to leave her house in order to get to her office by 8:00 a.m.? 6:34 a.m.

Mixed Review

Determine whether the given ordered pair is a solution of the system of equations.

22. (6, 1); $4y - x = -2$, $x - 7y = 2$

23. (2, 5); $y - 4x = -3$, $2x - y = -1$

Solve. **24.** $x^2 - 3x = 4$ **25.** $y^2 - 7y - 18 = 0$

Simplify. **26.** $\dfrac{x^4y^7}{xy^3}$ **27.** $\dfrac{a^9b^8}{a^4b^2}$ **28.** $\left(\dfrac{q^3s^5}{qs^2}\right)^3$ **29.** $\dfrac{x^{12}y^3z^5}{x^3yz^3}$

LOOKING FOR ERRORS

Each exercise has an error commonly made by algebra students. Can you find and correct the error?

1.
$$\begin{aligned} 3x - y &= 4 \\ 2x + y &= 16 \\ \hline 5x \quad &= 20 \\ x &= 4 \\ 3x - y &= 4 \\ 3(4) - y &= 4 \\ y &= 4 - 12 \\ y &= -8 \end{aligned}$$

The solution is $(4, -8)$.
The correct solution is (4, 8).

2.
$$\begin{aligned} 4x - y &= 17 \\ -x - y &= 7 \\ \hline 3x &= 24 \\ x &= 8 \\ 4(8) - y &= 17 \\ 32 - y &= 17 \\ -y &= -15 \\ y &= 15 \end{aligned}$$

The solution is (8, 15).
The correct solution is $(2, -9)$.

8-6 Problem Solving: Digit and Coin Problems

Objective: Use systems of equations to solve digit and coin problems.

Any two-digit number can be expressed as $10x + y$ where x is the digit in the tens place and y is the digit in the ones place. The number 23 can be written $10 \cdot 2 + 3$.

If we reverse the digits in the original number, the new number can be expressed as $10y + x$. The reverse of 23, 32, can be written $10 \cdot 3 + 2$. We use this relationship in the next example.

EXAMPLE 1

The sum of the digits of a two-digit number is 14. If the digits are reversed, the new number is 36 greater than the original number. Find the original number.

Let x = the tens digit and y = the ones digit.

There are two statements in this problem.

$$\underbrace{\text{The sum of the digits}}_{x + y} \ \underset{=}{\text{is}} \ \underset{14}{14.} \qquad \text{Translating}$$

$$\underbrace{\text{The new number}}_{10y + x} \ \underset{=}{\text{is}} \ \underset{36}{36} \ \underbrace{\text{greater than}}_{+} \ \underbrace{\text{the original number.}}_{10x + y} \qquad \text{Translating}$$

Simplifying the second equation gives

$$9x - 9y = -36$$

We have a system of equations.

$$\begin{aligned} x + \ \ y &= 14 \\ 9x - 9y &= -36 \end{aligned}$$

We can solve the system using the addition method. Multiply the first equation by 9 to make the y-terms additive inverses.

$$\begin{aligned} 9(x + y) = 9(14) &\longrightarrow & 9x + 9y &= 126 \\ 9x - 9y = -36 &\longrightarrow & 9x - 9y &= -36 \\ & & 18x \quad &= 90 \\ & & x &= 5 \quad \text{Tens digit} \end{aligned}$$

$5 + y = 14$ Substituting 5 for x in the first equation

$y = 9$ Solving for y

The solution is (5, 9). The original number is $5(10) + 9$ or 59.

8-6

FIRST FIVE MINUTES

1. If a car travels at a constant speed of 30 miles per hour, how long will it take to travel 96 miles?
   $\frac{96}{30} = 3.2$ hours
2. Zeb is 5 years older than Yolanda. The sum of their ages is 41. How old are they?
   Let z be the age of Zeb.
   Let y be the age of Yolanda.
   $z = y + 5$ (1)
   $z + y = 41$ (2)
   Substitute for z in (2).
   $(y + 5) + y = 41$
   $2y = 36$
   $y = 18$
   Substitute in (1).
   $z = (18) + 5$
   $z = 23$
   Zeb is 23. Yolanda is 18.

Remind students that there are two units for measuring money, dollars and cents. Cents were easier to use in Example 2, while dollars were easier to use in Example 3. Whichever they choose for a given problem, remind students to use the monetary unit consistently.

Key Question

- What is the value of 25 nickels? $1.25

Chalkboard Examples

1. The sum of the digits of a two-digit number is 10. If the digits are reversed, the new number is 36 less than the original number. Find the original number.
   Let x = the tens digit.
   Let y = the ones digit.
   $x + y = 10$
   $10x + y - 36 = 10y + x$
   Simplifying,
   $9x - 9y = 36$
   Multiplying the first equation by nine to make the y-terms additive inverses.
   $9x + 9y = 90$
   $9x - 9y = 36$
   $18x = 126$
   $x = 7$
   Substitute 7 for x in the first equation and solve for y.
   $7 + y = 10$
   $y = 3$
   The original number is 73.

2. A collection of nickels and dimes is worth \$3.95. There are 8 more dimes than nickels. How many dimes and how many nickels are there?
We use dollars as the unit of money. A nickel is worth 0.05 dollars. A dime is worth 0.10 dollars. Let n be the number of nickels.
Let d be the number of dimes.
$0.05n + 0.10d = 3.95$ (1)
Multiply by 100 to clear the decimals.
$5n + 10d = 395$ (1)
$d = n + 8$ (2)
Substitute for d in (1).
$5n + 10(n + 8) = 395$
$15n = 315$
$n = 21$
Substitute in (2).
$d = 29$
There are 29 dimes and 21 nickels.

3. A fork and knife weigh 50 grams and 70 grams, respectively. If the set contains 20 knives and forks and weighs 1220 grams, how many knives and forks are there?
Let f be the number of forks.
Let k be the number of knives.
$f + k = 20$ (1)
$50f + 70k = 1220$ (2)
Multiply (1) by -50.
$-50f - 50k = -1000$ (1)
Add (1) and (2).
$20k = 220$
$k = 11$
Substitute in (1).
$f + 11 = 20$
$f = 9$
There are 9 forks and 11 knives.

Try This Translate to a system of equations and solve.

a. The sum of the digits of a two-digit number is 5. If the digits are reversed, the new number is 27 more than the original number. Find the original number. 14

b. The sum of the digits of a two-digit number is 7. If the digits are reversed, the new number is 9 less than the original number. Find the original number. 43

EXAMPLE 2

Kami has some nickels and some dimes. The value of the coins is \$1.65. There are 12 more nickels than dimes. How many of each kind of coin does Kami have?

Let d = the number of dimes and n = the number of nickels. We write an equation for the **number** of coins.

$$d + 12 = n$$

The value of the nickels, in cents, is $5n$ since each nickel is worth 5¢. The value of the dimes is $10d$. Since we have the values of the coins in cents, we must use 165 cents for the total value. We write an equation for the **value** of the coins.

$$10d + 5n = 165$$

We can solve the system using the substitution method.

$$d + 12 = n$$
$$10d + 5n = 165$$

$$10d + 5(d + 12) = 165 \quad \text{Substituting } d + 12 \text{ for } n \text{ in the second equation}$$
$$10d + 5d + 60 = 165$$
$$15d = 105$$
$$d = 7$$

$$d + 12 = n \quad \text{Choosing the first equation}$$
$$7 + 12 = n \quad \text{Substituting 7 for } d$$
$$19 = n$$

The solution of this system is (7, 19). Kami has 7 dimes and 19 nickels.

Try This Translate to a system of equations and solve.

c. On a table there are 20 coins, some quarters and some dimes. Their value is \$3.05. How many of each are there? 7 quarters, 13 dimes

d. Calvin paid his \$1.35 skate rental with dimes and nickels only. There were 19 coins in all. How many of each coin were there? 8 dimes, 11 nickels

---

EXAMPLE 3

There were 411 people at a play. Admission was \$1 for adults and \$0.75 for children. The receipts were \$395.75. How many adults and how many children attended?

Let a = the number of adults and c = the number of children.

	Number	Admission Price (\$)	Receipts (\$)
Adult	a	1.00	a
Child	c	0.75	$0.75c$
Total	411		395.75

Since the total number of people is 411, we have this equation.

$$a + c = 411$$

The receipts from adults and from children equal the total receipts.

$$1.00a + 0.75c = 395.75$$

We have a system of equations. Clear the second equation of decimals and solve the system.

$$\begin{aligned} a + c &= 411 \\ 100a + 75c &= 39575 \end{aligned}$$

We multiply on both sides of the first equation by -100 and then add.

$$\begin{aligned} -100a - 100c &= -41100 \\ 100a + 75c &= 39575 \\ \hline -25c &= -1525 \\ c &= \frac{-1525}{-25} \\ c &= 61 \end{aligned}$$

$$\begin{aligned} a + c &= 411 && \text{Choosing the first equation} \\ a + 61 &= 411 && \text{Substituting 61 for } c \\ a &= 350 \end{aligned}$$

The solution of the system is (350, 61). There were 350 adults and 61 children at the play.

Try This Translate to a system of equations and solve.

e. There were 166 paid admissions to a game. The price was \$2 for adults and \$0.75 for children. The amount taken in was \$293.25. How many adults and how many children attended? 135, 31

LESSON QUIZ

1. A collection of nickels and dimes is worth 40 dollars (4000 cents). There are 500 coins. How many are there of each type?
300 dimes, 200 nickels

Assignment Guide
Minimum: 1–14 e/o, MR

Regular: 1–17 e/o, 18, MR

Advanced: 1–17 m3, 18–22, MR, assign w. Application

8-6 EXERCISES

A

1. The sum of the digits of a two-digit number is 9. If the digits are reversed, the new number is 63 greater than the original number. Find the original number. 18
2. The sum of the digits of a two-digit number is 10. When the digits are reversed, the new number is 36 more than the original number. Find the original number. 37
3. The sum of the digits of a two-digit number is 12. If the digits are reversed, the new number is 18 less than the original number. Find the original number. 75
4. The sum of the digits of a two-digit number is 16. If the digits are reversed, the new number is 18 less than the original number. Find the original number. 97
5. A jar of dimes and quarters contains $15.25. There are 103 coins in all. How many of each are there? 70 dimes, 33 quarters
6. A jar of quarters and nickels contains $1.25. There are 13 coins in all. How many of each are there? 3 quarters, 10 nickels
7. A vending machine takes only nickels and dimes. There are 5 times as many dimes as nickels in the machine. The face value of the coins is $4.40. How many of each coin are in the machine? 8 nickels, 40 dimes
8. A vending machine takes only nickels and dimes. At the end of the day there were three times as many nickels as dimes and a total of $25. How many of each coin were in the machine? 300 nickels, 100 dimes
9. There were 429 people at a play. Admission was $1 for adults and 75¢ for children. The receipts were $372.50. How many adults and how many children attended the play? 226 children, 203 adults
10. The attendance at a school concert was 578. Admission cost $2.00 for adults and $1.50 for children. The receipts were $985.00. How many adults and how many children attended the concert? 342 children, 236 adults
11. There were 200 tickets sold for a college basketball game. Tickets were $1.50 for students and $3 for adults. The total amount collected was $495. How many of each type of ticket were sold? 130 adults, 70 students
12. There were 203 tickets sold for a school wrestling match. For those who held activity cards, the price was $1.25. For those who did not hold activity cards, the price was $2.00. The total amount collected was $310. How many of each type of ticket were sold? 128 at $1.25, 75 at $2.00
13. A jar contains 5-gram bolts and 10-gram bolts. The contents of the jar weigh 2.35 kg (1000 g = 1 kg). If there are 300 bolts altogether, how many are there of each kind? 130 5-g bolts, 170 10-g bolts
14. A jar contains 5-gram bolts and 10-gram bolts. The contents of the jar weigh 3.8 kg. If there are 460 bolts, how many are there of each kind? 160 5-g bolts, 300 10-g bolts

B

15. The sum of the digits of a two-digit number is 14. If the number represented by reversing the digits is subtracted from the original number, the result is 18. What is the original number? 86

16. If 27 is added to a two-digit number, the result is a number with the same digits, but in reverse order. The sum of the digits is 11. What is the original number? 47

17. A two-digit number is 6 times the sum of its digits. The tens digit is 1 more than the units digit. Find the number. 54

18. ***Write a Convincing Argument*** Solve the problem below. Then write an argument that would convince a classmate that your solution is correct.

The sum of three digits is 5. The first and last digits are the same. If the middle digit is exchanged with the first digit, the new number is 90 less than the original number. Find the original number. 212

Challenge

19. A three-digit number is 28 times the sum of its digits. The units digit is twice as much as the tens digit and 3 more than the hundreds digit. Find the number.

20. Find all possible combinations of quarters and dimes that will total \$2.20. What is the smallest number of coins?

21. Laurel went to the bank to get \$20 worth of dimes and quarters. The teller made a mistake, interchanging the number of dimes and quarters Laurel asked for. How many dimes and how many quarters had she asked for if the teller gave her \$9 too much?

22. Glenda wrote a check to pay for a radio. She accidentally transposed the numbers. The store sent her a refund for \$36. She knew that the check was less than \$100 and was a whole dollar amount. What are the possible amounts that the radio could have cost?

Mixed Review

Factor. **23.** $16a^8 - 36$ **24.** $8x^3 + 10x^2 - 6x$ **25.** $c^2 - 5c$
26. $y^2 - 10y + 25$ **27.** $45m^2 - 106m + 45$ **28.** $2t^3 - 2t^2 - 4t$
Solve. **29.** $c^2 + 4c = 0$ **30.** $a^2 - 7a = -12$ **31.** $x^2 + 3x = 10$
Simplify. **32.** $\frac{x^4y^7}{x^2y^5}$ **33.** $\frac{x^9y^5z^4}{x^6y^2z}$ **34.** $\left(\frac{a^3b^7c}{a^3b}\right)^3$
Multiply. **35.** $(x + 1)^2$ **36.** $(x - 3)^2$ **37.** $(a + 7)^2$
38. $(r + 3)(r - 3)$ **39.** $(2a + 4)(a - 5)$ **40.** $(m - 4)^2$
Solve each system. **41.** $3x + y = 5$, $x + 2y = 0$ **42.** $2x + 3y = -2$, $3x + 2y = 7$

ADDITIONAL ANSWERS

Exercises

19. 336
20. Possible combinations of quarters and dimes: 8, 2; 6, 7; 4, 12; 2, 17; 0, 22; smallest number is 10.
21. 100 dimes, 40 quarters
22. \$15, \$26, \$37, \$48, \$59

Mixed Review

23. $4(2a^4 + 3)(2a^4 - 3)$
24. $2x(4x^2 + 5x - 3)$
25. $c(c - 5)$
26. $(y - 5)^2$
27. $(5m - 9)(9m - 5)$
28. $2t(t + 1)(t - 2)$
29. $0, -4$
30. $3, 4$
31. $2, -5$
32. x^2y^2
33. $x^3y^3z^3$
34. $b^{18}c^3$
35. $x^2 + 2x + 1$
36. $x^2 - 6x + 9$
37. $a^2 + 14a + 49$
38. $r^2 - 9$
39. $2a^2 - 6a - 20$
40. $m^2 - 8m + 16$
41. $x = 2, y = -1$
42. $x = 5, y = -4$

Problem Solving: College Entrance Exams

Point out that there are often other strategies using algebraic properties and principles that can be used to solve problems. The strategy used in Examples 1 and 2 use the addition and multiplication properties. In these problems, students are not asked to find x or y but some linear combination of x and y.

Problem Solving: College Entrance Exams

Systems of Equations

Some items on college entrance exams can be solved using the techniques you learned in this chapter for solving systems of equations. Some test items, however, can be solved more quickly using a variation of these methods.

EXAMPLE 1

If $2x + 3y = 27$ and $x + 2y = 7$, then $\frac{3x + 5y}{2} =$

(A) 10 **(B)** 12 **(C)** 17 **(D)** 20 **(E)** 34

While the addition method could be used to solve for x and y, this problem can be solved more easily using the addition principle and the multiplication principle to solve directly.

If we add the two equations and divide by 2, we find the answer immediately.

$$\begin{array}{r} 2x + 3y = 27 \\ x + 2y = 7 \\ \hline 3x + 5y = 34 \end{array} \qquad \frac{3x + 5y}{2} = 17$$

The answer is (C).

EXAMPLE 2

If $5x + 4y = 12$ and $2x + y = 8$, then $3x + 3y =$
(A) 5 **(B)** 4 **(C)** 3 **(D)** 2 **(E)** 1

Subtracting equations results in the answer directly.

$$\begin{array}{r} 5x + 4y = 12 \\ 2x + y = 8 \\ \hline 3x + 3y = 4 \end{array}$$

The answer is (B).

EXAMPLE 3

If $5x - 3y = 12$ and $x = \frac{7y}{5}$, then $y =$

(A) $\frac{3}{5}$ **(B)** $\frac{5}{7}$ **(C)** 3 **(D)** $\frac{3}{4}$ **(E)** $\frac{21}{5}$

Since x is expressed in terms of y, we use the substitution method.

$$5\left(\frac{7y}{5}\right) - 3y = 12$$

$$y = 3$$

The answer is (C).

Before solving a system, decide whether it would be easier to use the addition method, the substitution method, or a variation of these methods as shown in Examples 1 and 2.

Problems

Determine the best method and solve.

1. If $x + 2y = 6$ and $3x + y = 4$, then $4x + 3y =$
   (A) 8 **(B)** 9 **(C)** 10 **(D)** 11 **(E)** 12
2. If $5x - 3y = 8$ and $x = \frac{4y}{5}$, then $y =$
   (A) $\frac{4}{5}$ **(B)** $\frac{8}{5}$ **(C)** 6 **(D)** $\frac{8}{3}$ **(E)** 8
3. If $x + 4y = 9$ and $4x + 3y = 7$, then $5x + 7y =$
   (A) 8 **(B)** 9 **(C)** 16 **(D)** 18 **(E)** 20
4. If $3x + 3y = 17$ and $x + 4y = 3$, then $\frac{4x + 7y}{4} =$
   (A) 5 **(B)** 7 **(C)** 8 **(D)** 10 **(E)** 12
5. If $4x - 3y = 12$ and $x = \frac{7y}{4}$, then $y =$
   (A) 2 **(B)** 3 **(C)** 4 **(D)** 5 **(E)** 6
6. If $x + y = 3$ and $x - y = 2$, then $4x =$
   (A) 16 **(B)** 14 **(C)** 12 **(D)** 10 **(E)** 8
7. If $5x + 2y = 6$ and $2x + y = 4$, then $3x + y =$
   (A) 5 **(B)** 4 **(C)** 3 **(D)** 2 **(E)** 1
8. If $x + 2y = 4$ and $2x + y = 2$, then $6x + 6y =$
   (A) 8 **(B)** 9 **(C)** 10 **(D)** 11 **(E)** 12
9. If $3x - 2y = 13$ and $5x + 4y = 11$, then $\frac{8x + 2y}{6} =$
   (A) 24 **(B)** 6 **(C)** 4 **(D)** 3 **(E)** 2
10. If $5x + 2y = 12$ and $3x - 2y = 4$, then $\frac{2x + 4y}{4} =$
    (A) 16 **(B)** 8 **(C)** 6 **(D)** 4 **(E)** 2
11. If $3x + 2y = 10$ and $5x - 2y = 6$, then $2x =$
    (A) 1 **(B)** 2 **(C)** 3 **(D)** 4 **(E)** 8

ANSWERS

1. (C), variation
2. (E), substitution
3. (C), variation
4. (A), variation
5. (B), substitution
6. (D), addition
7. (D), variation
8. (E), variation
9. (C), variation
10. (E), variation
11. (D), variation

Problem Solving: Application

ANSWERS

1. No
2. No
3. Yes
4. Yes
5. $1.42
6. $1.90
7. $2.84
8. $2.37
9. $0.71
10. $0.95

Problem Solving: Application

Sales Taxes

Color Television Sets—This Week Only $290.00

How much would you really pay for a television set priced at $290.00? In most states, you would have to add sales tax, and would end up paying over $300.00. Sales tax is a percent of the price, and it varies by locality.

EXAMPLE 1

Gerry has $2.00 to buy a tube of toothpaste, which is priced at $1.88. The sales tax is 7%. Does he have enough money?

total = $1.88 + 0.07(1.88) = $2.01
He does not have enough money.

EXAMPLE 2

As the manager of a record store, you would like to sell singles at exactly one dollar including tax. If sales tax is $6\frac{1}{2}\%$, what price would bring the total cost to an even dollar?

$$\begin{aligned} x + 0.065x &= \$1.00 \\ 1.065x &= \$1.00 \\ x &= \$0.94 \end{aligned}$$

Rounding to the hundredths place

Problems

Assume the tax rate is 6%. State whether the spending money given is enough to pay for the item.

1. Soap, $1.68; spending money, $1.75
2. Clock radio, $29.98; spending money, $31.75
3. Baseball glove, $33.00; spending money, $35.00
4. Bicycle, $249.50; spending money, $270.00

You manage a cafeteria, and want to set prices that come to the total shown when sales tax of 5.5% is added. Give the price you would set for each.

5. Soup; total, $1.50
6. Chili; total, $2.00
7. Chicken sandwich; total, $3.00
8. Fruit salad; total, $2.50
9. Soft drink; total, $0.75
10. Ice cream; total, $1.00

Chapter 8 Summary and Review

8-1

A solution of a system of equations in two variables is an ordered pair that makes both equations true. One way to find a solution is to graph the two equations.

Determine whether the given ordered pair is a solution of the system of equations.

1. $(6, -1)$; $x - y = 3$, $2x + 5y = 6$

2. $(2, -3)$; $2x + y = 1$, $x - y = 5$

3. $(-2, 1)$; $x + 3y = 1$, $2x - y = -5$

4. $(-4, -1)$; $x - y = 3$, $x + y = -5$

Solve by graphing.

5. $x + y = 4$, $x - y = 8$

6. $x + 3y = 12$, $2x - 4y = 4$

7. $2x + y = 1$, $x = 2y + 8$

8. $3x - 2y = -4$, $2y - 3x = -2$

8-2

To solve a system of equations without graphing, you can use the substitution method. First solve one of the equations for a variable. Then substitute for that variable in the other equation.

Solve using the substitution method.

9. $y = 5 - x$, $3x - 4y = -20$

10. $x + 2y = 6$, $2x + 3y = 8$

11. $3x + y = 1$, $x = 2y + 5$

12. $x + y = 6$, $y = 3 - 2x$

13. $s + t = 5$, $s = 13 - 3t$

14. $x - y = 4$, $y = 2 - x$

Translate to a system of equations and solve.

15. The sum of two numbers is 30. Their difference is 40. Find the numbers.

8-3

The addition method is another way to solve a system of equations. Both equations must be in standard form $Ax + By = C$. Multiply one or both equations to make one of the terms of each equation additive inverses. Then add the two equations and solve for the variable. Substitute for that variable in either of the original equations and solve for the second variable.

ANSWERS

1. No
2. Yes
3. Yes
4. No
5. $(6, -2)$
6. $(6, 2)$
7. $(2, -3)$
8. No solution; lines are parallel
9. $(0, 5)$
10. $(-2, 4)$
11. $(1, -2)$
12. $(-3, 9)$
13. $(1, 4)$
14. $(3, -1)$
15. $(35, -5)$

16. (3, 1)
17. (1, 4)
18. (5, −3)
19. (−4, 1)
20. (−2, 4)
21. (−2, −6)
22. (3, 2)
23. (2, −4)
24. (12, 15)
25. Roberta 46, Cindy 21
26. length = 27.5, width = 10.5
27. 135 mi/h
28. 15
29. 60 quarters, 100 dimes

Solve using the addition method.

16. $x + y = 4$
$2x - y = 5$

17. $x + 2y = 9$
$3x - 2y = -5$

18. $x - y = 8$
$2x + y = 7$

19. $2x + 3y = -5$
$3x - y = -13$

20. $2x + 3y = 8$
$5x + 2y = -2$

21. $5x - 2y = 2$
$3x - 7y = 36$

22. $-x - y = -5$
$2x - y = 4$

23. $6x + 2y = 4$
$10x + 7y = -8$

Translate to a system of equations and solve.

24. The sum of two numbers is 27. One half of the first number plus one third of the second number is 11. Find the numbers.

8-4

Sometimes it is easier to use two variables when translating a word problem. Then you must find a system of two equations to solve in order to find the solution to the problem.

Translate to a system of equations and solve.

25. Roberta is 25 years older than her daughter, Cindy. In four years, Roberta will be twice as old as Cindy. How old are they now?

26. The perimeter of a rectangle is 76 cm. The length is 17 cm more than the width. Find the length and the width.

8-5

Use the formula, $d = r \cdot t$, to solve motion problems. *Drawing a diagram* and *making a table* may help you *write the equation.*

Translate to a system of equations and solve.

27. An airplane flew for 4 hours with a 15 mi/h tail wind. The return flight against the same wind took 5 hours. Find the speed of the airplane in still air.

8-6

A two-digit number can be written in the form $10x + y$. If the digits are reversed, the new number is $10y + x$. To solve coin problems, you can write one equation for the **number** of coins and/or dollars, and a second equation for the **value** of the coins and/or dollars.

28. The sum of the digits of a two-digit number is 6. When the digits are reversed, the new number is 36 more than the original number. Find the original number.

29. A collection of dimes and quarters is worth $25. There are 40 more dimes than quarters. How many of each are there?

Chapter 8 Test

Determine whether the given ordered pair is a solution of the system of equations.

1. $(4, 2)$; $x - y = 2$
$x + y = 6$

2. $(-8, -7)$; $x - 2y = 6$
$2x - 3y = 5$

Solve by graphing.

3. $x - y = 3$
$x + y = 5$

4. $x + 2y = 6$
$2x - 3y = 26$

5. $x = 2y + 4$
$y = 2x - 8$

6. $x = y - 1$
$3y = -2x - 2$

Solve using the substitution method.

7. $y = 6 - x$
$2x - 3y = 22$

8. $x + 2y = 5$
$x + y = 2$

9. $x + y = 31$
$x - y = 17$

10. $7x + y = 10$
$2y + 5x = 11$

Solve using the addition method.

11. $x - y = 6$
$3x + y = -2$

12. $3x - 4y = 7$
$x + 4y = 5$

13. $4x + 5y = 5$
$6x + 7y = 7$

14. $2x + 3y = 13$
$3x - 5y = 10$

15. $x + y = 4$
$2x + 3y = 7$

16. $8x - 10y = 2$
$7x - 5y = 13$

Translate to a system of equations and solve.

17. A motorboat traveled for 2 hours with an 8 km/h current. The return trip against the same current took 3 hours. Find the speed of the motorboat in still water.

18. The sum of two numbers is 8. Their difference is 12. Find the numbers.

19. A collection of dimes and quarters totals \$3.55. There are 25 coins in all. How many quarters are there?

20. Tickets to a junior high school play cost \$1.10 for each adult and \$0.40 for each child. If 360 tickets were sold for a total of \$282.60, how many tickets of each kind were sold?

21. One train leaves a station heading due west. Two hours later a second train leaves the same station heading due east. The second train is traveling 15 mi/h faster than the first. Six hours after the second train leaves, the two trains are 580 miles apart. Find the rate at which each train is traveling.

ANSWERS

1. Yes
2. Yes
3. $(4, 1)$
4. $(10, -2)$
5. $(4, 0)$
6. $(-1, 0)$
7. $(8, -2)$
8. $(-1, 3)$
9. $(24, 7)$
10. $(1, 3)$
11. $(1, -5)$
12. $\left(3, \frac{1}{2}\right)$
13. $(0, 1)$
14. $(5, 1)$
15. $(5, -1)$
16. $(4, 3)$
17. 40 km/h
18. 10 and -2
19. 7
20. 198 adult tickets, 162 child tickets
21. 35 mi/h, 50 mi/h

Test Item Analysis

Item	Lesson
1–6	8-1
7–10	8-2
11–16	8-3
17	8-5
18	8-2
19, 20	8-6
21	8-5

CHAPTER 9

Inequalities and Absolute Value

Chapter Overview

The geometric interpretation of inequalities in one and two variables is discussed using the language of sets. Set-builder notation and the set operations of union and intersection are introduced. The graphs of the conjunction and the disjunction of two inequalities in one variable are constructed. A discrete math topic discusses truth tables and the formal meaning of *and* and *or*. Equations and inequalities involving absolute value are discussed. Techniques are developed for removing absolute value signs and writing an equivalent expression as the conjunction or disjunction of a pair of inequalities. Inequalities in two variables are graphed as half-planes. Systems of linear inequalities in two variables are seen to be the intersection of half-planes.

Quantitative comparisons, which are often found on college entrance exams, are examined in the Problem Solving: College Entrance Exams section.

Objectives

9-1 ■ Name sets using set-builder notation.
■ Find intersections of sets.
■ Find unions of sets.
9-2 ■ Solve and graph a conjunction of two inequalities in one variable.
■ Solve and graph a disjunction of two inequalities in one variable.
9-3 ■ Solve equations involving absolute value.
9-4 ■ Solve and graph inequalities involving absolute value of the form $|A| < b$.
■ Solve and graph inequalities involving absolute value of the form $|A| > b$.
9-5 ■ Determine whether a given ordered pair is a solution of an inequality.
■ Graph inequalities in two variables.
9-6 ■ Graph systems of linear inequalities in two variables.

Cooperative Learning Opportunities

The *Suppose* activity in Lesson 9-1 lends itself to cooperative learning. Assign groups of 3 without definite roles but with the following procedures. First, brainstorm for a few minutes about how to go about solving the problem. Second, each student copies the diagram and writes in whatever information he or she can. Third, the students look at each other's diagrams and complete the solution together.

Lesson 9-5 on inequalities in two variables will also support cooperative learning. Assign groups of 3. Each group should do 5 of the exercises on page 419. Roles are: (1) draw the line; (2) decide which half-plane satisfies the inequality; (3) check. A student from each group can present one of the inequalities to the class with an explanation of that group's work.

The *Challenge* exercises on page 424 summarize much of what has come before. They are complex but not overly difficult. They can be done by students questioning each other in pairs.

Multicultural Note: *Georg Cantor*

Georg Cantor (1845–1918) was born in Russia but lived most of his life in Germany. He first studied engineering but then switched to pure mathematics and became the creator of the theory of sets. Cantor's ideas were new and some of the attacks on them were so savage that he suffered a temporary emotional collapse. But his achievements were finally recognized and he is one of the greats of modern mathematics.

The cardinal number of a set corresponds to the number of elements in the set. Thus, for example, the sets $A = \{1, 5, 8\}$ and $B = \{x, y, z\}$ have the same cardinal number, 3.

Two infinite sets have the same cardinal number if the elements of the two sets can be placed in one-to-one correspondence.

Alternative Assessment and Communication Ideas

The operations on sets and inequalities provide a variety of opportunities for alternative assessment. In Lesson 9-1, call on students to read and explain the meaning of the solution set for Exercises 19, 20, 29, and 30. Do this before students have worked the exercises with pencil and paper.

These exercises give students the opportunity to think on their feet, explain the meaning of the symbols, and talk through the logic that leads to the answer. As a student does this, you will be able to judge his or her understanding of the reasoning with sets.

In a similar way in Lesson 9-2, students should be able to talk through some of the inequalities on page 408. Try Exercises 1 to 4, and 21 to 24. Asks students to explain what the solution graphs will look like.

The **Writing to Learn** activity in Lesson 9-5 should be done as concisely and clearly as possible. Explain that they should edit their work, removing every unnecessary word.

Investigations and Projects

Working with set diagrams gives you a chance to review the use of conditions, an aspect of mathematics and of logical reasoning that is sometimes overlooked.

An example of conditions might be: To drive, you must be 16 years old, pass the driver's test, pay the required fee. Have students find out the conditions for the activities listed below and then draw a diagram to show the relationships among the different sets. Find the conditions to:

A. Get a driver's license.
B. Vote in a United States' election.
C. Be a United States citizen.
D. Join the Army.

The set diagram should show the relationships among all the sets. For example, voters is a subset of citizens; the set of licensed drivers intersects with each of the other three sets.

As a follow-up, you might have students devise their own sets along with the conditions.

MANAGING CHAPTER 9

Lesson	PACING CHART (DAYS) 2-Year* A for E	1-Year Minimum	1-Year Regular	1-Year Advanced	Opening Activity	Cooperative Activity	Seat or Group Work
9-1	3	1	1	1	First Five Minutes 9-1: ***FFMTM*** p. 28 or **TE** p. 400	Suppose: **SE** p. 404	Try This a–q
9-2	3	2	2	2	First Five Minutes 9-2: ***FFMTM*** p. 28 or **TE** p. 405; ***Overhead Transparencies*** T16	Connections: Discrete Math: **SE** p. 410	Try This a–i
9-3	2	1	1	1	First Five Minutes 9-3: ***FFMTM*** p. 28 or **TE** p. 411; ***Overhead Transparencies*** T17	Critical Thinking 9: ***Enrichment*** p. 26	Try This a–c
9-4	2	2	2	2	First Five Minutes 9-4: ***FFMTM*** p. 29 or **TE** p. 413; ***Overhead Transparencies*** T18	Explore: **SE** p. 413	Try This a–j
9-5	2	1	1	1	First Five Minutes 9-5: ***FFMTM*** p. 29 or **TE** p. 417; ***Overhead Transparencies*** T19, T20	Bonus Topic 9: ***Enrichment*** p. 10	Try This a–f
9-6	0	1	2	2	First Five Minutes 9-6: ***FFMTM*** p. 29 or **TE** p. 421; ***Overhead Transparencies*** T21a, T21b, T21c	✂ Manipulative Activity 9: ***Enrichment*** p. 42; Application: **SE** p. 421	Try This a–e
Review	2	1	1	1			
Test	1	1	1	1			

*2-Year Management Guide can be found in *Algebra for Everyone*.

FFMTM: First Five Minutes Transparency Masters

Enrichment	Review/Assess	Reteach	Technology	Lesson
Lesson Enrichment: **TE** p. 402; Suppose: **SE** p. 404	Lesson Quiz: **TE** p. 402		BASIC Computer Project 14: ***Technology*** p. 76	**9-1**
Connections: Discrete Math: **SE** p. 410	Mixed Review 17: ***SPMR*** p. 67; Lesson Quiz: **TE** p. 407; Quiz 17: ***Assessment*** p. 27	Skills Practice 24: ***SPMR*** p. 32		**9-2**
Critical Thinking 9: ***Enrichment*** p. 26	Geometry Review 1: ***SPMR*** p. 85; Mixed Practice 17: **SE** p. 700; Lesson Quiz: **TE** p. 411			**9-3**
Problem for Programmers: **SE** p. 416	Lesson Quiz: **TE** p. 414	Skills Practice 25: ***SPMR*** p. 33	Problem for Programmers **SE** p. 416	**9-4**
Writing to Learn: **SE** p. 420; Bonus Topic 9: ***Enrichment*** p. 10; Looking for Errors 9: ***Enrichment*** p. 58	Mixed Review 18: ***SPMR*** p. 68 Lesson Quiz: **TE** p. 419; Quiz 18: ***Assessment*** p. 28			**9-5**
✂ Manipulative Activity 9: ***Enrichment*** p. 42; Problem Solving: College Entrance Exams: **SE** pp. 425–426	Mixed Practice 18: **SE** p. 701; Lesson Quiz: **TE** p. 422	Skills Practice 26: ***SPMR*** p. 34	Spreadsheet Activity 6: ***Technology*** pp. 47–48	**9-6**
	Summary and Review: **SE** pp. 427–428; Test: **SE** p. 429	Strategy Problem Bank 9: ***Problem Bank*** p. 10		**Review**
	Chapter 9 Exam: ***A for E*** pp. 357–358; Chapter 9 Test: ***Assessment*** pp. 59–60 (min.), 119–124 (reg.), 179–180 (adv.)			**Test**

SPMR: Skills Practice Mixed Review

6. $x < -6$

7. $x > -13$

8. $x > 6$

9. $x \leq 0$

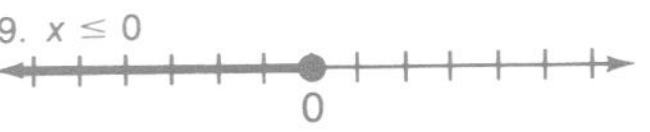

The solution to the problem posed on the facing page can be found on page 414.

Ready for Inequalities and Absolute Value?

2-2 Use $>$ or $<$ to write a true sentence.

1. $-6 < -4$

2. $4.5 > -4.5$

4-1 Determine whether the given number is a solution of the inequality.

3. $x \leq 6$
(a) -12 Yes **(b)** 0 Yes **(c)** 6 Yes

Graph on a number line.

4. $x > -3$

−3 0

5. $x \leq 1$

4-2 to 4-4 Solve and graph the solution. For answers, see top margin.

6. $2 - 3x > 20$

7. $28x + 18 > 26x - 8$

8. $8x - 10 > 7x - 4$

9. $8x - 13 \leq -13$

7-2 **10.** Determine whether the given point is a solution of $2x - y = 6$.
(a) $(1, 4)$ No **(b)** $(1, -4)$ Yes **(c)** $(2, -2)$ Yes

8-1 Determine whether the given ordered pair is a solution of the system of equations.

11. $(-4, -1)$; $2y - x = 2$, $x = 4y$ Yes

12. $(0, 2)$; $y + 2 = x$, $y - 2 = -x - 4$ No

Solve by graphing.

13. $x + 2y = 7$, $x = 3$ (3, 2)

14. $3y - 2x = 4$, $x + y = -2$ (−2, 0)

CHAPTER

9 Inequalities and Absolute Value

A lathe operator is making shoulder bolts for a lawn mower. The specifications require that the diameter (d) of the bolt satisfies the equation $|d - 2| \leq 0.01$ *cm. What are the acceptable diameters for the bolt?*

9-1

FIRST FIVE MINUTES

1. Art has 40 pennies and nickels in his pocket. The coins total one dollar. How many pennies and how many nickels are there?
   Let p be the number of pennies.
   Let n be the number of nickels.
   $p + n = 40$ (1)
   $p + 5n = 100$ (2)
   $n = 15, p = 25$
   There are 15 nickels and 25 pennies.

Set-Builder Notation

Three dots (. . .) are used to mean "and so on." This symbol is called an ellipsis. If an ellipsis appears at the end of a list, the list is infinite.

For better understanding, students should read aloud examples that include set-builder notation.

Three letters that are commonly associated with three familiar sets are

Z, the set of all integers.
Q, the set of all rationals.
R, the set of all reals.

The symbol $\in$ means "is an element of," and the symbol $\notin$ means "is not an element of."

Key Questions

- Is 3 a member of set R?
  Yes
- Is -3 a member of set Z?
  Yes
- If a number is in Q, must it be in Z?
  No; $\frac{1}{3} \in Q, \frac{1}{3} \notin Z$.

Chalkboard Examples

Write using
a. set-builder notation and
b. roster notation.

1. the set C of whole numbers greater than 5
   a. $C = \{x|\ x \text{ is a whole number and } x > 5\}$
   b. $C = \{6, 7, 8, \ldots\}$
2. the set N of negative integers
   a. $N = \{x|\ x \text{ is an integer and } x < 0\}$
   b. $N = \{-1, -2, -3, \ldots\}$

9-1 Sets, Intersections, and Unions

We think of many objects in the real world in terms of **sets.** We refer to sets of keys, a set of dishes, and a set of luggage. A **set** is a well-defined collection of objects called **members** or **elements.** We will use capital letters to represent sets. The letter Z is commonly used to represent the set of integers.

Set-Builder Notation

Objective: Name sets using set-builder notation.

We can write sets using two different notations, **roster notation,** which lists the members of the set, and **set-builder notation,** which gives a description of how the set is built.

Roster notation for the set of whole numbers greater than 20 is written

$$\{21, 22, 23, 24, \ldots\}$$

The three dots indicate that the numbers continue, following the pattern set by the first four numbers.

Set-builder notation for the set of whole numbers greater than 20 is written

variable — description

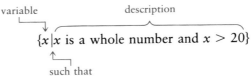

$$\{x|x \text{ is a whole number and } x > 20\}$$

such that

We read this as "the set of all x such that x is a whole number and x is greater than 20."

EXAMPLES Write using (a) roster notation and (b) set-builder notation.

1. the set B of whole numbers less than 7
(a) $B = \{0, 1, 2, 3, 4, 5, 6\}$
(b) $B = \{x|x \text{ is a whole number and } x < 7\}$

2. the set E of positive integers
(a) $E = \{1, 2, 3, 4, \ldots\}$ (b) $E = \{x|x \text{ is an integer and } x > 0\}$

Try This Write using (a) roster notation and (b) set-builder notation.

a. the set G of whole numbers greater than 5 See Additional Answers.
b. the set T of multiples of 5 less than 24
c. the set P of prime numbers less than 20

Intersection of Sets

Objective: Find intersections of sets.

The **intersection** of two sets A and B, written $A \cap B$, is the set of all members that are *common to both sets*. $A \cap B$ is read "A intersection B." In the diagram below, the circles represent sets A and B. The shaded region represents $A \cap B$.

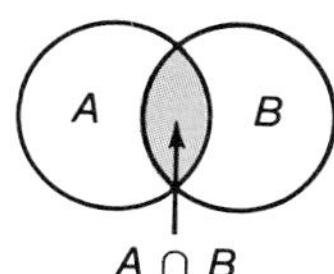

EXAMPLE 3 Let $A = \{1, 2, 3, 4, 5, 6\}$ and $B = \{-2, -1, 0, 1, 2, 3\}$. Find $A \cap B$. The numbers 1, 2, and 3 are common to both A and B.

$$A \cap B = \{1, 2, 3\}$$

Try This Let $P = \{-3, -2, 0, 1, 5\}$, $T = \{0, 1, 6, 9\}$, and $S = \{-3, 1, 6\}$.

d. Find $P \cap T$. $\{0, 1\}$ **e.** Find $T \cap S$. $\{1, 6\}$ **f.** Find $P \cap S$. $\{-3, 1\}$

We can find intersections of infinite sets.

EXAMPLE 4 Let W be the set of whole numbers and Z be the set of integers. Find $W \cap Z$.

Every whole number is common to W and Z. Thus $W \cap Z = W$.

Consider the intersection of the set of even numbers and the set of odd numbers. There are no members common to both sets. Thus the intersection is empty. We say the intersection is the **empty set**, which is symbolized by $\{ \ \}$ or $\emptyset$.

EXAMPLE 5 Let $G = \{0, 3, 6, 9\}$ and $H = \{2, 4, 8\}$. Find $G \cap H$.

There are no members common to G and H. $G \cap H = \emptyset$

Try This Let E be the set of even numbers, W be the set of whole numbers, $T = \{0, 2\}$, and $S = \{1, 5\}$.

g. Find $S \cap T$. $\emptyset$ **h.** Find $E \cap W$. E **i.** $T \cap E$. $\{0, 2\}$ or T

j. Find $E \cap S$. $\emptyset$ **k.** Find $W \cap S$. S **l.** Find $W \cap T$. T

Intersection of Sets

Emphasize that the set containing 0, $\{0\}$, is not the empty set, $\{ \ \}$. It has one element in it.

You may wish to mention that if the intersection of two or more sets is the empty set, the sets are said to be *disjoint.*

Key Questions

- What is the intersection of the set of people in this room with blond hair with the set of people in this room wearing blue?
  Answers may vary.
- What is the intersection of the set of people in this room with black hair with the set of people in this room with blond hair?
  $\emptyset$

Chalkboard Examples

1. Let $U = \{1, 3, 5, 7\}$ and $V = \{7, 6, 5, 4\}$. Find $U \cap V$.
   $U \cap V = \{5, 7\}$
2. Let R be the set of reals and Q be the set of rationals. Find $R \cap Q$.
   $R \cap Q = Q$, because every rational is a real.
3. Let $J = \{1, 2, 3, 5, 7, 9\}$ and $K = \{0, 2, 4, 6, 8\}$. Find $J \cap K$.
   $J \cap K = \{2\}$

Union of Sets

Point out that if an element is a member of both sets, then it needs to be listed only once in the union of those two sets.

Math Point
The circle diagrams are called *Venn diagrams* after the logician John Venn (1834–1923).

Chalkboard Examples

1. Let $C = \{0, 1, 2, 3\}$ and $D = \{1, 3, 5\}$. Find $C \cup D$.
   $C \cup D = \{0, 1, 2, 3, 5\}$
2. Let $R = \{1, 3, 5\}$. Find $R \cup R$.
   $R \cup R = \{1, 3, 5\} = R$
3. Let S be the set of positive divisors of 4 and let $T = \{1, 5, 10\}$. Find $S \cup T$.
   $S = \{1, 2, 4\}$
   $S \cup T = \{1, 2, 4, 5, 10\}$

LESSON ENRICHMENT

Have students check to see whether the commutative and associative properties hold for the intersection and union of sets.

1. The commutative properties
   $A \cap B = B \cap A$
   $A \cup B = B \cup A$
   True
2. The associative properties
   $(A \cap B) \cap C = A \cap (B \cap C)$
   $(A \cup B) \cup C = A \cup (B \cup C)$
   True

LESSON QUIZ

Let $A = \{1, 2, 3, 4\}$, $B = \{0, 2, 4, 6\}$, $C = \{1, 3, 5, 7\}$, Z be the integers.

1. Find $A \cap B$.
   $\{2, 4\}$
2. Find $A \cap C$.
   $\{1, 3\}$
3. Find $B \cap C$.
   $\emptyset$
4. Find $A \cup B$.
   $\{0, 1, 2, 3, 4, 6\}$
5. Find $B \cup C$.
   $\{0, 1, 2, 3, 4, 5, 6, 7\}$
6. Find $A \cap \{x \mid x \in Z \text{ and } x < 3\}$.
   $\{1, 2\}$
7. Find $A \cup \emptyset$.
   A

Union of Sets

Objective: Find unions of sets.

The **union** of two sets A and B, written $A \cup B$, is the set of all members that are in A or in B (or in both). In other words, we form the union of two sets by putting them together. In the diagram below, the circles represent the sets. The shaded region represents the union of the sets.

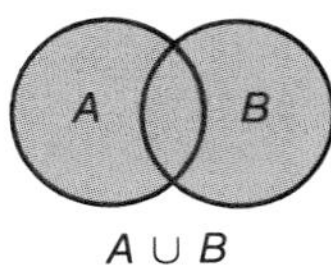

$A \cup B$

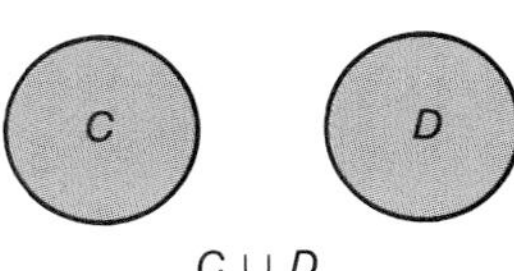

$C \cup D$

EXAMPLE 6 Let $A = \{2, 3, 4\}$ and $B = \{3, 5, 7\}$. Find $A \cup B$.

The members 2, 3, 4, 5, and 7 are either in A or in B (or in both).

$A \cup B = \{2, 3, 4, 5, 7\}$

Try This Let $W = \{-3, -2, 0, 4\}$, $X = \{-4, -2, 5, 6\}$, and $Y = \{1, 3, 5\}$.

m. Find $W \cup X$. $\{-4, -3, -2, 0, 4, 5, 6\}$ **n.** Find $W \cup Y$. $\{-3, -2, 0, 1, 3, 4, 5\}$

We can find unions involving infinite sets or the empty set.

EXAMPLE 7 Let $P = \{-2, -1, 4\}$. Find $P \cup \emptyset$.

The members -2, -1, and 4 are in P or in $\emptyset$.

$P \cup \emptyset = \{-2, -1, 4\} = P$

EXAMPLE 8 Let $S = \{4, 6, 8, 10\}$ and E be the set of even numbers. Find $S \cup E$.

All even numbers are in S or in E.

$S \cup E = E$

Try This Let $M = \{1, 3, 5\}$, E be the set of even whole numbers, and D be the set of odd whole numbers.

o. Find $M \cup D$. D **p.** Find $E \cup D$. $\{x \mid x \text{ is a whole number}\}$ **q.** Find $M \cup \emptyset$. M

9-1 EXERCISES

A

Write using (a) roster notation and (b) set-builder notation.

1. the set A of whole numbers less than 4
2. the set F of integers greater than or equal to 12
3. the set N of negative integers greater than -5
4. the set P of prime numbers less than 30
5. the set H of positive multiples of 3 less than or equal to 21
6. the set R of positive multiples of 4
7. the set E of positive even integers
8. the set T of positive factors of 12
9. the set M of even prime numbers
10. the set S of integers that are perfect squares less than 20

Let $A = \{-4, -3, -2, -1, 0\}$, $B = \{0, 1, 2\}$, $C = \{1, 2, 3, 4, 5\}$, and $D = \{4, 5, 6, 7, 8, 9, 10\}$. Find each of the following.

11. $B \cap C$ **12.** $A \cap B$ **13.** $C \cap D$ **14.** $C \cap B$

15. $A \cap C$ **16.** $B \cap D$ **17.** $A \cap \emptyset$ **18.** $D \cap \emptyset$

19. Let W be the set of whole numbers and E the set of even numbers. Find $W \cap E$.
20. Let Z be the set of integers and D the set of odd positive integers. Find $D \cap Z$.

Let $P = \{-5, -4, -3, -2, -1, 0\}$, $Q = \{-2, -1, 0\}$, $R = \{-1, 0, 1, 2, 3, 4\}$, and $S = \{5, 6, 7, 8\}$. Find each of the following.

21. $P \cup Q$ **22.** $Q \cup R$ **23.** $S \cup P$ **24.** $Q \cup S$

25. $R \cup S$ **26.** $R \cup P$ **27.** $P \cup \emptyset$ **28.** $S \cup \emptyset$

29. Let W be the set of whole numbers and E the set of even positive numbers. Find $W \cup E$. W
30. Let Z be the set of integers and D the set of odd positive integers. Find $D \cup Z$. Z

B

Let E be the set of even numbers, J the set of integers less than -9, and P the set of odd numbers between 7 and 29. To say that -9 is an element of Z, we write $-9 \in Z$. To say that $\frac{5}{8}$ is not a member of Z, we write $\frac{5}{8} \notin Z$.

Tell whether each of the following is true or false.

31. $2 \in E$ T **32.** $-7 \in J$ F **33.** $19 \in P$ T **34.** $0 \in J$ F

35. $-10 \in E$ T **36.** $23 \in P$ T **37.** $5 \notin P$ T **38.** $16 \notin E$ F

39. $-8 \in P$ F **40.** $10 \notin P$ T **41.** $-5 \notin J$ T **42.** $0 \notin E$ F

Assignment Guide
Minimum: 1–30 e/o, MR

Regular: 1–48 e/o, 49, MR

Advanced: 1–48 m3, 49–53, MR

ADDITIONAL ANSWERS

Try This

a. (a) $G = \{6, 7, 8 \ldots\}$
(b) $G = \{x \mid x$ is a whole number and $x > 5\}$

b. (a) $T = \{20, 15, 10, 5, 0, -5, \ldots\}$
(b) $T = \{x \mid x$ is a multiple of 5 and $x < 24\}$

c. (a) $P = \{2, 3, 5, 7, 11, 13, 17, 19\}$
(b) $P = \{x \mid x$ is a prime number and $x < 20\}$

Exercises

1. (a) $A = \{0, 1, 2, 3\}$
(b) $A = \{x \mid x$ is a whole number and $x < 4\}$

2. (a) $F = \{12, 13, 14, \ldots\}$
(b) $F = \{x \mid x$ is an integer and $x \geq 12\}$

3. (a) $N = \{-1, -2, -3, -4\}$
(b) $N = \{x \mid x$ is an integer and $-5 < x < 0\}$

4. (a) $P = \{2, 3, 5, 7, 11, 13, 17, 19, 23, 29\}$
(b) $P = \{x \mid x$ is a prime number and $x < 30\}$

5. (a) $H = \{3, 6, 9, 12, 15, 18, 21\}$
(b) $H = \{x \mid x$ is a multiple of 3 and $0 < x \leq 21\}$

6. (a) $R = \{4, 8, 12, 16, \ldots\}$
(b) $R = \{x \mid x$ is a multiple of 4 and $x > 0\}$

7. (a) $E = \{2, 4, 6, 8, \ldots\}$
(b) $E = \{x \mid x$ is an even integer and $x > 0\}$

8. (a) $T = \{1, 2, 3, 4, 6, 12\}$
(b) $T = \{x \mid x$ is a factor of 12 and $x > 0\}$

9. (a) $m = \{2\}$
(b) $m = \{x \mid x$ is an even prime number$\}$

10. (a) $s = \{0, 1, 4, 9, 16\}$
(b) $s = \{x \mid x$ is an integer, a perfect square, and $x < 20\}$

11. $\{1, 2\}$ **12.** $\{0\}$
13. $\{4, 5\}$ **14.** $\{1, 2\}$
15. $\emptyset$ **16.** $\emptyset$
17. $\emptyset$ **18.** $\emptyset$
19. $\{0, 2, 4, 6, 8, \ldots\}$ or E
20. $\{1, 3, 5, 7, 9, \ldots\}$ or D
21. $\{-5, -4, -3, -2, -1, 0\}$ or P

22. {−2, −1, 0, 1, 2, 3, 4}
23. {−5, −4, −3, −2, −1, 0, 5, 6, 7, 8}
24. {−2, −1, 0, 5, 6, 7, 8}
25. {−1, 0, 1, 2, 3, 4, 5, 6, 7, 8}
26. {−5, −4, −3, −2, −1, 0, 1, 2, 3, 4}
27. {−5, −4, −3, −2, −1, 0} or *P*
28. {5, 6, 7, 8} or *S*
29. {0, 1, 2, 3, ...}

47. {2, 4, 6, 8, ...}
48. {... −2, −1, 0, 1, 2 ...}
49. Answers may vary. Example: {5, 1, 0} and {1, 9}
50. $n(A \cup B) = n(A) + k$, where k is the number of elements in B which are not also in A. $k = n(B) - n(A \cap B)$. Thus $n(A \cup B) = n(A) + n(B) - n(A \cap B)$.
51.

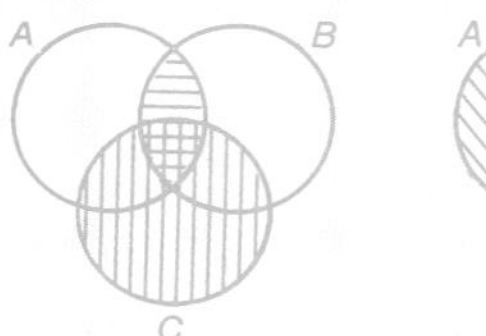

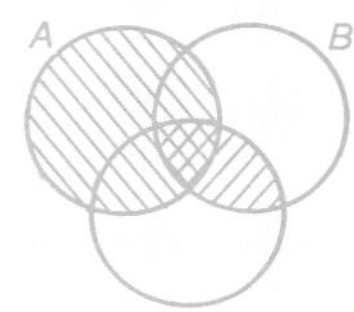

52.

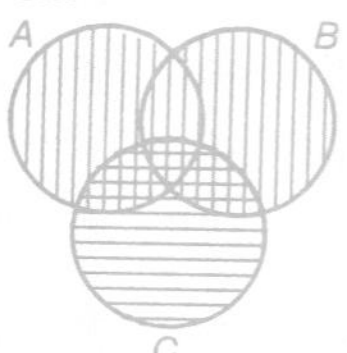

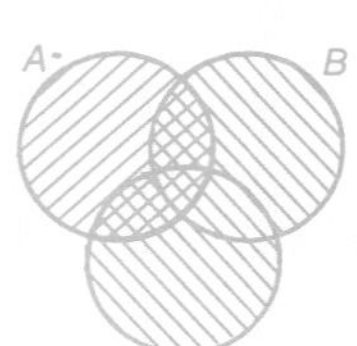

53. $B = \{3, 7, 10, 15\}$

Mixed Review

54. $3(3a + 1)(2a - 3)$
55. $(7 - 2c)(7 + 2c)$
56. $5(m - 5)(m + 5)$
57. $(2a - 3)^2$
58. $(2y + 7)^2$
59. $2(x + 3y)(4x - 3y)$
60. $(2, -3)$
61. $(5, 3)$
62. $(-2, -3)$
63. $y = 3x$
64. $y = -x + 2$
65. $y = \frac{1}{3}x - 4$
66. 18, 13
67. 9, 4
68. 55 paperback 31 hardcover

Let A be any set. Find the following.

43. $A \cap A$ A **44.** $A \cup \emptyset$ A **45.** $A \cup A$ A **46.** $A \cap \emptyset$ $\emptyset$

47. Find the intersection of the set of positive integers and the set of even integers.

48. Find the union of the set of integers and the set of whole numbers.

49. ***Critical Thinking*** Find two sets whose intersection is {1} and whose union is {5, 1, 0, 9}.

Challenge

50. Let $n(A)$ represent the number of members in set A. Show that $n(A \cup B) = n(A) + n(B) - n(A \cap B)$.

51. Use diagrams to show that $(A \cap B) \cap C = A \cap (B \cap C)$.

52. Use diagrams to show that $(A \cup B) \cup C = A \cup (B \cup C)$.

53. Let $A = \{3, 7, 10, 15\}$. Find a set B such that $A \cap B = A \cup B$.

Mixed Review

Factor. **54.** $18a^2 - 21a - 9$ **55.** $49 - 4c^2$ **56.** $5m^2 - 125$

57. $4a^2 - 12a + 9$ **58.** $4y^2 + 28y + 49$ **59.** $8x^2 + 18xy - 18y^2$

Solve. **60.** $y = x - 5$, $y = 11 - 7x$ **61.** $x = y + 2$, $x + y = 8$ **62.** $2x - y = -1$, $2y - x = -4$

Write an equation for the line that contains each pair of points.

63. (0, 0), (1, 3) **64.** (3, −1), (1, 1) **65.** (3, −3), (−3, −5)

66. The sum of two numbers is 31, the difference is 5. Find the numbers.

67. The sum of two numbers is 13, the product is 36. Find the numbers.

68. A bookstore sells paperback books for \$1.95 each and hardcover books for \$5.75 each. Last Tuesday, 86 books were sold for a total of \$285.50. How many each of paperback and hardcover books were sold?

SUPPOSE

There are 220 students in the sophomore class. Suppose

115 are taking Journalism,
60 are taking Ceramics,
95 are taking Spanish,
20 are taking Journalism and Ceramics,
30 are taking Journalism and Spanish,
25 are taking Ceramics and Spanish,
15 are taking all three subjects.

Ceramics Journalism
30 80
15
55
Spanish

How many students are taking only one of these three subjects?
Hint: Complete a diagram like the one above. 80 + 30 + 55 = 165 students

9-2 Compound Sentences

Conjunctions and Intersections

Objective: Solve and graph a conjunction of two inequalities in one variable.

A sentence like $x > 5$ and $x \le 12$ is called a **conjunction.** A conjunction of two statements is formed by connecting them with the word "and." A conjunction is true when *both* statements are true. A conjunction of two statements is similar to the intersection of two sets. The solution set of a conjunction is the intersection of the solution sets of the individual statements.

EXAMPLE 1 Graph the conjunction $x > 5$ *and* $x \le 12$.

$x > 5$

$x \le 12$

The graph of the conjunction is the intersection of the graphs of $x > 5$ and $x \le 12$.

$x > 5$ and $x \le 12$

The graph contains all numbers that are between 5 and 12, including 12. This can also be written as $5 < x \le 12$.

EXAMPLE 2 Graph the conjunction $x \ge -2$ and $x < 1$.

$x \ge -2$ and $x < 1$

This graph contains all numbers that are between -2 and 1, including -2. This can also be written as $-2 \le x < 1$.

9-2

FIRST FIVE MINUTES

Let $A = \{0, 1, 3, 8\}$,
$B = \{2, 4, 5, 6, 7, 9\}$,
$C = \{0, 1, 8\}$.
Find the following sets.

1. $A \cap B$
   $\emptyset$
2. $A \cap C$
   $\{0, 1, 8\} = C$
3. $A \cup B$
   $A \cup B = \{0, 1, 2, 3, 4, 5, 6, 7, 8, 9\}$

Conjunctions and Intersections

You may want to review number line graphing before beginning this lesson.

Emphasize the relationship between conjunction and intersection. An element is in the *intersection* of two sets if it is in the first set *and* in the second set.

Key Questions

- If C is the set $\{c, d, e\}$, and D is the set $\{d, e, f\}$, what is $C \cap D$?
  $\{d, e\}$
- If A is the set of integers greater than 2, and B is the set of integers less than 5, what is $A \cap B$?
  $A \cap B$ is the set of integers greater than 2 and less than 5.
  $A \cap B = \{3, 4\}$

Chalkboard Examples (*T16*)

1. Graph the conjunction $x < 7$ and $x > 2$.

2. Graph $4 < x < 8$.

3. Solve and graph.
   $2 \le x - 5 \le 7$
   The inequality may be rewritten
   $2 \le x - 5$ and $x - 5 \le 7$
   Solving separately,
   $7 \le x$ and $x \le 12$
   This may also be abbreviated
   $7 \le x \le 12$

a. −3 0 4

Try This Graph the conjunction.

b. −2 0 7

a. $-3 < x$ and $x < 4$ **b.** $-2 \le x$ and $x < 7$

EXAMPLE 3 Graph $-3 < x < 6$.

The inequality is the abbreviated form for the conjunction

$-3 < x$ *and* $x < 6$

The graph of the conjunction is the intersection of the individual graphs.

$-3 < x$

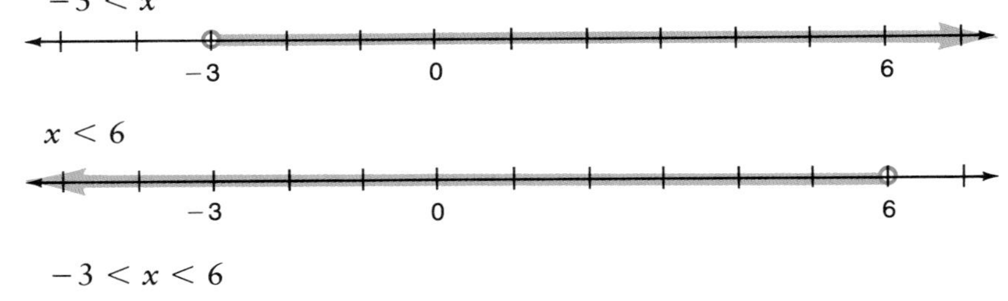

$-3 < x < 6$

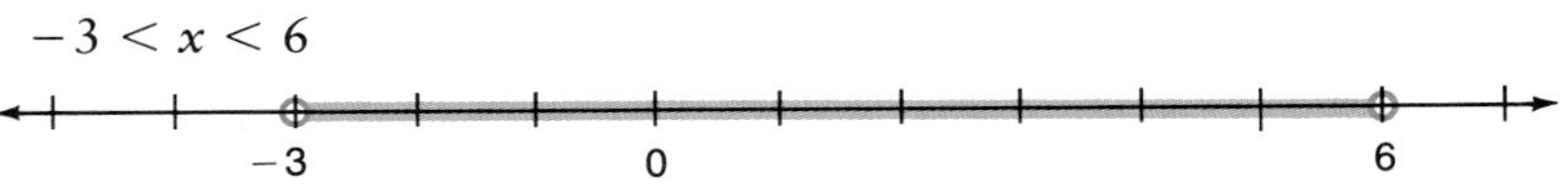

Try This Graph.

c. $-2 < x \le 4$ **d.** $-7 < x < -3$

EXAMPLE 4 Solve and graph.

$$-6 \le 2x + 4 < 10$$

$$-6 \le 2x + 4 \text{ and } 2x + 4 < 10 \quad \text{Writing the conjunction using } and$$

Solve each inequality separately.

$$\begin{array}{rcr} -6 \le 2x + 4 & \text{and} & 2x + 4 < 10 \\ -6 + (-4) \le 2x + 4 + (-4) & \text{and} & 2x + 4 + (-4) < 10 + (-4) \\ -10 \le 2x & \text{and} & 2x < 6 \\ -5 \le x & \text{and} & x < 3 \end{array}$$

We write the answer in abbreviated form and graph the solution.

$-5 \le x < 3$

−5 0 3

The solution set is $\{x|x \ge -5 \text{ and } x < 3\}$ or $\{x|-5 \le x < 3\}$.

Try This Solve and graph.

e. $-18 < 3x - 6 \leq -3$ $\{x \mid -4 < x \leq 1\}$

f. $5 < -2x + 1 \leq 3$ $\emptyset$

Disjunctions and Unions

Objective: Solve and graph a disjunction of two inequalities in one variable.

A sentence like $x < -3$ or $x > 6$ is called a **disjunction.** A disjunction of two statements is formed by connecting them with the word "or." A disjunction is true when *one or both* statements are true. A disjunction of two statements is like the union of two sets. The solution set of a disjunction is the union of the solution sets of the individual statements.

EXAMPLE 5 Graph the disjunction $x < -3$ or $x > 6$.

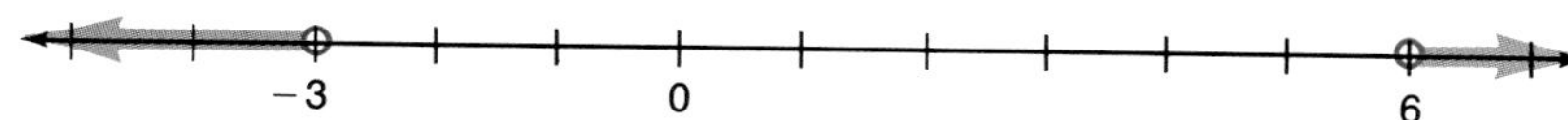

Try This Graph the disjunction.

g. $x \leq -1$ or $x > 4$

EXAMPLE 6 Solve and graph.

$$-3x - 4 > 8 \text{ or } x - 6 > 1$$

Solve each inequality separately.

$$\begin{array}{rcl} -3x - 4 > 8 & \text{or} & x - 6 > 1 \\ -3x - 4 + (4) > 8 + (4) & \text{or} & x - 6 + (6) > 1 + (6) \\ -3x > 12 & & \\ x < -4 & \text{or} & x > 7 \end{array}$$

We draw the graph of the solution set.

$x < -4$ or $x > 7$

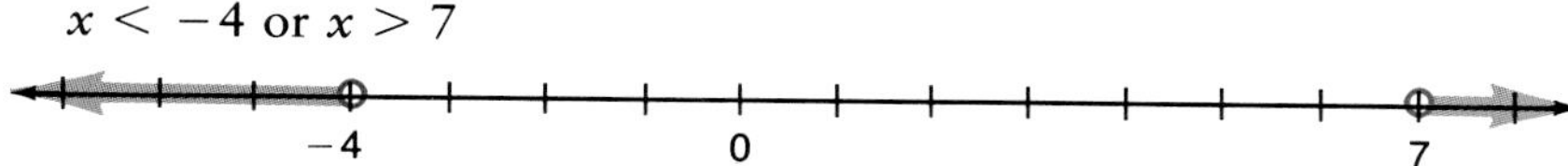

The solution set is $\{x \mid x < -4 \text{ or } x > 7\}$.

Try This Solve and graph. For graphs, see Additional Answers.

h. $-2x - 6 > 4$ or $x + 5 > 8$ $\{x \mid x < -5 \text{ or } x > 3\}$

i. $-5x + 2 > 27$ or $x - 3 > 2$ $\{x \mid x < -5 \text{ or } x > 5\}$

Disjunctions and Unions

Emphasize the relationship between union and disjunction. An element is in the *union* of two sets if it is in the first set *or* in the second set *or* both.

You may want to review the multiplication property for inequalities. Stress that the inequality sign is reversed when both sides are multiplied by a negative number.

Avoiding Common Errors

Students often try to write disjunctions such as $x < -3$ or $x > 6$ in an abbreviated form such as $6 < x < -3$. Point out that there is no abbreviated form for disjunctions as there is for conjunctions.

Chalkboard Examples (*T16*)

1. Graph the disjunction $x \leq 0$ or $x \geq 5$.

2. Solve and graph $2x - 1 < 5$ or $3x - 5 > 10$.
   Solve each inequality separately.
   $2x < 6$ or $3x > 15$
   $x < 3$ or $x > 5$

LESSON QUIZ

1. Graph $x > -3$ and $x < 3$.

2. Solve and graph $3x \leq 12$ and $2x \geq 4$.

3. Solve and graph $x - 3 \leq 0$ or $x \geq 5$.

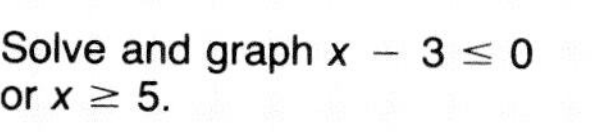

4. Solve and graph $3x - 2 \leq 4$ or $4x - 5 \geq 15$.

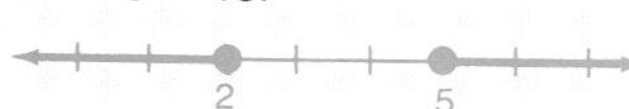

Assignment Guide
Minimum: Day 1: 1–20 e/o
Day 2: 21–34, MR
Regular: Day 1: 1–34 e/o, MR
Day 2: 35–50 e/o, 51, assign w. Connections
Advanced: Day 1: 1–34 m3, 35–40 e/o, MR
Day 2: 41–50 e/o, 51, 52–57 e/o, assign w. Connections

ADDITIONAL ANSWERS

Try This

h. −5 0 3

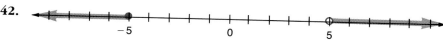

i. −5 0 5

Exercises

1–8. See Teacher's Answer Section.

For graphs of Exercises 9–20, see Teacher's Answer Section.

9. $\{x|1 < x < 3\}$
10. $\{x|0 < x < 6\}$
11. $\{x|-1 \le x < 4\}$
12. $\{x|6 < x < 10\}$
13. $\{x|-6 < x < 1\}$
14. $\{x|-4 \le x \le 3\}$
15. $\{x|1 < x < 6\}$
16. $\{x|3 \le x \le 4\}$
17. $\{x|0 < x \le 3\}$
18. $\{x|2 \le x \le 6\}$
19. $\{x|0 < x \le 4\}$
20. $\{x|-5 \le x < -2\}$

21–26. See Teacher's Answer Section.

For graphs of Exercises 27–34, see Teacher's Answer Section.

27. $\{x|x < 2 \text{ or } x > 7\}$
28. $\{x|x < 5 \text{ or } x > 6\}$
29. $\{x|x \le -1 \text{ or } x > 9\}$
30. $\{x|x < -4 \text{ or } x > 4\}$
31. $\{x|x < 4 \text{ or } x > 5\}$
32. $\{x|x < 7 \text{ or } x > 7\}$ or $\{x|x \neq 7\}$
33. $\{x|x \le -5 \text{ or } x > 3\}$
34. $\{x|x \le -2 \text{ or } x > 1\}$
35. $\{x|x$ is any rational number$\}$
36. $\{x|x$ is any rational number$\}$
37. $\emptyset$
38. $\{x|x < -2\}$
39. $\emptyset$
40. $\{x|x < 7\}$
41. $-5 < x$ and $x \le 2$ or $-5 < x \le 2$
42. $x \le -5$ or $x > 5$

9-2 EXERCISES

A

Graph these conjunctions.

1. $4 < x$ and $x < 9$
2. $-3 < x$ and $x < -1$
3. $0 < x$ and $x \le 5$
4. $1 \le x$ and $x < 10$
5. $-3 \le x$ and $x < 2$
6. $-7 \le x$ and $x \le 0$
7. $3 \le x < 12$
8. $-4 \le x < 5$

Solve and graph.

9. $3 < x + 2 < 5$
10. $-3 < x - 3 < 3$
11. $-4 \le x - 3 < 1$
12. $12 < 2x < 20$
13. $-18 < 3x < 3$
14. $-20 \le 5x \le 15$
15. $7 < 2x + 5 < 17$
16. $19 \le 5x + 4 \le 24$
17. $-5 < 7x - 5 \le 16$
18. $-11 \le -2x + 1 \le -3$
19. $-6 < 3x - 6 \le 6$
20. $-19 \le 5x + 6 < -4$

Graph these disjunctions.

21. $x < -1$ or $x > 2$
22. $x < -2$ or $x > 0$
23. $x \le -4$ or $x \ge 4$
24. $x < 0$ or $x > 5$
25. $x \le -6$ or $x > 2$
26. $x < 1$ or $x > -3$

Solve and graph.

27. $x + 8 < 10$ or $x - 5 > 2$
28. $x - 2 < 3$ or $x + 3 > 9$
29. $x + 1 \le 0$ or $x - 6 > 3$
30. $5x < -20$ or $3x > 12$
31. $4x < 16$ or $3x > 15$
32. $-2x > -14$ or $3x > 21$
33. $2x + 7 \le -3$ or $5x - 9 > 6$
34. $4x - 9 \le -17$ or $2x + 6 > 8$

B

Solve.

35. $x + 2 < 7$ or $x - 1 > -4$
36. $x - 5 < -3$ or $x + 8 > 7$
37. $3x + 12 \le 6$ and $2x - 4 > 2$
38. $-2x + 1 > 5$ and $-2x + 10 > 2$
39. $-6 > -3x - 6$ and $-3x - 6 \ge 6$
40. $3x - 8 < 13$ or $-3x + 10 > 5$

Write the inequality shown by each graph.

41. −5 0 5

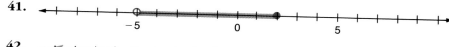

42. −5 0 5

43. 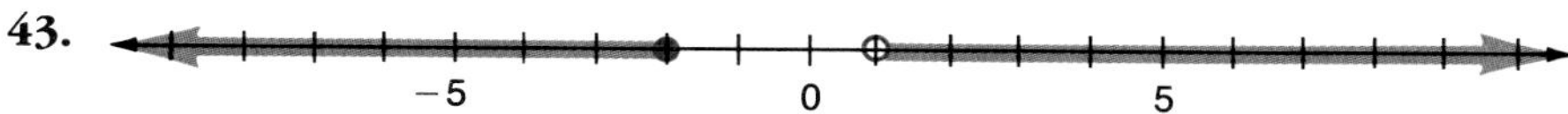

44. 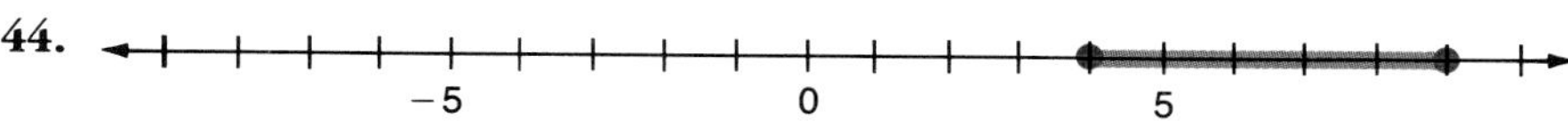

45.

46.

Write a compound sentence for each situation.

47. The length of an adult triceratops dinosaur was between 20 feet and 25 feet. (Let l be the length in feet.)

48. The Mesozoic era was 145 million years ago plus or minus 85 million years.

49. Lead must be at least 300° C and not more than 1700° C to be in liquid form.

50. Mercury is not a liquid if its temperature is below −39° C or above 357° C.

51. *Critical Thinking* If $a > b$ and $c > d$, is $ac > bd$ for all rational values of a, b, c, and d? Explain.

Challenge

Write a conjunction or disjunction to describe each graph.

52.

53.

Solve and graph.

54. $(x - 3)(x + 5) \geq 0$

55. $(x + 8)(x - 4) < 0$

56. $x^2 + x - 2 > 0$

57. $x^2 - x - 6 \leq 0$

Mixed Review

Identify the degree of each term and the degree of the polynomial.

58. $9a^2 - 25$ 59. $7x^3y^2 + 21x^2y - 14x + 5$ 60. $2a^2b^3c^4 - b^6$

Write an equation in slope-intercept form for the line that contains the given pair of points. 61. $(-3, 1), (4, 2)$ 62. $(0, 5), (-2, 1)$

Solve. 63. $x + y = -1$, $x - y = 3$ 64. $4x - 2y = 18$, $x + 3y = -20$ 65. $4x + 5y = -1$, $2x - 3y = 5$

66. A collection of nickels and dimes is worth \$3.40. There are 41 coins in all. How many are nickels and how many are dimes?

67. The difference of two numbers is 8; the product is 65. Find the numbers.

43. $x \leq -2$ or $x > 1$
44. $4 \leq x$ and $x \leq 9$ or $4 \leq x \leq 9$
45. $x < 0$ or $x > 6$
46. $x < 1$ or $x > 1$
47. $20 < l$ and $l < 25$ or $20 < l < 25$
48. $-230{,}000{,}000 \leq M$ and $M \leq -60{,}000{,}000$ or $-230{,}000{,}000 \leq M \leq -60{,}000{,}000$
49. $300 \leq L$ and $L \leq 1700$ or $300 \leq L \leq 1700$
50. $L < -39$ or $L > 357$
51. No, suppose $a = -1$, $b = -2$, $c = 1$, and $d = 0$. Then $ac = -1$ and $bd = 0$. -1 is not greater than 0.
52. $x \leq 2$ and $x \neq -3$ OR $x < -3$ or $(-3 < x$ and $x \leq 2)$
53. $x = -4$ or $x > 4$
For graphs of Exercises 54–57, see Teacher's Answer Section.
54. $x \leq -5$ or $x \geq 3$
55. $-8 < x$ and $x < 4$
56. $x < -2$ or $x > 1$
57. $-2 \leq x$ and $x \leq 3$

Mixed Review

58. 2, 0; 2
59. 5, 3, 1, 0; 5
60. 9, 6; 9
61. $y = \frac{1}{7}x + \frac{10}{7}$
62. $y = 2x + 5$
63. $(1, -2)$
64. $(1, -7)$
65. $(1, -1)$
66. 14 nickels, 27 dimes
67. 5, 13 or −5, −13

Connections: Discrete Math

Truth tables are part of another kind of algebra called Boolean algebra, named for its originator George Boole (1815–1864). This system of logic is used in the design of electrical switching circuits used by electronic computers and has other applications in the fields of engineering and probability.

Data bases written for computers commonly use *or* and *and* compound sentences to generate information.

For example, if you request a list of names of all people whose "last names begin with B and whose first names begin with B," you would receive a list of names such as Betty Bigelow, Bob Broter, Barney Banilow, etc. If you request a list of names of all people in the data base whose "last names begin with B or whose first names begin with B," you would receive a list of names such as Brenda Bartosh, Brian Smith, Gerry Brogg, Bart Agree, etc.

ANSWERS

1. False
2. True
3. True
4. False
5. True

 Connections: Discrete Math

Truth Tables

Recall that a statement is a sentence that is either true or false. A conjunction of two statements is only true if both statements are true. A disjunction of two statements is true if either statement is true. We can represent this with **truth tables** using T to indicate a true statement and F to indicate a false statement.

A	*B*	*A* and *B*
T	T	T
T	F	F
F	T	F
F	F	F

Truth Table for Conjunction

A	*B*	*A* or *B*
T	T	T
T	F	T
F	T	T
F	F	F

Truth Table for Disjunction

According to the table for conjunction, *A* and *B* is a true statement only if both *A* and *B* are true.

EXAMPLES

1. "Two is an even number and four is an even number" is true, since both individual statements are true.
2. "Five is an odd number and six is a prime number" is false, since one of the statements is false.

According to the table for disjunction, *A* and *B* is true in all cases except the one in which both *A* and *B* are false.

EXAMPLES

3. "Five is a prime number or eight is a prime number" is true, since one of the statements is true.
4. "Ten is a factor of twelve or eight is a prime number" is false, since both statements are false.

Exercises

True or false?

1. Five is a factor of 25 and six is a factor of 8.
2. Four is a prime number or two is a prime number.
3. Six is an even number or three is a prime number.
4. Ten is a factor of 11 or eight is an odd number.
5. An author of this book is Randall Charles and an author of this book is Stanley Smith.

9-3 Equations and Absolute Value

Objective: Solve equations involving absolute value.

Recall that the absolute value of a number is its distance from zero on the number line. $|x| = 3$ has two solutions, 3 and -3, since both have a distance of 3 units from 0 on the number line.

In general, we can state the following.

Solving Equations with Absolute Values

To solve an equation of the form $|A| = b$, where b is a positive number, solve the disjunction $A = b$ or $A = -b$.

EXAMPLE 1 Solve $|x + 3| = 5$.

There are two numbers whose distance from 0 is 5, namely 5 and -5. This gives us the disjunction $x + 3 = 5$ *or* $x + 3 = -5$.

$$x + 3 = 5 \quad \text{or} \quad x + 3 = -5$$
$$x = 2 \quad \text{or} \quad x = -8$$

Check:

$\lvert x + 3\rvert = 5$	
$\lvert 2 + 3\rvert$	5
$\lvert 5\rvert$	5
5	5 ✓

$\lvert x + 3\rvert = 5$	
$\lvert -8 + 3\rvert$	5
$\lvert -5\rvert$	5
5	5 ✓

The solution set is $\{2, -8\}$.

EXAMPLE 2 Solve $|2x - 4| = 10$.

There are two numbers whose distance from 0 is 10, namely 10 and -10.

$$2x - 4 = 10 \quad \text{or} \quad 2x - 4 = -10$$
$$2x = 14 \quad \text{or} \quad 2x = -6$$
$$x = 7 \quad \text{or} \quad x = -3$$

Substitution will show that both numbers check. The solution set is $\{7, -3\}$.

EXAMPLE 3 Solve $|5x - 3| = -17$.

Since by definition the absolute value of a number is positive or it is zero, there is no solution to this equation. The solution set is $\emptyset$.

Try This Solve.

a. $|x + 8| = 6$ $\{-2, -14\}$ **b.** $|x - 6| = 10$ $\{16, -4\}$ **c.** $|4x - 9| = -7$ $\emptyset$

9-3

FIRST FIVE MINUTES

1. Graph $2 \leq x \leq 7$.

2. Solve and graph.
$5x < 10$ and $x + 3 > 0$
$\{x \mid -3 < x < 2\}$

3. Solve and graph.
$2x < 4$ or $x - 3 > 2$
$\{x \mid x < 2 \text{ or } x > 5\}$

Remind students that a real number can be associated with a point on the number line. Emphasize the interpretation of $|x|$ as the distance of a point x from the point 0.

Key Questions

- What numbers have a distance of 8 units from 0?
$-8, 8$
- What numbers have a distance of -8 from 0?
None
- How far is -3 from 0?
3

Chalkboard Examples (*T17*)

1. Solve $|x - 3| = 2$.
$x - 3 = 2$ or $x - 3 = -2$
$x = 5$ or $x = 1$
2. Solve $|3x - 3| = 9$.
$3x - 3 = 9$ or $3x - 3 = -9$
$3x = 12$ or $3x = -6$
$x = 4$ or $x = -2$
3. Solve $|2x - 5| = -3$.
There are no solutions, since the absolute value is always nonnegative.

LESSON QUIZ

1. Solve $|x - 7| = 2$.
$x = 9$ or $x = 5$
2. Solve $|4x - 10| = 2$.
$x = 3$ or $x = 2$

Assignment Guide
Minimum: 1–21 e/o, MR

Regular: 1–33 e/o, 34, MR

Advanced: 1–33 m3, 34–37, MR

ADDITIONAL ANSWERS

Exercises

1. $\{9, -27\}$
2. $\{13, -5\}$
3. $\{-17, -5\}$
4. $\{-16, 30\}$
5. $\emptyset$
6. $\{-15, -19\}$
7. $\{5, -1\}$
8. $\left\{4, \frac{3}{2}\right\}$
9. $\left\{1, -\frac{3}{7}\right\}$
10. $\emptyset$
11. $\left\{2, \frac{8}{5}\right\}$
12. $\left\{16, -\frac{35}{2}\right\}$
13. $\left\{\frac{3}{8}, \frac{5}{8}\right\}$
14. $\emptyset$
15. $\left\{-\frac{1}{6}, -\frac{1}{2}\right\}$
16. $\left\{-\frac{3}{2}, -\frac{17}{10}\right\}$
17. $\emptyset$
18. $\{57, -3\}$
19. $\{-1, -9\}$
20. $\left\{2, -\frac{4}{3}\right\}$
21. $\{0.2, -0.28\}$

34. $|x + 3| = 3$
35. $\{x \mid x \geq 4\}$
36. $\left\{1, \frac{1}{7}\right\}$
37. $\left\{-\frac{3}{5}, -1\right\}$

Mixed Review

38. $m = \frac{1}{2}, b = -\frac{1}{2}$
39. $m = -4, b = -7$
40. $m = 3, b = 4$
41. $m = \frac{2}{5}, b = -1$
42. $m = -\frac{3}{4}, b = 3$
43. $2x(x - 3)(x + 1)$
44. $(2y - 1)(y - 4)$
45. $(3a + 2)(3a - 2)$
46. $(1, -3)$
47. $(1, -4)$
48. $(1, 1)$
49. $1, -2$
50. $-3, 0, 5$

9-3 EXERCISES

A

Solve.

1. $|x + 9| = 18$
2. $|x - 4| = 9$
3. $|x + 11| = 6$
4. $|m - 7| = 23$
5. $|x - 10| = -8$
6. $|x + 17| = 2$
7. $|2x - 4| = 6$
8. $|4b - 11| = 5$
9. $|7x - 2| = 5$
10. $|8x + 3| = -27$
11. $|5x - 9| = 1$
12. $|4x + 3| = 67$
13. $|2r - 1| = \frac{1}{4}$
14. $|4x + 3| = -5$
15. $|3x + 1| = 0.5$
16. $|5y + 8| = \frac{1}{2}$
17. $|2y - 6| = -9$
18. $\left|\frac{1}{3}x - 9\right| = 10$
19. $|0.2x + 1| = 0.8$
20. $|4.2x - 1.4| = 7$
21. $|5x + 0.2| = 1.2$

B

Solve.

22. $|2x + 5| - 9 = 12$ $\{8, -13\}$
23. $|3y - 2| + 4 = 21$ $\left\{\frac{19}{3}, -5\right\}$
24. $|2 - a| - 3 = 1$ $\{6, -2\}$
25. $8 - |1 - y| = 7$ $\{0, 2\}$
26. $3|y + 6| = 6$ $\{-4, -8\}$
27. $4|t + 3| = 16$ $\{1, -7\}$
28. $8 + |2c - 1| = 4$ $\emptyset$
29. $3|b - 2| + 7 = 10$ $\{3, 1\}$
30. $4|3 - z| - 8 = 8$ $\{-1, 7\}$
31. $10 + |5x + 2| = 7$ $\emptyset$
32. $6 - |3y - 2| = 10$ $\emptyset$
33. $-|x + 1| = -2$ $\{1, -3\}$
34. ***Critical Thinking*** Make one change in the equation $|x + 3| = 5$ so that the solution set of the new equation is $\{0, -6\}$.

Challenge

Solve.

35. $|x - 4| = x - 4$
36. $|3x| = |4x - 1|$
37. $|2y| = |3y + 2| + 1$

Mixed Review

Find the slope and y-intercept of each line.

38. $x - 2y = 1$
39. $-4x - y = 7$
40. $3x = y - 4$
41. $5y + 4 = 2x - 1$
42. $3x - 5 = -4y + 7$

Factor. 43. $2x^3 - 4x^2 - 6x$ 44. $2y^2 - 9y + 4$ 45. $9a^2 - 4$

Solve. 46. $3y + 4x = -5$, $x = y + 4$ 47. $2x + y = -2$, $y - x = -5$ 48. $3x - y = 2$, $2x + y = 3$

Solve. 49. $(m + 2)(m - 1) = 0$ 50. $a(2a + 6)(a - 5) = 0$

51. Ray is 42 years old. Eight years ago, Ray was twice as old as Roy. How old is Roy today? 25 yr

9-4 Inequalities and Absolute Value

Explore

We know that $|x| = 3$ has two solutions, $x = 3$ and $x = -3$. Both 3 and -3 are 3 units from 0. Copy the number line below. Test points on the number line to find four other points that satisfy the condition $|x| < 3$.

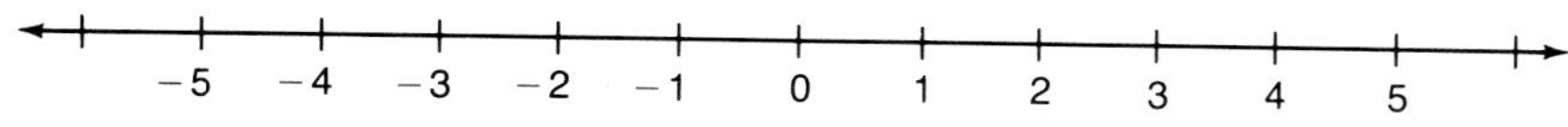

Conjunctions and Inequalities

Objective: Solve and graph inequalities involving absolute value of the form $|A| < b$.

For the absolute value of a number to be less than 3, its distance from 0 must be less than 3. Therefore, the inequality $|x| < 3$ is true for any number between 3 and -3.

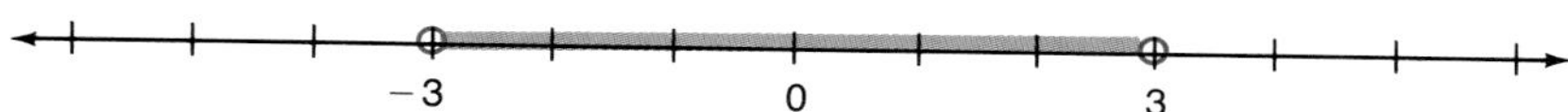

We write the solution as the conjunction $x < 3$ and $x > -3$, or $-3 < x < 3$. The solution set is $\{x| -3 < x < 3\}$.

Solving Inequalities with Absolute Values $|A| < b$

To solve an inequality of the form $|A| < b$ where b is a positive number, we solve the conjunction

$$-b < A < b$$

A similar rule holds for $|A| \le b$.

EXAMPLE 1 Solve and graph $|3x| < 15$.

We solve the conjunction as $-15 < 3x < 15$, first rewriting it using *and*.

$-15 < 3x$ and $3x < 15$

$-5 < x$ and $x < 5$ Solving each inequality

We can abbreviate this conjunction as $-5 < x < 5$ and graph the solution.

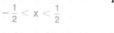

The solution set is $\{x| -5 < x < 5\}$.

9-4

FIRST FIVE MINUTES

1. Solve $|x - 5| = 4$.
$x - 5 = 4$ or $x - 5 = -4$
$x = 9$ or $x = 1$
2. Solve $|2x - 7| = 5$.
$2x - 7 = 5$ or $2x - 7 = -5$
$x = 6$ or $x = 1$

EXPLORE

Students should recognize that any number between -3 and 3 has an absolute value less than 3.

Conjunctions and Inequalities

Emphasize that $|x| < 6$ is equivalent to $-6 < x < 6$ and represents the set of numbers whose distance from 0, in either direction, is less than 6. Similarly, $|2x| < 6$ is equivalent to $-6 < 2x < 6$, and $|x - 1| < 6$ is equivalent to $-6 < x - 1 < 6$. Point out the similarity among the graphs of these three conjunctions.

Key Questions

- Is $|5| < 7$? Yes
- Is $|-2| < 5$? Yes
- Is $|-7| < -3$? No

Chalkboard Examples (*T18*)

1. Solve and graph $|x| < \frac{1}{2}$.
$-\frac{1}{2} < x < \frac{1}{2}$

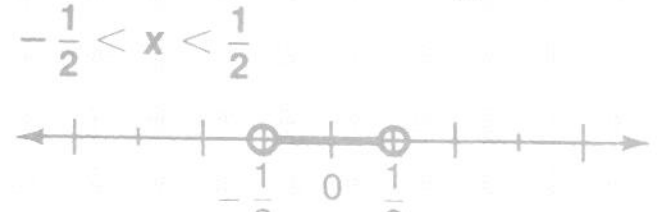

2. Solve and graph $|2x| \le 8$.
$-8 \le 2x \le 8$
$-8 \le 2x$ and $2x \le 8$
$-4 \le x$ and $x \le 4$
3. Solve and graph $|x - 3| \le 2$.
$-2 \le x - 3$ and $x - 3 \le 2$
$1 \le x$ and $x \le 5$

Disjunctions and Inequalities

Remind students that there is no abbreviated form for a disjunction.

Chalkboard Examples (*T18*)

1. Graph $|x| > 0$.
   $x < -0$ or $x > 0$
   $x < 0$ or $x > 0$
2. Solve and graph $|3x| > 12$.
   $3x > 12$ or $3x < -12$
   $x > 4$ or $x < -4$
3. Solve and graph $|2x - 4| > 2$.
   $2x - 4 > 2$ or $2x - 4 < -2$
   $2x > 6$ or $2x < 2$
   $x > 3$ or $x < 1$

LESSON QUIZ

1. Graph $|x| \le 3$ on the number line.
2. Solve and graph $|x - 1| < 3$.
   $\{x|-2 < x < 4\}$
3. Solve and graph $|2x| > 4$.
   $\{x|x < -2 \text{ or } x > 2\}$
4. Solve and graph $|4x - 10| > 2$.
   $\{x|x < 2 \text{ or } x > 3\}$

EXAMPLE 2

A lathe operator is making shoulder bolts for a lawn mower. The specifications require that the diameter (d) of the bolt satisfies the equation $|d - 2| \le 0.01$ cm. What are the acceptable diameters for the bolt?

We solve the conjunction
$-0.01 \le d - 2 \le 0.01$, first rewriting it using *and*.

$$-0.01 \le d - 2 \quad \text{and} \quad d - 2 \le 0.$$
$$1.99 \le d \quad \text{and} \quad d \le 2.$$

We can write this conjunction as $1.99 \le d \le 2.01$. The bolt's diameter must be equal to a number in the interval described by the inequality.

The solution set is $\{d|1.99 \le d \le 2.01\}$.

a. $\{x| -7 < x < 7\}$
b. $\{x| -6 < x < 6\}$
c. $\{x| -14 \le x \le 4\}$
d. $\left\{x\middle|\frac{2}{3} \le x \le 2\right\}$
For graphs, see Additional Answers.

Try This Solve and graph.

a. $|x| < 7$ **b.** $|3x| < 18$ **c.** $|x + 5| \le 9$ **d.** $|3x - 4| \le 2$

Disjunctions and Inequalities

Objective: Solve and graph inequalities involving absolute value of the form $|A| > b$.

The inequality $|x| > 2$ is true for any value whose distance from 0 on the number line is greater than 2.

EXAMPLE 3 Graph $|x| > 2$ on a number line. Find the solution set.

For the absolute value of a number to be greater than 2, its distance from 0 must be greater than 2. Thus x must be greater than 2 or less than -2.

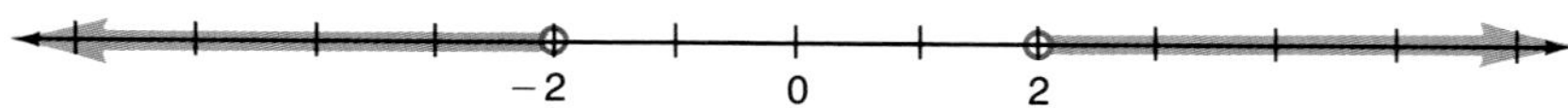

The solution is the disjunction $x < -2$ or $x > 2$.

Thus the solution set is $\{x|x < -2 \text{ or } x > 2\}$.

Try This Graph on a number line. Find the solution set.

e. $|x| > 1$ **f.** $|x| \ge 3$ **g.** $|x| > 5$
For graphs, see Additional Answers.

e. $\{x|x < -1 \text{ or } x > 1\}$
f. $\{x|x \le -3 \text{ or } x \ge 3\}$
g. $\{x|x < -5 \text{ or } x > 5\}$

Solving Inequalities with Absolute Values $|A| > b$

To solve an inequality of the form $|A| > b$ where b is a positive number, we solve the disjunction

$$A < -b \text{ or } A > b$$

A similar rule holds for $|A| \geq b$.

EXAMPLE 4 Solve and graph $|3x - 8| \geq 5$.

Solve the disjunction $3x - 8 \leq -5$ or $3x - 8 \geq 5$.

$$3x - 8 \leq -5 \quad \text{or} \quad 3x - 8 \geq 5$$
$$3x \leq 3 \qquad\qquad 3x \geq 13$$
$$x \leq 1 \qquad\qquad x \geq \frac{13}{3}$$

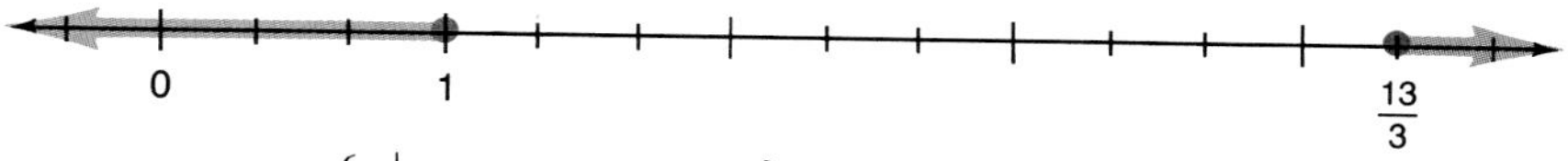

The solution set is $\left\{x \middle| x \leq 1 \text{ or } x \geq \frac{13}{3}\right\}$.

Try This Solve and graph. For graphs, see Teacher's Answer Section.

h. $|2x| > 10$ $\{x|x < -5 \text{ or } x > 5\}$ **i.** $|x - 4| \geq 5$ $\{x|x \leq -1 \text{ or } x \geq 9\}$ **j.** $|2x + 4| \geq 16$ $\{x|x \leq -10 \text{ or } x \geq 6\}$

9-4 EXERCISES

A

Solve and graph.

1. $|x| < 1$ **2.** $|t| \leq 4.5$ **3.** $|5x| \leq 20$ **4.** $|6x| \leq 24$

5. $|2x| < 11$ **6.** $|5y| \leq 5$ **7.** $|4t| < 28$ **8.** $|6x| \leq 36$

9. $|7x| \leq 35$ **10.** $|x - 3| < 12$ **11.** $|x + 2| \leq 5$ **12.** $|x - 5| \leq 7$

13. $|x + 6| < 2$ **14.** $|2y - 4| < 7$ **15.** $|4y - 2| < 7$

16. $|3x + 4| \leq 10$ **17.** $|2x + 1| \leq 5$ **18.** $|4z + 3| \leq 15$

In Example 2, suppose the diameter of the shoulder bolt satisfies the following equation. What are the acceptable diameters for the bolt?

19. $|d - 1| < 0.011$ **20.** $|2d - 2| \leq 1.1$ **21.** $|2d - 4| \leq 0.002$

Graph on a number line.

22. $|y| > 3$ **23.** $|t| > 4$ **24.** $|y| \geq 7$ **25.** $|x| \geq 9$

Assignment Guide
Minimum: Day 1: 1–21 e/o
Day 2: 22–37 e/o, MR
Regular: Day 1: 1–25 e/o
Day 2: 26–46 e/o, 47, MR
Advanced: Day 1: 1–25 e/o
Day 2: 26–46 e/o, 47, 48, MR

ADDITIONAL ANSWERS

Try This

a.

b.

c.

d.

e.

f.

g.
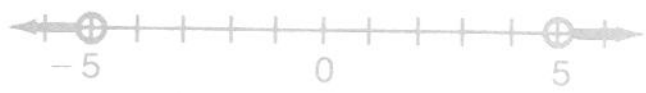

Exercises

For graphs of Exercises 1–37, see Teacher's Answer Section.

1. $\{x|-1 < x < 1\}$
2. $\{x|-4.5 \leq x \leq 4.5\}$
3. $\{x|-4 \leq x \leq 4\}$
4. $\{x|-4 \leq x \leq 4\}$
5. $\left\{x \middle| -\frac{11}{2} < x < \frac{11}{2}\right\}$
6. $\{y|-1 \leq y \leq 1\}$
7. $\{t|-7 < t < 7\}$
8. $\{x|-6 < x < 6\}$
9. $\{x|-5 \leq x \leq 5\}$
10. $\{x|-9 < x < 15\}$
11. $\{x|-7 \leq x \leq 3\}$
12. $\{x|-2 \leq x \leq 12\}$
13. $\{x|-8 < x < -4\}$
14. $\left\{y \middle| -\frac{3}{2} < y < \frac{11}{2}\right\}$
15. $\left\{y \middle| -\frac{5}{4} < y < \frac{9}{4}\right\}$
16. $\left\{x \middle| -\frac{14}{3} \leq x \leq 2\right\}$
17. $\{x|-3 \leq x \leq 2\}$
18. $\left\{z \middle| -\frac{9}{2} \leq z \leq 3\right\}$
19. $\{d|0.989 < d < 1.011\}$
20. $\{d|0.45 \leq d \leq 1.55\}$
21. $\{d|1.999 \leq d \leq 2.001\}$

26. $\{x|x < -4 \text{ or } x > 4\}$
27. $\{x|x \le -6 \text{ or } x \ge 6\}$
28. $\{t|t \le -3 \text{ or } t \ge 3\}$
29. $\{x|x < -2 \text{ or } x > 2\}$
30. $\{x|x \le -5 \text{ or } x \ge 7\}$
31. $\{x|x < -14 \text{ or } x > 4\}$
32. $\{x|x \le -2 \text{ or } x \ge 20\}$
33. $\left\{t|t \le -\frac{5}{2} \text{ or } t \ge \frac{7}{2}\right\}$
34. $\left\{y|y < -\frac{5}{3} \text{ or } y > 1\right\}$
35. $\left\{x|x \le -\frac{5}{2} \text{ or } x \ge 4\right\}$
36. $\left\{x|x \le -2 \text{ or } x \ge \frac{5}{3}\right\}$
37. $\left\{x|x < -\frac{15}{4} \text{ or } x > \frac{25}{4}\right\}$
38. $\left\{2, -\frac{3}{2}\right\}$
39. $\{x|-6 \le x \le 3\}$
40. $\left\{x|x < -\frac{4}{7} \text{ or } x > \frac{12}{7}\right\}$
41. $\{y|y \le -8 \text{ or } y \ge 7\}$
42. $\left\{x\middle|-\frac{22}{3} \le x \le 6\right\}$
43. $\left\{-\frac{3}{2}, -\frac{7}{4}\right\}$
44. $\left\{-1, -\frac{1}{3}\right\}$
45. $\emptyset$
46. $\left\{x|x \ne -\frac{5}{3}\right\}$

Mixed Review

49. $\{11, 13, 17, 19, 23, 29\}$
50. $\{4, 8, 12, 16, 20, 24\}$
51. $\{0, 2\}$
52. $\{-6, -4, -2, 0, 2, 4, 6\}$
53. $\{-2, -1, 0, 1, 2, 4, 6\}$
54. $\{0, 2\}$
55. $\{-6, -4, -2, -1, 0, 1, 2\}$
56. $\{-2, 0, 2\}$

Problem for Programmers

This program can be written using any programming language (BASIC, PASCAL, LOGO, etc.). Remind students that when using equations like $|x - 2| = 4$, $a = 1$, $b = -2$, and $c = 4$, and for equations like $|5x| = 8$, $a = 5$, $b = 0$, and $c = 8$.

The program for an absolute value inequality can also be written on a spreadsheet where the values of a, b, and c are each input in a separate column and the values of x are calculated in two other columns.

Solve and graph.

26. $|5x| > 20$ **27.** $|3x| \ge 18$ **28.** $|9t| \ge 27$

29. $|0.5x| > 1$ **30.** $|x - 1| \ge 6$ **31.** $|x + 5| > 9$

32. $|x - 9| \ge 11$ **33.** $\left|t - \frac{1}{2}\right| \ge 3$ **34.** $|3y + 1| > 4$

35. $|4x - 3| \ge 13$ **36.** $|6x + 1| \ge 11$ **37.** $\left|\frac{1}{5}x - \frac{1}{4}\right| > 1$

B

Solve.

38. $|4x - 1| = 7$ **39.** $|2x + 3| \le 9$ **40.** $|7x - 4| > 8$

41. $\left|\frac{2y + 1}{3}\right| \ge 5$ **42.** $\left|\frac{3x + 2}{4}\right| \le 5$ **43.** $\left|\frac{13}{4} + 2t\right| = \frac{1}{4}$

44. $|3x + 2| + 2 = 3$ **45.** $|2b - 4| < -5$ **46.** $|3x + 5| > 0$

47. ***Critical Thinking*** Write an absolute value inequality to describe each of the graphs below.

a.

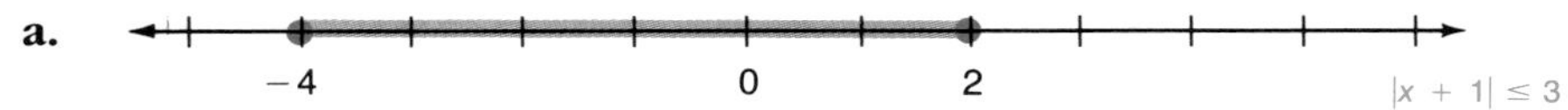

b.

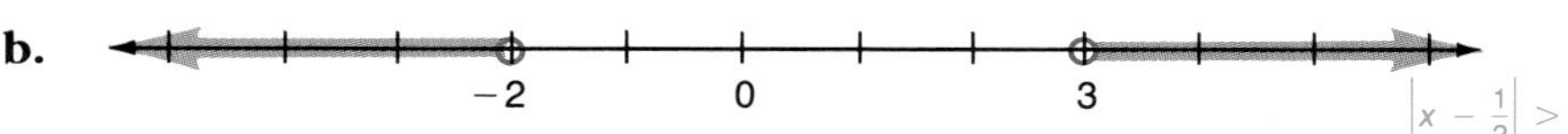

Challenge

For graph, see Teacher's Answer Section.

48. Solve and graph $|5x| \ge 20$ or $|2x| \le 4$. $\{x|x \le -4 \text{ or } -2 \le x \le 2 \text{ or } x \ge 4\}$

Mixed Review

Write using roster notation. **49.** the set A of prime numbers between 10 and 30 **50.** the set B of positive multiples of 4 less than 25

Find each of the following. Let $R = \{-6, -4, -2, 0, 2\}$, $S = \{-2, -1, 0, 1, 2\}$, $T = \{0, 2, 4, 6\}$. **51.** $R \cap T$ **52.** $R \cup T$ **53.** $S \cup T$ **54.** $S \cap T$ **55.** $R \cup S$ **56.** $R \cap S$

Problem for Programmers

Write a program that will solve an absolute value equation of the form $|ax + b| = c$. The values of a, b, and c will be the inputs, and both solutions will be the output. Test your program using Exercises 9-3.

Challenge: Write a program that will solve absolute value inequalities of the form $|ax + b| < c$ or $|ax + b| > c$. Test your program using Exercises 9-4.

9-5 Inequalities in Two Variables

Solutions of Inequalities in Two Variables

Objective: Determine whether a given ordered pair is a solution of an inequality.

The solutions of an inequality in two variables are the ordered pairs of numbers that make the inequality true.

EXAMPLE 1

Determine whether $(5, -3)$ is a solution of the inequality $2x - y > 5$. Replace x by 5 and y by -3.

$$2x - y > 5$$
$$2(5) - (-3) > 5$$
$$10 + 3 > 5$$
$$13 > 5 \quad \text{True}$$

Since $13 > 5$ is true, $(5, -3)$ is a solution.

Try This

a. Determine whether (2, 1) is a solution of $x + y < 4$. Yes

b. Determine whether (4, 8) is a solution of $y > 2x + 1$. No

Graphing Inequalities in Two Variables

Objective: Graph inequalities in two variables.

The graph of the linear equation $x + y = 3$ separates the coordinate plane into three sets:

the set of points on the line,
the set of points above the line,
and the set of points below the line.

We call the regions above the line and below the line **half-planes.** We call the line a **boundary line.**

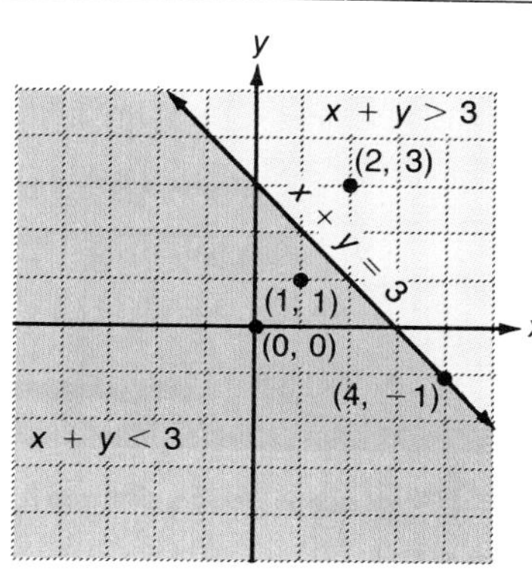

The solutions of an inequality in two variables are all the points in a half-plane and may include the points on the boundary line.

9-5

FIRST FIVE MINUTES

1. Solve and graph $|x - 4| < 2$.
$-2 < x - 4$ and $x - 4 < 2$
$2 < x$ and $x < 6$

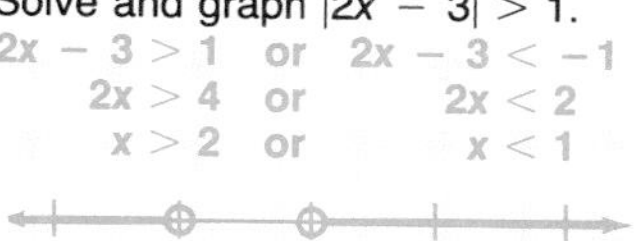

2. Solve and graph $|2x - 3| > 1$.
$2x - 3 > 1$ or $2x - 3 < -1$
$2x > 4$ or $2x < 2$
$x > 2$ or $x < 1$

1 2

Solutions of Inequalities in Two Variables

You may want to review the procedure for graphing linear equations in two variables. Remind students that the graph of a linear equation in two variables, such as $x + 2y = 7$, is a line.

Key Questions

- Is (2, 3) a solution of $3x + 2y = 12$? Yes
- Is (2, 3) a solution of $3x + 2y \le 12$? Yes
- Is (2, 3) a solution of $3x + 2y < 12$? No

Chalkboard Example

1. Determine whether (4, 1) is a solution of the inequality $3x + 2y < 20$.
$3(4) + 2(1) < 20$
The pair is a solution.

Graphing Inequalities in Two Variables

Emphasize that every point in the shaded half-plane satisfies the inequality and no points in the other half-plane satisfy the inequality. Have students verify this by picking points from both half-planes and substituting them into the inequality.

Encourage students to choose a "simple" point for testing the half-planes. (0, 0) is often the best choice if it is not on the boundary line.

Chalkboard Examples (*T19, T20*)

1. Graph $2x + 3y \le 12$.
   The graph contains the boundary line $2x + 3y = 12$ and all the points on one side of the line. The point (0, 0) satisfies the inequality, thus the graph consists of the line and all the points on the same side as the point (0, 0).

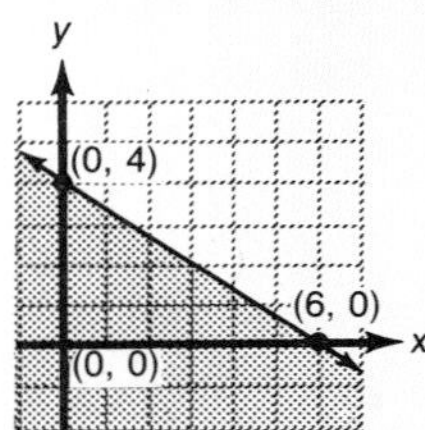

2. Graph $x \le 3$ on the plane.
   The graph contains the vertical line $x = 3$ and all the points to the left of the line.

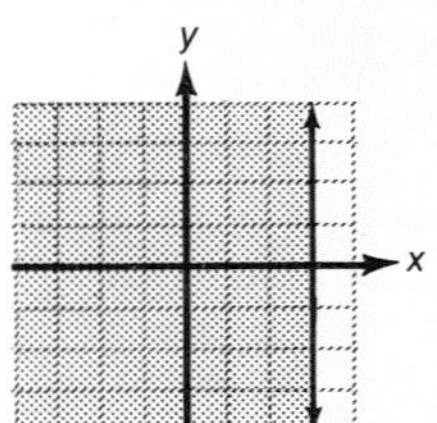

EXAMPLE 2 Graph $x + y < 4$ on a coordinate plane.

(a) We graph the boundary line $x + y = 4$ using any method learned in Chapter 7. We use a dashed line to show that the points on the line are not solutions of $x + y < 4$.

(b) The solutions of $x + y < 4$ must lie on one side of the boundary line. We test a point that is not on the line, such as (0, 0).

$$\begin{aligned} x + y &< 4 \\ 0 + 0 &< 4 \\ 0 &< 4 \quad \text{True} \end{aligned}$$

Since $0 < 4$ is true, the half-plane containing (0, 0) is the graph of the solution. We shade it to show that every point in that half-plane is a solution.

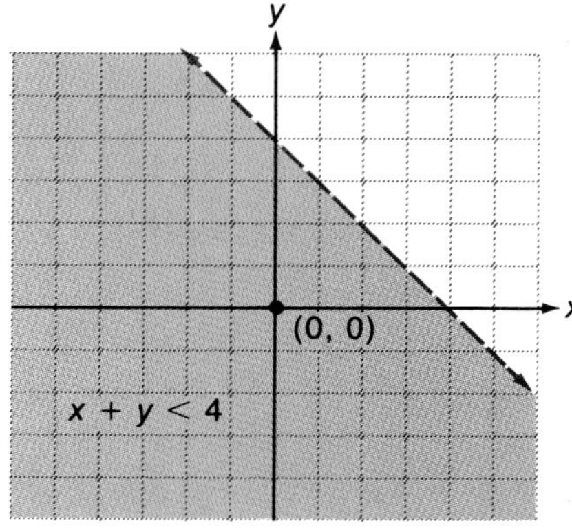

EXAMPLE 3 Graph $y - 2x \ge 0$ on a coordinate plane.

(a) We graph the boundary line $y - 2x = 0$. We use a solid line to show that the points on the line are solutions of $y - 2x \ge 0$.

(b) We determine which half-plane contains the solutions to $y - 2x \ge 0$ by testing a point that is not on the line, say (1, 1).

$$\begin{aligned} y - 2x &\ge 0 \\ 1 - 2(1) &\ge 0 \\ 1 - 2 &\ge 0 \\ -1 &\ge 0 \quad \text{False} \end{aligned}$$

Since $-1 \ge 0$ is *false,* the half-plane containing (1, 1) does *not* contain the solutions. The half-plane that does *not* contain (1, 1) is the graph of the solution. We shade it to show that every point in that half-plane is a solution.

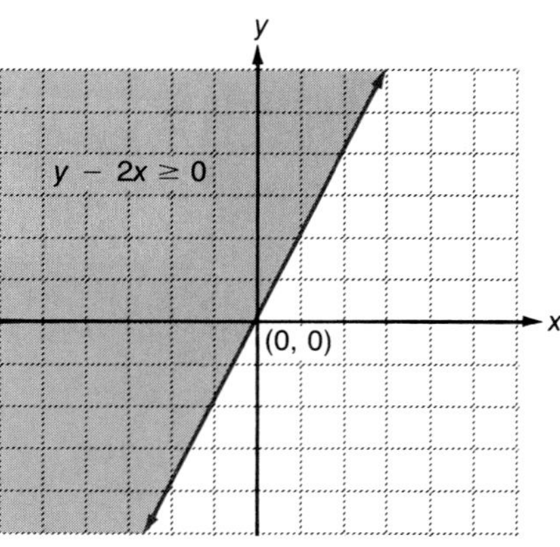

EXAMPLE 4 Graph $y < -2$ on a coordinate plane.

(a) We graph the boundary line $y = -2$, using a dashed line to show that the points on the line are not solutions of $y < -2$.

(b) We test a point that is not on the line, such as $(0, -3)$.

$$y < -2$$
$$-3 < -2 \quad \text{Substituting } -3 \text{ for } y$$

Since $-3 < -2$ is true, the half-plane containing $(0, -3)$ is the graph of the solution. We shade below the line to show that every point in that half-plane is a solution.

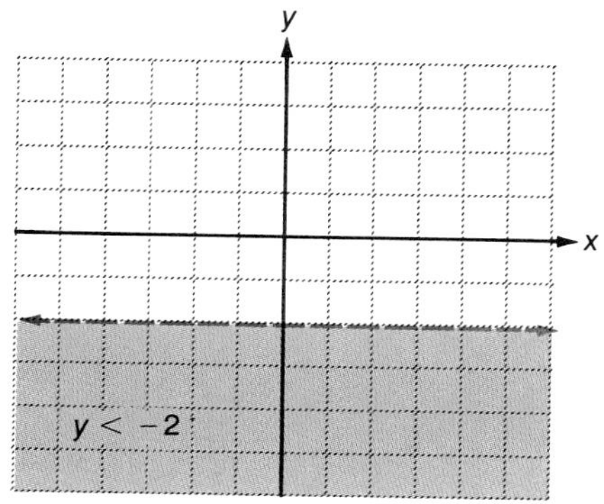

Try This Graph on a coordinate plane. See Additional Answers.

c. $y > x - 1$ **d.** $2x + y \leq 4$ **e.** $y - 3x < 0$ **f.** $x \geq 2$

9-5 EXERCISES

A

1. Determine whether $(-3, -5)$ is a solution of $-x - 3y < 18$. No
2. Determine whether $(5, -3)$ is a solution of $-2x + 4y \leq -2$. Yes
3. Determine whether $\left(\frac{1}{2}, -\frac{1}{4}\right)$ is a solution of $7y - 9x > -3$. No

Graph on a coordinate plane. See Teacher's Answer Section.

4. $x > 2y$	**5.** $x > 3y$	**6.** $y \leq x - 3$
7. $y \leq x - 5$	**8.** $y < x + 1$	**9.** $y < x + 4$
10. $y > 2$	**11.** $x \geq 3$	**12.** $x > 0$
13. $y \geq x - 2$	**14.** $y \geq x - 1$	**15.** $y \leq 2x - 1$
16. $y \leq 3x + 2$	**17.** $x + y \leq 3$	**18.** $x + y \leq 4$
19. $y \leq 0$	**20.** $y \geq -1$	**21.** $x \leq -2$
22. $x - y > 7$	**23.** $x - y > -2$	**24.** $x - 3y < 6$
25. $x - y < -10$	**26.** $2x + 3y \leq 12$	**27.** $5x + 4y \geq 20$
28. $y \geq 1 - 2x$	**29.** $y - 2x \leq -1$	**30.** $y + 4x > 0$
31. $y - x < 0$	**32.** $y > -3x$	**33.** $y < -5x$

LESSON QUIZ

1. Determine whether (2, 3) is a solution of the inequality $5x - 3y \leq 7$.
   The point is a solution.
2. Graph $5x - 2y \leq 10$ on the plane.

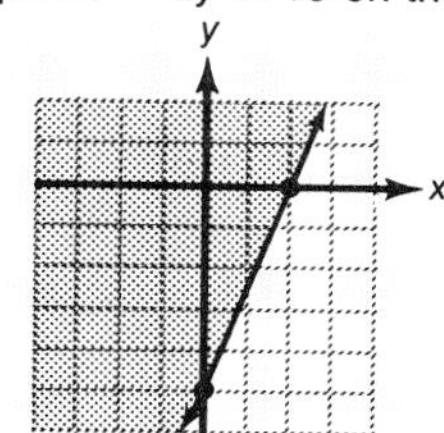

3. Graph $2x + 6y \leq 0$ on the plane.

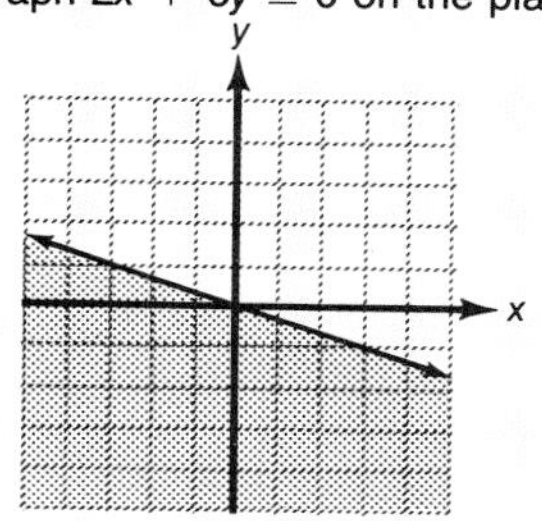

Assignment Guide

Minimum: 1–33 e/o, MR

Regular: 1–39 e/o, 40, MR

Advanced: 1–39 m3, 40–44, MR

ADDITIONAL ANSWERS

Try This

c.

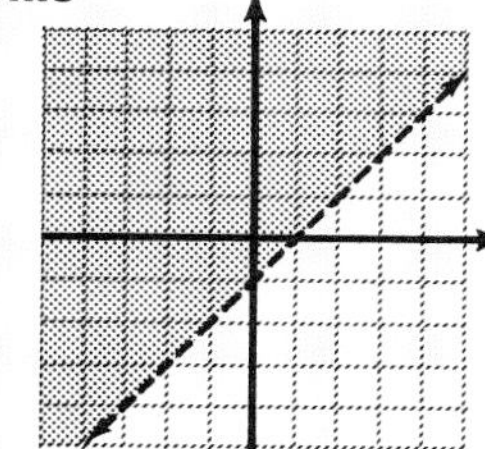

d.

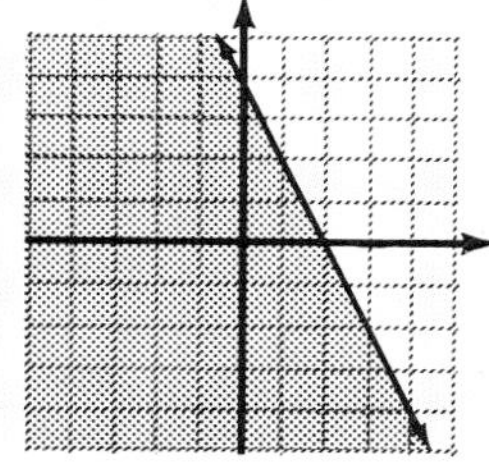

e.

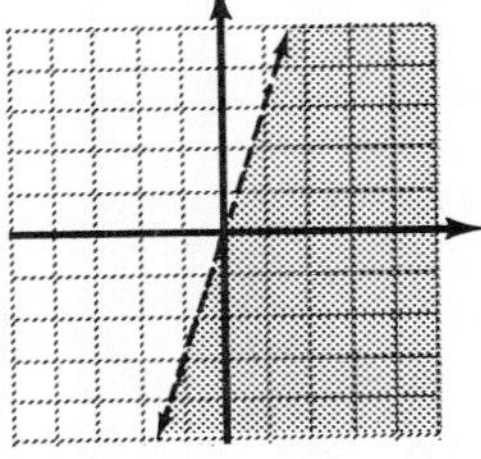

f.

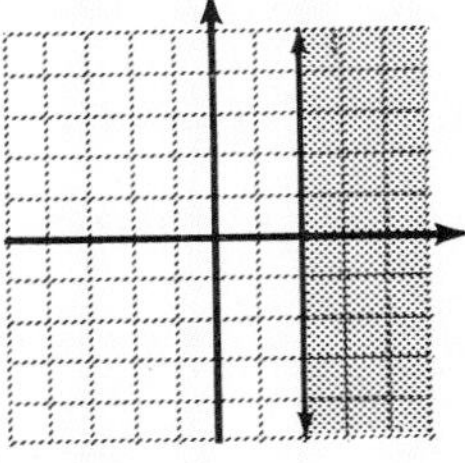

Exercises

40. ($x \geq 0$ and $y \leq 0$) or ($x \leq 0$ and $y \geq 0$); $xy \leq 0$

Mixed Review

45–47. See Teacher's Answer Section.
48. $-3 < x \leq 5$
49. $x \leq -4$ or $x > 3$
50. $(m - 5)(m - 10)$
51. $(2a + 7)(a - 6)$
52. $(2x + a)(x + a)$
53. $(3x + 5)(2x + 3)$

B

Write an inequality for each graph.

34.

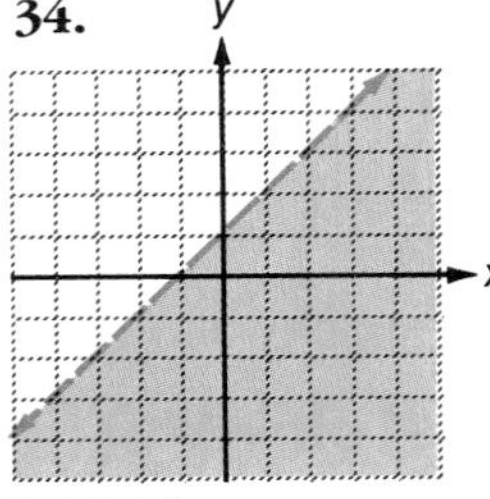

$y < x + 1$

35.

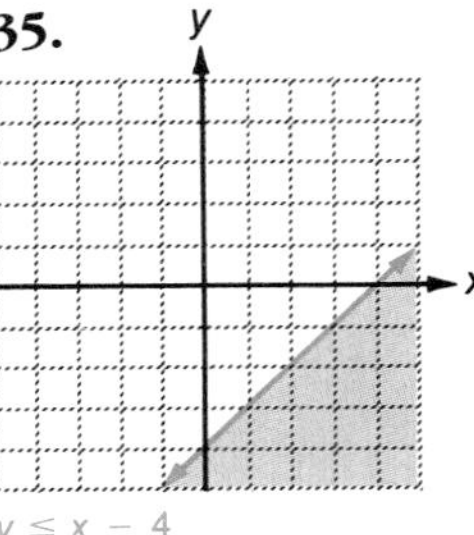

$y \leq x - 4$

36.

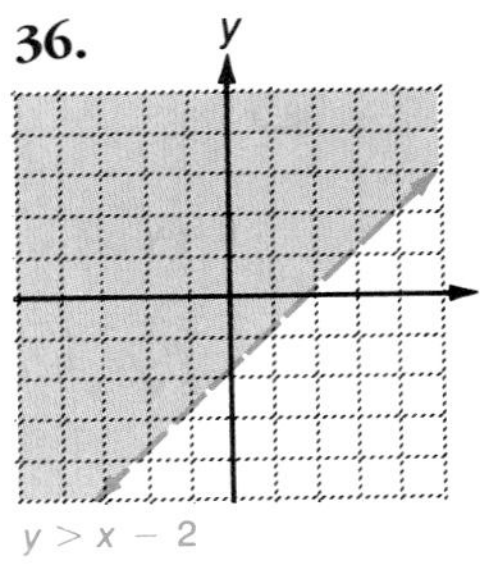

$y > x - 2$

37.

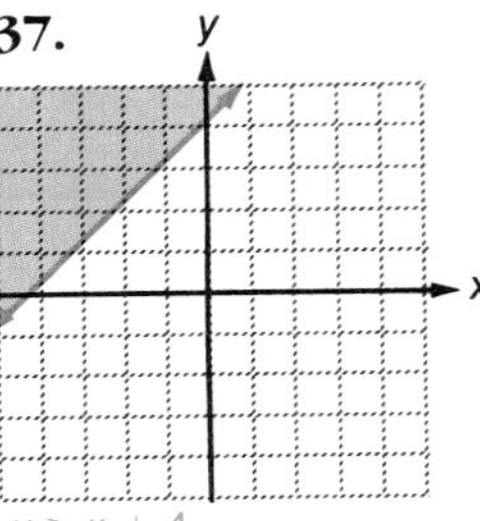

$y \geq x + 4$

38.

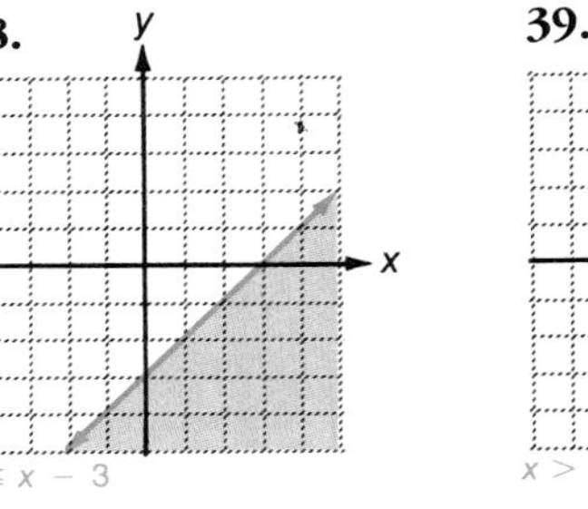

$y \leq x - 3$

39.

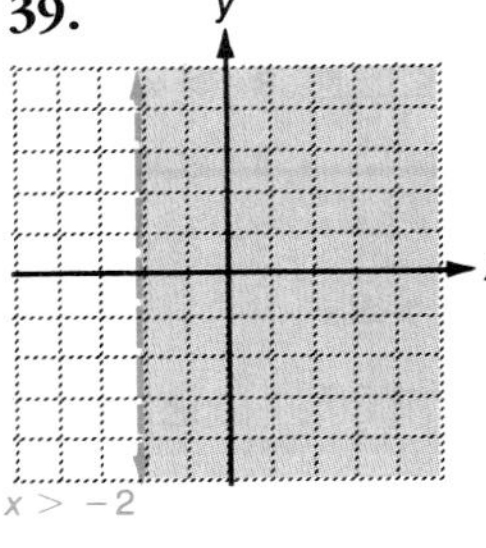

$x > -2$

40. ***Critical Thinking*** What compound inequality is shown in the graph? Can you find another inequality represented by the graph?

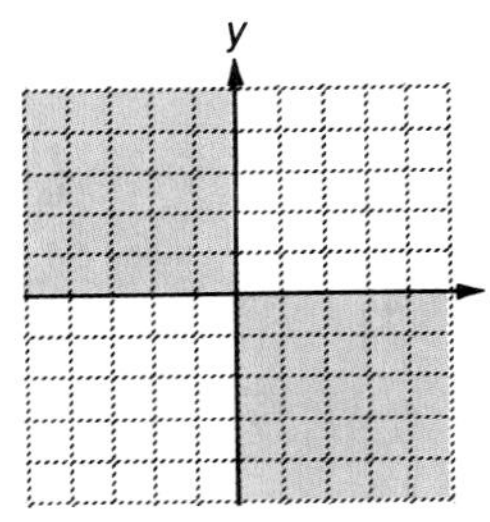

Challenge

Graph on a coordinate plane. See Teacher's Answer Section.

41. $|x| \leq y$
42. $|y| \geq x$
43. $|x| + |y| > 4$
44. $|x| - |y| \geq 6$

Mixed Review

Graph on a number line. **45.** $-5 \leq x$ and $x < 2$
46. $-4 < x$ and $x < -1$ **47.** $x \leq 0$ or $x > 3$
Solve. **48.** $5 < x + 8 \leq 13$ **49.** $2x + 1 \leq -7$ or $3x - 5 > 4$
Factor. **50.** $m^2 - 15m + 50$ **51.** $2a^2 - 5a - 42$
52. $2x^2 + 3xa + a^2$ **53.** $6x^2 + 19x + 15$

WRITING TO LEARN

Write a set of instructions in which you list the steps for graphing an inequality in two variables.

9-6 Graphing Systems of Linear Inequalities

Objective: Graph systems of linear inequalities in two variables.

Application

The Sanderson Water Company must supply at least 8 million gallons of water per day (mgd) to the city of Sanderson. The water will be provided from either the local reservoir or from a pipeline to a water supply located in the mountains. The local reservoir has a daily yield of 4 mgd, which may not be exceeded. The pipeline can supply no more than 8 mgd. However, in order to use the pipeline, the Sanderson Water Company must agree to use a minimum of 6 mgd. What are possible amounts from each source that will satisfy these conditions?

In real-world situations there are often many conditions or constraints that must be considered. Constraints can often be translated into mathematical inequalities. Two or more linear inequalities for which a common solution is sought are called a **system of inequalities**.

EXAMPLE 1 Solve this system by graphing.

$$2x + y \geq 8$$
$$2x - y > 1$$

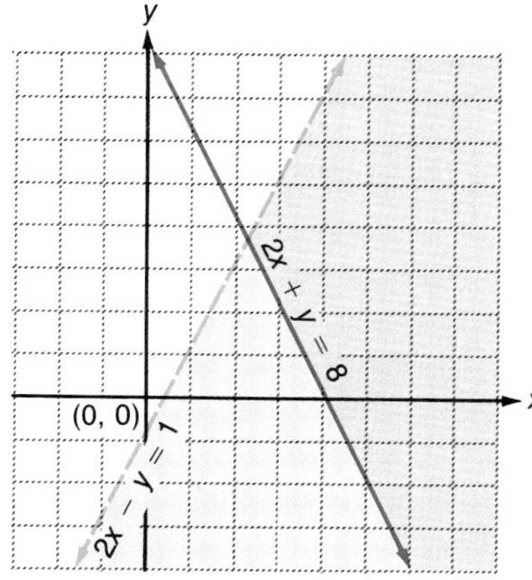

(a) Graph the inequality $2x + y \geq 8$, graphing the boundary line $2x + y = 8$ (solid), and shading the half-plane above the boundary line in one color.

(b) Graph the inequality $2x - y > 1$, graphing the boundary line $2x - y = 1$ (dashed), and shading the half-plane below the line in another color.

The region where the shadings overlap is the graph of the solution to the system of inequalities.

9-6

FIRST FIVE MINUTES

1. Graph on a coordinate plane.
   $6x - 2y \leq 6$

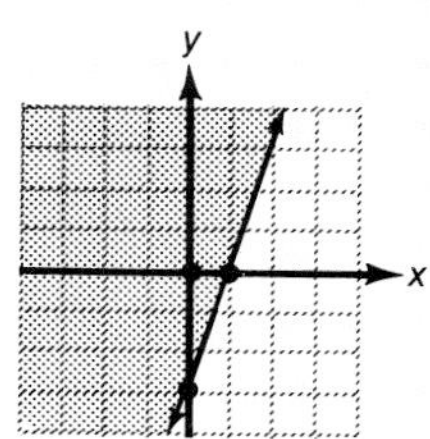

Remind students that the solution to a pair of linear equations corresponds to the point of intersection of a pair of lines. The solution to a pair of linear inequalities corresponds to a region formed by the intersection of two half-planes.

You may want to have students use hatch marks rather than color. They can, for example, shade one half-plane with horizontal lines and the other half-plane with vertical lines. The solution region will then be the crisscrossed area.

Key Questions

- How many half-planes are necessary to have a triangular solution region?
  Three
- Does every system of inequalities have a region of solution?
  No

Chalkboard Examples (*T21*)

1. Solve this system by graphing.
   $3x + 2y \geq 6$
   $4x + y \leq 4$
   Graph each boundary line separately, then shade the region that is in *both* half-planes.

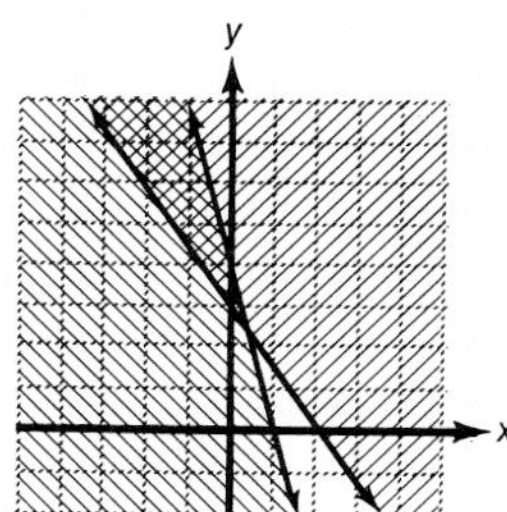

2. Samuel does odd jobs on Saturdays. He earns anywhere from \$3 to \$5 an hour. He can't work more than 8 hours, and he always does 3 hours of work for his next-door neighbor.

Write an inequality for each condition given in this situation and graph the inequalities.

Let the x-axis represent hours worked and the y-axis represent money earned.

Samuel earns between \$3 and \$5 an hour: $3x \leq y \leq 5x$.

He works at least 3 hours and no more than 8 hours: $3 \leq x \leq 8$.

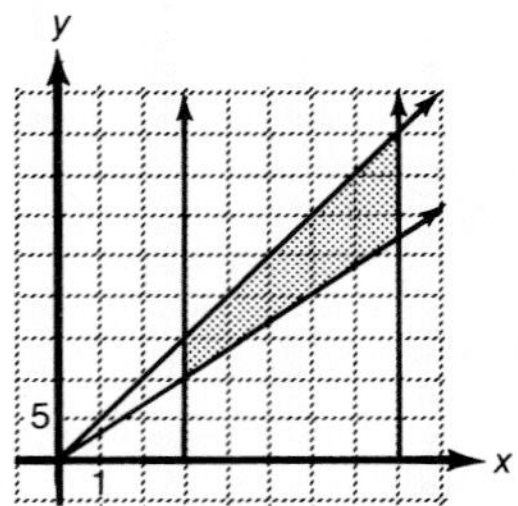

LESSON QUIZ

1. Solve the system by graphing.
$y \leq 2x + 1$
$x + y \leq 2$

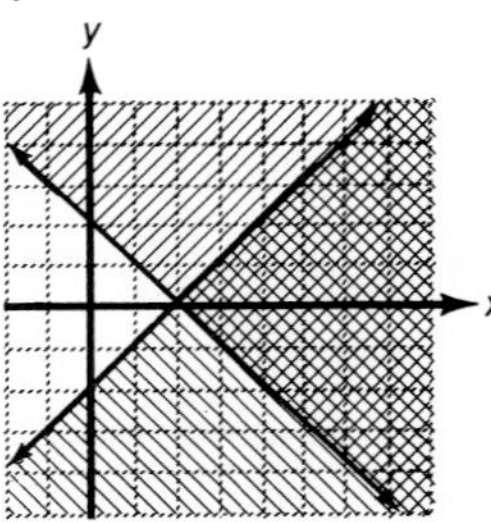

2. Solve the system by graphing.
$x + y \geq 2$
$x - y \geq 2$

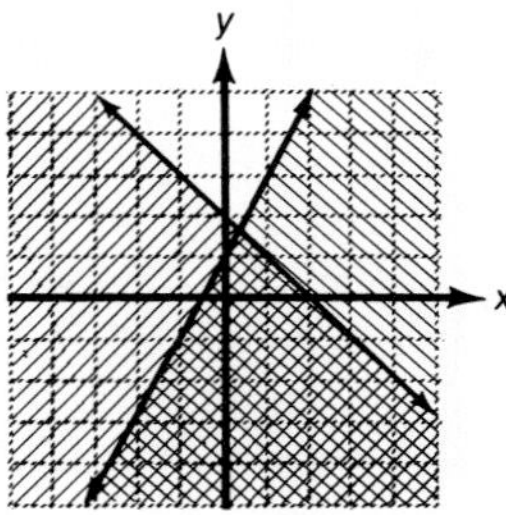

Try This Solve these systems by graphing. See Teacher's Answer Section.

a. $y > 4x - 1$
$y < -2x + 3$

b. $y \geq x$
$y \leq -x + 1$

c. $x \leq 0$
$x - y > 1$

d. $x + y < -1$
$3x - y > 4$

EXAMPLE 2 Write an inequality for each of the conditions given in the Application. Then graph these inequalities.

The Sanderson Water Company must supply at least 8 million gallons of water per day (mgd) to the city of Sanderson. The water will be provided from either the local reservoir or from a pipeline to a water supply located in the mountains. The local reservoir has a daily yield of 4 mgd, which may not be exceeded. The pipeline can supply no more than 8 mgd. However, in order to use the pipeline, the Sanderson Water Company must agree to use a minimum of 6 mgd. What are possible amounts from each source that will satisfy these conditions?

Let x = the amount of water (mgd) supplied from the reservoir.
Let y = the amount of water (mgd) supplied from the pipeline.

The water company must supply at least 8 mgd → $x + y \geq 8$

The reservoir can supply no more than 4 mgd → $x \leq 4$

The pipeline can supply no more than 8 mgd → $y \leq 8$

If used, the pipeline must supply at least 6 mgd → $y \geq 6$

Graph each of these inequalities on the same coordinate axes.

When graphing a system of three or more equations, we can use arrows to show which side of the boundary is included in the graph.

Finally, shade the region where all of the graphs overlap as indicated by the arrows.

The shaded area shows the values that satisfy all conditions.

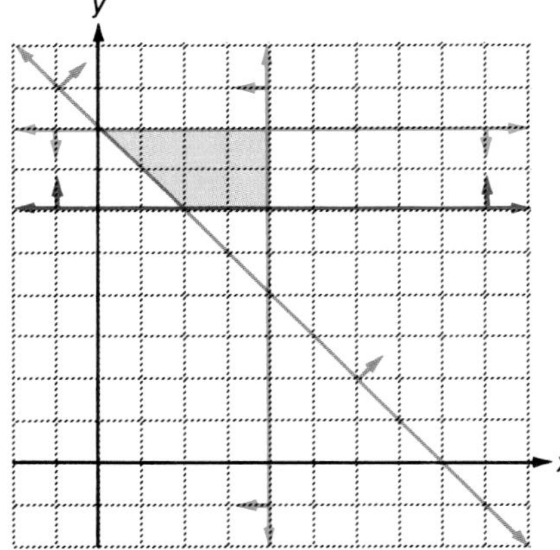

Try This

See Teacher's Answer Section.

e. The math club decides to raise money by selling pencils. They order 300 blue and 400 red pencils. They must sell 100 pencils to break even. Each of the twenty students in the club agrees to sell at least 10 pencils.

i. Write an inequality for each condition given in this situation.

ii. Graph the inequalities on the same coordinate axes.

iii. If the club sells 250 blue pencils and 300 red pencils, have they satisfied all of the conditions?

9-6 EXERCISES

A

Solve these systems by graphing.

1. $x > 2 + y$; $y > 1$
2. $y < 3x$; $x + y < 4$
3. $y < x$; $y < -x + 1$
4. $y > x$; $y > -x + 2$
5. $2y - y < 2$; $x > 3$
6. $y > 4$; $2y + x > 5$
7. $y > 4x - 1$; $y \leq -2x + 3$
8. $y > 5x + 2$; $y \leq -x + 1$
9. $x - 2y > 6$; $x + 2y \leq 4$
10. $2y - x > 5$; $x + y \leq 4$
11. $2x - 3y \geq 9$; $2y + x > 6$
12. $3x - 2y \leq 8$; $2x + y > 6$
13. $x + y < 3$; $x - y \leq 4$
14. $x - y < 3$; $x + y \geq 4$
15. $5x + 2y \geq 12$; $2x + 3y \leq 10$
16. $x \leq 4$; $x + y \leq 3$; $y \leq x$
17. $y \leq x$; $x \geq -2$; $y \leq 1 - x$
18. $y > 0$; $x > y$; $x + y \geq 2$
19. $y > 2x$; $y \leq x + 2$; $x > -1$
20. $y \leq x$; $y \geq -2$; $y < 2x - 3$
21. $x - y > 3$; $x > 0$; $x + y \leq 5$

22. Ouanh Nguyen is planning to pay for up to 30 minutes of computer time from a computer service, where she has a choice of games and a data search. She will need to use the data search for at least 10 minutes to research a term paper. The data search, however, must be used for at least 15 minutes at a time. In order to play a complete game, Ouanh must be connected to the games for at least 5 minutes.
    - **a.** Write an inequality for each condition given in this situation.
    - **b.** Graph the inequalities on the same coordinate axes.
    - **c.** If Ouanh uses the data search for 15 minutes and the games for 10 minutes, will all of the conditions be satisfied?

23. The school board is investigating ways to hire a faculty for the summer school program. They can hire teachers and aides. A minimum of 20 faculty members is needed to run the program, and there must be at least 12 teachers. For a proper teacher-to-aide ratio, the number of aides must be no more than twice the number of teachers. There can be no more than 50 faculty members altogether. (Note: There cannot be a negative number of teachers or aides.)
    - **a.** Write an inequality for each condition given in this situation.
    - **b.** Graph the inequalities on the same coordinate axes.
    - **c.** If the school board hires 12 teachers and 5 aides, will all of the conditions be satisfied?

Assignment Guide

Minimum: 1–22 e/o, MR, assign w. College Entrance Exams

Regular: 1–21 m3, 22–27 e/o, 28 MR

Advanced: 1–21 m4, 22–27 e/o, 28–31, MR

ADDITIONAL ANSWERS

Exercises

1–21. See Teacher's Answer Section.

22. a. $x + y \leq 30$
$x \geq 15$
$y \geq 5$

b.

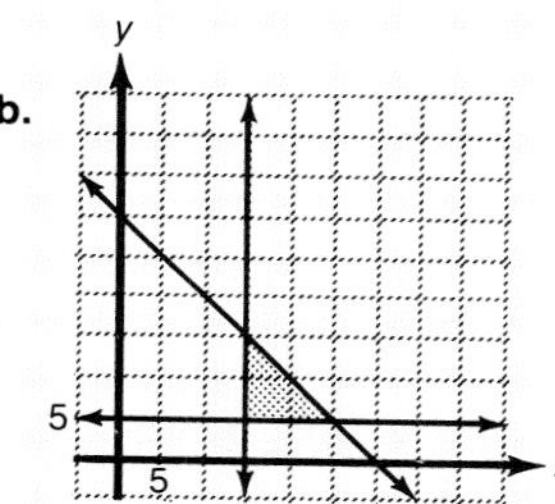

c. Yes

23. a. $x + y \geq 20$
$x \geq 12$
$y \leq 2x$
$x + y \leq 50$
$x \geq 0, y \geq 0$

b.

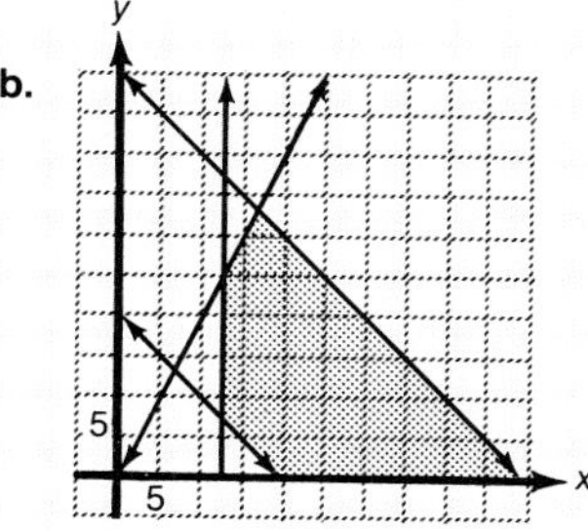

c. No

24. $x \geq -2, y \leq -2$
25. $y \geq 0, x > y$
26. $y \geq 1, y > x + 2$
27. $x < 3, y \leq 2, y \geq \frac{1}{2}x$
28. Answers may vary. Example: $0 \leq x \leq 5, 0 \leq y \leq 5$
29. $(-1, 1), (1, 0), (2, 1)$

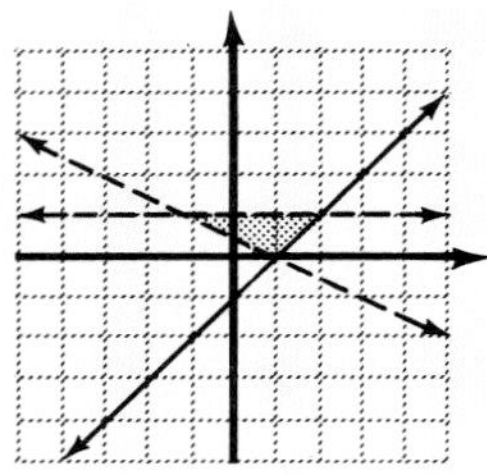

30. $(0, 1), (0, 3), (2, 2)$

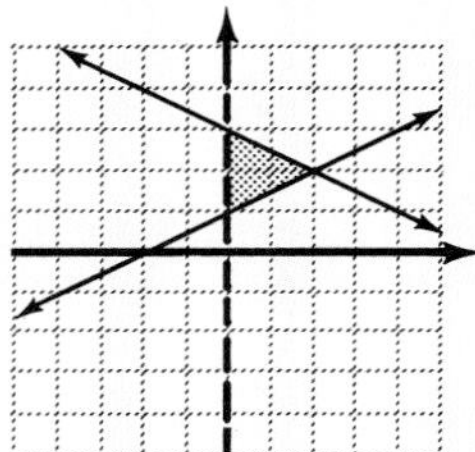

31.

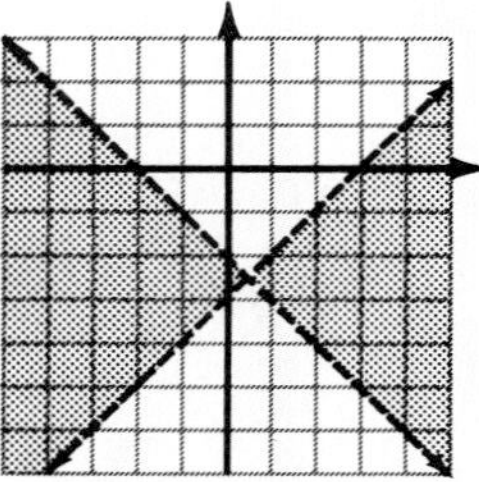

Mixed Review

32. $x \leq 11$ or $x > 8$
33. $1 < x \leq 3$
34. $x > 2$ or $x < -2$
35. $-2 < x < 2$
36. $y > 4$ or $y < -5$
37. $-5 < y < 4$
38. $(x + 2y)(x + y)$
39. $(b + 2)^2$
40. $(3x^2 - 5y)(3x^2 + 5y)$
41. 27 dimes, 54 quarters

B

Write a system of inequalities whose solution is shown by each graph.

24.

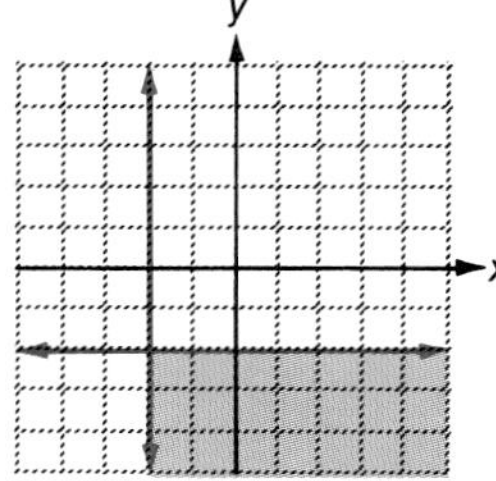

25.

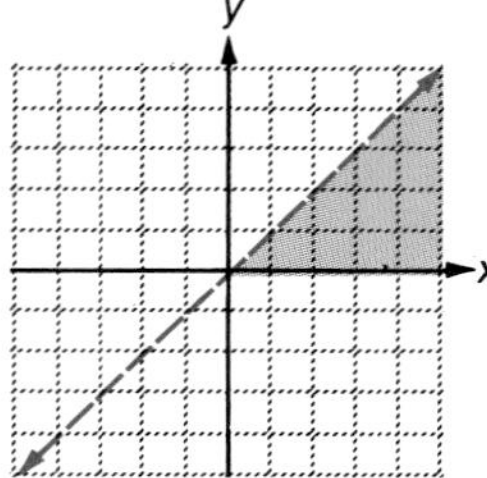

26.

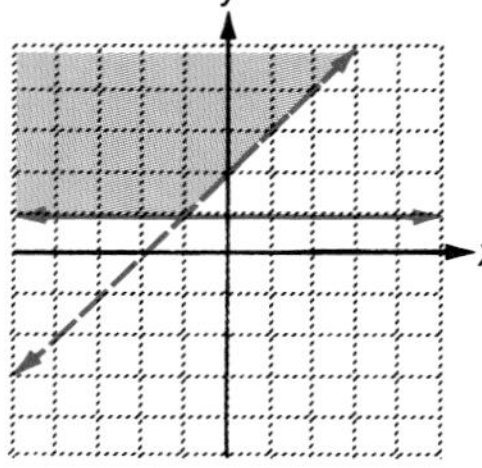

27.

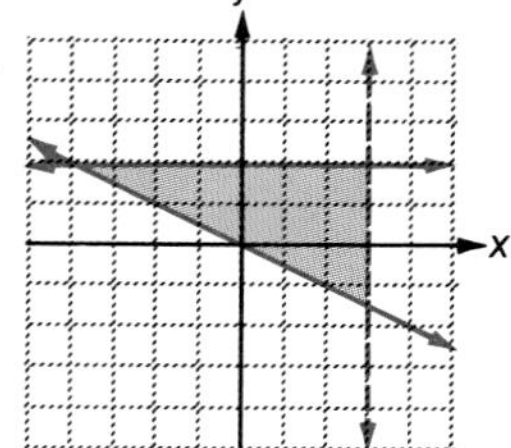

28. *Critical Thinking* Write a system of inequalities such that the graph of its solution forms a square region with one corner at the origin and two adjacent sides on the x- and y-axis.

Challenge

The corner points of the graph of a system of inequalities are the points where the boundary lines intersect. Graph each system of inequalities and give the coordinates of each corner point.

29. $x - y \leq 1$
$x + 2y > 1$
$y < 1$

30. $x > 0$
$2y + x \leq 6$
$x + 2 \leq 2y$

31. Graph $(x - y - 3)(x + y + 2) > 0$. (Hint: Under what conditions is a product of two numbers positive?)

Mixed Review

Solve. **32.** $x + 5 \leq 16$ or $x - 3 > 5$ **33.** $-7 \leq -3x + 2 < -1$

34. $|4x| > 8$ **35.** $|4x| < 8$ **36.** $|2y + 1| > 9$ **37.** $|2y + 1| < 9$

Factor. **38.** $x^2 + 3yx + 2y^2$ **39.** $b^2 + 4b + 4$ **40.** $9x^4 - 25y^2$

41. A collection of dimes and quarters is worth \$16.20. There are 81 coins in all. How many are dimes and how many are quarters?

Problem Solving: College Entrance Exams

Quantitative Comparisons

If you are asked to compare two expressions, you can often guess which expression is greater. However, you may want to check your answer by replacing the variables in the expressions with numbers. Select at least one positive integer, at least one negative integer, and zero as check points. If exponents are involved, you should also try a larger number like 10.

The choices for these kinds of test items are often:
(A) if the quantity in column A is greater
(B) if the quantity in column B is greater
(C) if the two quantities are equal
(D) if the relationship cannot be determined

In the examples below, decide which of the choices above is correct.

EXAMPLE 1

Column A		Column B	
$2x$		x	

You may guess that $2x$ is greater than x. However, is $2x$ greater than x for all acceptable replacements?

$2(1)$	$>$	(1)	Substituting 1
$2(0)$	$=$	(0)	Substituting 0
$2(-1)$	$<$	(-1)	Substituting -1

Since the expressions are $>$, $=$, and $<$, depending on the value of the variable, the correct answer is (D), the relationship cannot be determined.

EXAMPLE 2

Column A		Column B	
m^2		$1 + m^2$	
1^2	$<$	$1 + 1^2$	Substituting 1
0^2	$<$	$1 + 0^2$	Substituting 0
$(-1)^2$	$<$	$1 + (-1)^2$	Substituting -1

Since Column B is continuously larger than Column A, the answer is (B), the quantity in Column B is greater.

Problem Solving: College Entrance Exams

On college entrance exams, often as many as one third of the multiple choice questions are quantitative comparison questions.

ANSWERS

1. (D)
2. (B)
3. (D)
4. (D)
5. (B)
6. (A)
7. (A)
8. (D)
9. (D)
10. (C)

EXAMPLE 3

	Column A		Column B
	a, b, c are all positive		
	abc		$a + b + c$
First you let $a, b, c = 1$	$(1)(1)(1)$	$<$	$1 + 1 + 1$
Then you let $a, b, c = 2$	$(2)(2)(2)$	$>$	$2 + 2 + 2$

Since you get both $<$ and $>$, the answer must be (D), the relationship cannot be determined.

Problems

Compare the quantities in Column A with those in Column B, and choose statement (A), (B), (C), or (D).

	Column A		Column B
1.	$(x + 1)(x + 4)$	$x < 0$	$(x + 1)^2$
2.	c	$c < d < 0$	cd
3.	ab	$a < b < c$	bc
4.	$m + n$	$mn > 0$	$m - n$
5.	$5.0 \times 8{,}765$		$5.1 \times 8{,}765$
6.	c	$0 < c < d$	$-4d$
7.	$\frac{f}{e}$	$e > 1$ $f < 0$	ef
8.	$(a - 2)(a + 5)$	$a > 0$	$(a - 2)$
9.	$\frac{1}{d}$	$-3 < d < 3$ $d \neq 0$	d
10.	b	$(a + b) - c = a$	c

Chapter 9 Summary and Review

9-1

A set is a well-defined collection of objects called **members** or **elements.** To write a set using **roster notation,** list the elements of the set. To write a set using **set-builder notation,** specify a variable and a description of how to build the set.

Write using (a) roster notation and (b) set-builder notation.

1. the set A of whole numbers less than 9
2. the set B of odd whole numbers
3. the set C of positive multiples of 7 less than 30
4. the set D of negative integers greater than -5

The **intersection** of two sets A and B, $A \cap B$, is the set of all elements that are common to both sets. The **union** of the two sets A and B, $A \cup B$, is the set of all elements that are in A or B or both.

Let $A = (2, 4, 8, 16, 32)$, $B = (4, 8, 12, 16, 20)$ and $C = (3, 6, 9, 12, 15, 18)$. Find the following.

5. $A \cup B$
6. $A \cup C$
7. $A \cap B$
8. $B \cap C$
9. Let W be the set of whole numbers and P be the set of positive odd numbers. Find $W \cap P$.
10. Let Z be the set of integers and W be the set of whole numbers. Find $Z \cup W$.

9-2

A **conjunction** of two statements is formed by the word "and" connecting the two statements and is true when both statements are true. The graph of a conjunction is the *intersection* of the two individual graphs. A **disjunction** of two statements is formed by the word "or" connecting the two statements and is true when one or both of the statements are true. The graph of the disjunction is the *union* of the two individual graphs.

11. Graph the conjunction $x \geq -2$ and $x \leq 1$.
12. Graph the conjunction $-1 < p < 12$.
13. Graph the disjunction $x < -2$ or $x > 4$.

Solve and graph.

14. $-2 \leq x + 3 < 7$
15. $-1 \leq x + 4 < 4$
16. $12 + 2x < 0$ or $-2 - x \leq 3$
17. $x + 3 < 4$ or $x - 2 > -5$

ANSWERS

1. **a)** $A = \{0, 1, 2, 3, 4, 5, 6, 7, 8\}$ **b)** $A = \{x|x$ is a whole number and $x < 9\}$
2. **a)** $B = \{1, 3, 5, \ldots\}$ **b)** $B = \{x|x$ is a whole number and x is an odd number$\}$
3. **a)** $C = \{7, 14, 21, 28\}$ **b)** $C = \{x|x$ is a positive multiple of 7 and $x < 30\}$
4. **a)** $D = \{-4, -3, -2, -1\}$ **b)** $D = \{x|x$ is a negative integer and $x > -5\}$
5. $\{2, 4, 8, 12, 16, 20, 32\}$
6. $\{2, 3, 4, 6, 8, 9, 12, 15, 16, 18, 32\}$
7. $\{4, 8, 16\}$
8. $\{12\}$
9. $W \cap P = P$
10. $Z \cup W = Z$
11. −2 0 1
12. −1 0 12
13. −2 0 4
14. $-5 \leq x < 4$

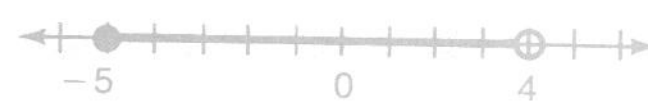

15. $-5 \leq x < 0$

16. $x < -6$ or $x \geq -5$

17. All numbers on the number line

18. $\{4, -12\}$
19. $\{-4, 8\}$
20. $\left\{\frac{18}{5}, -\frac{24}{5}\right\}$
21. $\emptyset$
22. $-3 < y < 3$

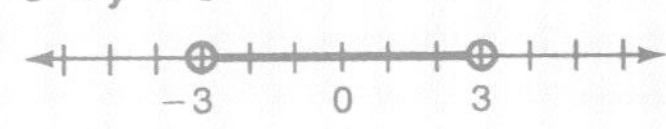

23. $-2 < y < 8$

24. $4 \le x \le 5$

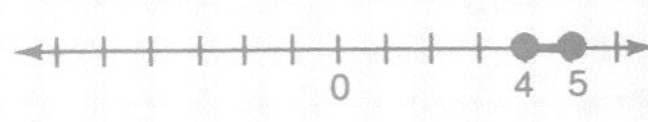

25. $x \le -5$ or $x \ge 5$

26. $a < -5$ or $a > -5$
All numbers except -5

27. $y < 1$ or $y > 4$

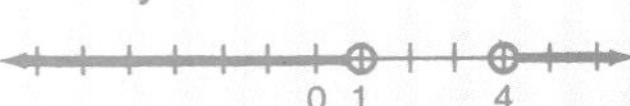

28. No
29. No
30. Yes
31. Yes
32–38. See Teacher's Answer Section.

9-3

To solve an equation with absolute value, such as $|x + 1| = 5$, solve the disjunction $x + 1 = 5$ or $x + 1 = -5$.

Solve.

18. $|x + 4| = 8$ **19.** $|3x - 6| = 18$

20. $|5x + 3| = 21$ **21.** $|3x - 5| = -7$

9-4

To graph an inequality such as $|x| < 5$, solve and graph the conjunction $-5 < x < 5$. To solve an inequality such as $|x| > 5$, solve and graph the disjunction $x > 5$ or $x < -5$.

Solve and graph.

22. $|5y| < 15$ **23.** $|y - 3| < 5$

24. $|2x - 9| \le 1$ **25.** $|3x| \ge 15$

26. $|5 + a| > 0$ **27.** $|-2y + 5| > 3$

9-5

To determine whether an ordered pair is a solution of an inequality, substitute the numbers in the ordered pair for the variables to see if the inequality is true.

Determine whether the given point is a solution of the inequality $x - 2y > 1$.

28. $(0, 0)$ **29.** $(1, 3)$

30. $(4, -1)$ **31.** $(-2, -2)$

To graph an inequality in two variables, graph the equation of the boundary line as a dashed or solid line. Then test a point that is not on the line to determine which half-plane contains the solution.

Graph on a coordinate plane.

32. $y \le 9$ **33.** $2x + y \ge 6$

34. $x > 2 - 2y$ **35.** $x < -2$

9-6

To find the solutions of a system of inequalities, graph both inequalities on a coordinate plane and find their intersection.

Solve these systems by graphing.

36. $y \ge x$, $y < x + 1$ **37.** $x > 1$, $y < -2$ **38.** $x + y < 6$, $2x - y < 7$

Chapter 9 Test

Write using (a) roster notation and (b) set-builder notation.

1. the set A of whole numbers greater than 4
2. the set B of negative integers greater than -3
3. the set C of positive multiples of 3 less than -3

Let $A = (2, 4, 6, 8, 10, 12)$, $B = (5, 10, 15)$, and $C = (2, 3, 5, 7, 11)$. Find the following.

4. $A \cap C$
5. $A \cap B$
6. $B \cap C$
7. $A \cup B$
8. $B \cup C$

Solve and graph.

9. $0 < x - 4 < 3$
10. $-10 \leq x - 5 < -8$
11. $x + 2 < 1$ or $x + 3 \geq 5$
12. $2x < -2$ or $3x - 1 > 2$

Solve.

13. $|x - 2| = 4$
14. $|3x - 6| = 21$

Solve and graph.

15. $|3p| < 21$
16. $|x + 4| < 2$
17. $|9 - r| \leq 9$
18. $|4x| \geq 12$
19. $|2a - 1| > 5$
20. $|-3y + 6| > 12$

Solve these systems by graphing.

21. $y \leq x$
    $y > x - 2$
22. $y > -3$
    $x < -2$
23. $y - x + 2 < 0$
    $2y - 2 > x$
24. $x - y > 2$
    $x + y < 1$

ANSWERS

1. (a) $A = \{5, 6, 7, \ldots\}$
(b) $A = \{x|x$ is a whole number and $x > 4\}$
2. (a) $B = \{-2, -1\}$
(b) $B = \{x|x$ is a negative integer and $x > -3\}$ or $\{x|x$ is an integer and $-3 < x < 0\}$
3. (a) $C = \emptyset$
(b) $C = \{x|x$ is a positive multiple of 3 and $x < -3\}$
4. $\{2\}$
5. $\{10\}$
6. $\{5\}$
7. $\{2, 4, 5, 6, 8, 10, 12, 15\}$
8. $\{2, 3, 5, 7, 10, 11, 15\}$
Graphs for 9–12. See Teacher's Answer Section.
9. $\{x|4 < x < 7\}$
10. $\{x|-5 \leq x < -3\}$
11. $\{x|x < -1$ or $x \geq 2\}$
12. $\{x|x < -1$ or $x > 1\}$
13. $\{6, -2\}$
14. $\{9, -5\}$
Graphs for 15–20. See Teacher's Answer Section.
15. $\{p|-7 < p < 7\}$
16. $\{x|-6 < x < -2\}$
17. $\{r|0 \leq r \leq 18\}$
18. $\{x|x \leq -3$ or $x \geq 3\}$
19. $\{a|a < -2$ or $a > 3\}$
20. $\{y|y < -2$ or $y > 6\}$
21–24. See Teacher's Answer Section.

Test Item Analysis

Item	Lesson
1–8	9-1
9–12	9-2
13, 14	9-3
15–20	9-4
21–24	9-5, 9-6

CHAPTER **10**

Rational Expressions and Equations

Chapter Overview

Techniques for manipulating rational algebraic expressions are covered in this chapter. Rational expressions are simplified by removing common factors as a ratio of 1. The rules for multiplying rational expressions are given. Division of rational expressions is accomplished by multiplying by the reciprocal. Rational expressions with like denominators are added and subtracted. Rational expressions with unlike denominators are added and subtracted by transforming to expressions with a common denominator. Rational equations in one variable are introduced and solved. In certain cases, extraneous solutions are seen to appear. The long-division algorithm for dividing two polynomials is introduced, and the quotient and remainder are discussed. Techniques for simplifying complex rational expressions involving rational expressions in the numerator or denominator are discussed. An optional section gives a detailed proof of some fundamental properties of fractions.

The Problem-Solving Guidelines are used to translate and solve problems that can be solved using rational equations. The problem-solving strategy *Work Backward* is introduced and all strategies can be used to solve the given problems.

Objectives

10-1 ▪ Simplify rational expressions.
10-2 ▪ Multiply rational expressions.
10-3 ▪ Divide rational expressions.
10-4 ▪ Add and subtract rational expressions with like denominators.
10-5 ▪ Find the least common multiple (LCM) of algebraic expressions.
▪ Add rational expressions with unlike denominators.
▪ Subtract rational expressions with unlike denominators.
10-6 ▪ Solve equations involving rational expressions.
10-7 ▪ Solve problems involving rational equations.
10-8 ▪ Solve problems involving the mixture of substances.
10-9 ▪ Divide a polynomial by a monomial.
▪ Divide a polynomial by a polynomial.
10-10 ▪ Simplify complex rational expressions.
10-11 ▪ Prove theorems involving multiplication and division.
10-12 ▪ Solve problems using the strategy *Work Backward* and other strategies.

Cooperative Learning Opportunities

Research has shown that cooperative learning is highly effective in developing skills. A cooperative learning quiz on the skills in Lessons 10-1 through 10-6 will serve several purposes. Students who have not yet caught on to these skills will receive help. They will feel less discouraged by a quiz taken in a group. Finally, this kind of quiz teaches while it evaluates. The approach is as follows.

Assign groups with 4 students to a group. Have each group do 3 to 5 exercises, different ones for each group to prevent interaction among groups. Tell the groups that each individual is to do the entire quiz but that you will select only one paper and its grade will be for all of the individuals in the group. This will force the students to work together, look at each other's work, point out mistakes to one another and do their best to see that everyone in the group has the work done correctly.

Multicultural Note: *The Maya*

The Maya lived in the Yucatan Peninsula of Mexico and their civilization flourished from about A.D. 300 to 800. They developed a complex civilization with magnificent temples, palaces, and observatories. Among their achievements were advances in mathematics and astronomy, as well as the creation of an accurate calendar. The Maya calendar was rather complex with several distinct reference points.

In fact there were three Mayan calendars.

1. A religious calendar with a 260-day cycle.
2. A 365-day solar calendar, containing 18 months, each with 20 days plus 5 extra days.
3. A 584-day cycle based on the planet Venus.

In preparation for algebraic least common multiples, you might have students do this time problem using least common multiples:

If the 260-day and 365-day Mayan calendars both start today, in how many days will they again start together? **Ans. In 18,980 days**

For more information, see page 113 of **Multiculturalism in Mathematics, Science, and Technology**.

Alternative Assessment and Communication Ideas

You can sometimes get students to focus on a problem–solving plan by asking for a self–assessment as part of a test or quiz. You can begin with an individual problem worth, say, 15 points. Offer 2 bonus points to any student who can correctly analyze his or her work, and score, based on the following model.

(1) I restated the problem (but I couldn't do it). +3
(2) I got started (but I couldn't develop a workable plan). +5
(3) I have the right plan (but I can't complete it). +10
(4) I had a good plan (but the answer doesn't seem quite right. I probably made a silly mistake). +13
(5) I solved it correctly. +15

Any of the problems in Lessons 10-7, 10-8, 10-11, and 10-12 can be done using this method.

The **Write a convincing argument** exercise on page 476 can be used as the basis for an oral presentation, with graphics, at the chalkboard.

Investigations and Projects

Continued fractions may be of interest to some of your students. They provide good practice in algebraic manipulation. The algebraic operations presented here can be checked arithmetically.

As a home assignment to start the project, ask students to evaluate the following continued fractions. Point out that they must simply work up from the bottom using what they know about the addition of fractions and reciprocals. After they have found the fractional equivalents to the two numerical problems, have them work out the algebraic generalizations.

Students may continue the project by investigating other continued fractions.

$$2+\cfrac{1}{2+\cfrac{1}{2+\cfrac{1}{2}}} \qquad 3+\cfrac{1}{3+\cfrac{1}{3+\cfrac{1}{3}}} \qquad x+\cfrac{1}{x+\cfrac{1}{x+\cfrac{1}{x}}}$$

The answers are: $\frac{29}{12}$, $\frac{109}{33}$, **and** $\frac{x^4+3x^2+1}{x^3+2x}$

MANAGING CHAPTER 10

Lesson	PACING CHART (DAYS) 2-Year* A for E	1-Year Minimum	1-Year Regular	1-Year Advanced	Opening Activity	Cooperative Activity	Seat or Group Work
10-1	2	1	1	1	First Five Minutes 10-1: ***FFMTM*** p. 29 or **TE** p. 432	Explore: **SE** p. 432	Try This a–f
10-2	2	1	2	2	First Five Minutes 10-2: ***FFMTM*** p. 30 or **TE** p. 436	Problem 48: **SE** p. 438	Try This a–c
10-3	2	1	1	1	First Five Minutes 10-3: ***FFMTM*** p. 30 or **TE** p. 439	Critical Thinking 10: ***Enrichment*** p. 27	Try This a–d
10-4	2	1	1	1	First Five Minutes 10-4: ***FFMTM*** p. 30 or **TE** p. 442	Problem 35: **SE** p. 444	Try This a–e
10-5	3	2	2	2	First Five Minutes 10-5: ***FFMTM*** p. 31 or **TE** p. 445	Connections: Geometry: **SE** p. 450	Try This a–l
10-6	2	2	2	2	First Five Minutes 10-6: ***FFMTM*** p. 31 or **TE** p. 451	Problem 43: **SE** p. 454	Try This a–e
10-7	3	1	1	1	First Five Minutes 10-7: ***FFMTM*** p. 31 or **TE** p. 455	Problem 1: **SE** p. 458; Calculator Worksheet 20: ***Technology*** p. 22	Try This a–c
10-8	0	1	1	1	First Five Minutes 10-8: ***FFMTM*** p. 31 or **TE** p. 460	Suppose: **SE** p. 464	Try This a–b
10-9	0	1	2	2	First Five Minutes 10-9: ***FFMTM*** p. 32 or **TE** p. 465	✂ Manipulative Activity 10: ***Enrichment*** p. 43	Try This a–d
10-10	0	1	1	1	First Five Minutes 10-10: ***FFMTM*** p. 32 or **TE** p. 469	Problem 28: **SE** p. 471	Try This a–b
10-11	0	0	0	1	First Five Minutes 10-11: ***FFMTM*** p. 32 or **TE** p. 472	Problem 2: **SE** p. 474	Try This a–b
10-12	3	1	1	1	First Five Minutes 10-2: ***FFMTM*** p. 33 or **TE** p. 475	Problem 5: **SE** p. 476	Problem 1: **SE** p. 476
Review	2	1	1	1			
Test	1	1	1	1			

*2-Year Management Guide can be found in *Algebra for Everyone.*

FFMTM: First Five Minutes Transparency Masters

Enrichment	Review/Assess	Reteach	Technology	Lesson
Looking for Errors: **SE** p. 435	Lesson Quiz: **TE** p. 434		Worksheet 8: ***Master Grapher*** pp. 35–37, 91–93, or 146–148	10-1
Worksheet 8: ***TI-81 Activities*** pp. 29–31	Geometry Review 2: ***SPMR*** p. 86; Lesson Quiz: **TE** p. 437		Worksheet 8: ***TI-81 Activities*** pp. 29–31	10-2
Critical Thinking 10: ***Enrichment*** p. 27	Mixed Review 19: ***SPMR*** p. 69; Lesson Quiz: **TE** p. 440; Quiz 19: ***Assessment*** p. 29	Skills Practice 27: ***SPMR*** p. 35		10-3
	Lesson Quiz: **TE** p. 443			10-4
Connections: Geometry: **SE** p. 450	Mixed Practice 19: **SE** p. 702; Mixed Review 20: ***SPMR*** p. 70; Lesson Quiz: **TE** p. 447			10-5
Worksheet 9: ***TI-81 Activities*** pp. 33–34	Lesson Quiz: **TE** p. 452; Quiz 20: ***Assessment*** p. 30	Skills Practice 28: ***SPMR*** p. 36	Worksheet 9: ***Master Grapher*** pp. 38–39, 94–95, or 149–150; Worksheet 9: ***TI-81 Activities*** pp. 33–34	10-6
Calculator Worksheet 20: ***Technology*** p. 22	Lesson Quiz: **TE** p. 457	Problem Bank 19: ***Problem Bank*** p. 36	Problem for Programmers **SE** p. 459; Calculator Worksheet 20: ***Technology*** p. 22	10-7
Suppose: **SE** p. 464	Lesson Quiz: **TE** p. 461	Problem Bank 20: ***Problem Bank*** p. 37	Spreadsheet Activity 7: ***Technology*** pp. 49–50	10-8
The Rule of False Position: SE p. 468; ✂ Manipulative Activity 10: ***Enrichment*** p. 43	Lesson Quiz: **TE** p. 466			10-9
Biographical Note: Mary Somerville: **SE** p. 471	Mixed Practice 20: **SE** p. 703; Lesson Quiz: **TE** p. 469	Skills Practice 29: ***SPMR*** p. 37		10-10
Bonus Topic 10: ***Enrichment*** p. 11	Lesson Quiz: **TE** p. 473			10-11
Looking for Errors 10: ***Enrichment*** p. 59; College Entrance Exam 3: ***Problem Bank*** pp. 57–61	Assessing Strategies 7: ***Assessment*** pp. 207–208	Strategy Problem Bank 10: ***Problem Bank*** p. 11		10-12
	Summary and Review: **SE** pp. 477–478; Test: **SE** p. 479			Review
	Chapter 10 Exam: ***A for E*** pp. 393–394; Chapter 10 Test: ***Assessment*** pp. 61–62 (min.), 125–130 (reg.), 181–182 (adv.)			Test

SPMR: Skills Practice Mixed Review

The solution to the problem posed on the facing page can be found on page 461.

Ready for Rational Expressions and Equations?

2-6 Find the reciprocal.

1. $\frac{3}{5}$ $\frac{5}{3}$

2. $\frac{3x}{y}$ $\frac{y}{3x}$

3-3 and 3-5 Solve.

3. $9 = 6(5x - 1)$ $\frac{1}{2}$

4. $11 - 2(y + 1) = 21$ -6

5. $5(d + 4) = 7(d - 1)$ $\frac{27}{2}$

6. $5(t + 3) + 4 = 3(t - 2) + 1$ -12

5-7, 5-8 Add or subtract.

7. $(2x^2 + 3x - 7) + (x^2 + x - 8)$ $3x^2 + 4x - 15$

8. $(x^2 + 6x + 8) - (x^2 - 3x - 4)$ $9x + 12$

5-9 to 5-11 Multiply.

9. $2x(3x + 2)$ $6x^2 + 4x$

10. $(x + 1)(x^2 - 2x - 1)$ $x^3 - x^2 - 3x - 1$

11. $(x - 2)(x + 2)$ $x^2 - 4$

12. $(x + 3)(x + 3)$ $x^2 + 6x + 9$

6-1 to 6-5 Factor.

13. $x^2 - 9$ $(x + 3)(x - 3)$

14. $x^2 - 6x + 9$ $(x - 3)(x - 3)$ or $(x - 3)^2$

15. $x^2 + 3x + 2$ $(x + 2)(x + 1)$

16. $16x^6 - 32x^5$ $16x^5(x - 2)$

17. $6a^2 + 5a - 6$ $(3a - 2)(2a + 3)$

6-8 Solve.

18. $x^2 - 5x + 6 = 0$ $2, 3$

19. $9x^2 - 4 = 0$ $\frac{2}{3}, -\frac{2}{3}$

6-9

20. One more than a number times one less than a number is 24. Find the number. $5, -5$

CHAPTER

10

Rational Expressions and Equations

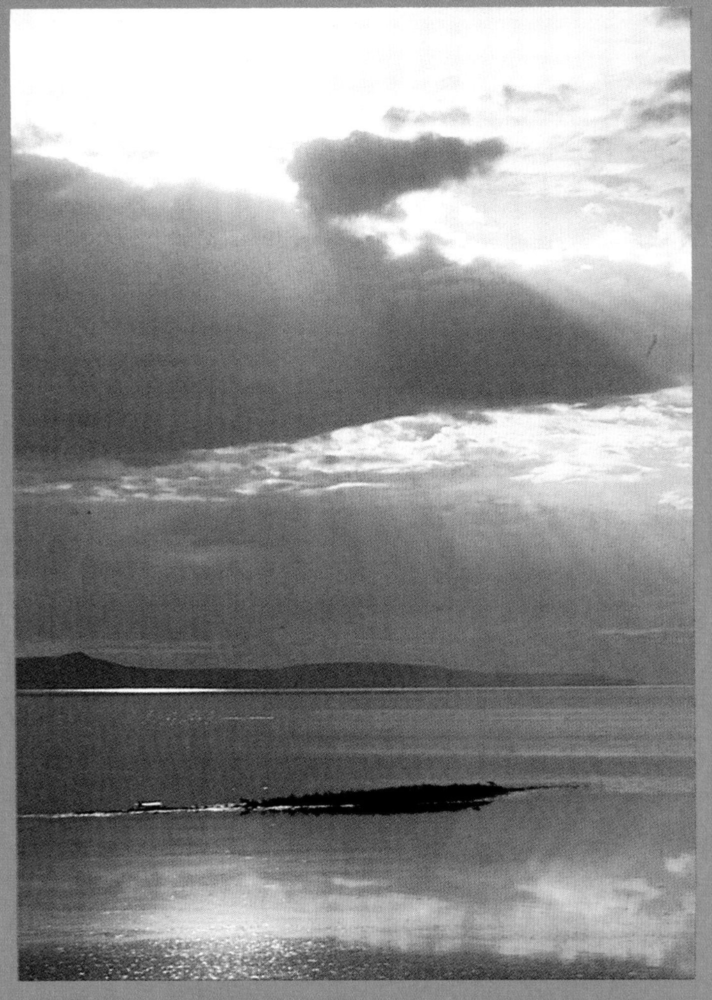

From 1963 to 1984, the water level in the Great Salt Lake rose, expanding the surface area of the lake from 900 square miles to 2300 square miles. During this period of time, the salinity of the lake dropped from 20 percent to 6 percent. How much water would you have to add to a liter of lake water that is 20 percent salt to get a solution that is only 6 percent salt?

10-1

FIRST FIVE MINUTES

Simplify.

1. $\frac{60}{15}$ 4
2. $\frac{6x^3}{2x^2}$ $3x$
3. $\frac{8-1}{1-8}$ -1

EXPLORE

The only regular polygons that tessellate the plane are equilateral triangles, squares, and hexagons ($n = 3$, 4, or 6). Here are sample sketches of how these polygons tessellate the plane.

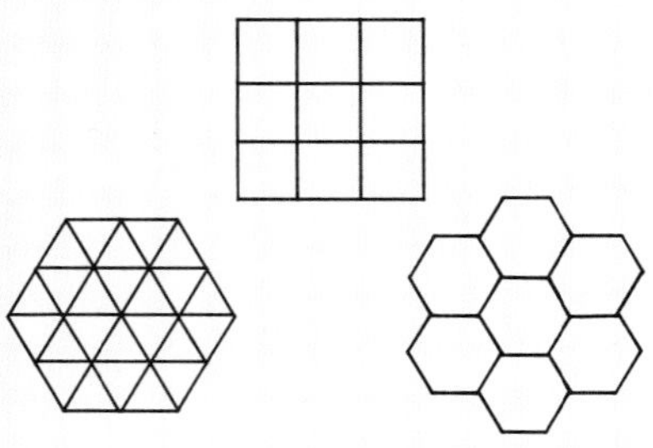

The value of $\frac{2n}{n-2}$ gives the number of polygons that must meet at each vertex when a polygon with n sides tessellates the plane.

Math Point

Hexagons cover the greatest area with the smallest perimeter. Bees use hexagons to make honeycomb because they provide the most efficient way to tessellate a plane.

Remind students of the meanings of *factor* and *term*. For example, the expression $a + b + c$ is the sum of three terms. The expression abc is the product of three factors and is one term.

Point out that just as $\frac{3}{-3}$ simplifies to -1, $\frac{x-4}{4-x}$ simplifies to -1. In each case, the numerator and denominator are additive inverses of each other.

Note that there may be many forms for the answers in this lesson. The answer for Example 5 could also have the form $\frac{1+y}{3-y}$.

10-1 Simplifying Rational Expressions

Objective: Simplify rational expressions.

Master Grapher Worksheet 8 can be used with this lesson.

Explore

Geometric patterns that use repeated shapes to cover the plane without gaps or overlaps are called **tessellations. Regular polygons** are figures whose sides have the same length. Tessellations made up of regular polygons are often used in architecture. Not all regular polygons tessellate the plane.

In the expression below, n represents the number of sides of a regular polygon. If the value of the expression is a whole number when you substitute for n, then the regular polygon with n sides will tessellate the plane.

$$\frac{2n}{n-2}$$

Find three values of n for which the expression gives a whole number. Sketch a tessellation using an n-sided polygon for each of the values of n you find. What relationship do you see between your sketches and the value of the above expression?

A **rational expression** is a quotient of two polynomials. A rational expression always indicates division. For example,

$$\frac{x^2 + 3x - 10}{3x + 2} \text{ means } (x^2 + 3x - 10) \div (3x + 2)$$

Rational expressions have the same properties as rational numbers. Since we cannot divide by 0, replacements for variables in the denominator that make the denominator 0 are not acceptable.

$\frac{5}{x}$ x cannot be 0.

$\frac{a}{b-2}$ b cannot be 2.

$\frac{5}{x-y}$ x cannot equal y.

A rational expression is in simplest form when the numerator and denominator have no common factors other than 1 or -1.

simplest form: $\frac{a + 2}{3a}$ Neither 3 nor a is a factor of $a + 2$.

not in simplest form: $\frac{5(x + 4)}{x(x + 4)}$ $x + 4$ is a factor of the numerator and the denominator.

To simplify rational expressions, factor the numerator and denominator. The common factors simplify to 1. We will restrict the values of the variables to values that will not make the denominator zero.

EXAMPLES Simplify.

1. $\frac{5x - 10}{5x} = \frac{5(x - 2)}{5x}$ Factoring the numerator

$= \frac{5(x - 2)}{5x}$ $\frac{5}{5} = 1$

$= \frac{x - 2}{x}$ Simplifying

2. $\frac{y^2 + 3y + 2}{y^2 - 1} = \frac{(y + 2)(y + 1)}{(y + 1)(y - 1)}$ Factoring the numerator and denominator

$= \frac{(y + 1)(y + 2)}{(y + 1)(y - 1)}$ $\frac{y + 1}{y + 1} = 1$

$= \frac{y + 2}{y - 1}$ Simplifying

Try This Simplify.

a. $\frac{12y + 24}{48y}$ $\frac{y + 2}{4y}$ **b.** $\frac{2x^2 + x}{3x^2 + 2x}$ $\frac{2x + 1}{3x + 2}$ **c.** $\frac{a^2 - 1}{2a^2 - a - 1}$ $\frac{a + 1}{2a + 1}$

The numerator and denominator in the rational expression $\frac{x - 4}{4 - x}$ do not appear to have any common factors other than 1. Since $(x - 4)$ and $(4 - x)$ are additive inverses of each other, however, we can rewrite one of them as the inverse of the other.

EXAMPLE 3 Simplify.

$\frac{x - 4}{4 - x} = \frac{-1(-x + 4)}{(4 - x)}$

$= \frac{-1(4 - x)}{(4 - x)}$ $\frac{4 - x}{4 - x} = 1$

$= -1$

Avoiding Common Errors

Some students may want to "cancel" the x's in Example 1, $\frac{x - 2}{x}$, to get $\frac{1 - 2}{1} = -1$. Remind them that only factors, not terms, can be factored or "cancelled."

Key Questions

What are some factors of the following expressions?

- $3x$
  $3, x$
- $3(x + 1)$
  $3, x + 1$
- $(x - 1)(x + 1)$
  $x - 1, x + 1$
- $5ab(x - y)$
  $5, a, b, x - y, 5a, 5b, 5ab$

What values of x are unacceptable replacements in the following expressions?

- $\frac{3x - 9}{2x - 8}$ 4
- $\frac{3}{(x - 1)(x + 3)}$ $1, -3$
- $\frac{5x + 3}{2 - 7}$ All values are acceptable.

Chalkboard Examples

Simplify.

1. $\frac{9x + 6}{3x}$
   $\frac{3(3x + 2)}{3x} = \frac{3x + 2}{x}$
2. $\frac{6x}{3(x + x^2)}$
   $\frac{3x \cdot 2}{3x(1 + x)} = \frac{2}{1 + x}$
3. $\frac{x^2 + 6x + 9}{3x + 9}$
   $\frac{(x + 3)^2}{3(x + 3)} = \frac{x + 3}{3}$
4. $\frac{a - 2b}{4b - 2a}$
   $\frac{a - 2b}{-2(a - 2b)} = \frac{-1}{2}$
5. $\frac{7x - 14}{2 - x}$
   $\frac{7(x - 2)}{-(x - 2)}$
   -7

LESSON QUIZ

Simplify.

1. $\frac{21x^2y}{7xy}$

   $3x$

2. $\frac{5x - 15}{5}$

   $x - 3$

3. $\frac{6x - 2}{3x - 1}$

   2

4. $\frac{t^2 + 9t + 14}{t + 2}$

   $t + 7$

5. $\frac{1 - y}{2y - 2}$

   $-\frac{1}{2}$

> ***Assignment Guide***
> Minimum: 1–30 e/o, MR
>
> Regular: 1–38 e/o, 39, MR
>
> Advanced: 1–38 m3, 39–42, MR

ADDITIONAL ANSWERS

Exercises

1. $\frac{2x}{y^2}$ **2.** $\frac{b}{-2a^2}$

3. $\frac{x - 3}{x}$ **4.** $\frac{y - 3}{2y}$

5. $\frac{m + 1}{2m + 3}$ **6.** $\frac{2(2y - 1)}{5(y - 1)}$

7. $\frac{x^3(6x - 1)}{x - 1}$ **8.** $\frac{1}{a^2}$

9. $\frac{1}{d - 7}$ **10.** $\frac{a - 3}{a + 2}$

11. $\frac{t - 5}{t - 4}$ **12.** $\frac{t + 2}{2(t - 4)}$

13. $a + 1$ **14.** $t - 1$

15. Already simplified

16. Already simplified

17. $\frac{3}{2}$ **18.** 2

19. $\frac{6}{x - 3}$ **20.** $\frac{5}{a + 6}$

21. $\frac{b - 3}{b - 4}$

EXAMPLES Simplify.

4. $\frac{3x - 6}{2 - x} = \frac{3(x - 2)}{2 - x}$ Factoring the numerator

$= \frac{3(x - 2)}{-1(x - 2)}$ $2 - x = -1(-2 + x) = -1(x - 2)$

$= -3$ Simplifying

5. $\frac{1 - y^2}{y^2 - 4y + 3} = \frac{(1 - y)(1 + y)}{(y - 1)(y - 3)}$ Factoring the numerator and denominator

$= \frac{-(y - 1)(1 + y)}{(y - 1)(y - 3)}$

$= \frac{-1(1 + y)}{(y - 3)}$

$= \frac{-1 - y}{y - 3}$

Try This Simplify.

d. $\frac{b - 7}{7 - b}$ -1 **e.** $\frac{5 - 2a}{3(2a - 5)}$ $-\frac{1}{3}$ **f.** $\frac{4x - 12}{6 - 2x}$ -2

10-1 EXERCISES

A

Simplify.

1. $\frac{4x^2y}{2xy^3}$ **2.** $\frac{a^3b^2}{-2a^5b}$ **3.** $\frac{4x - 12}{4x}$

4. $\frac{-2y + 6}{-4y}$ **5.** $\frac{3m^2 + 3m}{6m^2 + 9m}$ **6.** $\frac{4y^2 - 2y}{5y^2 - 5y}$

7. $\frac{6x^5 - x^4}{x^2 - x}$ **8.** $\frac{a^6 - a^5}{a^8 - a^7}$ **9.** $\frac{d + 7}{d^2 - 49}$

10. $\frac{a^2 - 9}{a^2 + 5a + 6}$ **11.** $\frac{t^2 - 25}{t^2 + t - 20}$ **12.** $\frac{2t^2 + 6t + 4}{4t^2 - 12t - 16}$

13. $\frac{a^2 - 1}{a - 1}$ **14.** $\frac{t^2 - 1}{t + 1}$ **15.** $\frac{x^2 + 1}{x + 1}$

16. $\frac{y^2 + 4}{y + 2}$ **17.** $\frac{6x^2 - 54}{4x^2 - 36}$ **18.** $\frac{8y^2 - 32}{4y^2 - 16}$

19. $\frac{6x + 12}{x^2 - x - 6}$ **20.** $\frac{5a + 5}{a^2 + 7a + 6}$ **21.** $\frac{b^2 - 10b + 21}{b^2 - 11b + 28}$

22. $\frac{2t - 8}{12 - 3t}$

23. $\frac{y^2 - 3y - 18}{y^2 - 2y - 15}$

24. $\frac{t^2 - 4}{(t + 2)^2}$

25. $\frac{(a - 3)^2}{a^2 - 9}$

26. $\frac{5x - 15}{3 - x}$

27. $\frac{6 - y}{y^2 - 2y - 24}$

28. $\frac{4 - 2y}{2y^2 + 10y - 28}$

29. $\frac{-12}{4x^2 - 1}$

30. $\frac{(a - b)^2}{b^2 - a^2}$

B

Simplify.

31. $\frac{a^4 - b^4}{b^2 - a^2}$

32. $\frac{x^4 - 16y^4}{(x^2 + 4y^2)(x - 2y)}$

33. $\frac{m^4 - n^4}{4m^2 + 4n^2}$

34. $\frac{2y^4 - 2z^4}{2y^2 - 2z^2}$

35. $\frac{(t - 3)^3(t^2 - 2t + 1)}{(t - 1)^3(t^2 - 4t + 4)}$

36. $\frac{(x^2 - y^2)(x^2 - 2xy + y^2)}{(x - y)^2(x^2 - 4xy - 5y^2)}$

Evaluate each expression before simplifying and after simplifying.

37. $\frac{(x + 3)^2}{x^2 - 9}$ for $x = 4$ 7; 7

38. $\frac{3a - 6}{2 - a}$ for $a = 2$ Not defined; −3

39. ***Critical Thinking*** Explain why $\frac{a^2 + b^2}{(a + b)^2}$ does not simplify to 1.

Challenge

Determine which replacements of x are not acceptable.

40. $\frac{x + 1}{x^2 + 4x + 4}$ −2

41. $\frac{x^2 - 16}{x^2 + 2x - 3}$ −3, 1

42. $\frac{x - 7}{x^3 - 9x^2 + 14x}$ 0, 2, 7

Mixed Review

Solve. 43. $x^2 - 12x + 35 = 0$ 44. $25x^2 - 9 = 0$

45. $6x^2 - x - 1 = 0$ 46. $3x^2 + 2x - 8 = 0$

47. $3x - 4y = 6$
$x + 4y = -14$

48. $x - y = -6$
$3x + 4y = -4$

49. $2y + 7x = -4$
$x = y - 7$

LOOKING FOR ERRORS

Tell which of the rational expressions below were simplified correctly. For those that were not done correctly, tell what error was made.

1. $\frac{8x^4y^2}{2x^3y^2} = 4x$

2. $\frac{\cancel{2y} - 7}{\cancel{2y}} = -7$

3. $\frac{(m - 2)^2}{m^2 - 4} = m + 2$

4. $\frac{8y^2 - 32}{4y^2 - 16} = 2y^2 - 2$

Answers

22. $-\frac{2}{3}$ 23. $\frac{y - 6}{y - 5}$

24. $\frac{t - 2}{t + 2}$ 25. $\frac{a - 3}{a + 3}$

26. -5 27. $\frac{-1}{y + 4}$

28. $\frac{-1}{y + 7}$

29. Already simplified

30. $\frac{b - a}{b + a}$

31. $-a^2 - b^2$ 32. $x + 2y$

33. $\frac{m^2 - n^2}{4}$ 34. $y^2 + z^2$

35. $\frac{(t - 3)^3}{(t - 1)(t - 2)^2}$ 36. $\frac{x - y}{x - 5y}$

39. $a^2 + b^2$ cannot be factored.

Mixed Review

43. 5, 7

44. $\frac{3}{5}, -\frac{3}{5}$

45. $\frac{1}{2}, -\frac{1}{3}$

46. $-2, \frac{4}{3}$

47. $(-2, -3)$

48. $(-4, 2)$

49. $(-2, 5)$

Looking for Errors

1. Correct
2. Incorrect; only factors can be simplified, not individual terms.
3. Incorrect; the expression was factored incorrectly. The correct answer is $\frac{m-2}{m+2}$.
4. Incorrect; the expression was factored incorrectly. The correct answer is 2.

10-2

FIRST FIVE MINUTES

Simplify.

1. $\frac{9x - 3}{3x - 1}$ 3
2. $\frac{4a^2}{a^3}$ $\frac{4}{a}$
3. $\frac{6 - y}{2y - 12}$ $-\frac{1}{2}$

Some students may try to find a common denominator before multiplying two fractions. Remind students that finding common denominators is not necessary when multiplying fractions.

Point out that the correct answer can have more than one form. In this chapter, polynomials are left in factored form, since this allows us to see whether there are any common factors, which allow us to reduce the expression.

Key Questions

- What is $\frac{2}{3} \cdot \frac{1}{4}$? $\frac{1}{6}$
- What is $\frac{4}{5} \cdot \frac{7}{8}$? $\frac{7}{10}$
- What is $\frac{a}{b} \cdot \frac{c}{d}$? $\frac{ac}{bd}$

Chalkboard Examples

Multiply. Simplify the product.

1. $\frac{3x^2}{2} \cdot \frac{4}{x}$

   $\frac{12x^2}{2x} = 6x$

2. $\frac{3y}{y - 1} \cdot \frac{2(y - 1)}{6y}$

   $\frac{6y(y - 1)}{6y(y - 1)} = 1$

3. $\frac{x + 3}{x + 5} \cdot \frac{x + 5}{x + 7}$

   $= \frac{(x + 3)(x + 5)}{(x + 5)(x + 7)}$

   $= \frac{x + 3}{x + 7}$

4. $\frac{3x - 6}{x - 1} \cdot \frac{1 - x}{3}$

   $= \frac{3(x - 2)(-1)(x - 1)}{3(x - 1)}$

   $= -(x - 2)$, or $2 - x$

10-2 Multiplying Rational Expressions

Objective: Multiply rational expressions.

To multiply rational numbers, we multiply the numerators and multiply the denominators.

$$\frac{3}{4} \cdot \frac{5}{6} = \frac{3 \cdot 5}{4 \cdot 6} = \frac{15}{24}$$

We multiply rational expressions in the same way.

EXAMPLES Multiply. Simplify the product.

1. $\frac{5a^3}{4} \cdot \frac{2}{5a} = \frac{5a^3 \cdot 2}{4 \cdot 5a}$ Multiplying numerators and multiplying denominators

$= \frac{10a^3}{20a}$

$= \frac{a^2}{2}$ Simplifying: $\frac{10}{20} = \frac{1}{2}$ $\frac{a^3}{a} = a^{3-1} = a^2$

2. $\frac{4}{5x^2} \cdot \frac{x - 2}{2x^3} = \frac{4(x - 2)}{10x^5}$ Multiplying numerators and multiplying denominators

$= \frac{2(x - 2)}{5x^5}$ Simplifying: $\frac{4}{10} = \frac{2}{5}$

3. $\frac{a - 2}{3} \cdot \frac{a + 2}{a + 3} = \frac{(a - 2)(a + 2)}{3(a + 3)}$ Multiplying numerators and multiplying denominators

There are no common factors other than 1. The answer is in simplest form. We could also write the product as $\frac{a^2 - 4}{3a + 9}$. However, we usually write products of polynomials in factored form.

EXAMPLE 4 Multiply. Simplify the product.

$\frac{-2}{2y + 6} \cdot \frac{3}{y - 5} = \frac{-2 \cdot 3}{(2y + 6)(y - 5)}$ Multiplying numerators and multiplying denominators

$= \frac{-2 \cdot 3}{2(y + 3)(y - 5)}$ Factoring the denominator

$= \frac{-3}{(y + 3)(y - 5)}$ Simplifying: $\frac{-2}{2} = -1$

Try This Multiply. Simplify the product.

a. $\frac{4a^4}{3} \cdot \frac{6}{5a^2}$ **b.** $\frac{x + 3}{5} \cdot \frac{5(x + 2)}{x + 4}$ **c.** $\frac{-3}{4m + 2} \cdot \frac{4}{2m - 1}$

a. $\frac{8a^2}{5}$
b. $\frac{(x + 3)(x + 2)}{x + 4}$
c. $\frac{-6}{(2m + 1)(2m - 1)}$

10-2 EXERCISES

A

Multiply. Simplify the product.

1. $\frac{4x^3}{3x} \cdot \frac{14}{x}$

2. $\frac{32}{b^4} \cdot \frac{3b^2}{8}$

3. $\frac{3c}{d^2} \cdot \frac{4d}{6c^3}$

4. $\frac{8}{3x} \cdot \frac{x + 7}{6x^2}$

5. $\frac{y + 6}{2y} \cdot \frac{4y^2}{y + 6}$

6. $\frac{-5}{m} \cdot \frac{m^6}{m + 2}$

7. $\frac{-2n}{7(n + 2)} \cdot \frac{7n + 7}{n + 1}$

8. $\frac{-3y}{6(y - 1)} \cdot \frac{2y - 2}{y^2}$

9. $\frac{a - 6}{a^2} \cdot \frac{a + 2}{a + 1}$

10. $\frac{3x}{2} \cdot \frac{x + 4}{x - 1}$

11. $\frac{4y}{5} \cdot \frac{y - 3}{2y}$

12. $\frac{a - 1}{a + 2} \cdot \frac{a + 1}{a - 1}$

13. $\frac{m - 2}{m - 5} \cdot \frac{m + 5}{m - 2}$

14. $\frac{2x + 3}{4} \cdot \frac{4}{x - 5}$

15. $\frac{-5}{6y - 4} \cdot \frac{-6}{5y + 6}$

16. $\frac{a - 5}{a^2 + 1} \cdot \frac{a + 1}{a^2 - 1}$

17. $\frac{t + 3}{t^2 - 2} \cdot \frac{t + 3}{t^2 - 9}$

18. $\frac{x + 1}{2 + x} \cdot \frac{x - 1}{x + 1}$

19. $\frac{2x}{2x} \cdot \frac{x - 1}{x + 4}$

20. $\frac{3y - 1}{2y + 1} \cdot \frac{y}{y}$

21. $\frac{-1}{-1} \cdot \frac{3 - x}{4 - x}$

22. $\frac{-1}{-1} \cdot \frac{4 - a}{5 - a}$

23. $\frac{4(x + 2)}{5x} \cdot \frac{6x^2}{2x}$

24. $\frac{6(m - 3)}{5m} \cdot \frac{4m^2}{2(m - 3)}$

25. $\frac{(y - 4)^2}{3y} \cdot \frac{(y - 2)}{(y + 4)(y - 4)}$

26. $\frac{(x + 1)^2}{x + 3} \cdot \frac{(x + 3)^3}{x + 1}$

27. $\frac{5(m - 1)}{(m + 3)^2} \cdot \frac{m + 3}{(m - 1)^2}$

28. $\frac{6a + 12}{5} \cdot \frac{15a}{7a + 14}$

29. $\frac{25 - x^2}{12} \cdot \frac{6}{5 - x}$

30. $\frac{3}{x^2 - 1} \cdot \frac{x + 1}{3}$

31. $\frac{4 - 3a}{6} \cdot \frac{3}{3a - 4}$

32. $\frac{1 - x}{7} \cdot \frac{14}{x - 1}$

33. $\frac{7x}{4x + 3} \cdot (8x + 6)$

34. $\frac{4c}{2c - 1} \cdot (8c - 4)$

LESSON QUIZ

Multiply and simplify.

1. $\frac{8x^4}{3} \cdot \frac{6}{4x^3}$ $4x$
2. $\frac{12x - 6}{5} \cdot \frac{25}{4x - 2}$ 15
3. $\frac{1 - x}{1 + x} \cdot \frac{1 + x}{x - 1}$ -1

Assignment Guide
Minimum: 1–34 e/o, MR

Regular: Day 1: 1–34 e/o, MR
Day 2: 35–47 e/o, 48
Advanced: Day 1: 1–34 e/o, MR
Day 2: 35–47 e/o, 48, 49–52 e/o

ADDITIONAL ANSWERS

Exercises

1. $\frac{56x}{3}$
2. $\frac{12}{b^2}$
3. $\frac{2}{c^2d}$
4. $\frac{4(x + 7)}{9x^3}$
5. $2y$
6. $\frac{-5m^5}{m + 2}$
7. $\frac{-2n}{n + 2}$
8. $\frac{-1}{y}$
9. $\frac{(a - 6)(a + 2)}{a^2(a + 1)}$
10. $\frac{3x(x + 4)}{2(x - 1)}$
11. $\frac{2(y - 3)}{5}$
12. $\frac{a + 1}{a + 2}$
13. $\frac{m + 5}{m - 5}$
14. $\frac{2x + 3}{x - 5}$
15. $\frac{15}{(3y - 2)(5y + 6)}$
16. $\frac{a - 5}{(a^2 + 1)(a - 1)}$
17. $\frac{t + 3}{(t^2 - 2)(t - 3)}$
18. $\frac{x - 1}{2 + x}$
19. $\frac{x - 1}{x + 4}$
20. $\frac{3y - 1}{2y + 1}$
21. $\frac{x - 3}{x - 4}$
22. $\frac{a - 4}{a - 5}$
23. $\frac{12(x + 2)}{5}$
24. $\frac{12m}{5}$
25. $\frac{(y - 4)(y - 2)}{3y(y + 4)}$
26. $(x + 1)(x + 3)^2$
27. $\frac{5}{(m + 3)(m - 1)}$
28. $\frac{18a}{7}$
29. $\frac{5 + x}{2}$
30. $\frac{1}{x - 1}$
31. $-\frac{1}{2}$
32. -2
33. $14x$
34. $16c$

35. $\frac{x+2}{x-2}$
36. $\frac{t}{t+2}$
37. $\frac{(a-3)(a+3)}{a(a+4)}$
38. 1
39. $\frac{2a}{a-2}$
40. $\frac{5(v-2)}{v-1}$
41. $\frac{(x-2)(x+2)}{(x-1)(x+1)}$
42. $\frac{(t-1)(t+1)}{(t-3)(t+3)}$
43. $\frac{(t-2)}{(t-1)}$
44. $\frac{y+4}{y+2}$
45. $(m-n)(m-3)$
46. $\frac{(a+b)^2(a-b)(2a-3b)}{2ab}$
47. $\frac{1}{x-y}$
48. Answers may vary. Possible answers are $\frac{2(a+3)}{a+5} \cdot \frac{4(a-1)}{a+8}$ or $\frac{8a+24}{a+5} \cdot \frac{a-1}{a+8}$.

Mixed Review

53. $\{-2, 0, 1, 2, 3, 4, 5\}$
54. $\{-2, 0\}$
55. $\{0, 1\}$
56. $\{-2, 0, 3, 5\}$
57. 4, −1
58. 1, 2
59. $\frac{5}{3}$, −1
60. (0, 5)
61. (4, 4)
62. 3, −7
63. 11, −5
64. 3, $-\frac{17}{3}$
65. (a) $p = 18y + 12$
(b) $246

B

Multiply. Simplify the product.

35. $\frac{x^2 - 3x - 10}{(x-2)^2} \cdot \frac{x-2}{x-5}$

36. $\frac{t^2}{t^2 - 4} \cdot \frac{t^2 - 5t + 6}{t^2 - 3t}$

37. $\frac{a^2 - 9}{a^2} \cdot \frac{a^2 - 3a}{a^2 + a - 12}$

38. $\frac{m^2 + 10m - 11}{m^2 - 1} \cdot \frac{m+1}{m+11}$

39. $\frac{4a^2}{3a^2 - 12a + 12} \cdot \frac{3a - 6}{2a}$

40. $\frac{5v + 5}{v - 2} \cdot \frac{v^2 - 4v + 4}{v^2 - 1}$

41. $\frac{x^4 - 16}{x^4 - 1} \cdot \frac{x^2 + 1}{x^2 + 4}$

42. $\frac{t^4 - 1}{t^4 - 81} \cdot \frac{t^2 + 9}{t^2 + 1}$

43. $\frac{(t-2)^3}{(t-1)^3} \cdot \frac{t^2 - 2t + 1}{t^2 - 4t + 4}$

44. $\frac{(y+4)^3}{(y+2)^3} \cdot \frac{y^2 + 4y + 4}{y^2 + 8y + 16}$

45. $\frac{m^2 - n^2}{2m + 1} \cdot \frac{2m^2 - 5m - 3}{m + n}$

46. $\frac{a^4 - b^4}{2ab} \cdot \frac{2a^2 - ab - 3b^2}{a^2 + b^2}$

47. $\frac{-4x^2 - 9xy - 2y^2}{x + 2y} \cdot \frac{-1}{4x^2 - 3xy - y^2}$

48. ***Critical Thinking*** Find two different pairs of rational expressions whose product is $\frac{8a^2 + 16a - 24}{a^2 + 13a + 40}$.

Challenge

Determine which replacements of x are not acceptable.

49. $\frac{x+1}{x^2 + 4x + 4}$ −2

50. $\frac{x^2 - 16}{x^2 + 2x - 3}$ 1, −3

51. $\frac{x - 7}{x^3 - 9x^2 + 14x}$ 0, 2, 7

52. $\frac{x^2 - 4}{x^3 + x^2 - 6x}$ 0, −3, 2

Mixed Review

Let $A = \{-2, 0, 3, 5\}$, $B = \{0, 1, 2, 3, 4\}$, and $C = \{-3, -2, 0, 1\}$. Find the following. **53.** $A \cup B$ **54.** $A \cap C$ **55.** $B \cap C$ **56.** $A \cup \emptyset$

Solve. **57.** $x^2 - 4 = 3x$ **58.** $2y^2 - 6y = -4$ **59.** $3a^2 - 5 = 2a$

Solve each system. **60.** $x - \frac{2}{5}y = -2$, $3x + 2y = 10$ **61.** $2x - y = 4$, $\frac{3}{4}x + y = 7$

Solve. **62.** $|y + 2| = 5$ **63.** $|2y - 6| = 16$ **64.** $|3x + 4| = 13$

65. Warne's Garden Supply sells topsoil by the cubic yard. Five cubic yards of topsoil cost $102; nine cubic yards of topsoil cost $174. Assume a linear relationship fits these data with some ordered pair (yards, price). **a.** Find the linear equation for the data points. **b.** Use this linear equation to find the cost of 13 cubic yards of topsoil.

10-3 Dividing Rational Expressions

Objective: Divide rational expressions.

We can divide rational expressions using the same procedure as dividing two rational numbers. To divide rational expressions, multiply the first expression by the reciprocal of the divisor.

EXAMPLES Divide and simplify.

1. $\frac{8n^5}{3} \div \frac{2n^2}{9} = \frac{8n^5}{3} \cdot \frac{9}{2n^2}$ Multiplying by the reciprocal of the divisor

$= \frac{72n^5}{6n^2}$ Multiplying numerators and multiplying denominators

$= 12n^3$ Simplifying

2. $\frac{2x+8}{3} \div \frac{x+4}{9} = \frac{2x+8}{3} \cdot \frac{9}{x+4}$ Multiplying by the reciprocal of the divisor

$= \frac{(2x+8)(9)}{3(x+4)}$ Multiplying

$= \frac{2(x+4)(9)}{(x+4)(3)}$ Factoring

$= 6$

3. $\frac{x+1}{x+2} \div \frac{x+1}{x+3} = \frac{x+1}{x+2} \cdot \frac{x+3}{x+1}$ Multiplying by the reciprocal of the divisor

$= \frac{(x+1)(x+3)}{(x+2)(x+1)}$ Factoring and identifying common factors

$= \frac{x+3}{x+2}$

4. $\frac{x+1}{x^2-1} \div \frac{x+1}{x^2-2x+1} = \frac{x+1}{x^2-1} \cdot \frac{x^2-2x+1}{x+1}$

$= \frac{(x+1)(x^2-2x+1)}{(x^2-1)(x+1)}$

$= \frac{(x+1)(x-1)(x-1)}{(x+1)(x-1)(x+1)}$ Factoring and identifying common factors

$= \frac{x-1}{x+1}$

Try This Divide and simplify.

a. $\frac{9a^4}{7} \div \frac{9a^2}{14}$ $2a^2$

b. $\frac{4m-8}{5} \div \frac{m-2}{10}$ 8

c. $\frac{3}{x^2-4} \div \frac{2}{x-1}$ $\frac{3(x-1)}{2(x+2)(x-2)}$

d. $\frac{x^2+5x+6}{x+5} \div \frac{x+2}{x+5}$ $x+3$

10-3

FIRST FIVE MINUTES

Multiply and simplify.

1. $\frac{3x-3}{5} \cdot \frac{5}{3x}$

$\frac{5 \cdot 3(x-1)}{15x} = \frac{x-1}{x}$

Divide and simplify.

2. $\frac{3}{5} \div \frac{7}{4}$ $\frac{12}{35}$

3. $\frac{4}{15} \div \frac{2}{5}$ $\frac{2}{3}$

Point out that after division problems are rewritten as multiplication by the reciprocals, the problems are similar to those in Lesson 10-2.

Remind students that just as the reciprocal of 4 is $\frac{1}{4}$, the reciprocal of $x - 2$ is $\frac{1}{x-2}$.

Avoiding Common Errors

Students may "invert" all fractions in the problem rather than just the divisor. Remind students that we multiply by the reciprocal of the divisor, which is the number on the right of the division symbol.

Chalkboard Examples

1. $\frac{3x}{5} \div \frac{6x}{15}$

$\frac{3x}{5} \cdot \frac{15}{6x} = \frac{45x}{30x} = \frac{3}{2}$

2. $\frac{5y-10}{3y} \div \frac{y-2}{y}$

$\frac{5(y-2)}{3y} \cdot \frac{y}{y-2} = \frac{5}{3}$

3. $\frac{2a+1}{4a+1} \div \frac{3a+1}{5a+1}$

$= \frac{2a+1}{4a+1} \cdot \frac{5a+1}{3a+1}$

$= \frac{(2a+1)(5a+1)}{(4a+1)(3a+1)}$

4. $\frac{x^2+8x+16}{x-1} \div \frac{x+4}{x^2-2x+1}$

$= \frac{x^2+8x+16}{x-1} \cdot \frac{x^2-2x+1}{x+4}$

$= \frac{(x+4)^2 \cdot (x-1)^2}{(x-1)(x+4)}$

$= (x+4)(x-1)$

LESSON QUIZ

Divide and simplify.

1. $\frac{3x}{2} \div \frac{9}{2x}$ $\quad \frac{x^2}{3}$
2. $\frac{2x-8}{3x} \div \frac{x-4}{6x}$ $\quad 4$
3. $\frac{x^2+3x+2}{6x} \div \frac{x+1}{2x}$ $\quad \frac{x+2}{3}$

Assignment Guide
Minimum: 1–34 e/o, MR
Regular: 1–40 e/o, 41, MR
Advanced: 1–40 m3, 41–45, MR

ADDITIONAL ANSWERS

Exercises

1. $2x^2$
2. $\frac{-5x^5}{14}$
3. $\frac{1}{a^3}$
4. $\frac{1}{4t^3}$
5. $\frac{3m^3}{5}$
6. $\frac{4a^5}{15}$
7. $\frac{15}{8}$
8. $\frac{1}{2}$
9. $\frac{15}{4}$
10. 3
11. $\frac{a-5}{3(a-1)}$
12. $\frac{t+1}{4(t+2)}$
13. $\frac{(x+2)^2}{x}$
14. $\frac{(x-1)^2}{x}$
15. $\frac{3}{2}$
16. $4y-8$
17. $\frac{c+1}{c-1}$
18. $\frac{2x}{x+5}$
19. $\frac{3(a-4)}{2}$
20. $\frac{3}{5(2x+3)}$
21. $\frac{y-3}{2y-1}$
22. $\frac{x+3}{x-5}$
23. $\frac{x+12}{x+2}$
24. 1
25. $\frac{1}{(c-5)^2}$
26. $\frac{1}{1+2z-z^2}$
27. $\frac{c+2}{c-2}$
28. $-\frac{x-7}{x+2}$ or $\frac{7-x}{x+2}$
29. $\frac{t+5}{t-5}$
30. $\frac{y-3}{y+3}$
31. $\frac{4(a+7)}{27}$
32. $\frac{2x-3}{2}$
33. $\frac{4^4(b-3)}{3^5}$
34. $\frac{(y+9)^4}{5^4}$

10-3 EXERCISES

A

Divide and simplify.

1. $\frac{5x^4}{3} \div \frac{5x^2}{6}$
2. $\frac{-2x^6}{7} \div \frac{4x}{5}$
3. $\frac{3}{a^5} \div \frac{3}{a^2}$
4. $\frac{2}{t^5} \div \frac{8}{t^2}$
5. $\frac{6m^4}{5} \div 2m$
6. $\frac{4a^7}{3} \div 5a^2$
7. $\frac{5x-5}{16} \div \frac{x-1}{6}$
8. $\frac{-4+2x}{8} \div \frac{x-2}{2}$
9. $\frac{-6+3x}{5} \div \frac{4x-8}{25}$
10. $\frac{-12+4x}{4} \div \frac{-6+2x}{6}$
11. $\frac{a+2}{a-1} \div \frac{3a+6}{a-5}$
12. $\frac{t-3}{t+2} \div \frac{4t-12}{t+1}$
13. $\frac{x^2-4}{x} \div \frac{x-2}{x+2}$
14. $\frac{x^2-1}{x} \div \frac{x+1}{x-1}$
15. $\frac{x^2-9}{4x+12} \div \frac{x-3}{6}$
16. $\frac{4y-8}{y+2} \div \frac{y-2}{y^2-4}$
17. $\frac{c^2+3c}{c^2+2c-3} \div \frac{c}{c+1}$
18. $\frac{x-5}{2x} \div \frac{x^2-25}{4x^2}$
19. $\frac{8a-32}{a+1} \div \frac{16}{3a+3}$
20. $\frac{17}{5x-10} \div \frac{34x+51}{3x-6}$
21. $\frac{2y^2-7y+3}{2y^2+3y-2} \div \frac{6y^2-5y+1}{3y^2+5y-2}$
22. $\frac{x^2-x-20}{x^2+7x+12} \div \frac{x^2-10x+25}{x^2+6x+9}$
23. $\frac{x^2+13x+12}{x+2} \div (x+1)$
24. $\frac{a^2-5a+6}{a-3} \div (a-2)$
25. $\frac{c^2+10c+21}{c^2-2c-15} \div (c^2+2c-35)$
26. $\frac{1-z}{1+2z-z^2} \div (1-z)$
27. $(c+3) \div \frac{c^2+c-6}{c+2}$
28. $(2-x) \div \frac{x^2-4}{x-7}$
29. $\frac{(t+5)^3}{(t-5)^3} \div \frac{(t+5)^2}{(t-5)^2}$
30. $\frac{(y-3)^3}{(y+3)^3} \div \frac{(y-3)^2}{(y+3)^2}$
31. $\left(\frac{a+7}{3}\right)^3 \div \left(\frac{a+7}{2}\right)^2$
32. $\left(\frac{2x-3}{2}\right)^4 \div \left(\frac{2x-3}{2}\right)^3$
33. $\left(\frac{4}{b-3}\right)^4 \div \left(\frac{3}{b-3}\right)^5$
34. $\left(\frac{5}{y+9}\right) \div \left(\frac{5}{y+9}\right)^5$

B

Divide and simplify.

35. $\dfrac{2a^2 - 5ab}{c - 3d} \div (4a^2 - 25b^2)$

36. $\dfrac{3a^2 - 5ab - 12b^2}{3ab + 4b^2} \div (3b^2 - ab)$

37. $x - 2a \div \dfrac{a^2x^2 - 4a^4}{a^2x + 2a^3}$

38. $\dfrac{3x^2 - 2xy - y^2}{x^2 - y^2} \div 3x^2 + 4xy + y^2$

39. $\dfrac{z^2 - 8z + 16}{z^2 + 8z + 16} \div \dfrac{(z - 4)^5}{(z + 4)^5}$

40. $xy \cdot \dfrac{y^2 - 4xy}{y - x} \div \dfrac{16x^2y^2 - y^4}{4x^2 - 3xy - y^2}$

41. ***Critical Thinking*** The volume of this figure is $a - 3$. What is its width? ◇

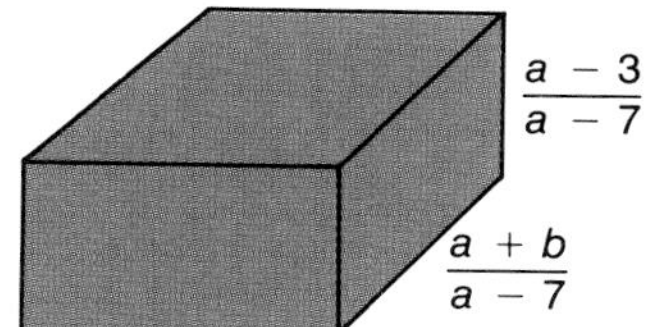

Challenge

Divide and simplify.

42. $\dfrac{x^2 - x + xy - y}{x^2 + 6x - 7} \div \dfrac{x^2 + 2xy + y^2}{4x + 4y}$ $\dfrac{4}{x + 7}$

43. $\dfrac{3x + 3y + 3}{9x} \div \dfrac{x^2 + 2xy + y^2 - 1}{x^4 + x^2}$ $\dfrac{x(x^2 + 1)}{3(x + y - 1)}$

44. $\left(\dfrac{y^2 + 5y + 6}{y^2} \cdot \dfrac{3y^3 + 6y^2}{y^2 - y - 12}\right) \div \dfrac{y^2 - y}{y^2 - 2y - 8}$ $\dfrac{3(y + 2)^3}{y(y - 1)}$

45. $\dfrac{a^4 - 81b^4}{a^2c - 6abc + 9b^2c} \cdot \dfrac{a + 3b}{a^2 + 9b^2} \div \dfrac{a^2 + 6ab + 9b^2}{(a - 3b)^2}$ $\dfrac{a - 3b}{c}$

Mixed Review

Determine whether the graphs of the equations are parallel.

46. $2x - 3y = 9$, $8x + 4 = -6y$ **47.** $4y + 9 = x$, $5 + 2y = 8x$ **48.** $6y - 21x = 5$, $8y - 5 = 28x$

Determine whether the graphs of the equations are perpendicular.

49. $5y = 2x - 10$, $2y + 5x = 2$ **50.** $4y + 1 = 3x$, $3y - 4x = 3$ **51.** $y = x + 3$, $y + x = -3$

Solve for the indicated letter. **52.** $Q = \dfrac{5mv}{s}$, for v **53.** $\dfrac{a}{b} = \dfrac{c}{d}$ for c

Solve. **54.** $2x + y = -1$, $5 - y = 4x$ **55.** $2x + 3y = 8$, $5y - x = 22$ **56.** $9y - 16 = 11x$, $5x + 1 = 2y$

Solve. **57.** $9a^2 - 81 = 0$ **58.** $c^2 - 2c = 35$ **59.** $|2x + 3| > 5$

60. Steve is half as old as Stacey. The sum of their ages five years ago was 8. How old are Steve and Stacey now?

35. $\dfrac{a}{(c - 3d)(2a + 5b)}$
36. $\dfrac{-1}{b^2}$
37. 1
38. $\dfrac{1}{(x + y)^2}$
39. $\dfrac{(z + 4)^3}{(z - 4)^3}$
40. x
41. $\dfrac{(a - 7)^2}{a + b}$

Mixed Review

46. No **47.** No
48. Yes **49.** Yes
50. No **51.** Yes
52. $v = \dfrac{Qs}{5m}$ **53.** $c = \dfrac{ad}{b}$
54. $(3, -7)$ **55.** $(-2, 4)$
56. $(1, 3)$ **57.** ± 3
58. $7, -5$
59. $x > 1, x < -4$
60. Steve is 6 years old. Stacey is 12 years old.

10-4

FIRST FIVE MINUTES

Add or subtract.

1. $\frac{5}{7} + \frac{3}{7}$

$\frac{8}{7}$

2. $\frac{13}{3} - \frac{8}{3}$

$\frac{5}{3}$

3. $\frac{5}{x} + \frac{3}{x}$

$\frac{8}{x}$

Point out that a fraction is simplified if its numerator and denominator have a greatest common factor of 1.

Key Questions

- What is $\frac{a}{b} + \frac{c}{b}$?

$\frac{a + c}{b}$

- What is $\frac{a}{b} - \frac{c}{b}$?

$\frac{a - c}{b}$

Chalkboard Examples

Add and simplify.

1. $\frac{6x}{5} + \frac{7x}{5}$

$\frac{6x + 7x}{5} = \frac{13x}{5}$

2. $\frac{3}{2x + 3} + \frac{2}{2x + 3}$

$\frac{5}{2x + 3}$

3. $\frac{3y + 2}{3y^2} + \frac{4y - 1}{3y^2}$

$\frac{3y + 2 + 4y - 1}{3y^2} = \frac{7y + 1}{3y^2}$

10-4 Addition and Subtraction: Like Denominators

Objective: Add and subtract rational expressions with like denominators.

To add or subtract rational expressions with like denominators, add or subtract the numerators, and write the sum or difference over the common denominator.

EXAMPLES Add and simplify.

1. $\frac{4m}{3} + \frac{5m}{3} = \frac{4m + 5m}{3}$ Writing the sum over the common denominator

$= \frac{9m}{3}$ Adding the numerators

$= 3m$ Simplifying

2. $\frac{6a^2}{a + 2} + \frac{4a^2}{a + 2} = \frac{6a^2 + 4a^2}{a + 2}$

$= \frac{10a^2}{a + 2}$

3. $\frac{2x^2 + 3x - 7}{2x + 1} + \frac{x^2 + x - 8}{2x + 1} = \frac{2x^2 + 3x - 7 + x^2 + x - 8}{2x + 1}$

$= \frac{3x^2 + 4x - 15}{2x + 1}$

$= \frac{(x + 3)(3x - 5)}{2x + 1}$ Factoring to look for common factors

Try This Add and simplify.

a. $\frac{3a}{4} + \frac{7a}{4}$ $\frac{5a}{2}$ **b.** $\frac{8x^2}{x + 4} + \frac{2x^2}{x + 4}$ $\frac{10x^2}{x + 4}$ **c.** $\frac{x^2 - 4x - 10}{x - 7} + \frac{x - 18}{x - 7}$ $x + 4$

EXAMPLE 4 Subtract and simplify.

$\frac{3a}{a + 2} - \frac{a - 4}{a + 2} = \frac{3a - (a - 4)}{a + 2}$ The parentheses are needed, since you must subtract the entire numerator.

$= \frac{3a - a + 4}{a + 2}$

$= \frac{2a + 4}{a + 2}$

$= \frac{2(a + 2)}{(a + 2)}$

$= 2$ Simplifying

Try This Subtract and simplify.

d. $\frac{4m+5}{m-1} - \frac{2m-1}{m-1}$ $\frac{2(m+3)}{m-1}$ **e.** $\frac{2y^2+4y-3}{y+3} - \frac{y^2-2y-12}{y+3}$ $y+3$

Any number of expressions with common denominators can be added or subtracted by adding or subtracting the numerators and placing the result over the common denominator.

LESSON QUIZ

Add or subtract and simplify.

1. $\frac{3x}{5} + \frac{x}{5}$
   $\frac{4x}{5}$
2. $\frac{7}{2z+7} - \frac{3}{2z+7}$
   $\frac{4}{2z+7}$
3. $\frac{2x^2+5x+3}{x+1} + \frac{x^2+x+1}{x+1}$
   $\frac{3x^2+6x+4}{x+1}$

Assignment Guide
Minimum: 1–24 e/o, MR

Regular: 1–24 m3, 25–34 e/o, 35, MR
Advanced: 1–34 m3, 35–37, MR

10-4 EXERCISES

A

Add or subtract. Simplify.

1. $\frac{3a}{5} + \frac{2a}{5}$ a

2. $\frac{6m}{11} + \frac{8m}{11}$ $\frac{14m}{11}$

3. $\frac{7s}{10} - \frac{2s}{10}$ $\frac{s}{2}$

4. $\frac{18xy}{7} - \frac{11xy}{7}$ xy

5. $\frac{6b^2}{c} + \frac{7b^2}{c}$ $\frac{13b^2}{c}$

6. $\frac{10x}{y} - \frac{7x}{y}$ $\frac{3x}{y}$

7. $\frac{4x+3}{x+2} + \frac{3x+4}{x+2}$ $\frac{7(x+1)}{x+2}$

8. $\frac{-6m}{m-5} + \frac{m-10}{m-5}$ $\frac{-5(m+2)}{m-5}$

9. $\frac{a-6}{a+1} - \frac{3a-4}{a+1}$ -2

10. $\frac{b+4}{b+2} - \frac{3b-8}{b+2}$ $\frac{-2(b-6)}{b+2}$

11. $\frac{y^2+5}{y+2} - \frac{4y+17}{y+2}$ $y-6$

12. $\frac{x^2+3}{x-2} - \frac{10x-7}{x-2}$ $\frac{x^2-10x+10}{x-2}$

13. $\frac{3a+5}{a-1} + \frac{2a-6}{a-1}$ $\frac{5a-1}{a-1}$

14. $\frac{4p-3}{p+2} + \frac{5-3p}{p+2}$ 1

15. $\frac{z-6}{2z+3} - \frac{5z}{2z+3}$ -2

16. $\frac{x-9}{3x+2} - \frac{7x-5}{3x+2}$ -2

17. $\frac{y-3}{y+5} - \frac{2y-7}{y+5}$ $\frac{-y+4}{y+5}$

18. $\frac{m+9}{m+3} - \frac{-4m-6}{m+3}$ 5

19. $\frac{n^2+3n}{n+4} + \frac{2n^2-13n-8}{n+4}$

20. $\frac{z+6}{z+5} + \frac{3z^2+19z+19}{z+5}$

21. $\frac{5x^2-3x+2}{2x-1} - \frac{3x^2+3x-2}{2x-1}$

22. $\frac{4y^2+2y-3}{5y+1} - \frac{3y^2-2y-4}{5y+1}$

23. $\frac{a-1}{a^2-2a+1} + \frac{5-3a}{a^2-2a+1}$

24. $\frac{3m-3}{m^2+3m-4} + \frac{m-7}{m^2+3m-4}$

ADDITIONAL ANSWERS

Exercises

19. $\frac{(3n+2)(n-4)}{n+4}$

20. $3z+5$

21. $\frac{2(x-2)(x-1)}{2x-1}$

22. $\frac{y^2+4y+1}{5y+1}$

23. $\frac{-2(a-2)}{(a-1)(a-1)}$

24. $\frac{2(2m-5)}{(m+4)(m-1)}$

25. $\frac{2(5a+3)}{a-2}$
26. $\frac{7x+1}{x+1}$
27. $\frac{a^2+a+9}{a+2}$
28. $\frac{2b^2+b-5}{b+4}$
29. $\frac{2x^2+4x+3}{x-1}$
30. $\frac{2(3a-4)(a+3)}{3a+4}$
31. $\frac{-y(3y+10)}{2y+1}$
32. $\frac{4p-5}{3p+8}$
33. $\frac{2(2x-1)}{x-1}$
34. $\frac{3(5b-2)}{5b+2}$

Mixed Review

38. $\frac{2x^2}{y}$
39. $\frac{m-6}{4}$
40. $\frac{-1}{a+4}$
41. $81t^8$
42. $\frac{y^8}{36}$
43. $\frac{m^{24}n^{12}}{64}$
44. $9a^2b^2$
45. $\frac{4x^2}{y^2}$
46. $-6, 4$
47. 11, 9

B

Add or subtract. Simplify.

25. $\frac{4a+5}{a-2}+\frac{6a-4}{a-2}+\frac{5}{a-2}$

26. $\frac{5x-3}{x+1}+\frac{2x}{x+1}+\frac{4}{x+1}$

27. $\frac{3a+3}{a+2}+\frac{a^2-2a}{a+2}+\frac{6}{a+2}$

28. $\frac{2b}{b+4}-\frac{4b}{b+4}-\frac{-2b^2-3b+5}{b+4}$

29. $\frac{x^2+3x-2}{x-1}+\frac{2x+4}{x-1}+\frac{x^2-x+1}{x-1}$

30. $\frac{4a^2+2a-3}{3a+4}+\frac{a^2+2a-15}{3a+4}+\frac{a^2+6a-6}{3a+4}$

31. $\frac{y^2-3y}{2y+1}-\frac{3y^2+4y}{2y+1}-\frac{y^2+3y}{2y+1}$

32. $\frac{p^2-6}{3p+8}+\frac{2p^2+5p-3}{3p+8}-\frac{3p^2+p-4}{3p+8}$

33. $\frac{3x^2+4x-12}{(3x+4)(x-1)}-\frac{5x^2-2x-6}{(3x+4)(x-1)}-\frac{-14x^2-4x+2}{(3x+4)(x-1)}$

34. $\frac{10b^2+b-2}{(5b+2)(2b+1)}+\frac{12b^2-5b}{(5b+2)(2b+1)}-\frac{-8b^2-7b+4}{(5b+2)(2b+1)}$

35. ***Critical Thinking*** The perimeter of the figure at the right is $2x+5$. Find the length of the missing side. $\frac{-2x-15}{x-6}$

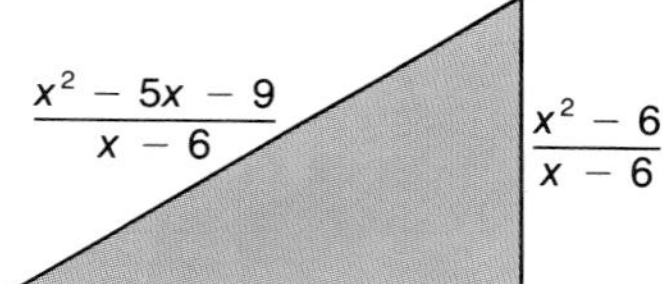

Challenge

Simplify.

36. $\frac{x^2}{3x^2-5x-2}-\frac{2x}{3x+1}\cdot\frac{1}{x-2}$ $\frac{x}{3x+1}$

37. $\frac{3}{x+4}\cdot\frac{2x+11}{x-3}-\frac{-1}{4+x}\cdot\frac{6x+3}{3-x}$ $\frac{30}{(x+4)(x-3)}$

Mixed Review

Simplify. **38.** $\frac{6x^2y}{3y^2}$ **39.** $\frac{m^2-36}{4m+24}$ **40.** $\frac{4-a}{a^2-16}$ **41.** $(-3t^2)^4$

42. $\left(\frac{y^4}{6}\right)^2$ **43.** $\left(\frac{m^4n^2}{2}\right)^6$ **44.** $(-3ab)^2$ **45.** $\left(\frac{-2x}{y}\right)^2$

Solve. **46.** Find two numbers whose sum is -2 and whose product is -24. **47.** The difference of two positive numbers is 2. The difference of the squares of the two numbers is 40. Find the numbers.

10-5 Addition and Subtraction: Unlike Denominators

Least Common Multiples

Objective: Find the least common multiple (LCM) of algebraic expressions.

To add rational expressions with unlike denominators, we begin by finding the least common multiple (LCM) of the denominators.

Finding the Least Common Multiple

To find the LCM of two or more algebraic expressions,
1. factor each expression.
2. form the product using each factor the greatest number of times it occurs.

EXAMPLES

1. Find the LCM of $8x^2y^2$ and $12xy^3$.

$$8x^2y^2 = 2 \cdot 2 \cdot 2 \cdot x \cdot x \cdot y \cdot y \qquad 12xy^3 = 2 \cdot 2 \cdot 3 \cdot x \cdot y \cdot y \cdot y$$
$$\text{LCM} = 2 \cdot 2 \cdot 2 \cdot 3 \cdot x \cdot x \cdot y \cdot y \cdot y = 24x^2y^3$$

2. Find the LCM of $x^2 + 5x - 6$ and $x^2 - 1$.

$$x^2 + 5x - 6 = (x + 6)(x - 1) \qquad x^2 - 1 = (x + 1)(x - 1)$$
$$\text{LCM} = (x + 6)(x + 1)(x - 1)$$

3. Find the LCM of $x^2 + 4$ and $x + 1$.
These expressions are not factorable, so the LCM is their product, $(x^2 + 4)(x + 1)$.

Try This Find the LCM.

a. $12xy^2$, $15x^3y$ **b.** $y^2 + 5y + 4$, $y^2 + 2y + 1$ **c.** $t^2 + 16$, $t - 2$

a. $60x^3y^2$
b. $(y + 1)^2(y + 4)$
c. $(t^2 + 16)(t - 2)$

If one of the factors is the additive inverse of another factor, we can use either one to form the LCM.

EXAMPLE 4 Find the LCM of $x^2 - y^2$ and $2y - 2x$.

$$x^2 - y^2 = (x + y)(x - y) \qquad 2y - 2x = 2(y - x)$$
$$\text{LCM} = 2(x + y)(x - y) \text{ or } 2(x + y)(y - x)$$

10-5

FIRST FIVE MINUTES

Add or subtract and simplify.

1. $\frac{3}{4} + \frac{7}{8}$
$\frac{13}{8}$
2. $\frac{4}{7} + \frac{2}{5}$
$\frac{34}{35}$
3. $\frac{4}{15} - \frac{1}{10}$
$\frac{1}{6}$

Least Common Multiples

Remind students that any two fractions can be expressed in a form in which their denominators are the same. The same technique works for algebraic fractions or rational expressions.

Key Questions

- What fraction with a denominator of 14 is equivalent to $\frac{3}{7}$?
$\frac{6}{14}$
- Can the LCM of two numbers be one of the numbers?
Yes

Chalkboard Examples

1. Find the LCM of x and y.
xy
2. Find the LCM of $3x^2$ and $2xy$.
$2 \cdot 3 \cdot x^2 \cdot y = 6x^2y$
3. Find the LCM of $x^2 + 6x + 5$ and $x^2 + 5x + 4$.
The factored expressions are $(x + 1)(x + 5)$ and $(x + 1)(x + 4)$.
The LCM is $(x + 1)(x + 4)(x + 5)$.
4. Find the LCM of $x^3 - 1$ and $x^2 - 1$.
The factored expressions are $(x - 1)(x^2 + x + 1)$ and $(x - 1)(x + 1)$.
The LCM is $(x - 1)(x + 1)(x^2 + x + 1)$.
5. Find the LCM of $3x + 6y$ and $x^2 + 4xy + 4y^2$.
The factored expressions are $3(x + 2y)$ and $(x + 2y)^2$.
The LCM is $3(x + 2y)^2$.

Addition with Unlike Denominators

Emphasize that when adding rational expressions or algebraic fractions we follow the same procedure used for adding ordinary fractions. The two fractions are each written in a form that has a common denominator. Then they can be added easily.

Chalkboard Examples

Add and simplify.

1. $\frac{x}{2} + \frac{3x}{5}$

   $\frac{5 \cdot x}{5 \cdot 2} + \frac{2 \cdot 3x}{2 \cdot 5} = \frac{11x}{10}$

2. $\frac{7}{3x + 15} + \frac{4}{x + 5}$

   The factored denominators are $3(x + 5)$ and $x + 5$. The LCM is $3(x + 5)$.

   $= \frac{7}{3(x + 5)} + \frac{3 \cdot 4}{3(x + 5)}$

   $= \frac{19}{3(x + 5)}$

3. $\frac{7}{3x^2 + x} + \frac{3}{6x + 2}$

   $= \frac{7}{x(3x + 1)} + \frac{3}{2(3x + 1)}$

   $= \frac{2 \cdot 7}{2x(3x + 1)} + \frac{x \cdot 3}{2x(3x + 1)}$

   $= \frac{3x + 14}{2x(3x + 1)}$

Try This Find the LCM.

d. $a^2 - b^2, 3b - 3a$ **e.** $x^2 - 2x + 1, 1 - x^2$

d. $3(a - b)(a + b)$ or $3(b - a)(b + a)$
e. $(x + 1)(x - 1)^2$

Addition with Unlike Denominators

Objective: Add rational expressions with unlike denominators.

To add rational expressions with unlike denominators,

1. find the LCM of the denominators. This is the least common denominator (LCD).
2. write each rational expression as an equivalent expression with the LCD. To write an equivalent rational expression, multiply by an expression equivalent to 1.
3. add the numerators. Write the sum over the LCD.

EXAMPLES Add and simplify.

5. $\frac{5x^2}{8} + \frac{7x}{12} = \frac{5x^2}{2 \cdot 2 \cdot 2} + \frac{7x}{2 \cdot 2 \cdot 3}$ LCM of the denominator is $2 \cdot 2 \cdot 2 \cdot 3$, or 24.

$= \frac{5x^2}{2 \cdot 2 \cdot 2} \cdot \frac{3}{3} + \frac{7x}{2 \cdot 2 \cdot 3} \cdot \frac{2}{2}$ Multiplying each term by a form of 1 to get the LCD

$= \frac{15x^2}{24} + \frac{14x}{24}$

$= \frac{15x^2 + 14x}{24}$

$= \frac{x(15x + 14)}{24}$

6. $\frac{3}{x + 1} + \frac{5}{x - 1} = \frac{3}{x + 1} \cdot \frac{x - 1}{x - 1} + \frac{5}{x - 1} \cdot \frac{x + 1}{x + 1}$ LCM is $(x + 1)(x - 1)$.

$= \frac{3(x - 1) + 5(x + 1)}{(x - 1)(x + 1)}$

$= \frac{3x - 3 + 5x + 5}{(x - 1)(x + 1)}$

$= \frac{8x + 2}{(x - 1)(x + 1)}$

$= \frac{2(4x + 1)}{(x - 1)(x + 1)}$

The numerator and denominator have no common factor, other than 1, so we cannot simplify further.

Try This Add and simplify.

f. $\frac{7x^2}{6} + \frac{3x}{16}$ $\frac{56x^2 + 9x}{48}$ **g.** $\frac{x}{x - 2} + \frac{4}{x + 2}$ $\frac{x^2 + 6x - 8}{(x - 2)(x + 2)}$

EXAMPLE 7 Add and simplify.

$$\frac{5}{x^2 + x} + \frac{4}{2x + 2} = \frac{5}{x(x + 1)} + \frac{4}{2(x + 1)} \qquad \text{LCM} = 2x(x + 1)$$

$$= \frac{5}{x(x + 1)} \cdot \frac{2}{2} + \frac{4}{2(x + 1)} \cdot \frac{x}{x}$$

$$= \frac{10}{2x(x + 1)} + \frac{4x}{2x(x + 1)}$$

$$= \frac{10 + 4x}{2x(x + 1)} \qquad \text{Adding}$$

$$= \frac{2(5 + 2x)}{2x(x + 1)} \qquad \text{Factoring numerator}$$

$$= \frac{5 + 2x}{x(x + 1)} \qquad \text{Simplifying}$$

Try This Add and simplify.

h. $\frac{3}{x^3 - x} + \frac{4}{x^2 + 2x + 1}$ **i.** $\frac{5}{x^2 + 17x + 16} + \frac{3}{x^2 + 9x + 8}$

h. $\frac{4x^2 - x + 3}{x(x - 1)(x + 1)^2}$

i. $\frac{8(x + 11)}{(x + 16)(x + 1)(x + 8)}$

Subtraction with Unlike Denominators

Objective: Subtract rational expressions with unlike denominators.

To subtract expressions with unlike denominators, follow steps 1 and 2 as given for addition with unlike denominators on the preceding page. Then subtract the numerators and write the difference over the LCD.

EXAMPLES Subtract and simplify.

8. $\frac{x + 2}{x - 4} - \frac{x + 1}{x + 4} = \frac{x + 2}{x - 4} \cdot \frac{x + 4}{x + 4} - \frac{x + 1}{x + 4} \cdot \frac{x - 4}{x - 4} \qquad \text{LCM} = (x - 4)(x + 4)$

$$= \frac{(x + 2)(x + 4)}{(x - 4)(x + 4)} - \frac{(x + 1)(x - 4)}{(x - 4)(x + 4)}$$

$$= \frac{(x + 2)(x + 4) - [(x + 1)(x - 4)]}{(x - 4)(x + 4)}$$

$$= \frac{x^2 + 6x + 8 - (x^2 - 3x - 4)}{(x - 4)(x + 4)} \qquad \text{Subtracting numerators}$$

$$= \frac{x^2 + 6x + 8 - x^2 + 3x + 4}{(x - 4)(x + 4)}$$

$$= \frac{9x + 12}{(x - 4)(x + 4)}$$

$$= \frac{3(3x + 4)}{(x - 4)(x + 4)}$$

Subtraction with Unlike Denominators

Emphasize that a subtraction sign affects the entire polynomial in a numerator, not just the first term. Before subtracting such a numerator, place the polynomial in parentheses. Then use the distributive property to remove the parentheses.

Chalkboard Examples

Subtract and simplify.

1. $\frac{x - 5}{x + 1} - \frac{x + 3}{x - 1}$

$$= \frac{(x - 5)(x - 1)}{(x + 1)(x - 1)} - \frac{(x + 1)(x + 3)}{(x + 1)(x - 1)}$$

$$= \frac{x^2 - 6x + 5 - (x^2 + 4x + 3)}{(x + 1)(x - 1)}$$

$$= \frac{-10x + 2}{(x + 1)(x - 1)}$$

$$= \frac{2(-5x + 1)}{(x + 1)(x - 1)} \text{ or } \frac{-2(5x - 1)}{(x + 1)(x - 1)}$$

2. $5 - \frac{5}{x - 2}$

$$= \frac{5(x - 2)}{x - 2} - \frac{5}{x - 2}$$

$$= \frac{5x - 10 - 5}{x - 2}$$

$$= \frac{5(x - 3)}{x - 2}$$

LESSON QUIZ

1. Find the LCM of $3ab^2$ and $6a^2b$.
   $6a^2b^2$

Add and simplify.

2. $\frac{9}{3x} + \frac{2}{5x}$
   $\frac{51}{15x}$
3. $\frac{4x}{x + 2} + \frac{7}{x}$
   $\frac{4x^2 + 7x + 14}{x(x + 2)}$

> ***Assignment Guide***
> Minimum: Day 1: 1–31 e/o, MR
> Day 2: 32–56 e/o
> Regular: Day 1: 1–56 e/o
> Day 2: 57–74 e/o, 75, MR
> Advanced: Day 1: 1–66 m3, MR
> Day 2: 67–74 e/o, 75–78

ADDITIONAL ANSWERS

Exercises

1. c^2d^2
2. $6x^2y$
3. $(x - y)(x + y)$
4. $(a - 5)(a + 5)$
5. $6(y - 3)$ or $6(3 - y)$
6. $8(x - 1)$ or $8(1 - x)$
7. $(t + 2)(t - 2)$
8. $(x + 3)(x - 3)$
9. $(x + 2)(x - 2)(x + 3)$
10. $(x + 1)(x - 2)(x + 2)$
11. $t(t + 2)^2(t - 4)$
12. $y^2(y + 1)(y - 1)$
13. $(a - 1)(a + 1)$
14. $(x + y)^2(x - y)$
15. $(m - 2)^2(m - 3)$
16. $(x + 2)(x - 1)(2x + 1)$
17. $\frac{7a^2}{8}$
18. $\frac{6y}{5}$
19. $\frac{44c}{75}$
20. $\frac{2x + 5}{x^2}$
21. $\frac{4(x + 2)}{x^2}$
22. $\frac{41}{24r}$
23. $\frac{37}{18t}$
24. $\frac{x^2 + 4xy + y^2}{x^2y^2}$
25. $\frac{c^2 + 3cd - d^2}{c^2d^2}$
26. $\frac{6x}{(x - 2)(x + 2)}$
27. $\frac{4x}{(x - 1)(x + 1)}$
28. $\frac{11x + 2}{3x(x + 1)}$
29. $\frac{11x + 15}{4x(x + 5)}$
30. $\frac{2(x^2 + 4x + 8)}{x(x + 4)}$
31. $\frac{2x^2 - 10x + 25}{x(x - 5)}$

9. $$3 - \frac{3}{x + 4} = \frac{3}{1}\cdot\frac{(x + 4)}{(x + 4)} - \frac{3}{x + 4}$$
$$= \frac{3x + 12}{x + 4} - \frac{3}{x + 4}$$
$$= \frac{3x + 12 - 3}{x + 4}$$
$$= \frac{3x + 9}{x + 4}$$
$$= \frac{3(x + 3)}{x + 4}$$

Try This Subtract and simplify.

j. $\frac{-3x}{x^2 - 16} - \frac{x + 1}{x + 4}$ **k.** $\frac{4a}{a^2 - 4} - \frac{3a - 2}{2 - a}$ **l.** $6 - \frac{1}{t - 2}$

j. $\frac{(2 + x)(2 - x)}{(x + 4)(x - 4)}$
k. $\frac{3a^2 + 8a - 4}{(a - 2)(a + 2)}$
l. $\frac{6t - 13}{t - 2}$

10-5 EXERCISES

A

Find the LCM.

1. c^2d, cd^2
2. $2x^2, 6xy$
3. $x - y, x + y$
4. $a - 5, a + 5$
5. $2(y - 3), 6(3 - y)$
6. $4(x - 1), 8(1 - x)$
7. $t + 2, t - 2$
8. $x + 3, x - 3$
9. $x^2 - 4, x^2 + 5x + 6$
10. $x^2 + 3x + 2, x^2 - 4$
11. $t^3 + 4t^2 + 4t, t^2 - 4t$
12. $y^3 - y^2, y^4 - y^2$
13. $a + 1, a^2 - 1$
14. $x^2 - y^2, x^2 + 2xy + y^2$
15. $m^2 - 5m + 6, m^2 - 4m + 4$
16. $2x^2 + 5x + 2, 2x^2 - x - 1$

Add and simplify.

17. $\frac{a^2}{2} + \frac{3a^2}{8}$
18. $\frac{8y}{10} + \frac{2y}{5}$
19. $\frac{4c}{15} + \frac{8c}{25}$
20. $\frac{2}{x} + \frac{5}{x^2}$
21. $\frac{4}{x} + \frac{8}{x^2}$
22. $\frac{5}{6r} + \frac{7}{8r}$
23. $\frac{2}{9t} + \frac{11}{6t}$
24. $\frac{x + y}{xy^2} + \frac{3x + y}{x^2y}$
25. $\frac{2c - d}{c^2d} + \frac{c + d}{cd^2}$
26. $\frac{3}{x - 2} + \frac{3}{x + 2}$
27. $\frac{2}{x - 1} + \frac{2}{x + 1}$
28. $\frac{3}{x + 1} + \frac{2}{3x}$
29. $\frac{2}{x + 5} + \frac{3}{4x}$
30. $\frac{x + 4}{x} + \frac{x}{x + 4}$
31. $\frac{x}{x - 5} + \frac{x - 5}{x}$

32. $\frac{2x}{x^2 - 16} + \frac{x}{x - 4}$

33. $\frac{4x}{x^2 - 25} + \frac{x}{x + 5}$

34. $\frac{5}{z + 4} + \frac{3}{3z + 12}$

35. $\frac{t}{t - 3} + \frac{5}{4t - 12}$

36. $\frac{3}{x - 1} + \frac{2}{(x - 1)^2}$

37. $\frac{2}{x + 3} + \frac{4}{(x + 3)^2}$

38. $\frac{4a}{5a - 10} + \frac{3a}{10a - 20}$

39. $\frac{3a}{4a - 20} + \frac{9a}{6a - 30}$

40. $\frac{x}{x^2 + 2x + 1} + \frac{1}{x^2 + 5x + 4}$

41. $\frac{7}{a^2 + a - 2} + \frac{5}{a^2 - 4a + 3}$

Subtract and simplify.

42. $\frac{x - 2}{6} - \frac{x + 1}{3}$

43. $\frac{a + 2}{2} - \frac{a - 4}{4}$

44. $\frac{y - 5}{y} - \frac{3y - 1}{4y}$

45. $\frac{x - 1}{4x} - \frac{2x + 3}{x}$

46. $\frac{4z - 9}{3z} - \frac{3z - 8}{4z}$

47. $\frac{3x - 2}{4x} - \frac{3x + 1}{6x}$

48. $\frac{5x + 3y}{2x^2y} - \frac{3x - 4y}{xy^2}$

49. $\frac{4x + 2t}{3xt^2} - \frac{5x - 3t}{x^2t}$

50. $\frac{5}{x + 5} - \frac{3}{x - 5}$

51. $\frac{2z}{z - 1} - \frac{3z}{z + 1}$

52. $\frac{5x}{x^2 - 9} - \frac{4}{x + 3}$

53. $\frac{8x}{x^2 - 16} - \frac{5}{x + 4}$

54. $\frac{3}{2t^2 - 2t} - \frac{5}{2t - 2}$

55. $\frac{4}{5b^2 - 5b} - \frac{3}{5b - 5}$

56. $\frac{2s}{t^2 - s^2} - \frac{s}{t - s}$

B

Add or subtract and simplify.

57. $\frac{3 - b}{b - 7} + \frac{2b - 5}{7 - b}$

58. $\frac{x}{x - 1} + \frac{1}{1 - x}$

59. $\frac{t^2}{t - 2} - \frac{4}{2 - t}$

60. $\frac{y^2}{y - 3} - \frac{9}{3 - y}$

61. $\frac{y - 8}{y^2 - 16} + \frac{y - 8}{16 - y^2}$

62. $\frac{a + 3}{a - 5} - \frac{2a - 1}{5 - a}$

63. $\frac{3(x - 2)}{2x - 3} - \frac{3(x - 1)}{3 - 2x}$

64. $\frac{m - 2}{m^2 - 25} + \frac{m - 2}{25 - m^2}$

65. $\frac{x}{x^2 + 5x + 6} - \frac{2}{x^2 + 3x + 2}$

66. $\frac{x}{x^2 + 11x + 30} - \frac{5}{x^2 + 9x + 20}$

Find the LCM.

67. $8x^2 - 8$, $6x^2 - 12x + 6$, and $10 - 10x$

68. $9x^3 - 9x^2 - 18x$, $6x^5 - 24x^4 + 24x^3$

69. $x^5 + 2x^4 + x^3$, $2x^3 - 2x$, $5x - 5$

70. $x^5 + 4x^4 + 4x^3$, $3x^2 - 12$, $2x + 4$

32. $\frac{x(x + 6)}{(x - 4)(x + 4)}$

33. $\frac{x(x - 1)}{(x + 5)(x - 5)}$

34. $\frac{6}{z + 4}$

35. $\frac{4t + 5}{4(t - 3)}$

36. $\frac{3x - 1}{(x - 1)^2}$

37. $\frac{2(x + 5)}{(x + 3)^2}$

38. $\frac{11a}{10(a - 2)}$

39. $\frac{9a}{4(a - 5)}$

40. $\frac{x^2 + 5x + 1}{(x + 1)^2(x + 4)}$

41. $\frac{12a - 11}{(a + 2)(a - 1)(a - 3)}$

42. $\frac{-x - 4}{6}$

43. $\frac{a + 8}{4}$

44. $\frac{y - 19}{4y}$

45. $\frac{-7x - 13}{4x}$

46. $\frac{7z - 12}{12z}$

47. $\frac{3x - 8}{12x}$

48. $\frac{-6x^2 + 13xy + 3y^2}{2x^2y^2}$

49. $\frac{4x^2 - 13xt + 9t^2}{3x^2t^2}$

50. $\frac{2(x - 20)}{(x + 5)(x - 5)}$

51. $\frac{z(5 - z)}{(z - 1)(z + 1)}$

52. $\frac{x + 12}{(x - 3)(x + 3)}$

53. $\frac{3x + 20}{(x - 4)(x + 4)}$

54. $\frac{3 - 5t}{2t(t - 1)}$

55. $\frac{4 - 3b}{5b(b - 1)}$

56. $\frac{s(2 - t - s)}{(t + s)(t - s)}$

57. $\frac{8 - 3b}{b - 7}$ or $\frac{3b - 8}{7 - b}$

58. 1

59. $\frac{t^2 + 4}{t - 2}$

60. $\frac{y^2 + 9}{y - 3}$

61. 0

62. $\frac{3a + 2}{a - 5}$

63. 3

64. 0

65. $\frac{x - 3}{(x + 1)(x + 3)}$

66. $\frac{x - 6}{(x + 4)(x + 6)}$

67. $120(x + 1)(x - 1)^2$

68. $18x^3(x - 2)^2(x + 1)$

69. $10x^3(x + 1)^2(x - 1)$

70. $6x^3(x + 2)^2(x - 2)$

71. $\frac{(z + 6)(2z - 3)}{z^2 - 4}$

72. $\frac{-2(y^2 - 5y - 30)}{(y - 3)^2(y + 3)}$

73. $\frac{11z^4 - 22z^2 + 6}{(2z^2 - 3)(z^2 + 2)(z^2 - 2)}$

74. $\frac{a}{a - b} + \frac{b}{a - b}$

75. Answers may vary. Example: $\frac{5x^2 + y}{x^2 + y^2} - \frac{2xy + y}{x^2 + y^2}$

Mixed Review

79. Yes
80. No
81. No
82. $\{x|x > 11 \text{ or } x < -11\}$

83. $\left\{x|x \geq 3 \text{ or } x \leq \frac{1}{3}\right\}$

84. $\{x|-12 \leq x \leq 12\}$

85. $\{x|x \neq 0\}$

86. $\{x|-4 \leq x \leq 6\}$

87. $\frac{a + 4}{a - 3}$
88. $3x - 5$
89. -3

Connections: Geometry

1. Perimeter $\frac{4(4y + 7)}{15}$; area $\frac{(y + 4)(y - 2)}{15}$

2. Perimeter $\frac{2(5x - 7)}{(x - 5)(x + 4)}$; area $\frac{6}{(x - 5)(x + 4)}$

Add and simplify.

71. $\frac{5}{z + 2} + \frac{4z}{z^2 - 4} + 2$

72. $\frac{-2}{y^2 - 9} + \frac{4y}{(y - 3)^2} + \frac{6}{3 - y}$

73. $\frac{3z^2}{z^4 - 4} + \frac{5z^2 - 3}{2z^4 + z^2 - 6}$

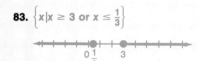

74. Write $\frac{a + b}{a - b}$ as the sum of two rational expressions.

75. ***Critical Thinking*** Write $\frac{5x^2 - 2xy}{x^2 + y^2}$ as the difference of two rational expressions, each having a multiple of y in the numerator.

Challenge

76. Two joggers leave the starting point of a circular course at the same time. One jogger completes one round in 6 minutes, and the second jogger finishes in 8 minutes. After how many minutes will they meet again at the starting place, assuming that they continue to run at the same pace? 24 min

The planets Earth, Jupiter, Saturn, and Uranus revolve around the sun about once each 1, 12, 30, and 84 years, respectively.

77. How often will Jupiter and Saturn appear in the same direction in the night sky as seen from Earth? Every 60 years

78. How often will Jupiter, Saturn, and Uranus all appear in the same direction in the night sky as seen from Earth? Every 420 years

Mixed Review

Determine whether the graphs of the equations are perpendicular.

79. $4y = 5x + 2$, $8x = 3 - 10y$ **80.** $y + 3x = 4$, $2x = 5 - 6y$ **81.** $6y + 4x = 11$, $21 - 15y = 10x$

Solve and graph. **82.** $|11x| > 121$ **83.** $|3x - 5| \geq 4$

84. $|9x| \leq 108$ **85.** $|2x - x| > 0$ **86.** $|x - 1| \leq 5$

Simplify. **87.** $\frac{a^2 + 7a + 12}{a^2 - 9}$ **88.** $\frac{9x^2 - 25}{3x + 5}$ **89.** $\frac{3x - 6}{2 - x}$

CONNECTIONS: GEOMETRY

Find the perimeter and area of each figure.

1. Rectangle with sides $\frac{y + 4}{3}$ and $\frac{y - 2}{5}$

2. Rectangle with sides $\frac{3}{x + 4}$ and $\frac{2}{x - 5}$

10-6 Solving Rational Equations

Objective: Solve equations involving rational expressions.

Master Grapher Worksheet 9 can be used with this lesson.

A **rational equation** is an equation containing one or more rational expressions. Here are some examples.

$$\frac{1}{x} = \frac{1}{4-x} \qquad x + \frac{6}{x} = -5 \qquad \frac{x^2}{x-1} = \frac{1}{x-1}$$

To solve a rational equation multiply on both sides by the LCM of all the denominators.

EXAMPLE 1 Solve.

$$\frac{1}{x} = \frac{1}{4-x} \quad \text{LCM is } x(4-x).$$

$$x(4-x)\cdot\frac{1}{x} = x(4-x)\cdot\frac{1}{4-x} \quad \text{Multiplying on both sides by LCM}$$

$$4 - x = x$$

$$4 = 2x$$

$$2 = x$$

Check: $\frac{1}{x} = \frac{1}{4-x}$

$\frac{1}{x}$	$\frac{1}{4-x}$
$\frac{1}{2}$	$\frac{1}{4-2}$
$\frac{1}{2}$	$\frac{1}{2}$ ✓

The solution is 2.

Try This Solve.

a. $\frac{3}{4} + \frac{5}{8} = \frac{x}{12}$ $\frac{33}{2}$ **b.** $\frac{1}{x} = \frac{1}{6-x}$ 3

EXAMPLE 2 Solve.

$$x + \frac{6}{x} = -5$$

$$x\left(x + \frac{6}{x}\right) = -5x \quad \text{LCM is } x.$$

$$x^2 + x\cdot\frac{6}{x} = -5x$$

$$x^2 + 6 = -5x$$

10-6

FIRST FIVE MINUTES

1. Add $\frac{3}{x} + \frac{1}{2x}$.

$\frac{2\cdot 3}{2\cdot x} + \frac{1}{2x} = \frac{7}{2x}$

2. Add $\frac{1}{2x+4} + \frac{5}{3x+6}$.

$\frac{1}{2(x+2)} + \frac{5}{3(x+2)}$

$= \frac{3\cdot 1}{3\cdot 2(x+2)} + \frac{2\cdot 5}{2\cdot 3(x+2)}$

$= \frac{13}{6(x+2)}$

Emphasize that the techniques of this section are not new. We multiply both sides of an equation by the LCM of the denominators in order to clear the fractions.

Emphasize the importance of checking solutions in the original equation. Point out that there is a difference between an extraneous solution and a wrong answer. Neither wrong answers nor extraneous solutions are solutions of the original equation. Only extraneous solutions, however, are solutions of the transformed equation.

Avoiding Common Errors

After solving rational equations, students often want to use the same technique to "get rid of" the denominators of rational expressions. Emphasize that this lesson involves equations. The multiplication property allows us to multiply *both* sides of an equation by the same quantity. Neither the multiplication property nor any other property allows us to multiply an *expression* by any number other than one.

Key Question

- If a rational equation has no variables in a denominator, how many extraneous roots are there? None

Chalkboard Examples

1. Solve and check.

   $\frac{1}{x+1} = \frac{2}{x}$

   Multiply through by the LCM $x(x + 1)$.

   $x = 2(x + 1)$
   $x = 2x + 2$
   $-x = 2$
   $x = -2$

2. Solve.

   $x + \frac{2}{x} = 3$

   Multiply through by x.

   $x^2 + 2 = 3x$
   $x^2 - 3x + 2 = 0$
   $(x - 1)(x - 2) = 0$
   $x = 1$ or $x = 2$

3. Solve.

   $\frac{4}{x+2} = \frac{x^2}{x+2}$

   Multiply through by $x + 2$.

   $4 = x^2$
   $x = 2$ or $x = -2$

   The number 2 is a solution, but the number -2 is an extraneous solution.

LESSON QUIZ

Solve and check.

1. $\frac{x}{3} + \frac{3}{2} = 1$

   $x = -\frac{3}{2}$

2. $x + \frac{5}{x} = 6$

   $x = 1$ or $x = 5$

3. $\frac{x-8}{x-5} = x$

   $x = 2$ or $x = 4$

This is a second degree equation. Thus we set the equation equal to zero.

$$x^2 + 5x + 6 = 0$$

$$(x + 3)(x + 2) = 0 \qquad \text{Factoring}$$

$$x + 3 = 0 \qquad x + 2 = 0$$

$$x = -3 \quad \text{or} \quad x = -2 \qquad \text{Using the principle of zero products}$$

Check:

$x + \frac{6}{x} = -5$	
$-3 + \frac{6}{-3}$	-5
$-3 - 2$	-5
-5	-5 ✓

$x + \frac{6}{x} = -5$	
$-2 + \frac{6}{-2}$	-5
$-2 - 3$	-5
-5	-5 ✓

Both numbers check, so there are two solutions, -3 and -2.

EXAMPLE 3 Solve.

$$\frac{x^2}{x-1} = \frac{1}{x-1}$$

$$(x-1)\cdot\frac{x^2}{x-1} = (x-1)\cdot\frac{1}{x-1} \qquad \text{LCM is } x - 1.$$

$$x^2 = 1$$

$$x^2 - 1 = 0$$

$$(x - 1)(x + 1) = 0$$

$$x - 1 = 0 \quad \text{or} \quad x + 1 = 0$$

$$x = 1 \quad \text{or} \quad x = -1$$

Check:

$\frac{x^2}{x-1}$	$= \frac{1}{x-1}$
$\frac{1^2}{1-1}$	$\frac{1}{1-1}$
$\frac{1}{0}$	$\frac{1}{0}$

$\frac{x^2}{x-1}$	$= \frac{1}{x-1}$
$\frac{(-1)^2}{-1-1}$	$\frac{1}{-1-1}$
$-\frac{1}{2}$	$-\frac{1}{2}$ ✓

The solution is -1. The number 1 is not a solution, as it makes a denominator zero.

When both sides of an equation are multiplied by a variable, the equation is transformed into a new equation that may have extra or extraneous solutions. In Example 3 the number 1 is an extraneous solution. *When solving rational equations, it is necessary to check each solution of the new equation in the original rational equation.*

Try This Solve.

c. $x + \frac{1}{x} = 2$ 1 **d.** $\frac{x^2}{x+2} = \frac{4}{x+2}$ 2 **e.** $\frac{1}{2x} + \frac{1}{x} = -12$ $-\frac{1}{8}$

10-6 EXERCISES

A

Solve.

1. $\frac{3}{8} + \frac{4}{5} = \frac{x}{20}$ $\frac{47}{2}$

2. $\frac{3}{5} + \frac{2}{3} = \frac{x}{9}$ $\frac{57}{5}$

3. $\frac{2}{3} - \frac{5}{6} = \frac{1}{x}$ -6

4. $\frac{1}{8} - \frac{3}{5} = \frac{1}{x}$ $-\frac{40}{19}$

5. $\frac{1}{6} + \frac{1}{8} = \frac{1}{t}$ $\frac{24}{7}$

6. $\frac{1}{8} + \frac{1}{10} = \frac{1}{t}$ $\frac{40}{9}$

7. $x + \frac{4}{x} = -5$ $-4; -1$

8. $x + \frac{3}{x} = -4$ $-3; -1$

9. $\frac{x}{4} - \frac{4}{x} = 0$ $4, -4$

10. $\frac{x}{5} - \frac{5}{x} = 0$ $5; -5$

11. $\frac{5}{x} = \frac{6}{x} - \frac{1}{3}$ 3

12. $\frac{4}{x} = \frac{5}{x} - \frac{1}{2}$ 2

13. $\frac{5}{3x} + \frac{3}{x} = 1$ $\frac{14}{3}$

14. $\frac{3}{4x} + \frac{5}{x} = 1$ $\frac{23}{4}$

15. $\frac{x - 7}{x + 2} = \frac{1}{4}$ 10

16. $\frac{a - 2}{a + 3} = \frac{3}{8}$ 5

17. $\frac{2}{x + 1} = \frac{1}{x - 2}$ 5

18. $\frac{5}{x - 1} = \frac{3}{x + 2}$ $-\frac{13}{2}$

19. $\frac{x}{6} - \frac{x}{10} = \frac{1}{6}$ $\frac{5}{2}$

20. $\frac{x}{8} - \frac{x}{12} = \frac{1}{8}$ 3

21. $\frac{x + 1}{3} - \frac{x - 1}{2} = 1$ -1

22. $\frac{x + 2}{5} - \frac{x - 2}{4} = 1$ -2

23. $\frac{a - 3}{3a + 2} = \frac{1}{5}$ $\frac{17}{2}$

24. $\frac{x - 1}{2x + 5} = \frac{1}{4}$ $\frac{9}{2}$

25. $\frac{x - 1}{x - 5} = \frac{4}{x - 5}$ No solution

26. $\frac{x - 7}{x - 9} = \frac{2}{x - 9}$ No solution

27. $\frac{2}{x + 3} = \frac{5}{x}$ -5

28. $\frac{3}{x + 4} = \frac{4}{x}$ -16

29. $\frac{x - 2}{x - 3} = \frac{x - 1}{x + 1}$ $\frac{5}{3}$

30. $\frac{2b - 3}{3b + 2} = \frac{2b + 1}{3b - 2}$ $\frac{1}{5}$

Solve.

31. $\frac{1}{x + 3} + \frac{1}{x - 3} = \frac{1}{x^2 - 9}$ $\frac{1}{2}$

32. $\frac{4}{x - 3} + \frac{2x}{x^2 - 9} = \frac{1}{x + 3}$ No solution

33. $\frac{x}{x + 4} - \frac{4}{x - 4} = \frac{x^2 + 16}{x^2 - 16}$ No solution

34. $\frac{5}{y - 3} - \frac{30}{y^2 - 9} = 1$ 2

Assignment Guide
Minimum: Day 1: 1–18 e/o, MR
Day 2: 19–34 e/o
Regular: Day 1: 1–20 e/o, MR
Day 2: 21–42 e/o, 43
Advanced: Day 1: 1–22 e/o, MR
Day 2: 23–42 e/o, 43–46

ADDITIONAL ANSWERS
Exercises

45. $\dfrac{\frac{x}{y}+\frac{w}{z}}{1-\frac{x}{y}\cdot\frac{w}{z}}$
$=\dfrac{\frac{xz+yw}{yz}}{\frac{yz-xw}{yz}}\cdot\dfrac{yz}{yz}$
$=\dfrac{xz+yw}{yz-xw}$

46. LCM is $(a-b)^2(a+b)^2$.
$\dfrac{\left(\frac{ab}{a-b}\right)^2-\left(\frac{ab}{a+b}\right)^2}{\left(\frac{ab}{a-b}\right)^2+\left(\frac{ab}{a+b}\right)^2}$
$=\dfrac{a^2b^2(a+b)^2-a^2b^2(a-b)^2}{a^2b^2(a+b)^2+a^2b^2(a-b)^2}$
$=\dfrac{(a+b)^2-(a-b)^2}{(a+b)^2+(a-b)^2}$
$=\dfrac{4ab}{2a^2+2b^2}=\dfrac{2ab}{a^2+b^2}$

Mixed Review

47. $\dfrac{(x+1)(x-3)}{x-5}$
48. $\dfrac{27(x+1)^2}{8}$
49. $\frac{1}{4}$
50. $\dfrac{x-2}{5(x-1)}$
51. $-2, 3$
52. $-5 \le x \le 11$
53. $x < -4$ or $x > 0$
54. $x < 5$ or $x > 7$
55. $y > -2$
56. $x > -4$
57. 2, 6

B

Solve.

35. $\dfrac{4}{y-2}-\dfrac{2y-3}{y^2-4}=\dfrac{5}{y+2}$ 7

36. $\dfrac{x}{x^2+3x-4}+\dfrac{x+1}{x^2+6x+8}=\dfrac{2x}{x^2+x-2}$ $\frac{-1}{6}$

37. $\dfrac{2a+7}{8a^2-2a-1}+\dfrac{a-4}{2a^2+5a-3}=\dfrac{4a-1}{4a^2+13a+3}$ 4, −2

38. $\dfrac{y}{y+0.2}-1.2=\dfrac{y-0.2}{y+0.2}$ $\frac{-1}{30}$

39. $\dfrac{x^2}{x^2-4}=\dfrac{x}{x+2}-\dfrac{2x}{2-x}$ 0, −1

40. $4a-3=\dfrac{a+13}{a+1}$ 2, −2

41. $\dfrac{14x-2}{x-3}=\dfrac{9x+8}{-2}$ $\frac{4}{3}, -\frac{7}{3}$

42. $\dfrac{y^2-4}{y+3}=2-\dfrac{y-2}{y+3}$ 4

43. ***Critical Thinking*** Solve the equation $\frac{8}{x}-4=\frac{2}{x}$ using any problem-solving strategy. $\frac{3}{2}$

Challenge

44. Solve. $\dfrac{n}{n-\frac{4}{9}}-\dfrac{n}{n+\frac{4}{9}}=\dfrac{1}{n}$ $\frac{4}{3}, \frac{-4}{3}$

45. Suppose $t=\frac{x}{y}$ and $r=\frac{w}{z}$. Show that $\dfrac{xz+yw}{yz-xw}=\dfrac{t+r}{1-tr}$.

46. Suppose $x=\dfrac{ab}{a+b}$ and $y=\dfrac{ab}{a-b}$. Show that $\dfrac{y^2-x^2}{y^2+x^2}=\dfrac{2ab}{a^2+b^2}$.

Mixed Review

Multiply or divide and simplify. **47.** $\dfrac{(x+1)^2}{(x-5)}\cdot\dfrac{(x-3)}{(x+1)}$

48. $\dfrac{3x+3}{2}\div\dfrac{4}{9x+9}$ **49.** $\dfrac{4a}{3a-3}\cdot\dfrac{3(a-1)}{16a}$ **50.** $\dfrac{x+2}{x-1}\div\dfrac{5x+10}{x-2}$

Solve. **51.** $|2x-1|=5$ **52.** $|x-3|\le 8$

53. $x-3<-7$ or $x+1>1$ **54.** $x-2<3$ or $x+4>11$

55. $11-8y<6y+39$ **56.** $3-7x<9x+67$

57. The difference of two numbers is 4. Five times the larger number is fifteen times the smaller. Find the numbers.

10-7 Problem Solving: Using Rational Equations

Objective: Solve problems involving rational equations.

PROBLEM-SOLVING GUIDELINES
■ UNDERSTAND the problem
■ Develop and carry out a PLAN
■ Find the ANSWER and CHECK

You can use the Problem-Solving Guidelines to help you solve problems involving rational equations.

Suppose it takes a person 4 hours to do a certain job. Then, in 1 hour, $\frac{1}{4}$ of the job gets done. This diagram helps show this relationship.

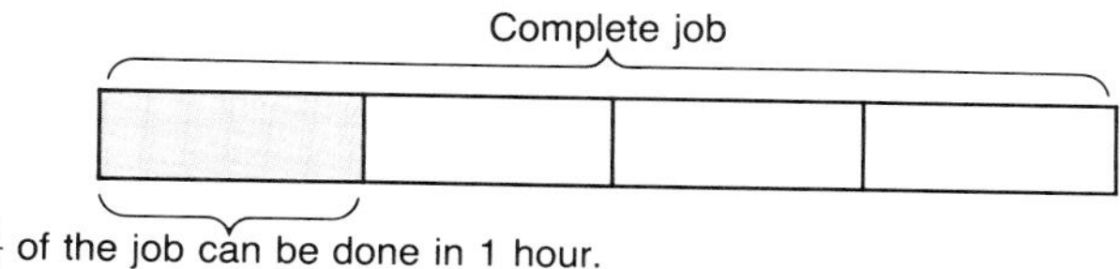

Complete job
$\frac{1}{4}$ of the job can be done in 1 hour.

In general, if a job can be done in t hours (or days, or some other unit of time), then $\frac{1}{t}$ of it can be done in 1 hour (or day, etc.).

EXAMPLE 1

Company A can install chairs in a theatre in 10 hours. Company B can install them in 15 hours. The owner of the theatre wants the chairs installed in less than one day (8 hours). If the companies work together, can they install the chairs in less than one day?

■ **UNDERSTAND the problem**

Question: Can the companies, working together, complete the job in less than 8 hours?

Data: Working alone, company A needs 10 hours and company B needs 15 hours.

■ **Develop and carry out a PLAN**

Company A can do $\frac{1}{10}$ of the job in 1 hour.

Company B can do $\frac{1}{15}$ of the job in 1 hour.

Let t = the total number of hours needed to complete the job.

$\frac{1}{t}$ = the part of the job that can be completed in 1 hour.

Working together, they can do $\frac{1}{10} + \frac{1}{15}$ of the job in 1 hour, so

$$\frac{1}{t} = \frac{1}{10} + \frac{1}{15}$$

10-7

FIRST FIVE MINUTES

Solve and check.

1. $\frac{x}{3} + \frac{1}{2} = 2$

$2x + 3 = 12$
$2x = 9$
$x = \frac{9}{2}$

2. $x + \frac{3}{x} = -4$

$x^2 + 3 = -4x$
$x^2 + 4x + 3 = 0$
$(x + 1)(x + 3) = 0$
$x = -1$ or $x = -3$

Emphasize that the first step of the Problem-Solving Guidelines involves understanding the situation. Remind students to draw and label a diagram or picture to help them understand the problem.

Remind students that it is important to specify the units of measurement of the numbers in the problem, especially of the unknown.

Key Questions

These questions refer to Example 1.

- Suppose both companies can install the seats in 10 hours. How long will it take them working together?
  5 hours
- Suppose both companies can install the seats in 15 hours. How long will it take them working together?
  $7\frac{1}{2}$ hours
- Without working the problem, can you answer the question?
  Company B works at a rate of 15 hours and Company A works at a faster rate, so the job can be done in less than $7\frac{1}{2}$ hours (which is less than 1 day).

Chalkboard Examples

1. Morton can eat a box of popcorn in 2 minutes. Wilbur can eat a box of popcorn in 3 minutes. They go to the movies and share one box of popcorn. How long will it take them to finish it?
   Let t be the time, in minutes, that it takes them to finish the popcorn. Morton can eat $\frac{1}{2}$ of a box of popcorn in one minute. Wilbur can eat $\frac{1}{3}$ of a box in one minute.
   Together they can eat $\frac{1}{t}$ of a box in one minute. So,
   $$\frac{1}{2} + \frac{1}{3} = \frac{1}{t}$$
   $$\frac{3}{6} + \frac{2}{6} = \frac{1}{t}$$
   $$\frac{5}{6} = \frac{1}{t}$$
   $$\frac{5}{6}t = 1$$
   $$t = \frac{6}{5}$$
   They will finish the popcorn in $\frac{6}{5}$ minute, or 1 minute, 12 seconds.
2. A bicyclist travels 20 miles per hour faster than a walker. The cyclist traveled 25 miles in the time it took the walker to walk 5 miles. Find their speeds.
   Let r = speed of the walker.
   $r + 20$ = speed of the cyclist.
   Let t = time each one traveled.

	Distance	Rate	Time
Cyclist	25	$r + 20$	t
Walker	5	r	t

If we solve the formula $d = rt$ for t, we get $t = \frac{d}{r}$. Using the rows of the tables, we get our two equations.

$$t = \frac{25}{r + 20}$$
$$t = \frac{5}{r}$$

These combine into the following equation.

$$\frac{5}{r} = \frac{25}{r + 20}$$
$$5(r + 20) = 25r$$
$$5r + 100 = 25r$$
$$100 = 20r$$
$$5 = r$$

The walker travels 5 miles per hour, the cyclist travels 25 miles per hour.

We solve this equation for t.

$$\frac{1}{t} = \frac{3}{30} + \frac{2}{30}$$
$$\frac{1}{t} = \frac{1}{6}$$
$$t = 6$$

Find the ANSWER and CHECK

The job can be completed in 6 hours with both companies working together. Thus it can be completed in less than 1 day (8 hours). This is reasonable, since company A could do $\frac{5}{10}$ or half of the job in 5 hours, and company B could do about half of the job $\left(\frac{7}{15}\right)$ in 7 hours.

Try This Solve.

a. A contractor finds that it takes crew A 6 hours to construct a wall of a certain size. Crew B takes 8 hours to construct a wall of the same size. How long will it take if they work together? $3\frac{3}{7}$ h

EXAMPLE 2

One car travels 20 km/h faster than another. While one of them travels 240 km, the other travels 180 km. Find their speeds.

UNDERSTAND the problem

Question: What are the speeds of the cars?
Data: One car travels 20 km/h faster than the other car. The faster car goes 240 km. The slower car goes 180 km. The time traveled is the same for both.

Develop and carry out a PLAN

Let r = the speed (rate) of the slower car.

$r + 20$ = speed of faster car

Let t = time each car traveled.

	Distance	Rate	Time
Slower car	180	r	t
Faster car	240	$r + 20$	t

Recording the data in a table helps show relationships.

If we solve the formula $d = rt$ for t, we get $t = \frac{d}{r}$. From the rows of the table, we can find two equations.

$$t = \frac{180}{r} \quad \text{and} \quad t = \frac{240}{r + 20}$$

Since the times are the same, we have the following equation.

$$\frac{180}{r} = \frac{240}{r + 20}$$

$$\frac{180 \cdot r(r + 20)}{r} = \frac{240 \cdot r(r + 20)}{r + 20}$$ Multiplying on both sides by the LCM, $r(r + 20)$

$$180(r + 20) = 240r$$

$$180r + 3600 = 240r$$

$$\frac{3600}{60} = r$$

$$60 = r$$ Rate of the slower car

$$80 = r + 20$$ Rate of the faster car

■ **Find the ANSWER and CHECK**

The speeds are 60 km/h for the slower car and 80 km/h for the faster car. In 3 hours the slow car would travel $60 \times 3 = 180$ km, and in 3 hours the faster car would travel $80 \times 3 = 240$ km. The answers check.

Try This Solve.

b. One boat travels 10 km/h faster than another. While one boat travels 120 km, the other travels 155 km. Find their speeds. $34\frac{2}{7}$ km/h, $44\frac{2}{7}$ km/h

---

EXAMPLE 3

The reciprocal of 2 less than a certain number is twice the reciprocal of the number itself. What is the number?

Let x = the number.

(Reciprocal of 2 less than the number) is (twice the reciprocal of the number.)

$$\frac{1}{x - 2} = 2 \cdot \frac{1}{x}$$ Translating

$$\frac{1}{x - 2} = \frac{2}{x}$$

$$\frac{x(x - 2)}{x - 2} = \frac{2x(x - 2)}{x}$$ Multiplying by LCM

$$x = 2(x - 2)$$ Simplifying

$$x = 2x - 4$$

$$x = 4$$

The number is 4.

Try This Solve.

c. The reciprocal of two more than a number is three times the reciprocal of the number. Find the number. -3

LESSON QUIZ

1. A tank can be emptied through either of two pipes. The first pipe empties the tank in 4 hours. The second pipe empties the tank in 3 hours. How long will it take to empty the tank using both pipes?

   $\frac{12}{7}$ hours

Assignment Guide
Minimum: 1–10 e/o, MR

Regular: 1–16 m3, 17, MR

Advanced: 1–16 m4, 17–20, MR

10-7 EXERCISES

A

Solve.

1. It takes painter A 3 hours to paint a certain area of a house. It takes painter B 5 hours to do the same job. How long would it take them, working together, to do the painting job? $1\frac{7}{8}$ h
2. By checking work records, a plumber finds that worker A can do a certain job in 12 hours. Worker B can do the same job in 9 hours. How long would it take if they worked together? $5\frac{1}{7}$ h
3. A tank can be filled in 18 hours by pipe A or in 24 hours by pipe B. How long would it take both pipes to fill the tank? $10\frac{2}{7}$ h
4. Team A can set up chairs in the gym in 15 minutes and team B can set up the chairs in 20 minutes. How long would it take them, working together, to set up the same chairs? $8\frac{4}{7}$ min
5. One car travels 40 km/h faster than another. While one travels 150 km, the other goes 350 km. Find their speeds. 30 km/h, 70 km/h
6. A person traveled 120 miles in one direction. The return trip was accomplished at double the speed and took 3 hours less time. Find the speed going. 20 mi/h
7. The speed of a freight train is 14 km/h slower than the speed of a passenger train. The freight train travels 330 km in the same time that it takes the passenger train to travel 400 km. Find the speed of each train. p: 80 km/h, f: 66 km/h
8. The reciprocal of 4 plus the reciprocal of 5 is the reciprocal of what number? $\frac{20}{9}$, or $2\frac{2}{9}$
9. The sum of half a number and its reciprocal is the same as 51 divided by the number. Find the number. $\frac{1}{2}x + \frac{1}{x} = \frac{51}{x}$, $x = 10$ or -10
10. The additive inverse of a number divided by twelve is the same as one less than three times its reciprocal. Find the number. $\frac{-x}{12} = \frac{3}{x} - 1$, $x = 6$

B

11. Kirsten can type a 50-page paper in 8 hours. Last month Kirsten and Courtney, together, typed a 50-page paper in 6 hours. How long would it take Courtney to type a 50-page paper on her own? 24 h
12. Two road crews, working together, repaired 1 mile of a road in 4 hours. Working separately, one of the crews takes about 6 hours to repair a similar road. How long would it take the other crew, working alone, to repair a similar road? 12 h
13. One machine in a print shop can produce a certain number of pages twice as fast as another machine. Operating together, these machines can produce this number of pages in 8 minutes. How long would it take each machine, working alone, to produce this number of pages? 12 min, 24 min

14. One watering system needs about 3 times as long to complete a job as another watering system. When both systems operate at the same time, the job can be completed in 9 minutes. How long does it take each system to do the job alone? 12 min, 36 min

15. It takes 10 hours to fill a pool with water, and 20 hours to drain it. If the pool is empty and the drain is open, how long will it take to fill the pool? 20 h

16. It takes 8 hours to fill a tank with a particular chemical. Without treatment, all of the chemical in the tank would evaporate in 12 hours. If the tank is empty to start, and the chemical is not being treated as it enters the tank, how long will it take to have a full tank? 24 h

17. *Critical Thinking* In Exercise 16, suppose it takes 9 hours to fill the tank. Without treatment, how long will it take to fill the tank? 36 h

Challenge

18. A carpenter can complete a certain job in 5 hours. After working on the job for 2 hours, an assistant helped finish the job. Together they completed the job in 1 hour. How long might it take the assistant, working alone, to complete a job similar to this one? $2\frac{1}{2}$ h

19. Dr. Wright allowed one hour to reach an appointment 50 miles away. After driving 30 miles she realized that her speed would have to be increased 15 mi/h for the remainder of the trip. What was her speed for the first 30 miles? $\frac{30}{r} + \frac{20}{r+15} = 1$; 45 mi/h

20. Together, Michelle, Bernie, and Kurt can do a job in 1 hour and 20 minutes. To do the job alone, Michelle needs twice the time that Bernie needs and two hours more than Kurt. How long would it take each to complete the job working alone? Michelle 6 h, Bernie 3 h, Kurt 4 h

Mixed Review

Add or subtract. Simplify. **21.** $\frac{5x-2}{x-1} + \frac{3x-1}{x-1}$ **22.** $\frac{x^2+7}{x-3} + \frac{7x+3}{x-3}$

23. $\frac{x^2+6x}{x+4} - \frac{3x+5}{x+4} + \frac{1}{x+4}$ **24.** $\frac{3}{x+1} + \frac{3}{x-1}$

Solve. **25.** $m^2 - 5m = 14$ **26.** $9n^2 = 16$ **27.** $x^3 + 3x^2 + 2x = 0$

Problem for Programmers

Write a program that will solve a typical work problem: If A can do a job in *a* amount of time and B can do a job in *b* amount of time, how long will it take A and B to do the job together? The amounts *a* and *b* will be the inputs, and the time to do the job together, *t*, will be the output. Hint: Write an equation and solve for *t* first.

Use the exercises in this section to test your program.

ADDITIONAL ANSWERS

Mixed Review

21. $\frac{(8x-3)}{(x-1)}$

22. $\frac{(x+5)(x+2)}{(x-3)}$

23. $x - 1$

24. $\frac{6x}{(x+1)(x-1)}$

25. 7, −2

26. $\frac{4}{3}, -\frac{4}{3}$

27. 0, −1, −2

Problem for Programmers

This program can be written using any programming language (BASIC, PASCAL, LOGO, etc.). Students may need help solving the equation $\frac{1}{a} + \frac{1}{b} = \frac{1}{t}$ for *t*. You may wish to give them the equation $t = \frac{ab}{a+b}$.

This program can also be written on a spreadsheet where the values of *a* and *b* are each input in a separate column and the value of *t* is calculated in a third column.

10-8

FIRST FIVE MINUTES

Solve.

1. $0.5x + 0.4(100 - x) = 42$

   $0.5x + 40 - 0.4x = 42$
   $0.1x = 2$
   $x = 20$

2. $0.04x + 0.4(200 - x) = 62$

   $0.04x + 80 - 0.4x = 62$
   $-0.36x = -18$
   $x = \frac{-18}{-0.36}$
   $x = 50$

You may want to point out that students can find the amount of acid in a solution by multiplying the quantity of solution by the percent of acid in it. Thus, a 100 L solution that is 50% acid contains 50 L of acid. Remind students that since 200 L of solution are needed in Example 1, the amount of the first solution plus the amount of the second solution must add to 200.

Emphasize the importance of making a table for mixture problems.

Mixture problems can be worked using two variables and two equations as well as the way shown in the examples. There is often more than one way to find an answer to a problem.

Math Point
The Great Salt Lake has risen more than 19 feet since its historic low in 1963. The rise has been caused by a period of unusually high levels of rain and snow in the area. The addition of fresh-water precipitation has also decreased the lake's salinity.

Key Questions

- If a solution of acid and water is 80% acid, what percent is water? 20%
- How much acid is in 200 L of solution that is 62% acid? 124 L
- If a solution of salt and water is 6% salt, what percent is water? 94%
- How much salt is in 1 L of water that is 6% salt? 0.06 L

10-8 Problem Solving: Mixture Problems

Objective: Solve problems involving the mixture of substances.

PROBLEM-SOLVING GUIDELINES
■ UNDERSTAND the problem
■ Develop and carry out a PLAN
■ Find the ANSWER and CHECK

Some real-world situations require that two or more substances be combined to produce a mixture.

EXAMPLE 1

A chemist has one solution that is 80% acid and one that is 30% acid. How much of each solution is needed to make a 200 L solution that is 62% acid?

■ UNDERSTAND the problem

Question: How much of each solution is needed?
Data: first solution—80% acid
second solution—30% acid
final solution—200 L, 62% acid

■ Develop and carry out a PLAN

Let x = amount of the first solution.
$200 - x$ = the amount of the second solution
To solve this problem, it is helpful to record the data given and the unknowns in a table.

	Amount of solution	Percent acid	Amount of acid
1st solution	x	80%	$0.8x$
2nd solution	$200 - x$	30%	$0.3(200 - x)$
final solution	200	62%	$0.62(200)$

We can now write an equation using the data in the table.

The sum of the amounts of acid in the two solutions gives the amount of acid in the final solution. Thus we have the equation

$$0.8x + 0.3(200 - x) = 0.62(200)$$
$$0.8x + 60 - 0.3x = 124$$
$$0.5x = 64$$
$$x = 128 \quad \text{The amount of the first solution needed}$$

Thus $200 - x = 200 - 128$. Substituting to find the amount of the second solution

Find the ANSWER and CHECK

128 L of the 80% solution and 72 L of the 30% solution are needed. 80% of 128 is about 100, and 30% of 72 is about 20. The total, $100 + 20 = 120$, is 60% of 200. The answer is reasonable.

EXAMPLE 2

From 1963 to 1984, the level of water in the Great Salt Lake rose, expanding the surface area of the lake from 900 square miles to 2300 square miles. During this period of time, the salinity of the lake dropped from 20 percent to 6 percent. How much water would you have to add to a liter of lake water that is 20 percent salt to get a solution that is only 6 percent salt?

UNDERSTAND the problem

Question: What amount of water must be added?
Data: original solution of 1 liter of water is 20% salt;
final solution is to be 6% salt

Develop and carry out a PLAN

Let x = the amount of water added to the solution.
$1 + x$ = the amount in the new solution

Make a table to organize the data and the unknown information.

	Amount of solution	Percent salt	Amount of salt
Original solution	1	20%	0.20(1)
Added water	x	0%	0
Final solution	$1 + x$	6%	$0.06(1 + x)$

The amount of salt in the original solution plus the amount added gives the amount of salt in the new solution. Notice that since no salt is added, the total amount of salt does not change.

$$0.20(1) + 0 = 0.06(1 + x)$$
$$20 = 6 + 6x$$
$$x \approx 2.33$$

Find the ANSWER and CHECK

The addition of approximately 2.33 liters of salt-free water for every existing liter of lake water with 20 percent salinity will result in 6 percent salinity in the lake.

Chalkboard Example

1. A chemist has one solution that is 60% acid and another that is 30% acid. How much of each solution is needed to make a 750 mL solution that is 50% acid?
Let x = amount of the first acid.
$750 - x$ = amount of the second solution

	% acid	Amount of solution	Amount of acid
1st sol	60%	x	$0.6x$
2nd sol	30%	$750 - x$	$0.3(750 - x)$
3rd sol	50%	750	0.5(750)

We can now write an equation using the data in the chart.

$$0.6x + 0.3(750 - x) = 0.5(750)$$
$$0.6x + 225 - 0.3x = 375$$
$$0.3x = 150$$
$$x = 500$$

500 mL of the first solution and 250 mL of the second solution are needed.

LESSON QUIZ

1. A chemist has 5 liters of a certain solution that is 70% salt. How much water should be added to this solution to make a new solution that is only 50% salt?
2 liters

Assignment Guide
Minimum: 1–8, MR

Regular: 1–10 e/o, 11, MR

Advanced: 1–10 e/o, 11, 12, MR

ADDITIONAL ANSWERS

Exercises

1. 50 L of 60%, 50 L of 40%
2. 50 gal of skim milk
3. e. $0.50x + 0.80(100 - x) = 0.68(100)$; 40 mL of A, 60 mL of B

Try This

a. A 280 mL solution is 20% salt. How much water should be added to make the solution 14% salt? 120 mL

b. A grocer wishes to mix some nuts worth 90¢ per pound with some nuts worth \$1.60 per pound to make 175 pounds of a mixture that is worth \$1.30 per pound. How much of each should she use? 75 lb, 100 lb

10-8 EXERCISES

A

1. A chemist has one solution that is 60% chlorinated and another that is 40% chlorinated. How much of each solution is needed to make a 100 L solution that is 50% chlorine?

	Amount of solution	Percent chlorine	Amount of chlorine
1st solution	x	60%	$0.60x$
2nd solution	$100 - x$	40%	$0.40(100 - x)$
Final solution	100	50%	$0.50(100)$

2. A 50-gallon barrel of milk is 6% butterfat. How much skim milk (no butterfat) should be mixed to make milk that is 3% butterfat?

	Amount (gallons)	Percent butterfat	Amount butterfat (gallons)
Original solution	50	6%	$0.06(50)$
Skim milk	x	0%	0
Final Solution	$50 + x$	3%	$0.03(50 + x)$

3. Solution A is 50% acid and solution B is 80% acid. How much of each should be used to make 100 milliliters of a solution that is 68% acid.

a. Copy the table below. Write labels for the sections of the table that are shaded.

	Amount of solution	Percent acid	Amount of acid
Solution A	x	50%	$0.50x$
Solution B	$100 - x$	80%	$0.80(100 - x)$
Final solution	100	68%	$0.68(100)$

b. Let x be the amount of the first solution. Complete the columns that show the amount of solution and the percent of acid.

c. To find the *amount* of acid in a solution, what two quantities must be multiplied? (Percent acid)(Amount solution)

d. Write expressions that show the amount of acid in each solution.

e. Write and solve an equation to answer the problem.

4. Seminole Dairy Farm has 100 gal of milk that is 4.6% butterfat. How much skim milk (no butterfat) should be mixed with it to make milk that is 3.2% fat?

a. Copy the table below. Write labels for the sections of the table that are shaded.

	Amount (gallons)	Percent butterfat	Amount butterfat (gallons)
Original solution	100	4.6%	0.046(100)
Skim milk	x	0%	0
Final solution	$100 + x$	3.2%	$0.032(100 + x)$

b. Let x be the amount of skim milk. Complete the columns that show the amount and the percent of butterfat.

c. To find the *amount* of butterfat in a solution, what two quantities must be multiplied? (Percent butterfat)(Amount)

d. Write expressions that show the amount of butterfat in each solution.

e. Write and solve an equation to answer the problem.

5. A solution containing 30% insecticide is to be mixed with a solution containing 50% insecticide to make 200 L of a solution containing 42% insecticide. How much of each solution should be used?

6. A solution containing 28% fungicide is to be mixed with a solution containing 40% fungicide to make 300 L of a solution containing 36% fungicide. How much of each solution should be used?

7. The Nut Shoppe has 10 kg of mixed cashews and pecans, which sell for \$8.40 per kilogram. Cashews alone sell for \$8 per kilogram, and pecans sell for \$9 per kilogram. How many kilograms of each are in the mix?

8. A coffee shop mixes Brazilian coffee worth \$5 per kilogram with Turkish coffee worth \$8 per kilogram. The mixture is to sell for \$7 per kilogram. How much of each type of coffee should be used to make 300 kg of the mixture?

B

9. Northern Maywood voted 60% to 40% in favor of a water project. Southern Maywood voted 90% to 10% against the project. The project passed 55% to 45%. If 5900 people voted, how many were from Southern Maywood?

4. e. $0.046(100) = 0.032(100 + x)$; 43.75 gal
5. 80 L of 30%, 120 L of 50%
6. 100 L of 28%, 200 L of 40%
7. 6 kg of cashews, 4 kg of pecans
8. 100 kg of Brazilian coffee 200 kg of Turkish coffee
9. 590 from Southern Maywood

10. 10 people at \$40
5 people at \$50
11. 1770
12. 16 liters of the combined A and B solution and 8 liters of the C solution are needed, but there are only 15 liters of the A-B solution, so it can't be done.

Mixed Review

13. 4, −10
14. 10, −6
15. 6, −6
16. $-4 < x < 4$
17. $-3 \le x \le \frac{17}{13}$
18. No solution
19. 46 dimes, 37 quarters

10. An employer has a daily payroll of \$650 when employing some workers at \$40 per day and others at \$50 per day. When the number of \$40 workers is increased by 50% and the number of \$50 workers is decreased $\frac{1}{5}$, the new daily payroll is \$800. Find how many workers were originally employed at each rate.

11. *Critical Thinking* In Exercise 9, suppose that the project failed 45% to 55%. How many voters were from Southern Maywood?

Challenge

12. Bottle A, containing 12 L of 15% acid, is combined with bottle B, containing 3 L of 25% acid. Bottle C is 26% acid. How much of each solution is needed to have 24 L of a 20% acid solution?

Mixed Review

Solve. **13.** $|x + 3| = 7$ **14.** $|2x - 4| = 16$ **15.** $|4x| - 5 = 19$

16. $8 - |x| > 4$ **17.** $|3x - 4| \le 13$ **18.** $|5x - 4| + 3 < -19$

19. A collection of dimes and quarters is worth \$13.85. There are 83 coins in all. How many are dimes and how many are quarters?

SUPPOSE

Problem: Aretha needs an antifreeze solution that is 50% alcohol. She has antifreeze that is 40% alcohol and antifreeze that is 60% alcohol. How much of each solution does she need to get 10 liters of the antifreeze that is 50% alcohol? 5 L of each

Solution A:

	Amount of solution	Percent alcohol	Amount of alcohol
1st antifreeze	x	0.60	$0.60x$
2nd antifreeze	$10 - x$	0.40	$0.40(10 - x)$
Final solution	10	0.50	0.50(10)

Solution B:

	Amount of solution	Percent alcohol	Amount of alcohol
1st antifreeze	x	0.60	$0.60x$
2nd antifreeze	y	0.40	$0.40y$
Final solution	10	0.50	0.50(10)

Complete both tables and use the information in them to solve the problem. What mathematical concept is involved in Solution B?
Systems of equations

10-9 Dividing Polynomials

Dividing by a Monomial

Objective: Divide a polynomial by a monomial.

Rational expressions indicate division. To divide a polynomial by a monomial, divide each term by that monomial.

EXAMPLES Divide.

1. $\frac{6x^2 + 3x - 2}{3} = \frac{6x^2}{3} + \frac{3x}{3} - \frac{2}{3}$ Dividing each term by 3

$= 2x^2 + x - \frac{2}{3}$

2. $(x^3 + 10x^2 + 8x) \div 2x$

$\frac{x^3 + 10x^2 + 8x}{2x} = \frac{x^3}{2x} + \frac{10x^2}{2x} + \frac{8x}{2x}$ Dividing each term by $2x$

$= \frac{1}{2}x^2 + 5x + 4$

Try This Divide.

a. $\frac{4x^3 + 6x - 5}{2}$ **b.** $\frac{2x^3 + 6x^2 + 4x}{2x}$

a. $2x^3 + 3x - \frac{5}{2}$
b. $x^2 + 3x + 2$

Dividing by a Binomial

Objective: Divide a polynomial by a polynomial.

When the divisor is not a monomial, we can use long division.

EXAMPLE 3 Divide.

$(x^2 + 5x + 6) \div (x + 2)$

$$
\begin{array}{r l}
x & \leftarrow \text{Dividing first term by first term to get } x \\
x + 2 \overline{\big)\, x^2 + 5x + 6} & \\
x^2 + 2x & \leftarrow \text{Multiplying } x \text{ by divisor } x + 2 \\
\hline
3x & \leftarrow \text{Subtracting}
\end{array}
$$

10-9

FIRST FIVE MINUTES

1. $172 \div 13$
   13 remainder 3
2. $625 \div 25$
   25

Dividing by a Monomial

Remind students that a quotient of a polynomial and a monomial has two forms, both of which are correct. For example,

$\frac{x + y}{z}$

may also be written in the equivalent form

$\frac{x}{z} + \frac{y}{z}$

Point out that one form may be more useful in a particular situation.

Chalkboard Examples

1. Divide $8x^2 + 4x + 1$ by 2.
   $\frac{8x^2 + 4x + 1}{2}$
   $= \frac{8x^2}{2} + \frac{4x}{2} + \frac{1}{2}$
   $= 4x^2 + 2x + \frac{1}{2}$
2. Divide $4x^4 + 12x^2 + 8x$ by $4x$.
   $\frac{4x^4 + 12x^2 + 8x}{4x}$
   $= \frac{4x^4}{4x} + \frac{12x^2}{4x} + \frac{8x}{4x}$
   $= x^3 + 3x + 2$

Dividing by a Binomial

Point out the similarities between long division of polynomials and long division of numbers. Remind students that they can check their division by multiplying the divisor and the quotient, and adding the remainder, if any.

Key Question

- If both the divisor and the quotient are polynomials of degree 3, what is the degree of the dividend?
  6

Chalkboard Examples

1. Divide $x^2 + 3x + 2$ by $x + 1$.

$$\begin{array}{r} x + 2 \\ x + 1\overline{)x^2 + 3x + 2} \\ \underline{x^2 + x } \\ 2x + 2 \\ \underline{2x + 2} \\ 0 \end{array}$$

The quotient is $x + 2$.

2. Divide $x^2 + x + 1$ by $x + 1$.

$$\begin{array}{r} x \\ x + 1\overline{)x^2 + x + 1} \\ \underline{x^2 + x } \\ 1 \end{array}$$

The quotient is $x + \frac{1}{x + 1}$.

3. Divide $x^4 + x^2 + 1$ by $x + 1$.

$$\begin{array}{r} x^3 - x^2 + 2x - 2 \\ x + 1\overline{)x^4 + 0 + x^2 + 0 + 1} \\ \underline{x^4 + x^3 } \\ -x^3 + x^2 + 0 + 1 \\ \underline{-x^3 - x^2 } \\ 2x^2 + 0 + 1 \\ \underline{2x^2 + 2x } \\ -2x + 1 \\ \underline{-2x - 2} \\ 3 \end{array}$$

The quotient is $x^3 - x^2 + 2x - 2 + \frac{3}{x + 1}$.

LESSON QUIZ

1. Divide $\frac{9x^2 + 3x + 12}{3}$.
   $3x^2 + x + 4$
2. Divide $5x^4 + 20x^2 + 15x$ by $5x$.
   $x^3 + 4x + 3$
3. Divide $5x^2 - 2x - 3$ by $x - 1$.
   $5x + 3$

We now "bring down" the next term of the dividend, 6.

$$\begin{array}{rl} x + 3 & \leftarrow \text{Dividing first term by first term to get 3} \\ x + 2\overline{)x^2 + 5x + 6} & \\ \underline{x^2 + 2x } & \\ 3x + 6 & \\ \underline{3x + 6} & \leftarrow \text{Multiplying 3 by divisor } x + 2 \\ 0 & \leftarrow \text{Subtracting} \end{array}$$

The quotient is $x + 3$. To check, multiply the quotient by the divisor and add the remainder, if any, to see if you get the dividend.

$(x + 2)(x + 3) = x^2 + 5x + 6$. The division checks.

EXAMPLE 4 Divide.

$(x^2 + 2x - 12) \div (x - 3)$

$$\begin{array}{rl} x + 5 & \\ x - 3\overline{)x^2 + 2x - 12} & \\ \underline{x^2 - 3x } & \\ 5x - 12 & \\ \underline{5x - 15} & \\ 3 & \leftarrow \text{Remainder} \end{array}$$

Check:
$$\begin{aligned} (x - 3)(x + 5) + 3 &= x^2 + 2x - 15 + 3 \\ &= x^2 + 2x - 12 \end{aligned}$$

The answer can be written as quotient plus remainder over divisor.

$$\underbrace{x + 5}_{\text{Quotient}} + \frac{3 \leftarrow \text{Remainder}}{\underbrace{x - 3}_{\text{Divisor}}}$$

When there are missing terms, we may represent them with 0's.

EXAMPLE 5 Divide.

$(x^3 + 1) \div (x + 1)$

$$\begin{array}{rl} x^2 - x + 1 & \\ x + 1\overline{)x^3 + 0 \cdot x^2 + 0x + 1} & \text{Writing in the missing terms} \\ \underline{x^3 + x^2 } & \\ -x^2 + 0x & \\ \underline{-x^2 - x } & \\ x + 1 & \\ \underline{x + 1} & \end{array}$$

Try This Divide.

c. $x - 2\overline{)x^2 + 2x - 9}$ $x + 4 + \frac{-1}{x - 2}$ d. $(x^3 - 1) \div (x - 1)$ $x^2 + x + 1$

10-9 EXERCISES

A

Divide.

1. $\dfrac{24x^4 - 4x^3 + x^2 - 16}{8}$

2. $\dfrac{12a^4 - 3a^2 + a - 6}{6}$

3. $\dfrac{u - 2u^2 - u^5}{u}$

4. $\dfrac{50x^5 - 7x^4 + x^2}{x}$

5. $\dfrac{15t^3 + 24t^2 - 6t}{3t}$

6. $\dfrac{25t^3 + 15t^2 - 30t}{5t}$

7. $\dfrac{20x^6 - 20x^4 - 5x^2}{-5x^2}$

8. $\dfrac{24x^6 + 32x^5 - 8x^2}{-8x^2}$

9. $\dfrac{24x^5 - 40x^4 + 6x^3}{4x^3}$

10. $\dfrac{18x^6 - 27x^5 - 3x^3}{9x^3}$

11. $\dfrac{9r^2s^2 + 3r^2s - 6rs^2}{-3rs}$

12. $\dfrac{4x^4y - 8x^6y^2 + 12x^8y^6}{4x^4y}$

Divide.

13. $(x^2 + 4x + 4) \div (x + 2)$

14. $(x^2 - 6x + 9) \div (x - 3)$

15. $(x^2 - 10x - 25) \div (x - 5)$

16. $(x^2 + 8x - 16) \div (x + 4)$

17. $(x^2 + 4x - 14) \div (x + 6)$

18. $(x^2 + 5x - 9) \div (x - 2)$

19. $(x^2 - 9) \div (x + 3)$

20. $(x^2 - 25) \div (x + 5)$

21. $(x^5 + 1) \div (x + 1)$

22. $(x^5 - 1) \div (x - 1)$

23. $\dfrac{a^3 + 6a^2 + 12a + 8}{a + 2}$

24. $\dfrac{x^3 - 4x^2 + x + 6}{x - 2}$

25. $\dfrac{6x^3 + 11x^2 + 4x + 35}{2x + 5}$

26. $\dfrac{24a^3 + 2a^2 - 15}{3a - 2}$

27. $\dfrac{8x^3 - 22x^2 - 5x + 12}{4x + 3}$

28. $\dfrac{2x^3 - 9x^2 + 11x - 3}{2x - 3}$

29. $(x^6 - 13x^3 + 42) \div (x^3 - 7)$

30. $(x^6 + 5x^3 - 24) \div (x^3 - 3)$

31. $(x^4 - 16) \div (x - 2)$

32. $(x^4 - 81) \div (x - 3)$

33. $(t^3 - t^2 + t - 1) \div (t - 1)$

34. $(t^3 - t^2 + t - 1) \div (t + 1)$

B

Divide.

35. $(x^4 + 9x^2 + 20) \div (x^2 + 4)$ $x^2 + 5$

36. $(y^4 + a^2) \div (y + a)$ $y^3 - ay^2 + a^2y - a^3 + \frac{a^2(a^2 + 1)}{y + a}$

37. $(5a^3 + 8a^2 - 23a - 1) \div (5a^2 - 7a - 2)$ $a + 3 + \frac{5}{5a^2 - 7a - 2}$

38. $(15y^3 - 30y + 7 - 19y^2) \div (3y^2 - 2 - 5y)$ $5y + 2 + \frac{-10y + 11}{3y^2 - 5y - 2}$

Assignment Guide

Minimum: 1–34 e/o, MR

Regular: Day 1: 1–34 e/o
Day 2: 35–43, MR

Advanced: Day 1: 1–34 e/o
Day 2: 35–48, MR

ADDITIONAL ANSWERS

Exercises

1. $3x^4 - \frac{x^3}{2} + \frac{x^2}{8} - 2$
2. $2a^4 - \frac{a^2}{2} + \frac{a}{6} - 1$
3. $1 - 2u - u^4$
4. $50x^4 - 7x^3 + x$
5. $5t^2 + 8t - 2$
6. $5t^2 + 3t - 6$
7. $-4x^4 + 4x^2 + 1$
8. $-3x^4 - 4x^3 + 1$
9. $6x^2 - 10x + \frac{3}{2}$
10. $2x^3 - 3x^2 - \frac{1}{3}$
11. $-3rs - r + 2s$
12. $1 - 2x^2y + 3x^4y^5$
13. $x + 2$
14. $x - 3$
15. $x - 5 + \frac{-50}{x - 5}$
16. $x + 4 + \frac{-32}{x + 4}$
17. $x - 2 + \frac{-2}{x + 6}$
18. $x + 7 + \frac{5}{(x - 2)}$
19. $x - 3$
20. $x - 5$
21. $x^4 - x^3 + x^2 - x + 1$
22. $x^4 + x^3 + x^2 + x + 1$
23. $a^2 + 4a + 4$
24. $x^2 - 2x - 3$
25. $3x^2 - 2x + 7$
26. $8a^2 + 6a + 4 + \frac{-7}{3a - 2}$
27. $2x^2 - 7x + 4$
28. $x^2 - 3x + 1$
29. $x^3 - 6$
30. $x^3 + 8$
31. $x^3 + 2x^2 + 4x + 8$
32. $x^3 + 3x^2 + 9x + 27$
33. $t^2 + 1$
34. $t^2 - 2t + 3 + \frac{-4}{t + 1}$

41. $a^5 + a^4b + a^3b^2 + a^2b^3 + ab^4 + b^5$
42. $x^4 - x^3y + x^2y^2 - xy^3 + y^4$

Mixed Review

49. $-18(y - 1)$ or $18(y - 1)$
50. $\frac{(x + y)^2}{x^2y^2}$
51. $\frac{9}{14m}$
52. $\frac{-1(x + 10)}{(x + 2)(x - 2)}$
53. $\frac{-1(2x - 1)}{(x + 3)(x - 3)}$
54. $\frac{(5x + 1)}{(2x - 1)}$
55. $-1, 3$
56. 8
57. 6

39. $(6x^5 - 13x^3 + 5x + 3 - 4x^2 + 3x^4) \div (3x^3 - 2x - 1)$ $2x^2 + x - 3$
40. $(5x^7 - 3x^4 + 2x^2 - 10x + 2) \div (x^2 - x + 1)$ $5x^5 + 5x^4 - 8x^2 - 8x + 2$
41. $(a^6 - b^6) \div (a - b)$ 42. $(x^5 + y^5) \div (x + y)$
43. *Critical Thinking* What polynomial has a quotient of $3a^2 + ab - b$ with a remainder of a when divided by $2a^2 - b$? $6a^4 + 2a^3b - 5a^2b - ab^2 + b^2 + a$

Challenge

44. Divide $6a^{3h} + 13a^{2h} - 4a^h - 15$ by $2a^h + 3$. $3a^{2h} + 2a^h - 5$

If the remainder is 0 when one polynomial is divided by another, then the divisor is a factor of the dividend. Find the value(s) of c for which $x - 1$ is a factor of each polynomial.

45. $x^2 + 4x + c$ -5 46. $2x^2 + 3cx - 8$ 2 47. $c^2x^2 - 2cx + 1$ 1
48. One factor of $x^3 + 2x^2 - x - 2$ is $x + 2$. Find two other factors of this polynomial. $(x + 1)(x - 1)$

Mixed Review

Find the least common multiple (LCM). 49. $6(y - 1), 9 - 9y$

Add or subtract. Simplify. 50. $\frac{(x + y)}{x^2y} + \frac{(x + y)}{xy^2}$ 51. $\frac{4}{7m} + \frac{1}{14m}$

52. $\frac{2}{x + 2} - \frac{3}{x - 2}$ 53. $\frac{7}{x^2 - 9} - \frac{4}{2x - 6}$ 54. $\frac{(x - 3)}{2x - 1} - \frac{4(x + 1)}{1 - 2x}$

Solve. 55. $x - \frac{3}{x} = 2$ 56. $\frac{x - 3}{x + 2} = \frac{1}{2}$ 57. $\frac{x + 2}{4} - \frac{x - 3}{3} = 1$

THE RULE OF FALSE POSITION

Suppose you know that a number plus a seventh of the number is nineteen. How can you find the number? One way is to write a linear equation, $x + \frac{1}{7}x = 19$, and solve it for x. Another way is to use the *rule of false position.*

To use the rule of false position, choose any value for x. Then try it in the equation. Suppose $x = 7$. Then $x + \frac{1}{7}x = 8$, not 19. But you can use your false answer to find the true answer. The ratio of the true value of x is to 7 as 19 is to 8. So, the following proportion can be solved for x.

$$\frac{x}{7} = \frac{19}{8} \qquad x = \frac{7 \cdot 19}{8} \qquad x = 16\frac{5}{8}$$

The solution to $x + \frac{1}{7}x = 19$ is $16\frac{5}{8}$.

The rule of false position only works for linear equations with no constant terms on the left.

10-10 Complex Rational Expressions

Objective: Simplify complex rational expressions.

A **complex rational expression** has a rational expression in its numerator or denominator or both. Here are some examples.

$$\frac{1+\frac{2}{x}}{3} \qquad \frac{\frac{x+y}{2}}{\frac{2x}{x+1}} \qquad \frac{\frac{1}{3}+\frac{1}{5}}{\frac{2}{x}-\frac{x}{y}}$$

To simplify a complex rational expression, multiply the numerator and denominator by an expression equivalent to 1. The expression selected should be the least common multiple of any denominators found in the numerator or denominator of the complex rational expression.

EXAMPLE 1 Simplify.

$$\frac{\frac{3}{4}+\frac{x}{2}}{\frac{x}{8}} = \frac{\frac{3}{4}+\frac{x}{2}}{\frac{x}{8}}\cdot\frac{8}{8}$$ The LCM of the denominators is 8.

$$= \frac{\frac{3}{4}\cdot 8+\frac{x}{2}\cdot 8}{\frac{x}{8}\cdot 8}$$ Using the distributive property

$$= \frac{6+4x}{x}$$ Simplifying

EXAMPLE 2 Simplify.

$$\frac{1-\frac{1}{x}}{1-\frac{1}{x^2}} = \frac{1-\frac{1}{x}}{1-\frac{1}{x^2}}\cdot\frac{x^2}{x^2}$$ The LCM of x and x^2 is x^2.

$$= \frac{x^2(1)-x^2\left(\frac{1}{x}\right)}{x^2(1)-x^2\left(\frac{1}{x^2}\right)}$$ Using the distributive property

$$= \frac{x^2-x}{x^2-1}$$

$$= \frac{x(x-1)}{(x+1)(x-1)}$$ Factoring

$$= \frac{x}{x+1}$$ Simplifying

10-10

FIRST FIVE MINUTES

1. Divide $6x^3 + 12x^2 + 18x$ by $3x$.
   $2x^2 + 4x + 6$
2. Divide $4x^2 + 9x + 2$ by $x + 2$.

$$\begin{array}{r} 4x + 1 \\ x+2\overline{)4x^2 + 9x + 2} \\ \underline{4x^2 + 8x} \\ x + 2 \\ \underline{x + 2} \\ 0 \end{array}$$

The quotient is $4x + 1$.

Point out that all of these could be worked as division of polynomials, since the fraction bar means "divided by."

Chalkboard Examples

1. Simplify.

$$\frac{\frac{5}{3}+\frac{3}{4}}{\frac{1}{2}+\frac{2}{3}}$$

$$\frac{\frac{5}{3}+\frac{3}{4}}{\frac{1}{2}+\frac{2}{3}}\cdot\frac{12}{12} = \frac{20+9}{6+8} = \frac{29}{14}$$

2. Simplify.

$$\frac{2+\frac{1}{a}}{2+\frac{3}{a}}$$

$$\frac{2+\frac{1}{a}}{2+\frac{3}{a}}\cdot\frac{a}{a}$$

$$\frac{2a+1}{2a+3}$$

LESSON QUIZ

Simplify.

1. $\dfrac{\frac{1}{3}+\frac{3}{5}}{\frac{4}{6}}$

   $\frac{7}{5}$

2. $\dfrac{\frac{3}{x}+\frac{2}{x^2}}{\frac{1}{x}+\frac{5}{x^2}}$

   $\frac{3x+2}{x+5}$

Assignment Guide
Minimum: 1–24 e/o, MR

Regular: 1–27 e/o, 28, MR

Advanced: 1–27 m3, 28–30, MR

ADDITIONAL ANSWERS
Exercises

1. $\frac{20}{21}$
2. $\frac{22}{5}$
3. $\frac{4(x + 2)}{3x}$
4. $\frac{12 + 2x}{5}$
5. $\frac{25}{4}$
6. $\frac{-65}{18}$
7. $\frac{1 + 3x}{1 - 5x}$
8. $\frac{9}{2}$
9. $\frac{28}{y + 8}$
10. $\frac{c + 3d}{4d + c}$
11. $\frac{9 + 3s^2}{4s^2}$
12. $\frac{5}{3y^2}$
13. $\frac{2x + 1}{x}$
14. $\frac{1}{y + x}$
15. $\frac{a - b}{2}$
16. $\frac{x + y}{x}$
17. $x - y$
18. $-\frac{1}{2a}$
19. $\frac{a}{b(2a + 1)}$
20. $\frac{m(m + n)}{(n + 1)(m - n)}$
21. $\frac{st(pr + q^2)}{qr(rt + s^2)}$
22. $\frac{de(ac + b^2)}{bc(ce + d^2)}$
23. $\frac{4f + 3fg + g}{2(fg^2 + 2fg + 3f + 2g + 3)}$
24. $\frac{x(x^2 + 2x + 2)}{x^3 + x + 2}$

Try This Simplify.

a. $\dfrac{\frac{x}{2} + \frac{x}{3}}{\frac{1}{2}}$ $\frac{5x}{3}$ **b.** $\dfrac{1 + \frac{1}{x}}{1 - \frac{1}{x^2}}$ $\frac{x}{x - 1}$

10-10 EXERCISES

A

Simplify.

1. $\dfrac{\frac{2}{7} + \frac{3}{7}}{\frac{3}{4}}$
2. $\dfrac{3 + \frac{5}{2}}{\frac{5}{4}}$
3. $\dfrac{1 + \frac{2}{x}}{\frac{3}{4}}$
4. $\dfrac{3 + \frac{x}{2}}{\frac{5}{4}}$
5. $\dfrac{1 + \frac{9}{16}}{1 - \frac{3}{4}}$
6. $\dfrac{\frac{5}{27} - 5}{\frac{1}{3} + 1}$
7. $\dfrac{\frac{1}{x} + 3}{\frac{1}{x} - 5}$
8. $\dfrac{\frac{3}{a}}{\frac{1}{a} - \frac{1}{3a}}$
9. $\dfrac{\frac{7}{y}}{\frac{1}{4} + \frac{2}{y}}$
10. $\dfrac{\frac{c}{d} + 3}{4 + \frac{c}{d}}$
11. $\dfrac{\frac{3}{s} + s}{\frac{s}{3} + s}$
12. $\dfrac{\frac{2}{y} + \frac{1}{2y}}{y + \frac{y}{2}}$
13. $\dfrac{4 - \frac{1}{x^2}}{2 - \frac{1}{x}}$
14. $\dfrac{\frac{1}{xy}}{\frac{1}{x} + \frac{1}{y}}$
15. $\dfrac{\frac{2}{a + b}}{\frac{4}{a^2 - b^2}}$
16. $\dfrac{\frac{x}{x - y}}{\frac{x^2}{x^2 - y^2}}$
17. $\dfrac{\frac{x}{y} - \frac{y}{x}}{\frac{1}{y} + \frac{1}{x}}$
18. $\dfrac{\frac{1}{a} - \frac{1}{2}}{a - 2}$
19. $\dfrac{\frac{a}{(a + b)(2a + 1)}}{\frac{b}{(a + b)}}$
20. $\dfrac{\frac{m}{(m - n)(m + n)}}{\frac{n + 1}{(m + n)^2}}$
21. $\dfrac{\frac{p}{q} + \frac{q}{r}}{\frac{r}{s} + \frac{s}{t}}$
22. $\dfrac{\frac{a}{b} + \frac{b}{c}}{\frac{c}{d} + \frac{d}{e}}$
23. $\dfrac{\frac{g}{2f} + \frac{g + 2}{f + 1}}{\frac{g^2}{f + 1} + \frac{2g + 3}{f}}$
24. $\dfrac{\frac{x + 1}{x + 2} + \frac{1}{x}}{\frac{x}{x + 2} + \frac{1}{x^2}}$

B

Simplify.

25. $\dfrac{1 + \dfrac{a}{b-a}}{\dfrac{a}{a+b} - 1}$ $\frac{a+b}{a-b}$

26. $\dfrac{\dfrac{a}{b} + \dfrac{c}{d}}{\dfrac{b}{a} + \dfrac{d}{c}}$ $\frac{ac}{bd}$

27. $\dfrac{\dfrac{a}{b} - \dfrac{c}{d}}{\dfrac{b}{a} - \dfrac{d}{c}}$ $\frac{-ac}{bd}$

28. *Critical Thinking* What values of a are unacceptable because they would make the denominator 0 in the fraction $\dfrac{\dfrac{2a-4}{a+1}}{\dfrac{a+2}{a-2}}$? $-1, \pm 2$

Challenge

Solve.

29. $\dfrac{\dfrac{2a+3}{a+1}}{\dfrac{a-2}{a+1}} = 12$ $\frac{27}{10}$

30. $\dfrac{\dfrac{x+1}{x-1} + 1}{\dfrac{x+1}{x-1} - 1} = 10$ 10

Mixed Review

Calculate and simplify. **31.** $\dfrac{4x+5}{x+5} - \dfrac{x+11}{x+5}$ **32.** $\dfrac{5}{y+2} + \dfrac{5}{y-2}$

33. $\dfrac{m^2}{m-5} + \dfrac{25}{5-m}$ **34.** $\dfrac{2}{x+1} + \dfrac{5}{2x}$ **35.** $\dfrac{x-1}{x} - \dfrac{3x+5}{2x}$

Solve. **36.** $\dfrac{5}{x+1} = \dfrac{4}{x-1}$ **37.** $\dfrac{x}{4} - \dfrac{x}{6} = \dfrac{1}{4}$ **38.** $\dfrac{x-2}{3x} = \dfrac{1}{4}$

39. Find two numbers whose sum is -13 and whose difference is 21.

BIOGRAPHICAL NOTE: MARY SOMERVILLE

In spite of the limitations that society placed on women during the 18th century, Mary Somerville (born in Scotland in 1780) was recognized as one of the prominent scholars and mathematicians of her time. She was one of the first women elected to the Royal Astronomical Society, and by the end of her long life, she was widely recognized for her writing in the fields of mathematics and science.

Although at the age of nine Mary had not learned to either read or write, she later blossomed into a young woman with an incredible thirst for knowledge. At thirteen, she discovered the mysterious sounding word *algebra* in a magazine, and was determined to find out more about this strange kind of arithmetic. That was the beginning of her lifelong passion for the study of mathematics. Even as an elderly woman of 92, she would rise early every morning, and for four or five hours she would read books on higher algebra.

Mixed Review

31. $\frac{3(x-2)}{(x+5)}$
32. $\frac{10y}{(y+2)(y-2)}$
33. $(m+5)$
34. $\frac{(9x+5)}{2x(x+1)}$
35. $\frac{-1(x+7)}{2x}$
36. 9
37. 3
38. 8
39. $-17, 4$

10-11

FIRST FIVE MINUTES

1. Simplify.

$$\frac{2 + \frac{3}{x}}{4 + \frac{5}{x}}$$

$$\frac{2 + \frac{3}{x}}{4 + \frac{5}{x}} \cdot \frac{x}{x} = \frac{2x + 3}{4x + 5}$$

2. Simplify.

$$\frac{\frac{a + b}{c}}{\frac{a + b}{c^2}}$$

$$\frac{\frac{a + b}{c}}{\frac{a + b}{c^2}} \cdot \frac{c^2}{c^2} = \frac{(a + b)c}{a + b} = c$$

This section serves as an excellent introduction to the logic used in geometry.

Key Questions

- What property guarantees that $(a + b)c = ac + bc$? Distributive
- What property guarantees that $(a + b)c = c(a + b)$? Commutative

Chalkboard Example

1. Complete the proof of the following theorem by supplying the reasons. For any numbers a, b, and any nonzero number c,

$$\frac{a}{c} + \frac{b}{c} = \frac{a + b}{c}.$$

1. $\frac{a}{c} + \frac{b}{c} = a \cdot \frac{1}{c} + b \cdot \frac{1}{c}$	Div. thm.
2. $= (a + b)\frac{1}{c}$	Dist. prop.
3. $= \frac{a + b}{c}$	Div. thm.
4. $\frac{a}{c} + \frac{b}{c} = \frac{a + b}{c}$	Trans. prop.

10-11 Proofs

(Optional)

Objective: Prove theorems involving multiplication and division.

In our work with division of rational numbers and division of rational expressions, we used the division rule of multiplying by the reciprocal of the divisor. We can prove this rule.

Theorem

The Division Theorem

For any number a and any nonzero number b,

$$\frac{a}{b} = a \cdot \frac{1}{b}$$

EXAMPLE 1

To prove this theorem we will use the definition of division. That is, $\frac{a}{b} = c$ if $c \cdot b = a$. Thus to show that $a \cdot \frac{1}{b}$ is the quotient $\frac{a}{b}$, we will need to show that when b is multiplied by $a \cdot \frac{1}{b}$ the result is a.

Proof

1. $\left(a \cdot \frac{1}{b}\right) \cdot b = a \cdot \left(\frac{1}{b} \cdot b\right)$	1. Associative property of multiplication
2. $= a \cdot (1)$	2. Definition of reciprocal
3. $= a$	3. Multiplicative identity
4. $\left(a \cdot \frac{1}{b}\right) \cdot b = a$	4. Transitive property of equality

Thus, by the definition of division, $a \cdot \frac{1}{b} = \frac{a}{b}$.

Another theorem related to reciprocals concerns the reciprocal of a product.

Theorem

The Reciprocal Theorem

For any rational numbers a and b,

$$\frac{1}{ab} = \frac{1}{a} \cdot \frac{1}{b}$$

(The reciprocal of the products is the product of the reciprocal.)

EXAMPLE 2

To prove this theorem we will use the commutative and associative properties to show that $(ab) \cdot \left(\frac{1}{a} \cdot \frac{1}{b}\right)$ is 1.

Proof

1. $ab\left(\frac{1}{a} \cdot \frac{1}{b}\right) = \left(ab \cdot \frac{1}{a}\right) \cdot \frac{1}{b}$	1. Associative property of multiplication
2. $= \left(a \cdot \frac{1}{a} \cdot b\right) \cdot \frac{1}{b}$	2. Commutative property of multiplication
3. $= \left(a \cdot \frac{1}{a}\right)\left(b \cdot \frac{1}{b}\right)$	3. Associative property of multiplication
4. $= 1 \cdot 1$	4. Definition of reciprocal
5. $= 1$	5. Multiplicative identity
6. $ab\left(\frac{1}{a} \cdot \frac{1}{b}\right) = 1$	6. Transitive property of equality

Thus $\frac{1}{ab} = \frac{1}{a} \cdot \frac{1}{b}$.

Theorem

For any rational numbers a, c, and any nonzero rational numbers b, d,

$$\frac{a}{b} \cdot \frac{c}{d} = \frac{ac}{bd}$$

Try This

a. Complete the following proof of the theorem presented above.

Proof

1. $\frac{a}{b} = a \cdot \frac{1}{b}$ and $\frac{c}{d} = c \cdot \frac{1}{d}$	1. Division theorem
2. $\frac{a}{b} \cdot \frac{c}{d} = \left(a \cdot \frac{1}{b}\right)\left(c \cdot \frac{1}{d}\right)$	2. Substituting $a \cdot \frac{1}{b}$ for $\frac{a}{b}$ and $c \cdot \frac{1}{d}$ for $\frac{c}{d}$
3. $= (a \cdot c)\left(\frac{1}{b} \cdot \frac{1}{d}\right)$	3. Associative and commutative properties
4. $= ac\left(\frac{1}{bd}\right)$	4. Reciprocal theorem
5. $= \frac{ac}{bd}$	5. Division theorem
6. $\frac{a}{b} \cdot \frac{c}{d} = \frac{ac}{bd}$	6. Transitive property of equality

b. The subtraction theorem states that for any real numbers a and b, $a - b = a + (-b)$. Write a proof of the subtraction theorem.

LESSON QUIZ

1. What property guarantees that $(a + b) + c = a + (b + c)$? Associative
2. What property guarantees that $(a + b) + c = c + (a + b)$? Commutative

Assignment Guide

Minimum: Omit

Regular: Omit

Advanced: 1–4, MR

ADDITIONAL ANSWERS

Try This

b.

1. $[a + (-b)] + b = a + [(-b) + b]$	Assoc. prop.
2. $= a + 0$	Prop. of add. inv.
3. $= a$	Identity prop.
4. $[a + (-b)] + b = a$	Trans. prop.

Thus, by the definition of subtraction, $a + (-b) = a - b$.

Exercises

2.

1. $\frac{a}{c} = a \cdot \frac{1}{c}$ and $\frac{b}{c} = b \cdot \frac{1}{c}$	Div. thm.
2. $\frac{a}{c} - \frac{b}{c} = a \cdot \frac{1}{c} - b \cdot \frac{1}{c}$	Subst.
3. $= (a - b)\frac{1}{c}$	Dist.
4. $= \frac{a - b}{c}$	Div. thm.
5. $\frac{a}{c} - \frac{b}{c} = \frac{a - b}{c}$	Trans. prop.

3, 4. See Teacher's Answer Section.

Mixed Review

5. $32w^5$
6. $\frac{ab}{c}$
7. y^{81}
8. $81m^{20}$
9. $(9c + 4)(9c - 4)$
10. $5(x + 3)(x - 2)$
11. $(2x + 5)(x - 1)$
12. $(x + 4)(6x + 1)$
13. $(3x + 1)(2x + 3)$
14. $(2x + 3)(5x + 4)$
15. $7, -7$
16. $2, -2$
17. 5
18. $(2, 2)$
19. $(-1, 1)$

10-11 EXERCISES

A

1. Complete the proof of the following theorem by supplying the reasons. For any numbers a, b, and any non-zero number c,

$$\frac{a}{c} + \frac{b}{c} = \frac{a + b}{c}.$$

(a) $\frac{a}{c} = a \cdot \frac{1}{c}$ and $\frac{b}{c} = b \cdot \frac{1}{c}$	(a) Division theorem
(b) $\frac{a}{c} + \frac{b}{c} = a \cdot \frac{1}{c} + b \cdot \frac{1}{c}$	(b) Substituting $a \cdot \frac{1}{c}$ for $\frac{a}{c}$ and $b \cdot \frac{1}{c}$ for $\frac{b}{c}$
(c) $= (a + b)\frac{1}{c}$	(c) Distributive property
(d) $= \frac{a + b}{c}$	(d) Division theorem
(e) $\frac{a}{c} + \frac{b}{c} = \frac{a + b}{c}$	(e) Transitive property of equality

2. Write a proof of the following theorem. For any numbers a, b, and any nonzero number c,

$$\frac{a}{c} - \frac{b}{c} = \frac{a - b}{c}$$

(Hint: Use Exercise 1 as a model for your proof.)

3. Prove that if $\frac{a}{b}$ is any nonzero rational number, then its reciprocal is $\frac{b}{a}$. (Hint: Show that $\frac{b}{a}$ satisfies the definition of reciprocal.)

4. Prove the property of proportion:

$$\text{if } \frac{a}{b} = \frac{c}{d}, \text{ then } ad = bc.$$

Mixed Review

Simplify. **5.** $(2w)^5$ **6.** $\frac{a^2b^3}{ab^2c}$ **7.** $(y^9)^9$ **8.** $(-3m^5)^4$

Factor. **9.** $81c^2 - 16$ **10.** $5x^2 + 5x - 30$ **11.** $2x^2 + 3x - 5$
12. $6x^2 + 25x + 4$ **13.** $6x^2 + 11x + 3$ **14.** $10x^2 + 23x + 12$

Solve. **15.** $\frac{x}{7} - \frac{7}{x} = 0$ **16.** $x - \frac{4}{x} = 0$ **17.** $\frac{a + 3}{2a + 2} = \frac{2}{3}$

18. $3x + y = 8$
$5x - y = 8$

19. $2x + 5y = 3$
$5x - 2y = -7$

10-12 Problem Solving: Strategies

Work Backward

Objective: Solve problems using the strategy *Work Backward* and other strategies.

PROBLEM-SOLVING GUIDELINES
■ UNDERSTAND the problem
■ Develop and carry out a PLAN
■ Find the ANSWER and CHECK

Sometimes a problem describes a sequence of actions involving numbers, gives the result, and asks for the original number. A problem of this type can be solved using a strategy called Work Backward.

EXAMPLE

Ken had a package of graph paper for math class that he shared with 3 friends. He gave one quarter of the pack to Adele. Terry got one third of what was left. Then Phyllis took one sixth of the remainder. Ken had 30 sheets left to himself. How many sheets did he have to start?

To solve this problem, start with the number of sheets Ken had left to himself and *work backward* using the inverse operations.

Data in the Story	Work Backward
Ken started with some number of sheets of graph paper. ↓	Ken started with 72 sheets.
Adele took $\frac{1}{4}$. ↓	↑ If Adele took $\frac{1}{4}$ of the pack, then the 54 sheets left must be $\frac{3}{4}$ of what was there. If $\frac{3}{4}x = 54$, then $x = 72$.
Terry took $\frac{1}{3}$ of what was left. ↓	↑ If Terry took $\frac{1}{3}$ of what was left, then the 36 sheets left must be $\frac{2}{3}$ of what was there. If $\frac{2}{3}x = 36$, then $x = 54$.
Phyllis took $\frac{1}{6}$ of the remainder. ↓	↑ If $\frac{5}{6}x = 30$ then $x = 36$. There were 36 sheets before Phyllis took hers.
Ken had 30 sheets left. →	↑ If Phyllis took $\frac{1}{6}$ of the remaining sheets, then 30 must be $\frac{5}{6}$ of the amount.

Ken had a total of 72 sheets of graph paper to start.

10-12

FIRST FIVE MINUTES

1. Four consecutive numbers add up to 66. What are they?
   15, 16, 17, 18
   (Guess, Check, Revise or Write an Equation)
2. Find A and B if
   $$\frac{3x + 1}{x(x + 1)} = \frac{A}{x} + \frac{B}{x + 1}$$
   $A = 1, B = 2$
   (Guess, Check, Revise)

Work Backward

Problems that involve a series of events can often be difficult to solve using an equation. The strategy *Work Backward* is ideal for solving this kind of problem. Note that listing the steps, as in the example, is a useful part of the strategy.

In the example, the arrows indicate the order in which the problem is solved. First the data in the problem is listed in the order it was given. In a column opposite, working *from the bottom up,* the number of sheets of paper left at each step is worked out.

Key Question

- What other strategy might you use to solve the example?
  Guess, check, revise

Chalkboard Example

1. Dolores, Chip, Serena, and Tony are in training. One Saturday, Dolores biked 4 times as far as Chip ran, Serena swam one twelfth as far as Dolores biked, and Tony rode his horse 6 times as far as Serena swam. If Tony rode 18 miles, how far did Chip run?
   Work backward. Serena swam one sixth as far as Tony rode, or 3 miles. Dolores biked 12 times as far as Serena swam, or 36 miles. Chip ran one fourth as far as Dolores biked, or 9 miles.

Hints for Problems

1. Try the strategy *Work Backward.*
2. Draw a diagram of the swimming pool. Imagine it filled 2 ft from the top.
3. Work backward from the 4th turnpike, retracing Ramon's steps.
4. Try filling the 9-qt bucket first and pouring it into the other.
5. Write an equation and find a common denominator.
6. Make a table to record the number of cannonballs on each layer. How many layers will there be?

ANSWERS

1. Together they found 44 new stores. They did not get the bonus.
2. It will cost $90 to fill the swimming pool to a line 2 ft from the top.
3. Before entering the first turnpike, Ramon had $22.50.
4. Fill the 9-qt pail; pour into 4-qt pail, leaving 5 qt. Empty 4-qt pail and fill from large pail, leaving 1 qt in large pail. Empty 4-qt pail and transfer 1 qt to smaller pail. Fill the 9-qt pail and pour into smaller pail. It will take 3 qt to fill the smaller pail, leaving 6 qt in the large pail.
5. The number is 42.
6. 385 cannonballs were used to build the monument.

Problem-Solving Strategies		
Draw a Diagram	Guess, Check, Revise	Write an Equation
Make an Organized List	Use Logical Reasoning	Make a Table
Look for a Pattern	Simplify the Problem	Work Backward

10-12 PROBLEMS

Solve using one or more of the strategies.

1. Four salespeople were sent into a particular region to find new stores to carry their product. If, together, they found 50 new stores to carry their product, they would each get a $500 bonus. Neil found twice as many stores as Gus. Gus found 4 fewer stores than Salvatore, and Salvatore found 4 more than Bonnie. Bonnie found 8 stores. Did each salesperson get the $500 bonus?
2. A rectangular swimming pool is 50 ft wide, 100 ft long, and 10 ft deep. The pool will be filled to a line 2 ft from the top. The water company charges $2.25/1000 ft^3. How much does it cost to fill this pool?
3. Ramon was going to visit his girlfriend in a distant city. He had to travel on four different turnpikes to get there. He had to pay 50¢ to enter each turnpike and 50¢ to exit. On each turnpike, he stopped at one store for a snack and spent $\frac{1}{2}$ of the money he had after he entered that turnpike. After paying 50¢ to leave the last turnpike, Ramon was out of money. How much did he start with before entering the first turnpike?
4. You have two pails, one that will hold 4 qt and one that will hold 9 qt. There are no markings on either pail to indicate smaller quantities. How can you measure out 6 qt of water using these two pails? (Assume there is an unlimited supply of water.)
5. If a certain number, two thirds of it, half of it, and a seventh of it are added together, the result is 97. What is the number?*
6. ***Write a convincing argument*** Solve the problem below. Then write an argument that would convince a classmate that your solution is correct.

   An architect was hired to build a monument to a Civil War battle. The structure was a pyramid made out of cannonballs. The base was made of 100 cannonballs in the shape of a square, with 10 cannonballs on a side; the row on top of the base had 81 cannonballs with 9 on a side; and so on. How many cannonballs were used to build the monument?

*This problem appears in the Rhind Papyrus, which is probably the oldest mathematical book known, written around 1650 B.C. in Egypt.

Chapter 10 Summary and Review

10-1

A rational expression is in simplest form when the only common factor of the numerator and denominator is 1 or −1. To simplify a rational expression, factor the numerator and the denominator, and find common factors that simplify to 1.

Simplify.

1. $\frac{3x+9}{3x}$
2. $\frac{6y^2+3y}{3y^2+6y}$
3. $\frac{3x-3}{3x+6}$
4. $\frac{3c+5d}{25d^2-9c^2}$

10-2

To multiply two rational expressions, multiply the numerators and multiply the denominators.

Multiply. Simplify the product.

5. $\frac{9y^2}{5y^2} \cdot \frac{(y-3)}{3}$
6. $\frac{2x}{x+1} \cdot \frac{x+1}{4x}$
7. $\frac{7(m-2)}{5m} \cdot \frac{4m^2}{m-2}$

10-3

To divide rational expressions, multiply the first expression by the reciprocal of the divisor.

Divide and simplify.

8. $\frac{3x+3}{3} \div \frac{x+1}{6}$
9. $\frac{y+2}{y-3} \div \frac{y+2}{y+1}$
10. $\frac{y+3}{y^2-9} \div \frac{y-3}{y^2-5y+6}$
11. $\frac{b-2}{b^2+b} \div \frac{b^2-4}{b+1}$
12. $\frac{4x-6}{5} \div \frac{6x-9}{25}$
13. $\frac{x^2-y^2}{xy^2} \div \frac{xy+y^2}{x}$

10-4, 10-5

To add or subtract rational expressions, first determine the least common denominator and if necessary rewrite each expression as an equivalent expression with the LCD. Add or subtract the numerators, and write the sum or difference over the denominator.

Add or subtract. Simplify.

14. $\frac{3x^2+2x-5}{5x+1} + \frac{2x^2-x+6}{5x+1}$
15. $\frac{5b}{2+b} - \frac{b-3}{2+b}$
16. $\frac{3a}{3a} + \frac{-1}{a}$
17. $\frac{2a}{a+1} + \frac{4a}{a^2-1}$
18. $\frac{3}{3x-9} + \frac{x-2}{3-x}$
19. $\frac{3x-1}{2x} - \frac{x-1}{x}$
20. $\frac{15}{b^2-4} - \frac{7}{b-2}$
21. $\frac{1}{x^2-25} - \frac{x-5}{x^2-4x-5}$

ANSWERS

1. $\frac{x+3}{x}$
2. $\frac{2y+1}{y+2}$
3. $\frac{x-1}{x+2}$
4. $\frac{1}{5d-3c}$
5. $\frac{3(y-3)}{5}$
6. $\frac{1}{2}$
7. $\frac{28m}{5}$
8. 6
9. $\frac{y+1}{y-3}$
10. $\frac{y-2}{y-3}$
11. $\frac{1}{b(b+2)}$
12. $\frac{10}{3}$
13. $\frac{x-y}{y^3}$
14. $\frac{5x^2+x+1}{5x+1}$
15. $\frac{4b+3}{2+b}$
16. $\frac{a-1}{a}$
17. $\frac{2a}{a-1}$
18. −1
19. $\frac{x+1}{2x}$
20. $\frac{-7b+1}{(b+2)(b-2)}$
21. $\frac{-x^2+x+26}{(x-5)(x+5)(x+1)}$

22. 8
23. $(-5, 3)$
24. 3
25. $(-1, -5)$
26. $(5, 2)$
27. $5\frac{1}{7}$ hours
28. 240 km/h, 280 km/h
29. 40 liters of each
30. $4y^3 + \frac{8}{3}y - 1$
31. $2x - 5$
32. $\frac{x}{1 - x}$
33. $\frac{y(xy + 3)}{xy^2 - 2}$

10-6

To solve an equation with rational expressions, first multiply both sides of the equation by the LCM of all the denominators.

Solve.

22. $\frac{3}{y} - \frac{1}{4} = \frac{1}{y}$

23. $\frac{15}{x} - \frac{15}{x + 2} = 2$

24. $\frac{4x}{3} - \frac{2x - 1}{5} = \frac{x + 3}{2}$

25. $\frac{5}{x} + x = -6$

26. $\frac{x}{x - 1} - \frac{2}{1 - x^2} = \frac{8}{x + 1}$

10-7

If a job requires n hours, then $\frac{1}{n}$ of the job can be done in 1 hour. You can use this principle to write an equation to solve work problems.

27. In checking records a contractor finds that crew A can pave a certain length of highway in 9 hours. Crew B can do the same job in 12 hours. How long would it take if both crews worked together?

The formula $d = r \cdot t$ or $t = \frac{d}{r}$ can be used to make a table and write an equation for solving motion problems.

28. A lab is testing two high speed trains. One train travels 40 km/h faster than the other train. While one train travels 70 km, the other travels 60 km. Find their speeds.

10-8

29. Solution A is 30% alcohol and solution B is 60% alcohol. How much of each is needed to make 80 liters of a solution that is 45% alcohol?

10-9

To divide a polynomial by a monomial, divide each term by that monomial. To divide a polynomial by another polynomial, use the long division method.

Divide.

30. $\frac{12y^3 + 8y - 3}{3}$

31. $(2x^2 + 3x - 20) \div (x + 4)$

10-10

To simplify a complex rational expression, multiply both the numerator and the denominator by the LCM of all denominators in the complex expression.

Simplify.

32. $\frac{\frac{1}{x} + 1}{\frac{1}{x^2} - 1}$

33. $\frac{x + \frac{3}{y}}{x - \frac{2}{y^2}}$

Chapter 10 Test

Simplify.

1. $\frac{5y + 15}{10}$
2. $\frac{14y^2 + 7y}{49y^2 + 14y}$
3. $\frac{4x^2 - 8xy + 4y^2}{3x - 3y}$

Multiply. Simplify the product.

4. $\frac{2x + 3y}{5} \cdot \frac{10}{4x + 6y}$
5. $\frac{25 - x^2}{12} \cdot \frac{6}{5 - x}$
6. $\frac{x^2 + x}{x^2} \cdot \frac{3x - 3}{x^2 - 1}$

Divide and simplify.

7. $\frac{4x - 6}{5} \div \frac{6x - 9}{25}$
8. $\frac{2x + x^2}{4x - 5} \div \frac{4x^2 + 2x^3}{16x - 20}$

Add or subtract. Simplify.

9. $\frac{16 + x}{x^3} + \frac{7 - 4x}{x^3}$
10. $\frac{5 - t}{t^2 + 1} - \frac{t - 3}{t^2 + 1}$
11. $\frac{x - 5}{x^2 - 1} + \frac{5}{x^2 - 1}$

Add or subtract. Simplify.

12. $\frac{x - 4}{x - 3} + \frac{x - 1}{3 - x}$
13. $\frac{5}{t - 1} + \frac{3}{t}$
14. $\frac{1}{x^2 - 16} - \frac{x + 4}{x^2 - 3x - 4}$
15. $\frac{6}{9 - a^2} - \frac{3}{12 + 4a}$
16. $\frac{4}{x^2 - 1} - \frac{2}{x^2 - 2x + 1}$
17. $\frac{3}{2a + 18} + \frac{27}{a^2 - 81}$

Solve.

18. $\frac{7}{y} - \frac{1}{3} = \frac{1}{4}$
19. $\frac{15}{x} - \frac{15}{x - 2} = -2$
20. Solution A is 25% acid and solution B is 40% acid. How much of each is needed to make 60 liters of a solution that is 30% acid?
21. Mrs. Crowley has a stack of letters to be typed. If she can type all of the letters in 6 hours and Mr. Crowley can type all of the letters in 9 hours, how long will it take them if they work together?

Divide.

22. $(12x^4 + 9x^3 - 15x^2) \div 3x^2$
23. $\frac{6x^3 - 8x^2 - 14x + 13}{3x + 2}$

Simplify.

24. $\dfrac{\frac{1}{14y} - \frac{1}{2y^2}}{\frac{1}{7} - \frac{6}{7y} - \frac{1}{y^2}}$
25. $\dfrac{25 - \frac{9}{x^2}}{5 + \frac{3}{x}}$

ANSWERS

1. $\frac{y + 3}{2}$
2. $\frac{2y + 1}{7y + 2}$
3. $\frac{4(x - y)}{3}$
4. 1
5. $\frac{5 + x}{2}$
6. $\frac{3}{x}$
7. $\frac{10}{3}$
8. $\frac{2}{x}$
9. $\frac{23 - 3x}{x^3}$
10. $\frac{8 - 2t}{t^2 + 1}$
11. $\frac{x}{x^2 - 1}$
12. $\frac{-3}{x - 3}$
13. $\frac{8t - 3}{t(t - 1)}$
14. $\frac{-x^2 - 7x - 15}{(x - 4)(x + 4)(x + 1)}$
15. $\frac{3(5 + a)}{4(3 - a)(3 + a)}$
16. $\frac{2(x - 3)}{(x + 1)(x - 1)^2}$
17. $\frac{3}{2(a - 9)}$
18. 12
19. 5, −3
20. 40 liters of A; 20 liters of B
21. $3\frac{3}{5}$ hours
22. $4x^2 + 3x - 5$
23. $2x^2 - 4x - 2 + \frac{17}{3x + 2}$
24. $\frac{1}{2(y + 1)}$
25. $\frac{5x - 3}{x}$

Test Item Analysis

Item	Lesson
1–3	10-1
4–6	10-2
7, 8	10-3
9–11	10-4
12–17	10-5
18, 19	10-6
20	10-8
21	10-7
22, 23	10-9
24, 25	10-10

CHAPTER **11**

Radical Expressions and Equations

Chapter Overview

This chapter begins with a discussion of real numbers. The density property is then expanded to include real numbers. Techniques of manipulating numeric and algebraic radical expressions are then covered. The major emphasis is on square roots, to provide a sound background for solving quadratic equations in Chapter 13. Two bonus topics, however, cover cube roots and higher roots along with rational exponents. Two useful applications of radicals, the Pythagorean theorem and the distance formula (a bonus topic), give geometric meaning to irrational square roots.

Problems that can be solved using the Pythagorean theorem are introduced in the problem-solving section. Problem Solving: College Entrance Exams gives suggestions for solving "odd-even" problems on college entrance exams.

Objectives

11-1
- Find the square roots of perfect squares.
- Tell whether a real number is rational or irrational.
- Use a table or a calculator to give an approximation for an irrational number.

11-2
- Determine acceptable replacements for radicands.
- Simplify perfect square radicands.

11-3
- Simplify radical expressions.

B.T.
- Find cube roots.

11-4
- Multiply radical expressions.

B.T.
- Find rational approximations of square roots.

11-5
- Divide expressions involving radicals.
- Rationalize the denominator.

B.T.
- Simplify expressions with rational exponents.

11-6
- Add and subtract radical expressions.

11-7
- Solve triangles using the Pythagorean theorem.

B.T.
- Find the distance between two points on the coordinate plane.

11-8
- Solve problems using the Pythagorean theorem.

11-9
- Solve equations involving radicals.
- Solve problems involving the solution of equations with radicals.

TEACHING CHAPTER 11

Cooperative Learning Opportunities

Study groups in mathematics and science are becoming increasingly popular among college students. Study groups for high school students can be very helpful to review homework, reinforce difficult concepts, and prepare for tests. There is no ideal number of members nor are there required roles and procedures. The only prerequisites are that students be serious and able to work together. Classroom trials will help you determine which students profit from study groups.

The exercises on pages 496, 501, and 505 are good candidates for small–group review after homework. Have students, in groups of 2 or 3, check their answers and their work.

The extra bit of difficulty found in the exercises on pages 517 and 518 is enough to discourage some students. But there are no real tricks in these problems and students working in groups of 3 or 4 will probably be able to do most of them. Study groups in class can get started on homework assignments.

Multicultural Note: *Squares and Square Roots in Babylonia*

In the dry climate of ancient Babylonia, located in present–day Iraq, clay tablets have been well preserved for over 4,000 years. As these tablets are found and translated, scientists are learning a lot about the people of Babylonia. One of these tablets contains a table of number pairs, part of which is shown here in base 10.

In connection with Lesson 11-7, you can present this table to students and tell them that the first column contains a number that forms a Pythagorean relationship with the other two. What you are *not* telling them is whether these numbers are squares or square roots and whether the third number is a side or a hypotenuse.

For more information, see page 21 of **Multiculturalism in Mathematics, Science, and Technology**.

	119	169
	3367	4825
	4601	6649
	65	97
	319	481

Solution: The number in the third column represents the hypotenuse. The missing number is the second leg. **120, 3456, 4800, 72, 360.**

Alternative Assessment and Communication Ideas

Students will be hearing about rational and irrational numbers in all of their future math courses. You can evaluate their present understanding of these concepts by asking for a paragraph that explains what these number sets are and how they are different from each other. Tell students to include something about different kinds of decimals and the meaning of ratio.

Using a scientific calculator, students can self-check after simplifying the numerical radical expressions found throughout Chapter 11.

$\sqrt{\frac{5}{6}} - \sqrt{\frac{6}{5}}$ can be simplified to $-\frac{\sqrt{30}}{30}$ and both of these give -0.1825741858 on the calculator. This demonstrates that they are equivalent expressions.

The **Writing to Learn** activity in Lesson 11-8 forces students to express themselves clearly about mathematical concepts and procedures.

Investigations and Projects

Students often think that math is a static discipline, unchanged and unchanging. A project on the history of numbers can focus on the human face of mathematics.

Have students do library research on the origins of different kinds of numbers. Suggest that they select particular cultures and topics to study. There are many choices to be made and students will have to use their judgment in analyzing certain developments. The following are possible areas on which to focus.

(1) Cultures. Study the number system of Babylonia, Egypt, Greece, or the Maya.

(2) Zero. Research math without zero and early uses of zero. (A similar report could be done on π.)

(3) Expansion of the number system. Separate reports can be done on the development of negative, rational, and irrational numbers.

MANAGING CHAPTER 11

Lesson	PACING CHART (DAYS) 2-Year* A for E	1-Year Minimum	1-Year Regular	1-Year Advanced	Opening Activity	Cooperative Activity	Seat or Group Work
11-1	3	1	1	1	First Five Minutes 11-1: ***FFMTM*** p. 33 or **TE** p. 482	The Density Property: **SE** p. 486; Calculator Worksheet 21: ***Technology*** p. 23	Try This a–k
11-2	2	1	1	1	First Five Minutes 11-2: ***FFMTM*** p. 33 or **TE** p. 487	Connections: Geometry: **SE** p. 490	Try This a–k
11-3	2	1	1	1	First Five Minutes 11-3: ***FFMTM*** p. 33 or **TE** p. 491	Explore: **SE** p. 491	Try This a–i
11-4	3	1	1	1	First Five Minutes 11-4: ***FFMTM*** p. 34 or **TE** p. 495	Problem 63: **SE** p. 496	Try This a–i
11-5	0	2	2	2	First Five Minutes 11-5: ***FFMTM*** p. 34 or **TE** p. 498	Explore: **SE** p. 498; Critical Thinking 11: ***Enrichment*** p. 28	Try This a–p
11-6	1	1	1	1	First Five Minutes 11-6: ***FFMTM*** p. 34 or **TE** p. 504	Problem Solving: Application: **SE** pp. 507–508	Try This a–h
11-7	3	1	1	1	First Five Minutes 11-7: ***FFMTM*** p. 34 or **TE** p. 509; ***Overhead Transparencies*** T22, T23	✂ Manipulative Activity 11: ***Enrichment*** p. 44	Try This a–d
11-8	2	1	1	1	First Five Minutes 11-8: ***FFMTM*** p. 35 or **TE** p. 514; ***Overhead Transparencies*** T24	Calculator Worksheet 24: ***Technology*** p. 26	Try This a–b
11-9	3	2	2	3	First Five Minutes 11-9: ***FFMTM*** p. 35 or **TE** p. 519; Application: **SE** p. 519	Bonus Topic 11: ***Enrichment*** p. 12	Try This a–f
Review	2	1	1	1			
Test	1	1	1	1			
Cum. Review	3	0	0	0			
Mid-Year Test	1	0	0	0			

*2-Year Management Guide can be found in *Algebra for Everyone*.

FFMTM: First Five Minutes Transparency Masters

Enrichment	Review/Assess	Reteach	Technology	Lesson
The Density Property: **SE** p. 486	Mixed Review 21: ***SPMR*** p. 71; Lesson Quiz: **TE** p. 485		Square Roots: **SE** p. 484; Calculator Worksheet 21: ***Technology*** p. 23; Spreadsheet Activity 8: ***Technology*** pp. 51–52	**11-1**
Connections: Geometry: **SE** p. 490	Lesson Quiz: **TE** p. 488		Evaluating Radical Expressions: **SE** p. 488; Calculator Worksheet 22: ***Technology*** p. 24	**11-2**
Bonus Topic: **SE** p. 494	Lesson Quiz: **TE** p. 492	Skills Practice 30: ***SPMR*** p. 38		**11-3**
Bonus Topic: **SE** p. 497	Lesson Quiz: **TE** p. 495; Quiz 21: ***Assessment*** p. 31			**11-4**
Bonus Topic: **SE** p. 503; Critical Thinking 11: ***Enrichment*** p. 28	Mixed Review 22: ***SPMR*** p. 72; Lesson Quiz: **TE** p. 500	Skills Practice 31: ***SPMR*** p. 39; Mixed Practice 21: **SE** p. 704	Finding Roots: **SE** p. 503; Calculator Worksheet 23: ***Technology*** p. 25	**11-5**
Problem Solving: Application: **SE** pp. 507–508	Lesson Quiz: **TE** p. 505			**11-6**
✂ Manipulative Activity 11: ***Enrichment*** p. 44; Bonus Topic: **SE** p. 513	Geometry Review 3: ***SPMR*** p. 87; Lesson Quiz: **TE** p. 510		Finding Missing Lengths: **SE** p. 510; Problem for Programmers **SE** p. 512; Spreadsheet Activity 9: ***Technology*** pp. 53–54	**11-7**
Writing to Learn: **SE** p. 518; Looking for Errors 11: ***Enrichment*** p. 60	Lesson Quiz: **TE** p. 514; Quiz 22: ***Assessment*** p. 32	Problem Bank 21: ***Problem Bank*** p. 38	Calculator Worksheet 24: ***Technology*** p. 26	**11-8**
Bonus Topic 11: ***Enrichment*** p. 12; Problem Solving College Entrance Exams: **SE** pp. 523–524	Lesson Quiz: **TE** p. 521 Problem Bank 22: ***Problem Bank*** p. 39	Mixed Practice 22: **SE** p. 705; Skills Practice 32: ***SPMR*** p. 40	BASIC Computer Project 15: ***Technology*** p. 77	**11-9**
	Summary and Review: **SE** pp. 525–527; Test: **SE** p. 528	Strategy Problem Bank 11: ***Problem Bank*** p. 12		**Review**
	Chapter 11 Exam: ***A for E*** pp. 427–428; Chapter 11 Test: ***Assessment*** pp. 63–64 (min.), 131–136 (reg.), 183–184 (adv.)			**Test**
	Cumulative Review: **SE** pp. 529–533			**Cum. Review**
	Cumulative Exam: ***Algebra for Everyone*** pp. T67–T70			**Mid-Year Test**

SPMR: Skills Practice Mixed Review

The solution to the problem posed on the facing page can be found on page 520.

Ready for Radical Expressions and Equations?

1-2 Simplify.

1. $\frac{18}{50}$ $\frac{9}{25}$ **2.** $\frac{18}{66}$ $\frac{3}{11}$ **3.** $\frac{81}{27}$ 3 **4.** $\frac{100}{50}$ 2

1-3 What is the meaning of each?

5. 5^2 5×5 **6.** 4^3 $4 \times 4 \times 4$ **7.** x^5 $x \times x \times x \times x \times x$ **8.** 7^6 $7 \times 7 \times 7 \times 7 \times 7 \times 7$

2-1 Simplify.

9. $|-8|$ 8 **10.** $|-15|$ 15 **11.** $|0|$ 0

2-5 Multiply.

12. $\frac{5}{3} \cdot \frac{5}{3}$ $\frac{25}{9}$ **13.** $\left(-\frac{2}{9}\right) \cdot \frac{2}{9}$ $-\frac{4}{81}$ **14.** $\left(-\frac{3}{16}\right) \cdot \left(-\frac{3}{16}\right)$ $\frac{9}{256}$

15. $\frac{11}{4} \cdot \left(-\frac{11}{4}\right)$ $-\frac{121}{16}$ **16.** $(-5)(-5)$ 25 **17.** $(-6)(-6)(-6)$ -216

18. $\left(-\frac{3}{4}\right)\left(-\frac{3}{4}\right)$ $\frac{9}{16}$ **19.** $\left(-\frac{1}{5}\right)\left(-\frac{1}{5}\right)\left(-\frac{1}{5}\right)$ $-\frac{1}{125}$

5-1 Multiply or divide. Simplify.

20. $x^3 \cdot x^3$ x^6 **21.** $(a^2b^3)(ab^2)$ a^3b^5

22. $\frac{x^9}{x^4}$ x^5 **23.** $\frac{ab^3}{ab}$ b^2

6-1 to 6-5 Factor.

24. $x^3 - x^2$ $x^2(x - 1)$ **25.** $5x - 30x^2$ $5x(1 - 6x)$

26. $x^2 + 2x + 1$ $(x + 1)^2$ **27.** $x^2 - 14x + 49$ $(x - 7)^2$

CHAPTER

11 Radical Expressions and Equations

How far, to the nearest kilometer, can you see through an airplane window at a height, or altitude, of 12,321 meters?

11-1

FIRST FIVE MINUTES

1. Find two numbers x such that $x^2 = 121$.
   $x = 11, x = -11$
2. Solve $x^2 = 144$.
   $x = \pm 12$
3. Solve $x^2 = 16$.
   $x = \pm 4$

Square Roots

Stress the difference among the symbols, $\sqrt{7}$, $-\sqrt{7}$, and $\pm\sqrt{7}$. $\sqrt{7}$ is read, "the positive square root of 7" or "the principal square root of 7."

Avoiding Common Errors

When students use ± 3 to designate the square roots of 9, they often forget that this represents two answers, $+3$ and -3. In this lesson, the use of the symbol $\pm$ is minimized for this reason. Stress that all positive numbers have two square roots.

Key Questions

- How many square roots does every positive number have?
  Two
- Is there a number that has only one square root?
  Yes, 0

Chalkboard Examples

1. Find the square roots of 400.
   20, -20
2. Simplify $\sqrt{169}$.
   $\sqrt{169} = 13$, the principal root
3. Simplify $-\sqrt{81}$.
   $-\sqrt{81} = -9$, the negative root

11-1 Real Numbers

Square Roots

Objective: Find the square roots of perfect squares.

When we raise a number to the second power, we have squared the number. Sometimes we may need to find the number that was squared. We call this process finding a square root of a number.

Definition

The number c is a **square root** of a if $c^2 = a$.

Every positive number has two square roots, a positive square root and a negative square root. For example, the square roots of 25 are 5 and -5, because $5^2 = 25$ and $(-5)^2 = 25$.

The positive square root is also called the principal square root. The $\sqrt{\ }$ symbol is called a radical sign. The radical sign is used to denote the principal square root. To name the negative square root of a number, we use $-\sqrt{\ }$. Thus,

$$\sqrt{25} = 5 \text{ and } -\sqrt{25} = -5.$$

We can use the symbol $\pm\sqrt{\ }$ to name the positive and negative square root.

The number 0 has only one square root, 0. Since any positive or negative number squared is positive, negative numbers do not have square roots in the set of real numbers.

EXAMPLE 1 Find the square roots of 81.

The numbers 9 and -9 are square roots. $9^2 = 81$; $(-9)^2 = 81$

EXAMPLES Simplify.

2. $\sqrt{225} = 15$ Taking the principal square root

3. $-\sqrt{64} = -8$ Taking the negative square root

Try This

a. Find the square roots of 169. 13, -13

Simplify. **b.** $-\sqrt{100}$ -10 **c.** $\sqrt{256}$ 16

Real Numbers

Objective: Tell whether a real number is rational or irrational.

Each rational number can be matched to exactly one point on a number line. There are many points on the number line, however, for which there are no rational numbers. These points correspond to **irrational numbers.** Every point on a number line is associated with either a rational number or an irrational number. Combined, these numbers form the set of **real numbers.**

Definition

The **real numbers** consist of the rational numbers and the irrational numbers.

Recall that any rational number can be written in the form $\frac{a}{b}$ where a and b are integers and $b \neq 0$.

We also know that decimal notation for a rational number either ends or continues to repeat the same group of digits.

$\frac{1}{4} = 0.25$ The decimal ends.

$\frac{1}{3} = 0.333\ldots$ The 3 repeats.

$\frac{5}{11} = 0.45\overline{45}$ The bar indicates that 45 repeats.

An irrational number cannot be expressed as a ratio of two integers. Decimal notation for an irrational number never ends and does not repeat any group of digits. The number π is an example.

$\pi = 3.1415926535\ldots$ and continues endlessly.

The numbers 3.1416, 3.14, or $\frac{22}{7}$ are only rational approximations for π.

Is $\sqrt{2}$ a rational number? If we look for a number $\frac{a}{b}$ for which $\left(\frac{a}{b}\right)^2 = 2$, we can find rational numbers whose squares are quite close to 2. But we can never find one whose square is exactly 2. Therefore, $\sqrt{2}$ cannot be expressed as the ratio of two integers and is not a rational number. $\sqrt{2}$ is an *irrational number.*

Definition

An **irrational number** is a real number that cannot be written in the form $\frac{a}{b}$ where a and b are integers and $b \neq 0$.

Real Numbers

The repeating pattern for a decimal such as $\frac{5}{11}$ may be difficult for students to visualize; you may want to have students do the long division as a demonstration. Using some calculators, $5 \div 11 = 0.4545455$. Point out that this is an approximation in which the last digit has been rounded off.

Key Questions

- What fraction is represented by $0.\overline{3}$?
  $\frac{1}{3}$
- What fraction is represented by $0.\overline{6}$?
  $\frac{2}{3}$
- What fraction is represented by $0.\overline{4}$?
  $\frac{4}{9}$
- What fraction is represented by $0.\overline{7}$?
  $\frac{7}{9}$

Chalkboard Examples

Identify as rational or irrational.

1. $\sqrt{13}$
   $\sqrt{13}$ is irrational, since 13 is not a perfect square.
2. $\sqrt{100}$
   $\sqrt{100} = 10$, a rational number.
3. $\sqrt{12}$
   $\sqrt{12}$ is irrational, since 12 is not a perfect square.

Approximating Irrational Numbers

Math Point
In 1761, the mathematician Johann Heinrich Lambert presented to the Berlin Academy the first proof that π is irrational. The decimal representation of π never ends and never repeats. It is possible to approximate π to any degree of accuracy by a fraction. Here are some rational approximations to π. The decimals are given far enough to show the deviation of each approximation from the true value of π.

$\pi \approx 3.14159265358979323846264 3$

$$\frac{3}{1} = 3.0$$

$$\frac{22}{7} = 3.1428$$

$$\frac{333}{106} = 3.141509$$

$$\frac{355}{113} = 3.1415929$$

$$\frac{103993}{33102} = 3.141592653$$

Key Questions

- $\sqrt{8}$ is between what two integers?
  2 and 3
- $\sqrt{21}$ is between what two integers?
  4 and 5
- $\sqrt{145}$ is between what two integers?
  12 and 13

Chalkboard Example

1. Use a calculator or Table 1 to approximate $\sqrt{13}$.
   $\sqrt{13} \approx 3.606$, rounded to 3 decimal digits

Point out that a calculator cannot store an irrational number. A calculator stores a rational approximation in the form of a terminating decimal.

You may want students to try to find a perfect square root of 2. Students may conclude that 1.4142136 is a perfect square root of 2. Check this by reentering the number and squaring.

The square roots of most whole numbers are irrational. Only the perfect squares 0, 1, 4, 9, 16, 25, 36, and so on have rational square roots.

EXAMPLES Identify the rational numbers and the irrational numbers.

4. $\sqrt{3}$ — $\sqrt{3}$ is irrational, since 3 is not a perfect square.
5. $\sqrt{25}$ — $\sqrt{25}$ is rational, since 25 is a perfect square.
6. $\sqrt{35}$ — $\sqrt{35}$ is irrational, since 35 is not a perfect square.
7. $-\sqrt{49}$ — $-\sqrt{49}$ is rational, since 49 is a perfect square.

Try This Identify the rational numbers and the irrational numbers.

d. $\sqrt{5}$ Irrational **e.** $-\sqrt{36}$ Rational **f.** $-\sqrt{32}$ Irrational **g.** $\sqrt{101}$ Irrational

Approximating Irrational Numbers

Objective: Use a table or a calculator to give an approximation for an irrational number.

We can use a rational number to approximate an irrational number. Table 1 in the Appendix contains rational approximations for square roots. We can also use a calculator to find rational approximations for square roots.

EXAMPLE 8 Approximate $\sqrt{10}$.

Using Table 1, find 10 in the first column headed N. Look in the third column headed $\sqrt{N}$ opposite 10. Thus $\sqrt{10} \approx 3.162$. The symbol $\approx$ means "is approximately equal to."

Calculators are very useful for finding square roots.

Square Roots

Most calculators have a square root key that is usually accessed using an INV or 2nd key with the x^2 key.

$\sqrt{10} \rightarrow 10$ 2nd x^2 $\rightarrow$ 3.1622777

Since $\sqrt{10}$ is an irrational number, the decimal shown on the calculator is a rational approximation.

For additional calculator practice, see Calculator Worksheet 21.

Using either method, we find $\sqrt{10} \approx 3.162$ to the nearest thousandth.

Try This Approximate these square roots to the nearest thousandth.

h. $\sqrt{7}$ 2.646 **i.** $\sqrt{72}$ 8.485 **j.** $\sqrt{18}$ 4.243 **k.** $\sqrt{45}$ 6.708

11-1 EXERCISES

A

Find the square roots of each number.

1. 1 1, −1 **2.** 4 2, −2 **3.** 16 4, −4 **4.** 9 3, −3

5. 100 10, −10 **6.** 121 11, −11 **7.** 169 13, −13 **8.** 144 12, −12

9. 324 18, −18 **10.** 25 5, −5 **11.** 225 15, −15 **12.** 256 16, −16

Simplify.

13. $\sqrt{4}$ **14.** $\sqrt{1}$ **15.** $-\sqrt{9}$ **16.** $-\sqrt{25}$

17. $-\sqrt{64}$ **18.** $-\sqrt{81}$ **19.** $-\sqrt{225}$ **20.** $\sqrt{400}$

21. $\sqrt{361}$ **22.** $\sqrt{441}$ **23.** $\sqrt{196}$ **24.** $-\sqrt{49}$

25. $-\sqrt{324}$ **26.** $\sqrt{289}$ **27.** $-\sqrt{36}$ **28.** $\sqrt{625}$

Identify each square root as rational or irrational.

29. $\sqrt{2}$ **30.** $\sqrt{6}$ **31.** $\sqrt{8}$ **32.** $\sqrt{10}$

33. $\sqrt{49}$ **34.** $\sqrt{100}$ **35.** $\sqrt{98}$ **36.** $\sqrt{75}$

37. $-\sqrt{4}$ **38.** $-\sqrt{1}$ **39.** $-\sqrt{12}$ **40.** $-\sqrt{14}$

41. $-\sqrt{125}$ **42.** $-\sqrt{196}$ **43.** $-\sqrt{150}$ **44.** $-\sqrt{200}$

Approximate these square roots to the nearest thousandth.

45. $\sqrt{5}$ **46.** $\sqrt{6}$ **47.** $\sqrt{17}$ **48.** $\sqrt{19}$

49. $\sqrt{93}$ **50.** $\sqrt{43}$ **51.** $\sqrt{40}$ **52.** $\sqrt{51}$

53. $\sqrt{60}$ **54.** $\sqrt{54}$ **55.** $\sqrt{111}$ **56.** $\sqrt{78}$

B

Identify each number as rational or irrational. If it is rational, is it best described as a whole number, an integer, or a rational number?

57. $-\sqrt{81}$ **58.** $\sqrt{120}$ **59.** $\sqrt{0.49}$

60. $\sqrt{196}$ **61.** $\sqrt{\frac{36}{25}}$ **62.** $-\sqrt{215}$

Simplify.

63. $\sqrt{\sqrt{16}}$ **64.** $\sqrt{3^2 + 4^2}$

65. $\sqrt{(3 + 4)^2}$ **66.** $(\sqrt{5} + 13)^2$

67. Between what two consecutive integers is $-\sqrt{33}$?

68. Between what two consecutive integers is $-\sqrt{57}$?

69. ***Critical Thinking*** When asked his age, Augustus De Morgan, a nineteenth-century English mathematician, responded,

"I was x years old in the year x^2."

In what year was he born? 1806

LESSON QUIZ

1. Find the square roots of 256.
   $\pm\sqrt{256} = 16$ or -16
2. Simplify $\sqrt{900}$.
   $\sqrt{900} = 30$
3. Is $\sqrt{75}$ rational or irrational?
   75 is not a perfect square, hence $\sqrt{75}$ is irrational.
4. Use Table 1 or a calculator to find $\sqrt{17}$ to three decimal places.
   $\sqrt{17} = 4.123$

Assignment Guide
Minimum: 1–56 e/o, MR

Regular: 1–56 m3, 57–68 e/o, 69, MR
Advanced: 1–68 m3, 69, 70–80 e/o, MR

ADDITIONAL ANSWERS

Exercises

13. 2 **14.** 1
15. −3 **16.** −5
17. −8 **18.** −9
19. −15 **20.** 20
21. 19 **22.** 21
23. 14 **24.** −7
25. −18 **26.** 17
27. −6 **28.** 25
29. Irrational **30.** Irrational
31. Irrational **32.** Irrational
33. Rational **34.** Rational
35. Irrational **36.** Irrational
37. Rational **38.** Rational
39. Irrational **40.** Irrational
41. Irrational **42.** Rational
43. Irrational **44.** Irrational
45. 2.236 **46.** 2.449
47. 4.123 **48.** 4.359
49. 9.644 **50.** 6.557
51. 6.325 **52.** 7.141
53. 7.746 **54.** 7.348
55. 10.536 **56.** 8.832
57. Rational, integer
58. Irrational
59. Rational, rational
60. Rational, whole number
61. Rational, rational
62. Irrational
63. 2 **64.** 5
65. 7 **66.** 18
67. −5, −6 **68.** −8, −7

70. $\sqrt{73}$
71. $\sqrt{17}$
72. $\sqrt{59}$
73. $\sqrt{26}$
74. $\sqrt{3}$
75. $\sqrt{44}$
76. $\sqrt{113}$
77. $\frac{x + y}{2}$
78. 1 is $(-1)^2$ and 1^3, 64 is 8^2 and 4^3
79. $\sqrt{5} \approx 2.2$
80. a. 3 b. 43 c. −6 d. 94

Mixed Review

81. $\frac{x^4y}{-3}$
82. $\frac{x + 1}{4}$
83. $\frac{x^2(x + 1)}{15}$
84. $x + 2$
85. $\frac{-2x}{(x + 2)(x - 2)}$
86. $5(5x + 2)(5x - 2)$
87. $(a + c)(a - c)$
88. $\frac{11}{2}$
89. 27
90. 4
91. $\frac{15}{7}$
92. $\frac{18}{11}$
93. $-\frac{12}{7}$
94. $x - 5$
95. $y^3 + 3y^2 + 9y + 27$
96. (1, 7)
97. $\left(-\frac{3}{2}, 2\right)$

Challenge

For which irrational numbers could these be approximations? Use Table 1.

70. 8.544 **71.** 4.123 **72.** 7.681

73. 5.099 **74.** 1.732 **75.** 6.633

76. 10.63 could be an approximation for what square root?

77. What number is halfway between x and y?

78. Find a number that is the square of an integer and the cube of a different integer.

79. A formula for the energy of an object of mass (m) and velocity (v) is given by $E = \frac{1}{2}mv^2$. Find v to the nearest tenth if $E = 20$, and $m = 8$.

80. Find y if $\sqrt{y + 6}$ is

a. 3 **b.** 7 **c.** 0 **d.** 10

Mixed Review

Simplify. **81.** $\frac{x^5y^2}{-3xy}$ **82.** $\frac{5(x + 1)}{8x} \cdot \frac{4x}{10}$ **83.** $\frac{3(x + 1)}{5x^2} \cdot \frac{x^4}{9}$

84. $\frac{x^2 + 8x}{x + 3} - \frac{3x + 2}{x + 3} + \frac{8}{x + 3}$ **85.** $\frac{3x - 10}{x^2 - 4} - \frac{5}{x + 2}$

Find the LCM. **86.** $25x - 10, 5x + 2$ **87.** $a + c, a - c$

Solve. **88.** $\frac{2}{3} + \frac{1}{4} = \frac{x}{6}$ **89.** $\frac{5}{8} + \frac{1}{2} = \frac{y}{24}$ **90.** $\frac{4}{9} - \frac{1}{3} = \frac{x}{36}$

91. $\frac{2}{3} - \frac{1}{5} = \frac{1}{a}$ **92.** $\frac{1}{6} + \frac{4}{9} = \frac{1}{a}$ **93.** $\frac{1}{4} - \frac{5}{6} = \frac{1}{b}$

Divide. **94.** $(x^2 - 9x + 20) \div (x - 4)$ **95.** $(y^4 - 81) \div (y - 3)$

Solve. **96.** $y - 6x = 1$, $5x + y = 12$ **97.** $4x + y = -4$, $10x + 3y = -9$

THE DENSITY PROPERTY

Recall the density property of rational numbers. No matter how close two rational numbers are, we can find a rational number between them. Does a real number exist between any two real numbers? Answers may vary.

- Find a real number between $\frac{3}{7}$ and $\frac{4}{7}$. $\frac{1}{2}$
- Find a real number between −0.23 and −0.24. −0.235
- Find a real number between $\sqrt{2}$ and $\sqrt{3}$. 1.5
- Find a real number between $\sqrt{10}$ and $\sqrt{11}$. 3.2

Do you think the density property holds for real numbers? Yes

11-2 Radical Expressions

Math History

Before symbols were used to describe mathematics, the words *root* or *side* were used to refer to the square root of a number. Because Arabic writers thought of a square number growing out of or being extracted from a root, works translated from Arabic used the word *radix* (root). Late medieval writers represented *radix* using the single symbol ℞, which was used for over a century. In 1484 the symbol $℞^2$ appeared for square root. The symbol $\sqrt{\ }$ first appeared in print (in *Die Coss* by Christoff Rudolff) in 1525 and by the seventeenth century was widely accepted.

Nonnegative Radicands

Objective: Determine acceptable replacements for radicands.

When an expression is written under a radical, we have a **radical expression.** These are radical expressions.

$$\sqrt{14} \qquad \sqrt{x} \qquad \sqrt{x^2 + 4} \qquad \sqrt{\frac{x^2 - 5}{2}}$$

The expression written under the radical is called the **radicand.**

The square of any real number is always a positive number or zero. For example, $8^2 = 64$ and $(-11)^2 = 121$. Since there are no real numbers that can be squared to get negative numbers, radical expressions with negative radicands have no meaning in the real number system.

The following expressions do *not* represent real numbers.

$$\sqrt{-100} \qquad \sqrt{-49} \qquad -\sqrt{-3}$$

EXAMPLE 1

Evaluate the expression $\sqrt{1 - y}$ for $y = 6$. Is the result a real number?

If we replace y by 6, we get $\sqrt{1 - 6} = \sqrt{-5}$, which has a negative radicand and has no meaning in the real number system. This is not a real number.

EXAMPLES

Determine the values of x that make each expression a real number.

2. $\sqrt{x}$ Any number greater than or equal to 0 can be used.
3. $\sqrt{x + 2}$ We solve the inequality $x + 2 \geq 0$. Any number greater than or equal to -2 can be used.

11-2

FIRST FIVE MINUTES

1. Find the square roots of 2500.
   50, -50
2. Simplify $\sqrt{121}$.
   $\sqrt{121} = 11$
3. Is $\sqrt{8}$ rational or irrational?
   Irrational
4. Use Table 1 or a calculator to find $\sqrt{11}$, rounded to three decimal places.
   3.317

Nonnegative Radicands

This section shows that caution is necessary when working with radical expressions involving variables. Point out that if a variable is squared, it will represent a positive number for any replacement.

Key Questions

- Is $\sqrt{-2}$ a real number?
  No
- Is $\sqrt{5}$ a real number?
  Yes; $\sqrt{5}$ is an irrational number, which is a real number.
- Is $\sqrt{1 - 8}$ a real number?
  No; $\sqrt{1 - 8} = \sqrt{-7}$, which is not a real number.

Chalkboard Examples

1. Evaluate the expression $\sqrt{x - 5}$ for $x = 1$. Is the result a real number?
   $\sqrt{1 - 5} = \sqrt{-4}$
   $\sqrt{-4}$ is not a real number.
2. For what values of x is $\sqrt{1 - x}$ a real number?
   $\sqrt{1 - x}$ is real for $x \leq 1$.
3. For what values of x is $\sqrt{-x}$ a real number?
   $\sqrt{-x}$ is real for $x \leq 0$.
4. For what values of x is $\sqrt{(x - 1)^2}$ a real number?
   Since $(x - 1)^2$ is always nonnegative, any x will work.
5. For what values of x is $\sqrt{x^2 - 1}$ a real number?
   $x^2 - 1$ must be nonnegative.
   $x^2 \geq 1$
   $x \geq 1$ or $x \leq -1$

Perfect Square Radicands

Point out that the principal square root is always nonnegative. Thus we must take the absolute value of variables to assure a nonnegative number. Following this lesson, however, the radicands will be assumed to be nonnegative numbers, which will eliminate the need for absolute value.

Chalkboard Examples

Simplify.

1. $\sqrt{(5x)^2}$
   $|5x|$, or $5|x|$
2. $\sqrt{9x^2}$
   $\sqrt{(3x)^2} = |3x| = 3|x|$
3. $\sqrt{x^2 + 6x + 9}$
   $\sqrt{(x + 3)^2} = |x + 3|$

If students receive an error message, they have probably attempted to find the square root of a negative number.

Students may also use [y^x] 2 and [INV] [y^x] 2 to find squares and square roots.

LESSON QUIZ

1. For what values of x is $\sqrt{x^2 - 4}$ real?
   $x \leq -2$ or $x \geq 2$
2. Simplify $\sqrt{16x^2}$.
   $4|x|$
3. Simplify $\sqrt{x^2 + 8x + 16}$.
   $|x + 4|$

EXAMPLE 4 Determine the values of x that make $\sqrt{x^2}$ a real number.

Squares of real numbers are never negative. All real number replacements are acceptable.

Try This

a. Evaluate the expression $\sqrt{15 - 2x}$ for $x = 8$. Is the result a real number? $\sqrt{-1}$; No

Determine the values of x that make each expression a real number.

b. $\sqrt{x + 1}$ $x \geq -1$ **c.** $\sqrt{x - 3}$ $x \geq 3$ **d.** $\sqrt{2x - 5}$ $x \geq \frac{5}{2}$ **e.** $\sqrt{x^2 + 3}$ All replacements

Perfect Square Radicands

Objective: Simplify perfect square radicands.

Remember that $\sqrt{a}$ means the principal square root (positive or zero) of a. The symbol $\sqrt{x^2}$ means to square x and then find the principal square root. Is $\sqrt{x^2} = x$? Not necessarily.

Suppose $x = 3$. Then $\sqrt{x^2} = \sqrt{3^2}$, which is $\sqrt{9}$, or 3.
Suppose $x = -3$. Then $\sqrt{x^2} = \sqrt{(-3)^2}$, which is $\sqrt{9}$, or 3.

In either case, we have $\sqrt{x^2} = |x|$. In general, any radical expression $\sqrt{a^2}$ can be simplified to $|a|$.

EXAMPLES Simplify.

5. $\sqrt{(3x)^2} = |3x|$ or $3|x|$ 6. $\sqrt{a^2b^2} = \sqrt{(ab)^2} = |ab|$

7. $\sqrt{x^2 + 2x + 1} = \sqrt{(x + 1)^2} = |x + 1|$

Try This Simplify.

f. $\sqrt{(xy)^2}$ $|xy|$ **g.** $\sqrt{x^2y^2}$ $|xy|$ **h.** $\sqrt{(x - 1)^2}$ $|x - 1|$

i. $\sqrt{x^2 + 8x + 16}$ $|x + 4|$ **j.** $\sqrt{25y^2}$ $5|y|$ **k.** $\sqrt{\frac{1}{4}t^2}$ $\frac{1}{2}|t|$

Evaluating Radical Expressions

You can use a calculator to evaluate radical expressions.
Evaluate $\sqrt{4x^2 - 5}$ for $x = 3$. Express the answer as a decimal to the nearest hundredth.

[( ] 4 [×] 3 [x^2] [−] 5 [ )]

[2nd] [x^2] 5.5677644 ≈ 5.57

For additional calculator practice, see Calculator Worksheet 22.

11-2 EXERCISES

A

1. Evaluate the expression $\sqrt{3x - 12}$ for $x = 4$. Is the result a real number? 0; Yes
2. Evaluate the expression $\sqrt{8 - 4y}$ for $y = 10$. Is the result a real number? $\sqrt{-32}$; No
3. Evaluate $\sqrt{x + 12}$ for $x = -6$. Is the result a real number? $\sqrt{6}$; Yes
4. Evaluate $\sqrt{3y + 12}$ for $y = -5$. Is the result a real number? $\sqrt{-3}$; No

Determine the values for the variable that will make each expression a real number.

5. $\sqrt{5x}$
6. $\sqrt{3y}$
7. $\sqrt{t - 5}$
8. $\sqrt{y - 8}$
9. $\sqrt{y + 8}$
10. $\sqrt{x + 6}$
11. $\sqrt{x + 20}$
12. $\sqrt{m - 18}$
13. $\sqrt{2y - 7}$
14. $\sqrt{3x + 8}$
15. $\sqrt{t^2 + 5}$
16. $\sqrt{y^2 + 1}$

Simplify.

17. $\sqrt{t^2}$
18. $\sqrt{x^2}$
19. $\sqrt{9x^2}$
20. $\sqrt{4a^2}$
21. $\sqrt{(-7)^2}$
22. $\sqrt{(-5)^2}$
23. $\sqrt{(-4d)^2}$
24. $\sqrt{(-3b)^2}$
25. $\sqrt{(x + 3)^2}$
26. $\sqrt{(x - 7)^2}$
27. $\sqrt{a^2 - 10a + 25}$
28. $\sqrt{x^2 + 2x + 1}$
29. $\sqrt{4a^2 - 4a + 1}$
30. $\sqrt{9a^2 - 12a + 4}$

B

Solve.

31. $\sqrt{x^2} = 6$
32. $\sqrt{y^2} = -7$
33. $-\sqrt{x^2} = -3$
34. $t^2 = 49$
35. $\sqrt{(x - 3)^2} = 5$
36. $\sqrt{4a^2 - 12a + 9} = 3$

Simplify.

37. $\sqrt{(3a)^2}$
38. $\sqrt{(4a)^2(4a)^2}$
39. $\sqrt{\dfrac{144x^8}{36y^6}}$
40. $\sqrt{\dfrac{y^{12}}{8100}}$
41. $\sqrt{\dfrac{169}{m^{16}}}$
42. $\sqrt{\dfrac{p^2}{3600}}$
43. Determine the values for the variable that will make each expression a real number.
    a. $\sqrt{m(m + 3)}$ $m \geq 0$ or $m \leq -3$
    b. $\sqrt{x^2(x - 3)}$ $x \geq 3$ or $x = 0$
44. *Critical Thinking* Given a and c, what must be true of b to make $\sqrt{b^2 - 4ac}$ a real number?
    a. $a = -3, c = 2$ Any real number
    b. $a = 2, c = 8$ $b \leq -8$ or $b \geq 8$

Assignment Guide
Minimum: 1–30 e/o, MR

Regular: 1–43 e/o, 44, MR

Advanced: 1–43 m3, 44–49, MR

ADDITIONAL ANSWERS

Exercises

5. $x \geq 0$
6. $y \geq 0$
7. $t \geq 5$
8. $y \geq 8$
9. $y \geq -8$
10. $x \geq -6$
11. $x \geq -20$
12. $m \geq 18$
13. $y \geq \frac{7}{2}$
14. $x \geq -\frac{8}{3}$
15. Any value
16. Any value
17. $|t|$
18. $|x|$
19. $3|x|$
20. $2|a|$
21. 7
22. 5
23. $4|d|$
24. $3|b|$
25. $|x + 3|$
26. $|x - 7|$
27. $|a - 5|$
28. $|x + 1|$
29. $|2a - 1|$
30. $|3a - 2|$
31. 6, −6
32. No value
33. 3, −3
34. 7, −7
35. −2, 8
36. 0, 3
37. $3|a|$
38. $16a^2$
39. $\frac{2x^4}{|y^3|}$
40. $\frac{y^6}{90}$
41. $\frac{13}{m^8}$
42. $\frac{|p|}{60}$

45. $x \geq 2$ or $x \leq -3$
46. $x \leq -4$ or $x \geq -3$
47. $x \geq 2$ or $x \leq -2$
48. $x \geq \frac{1}{2}$ or $x \leq -\frac{1}{2}$
49. **a.** Real **b.** Real **c.** Not real **d.** Not real **e.** Real **f.** Not real

Mixed Review

50. $-4 < x < -2$
51. No solution
52. $y \leq -8$ or $y \geq 2$
53. -2
54. $\frac{4(x + 1)}{x - 3}$
55. $\frac{5y + 27}{(y + 5)^2}$
56. $\frac{2y + 3}{(y + 3)(y + 4)}$
57. 6, -1
58. 2
59. 7

Challenge

Determine the values for the variable that will make each expression a real number.

45. $\sqrt{(x + 3)(x - 2)}$ **46.** $\sqrt{x^2 + 7x + 12}$

47. $\sqrt{x^2 - 4}$ **48.** $\sqrt{4x^2 - 1}$

49. For a polynomial of the form $ax^2 + bx + c = 0$ to have real solutions, $\sqrt{b^2 - 4ac}$ must be a real number. Which of the following polynomials have real solutions?

a. $x^2 - 12x + 3 = 0$ **b.** $x^2 + 2x - 50 = 0$
c. $x^2 + 5x + 7 = 0$ **d.** $5x^2 + 2x + 1 = 0$
e. $-x^2 + x + 1 = 0$ **f.** $-x^2 + x - 1 = 0$

Mixed Review

Solve. **50.** $|x + 3| < 1$ **51.** $|x - 9| = -3$ **52.** $|y + 3| \geq 5$

Simplify. **53.** $\frac{x - 3}{x + 2} - \frac{3x + 1}{x + 2}$ **54.** $\frac{6x + 7}{x - 3} - \frac{2x + 3}{x - 3}$

55. $\frac{5}{y + 5} + \frac{2}{(y + 5)^2}$ **56.** $\frac{5}{y + 4} - \frac{3}{y + 3}$

Solve. **57.** $x - \frac{6}{x} = 5$ **58.** $\frac{6}{x} = \frac{5}{x} + \frac{1}{2}$ **59.** $\frac{y + 1}{y - 3} = 2$

CONNECTIONS: GEOMETRY

The formula for the volume of a cylinder is $V = \pi r^2 h$. The height of each cylinder and the volume are given. Find the radius of each figure. If you do not have a calculator with a π key, use 3.14 for π. Round the radius to the nearest whole number.

1.

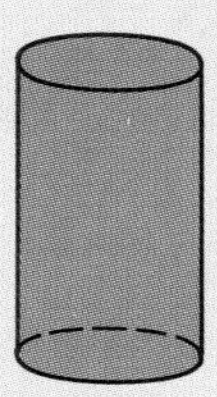

$h = 25$ in., $V = 2826$ in.^{3} 6 in.

2.

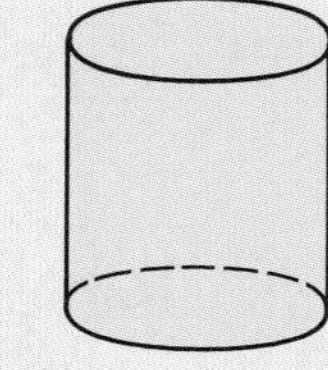

$h = 6.2$ cm, $V = 175$ cm^3 3 cm

3.

$h = 40.5$ yd, $V = 6234$ yd^3 7 yd

11-3 Simplifying Radical Expressions

Objective: Simplify radical expressions.

Explore

Find the following square roots.

$\sqrt{225}$ 15 $\qquad$ $\sqrt{9} \cdot \sqrt{25}$ $3 \cdot 5 = 15$

$\sqrt{400}$ 20 $\qquad$ $\sqrt{4} \cdot \sqrt{100}$ $2 \cdot 10 = 20$

What do you notice about the results?

The above relationship suggests the following fact about square roots.

Product Property for Radicals

For any nonnegative real numbers a and b, $\sqrt{ab} = \sqrt{a} \cdot \sqrt{b}$.

To simplify radical expressions, we look for perfect square factors in the radicand. To simplify $\sqrt{50}$, we identify the perfect square 25.

$$\sqrt{50} = \sqrt{25 \cdot 2}$$

Then we use the Product Property for Radicals to rewrite the expression.

$$= \sqrt{25} \cdot \sqrt{2}$$
$$= 5\sqrt{2}$$

A **radical expression** has been **simplified** when its radicand contains no perfect square factors. The radical expression $5\sqrt{2}$ is in its simplest form.

If you do not recognize perfect squares, try factoring the radicand into its prime factors.

$$\sqrt{50} = \sqrt{2 \cdot 5 \cdot 5} = 5\sqrt{2}$$

In many formulas and problems involving radical notation, variables do not represent negative numbers. Thus, absolute value is not necessary. *From now on we will assume that all radicands are nonnegative.*

EXAMPLE 1 Simplify.

$\sqrt{18} = \sqrt{9 \cdot 2}$ Factoring the radicand with a perfect square factor

$= \sqrt{9} \cdot \sqrt{2}$ Using the product property for radicals

$= 3\sqrt{2}$ The radicand has no factors that are perfect squares.

11-3

FIRST FIVE MINUTES

1. Simplify $\sqrt{25x^2}$.
   $5|x|$
2. Simplify $\sqrt{x^2 - 10x + 25}$.
   $|x - 5|$
3. For what values of x is $\sqrt{(x - 1)^2}$ real?
   Since $(x - 1)^2$ is always nonnegative any x will work.

EXPLORE

Students will find that $\sqrt{225} = \sqrt{9} \cdot \sqrt{25}$ and $\sqrt{400} = \sqrt{4} \cdot \sqrt{100}$. They should also notice that $225 = 9 \cdot 25$ and $400 = 4 \cdot 100$. From this, some students may be able to generalize the product property for radicals.

Point out that the product property for radicals allows us to find the root of a large number by finding the roots of the factors. For example,

$$\sqrt{1225} = \sqrt{25 \cdot 49} = \sqrt{25} \cdot \sqrt{49} = 5 \cdot 7$$

It is very helpful to arrange the factors into two groups, those that are perfect squares and those that are not.

Stress that we have not just stopped using the absolute value with variables; we are assuming that all numbers in the radicand are nonnegative.

Key Questions

- Can you simplify $\sqrt{15}$?
  No; there are no factors that are perfect squares.

Can you find the largest perfect square factor for each?

- 27 9
- 32 16
- 75 25
- x^{15} x^{14}

Chalkboard Examples

Simplify.

1. $\sqrt{45}$
   $\sqrt{45} = \sqrt{9 \cdot 5} = \sqrt{9} \cdot \sqrt{5} = 3\sqrt{5}$
2. $\sqrt{49x}$
   $\sqrt{49} \cdot \sqrt{x} = 7\sqrt{x}$
3. $\sqrt{52t}$
   $\sqrt{4 \cdot 13t} = 2\sqrt{13t}$
4. $\sqrt{2x^2 + 20x + 50}$
   $\sqrt{2(x^2 + 10x + 25)} = \sqrt{2}(x + 5)$
5. $\sqrt{x^{12}}$
   $\sqrt{(x^6)^2} = x^6$
6. $\sqrt{x^{26}}$
   $\sqrt{(x^{13})^2} = x^{13}$
7. $\sqrt{x^{13}}$
   $\sqrt{x^{12}x} = \sqrt{(x^6)^2 x} = x^6\sqrt{x}$

LESSON QUIZ

Simplify.

1. $\sqrt{28}$
   $\sqrt{4 \cdot 7} = 2\sqrt{7}$
2. $\sqrt{7x^2 + 14x + 7}$
   $\sqrt{7(x^2 + 2x + 1)} = \sqrt{7}(x + 1)$
3. $\sqrt{x^{14}}$
   x^7
4. $\sqrt{9(a + 2)^2}$
   $3(a + 2)$

EXAMPLES Simplify.

2. $\sqrt{48t} = \sqrt{16 \cdot 3t}$ Identifying perfect square factors
   $= \sqrt{16} \cdot \sqrt{3t}$ Using the product property for radicals
   $= 4\sqrt{3t}$

3. $\sqrt{72x^2} = \sqrt{36x^2 \cdot 2}$ Identifying perfect square factors
   $= \sqrt{36x^2} \cdot \sqrt{2}$ Using the product property for radicals
   $= 6x\sqrt{2}$

4. $\sqrt{3x^2 + 6x + 3} = \sqrt{3(x^2 + 2x + 1)}$
   $= \sqrt{3} \cdot \sqrt{x^2 + 2x + 1}$ Using the product property for radicals
   $= \sqrt{3} \cdot \sqrt{(x + 1)^2}$
   $= \sqrt{3}(x + 1)$

Try This Factor and simplify.

a. $\sqrt{32}$ $4\sqrt{2}$ **b.** $\sqrt{25x^2}$ $5x$ **c.** $\sqrt{60x}$ $2\sqrt{15x}$
d. $\sqrt{45x^2}$ $3x\sqrt{5}$ **e.** $\sqrt{7x^2 - 14x + 7}$ $\sqrt{7}(x - 1)$

To take a square root of a power such as x^8, the exponent must be even. We then take half the exponent. Recall that $(x^4)^2 = x^8$.

EXAMPLES Simplify.

5. $\sqrt{x^6} = \sqrt{(x^3)^2}$
   $= x^3$

6. $\sqrt{x^{10}} = \sqrt{(x^5)^2}$
   $= x^5$

7. $\sqrt{x^{22}} = x^{11}$

When odd powers occur, express the power as the product of the largest even power and x. Then simplify the even power.

EXAMPLE 8 Simplify.

$$\sqrt{x^9} = \sqrt{x^8 \cdot x} = \sqrt{x^8} \cdot \sqrt{x} = x^4\sqrt{x}$$

Try This Simplify.

f. $\sqrt{y^8}$ y^4 **g.** $\sqrt{(x + y)^{14}}$ $(x + y)^7$
h. $\sqrt{t^{15}}$ $t^7\sqrt{t}$ **i.** $\sqrt{a^{25}}$ $a^{12}\sqrt{a}$

11-3 EXERCISES

A

Simplify. Assume that all variables are nonnegative.

1. $\sqrt{12}$
2. $\sqrt{8}$
3. $\sqrt{20}$
4. $\sqrt{45}$
5. $\sqrt{75}$
6. $\sqrt{50}$
7. $\sqrt{200}$
8. $\sqrt{300}$
9. $\sqrt{3x^2}$
10. $\sqrt{5y^2}$
11. $\sqrt{16a}$
12. $\sqrt{49b}$
13. $\sqrt{13x^2}$
14. $\sqrt{29t^2}$
15. $\sqrt{9x}$
16. $\sqrt{4y}$
17. $\sqrt{64y^2}$
18. $\sqrt{9x^2}$
19. $\sqrt{8t^2}$
20. $\sqrt{125a^2}$
21. $\sqrt{4x^2 + 8x + 4}$
22. $\sqrt{3x^2 + 12x + 12}$
23. $\sqrt{2x^2 + 12x + 18}$
24. $\sqrt{5x^2 + 30x + 45}$
25. $\sqrt{4x^2 + 12xy + 9y^2}$
26. $\sqrt{3x^2 + 30xy + 75y^2}$

Simplify.

27. $\sqrt{x^6}$ x^3
28. $\sqrt{x^{10}}$ x^5
29. $\sqrt{x^{12}}$ x^6
30. $\sqrt{x^{16}}$ x^8
31. $\sqrt{x^5}$ $x^2\sqrt{x}$
32. $\sqrt{x^3}$ $x\sqrt{x}$
33. $\sqrt{t^{19}}$ $t^9\sqrt{t}$
34. $\sqrt{p^{17}}$ $p^8\sqrt{p}$
35. $\sqrt{(y-2)^8}$ $(y-2)^4$
36. $\sqrt{(x+3)^6}$ $(x+3)^3$
37. $\sqrt{4(x+5)^{10}}$ $2(x+5)^5$
38. $\sqrt{16(a-7)^4}$ $4(a-7)^2$
39. $\sqrt{36m^3}$ $6m\sqrt{m}$
40. $\sqrt{250y^3}$ $5y\sqrt{10y}$
41. $\sqrt{8a^5}$ $2a^2\sqrt{2a}$
42. $\sqrt{12b^7}$ $2b^3\sqrt{3b}$
43. $\sqrt{448x^6y^3}$ $8x^3y\sqrt{7y}$
44. $\sqrt{243x^5y^4}$ $9x^2y^2\sqrt{3x}$

B

Simplify. Assume that all variables are nonnegative real numbers.

45. $3\sqrt{200}$
46. $2\sqrt{75}$
47. $4\sqrt{12}$
48. $-3\sqrt{72}$
49. $-2\sqrt{1000}$
50. $6\sqrt{36x}$
51. $4m\sqrt{20m^2}$
52. $2x\sqrt{50x^4}$
53. $5r^2\sqrt{32r^4s^3}$
54. $3a^3\sqrt{28a^3b^5}$

Evaluate and simplify for $r = 5$ and $s = \sqrt{5}$.

55. $\sqrt{3 + r^2}$
56. $\sqrt{r^2 - 1}$
57. $\sqrt{r + s^2}$
58. $\sqrt{50 - s^2}$

59. *Critical Thinking* Find $\sqrt{49}$, $\sqrt{490}$, $\sqrt{4900}$, $\sqrt{49{,}000}$, and $\sqrt{490{,}000}$. What pattern do you see?

Assignment Guide
Minimum: 1–44 e/o, MR

Regular: 1–44 m3, 45–58 e/o, 59, MR
Advanced: 1–58 m3, 59, 60–69 e/o, MR, assign w. Bonus Topic

ADDITIONAL ANSWERS

Exercises

1. $2\sqrt{3}$
2. $2\sqrt{2}$
3. $2\sqrt{5}$
4. $3\sqrt{5}$
5. $5\sqrt{3}$
6. $5\sqrt{2}$
7. $10\sqrt{2}$
8. $10\sqrt{3}$
9. $x\sqrt{3}$
10. $y\sqrt{5}$
11. $4\sqrt{a}$
12. $7\sqrt{b}$
13. $x\sqrt{13}$
14. $t\sqrt{29}$
15. $3\sqrt{x}$
16. $2\sqrt{y}$
17. $8y$
18. $3x$
19. $2t\sqrt{2}$
20. $5a\sqrt{5}$
21. $2(x + 1)$
22. $(x + 2)\sqrt{3}$
23. $(x + 3)\sqrt{2}$
24. $(x + 3)\sqrt{5}$
25. $2x + 3y$
26. $(x + 5y)\sqrt{3}$

45. $30\sqrt{2}$
46. $10\sqrt{3}$
47. $8\sqrt{3}$
48. $-18\sqrt{2}$
49. $-20\sqrt{10}$
50. $36\sqrt{x}$
51. $8m^2\sqrt{5}$
52. $10x^3\sqrt{2}$
53. $20r^4s\sqrt{2s}$
54. $6a^4b^2\sqrt{7ab}$
55. $2\sqrt{7}$
56. $2\sqrt{6}$
57. $\sqrt{10}$
58. $3\sqrt{5}$
59. $\sqrt{49} = 7$ $\quad \sqrt{490} = 7\sqrt{10}$
$\sqrt{4900} = 70$ $\quad \sqrt{49{,}000} = 70\sqrt{10}$
$\sqrt{490{,}000} = 700$
$\sqrt{49 \times 10^n} = \sqrt{49} \cdot \sqrt{10^n} = 7\sqrt{10^n}$

Mixed Review

70. $(-1, -4)$
71. $(4, 1)$
72. $(3, -2)$
73. $\frac{a^2 + 4}{2a^2 + 3a + 7}$
74. $\frac{x + 2}{x^2}$
75. 35, 16

Bonus Topic

When simplifying cube roots, it is helpful to arrange the factors into two groups, those that are perfect cubes and those that are not. You may want to have students practice finding perfect cube roots of the following.
8, 64, 125, 216, 1000, a^{12}
2, 4, 5, 6, 10, a^4

ANSWERS

1. 2 **2.** 3
3. 5 **4.** 10
5. -2 **6.** -4
7. -1 **8.** -20
9. x **10.** y
11. ab **12.** $n\sqrt[3]{m}$
13. $3x^2y$ **14.** $5m^3n^4$
15. $-2a^2b^3$ **16.** $-5p^4$
17. xy^2 **18.** m^2n^4
19. $a^2b^3\sqrt[3]{30ab^2}$

Challenge

Use the proper symbol (>, <, or =) between each pair of values. Assume x is positive.

60. $15 > \sqrt{14}$ **61.** $15\sqrt{2} = \sqrt{450}$ **62.** $16 > \sqrt{15}\sqrt{17}$
63. $3\sqrt{11} > 7\sqrt{2}$ **64.** $5\sqrt{7} < 4\sqrt{11}$ **65.** $8 < \sqrt{15}\sqrt{17}$
66. $3\sqrt{x} < 2\sqrt{2.5x}$ **67.** $4\sqrt{x} = 5\sqrt{0.64x}$
68. $90\sqrt{100x} < 100\sqrt{90x}$ **69.** $4\sqrt{5x} < \sqrt{12x} + 4\sqrt{2x}$

Mixed Review

Solve. **70.** $5x + y = -9$, $2x - y = 2$ **71.** $2x + 3y = 11$, $5y - x = 1$ **72.** $5y + 3x = -1$, $2x - 2y = 10$

Simplify. **73.** $\frac{6a^2 + 24}{12a^2 + 18a + 42}$ **74.** $\frac{(x + 3)}{x^2} \cdot \frac{(x + 2)}{(x + 3)}$

Solve. **75.** The sum of two numbers is 51 and the difference of the two numbers is 19. Find the two numbers.

Bonus Topic: Cube Roots

Objective: Find cube roots.

The number c is called the **cube root** of a if $c^3 = a$. We write this as $c = \sqrt[3]{a}$.

$\sqrt[3]{216} = 6$, since $6^3 = 216$ and $\sqrt[3]{-216} = -6$, since $(-6)^3 = -216$

The procedures you have learned for multiplying, factoring, and simplifying expressions involving square roots also apply to cube roots.

EXAMPLE Simplify.

$$\begin{aligned}\sqrt[3]{16a^4} &= \sqrt[3]{8 \cdot 2 \cdot a^3 \cdot a} && \text{Identifying factors that are perfect cubes} \\ &= \sqrt[3]{2^3 \cdot 2 \cdot a^3 \cdot a} \\ &= \sqrt[3]{2^3 \cdot a^3} \cdot \sqrt[3]{2a} \\ &= 2a\sqrt[3]{2a}\end{aligned}$$

Exercises

Simplify.

1. $\sqrt[3]{8}$ **2.** $\sqrt[3]{27}$ **3.** $\sqrt[3]{125}$ **4.** $\sqrt[3]{1000}$
5. $\sqrt[3]{-8}$ **6.** $\sqrt[3]{-64}$ **7.** $\sqrt[3]{-1}$ **8.** $\sqrt[3]{-8000}$
9. $\sqrt[3]{x^3}$ **10.** $\sqrt[3]{y^3}$ **11.** $\sqrt[3]{a^3b^3}$ **12.** $\sqrt[3]{mn^3}$
13. $\sqrt[3]{27x^6y^3}$ **14.** $\sqrt[3]{125m^9n^{12}}$ **15.** $\sqrt[3]{-8a^6b^9}$ **16.** $\sqrt[3]{-125p^{12}}$
17. $\sqrt[3]{x^2y} \cdot \sqrt[3]{xy^5}$ **18.** $\sqrt[3]{m^4n^5} \cdot \sqrt[3]{m^2n^7}$ **19.** $\sqrt[3]{6a^4b^4} \cdot \sqrt[3]{5a^3b^7}$

11-4 Multiplying Radical Expressions

Objective: Multiply radical expressions.

We know that for nonnegative numbers,

$$\sqrt{ab} = \sqrt{a} \cdot \sqrt{b}$$

We can use the product property for radicals to multiply radicals. It can also be used to simplify radicals.

EXAMPLES Multiply.

1. $\sqrt{5} \cdot \sqrt{7} = \sqrt{5 \cdot 7} = \sqrt{35}$
2. $\sqrt{8} \cdot \sqrt{8} = \sqrt{8 \cdot 8} = \sqrt{64} = 8$
3. $\sqrt{\frac{2}{3}} \cdot \sqrt{\frac{4}{5}} = \sqrt{\frac{2}{3} \cdot \frac{4}{5}} = \sqrt{\frac{8}{15}}$
4. $\sqrt{2x} \cdot \sqrt{3x - 1} = \sqrt{2x(3x - 1)} = \sqrt{6x^2 - 2x}$

Try This Multiply.

a. $\sqrt{3} \cdot \sqrt{7}$ $\sqrt{21}$ **b.** $\sqrt{5} \cdot \sqrt{5}$ $\sqrt{25}$, or 5 **c.** $\sqrt{x} \cdot \sqrt{x + 1}$ $\sqrt{x^2 + x}$ **d.** $\sqrt{x + 1} \cdot \sqrt{x - 1}$ $\sqrt{x^2 - 1}$

Sometimes we can simplify after multiplying. We can find perfect square factors and take their square roots.

EXAMPLES Multiply and simplify.

5. $\sqrt{2} \cdot \sqrt{14} = \sqrt{2 \cdot 14}$ Multiplying
$= \sqrt{2 \cdot 2 \cdot 7}$ Factoring to find perfect square factors
$= \sqrt{2 \cdot 2} \cdot \sqrt{7}$
$= 2\sqrt{7}$

6. $\sqrt{3x^2} \cdot \sqrt{9x^3} = \sqrt{3 \cdot 9x^5}$ Multiplying
$= \sqrt{3 \cdot 9 \cdot x^4 \cdot x}$ Factoring to find perfect square factors
$= \sqrt{9 \cdot x^4 \cdot 3 \cdot x}$ Identifying perfect squares
$= \sqrt{9} \cdot \sqrt{x^4} \cdot \sqrt{3x}$
$= 3x^2\sqrt{3x}$

Try This Multiply and simplify.

e. $\sqrt{3y} \cdot \sqrt{6}$ $3\sqrt{2y}$ **f.** $\sqrt{2x} \cdot \sqrt{50x}$ $10x$ **g.** $\sqrt{2x^3} \cdot \sqrt{8x^3y^4}$ $4x^3y^2$
h. $\sqrt{10xy^2} \cdot \sqrt{5x^2y^3}$ $5xy^2\sqrt{2xy}$ **i.** $\sqrt{12x^3y^2} \cdot \sqrt{3x^2y^6}$ $6x^2y^4\sqrt{x}$

11-4

FIRST FIVE MINUTES

1. Multiply $\sqrt{7} \cdot \sqrt{6}$.
$\sqrt{42}$
2. Multiply $\sqrt{2x} \cdot \sqrt{x + 1}$.
$\sqrt{2x(x + 1)} = \sqrt{2x^2 + 2x}$
3. Simplify $\sqrt{16x}$.
$\sqrt{16} \cdot \sqrt{x} = 4\sqrt{x}$

Key Question

- Why can't we multiply and simplify $\sqrt{-5} \cdot \sqrt{-5} = \sqrt{25} = 5$?
Because the product property for radicals is only true for nonnegative radicands.

Chalkboard Examples

Multiply.

1. $\sqrt{3} \cdot \sqrt{12}$
$\sqrt{36} = 6$
2. $\sqrt{7} \cdot \sqrt{7}$
$\sqrt{49} = 7$
3. $\frac{\sqrt{5}}{3} \cdot \frac{\sqrt{7}}{2}$
$\frac{\sqrt{5}}{3} \cdot \frac{\sqrt{7}}{2} = \frac{\sqrt{35}}{6}$
4. $\sqrt{3x}\sqrt{5x + 2}$
$\sqrt{3x(5x + 2)} = \sqrt{15x^2 + 6x}$

Multiply and simplify.

5. $\sqrt{6} \cdot \sqrt{54}$
$\sqrt{6} \cdot \sqrt{6} \cdot \sqrt{9} = 6 \cdot 3 = 18$
6. $\sqrt{5x}\sqrt{20x^3}$
$\sqrt{100x^4} = 10x^2$

LESSON QUIZ

1. Multiply $\sqrt{7} \cdot \sqrt{11}$.
$\sqrt{77}$
2. Multiply $\sqrt{x + 1} \cdot \sqrt{x - 1}$.
$\sqrt{(x + 1)(x - 1)} = \sqrt{x^2 - 1}$
3. Multiply and simplify $\sqrt{2} \cdot \sqrt{50}$.
10
4. Multiply and simplify $\sqrt{3x} \cdot \sqrt{12x}$.
$6x$

Assignment Guide
Minimum: 1–50 e/o, MR

Regular: 1–62 m3, 63, MR

Advanced: 1–62 m4, 63–66, MR, assign w. Bonus Topic

ADDITIONAL ANSWERS

Exercises

1. $\sqrt{6}$ **2.** $\sqrt{15}$
3. 17 **4.** $5\sqrt{3}$
5. $\sqrt{2x}$ **6.** $\sqrt{3a}$
7. $\sqrt{x^2 - 3x}$ **8.** $\sqrt{10x - 5}$
9. $\sqrt{x^2 + 3x + 2}$ **10.** $\sqrt{x^2 - 16}$
11. $\sqrt{2x^2 - 2x - 12}$
12. $\sqrt{2x^2 - 3x - 20}$
13. $\sqrt{2xy + y^2}$ **14.** $\sqrt{9a^2 + 6ab}$
15. $\sqrt{3x^2 + 4xy}$ **16.** $\sqrt{x^2 - y^2}$
17. $\sqrt{a^2 - b^2}$ **18.** $\sqrt{x^2 + x - 12}$
19. $3\sqrt{6}$ **20.** $5\sqrt{2}$
21. $3\sqrt{10}$ **22.** 9
23. $6\sqrt{7x}$ **24.** $6\sqrt{6x}$
25. $6\sqrt{xy}$ **26.** $7\sqrt{3xy}$
27. 10 **28.** $11\sqrt{x}$
29. $5b\sqrt{3}$ **30.** $6a\sqrt{3}$
31. $2t$ **32.** $3a$
33. $a\sqrt{bc}$ **34.** $x\sqrt{yz}$
35. $2xy\sqrt{2xy}$ **36.** $5mn\sqrt{3mn}$
37. $6xy^3\sqrt{3xy}$ **38.** $4x^2y\sqrt{6y}$
39. $10ab^2\sqrt{5ab}$ **40.** $10a\sqrt{b}$
41. $12x\sqrt{y}$ **42.** $7a^2b\sqrt{6ab}$
43. $8xy^4\sqrt{7x}$ **44.** $2x^5y^2\sqrt{5x}$
45. $3x^2y^8\sqrt{5y}$ **46.** $4x^2yz^2\sqrt{5y}$
47. $2x^2y^3z\sqrt{15y}$ **48.** $30x^2\sqrt{3}$
49. $42x^5\sqrt{2}$ **50.** $10x^7\sqrt{3}$
51. $4y\sqrt{3}$ **52.** $a^2 - 5\sqrt{a}$
53. $18(x + 1)\sqrt{y(x + 1)}$
54. $6(x - 2)^2\sqrt{10}$
55. $2x^3\sqrt{5x}$
56. $0.2x^{2n}$
57. $2^{54}x^{158}\sqrt{2x}$
58. $7y^{13}x^{157}\sqrt{3xy}$
59. $(x + 9)^{51}\sqrt{x + 9}$
60. $(a + 2b)^{17}$
61. $x^ny^n\sqrt{y}$
62. $x^{n+1}y^{2n}\sqrt{xy}$
63. No. Consider $a = 1$ and $b = 1$. $\sqrt{1} + \sqrt{1} = 2$; $\sqrt{1 + 1} = \sqrt{2}$

11-4 EXERCISES

A

Multiply.

1. $\sqrt{2} \cdot \sqrt{3}$ **2.** $\sqrt{3} \cdot \sqrt{5}$ **3.** $\sqrt{17} \cdot \sqrt{17}$
4. $\sqrt{25} \cdot \sqrt{3}$ **5.** $\sqrt{2} \cdot \sqrt{x}$ **6.** $\sqrt{3} \cdot \sqrt{a}$
7. $\sqrt{x} \cdot \sqrt{x - 3}$ **8.** $\sqrt{5} \cdot \sqrt{2x - 1}$ **9.** $\sqrt{x + 2} \cdot \sqrt{x + 1}$
10. $\sqrt{x + 4} \cdot \sqrt{x - 4}$ **11.** $\sqrt{x - 3} \cdot \sqrt{2x + 4}$ **12.** $\sqrt{2x + 5} \cdot \sqrt{x - 4}$
13. $\sqrt{y} \cdot \sqrt{2x + y}$ **14.** $\sqrt{3a} \cdot \sqrt{3a + 2b}$ **15.** $\sqrt{x} \cdot \sqrt{3x + 4y}$
16. $\sqrt{x + y} \cdot \sqrt{x - y}$ **17.** $\sqrt{a - b} \cdot \sqrt{a + b}$ **18.** $\sqrt{x - 3} \cdot \sqrt{x + 4}$

Multiply and simplify.

19. $\sqrt{3} \cdot \sqrt{18}$ **20.** $\sqrt{5} \cdot \sqrt{10}$ **21.** $\sqrt{15} \cdot \sqrt{6}$
22. $\sqrt{3} \cdot \sqrt{27}$ **23.** $\sqrt{18} \cdot \sqrt{14x}$ **24.** $\sqrt{12} \cdot \sqrt{18x}$
25. $\sqrt{3x} \cdot \sqrt{12y}$ **26.** $\sqrt{7x} \cdot \sqrt{21y}$ **27.** $\sqrt{10} \cdot \sqrt{10}$
28. $\sqrt{11} \cdot \sqrt{11x}$ **29.** $\sqrt{5b} \cdot \sqrt{15b}$ **30.** $\sqrt{6a} \cdot \sqrt{18a}$
31. $\sqrt{2t} \cdot \sqrt{2t}$ **32.** $\sqrt{3a} \cdot \sqrt{3a}$ **33.** $\sqrt{ab} \cdot \sqrt{ac}$
34. $\sqrt{xy} \cdot \sqrt{xz}$ **35.** $\sqrt{2x^2y} \cdot \sqrt{4xy^2}$ **36.** $\sqrt{15mn^2} \cdot \sqrt{5m^2n}$
37. $\sqrt{18x^2y^3} \cdot \sqrt{6xy^4}$ **38.** $\sqrt{12x^3y^2} \cdot \sqrt{8xy}$ **39.** $\sqrt{50ab} \cdot \sqrt{10a^2b^4}$
40. $\sqrt{5a} \cdot \sqrt{20ab}$ **41.** $\sqrt{6xy} \cdot \sqrt{24x}$ **42.** $\sqrt{7a^2b} \cdot \sqrt{42a^3b^2}$
43. $\sqrt{56x^2y^7} \cdot \sqrt{8xy}$ **44.** $\sqrt{10x^6y^3} \cdot \sqrt{2x^5y}$ **45.** $\sqrt{15xy^{12}} \cdot \sqrt{3x^3y^5}$
46. $\sqrt{8xyz^3} \cdot \sqrt{10x^3y^2z}$ **47.** $\sqrt{12x^3y^5z} \cdot \sqrt{5xy^2z}$ **48.** $\sqrt{12x^3} \cdot \sqrt{5x} \cdot \sqrt{45}$
49. $\sqrt{12x^6} \cdot \sqrt{7x^3} \cdot \sqrt{42x}$ **50.** $\sqrt{6x^3} \cdot \sqrt{5x^5} \cdot \sqrt{10x^6}$

B

Multiply and simplify.

51. $(\sqrt{2y})(\sqrt{3})(\sqrt{8y})$ **52.** $\sqrt{a}(\sqrt{a^3} - 5)$
53. $\sqrt{27(x + 1)} \cdot \sqrt{12y(x + 1)^2}$ **54.** $\sqrt{18(x - 2)} \cdot \sqrt{20(x - 2)^3}$
55. $\sqrt{x} \cdot \sqrt{2x} \cdot \sqrt{10x^5}$ **56.** $\sqrt{0.04x^{4n}}$
57. $\sqrt{2^{109}} \cdot \sqrt{x^{306}} \cdot \sqrt{x^{11}}$ **58.** $\sqrt{147} \cdot \sqrt{y^{27}} \cdot \sqrt{x^{315}}$
59. $\sqrt{(x + 9)^4} \cdot \sqrt{(x + 9)^{99}}$ **60.** $\sqrt{a^2 + 4ab + 4b^2} \cdot \sqrt{(a + 2b)^{32}}$
61. $\sqrt{x^{2n}} \cdot \sqrt{y^{2n+1}}$ **62.** $\sqrt{x^{2n}} \cdot \sqrt{x^3y^{3n}} \cdot \sqrt{y^{n+1}}$

63. ***Critical Thinking*** We know that $\sqrt{a} \cdot \sqrt{b} = \sqrt{ab}$ for positive real numbers. Is it also true that $\sqrt{a} + \sqrt{b} = \sqrt{a + b}$? Explain.

Challenge

64. Simplify $\sqrt{y^n}$, given n is an even whole number ≥ 2. $y^{(n/2)}$

65. Simplify $\sqrt{y^n}$, given n is an odd whole number ≥ 3. $y^{[(n-1)/2]}\sqrt{y}$

66. Multiply $(x^2 + \sqrt{2}xy + y^2)$ by $(x^2 - \sqrt{2}xy + y^2)$. Use your result to factor $x^8 + y^8$. $x^4 + y^4$; $(x^4 + \sqrt{2}x^2y^2 + y^4)(x^4 - \sqrt{2}x^2y^2 + y^4)$

Mixed Review

Simplify. **67.** $m^6 \cdot m^2$ **68.** $(3y^2)^3$ **69.** $(4x^3)(x^2)$ **70.** $(4c^2)(-2c^3)$

Factor. **71.** $a^2 - b^2$ **72.** $144y^2 - 1$ **73.** $4m^2 - 9n^2$

Simplify. **74.** $\frac{-7x}{x+3} - \frac{2x+9}{x+3}$ **75.** $\frac{4}{x} + \frac{3}{x^2}$ **76.** $\frac{x+1}{2} - \frac{x-3}{4}$

Find the square roots of each number. **77.** 36 **78.** 121 **79.** 625

Simplify. **80.** $\sqrt{16}$ **81.** $-\sqrt{36}$ **82.** $-\sqrt{225}$ **83.** $\sqrt{81}$

Bonus Topic: Approximating Square Roots

Objective: Find rational approximations of square roots.

You can find a rational approximation of a square root by using a calculator or using a table of square roots. Table 1 in the Appendix lists square root approximations for numbers less than or equal to 100. Square root approximations for numbers greater than 100 can often be found by first factoring and then using the table of square root approximations.

EXAMPLES Approximate these square roots.

1. $\sqrt{160}$

Using Table 1: $\sqrt{160} = \sqrt{16 \cdot 10}$ — Choosing a factor of the radicand as a perfect square

$= \sqrt{16} \cdot \sqrt{10}$

$= 4\sqrt{10}$

$\approx 4(3.162)$ — Using Table 1, $\sqrt{10} \approx 3.162$

≈ 12.648

Using a calculator: $\sqrt{160} \approx 12.649111$

≈ 12.649 — Rounding to the nearest thousandth

2. $\sqrt{341}$

Using Table 1: $\sqrt{341} = \sqrt{11 \cdot 31}$ — There is no perfect square factor.

$= \sqrt{11} \cdot \sqrt{31}$

$\approx 3.317 \times 5.568$

≈ 18.469 — Rounding to the nearest thousandth

Using a calculator: $\sqrt{341} \approx 18.466185$

≈ 18.466 — Rounding to the nearest thousandth

Exercises

Approximate these square roots.

1. $\sqrt{125}$ **2.** $\sqrt{124}$ **3.** $\sqrt{180}$ **4.** $\sqrt{150}$

5. $\sqrt{360}$ **6.** $\sqrt{250}$ **7.** $\sqrt{105}$ **8.** $\sqrt{115}$

9. $\sqrt{4500}$ **10.** $\sqrt{3200}$ **11.** $\sqrt{15{,}000}$ **12.** $\sqrt{60{,}000}$

Mixed Review

67. m^8
68. $27y^6$
69. $4x^5$
70. $-8c^5$
71. $(a + b)(a - b)$
72. $(12y - 1)(12y + 1)$
73. $(2m + 3n)(2m - 3n)$
74. $\frac{-9(x+1)}{x+3}$
75. $\frac{4x+3}{x^2}$
76. $\frac{x+5}{4}$
77. ± 6
78. ± 11
79. ± 25
80. 4
81. -6
82. -15
83. 9

Bonus Topic

Note the differences that occur in the approximations of square roots when using a table and when using a calculator. The differences are due to the fact that a table is rounded to the thousandths place. In Example 1, the square root of 10, 3.162, is multiplied by four, which accentuates the error.

Differences can also occur from using different factors before using the square root table. Example 1 could be factored as $\sqrt{4} \cdot \sqrt{40} = 2(6.325) = 12.65$.

You may want to ask students to determine which answer is more accurate. They could use their calculators to find the square of each answer and compare.

ANSWERS

	Using Table 1	Using a calculator
1.	11.180	11.180
2.	11.136	11.136
3.	13.416	13.416
4.	12.245	12.247
5.	18.972	18.974
6.	15.810	15.811
7.	10.247 or 10.248	10.247
8.	10.724	10.724
9.	67.08	67.082
10.	56.57	56.569
11.	122.464	122.474
12.	244.9	244.949

11-5

FIRST FIVE MINUTES

1. Simplify $\sqrt{2x} \cdot \sqrt{18x^3}$.
   $\sqrt{36x^4} = 6x^2$
2. Simplify $\sqrt{7x} \cdot \sqrt{7xy^2}$.
   $\sqrt{49x^2y^2} = 7xy$
3. Simplify $\sqrt{x^{18}}$.
   x^9
4. Simplify $\sqrt{121x^4y^3}$.
   $11x^2y\sqrt{y}$

EXPLORE

Students should realize that $\frac{\sqrt{36}}{\sqrt{9}} = \sqrt{\frac{36}{9}}$. From this, they may be able to generalize the division property for radicals.

Dividing with Radicals

Assume that all variables in the radicand are nonnegative in this lesson.

Some students may find a verbal rule useful. "The radical of a quotient is the quotient of the radicals."

Key Questions

- Which is greater, 38 or 38^2?
  38^2
- Which is greater, $\frac{3}{8}$ or $\left(\frac{3}{8}\right)^2$?
  $\frac{3}{8}$

Chalkboard Examples

Simplify.

1. $\sqrt{\frac{36}{25}}$ $\frac{6}{5}$
2. $\sqrt{\frac{12}{75}}$ $\sqrt{\frac{4 \cdot 3}{25 \cdot 3}} = \frac{2}{5}$

Divide.

3. $\frac{\sqrt{125}}{\sqrt{5}}$
   $\sqrt{\frac{125}{5}} = \sqrt{25} = 5$
4. $\frac{\sqrt{40b^3}}{\sqrt{10b^2}}$
   $\sqrt{\frac{40b^3}{10b^2}} = \sqrt{4b} = 2\sqrt{b}$

11-5 Dividing and Simplifying

Explore

Compare the following square roots.

$\frac{\sqrt{36}}{\sqrt{9}}$ $\frac{6}{3} = 2$ $\qquad$ $\sqrt{\frac{36}{9}}$ $\sqrt{4} = 2$

What do you notice about the results? They are the same.

Dividing with Radicals

Objective: Divide expressions involving radicals.

The above relationship suggests the following fact about square roots.

Division Property for Radicals

For any nonnegative real numbers a and b, where $b \neq 0$,

$$\sqrt{\frac{a}{b}} = \frac{\sqrt{a}}{\sqrt{b}} \quad \text{and} \quad \frac{\sqrt{a}}{\sqrt{b}} = \sqrt{\frac{a}{b}}$$

Fractional radicands with a perfect square numerator and a perfect square denominator can be simplified.

EXAMPLES Simplify.

1. $\sqrt{\frac{25}{9}} = \frac{5}{3}$, since $\frac{5}{3} \cdot \frac{5}{3} = \frac{25}{9}$ $\qquad$ 2. $\sqrt{\frac{1}{16}} = \frac{1}{4}$, since $\frac{1}{4} \cdot \frac{1}{4} = \frac{1}{16}$

Sometimes a fractional radicand can be simplified to a perfect square.

EXAMPLE 3 Simplify.

$$\sqrt{\frac{18}{50}} = \sqrt{\frac{9}{25} \cdot \frac{2}{2}} = \sqrt{\frac{9}{25}} = \frac{3}{5}$$

Try This Simplify.

a. $\sqrt{\frac{16}{9}}$ $\frac{4}{3}$ **b.** $\sqrt{\frac{1}{25}}$ $\frac{1}{5}$ **c.** $\sqrt{\frac{1}{9}}$ $\frac{1}{3}$ **d.** $\sqrt{\frac{18}{32}}$ $\frac{3}{4}$ **e.** $\sqrt{\frac{2250}{2560}}$ $\frac{15}{16}$

We can use the division property for radicals to simplify radicals with fractions and to divide radicals.

EXAMPLES Divide and simplify.

4. $\frac{\sqrt{27}}{\sqrt{3}} = \sqrt{\frac{27}{3}} = \sqrt{9} = 3$

5. $\frac{\sqrt{30a^3}}{\sqrt{6a^2}} = \sqrt{\frac{30a^3}{6a^2}} = \sqrt{5a}$

Try This Divide and simplify.

f. $\frac{\sqrt{50}}{\sqrt{2}}$ 5 **g.** $\frac{\sqrt{42x^4}}{\sqrt{7x^2}}$ $x\sqrt{6}$

Rationalizing the Denominator

Objective: Rationalize the denominator.

An expression containing radicals is simplified when the following conditions are met.

- The radicand contains no perfect square factors.
- A fraction in simplest form does not have a radical in the denominator.
- A simplified radical does not contain a fractional radicand.

The process of removing a fraction from the radicand or a radical from the denominator is called **rationalizing the denominator**

EXAMPLES Simplify.

6. $\frac{\sqrt{2}}{\sqrt{3}} = \frac{\sqrt{2}}{\sqrt{3}} \cdot \frac{\sqrt{3}}{\sqrt{3}}$ Multiplying by 1; $\frac{\sqrt{3}}{\sqrt{3}} = 1$

$= \frac{\sqrt{2} \cdot \sqrt{3}}{\sqrt{3} \cdot \sqrt{3}}$

$= \frac{\sqrt{6}}{3}$ or $\frac{1}{3}\sqrt{6}$

7. $\frac{6}{\sqrt{2}} = \frac{6}{\sqrt{2}} \cdot \frac{\sqrt{2}}{\sqrt{2}}$ Multiplying by 1; $\frac{\sqrt{2}}{\sqrt{2}} = 1$

$= \frac{6 \cdot \sqrt{2}}{\sqrt{2} \cdot \sqrt{2}}$

$= \frac{6\sqrt{2}}{2}$

$= 3\sqrt{2}$

Rationalizing the Denominator

Using a table and computing without a calculator,

$\frac{\sqrt{2}}{\sqrt{3}} = 1.414 \div 1.732$

is more difficult to compute than

$\frac{\sqrt{6}}{3} = 2.449 \div 3$

Before the advent of the calculator, rationalizing the denominator was very important for the purpose of calculation. With calculators, a radical in the denominator is no longer a problem. The answers in this book, however, will be in what is traditionally known as simplified form, with the denominators rationalized.

Point out that when rationalizing a denominator, the first step is to multiply by the smallest number that will make the denominator a perfect square. Multiplying by the denominator will always give a perfect square. Sometimes, you can multiply by something other than the denominator, as shown in Example 10.

Chalkboard Examples

Rationalize the denominator.

1. $\frac{\sqrt{5}}{\sqrt{7}}$

$\frac{\sqrt{5}}{\sqrt{7}} \cdot \frac{\sqrt{7}}{\sqrt{7}} = \frac{\sqrt{35}}{7}$ or $\frac{1}{7}\sqrt{35}$

2. $\frac{3}{\sqrt{2}}$

$\frac{3}{\sqrt{2}} \cdot \frac{\sqrt{2}}{\sqrt{2}} = \frac{3\sqrt{2}}{2}$ or $\frac{3}{2}\sqrt{2}$

3. $\frac{\sqrt{7}}{\sqrt{y}}$

$\frac{\sqrt{7}}{\sqrt{y}} \cdot \frac{\sqrt{y}}{\sqrt{y}} = \frac{\sqrt{7y}}{y}$ or $\frac{1}{y}\sqrt{7y}$

4. $\frac{\sqrt{81z^3}}{\sqrt{6}}$

Simplify the numerator first.

$\frac{\sqrt{81z^3}}{\sqrt{6}} = \frac{9z\sqrt{z}}{\sqrt{6}} \cdot \frac{\sqrt{6}}{\sqrt{6}}$

$= \frac{9z\sqrt{6z}}{6} = \frac{3z\sqrt{6z}}{2}$

LESSON QUIZ

1. Simplify $\frac{\sqrt{100}}{\sqrt{64}}$. $\frac{5}{4}$
2. Divide and simplify. $\frac{\sqrt{27x^3}}{\sqrt{3x}}$ $3x$
3. Rationalize the denominator. $\frac{\sqrt{7x}}{\sqrt{5}}$ $\frac{\sqrt{35x}}{5}$

8. $\frac{\sqrt{5}}{\sqrt{x}} = \frac{\sqrt{5}}{\sqrt{x}} \cdot \frac{\sqrt{x}}{\sqrt{x}}$ Multiplying by 1; $\frac{\sqrt{x}}{\sqrt{x}} = 1$

$= \frac{\sqrt{5} \cdot \sqrt{x}}{\sqrt{x} \cdot \sqrt{x}}$

$= \frac{\sqrt{5x}}{x}$

Try This Simplify.

h. $\frac{\sqrt{5}}{\sqrt{7}}$ $\frac{\sqrt{35}}{7}$ **i.** $\frac{8}{\sqrt{6}}$ $\frac{4\sqrt{6}}{3}$ **j.** $\frac{\sqrt{x}}{\sqrt{y}}$ $\frac{\sqrt{xy}}{y}$

If the radicand is a fraction, it can be simplified by writing it as a division of radicals and proceeding as above.

EXAMPLES Simplify.

9. $\sqrt{\frac{3}{4}} = \frac{\sqrt{3}}{\sqrt{4}}$ Writing as a division of radicals

$= \frac{\sqrt{3}}{2}$

10. $\sqrt{\frac{5}{12}} = \frac{\sqrt{5}}{\sqrt{12}} \cdot \frac{\sqrt{3}}{\sqrt{3}}$ Multiplying by 1; $\frac{\sqrt{3}}{\sqrt{3}} = 1$

$= \frac{\sqrt{15}}{\sqrt{36}}$

$= \frac{\sqrt{15}}{6}$

11. $\sqrt{\frac{2y}{5x^3}} = \frac{\sqrt{2y}}{\sqrt{5x^3}}$

$= \frac{\sqrt{2y}}{\sqrt{5x^3}} \cdot \frac{\sqrt{5x}}{\sqrt{5x}}$ Multiplying by 1; $\frac{\sqrt{5x}}{\sqrt{5x}} = 1$

$= \frac{\sqrt{10yx}}{\sqrt{25x^4}}$

$= \frac{\sqrt{10yx}}{5x^2}$

Try This Simplify.

k. $\sqrt{\frac{3}{7}}$ $\frac{\sqrt{21}}{7}$ **l.** $\sqrt{\frac{5}{8}}$ $\frac{\sqrt{10}}{4}$ **m.** $\sqrt{\frac{2}{27}}$ $\frac{\sqrt{6}}{9}$ **n.** $\sqrt{\frac{5}{2a}}$ $\frac{\sqrt{10a}}{2a}$

o. $\sqrt{\frac{7}{3b^5}}$ $\frac{\sqrt{21b}}{3b^3}$ **p.** $\sqrt{\frac{x}{18y^3}}$ $\frac{\sqrt{2xy}}{6y^2}$

11-5 EXERCISES

A

Simplify.

1. $\sqrt{\frac{9}{49}}$ $\frac{3}{7}$ **2.** $\sqrt{\frac{16}{25}}$ $\frac{4}{5}$ **3.** $\sqrt{\frac{1}{36}}$ $\frac{1}{6}$ **4.** $\sqrt{\frac{1}{4}}$ $\frac{1}{2}$

5. $-\sqrt{\frac{16}{81}}$ $-\frac{4}{9}$ **6.** $-\sqrt{\frac{25}{49}}$ $\frac{-5}{7}$ **7.** $\sqrt{\frac{64}{289}}$ $\frac{8}{17}$ **8.** $\sqrt{\frac{81}{361}}$ $\frac{9}{19}$

9. $-\sqrt{\frac{9}{100}}$ $-\frac{3}{10}$ **10.** $-\sqrt{\frac{49}{100}}$ $-\frac{7}{10}$ **11.** $\sqrt{\frac{27}{75}}$ $\frac{3}{5}$ **12.** $\sqrt{\frac{50}{18}}$ $\frac{5}{3}$

Divide and simplify.

13. $\frac{\sqrt{18}}{\sqrt{2}}$ 3 **14.** $\frac{\sqrt{20}}{\sqrt{5}}$ 2 **15.** $\frac{\sqrt{60}}{\sqrt{15}}$ 2 **16.** $\frac{\sqrt{108}}{\sqrt{3}}$ 6

17. $\frac{\sqrt{75}}{\sqrt{15}}$ $\sqrt{5}$ **18.** $\frac{\sqrt{18}}{\sqrt{3}}$ $\sqrt{6}$ **19.** $\frac{\sqrt{3}}{\sqrt{75}}$ $\frac{1}{5}$ **20.** $\frac{\sqrt{3}}{\sqrt{48}}$ $\frac{1}{4}$

21. $\frac{\sqrt{12}}{\sqrt{75}}$ $\frac{2}{5}$ **22.** $\frac{\sqrt{18}}{\sqrt{32}}$ $\frac{3}{4}$ **23.** $\frac{\sqrt{8x}}{\sqrt{2x}}$ 2 **24.** $\frac{\sqrt{18b}}{\sqrt{2b}}$ 3

25. $\frac{\sqrt{63y^3}}{\sqrt{7y}}$ $3y$ **26.** $\frac{\sqrt{48x^3}}{\sqrt{3x}}$ $4x$ **27.** $\frac{\sqrt{15x^5}}{\sqrt{3x}}$ $x^2\sqrt{5}$ **28.** $\frac{\sqrt{30a^5}}{\sqrt{5a}}$ $a^2\sqrt{6}$

29. $\frac{\sqrt{7}}{\sqrt{3}}$ $\frac{1}{3}\sqrt{21}$ **30.** $\frac{\sqrt{2}}{\sqrt{5}}$ $\frac{1}{5}\sqrt{10}$ **31.** $\frac{\sqrt{9}}{\sqrt{8}}$ $\frac{3}{4}\sqrt{2}$ **32.** $\frac{\sqrt{4}}{\sqrt{27}}$ $\frac{2}{9}\sqrt{3}$

Simplify.

33. $\sqrt{\frac{2}{5}}$ **34.** $\sqrt{\frac{2}{7}}$ **35.** $\sqrt{\frac{3}{8}}$ **36.** $\sqrt{\frac{7}{8}}$

37. $\sqrt{\frac{7}{12}}$ **38.** $\sqrt{\frac{1}{12}}$ **39.** $\sqrt{\frac{1}{18}}$ **40.** $\sqrt{\frac{5}{18}}$

41. $\sqrt{\frac{1}{2}}$ **42.** $\sqrt{\frac{1}{3}}$ **43.** $\sqrt{\frac{8}{3}}$ **44.** $\sqrt{\frac{12}{5}}$

45. $\sqrt{\frac{3}{x}}$ **46.** $\sqrt{\frac{2}{x}}$ **47.** $\sqrt{\frac{x}{y}}$ **48.** $\sqrt{\frac{a}{b}}$

49. $\sqrt{\frac{x^2}{18}}$ **50.** $\sqrt{\frac{x^2}{20}}$ **51.** $\sqrt{\frac{6c}{2d^3}}$ **52.** $\sqrt{\frac{x}{8y^7}}$

Simplify.

53. $\frac{\sqrt{2}}{\sqrt{5}}$ $\frac{\sqrt{10}}{5}$ **54.** $\frac{\sqrt{3}}{\sqrt{2}}$ $\frac{\sqrt{6}}{2}$ **55.** $\frac{2}{\sqrt{2}}$ $\sqrt{2}$ **56.** $\frac{3}{\sqrt{3}}$ $\sqrt{3}$

57. $\frac{\sqrt{48}}{\sqrt{32}}$ $\frac{\sqrt{6}}{2}$ **58.** $\frac{\sqrt{56}}{\sqrt{40}}$ $\frac{\sqrt{35}}{5}$ **59.** $\frac{\sqrt{450}}{\sqrt{18}}$ 5 **60.** $\frac{\sqrt{224}}{\sqrt{14}}$ 4

61. $\frac{\sqrt{3}}{\sqrt{x}}$ $\frac{\sqrt{3x}}{x}$ **62.** $\frac{\sqrt{2}}{\sqrt{y}}$ $\frac{\sqrt{2y}}{y}$ **63.** $\frac{4y}{\sqrt{3}}$ $\frac{4y\sqrt{3}}{3}$ **64.** $\frac{8x}{\sqrt{5}}$ $\frac{8x\sqrt{5}}{5}$

Assignment Guide

Minimum: Day 1: 1–32 e/o
Day 2: 33–72 e/o, MR

Regular: Day 1: 1–32 e/o, assign w. Application
Day 2: 33–78 e/o, 79, MR

Advanced: Day 1: 1–72 m3, MR
Day 2: 73–84, assign w. Bonus Topic

ADDITIONAL ANSWERS

Exercises

33. $\frac{1}{5}\sqrt{10}$
34. $\frac{1}{7}\sqrt{14}$
35. $\frac{1}{4}\sqrt{6}$
36. $\frac{1}{4}\sqrt{14}$
37. $\frac{1}{6}\sqrt{21}$
38. $\frac{1}{6}\sqrt{3}$
39. $\frac{1}{6}\sqrt{2}$
40. $\frac{1}{6}\sqrt{10}$
41. $\frac{1}{2}\sqrt{2}$
42. $\frac{1}{3}\sqrt{3}$
43. $\frac{2}{3}\sqrt{6}$
44. $\frac{2}{5}\sqrt{15}$
45. $\frac{1}{x}\sqrt{3x}$
46. $\frac{1}{x}\sqrt{2x}$
47. $\frac{1}{y}\sqrt{xy}$
48. $\frac{1}{b}\sqrt{ab}$
49. $\frac{x\sqrt{2}}{6}$
50. $\frac{x\sqrt{5}}{10}$
51. $\frac{\sqrt{3cd}}{d^2}$
52. $\frac{\sqrt{2xy}}{4y^4}$

Mixed Review

85. Irrational
86. Rational
87. Irrational
88. Rational
89. Rational
90. Irrational
91. Rational
92. $(4a + 5c^2)(4a - 5c^2)$
93. $(x + 3)(x - 5)$
94. $5(m - 3)^2$
95. $(m - 3n)(2a + b)$
96. $\frac{11}{2}$
97. 4
98. 3
99. $x \geq 0$
100. Any real number
101. $x \geq 2$
102. $x \geq -\frac{5}{2}$

65. $\frac{\sqrt{a^3}}{\sqrt{8}}$ $\frac{a\sqrt{2a}}{4}$ **66.** $\frac{\sqrt{x^3}}{\sqrt{27}}$ $\frac{x\sqrt{3x}}{9}$ **67.** $\frac{\sqrt{56}}{\sqrt{12x}}$ $\frac{\sqrt{42x}}{3x}$ **68.** $\frac{\sqrt{45}}{\sqrt{8a}}$ $\frac{3\sqrt{10a}}{4a}$

69. $\frac{\sqrt{27c}}{\sqrt{32c^3}}$ $\frac{3\sqrt{6}}{8c}$ **70.** $\frac{\sqrt{7x^3}}{\sqrt{12x}}$ $\frac{x\sqrt{21}}{6}$ **71.** $\frac{\sqrt{y^5}}{\sqrt{xy^2}}$ $\frac{y\sqrt{xy}}{x}$ **72.** $\frac{\sqrt{x^3}}{\sqrt{xy}}$ $\frac{x\sqrt{y}}{y}$

B

Rationalize the denominator.

73. $\frac{\sqrt{2}}{3\sqrt{3}}$ $\frac{\sqrt{6}}{9}$ **74.** $\frac{3\sqrt{6}}{6\sqrt{2}}$ $\frac{\sqrt{3}}{2}$ **75.** $\frac{5\sqrt{2}}{3\sqrt{5}}$ $\frac{\sqrt{10}}{3}$

76. $\frac{3\sqrt{15}}{5\sqrt{32}}$ $\frac{3\sqrt{30}}{40}$ **77.** $\frac{4\sqrt{\frac{6}{7}}}{\sqrt{\frac{12}{63}}}$ $6\sqrt{2}$ **78.** $\frac{\sqrt{\frac{2}{3}}}{\sqrt{\frac{3}{2}}}$ $\frac{2}{3}$

79. ***Critical Thinking*** Rationalize the denominator of $\frac{a\sqrt{b}}{b\sqrt{a}}$. $\frac{\sqrt{ab}}{b}$

Challenge

Multiply.

80. $(\sqrt{5} + 7)(\sqrt{5} - 7)$ -44 **81.** $(1 + \sqrt{5})(1 - \sqrt{5})$ -4

82. $(\sqrt{6} - \sqrt{3})(\sqrt{6} + \sqrt{3})$ 3 **83.** $(\sqrt{3} + \sqrt{2})(\sqrt{3} + \sqrt{2})$ $5 + 2\sqrt{6}$

84. The period T of a pendulum is the time it takes for a pendulum of length L to move from one side to the other and back. A formula for the period is $T = 2\pi\sqrt{\frac{L}{32}}$ where T is in seconds and L is in feet. Use 3.14 for π.

a. Find the periods of pendulums of lengths 2 ft, 8 ft, 64 ft, and 100 ft. 1.57 s, 3.14 s, 8.88 s, 11.10 s

b. Find the period of a pendulum of length $\frac{2}{3}$ in. 0.262 s

c. The pendulum of a grandfather clock is $\frac{32}{\pi^2}$ feet long. How long does it take to swing from one side to the other? 1 s

Mixed Review

Identify the rational and irrational numbers. **85.** $\sqrt{7}$ **86.** $\sqrt{9}$ **87.** $\sqrt{135}$ **88.** $\sqrt{16}$ **89.** $\sqrt{144}$ **90.** $\sqrt{220}$ **91.** $\sqrt{0}$

Factor. **92.** $16a^2 - 25c^4$ **93.** $x^2 - 2x - 15$ **94.** $5m^2 - 30m + 45$ **95.** $2am + bm - 6an - 3bn$

Solve. **96.** $\frac{7}{2x} + \frac{2}{x} = 1$ **97.** $\frac{12}{x + 4} = \frac{3}{x - 2}$ **98.** $\frac{a + 1}{4a - 4} = \frac{1}{2}$

Determine the replacements for the variables that give real numbers. **99.** $\sqrt{3x}$ **100.** $\sqrt{2x^2}$ **101.** $\sqrt{x - 2}$ **102.** $\sqrt{2x + 5}$

Bonus Topic: Rational Exponents

Objective: Simplify expressions with rational exponents.

Your work with exponents thus far has been with integer exponents. Exponents can also be rational numbers.

If rational exponents are to follow the same rules as for integer exponents, it must be true that

$$3^{\frac{1}{2}} \cdot 3^{\frac{1}{2}} = 3^{\frac{1}{2}+\frac{1}{2}} = 3^1 = 3.$$

If we define $3^{\frac{1}{2}} = \sqrt{3}$, then our rules will work, since

$$\sqrt{3} \cdot \sqrt{3} = \sqrt{3^2} = 3$$

In general,

Definition

$a^{\frac{1}{k}} = \sqrt[k]{a}$ for any natural number k and any a, $a > 0$.

EXAMPLES Simplify.

1. $25^{\frac{1}{2}} = \sqrt{25} = 5$
2. $8^{\frac{1}{3}} = \sqrt[3]{8} = 2$

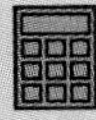

Finding Roots

Most calculators do not have cube root or other root keys. You can find a cube root or other roots of a number, however, using the y^x key.

For example, to find the cube root of 8, we first write $\sqrt[3]{8}$ using exponential notation.

$$\sqrt[3]{8} = 8^{\frac{1}{3}}$$

$8^{\frac{1}{3}} \rightarrow$ 8 [y^x] [( ] 1 [÷] 3 [ )] [=] $\rightarrow$ 2

For additional calculator practice, see Calculator Worksheet 23.

Exercises

Simplify.

1. $16^{\frac{1}{2}}$ 2. $81^{\frac{1}{2}}$ 3. $27^{\frac{1}{3}}$ 4. $125^{\frac{1}{3}}$ 5. $343^{\frac{1}{3}}$

6. $\left(9^{\frac{1}{2}}\right)^3$ 7. $\left(4^{\frac{1}{2}}\right)^3$ 8. $\left(64^{\frac{1}{3}}\right)^2$ 9. $\left(27^{\frac{1}{3}}\right)^2$ 10. $\left(125^{\frac{1}{3}}\right)^2$

Bonus Topic

Ask students to find the cube root of a number with their calculators, and most will respond that their calculator does not have a cube root key. This is a good way to give a practical demonstration of the use of rational exponents. Rational exponents allow us to find the cube root of any number. This can also be extended to finding any root desired, using $\frac{1}{4}$ to find the fourth root, $\frac{1}{5}$ to find the fifth root, and so on.

ANSWERS

1. 4
2. 9
3. 3
4. 5
5. 7
6. 27
7. 8
8. 16
9. 9
10. 25

11-6

FIRST FIVE MINUTES

1. Simplify $\frac{\sqrt{9}}{\sqrt{16}}$.

   $\frac{3}{4}$

2. Simplify $\frac{\sqrt{50x^3}}{\sqrt{2x}}$.

   $5x$

3. Rationalize the denominator. $\frac{\sqrt{3x}}{\sqrt{5}}$

   $\frac{\sqrt{15x}}{5}$

Emphasize that an expression such as $\sqrt{2}$ is a real number and can be manipulated like any other number. $3\sqrt{5} + 4\sqrt{5}$ can be added just as can $3x + 4x$.

Stress that $\sqrt{3} + \sqrt{2}$ cannot be added, just as $x + y$ cannot be added.

Key Questions

- Does $\sqrt{5} + \sqrt{6} = \sqrt{11}$?
  No
- Does $2\sqrt{3} + 3\sqrt{3} = 5\sqrt{3}$?
  Yes
- Does $\sqrt{3} + 2\sqrt{3} = 3\sqrt{6}$?
  No

Chalkboard Examples

Add or subtract.

1. $2\sqrt{7} + 6\sqrt{7}$
   $(2 + 6)\sqrt{7} = 8\sqrt{7}$
2. $\sqrt{12} - \sqrt{3}$
   $2\sqrt{3} - \sqrt{3} = \sqrt{3}$
3. $\sqrt{9y} + \sqrt{16y}$
   $3\sqrt{y} + 4\sqrt{y} = 7\sqrt{y}$
4. $\sqrt{a^5 + 2a^4} + \sqrt{a + 2}$
   $= \sqrt{a^4(a + 2)} + \sqrt{a + 2}$
   $= a^2\sqrt{a + 2} + \sqrt{a + 2}$
   $= (a^2 + 1)\sqrt{a + 2}$
5. $\sqrt{7} + \frac{\sqrt{1}}{\sqrt{7}}$
   $= \sqrt{7} + \frac{\sqrt{1}}{\sqrt{7}} \cdot \frac{\sqrt{7}}{\sqrt{7}}$
   $= \sqrt{7} + \frac{\sqrt{7}}{7}$
   $= \sqrt{7}\left(1 + \frac{1}{7}\right)$
   $= \frac{8}{7}\sqrt{7}$

11-6 Addition and Subtraction

Objective: Add and subtract radical expressions.

When we have radical expressions with the same radicands we can simplify using the distributive property.

EXAMPLE 1 Add.

$$3\sqrt{5} + 4\sqrt{5} = (3 + 4)\sqrt{5} \quad \text{Using the distributive property}$$
$$= 7\sqrt{5}$$

Sometimes we need to simplify the radicand before adding or subtracting.

EXAMPLES Add or subtract.

2. $\sqrt{2} - \sqrt{8} = \sqrt{2} - \sqrt{4 \cdot 2}$
$= \sqrt{2} - 2\sqrt{2}$ Simplifying
$= (1 - 2)\sqrt{2}$ Using the distributive property
$= -\sqrt{2}$

3. $\sqrt{x} + \sqrt{4x} = \sqrt{x} + 2\sqrt{x} = 3\sqrt{x}$

4. $\sqrt{x^3 - x^2} + \sqrt{4x - 4} = \sqrt{x^2(x - 1)} + \sqrt{4(x - 1)}$ Factoring radicands
$= \sqrt{x^2}\sqrt{x - 1} + \sqrt{4}\sqrt{x - 1}$
$= x\sqrt{x - 1} + 2\sqrt{x - 1}$
$= (x + 2)\sqrt{x - 1}$ Using the distributive property

Try This Add or subtract.

a. $3\sqrt{2} + 9\sqrt{2}$ $12\sqrt{2}$ **b.** $8\sqrt{5} - 3\sqrt{5}$ $5\sqrt{5}$ **c.** $2\sqrt{10} - 7\sqrt{40}$ $-12\sqrt{10}$
d. $\sqrt{24y} + \sqrt{54y}$ $5\sqrt{6y}$ **e.** $\sqrt{9x + 9} - \sqrt{4x + 4}$ $\sqrt{x + 1}$

Sometimes after rationalizing denominators, we can factor and combine expressions.

EXAMPLE 5

$$\sqrt{3} + \sqrt{\frac{1}{3}} = \sqrt{3} + \frac{\sqrt{1}}{\sqrt{3}}$$
$$= \sqrt{3} + \frac{\sqrt{1}}{\sqrt{3}} \cdot \frac{\sqrt{3}}{\sqrt{3}}$$
$$= \sqrt{3} + \frac{\sqrt{3}}{3}$$
$$= \frac{4}{3}\sqrt{3}$$

Try This Add or subtract.

f. $\sqrt{2} + \sqrt{\frac{1}{2}}$ $\frac{3}{2}\sqrt{2}$ **g.** $\sqrt{\frac{5}{3}} - \sqrt{\frac{3}{5}}$ $\frac{2\sqrt{15}}{15}$ **h.** $\frac{x}{\sqrt{x}} + \sqrt{x}$ $2\sqrt{x}$

11-6 EXERCISES

A

Add or subtract.

1. $3\sqrt{2} + 4\sqrt{2}$ $7\sqrt{2}$
2. $8\sqrt{3} + 3\sqrt{3}$ $11\sqrt{3}$
3. $7\sqrt{5} - 3\sqrt{5}$ $4\sqrt{5}$
4. $8\sqrt{2} - 5\sqrt{2}$ $3\sqrt{2}$
5. $6\sqrt{x} + 7\sqrt{x}$ $13\sqrt{x}$
6. $9\sqrt{y} + 3\sqrt{y}$ $12\sqrt{y}$
7. $9\sqrt{x} - 11\sqrt{x}$ $-2\sqrt{x}$
8. $6\sqrt{a} - 14\sqrt{a}$ $-8\sqrt{a}$
9. $5\sqrt{8} + 15\sqrt{2}$ $25\sqrt{2}$
10. $3\sqrt{12} + 2\sqrt{3}$ $8\sqrt{3}$
11. $\sqrt{27} - 2\sqrt{3}$ $\sqrt{3}$
12. $7\sqrt{50} - 3\sqrt{2}$ $32\sqrt{2}$
13. $\sqrt{45} - \sqrt{20}$ $\sqrt{5}$
14. $\sqrt{27} - \sqrt{12}$ $\sqrt{3}$
15. $\sqrt{72} + \sqrt{98}$ $13\sqrt{2}$
16. $\sqrt{45} + \sqrt{80}$ $7\sqrt{5}$
17. $2\sqrt{12} + \sqrt{27} - \sqrt{48}$
18. $9\sqrt{8} - \sqrt{72} + \sqrt{98}$
19. $3\sqrt{18} - 2\sqrt{32} - 5\sqrt{50}$
20. $\sqrt{18} - 3\sqrt{8} + \sqrt{50}$
21. $2\sqrt{27} - 3\sqrt{48} + 2\sqrt{18}$
22. $3\sqrt{48} - 2\sqrt{27} - 2\sqrt{18}$
23. $\sqrt{4x} + \sqrt{81x^3}$
24. $\sqrt{12x^2} + \sqrt{27}$
25. $\sqrt{27} - \sqrt{12x^2}$
26. $\sqrt{81x^3} - \sqrt{4x}$
27. $\sqrt{8x + 8} + \sqrt{2x + 2}$
28. $\sqrt{12x + 12} + \sqrt{3x + 3}$
29. $\sqrt{x^5 - x^2} + \sqrt{9x^3 - 9}$
30. $\sqrt{16x - 16} + \sqrt{25x^3 - 25x^2}$
31. $3x\sqrt{y^3x} - x\sqrt{yx^3} + y\sqrt{y^3x}$
32. $4a\sqrt{a^2b} + a\sqrt{a^2b^3} - 5\sqrt{b^3}$
33. $\sqrt{4(a + b)} - \sqrt{(a + b)^3}$
34. $\sqrt{x^2y} + \sqrt{4x^2y} + \sqrt{9y} - \sqrt{y^3}$
35. $\sqrt{3} - \sqrt{\frac{1}{3}}$ $\frac{2\sqrt{3}}{3}$
36. $\sqrt{2} - \sqrt{\frac{1}{2}}$ $\frac{\sqrt{2}}{2}$
37. $5\sqrt{2} + 3\sqrt{\frac{1}{2}}$ $\frac{13\sqrt{2}}{2}$
38. $4\sqrt{3} + 2\sqrt{\frac{1}{3}}$ $\frac{14\sqrt{3}}{3}$
39. $\sqrt{\frac{2}{3}} - \sqrt{\frac{1}{6}}$ $\frac{\sqrt{6}}{6}$
40. $\sqrt{\frac{1}{2}} - \sqrt{\frac{1}{8}}$ $\frac{\sqrt{2}}{4}$
41. $\sqrt{\frac{1}{12}} - \sqrt{\frac{1}{27}}$ $\frac{\sqrt{3}}{18}$
42. $\sqrt{\frac{5}{6}} - \sqrt{\frac{6}{5}}$ $\frac{-\sqrt{30}}{30}$

B

43. Three students were asked to simplify $\sqrt{10} + \sqrt{50}$. Their answers were $\sqrt{10}(1 + \sqrt{5})$, $\sqrt{10} + 5\sqrt{2}$, and $\sqrt{2}(5 + \sqrt{5})$.
    a. Which, if any, is incorrect? None
    b. Which is in simplest form? $\sqrt{10} + 5\sqrt{2}$

LESSON QUIZ

Add or subtract.

1. $8\sqrt{11} + 3\sqrt{11}$ $11\sqrt{11}$
2. $7\sqrt{45} - 4\sqrt{5}$ $17\sqrt{5}$
3. $3\sqrt{4a} + 5\sqrt{9a^3}$ $(6 + 15a)\sqrt{a}$

Assignment Guide

Minimum: 1–42 e/o, MR

Regular: 1–42 m3, 43–51 e/o, 52, MR

Advanced: 1–51 m3, 52–57, MR

ADDITIONAL ANSWERS

Exercises

17. $3\sqrt{3}$
18. $19\sqrt{2}$
19. $-24\sqrt{2}$
20. $2\sqrt{2}$
21. $6\sqrt{2} - 6\sqrt{3}$
22. $6\sqrt{3} - 6\sqrt{2}$
23. $(2 + 9x)\sqrt{x}$
24. $(2x + 3)\sqrt{3}$
25. $(3 - 2x)\sqrt{3}$
26. $(9x - 2)\sqrt{x}$
27. $3\sqrt{2x + 2}$
28. $3\sqrt{3x + 3}$
29. $(x + 3)\sqrt{x^3 - 1}$
30. $(4 + 5x)\sqrt{x - 1}$
31. $(-x^2 + 3xy + y^2)\sqrt{xy}$
32. $(4a^2 + a^2b - 5b)\sqrt{b}$
33. $(2 - a - b)\sqrt{a + b}$
34. $(3x + 3 - y)\sqrt{y}$

Mixed Review
58. $5y$
59. 6
60. $x + 2$
61. $y + 5$
62. $5\sqrt{3}$
63. $4\sqrt{3}$
64. 11
65. $\sqrt{a^2 - c^2}$
66. $2\sqrt{5}$
67. $4x\sqrt{y}$
68. $(x - 2)\sqrt{x}$

69.
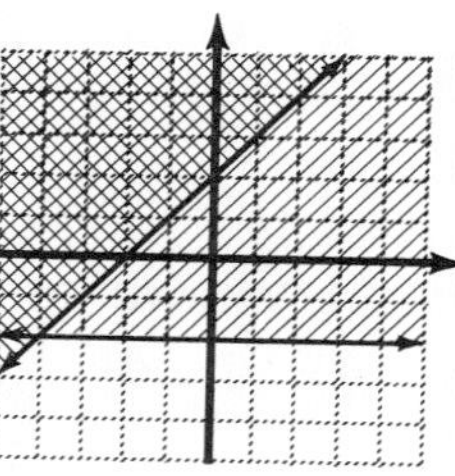

70.
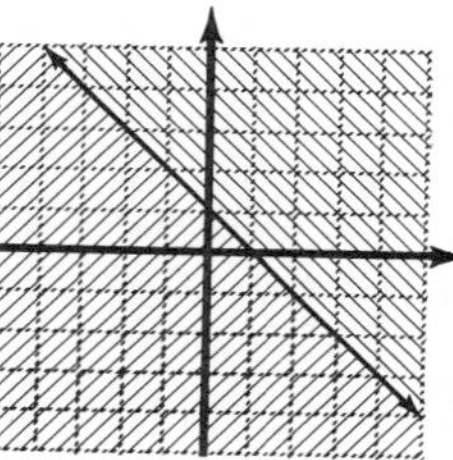

71.
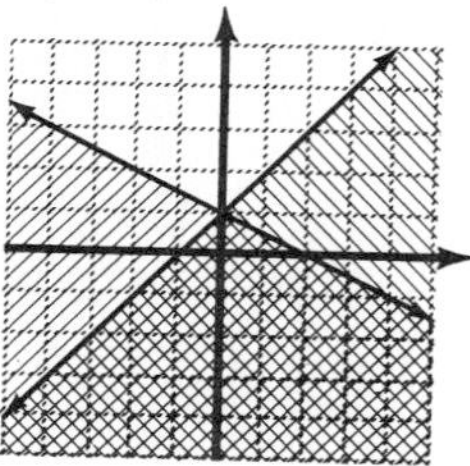

Add or subtract.

44. $\sqrt{125} - \sqrt{45} + 2\sqrt{5}$ $4\sqrt{5}$

45. $3\sqrt{\frac{1}{2}} + \frac{5}{2}\sqrt{18} + \sqrt{98}$ $16\sqrt{2}$

46. $\frac{3}{5}\sqrt{24} + \frac{2}{5}\sqrt{150} - \sqrt{96}$ $\frac{-4\sqrt{6}}{5}$

47. $\frac{1}{3}\sqrt{27} + \sqrt{8} + \sqrt{300} - \sqrt{18} - \sqrt{162}$ $11\sqrt{3} - 10\sqrt{2}$

48. $\sqrt{ab^6} + b\sqrt{a^3} + a\sqrt{a}$ $(b^3 + ab + a)\sqrt{a}$

49. $x\sqrt{2y} - \sqrt{8x^2y} + \frac{x}{3}\sqrt{18y}$ 0

50. $7x\sqrt{12xy^2} - 9y\sqrt{27x^3} + 5\sqrt{300x^3y^2}$ $37xy\sqrt{3x}$

51. $\sqrt{x} + \sqrt{\frac{1}{x}}$ $\frac{x+1}{x}\sqrt{x}$

52. ***Critical Thinking*** You know that $\sqrt{x^2 + y^2} = \sqrt{x^2} + \sqrt{y^2}$ is not true for *all* real numbers. For what numbers is it true? $x = 0$ or $y = 0$

Challenge

Add or subtract. Simplify when possible.

53. $5\sqrt{\frac{3}{10}} + 2\sqrt{\frac{5}{6}} - 6\sqrt{\frac{15}{32}}$ $\frac{\sqrt{30}}{12}$

54. $2\sqrt{\frac{2a}{b}} - 4\sqrt{\frac{b}{2a^3}} + 5\sqrt{\frac{1}{8}a^3b}$ $\left[\frac{2}{b} - \frac{2}{a^2} + \frac{5a}{4}\right]\sqrt{2ab}$

55. Evaluate for $a = 1, b = 3, c = 2, d = 4$.
 a. $\sqrt{a^2 + c^2}, \sqrt{a^2} + \sqrt{c^2}$ $\sqrt{5}, 3$
 b. $\sqrt{b^2 + c^2}, \sqrt{b^2} + \sqrt{c^2}$ $\sqrt{13}, 5$
 c. $\sqrt{a^2 + d^2}, \sqrt{a^2} + \sqrt{d^2}$ $\sqrt{17}, 5$
 d. $\sqrt{b^2 + d^2}, \sqrt{b^2} + \sqrt{d^2}$ 5, 7
 e. $\sqrt{a^2 + b^2}, \sqrt{a^2} + \sqrt{b^2}$ $\sqrt{10}, 4$
 f. $\sqrt{c^2 + d^2}, \sqrt{c^2} + \sqrt{d^2}$ $2\sqrt{5}, 6$

Binomial pairs such as $1 + \sqrt{2}$ and $1 - \sqrt{2}$ are called **conjugates**. We can use conjugates to rationalize binomial denominators containing radicals. Rationalize each denominator.

56. $\frac{5}{1 - \sqrt{2}}$ $-5 - 5\sqrt{2}$

57. $\frac{8 + \sqrt{3}}{3 - \sqrt{2}}$ $\frac{24 + 3\sqrt{3} + 8\sqrt{2} + \sqrt{6}}{7}$

Mixed Review

Simplify. 58. $\sqrt{25y^2}$ 59. $\sqrt{(-6)^2}$ 60. $\sqrt{(x + 2)^2}$
61. $\sqrt{y^2 + 10y + 25}$

Multiply. 62. $\sqrt{5}\sqrt{15}$ 63. $\sqrt{6}\sqrt{8}$ 64. $\sqrt{11}\sqrt{11}$
65. $\sqrt{a + c}\sqrt{a - c}$

Factor and simplify. 66. $\sqrt{20}$ 67. $\sqrt{16x^2y}$ 68. $\sqrt{x^3 - 4x^2 + 4x}$

Solve by graphing. 69. $x + 2 \leq y$, $y \geq -2$ 70. $x + y \leq 1$, $x + y \geq 1$ 71. $y - x \leq 1$, $2y + x \leq 2$

Problem Solving: Application

Injury Severity Score

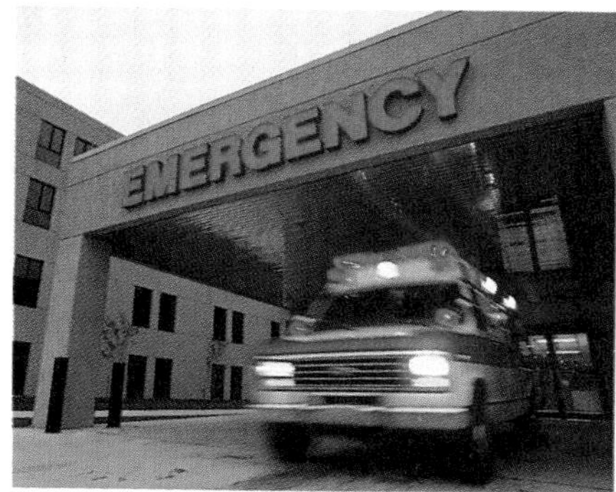

Doctors in hospital emergency rooms must decide the order in which patients should be treated. Obviously, patients with the most serious injuries should be treated before those with less serious injuries. How do doctors determine the severity of an injury? Several scoring systems have been devised, the Injury Severity Score (ISS) among them. In the ISS system, each injury is assigned a severity code ranging from 1, for minor injuries, to 6, for injuries that are life-threatening. The ISS also assigns six body regions the letters A through F:

A Head and neck	D Abdomen
B Face	E Extremities
C Chest	F Skin

To compute the ISS, the doctor identifies the highest severity code for each region in which the patient has an injury. If the patient has any code 6 injury, the ISS is 75. Otherwise, the ISS is found by identifying the three highest codes from different body regions, squaring them, and finding their sum.

Suppose the three highest severity codes for a patient are as follows: Head and neck 2; Chest 1; Abdomen 4. Find the ISS.

First, square each code: $2^2 = 4$, $1^2 = 1$, and $4^2 = 16$.
Next, find the sum of the squares: $4 + 1 + 16 = 21$.
The ISS for this patient is 21.

Suppose a patient has eight injuries as shown by the eight codes in the chart below. Find the ISS.

Region	Codes
A	5, 5, 4
C	3, 2
D	1
E	4, 4

Select the three highest codes from different body regions. They are 5 (from region A), 3 (from region C), and 4 (from region E). Thus the ISS is $5^2 + 3^2 + 4^2 = 25 + 9 + 16 = 50$.

ANSWERS

1. 35
2. 50
3. 62
4. 30
5. 38
6. 50
7. 43
8. 57
9. 50
10. 30
11. From highest score to lowest: 8, 6, 9, 7, 5, 10 or 8, 9, 6, 7, 5, 10
12. (5) 77% (6) 61% (7) 71% (8) 49% (9) 61% (10) 86%

Problems

Find the ISS for patients having these three highest codes.

1. Abdomen 3; Extremities 5; Skin 1
2. Head and neck 4; Face 5; Skin 3
3. Chest 5; Abdomen 6; Extremities 1
4. Head and neck 1; Abdomen 2; Skin 5

Find the ISS for the following cases.

5.

Region	Codes
A	5, 2
B	3
C	2, 1
D	2

6.

Region	Codes
A	4, 3
C	5, 2
E	3, 1

7.

Region	Codes
A	3, 2
B	5, 3
D	3, 1, 1
E	2

8.

Region	Codes
A	4, 4, 4, 4, 4, 4
C	5, 4, 4, 4, 4
E	4, 4, 3, 4, 4

9.

Region	Codes
A	5, 5, 5, 5
B	3, 3, 3, 3, 3
C	2, 2, 2, 4
D	3, 3, 3, 1, 1
F	2, 2

10.

Region	Codes
A	5, 4, 1
B	2, 2
C	1, 1
D	1, 1, 1

11. Determine the order in which the patients in cases 5 through 10 should be treated.
12. If the probability of surviving injuries is found using the formula $P = 1 - \left(\frac{ISS}{80}\right)^2$, find the probability of survival for the patients in cases 5 through 10.

11-7 The Pythagorean Theorem 

Objective: Solve triangles using the Pythagorean theorem.

In a right triangle, the longest side is called the **hypotenuse**. The hypotenuse is always the side opposite the right angle. The other two sides are called the **legs** of the triangle. We usually use the variables a and b to identify the legs and c for the hypotenuse. They are related as follows.

The Pythagorean Theorem

In any right triangle, if a and b are the lengths of the legs and c is the length of the hypotenuse, then

$$a^2 + b^2 = c^2$$

The diagram below shows the relationship between the legs and the hypotenuse in a right triangle.

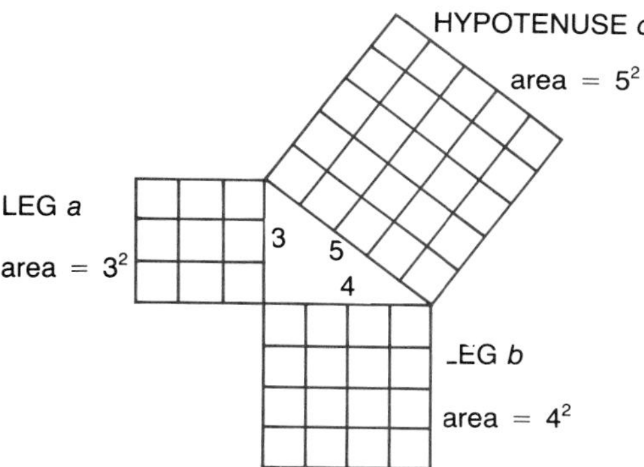

$$a^2 + b^2 = c^2$$
$$3^2 + 4^2 = 5^2$$
$$9 + 16 = 25$$

If we know the lengths of any two sides, we can find the length of the third side.

EXAMPLE 1

Find the length of the hypotenuse of this right triangle to the nearest thousandth.

$$4^2 + 5^2 = c^2$$
$$16 + 25 = c^2$$
$$41 = c^2$$
$$c = \sqrt{41}$$
$$c \approx 6.403$$

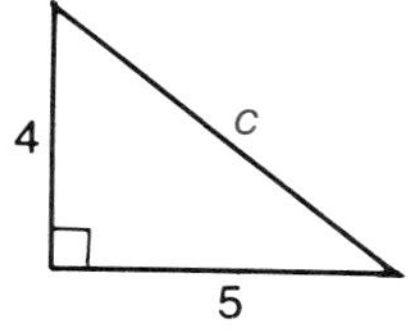

11-7

FIRST FIVE MINUTES

Add or subtract.

1. $3\sqrt{7} + 5\sqrt{7}$
   $8\sqrt{7}$
2. $5\sqrt{12} + 4\sqrt{3}$
   $14\sqrt{3}$
3. $\sqrt{9x} + 2\sqrt{4x}$
   $7\sqrt{x}$

You can use multiples of the commonly used 3-4-5 and 5-12-13 right triangles as examples of the Pythagorean theorem. For example, 6-8-10 or 10-24-26 satisfy the Pythagorean theorem. You may want to have students try to come up with their own Pythagorean triangles.

Key Question

- How can you tell which side is the hypotenuse? It is the side opposite the right angle.

Chalkboard Examples (*T22*)

1. Find the length of the hypotenuse of the right triangle with sides 5 and 12.
   $c^2 = 5^2 + 12^2$
   $c^2 = 169$
   $c = \sqrt{169} = 13$
2. Find the length of the leg of the right triangle with one leg of length 7 and hypotenuse of length 9.
   $a^2 + 7^2 = 9^2$
   $a^2 = 9^2 - 7^2$
   $a^2 = 32$
   $a = \sqrt{32} \approx 5.657$
3. Find the length of the leg of the right triangle with hypotenuse 8 and leg 3.
   $a^2 + 3^2 = 8^2$
   $a^2 = 8^2 - 3^2$
   $a^2 = 55$
   $a = \sqrt{55} \approx 7.416$
4. Find the length of the leg of the right triangle with leg 6 and hypotenuse 11.
   $a^2 + 6^2 = 11^2$
   $a^2 = 11^2 - 6^2$
   $a^2 = 85$
   $a = \sqrt{85} \approx 9.220$

LESSON ENRICHMENT (*T23*)
You may want to show the following informal proof of the Pythagorean theorem based on the figures below.

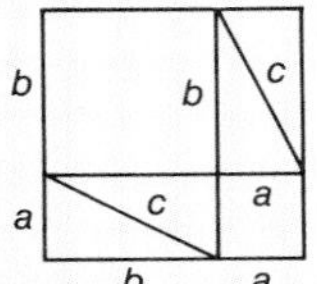

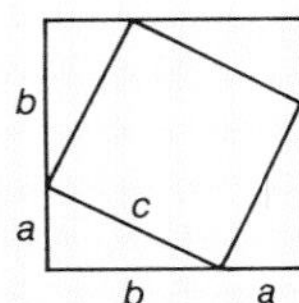

The two large squares have equal areas. Equal areas remain after removing the four right triangles from each large square. The remaining area in the left square is $a^2 + b^2$. The remaining area in the right square is c^2. Therefore, $a^2 + b^2 = c^2$.

LESSON QUIZ

1. Find the hypotenuse of the right triangle with sides $\sqrt{8}$ and 1.
   3
2. Find the leg of the right triangle with leg 2 and hypotenuse $\sqrt{13}$.
   3

EXAMPLE 2

Find the length of the leg of this right triangle to the nearest thousandth.

$$\begin{aligned} 1^2 + b^2 &= (\sqrt{7})^2 \\ 1 + b^2 &= 7 \\ b^2 &= 7 - 1 \\ b^2 &= 6 \\ b &= \sqrt{6} \\ b &\approx 2.449 \end{aligned}$$

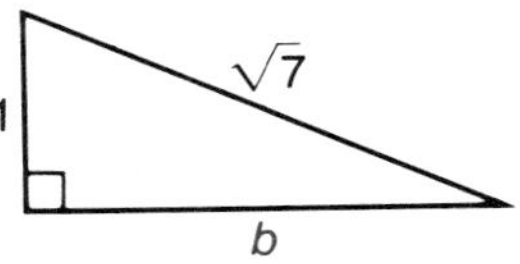

Try This Find the missing length in each right triangle.

a.

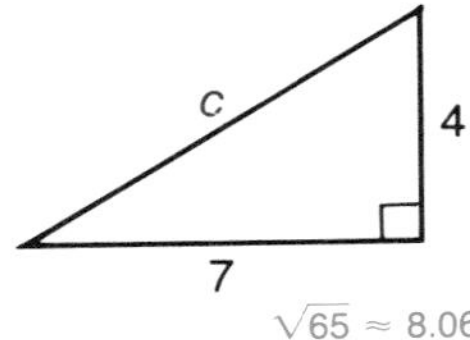

$\sqrt{65} \approx 8.062$

b.

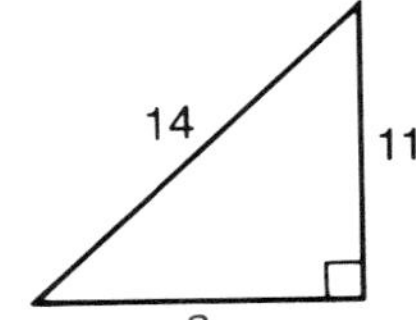

$\sqrt{75} \approx 8.660$

c.

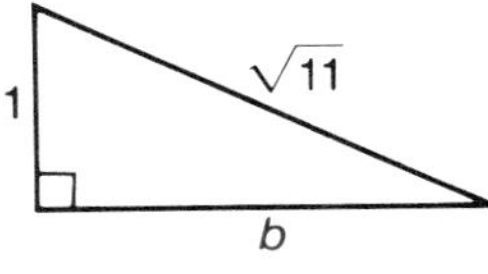

$\sqrt{10} \approx 3.162$

d.

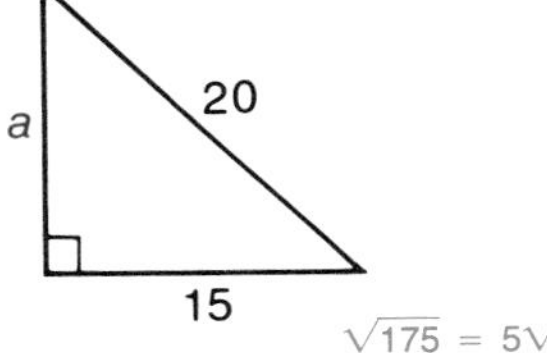

$\sqrt{175} = 5\sqrt{7} \approx 13.229$

Finding Missing Lengths

We can use the [2nd] key and the [x^2] key to solve problems involving the Pythagorean theorem.

Find the length of the leg of this right triangle to the nearest thousandth of an inch.

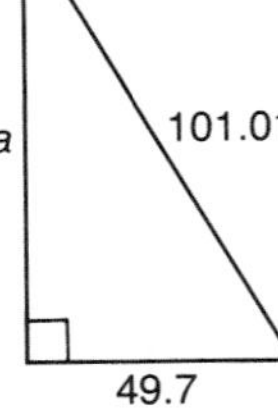

Solve $a^2 = 101.01^2 - 49.7^2$.
$a = \sqrt{101.01^2 - 49.7^2}$

Using a calculator we get

[(] 101.01 [x^2] [−] 49.7 [x^2] [)]

[2nd] [x^2]

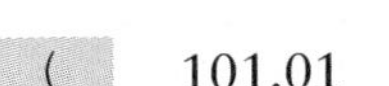

To the nearest thousandth, the length is 87.937 in.

For additional calculator practice, see Calculator Worksheet 24.

11-7 EXERCISES

A

Find the length of the third side of each right triangle.

1.

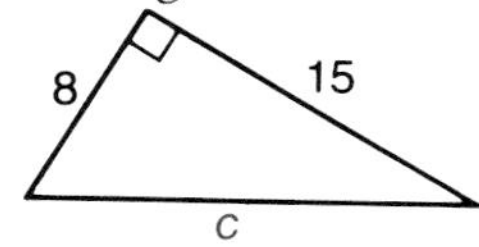

2.

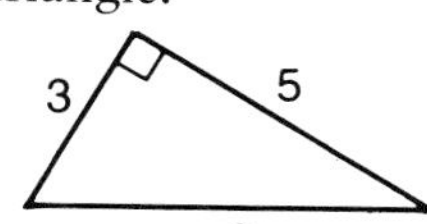

3.

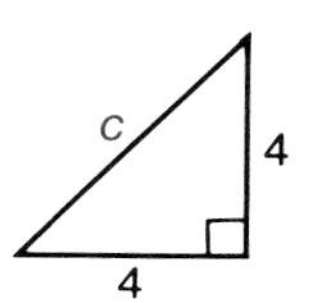

4.

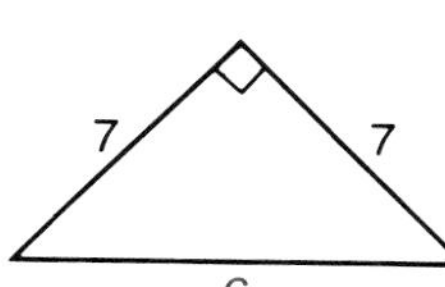

5.

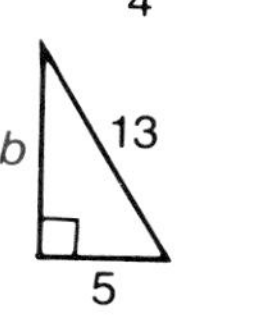

6.

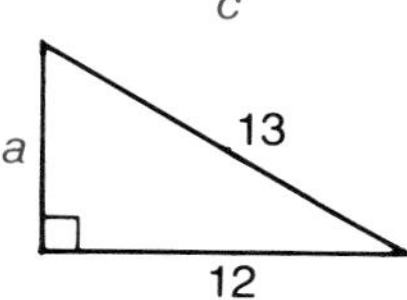

7.

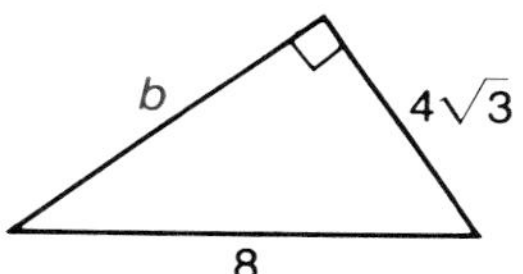

8.

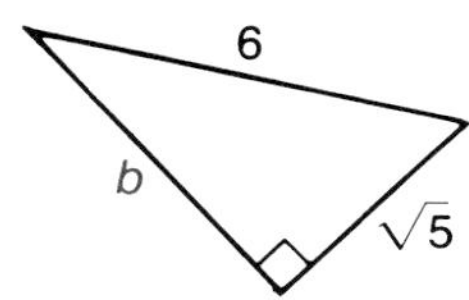

Find the length of the side not given for a right triangle with hypotenuse c and legs a and b.

9. $a = 10, b = 24$ 26

10. $a = 5, b = 12$ 13

11. $a = 9, c = 15$ 12

12. $a = 18, c = 30$ 24

13. $b = 1, c = \sqrt{5}$ 2

14. $b = 1, c = \sqrt{2}$ 1

15. $a = 1, c = \sqrt{3}$ $\sqrt{2}$

16. $a = \sqrt{3}, b = \sqrt{5}$ $2\sqrt{2}$

17. $c = 10, b = 5\sqrt{3}$ 5

18. $a = 3\sqrt{3}, c = 5\sqrt{3}$ $b = 4\sqrt{3}$

B

An equilateral triangle is shown to the right.

19. Find an expression for height h in terms of a.

20. Find an expression for area A in terms of a.

21. Find an expression for area A in terms of h.

22. Figure $ABCD$ is a square. Find AC.

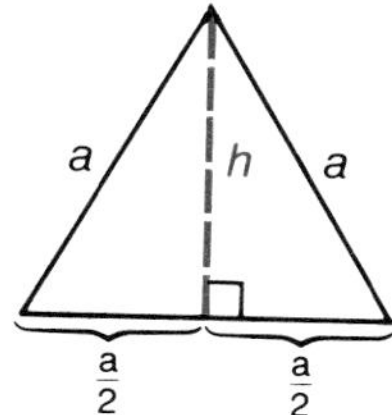

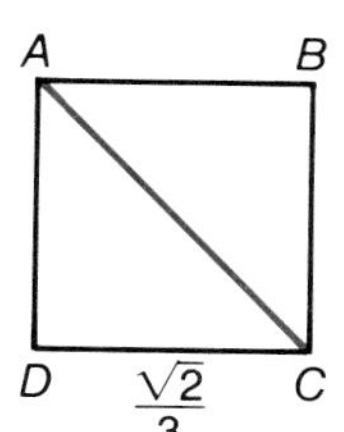

Assignment Guide
Minimum: 1–18, MR

Regular: 1–23, MR

Advanced: 1–18 e/o, 19–27, MR, assign w. Bonus Topic

ADDITIONAL ANSWERS

Exercises

1. 17
2. $\sqrt{34}$ or 5.831
3. $4\sqrt{2}$ or 5.657
4. $7\sqrt{2}$ or 9.899
5. 12
6. 5
7. 4
8. $\sqrt{31}$ or 5.568

19. $\frac{a}{2}\sqrt{3}$

20. $\frac{a^2}{4}\sqrt{3}$

21. $A = \frac{h^2\sqrt{3}}{3}$

22. $\frac{2}{3}$

Mixed Review

28. -13
29. $x + 3$
30. $5\sqrt{y}$
31. $4a\sqrt{2}$
32. $x^3\sqrt{x}$
33. a^{10}
34. $(x + 5)^2$
35. $(x - 3)\sqrt{x - 3}$
36. $2a^2\sqrt{3a}$
37. $6x^2\sqrt{6}$
38. $2x\sqrt{3xy}$
39. $3ab^2\sqrt{2a}$
40. 2
41. 3
42. 3, 4
43. 14, 15
44. -5, 12

Problems for Programmers

These programs can be written using any programming language (BASIC, PASCAL, LOGO, etc.). These programs can also be written on a spreadsheet.

23. *Critical Thinking* A right triangle has sides whose lengths are consecutive integers. Find the lengths of the sides. 3, 4, 5

Challenge

24. Find the length of the diagonal of a 10 cm cube. $10\sqrt{3}$

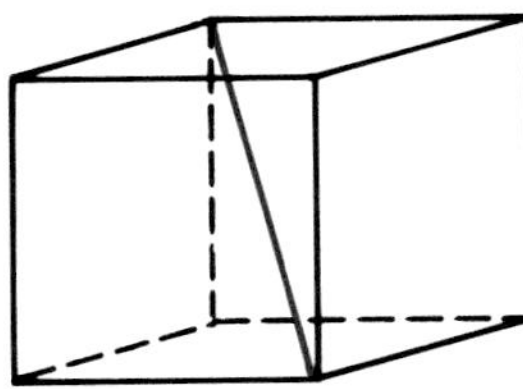

Find x.

25. $12 - 2\sqrt{6} \approx 7.1$ **26.**  $\frac{\sqrt{3}}{2} \approx 0.87$ **27.**  6

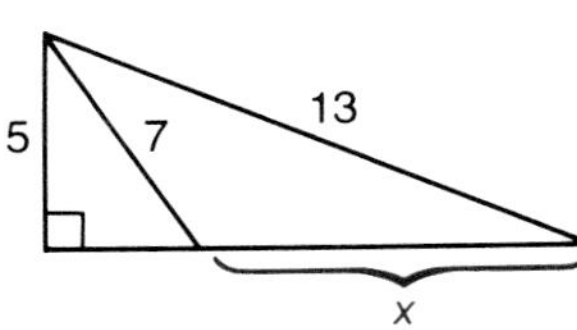

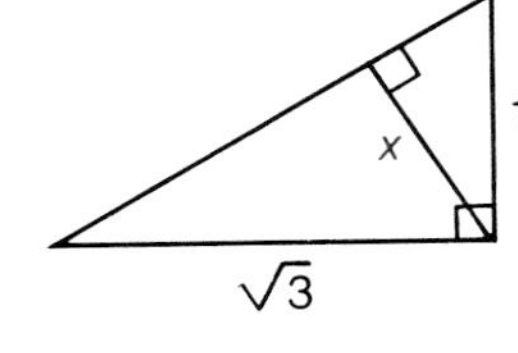

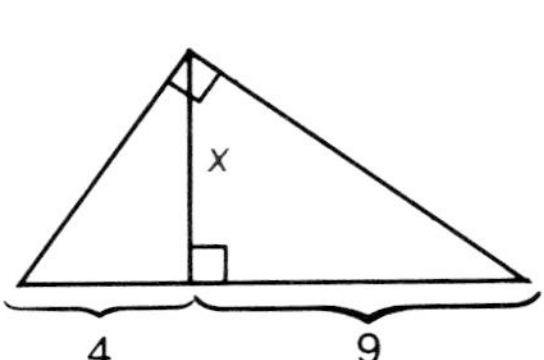

Mixed Review

Simplify. **28.** $-\sqrt{169}$ **29.** $\sqrt{(x + 3)^2}$ **30.** $\sqrt{25y}$ **31.** $\sqrt{32a^2}$ **32.** $\sqrt{x^7}$ **33.** $\sqrt{a^{20}}$ **34.** $\sqrt{(x + 5)^4}$ **35.** $\sqrt{(x - 3)^3}$ **36.** $\sqrt{12a^5}$ **37.** $\sqrt{216x^4}$ **38.** $\sqrt{12x^3y}$ **39.** $\sqrt{18a^3b^4}$

Solve. **40.** $\frac{3}{2x} + \frac{1}{2} = \frac{10}{4x}$ **41.** $\frac{x}{4} - \frac{x}{12} = \frac{1}{2}$ **42.** $x + \frac{12}{x} = 7$

43. The product of two consecutive positive integers is 210. Find the numbers. **44.** The sum of two numbers is 7. The difference of the two numbers is -17. Find the numbers.

Problems for Programmers

Write a program that will solve the Pythagorean theorem, $a^2 + b^2 = c^2$, for c, the hypotenuse.

Write a program that will solve the Pythagorean theorem, $a^2 + b^2 = c^2$, for either leg a or leg b.

Test your programs using Exercises 1–18 in this section.

Bonus Topic: The Distance Formula

Objective: Find the distance between two points on the coordinate plane.

The **distance formula** is based on the Pythagorean theorem and is used to find the distance between any two points in the plane if the coordinates of the points are known.

EXAMPLE 1 Find the distance between the points (3, 2) and (−3, −2).

We plot these points on a coordinate plane and construct a triangle as shown. The distance between the points (3, 2) and (−3, −2) is the hypotenuse of this triangle.

We can use the Pythagorean theorem to find this length.

$$\begin{aligned} c^2 &= a^2 + b^2 \\ &= 6^2 + 4^2 \\ &= 36 + 16 \\ &= 52 \\ c &= \pm\sqrt{52} \end{aligned}$$

Since distance cannot be negative, the distance is $\sqrt{52} \approx 7.2$.

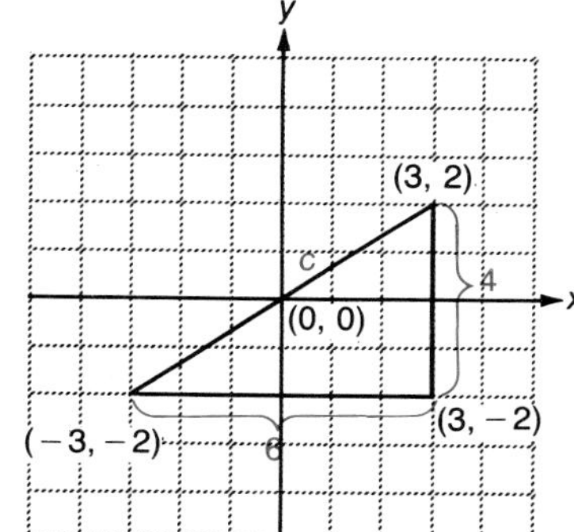

The distance formula, which is derived from the Pythagorean theorem, can be used to compute the distance between two points.

Distance Formula

The distance between any two points (x_1, y_1) and (x_2, y_2) is given by

$$d = \sqrt{(x_1 - x_2)^2 + (y_1 - y_2)^2}$$

EXAMPLE 2 Find the distance between (2, 2) and (5, 6).

$$\begin{aligned} d &= \sqrt{(2-5)^2 + (2-6)^2} = \sqrt{(-3)^2 + (-4)^2} \\ &= \sqrt{9 + 16} = \sqrt{25} \\ d &= 5 \end{aligned}$$

Exercises

Use the distance formula to find the distance between each pair of points.

1. (8, −5) and (3, 7)
2. (0, 4) and (−4, 6)
3. (−3, −5) and (−6, −8)
4. (5, 6) and (−2, 6)
5. (−4, −4) and (4, 4)
6. (7, 0) and (−6, 4)

Bonus Topic

You may want to present the following proof of the distance formula.

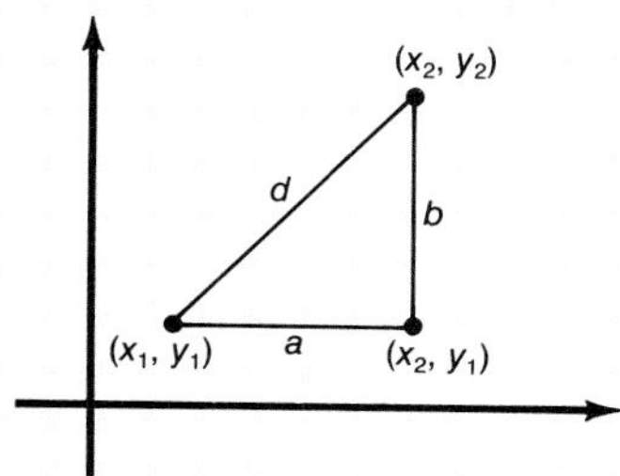

Let segment a be horizontal and let segment b be vertical. Since a is horizontal, its length is simply $x_2 - x_1$. The length of b is $y_2 - y_1$. Using the Pythagorean theorem, $d^2 = a^2 + b^2$, we substitute for a and b.

$d^2 = (x_2 - x_1)^2 + (y_2 - y_1)^2$

$d = \sqrt{(x_2 - x_1)^2 + (y_2 - y_1)^2}$

ANSWERS

1. 13
2. $2\sqrt{5}$
3. $3\sqrt{2}$
4. 7
5. $8\sqrt{2}$
6. $\sqrt{185}$

11-8

FIRST FIVE MINUTES

1. Find the hypotenuse of a right triangle with sides 7 and $\sqrt{15}$.
   $c^2 = 49 + 15$
   $c^2 = 64$
   $c = 8$
2. Find the leg of the right triangle with hypotenuse 9 and leg $\sqrt{17}$.
   $a^2 = 81 - 17$
   $a^2 = 64$
   $a = 8$

Point out that the Pythagorean theorem allows the computation of a distance not easily measured, and that it allows us to test whether a triangle is a right triangle.

You may want to have students try to make up their own word problems using the Pythagorean theorem.

Key Question

- Is a triangle with sides 1, 2, and 3 a right triangle? Why or why not?
  No; $3^2 \neq 1^2 + 2^2$

Chalkboard Example (*T24*)

1. A playing field is 100 yards long by 50 yards wide. What is the diagonal distance across the field?
   The diagonal is the hypotenuse of a right triangle with sides 100 yards and 50 yards long. The length d of the diagonal is such that
   $d^2 = 100^2 + 50^2$
   $d^2 = 12500$
   $d = \sqrt{12500} \approx 111.803$
   The diagonal distance is about 111.8 yards.

LESSON QUIZ

1. A support cable stretches from the top of a 40-foot antenna tower to a point 30 feet out from the base of the tower. How long is the cable?
   50 feet
2. A square gate is braced with a cable stretched across its diagonal. The length of the cable is $\sqrt{8}$ feet. How wide is the gate?
   2 feet

11-8 Problem Solving: Using the Pythagorean Theorem

Objective: Solve problems using the Pythagorean theorem.

PROBLEM-SOLVING GUIDELINES
■ UNDERSTAND the problem
■ Develop and carry out a PLAN
■ Find the ANSWER and CHECK

Many real-world problems can be solved using the Pythagorean theorem. Use the Pythagorean theorem and the Problem-Solving Guidelines to help you solve these problems.

EXAMPLE 1

On a little league baseball diamond, the distance between the bases is 60 ft. What is the distance from home plate to second base?

■ UNDERSTAND the problem

Question: What is the distance (d) from home plate to second base?
Data: Distance between home and first base = 60 ft; distance between first and second base = 60 ft.

■ Develop and carry out a PLAN

We can write and solve an equation using the Pythagorean theorem.

$$60^2 + 60^2 = d^2$$
$$3600 + 3600 = d^2$$
$$7200 = d^2$$
$$\sqrt{7200} = d$$
$$84.9 \approx d$$

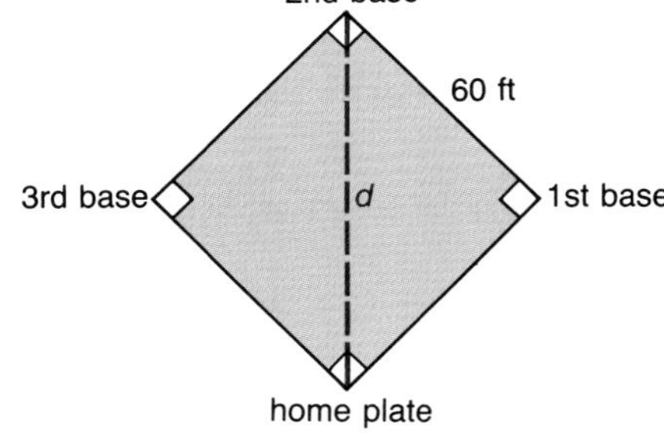

■ Find the ANSWER and CHECK

The distance from home plate to second base is about 84.9 ft. This answer is reasonable since the hypotenuse is greater than either leg.

Try This Solve.

a. How long is a guy wire that reaches from the top of a 15-ft pole to a point on the ground 10 ft from the bottom of the pole? ≈18.0 ft

b. A 12-ft ladder is leaning against a building. The bottom of the ladder is 7 ft from the building. How high is the top of the ladder? ≈9.7 ft

11-8 EXERCISES

A

Solve. Round answers to nearest tenth.

1. A 10-m ladder is leaning against a building. The bottom of the ladder is 5 m from the building. How high is the top of the ladder?

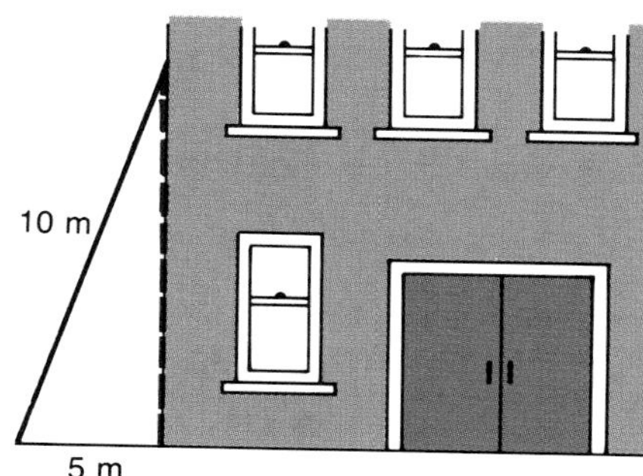

2. How long must a wire be to reach from the top of a 13-m telephone pole to a point on the ground 9 m from the foot of the pole?

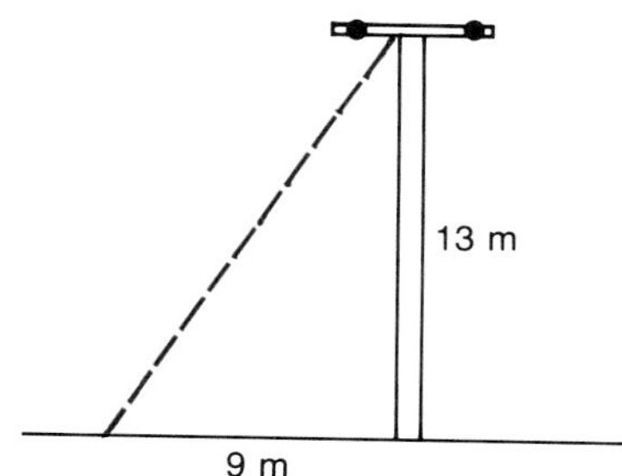

3. What amount of wire is needed to connect the top of the antenna to the hook 15 ft from the base of the antenna, as shown at right?

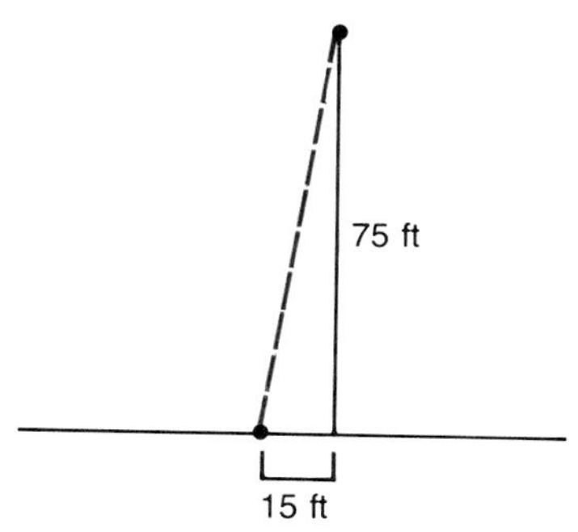

4. The distance between consecutive bases in major league baseball is 90 ft. Find the distance from home plate to second base.

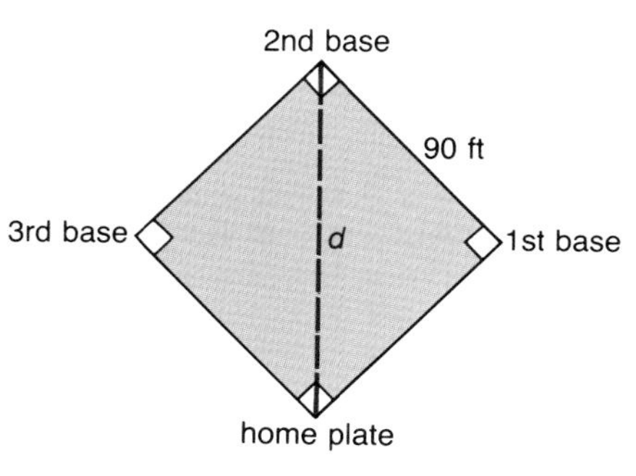

Assignment Guide
Minimum: 1 – 9, MR

Regular: 1–17, MR

Advanced: 1–9 e/o, 10–19, MR

ADDITIONAL ANSWERS

Exercises

1. ≈ 8.7 m
2. ≈ 15.8 m
3. ≈ 76.5 ft
4. ≈ 127.3 ft

5. ≈ 68.0 m
6. ≈ 43.0 m
7. ≈ 77.6 mi
8. ≈ 61.8 ft
9. ≈ 14.5 km

5. What is the distance across the garden shown at the right?

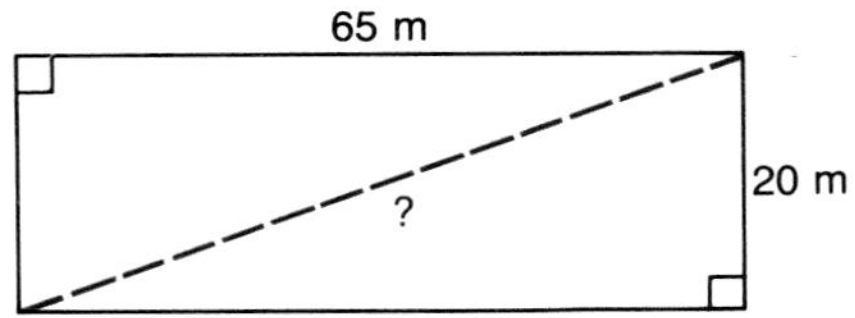

6. A surveyor had poles marked at points A, B, and C. The distances that could be measured are shown on the drawing. What is the approximate distance from A to C?

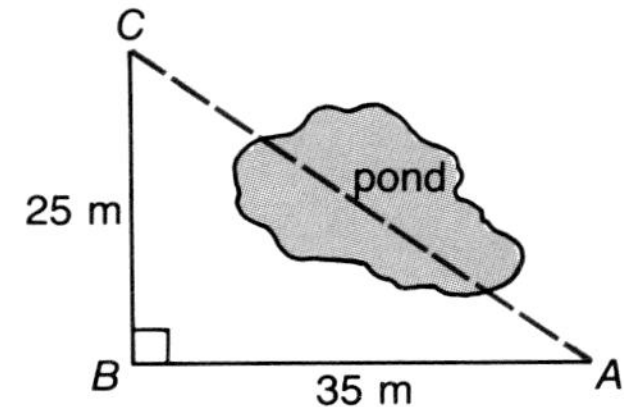

7. Carla Chew lives 20 miles due north of her favorite radio station. While driving due east from her house, she was able to keep the radio signal for about 75 miles. What is the broadcasting range of her favorite radio station?

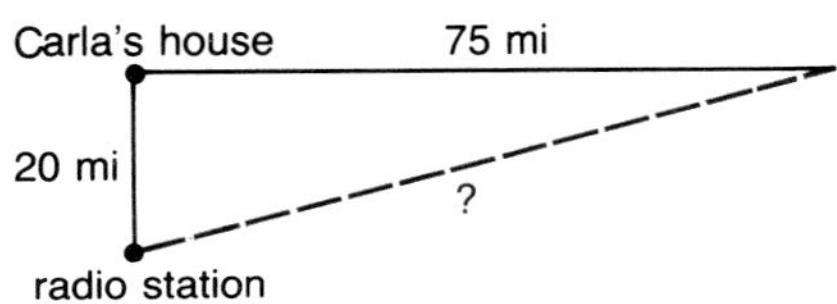

8. A cable television company needed to wire from its box at the corner of a lot to a corner of a house. The owner knew the house was 15 ft from the side of the lot and 60 ft from the back of the lot. How much wire was needed to go from the box to the house?

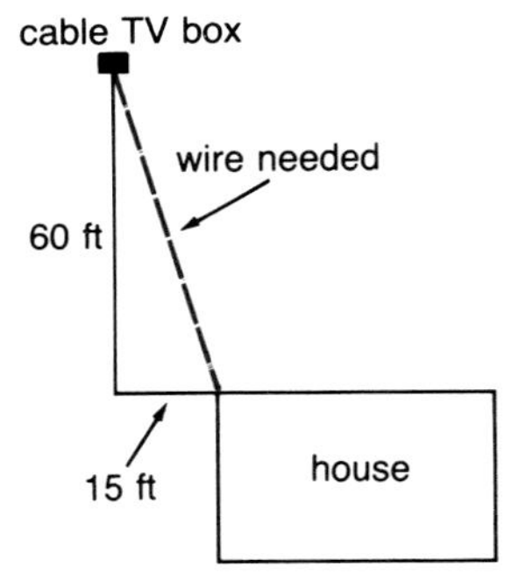

9. An airplane is flying at an altitude of 4.1 km. The plane's slant distance from the runway is 15.1 km. How far must the plane travel to be directly above the runway?

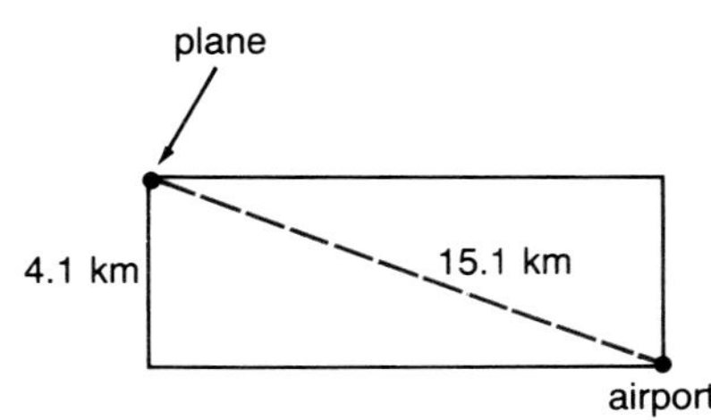

B

10. Suppose an outfielder catches the ball on the third base line about 40 feet behind third base. About how far would the outfielder have to throw the ball to first base?

11. An A-frame tent is in the shape of an isosceles triangle. The base of the triangle is 10 ft and the two congruent sides are each 8 ft. What is the height of the tent?

12. How far out is the ship? Using geometry, Kala found triangle *CDE* to be *congruent* (same size and shape) to triangle *ABC*.

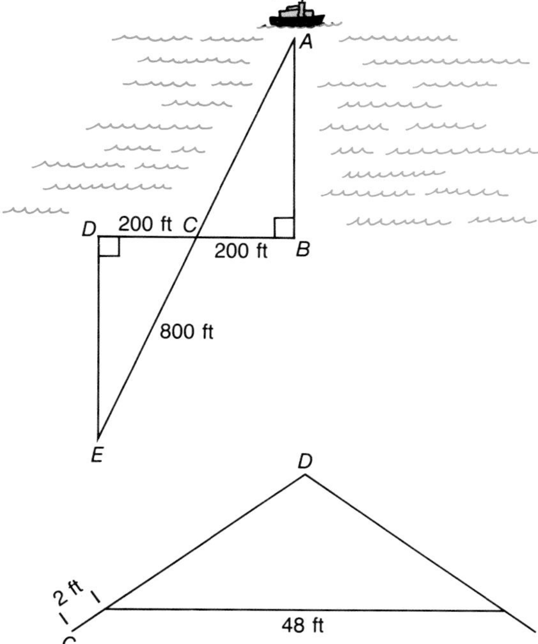

13. A 48-ft-wide building has a roof that rises 4 ft for each 12-foot horizontal change. If the roof has a 2-foot overhang, what is the length of *CD*?

14. The diagonal of a square has length $8\sqrt{2}$ ft. Find the length of a side of the square.

15. Find the length of the diagonal of a rectangle whose length is 12 in. and whose width is 7 in.

16. One leg of a right triangle is 5 times the other leg. Find the longer leg if the hypotenuse is 60 ft.

10. $50\sqrt{10} \approx 158.1$ ft
11. $\sqrt{39} \approx 6.2$ ft
12. $200\sqrt{15} \approx 774.6$ ft
13. $8\sqrt{10} + 2 \approx 27.3$ ft
14. 8 ft
15. $\sqrt{193} \approx 13.9$ in.
16. 58.8 ft

17. $3\sqrt{73} + 2 \approx 27.6$ ft
18. Old road 2.5 h, major highways 2.1 h; major highways
19. $\sqrt{1525} = 5\sqrt{61} \approx 39.05$ mi, 1.28 h

Mixed Review

20. $\frac{\sqrt{15}}{5}$
21. $\frac{2\sqrt{y}}{y}$
22. $\frac{\sqrt{x}}{x}$
23. $5\sqrt{6}$
24. $xy\sqrt{z}$
25. $5\sqrt{2}$
26. $6\sqrt{3}$
27. $8\sqrt{3}$
28. $5\sqrt{5}$
29. $22\sqrt{2}$
30. $\sqrt{6}$
31. $-\sqrt{2}$

Writing to Learn

Answers may vary, but students should recognize that the square of the hypotenuse equals the sum of the squares of the legs, regardless of what variables are used to name them.

17. ***Critical Thinking*** In Exercise 13, suppose that the roof rises 3 feet for each 8-foot horizontal change, and that all other measurements remain the same. What is the length of CD?

Challenge

18. Two major highways meet at a 90° angle. The known distances between cities are marked on the map at the right. An old road connects these cities. On the major highways, one can average 50 mi/h from point A to point C. On the old road, one can average only 30 mi/h. Which path would get you from A to C in the least time?

19. Two cars leave a service station at the same time. One car travels east at a speed of 50 mi/h, and the other travels south at a speed of 60 mi/h. After one-half hour, how far apart are they? When will they be 100 miles apart?

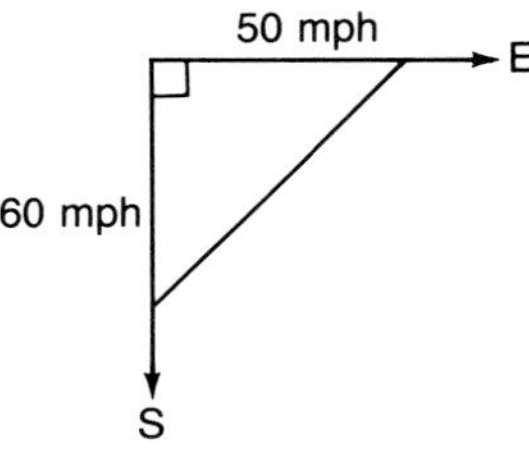

Mixed Review

Rationalize denominator. **20.** $\sqrt{\frac{3}{5}}$ **21.** $\frac{\sqrt{20}}{\sqrt{5y}}$ **22.** $\frac{\sqrt{y}}{\sqrt{xy}}$

Multiply and simplify. **23.** $\sqrt{15}\sqrt{10}$ **24.** $\sqrt{xy}\sqrt{xyz}$

Add or subtract. **25.** $\sqrt{2} + 4\sqrt{2}$ **26.** $4\sqrt{12} - 2\sqrt{3}$

27. $6\sqrt{12} - 4\sqrt{3}$ **28.** $\sqrt{45} + \sqrt{20}$ **29.** $2\sqrt{8} + 6\sqrt{18}$

30. $\sqrt{24} - \sqrt{6}$ **31.** $\sqrt{18} - 5\sqrt{8} + \sqrt{72}$

WRITING TO LEARN

Suppose one of your classmates claims that the Pythagorean theorem is $x^2 + y^2 = z^2$. Another classmate responds, "It depends." Write a paragraph explaining why the second classmate is correct.

11-9 Equations with Radicals

Application

Finding the speed of an automobile involved in an accident is important information that can help prevent future accidents. The formula $r = 2\sqrt{5L}$ can be used to approximate the speed (r), in miles per hour, of a car that has left a skid mark of length L, in feet.

Solving Equations with Radicals

Objective: Solve equations involving radicals.

To solve equations with radicals, we first convert them to equations without radicals. We do this by squaring both sides of the equation.

The Principle of Squaring

If an equation $a = b$ is true, then the equation $a^2 = b^2$ is true.

EXAMPLE 1 Solve.

$$\sqrt{2x} - 4 = 7$$
$$\sqrt{2x} = 11 \quad \text{Getting the radical alone on one side}$$
$$(\sqrt{2x})^2 = 11^2 \quad \text{Squaring both sides}$$
$$2x = 121$$
$$x = \frac{121}{2}$$

Check:

$\sqrt{2x} - 4$	$= 7$
$\sqrt{2 \cdot \frac{121}{2}} - 4$	7
$\sqrt{121} - 4$	7
$11 - 4$	7
7	7 ✓

The solution is $\frac{121}{2}$.

It is important to check. *When we square both sides of an equation, it is transformed into a new equation that may have extraneous solutions.* For example, the equation $x = 1$ has one solution, the number 1. When we square both sides we get $x^2 = 1$, which has two solutions, 1 and -1.

11-9

FIRST FIVE MINUTES

1. Find the length of the diagonal of a rectangle with sides 60 feet and 80 feet.
   Let d be the length of the diagonal.
   $d^2 = 60^2 + 80^2$
   $d = 100$
2. What is the length of the side of a square with diagonal of length $\sqrt{18}$?
   Let x be the length of the side.
   $x^2 + x^2 = (\sqrt{18})^2$
   $2x^2 = 18$
   $x^2 = 9$
   $x = 3$

APPLICATION

The formula $r = 2\sqrt{5L}$ is used in Exercises 23 and 24.

Solving Equations with Radicals

Point out that the principle of squaring is a special case of the general principle that if identical operations are applied to both sides of an equation, then the result is a true equation. In this case, however, the new equation may have solutions that the original does not. Emphasize that possible answers must be checked in the original equation.

Key Question

- If $a^2 = b^2$, does $a = b$?
  No; consider $a = 2$ and $b = -2$.

Chalkboard Examples

1. Solve $\sqrt{5x} + 7 = 10$.
   $\sqrt{5x} = 3$
   $5x = 9$
   $x = \frac{9}{5}$

Check:

$\sqrt{5 \cdot \frac{9}{5}} + 7$	$= 10$
$\sqrt{9} + 7$	10
$3 + 7$	10
10	10 ✓

2. Solve $\sqrt{3x - 1} = \sqrt{x + 5}$.
Square both sides.
$3x - 1 = x + 5$
$2x = 6$
$x = 3$

Check:

$\sqrt{3 \cdot 3 - 1}$	$\sqrt{3 + 5}$
$\sqrt{9 - 1}$	$\sqrt{8}$
$\sqrt{8}$	$\sqrt{8}$ ✓

Problem Solving

Point out that the formula $V = 3.5\sqrt{h}$ is a good approximation when the height h is small.

Chalkboard Example

1. How far can you see from the top of the radio mast on top of Sears' Tower building in Chicago? The top of the mast is about 475 meters high.
The distance to the horizon, in kilometers is
$V = 3.5\sqrt{475} = 3.5\sqrt{25 \cdot 19}$
$= 3.5 \cdot 5 \cdot \sqrt{19}$
$\approx 3.5 \cdot 5 \cdot 4.359$
≈ 76.28 kilometers

LESSON ENRICHMENT

The radius of the earth is approximately 4000 miles. A person at a height h, in miles, can see a distance V to the horizon. Find V in terms of h.

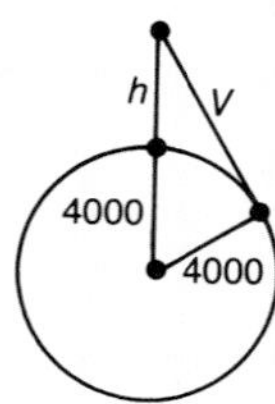

V is one side of a right triangle with hypotenuse $h + 4000$ and leg 4000.
$V^2 + 4000^2 = (h + 4000)^2$
$V^2 + 4000^2 = h^2 + 8000h + 4000^2$
$V^2 = h^2 + 8000h$
$V = \sqrt{h(h + 8000)}$

EXAMPLE 2 Solve.

$$\sqrt{x + 1} = \sqrt{2x - 5}.$$
$$(\sqrt{x + 1})^2 = (\sqrt{2x - 5})^2 \quad \text{Squaring both sides}$$
$$x + 1 = 2x - 5$$
$$x = 6$$

Check: $\sqrt{x + 1} = \sqrt{2x - 5}$

$\sqrt{6 + 1}$	$\sqrt{2(6) - 5}$
$\sqrt{7}$	$\sqrt{12 - 5}$
$\sqrt{7}$	$\sqrt{7}$ ✓

The solution is 6.

Try This Solve.

a. $\sqrt{3x} - 5 = 3$ $\frac{64}{3}$ **b.** $\sqrt{3x + 1} = \sqrt{2x + 3}$ 2

c. $\sqrt{x - 2} - 5 = 3$ 66

Problem Solving

Objective: Solve problems involving the solution of equations with radicals.

The following formula tells how many kilometers (V) you can see from a height of h meters above the earth.

$$V = 3.5\sqrt{h}$$

EXAMPLE 3

How far, to the nearest kilometer, can you see through an airplane window at a height, or altitude, of 12,321 meters?

$$V = 3.5\sqrt{12,321} \quad \text{Substituting 12,321 for } h$$
$$V = 388.5 \text{ km}$$

Try This Approximate answers to the nearest kilometer.

d. How far can you see to the horizon through an airplane window at a height of 8000 m? ≈313 km

e. How far can a sailor see to the horizon from the top of a 20-m mast? ≈16 km

EXAMPLE 4

A person can see about 50 kilometers to the horizon from the top of a cliff. How high is the cliff to the nearest meter? Use $V = 3.5\sqrt{h}$.

$$50 = 3.5\sqrt{h} \quad \text{Substituting 50 for } V$$

$$\frac{50}{3.5} = \sqrt{h}$$

$$14.3 \approx \sqrt{h} \quad \text{Rounding to the nearest tenth}$$

$$(14.3)^2 \approx (\sqrt{h})^2$$

$$(14.3)^2 \approx h$$

$$204 \text{ m} \approx h$$

The cliff is about 204 meters high.

Try This Approximate to the nearest meter.

f. A person can see 61 km to the horizon from the roof of a building. How high is the rooftop? About 300 m

11-9 EXERCISES

A

Solve.

1. $\sqrt{x} = 5$ 25
2. $\sqrt{x} = 7$ 49
3. $\sqrt{x} = 6.2$ 38.44
4. $\sqrt{x} = 4.3$ 18.49
5. $\sqrt{x + 3} = 20$ 397
6. $\sqrt{x + 4} = 11$ 117
7. $\sqrt{2x + 4} = 25$ 310.5
8. $\sqrt{2x + 1} = 13$ 84
9. $3 + \sqrt{x - 1} = 5$ 5
10. $4 + \sqrt{y - 3} = 11$ 52
11. $6 - 2\sqrt{3n} = 0$ 3
12. $8 - 4\sqrt{5n} = 0$ $\frac{4}{5}$
13. $\sqrt{5x - 7} = \sqrt{x + 10}$ $\frac{17}{4}$
14. $\sqrt{4x - 5} = \sqrt{x + 9}$ $\frac{14}{3}$
15. $\sqrt{x} = -7$ No value
16. $-\sqrt{x} = 5$ No value
17. $\sqrt{2y + 6} = \sqrt{2y - 5}$ No value
18. $2\sqrt{x - 2} = \sqrt{7 - x}$ 3

Solve. Use $V = 3.5\sqrt{h}$ for Exercises 19–22.

19. How far can you see to the horizon from an airplane at 9800 m?

20. How far can a sailor see to the horizon from the top of a 24-m mast?

21. A person can see about 350 km to the horizon from an airplane window. How high is the airplane?

22. A person can see about 100 km to the horizon from the top of a hill. How high is the hill?

The formula $r = 2\sqrt{5L}$ can be used to approximate the speed (r), in mi/h, of a car that has left a skid mark of length L, in feet. Note: $L = \frac{r^2}{20}$

23. How far will a car skid at 50 mi/h? at 70 mi/h? 125 ft, 245 ft

24. How far will a car skid at 60 mi/h? at 100 mi/h? 180 ft, 500 ft

LESSON QUIZ

1. Solve $\sqrt{x + 5} = 7$.
   $x = 44$
2. Solve using $V = 3.5\sqrt{h}$.
   A person can see 140 km to the horizon from an airplane window. How high is the airplane?
   The airplane is at an altitude of about 1600 meters.

Assignment Guide

Minimum: 1–24 e/o, MR

Regular: 1–30 e/o, 31, MR

Advanced: Day 1: 1–24 e/o, assign w. Application
Day 2: 25–30 e/o, 31, 32–41 e/o, MR

ADDITIONAL ANSWERS

Exercises

19. ≈ 346 km
20. ≈ 17 km
21. ≈ 10,000 m
22. ≈ 818 m

Mixed Review
42. $x \geq -1$
43. $x \geq 1$
44. $x \geq -\frac{1}{5}$
45. Any real number
46. 15
47. m
48. $(x - 1)$
49. $9a$
50. $y^6\sqrt{y}$
51. $3(y + 7)^2$
52. $12m^2\sqrt{m}$
53. $\frac{1}{3}, \frac{1}{5}$
54. $-\frac{1}{3}, \frac{1}{4}$

B

Solve.

25. $\sqrt{5x^2 + 5} = 5$ 2 or −2

26. $\sqrt{x} = -x$ 0

27. Find a number such that twice its square root is 14. 49

28. Find a number such that the inverse of three times its square root is -33. 121

The formula $T = 2\pi\sqrt{\frac{L}{32}}$ can be used to find the period (T), in seconds, of a pendulum of length L, in feet. Note: $L = 8\left(\frac{T}{\pi}\right)^2$

29. What is the length of a pendulum that has a period of 1.6 sec? Use 3.14 for π. 2.1 ft

30. What is the length of a pendulum that has a period of 3 sec? Use 3.14 for π. 7.3 ft

31. ***Critical Thinking*** Find a number such that the square root of 4 more than 5 times the number is 8. 12

Challenge

Solve.

32. $x - 1 = \sqrt{x + 5}$ 4

33. $\sqrt{y^2 + 6} + y - 3 = 0$ $\frac{1}{2}$

34. $\sqrt{x - 5} + \sqrt{x} = 5$ (Use the principle of squaring twice.) 9

35. $\sqrt{3x + 1} = 1 + \sqrt{x + 4}$ 5

36. $4 + \sqrt{10 - x} = 6 + \sqrt{4 - x}$ $\frac{15}{4}$

37. $x = (x - 2)\sqrt{x}$ 0 or 4. (1 is not a solution.)

38. Solve $A = \sqrt{1 + \frac{a^2}{b^2}}$ for b. $\sqrt{\frac{a^2}{A^2 - 1}}$

The formula $t = \sqrt{\frac{2s}{g}}$ gives the time in seconds for an object, initially at rest, to fall s feet.

39. Solve the formula for s. $\frac{t^2g}{2}$

40. If $g = 32.2$, find the distance an object falls in the first 5 seconds. 402.5 ft

41. Find the distance an object falls in the first 10 seconds. 1610 ft

Mixed Review

Determine the replacements for the variable that give real numbers.

42. $\sqrt{x + 1}$ **43.** $\sqrt{x - 1}$ **44.** $\sqrt{5x + 1}$ **45.** $\sqrt{x^2 + 4}$

Simplify. **46.** $\sqrt{225}$ **47.** $\sqrt{m^2}$ **48.** $\sqrt{x^2 - 2x + 1}$

49. $\sqrt{(-9a)^2}$ **50.** $\sqrt{y^{13}}$ **51.** $\sqrt{9(y + 7)^4}$ **52.** $\sqrt{144m^5}$

Solve. **53.** $y^2 - \frac{8}{15}y + \frac{15}{225} = 0$ **54.** $x^2 + \frac{1}{12}x - \frac{12}{144} = 0$

Problem Solving: College Entrance Exams

Odd and Even Problems

A common type of problem found on college entrance exams is the "odd and even" problem. A variable is given to be an odd or an even number, and you must determine whether any of several expressions are odd or even. It is helpful to think about the following relationships involving the addition and multiplication of odd and even numbers.

odd + odd = even	odd × odd = odd
odd + even = odd	odd × even = even
even + even = even	even × even = even

EXAMPLE 1

If n is odd, which of the following can't be odd?

(A) $3n + 2$ **(B)** $3n + 4$ **(C)** $2n + 3$
(D) $6n + 3$ **(E)** $5n + 5$

We will look at the patterns above and determine whether the given expressions are even or odd.

(A) 3(odd) × n(odd) + 2(even) = odd + even = odd
(B) 3(odd) × n(odd) + 4(even) = odd + even = odd
(C) 2(even) × n(odd) + 3(odd) = even + odd = odd
(D) 6(even) × n(odd) + 3(odd) = even + odd = odd
(E) 5(odd) × n(odd) + 5(odd) = odd + odd = even

The correct answer is (E).

Another strategy is to substitute numbers according to the conditions given in the problem and evaluate the expressions.

EXAMPLE 2

If x is a positive integer, which of the following *must* be an even integer?

(A) $x^3 + 3$ **(B)** $5x + 1$ **(C)** $4x + 2$
(D) $x^2 + 1$ **(E)** $x^2 + x + 3$

Since x can be either odd or even, we will substitute an odd number and an even number and check each answer. If one odd number makes the answer even, any odd number will make the answer even.

(A) $x^3 + 3 = (1)^3 + 3 = 4$
$x^3 + 3 = (0)^3 + 3 = 3$

(B) $5x + 1 = 5(0) + 1 = 1$ Since the answer is odd, you need not evaluate the second expression.

(C) $4x + 2 = 4(0) + 2 = 2$
$4x + 2 = 4(1) + 2 = 6$

At this point, we know (C) is correct because both answers are even.

ANSWERS

1. (D)
2. (D)
3. (B)
4. (D)
5. (C)
6. (E)

Problems

1. If a and b are odd integers, which of the following must be true?

I. $\frac{a + b}{2}$ is odd.
II. $a - b$ is even.
III. $a + b$ is divisible by 2.

(A) III only
(B) I and II only
(C) I and III only
(D) II and III only
(E) I, II, and III

2. For any integer n, which of the following represents three consecutive odd integers?
(A) $n, n + 1, n + 2$
(B) $n + 1, n + 3, n + 5$
(C) $3n, 5n, 7n$
(D) $2n + 1, 2n + 3, 2n + 5$
(E) $2n, 2n + 2, 2n + 4$

3. For what whole number (W) is the sum of W, $W + 1$, and $W + 2$ odd?
(A) For all W **(B)** For all even numbers W
(C) For all odd numbers W **(D)** For no W
(E) For some W, but for none of the sets above

4. If M is an odd integer and N is an even integer, which of the following *could* be an even integer?

(A) $M + N$ **(B)** $M - N$ **(C)** $\frac{M}{2} + N$
(D) $(M \times M) + M$ **(E)** $\frac{M}{2} + \frac{N}{2}$

5. If X, Y, and Z are integers such that $XY + Z$ is even, which of the following *might* be TRUE?
(A) X and Y are even; Z is odd.
(B) X and Y are odd; Z is even.
(C) X and Z are even; Y is odd.
(D) X and Z are odd; Y is even.
(E) Y and Z are odd; X is even.

6. In the equations below, a is an odd integer and b is an even integer. Which of the following expressions must be odd?

$$a^2 + ab^2 + 2b^3 = c$$
$$b^2 + ba^2 + 2a^3 = d$$

I. $c^2 + cd^2 + 2d^2$
II. $3c^3 + 3d^2 + 2c^2$
III. $c^2 + dc^2 + 2d^3$

(A) I only **(B)** II only **(C)** III only **(D)** I and II only
(E) I, II, and III

Chapter 11 Summary and Review

11-1

The number c is a **square root** of a if $c^2 = a$. The square roots of 64 are 8 and -8. The **principal square root** of 64 is written $\sqrt{64} = 8$. The negative square root of 64 is written $-\sqrt{64} = -8$.

Simplify.

1. $\sqrt{36}$ **2.** $-\sqrt{81}$ **3.** $\sqrt{49}$ **4.** $-\sqrt{169}$

An **irrational number** cannot be named by fractional notation $\frac{a}{b}$. The rational numbers and irrational numbers make up the set of **real numbers.**

Identify each square root as rational or irrational.

5. $\sqrt{3}$ **6.** $\sqrt{36}$ **7.** $-\sqrt{12}$ **8.** $-\sqrt{4}$

11-2

In a radical expression, the expression written under the radical $\sqrt{x^2 + 5}$ is called the **radicand.** Radical expressions with negative radicands have no meaning in the real number system.

Determine the replacements for the variable so that the expression represents a real number.

9. $\sqrt{x + 7}$ **10.** $\sqrt{x - 10}$

Simplify.

11. $\sqrt{m^2}$ **12.** $\sqrt{49t^2}$

13. $\sqrt{p^2}$ **14.** $\sqrt{(x - 4)^2}$

11-3

For any nonnegative numbers, a and b, $\sqrt{ab} = \sqrt{a} \cdot \sqrt{b}$. You can use this property to simplify radical expressions. A simplified radical expression has no factors under the radical sign that are perfect squares.

To find the square root of an even power such as x^{10}, take half of the exponent. If the exponent is odd, write the power as a product of the largest even power and x. Then simplify the even power.

Factor and simplify. Assume that all variables are nonnegative.

15. $-\sqrt{48}$ **16.** $\sqrt{x^2 - 14x + 49}$

17. $\sqrt{64x^2}$ **18.** $\sqrt{36x}$

19. $\sqrt{x^{12}}$ **20.** $\sqrt{y^5}$

21. $\sqrt{(x - 2)^4}$ **22.** $\sqrt{75y^{15}}$

23. $\sqrt{25x^9}$ **24.** $\sqrt{(y + 7)^{10}}$

ANSWERS

1. 6
2. -9
3. 7
4. -13
5. Irrational
6. Rational
7. Irrational
8. Rational
9. $x \geq -7$
10. $x \geq 10$
11. $|m|$
12. $7|t|$
13. $|p|$
14. $|x - 4|$
15. $-4\sqrt{3}$
16. $x - 7$
17. $8x$
18. $6\sqrt{x}$
19. x^6
20. $y^2\sqrt{y}$
21. $(x - 2)^2$
22. $5y^7\sqrt{3y}$
23. $5x^4\sqrt{x}$
24. $(y + 7)^5$

25. $\sqrt{21}$
26. $\sqrt{at}$
27. $\sqrt{x^2 - 9}$
28. $\sqrt{6xy}$
29. $\sqrt{\frac{15}{28}}$
30. $\sqrt{6x^2 + 3x}$
31. $3\sqrt{2}$
32. $x^3\sqrt{10x}$
33. $b\sqrt{ac}$
34. $5b^2\sqrt{3}$
35. $\frac{3}{4}$
36. $\frac{1}{5}$
37. $\frac{2}{3}$
38. $\frac{3\sqrt{2}}{8}$
39. 4
40. $x^2\sqrt{5}$
41. 2
42. 4
43. $\frac{\sqrt{15}}{5}$
44. $\frac{5\sqrt{3}}{3}$
45. $\frac{2\sqrt{2x}}{x}$
46. $\frac{4a\sqrt{6a}}{3}$
47. $\frac{\sqrt{2}}{4}$
48. $\frac{\sqrt{5y}}{y}$

11-4

We can use the product property for radicals to multiply radicals. Sometimes we can simplify after multiplying. We can find perfect square factors and take their square roots.

Multiply.

25. $\sqrt{3} \cdot \sqrt{7}$

26. $\sqrt{a} \cdot \sqrt{t}$

27. $\sqrt{x - 3} \cdot \sqrt{x + 3}$

28. $\sqrt{2x} \cdot \sqrt{3y}$

29. $\sqrt{\frac{3}{4}} \cdot \sqrt{\frac{5}{7}}$

30. $\sqrt{3x} \cdot \sqrt{2x + 1}$

Multiply and simplify.

31. $\sqrt{3} \cdot \sqrt{6}$

32. $\sqrt{2x^2} \cdot \sqrt{5x^5}$

33. $\sqrt{ab} \cdot \sqrt{bc}$

34. $\sqrt{5b} \cdot \sqrt{15b^3}$

11-5

For any nonnegative radicands A and B, $\frac{\sqrt{A}}{\sqrt{B}} = \sqrt{\frac{A}{B}}$.

A simplified expression may not have a radical in the denominator or a fractional radicand; you must remove the fraction from the radicand or the radical from the denominator by **rationalizing the denominator.**

Simplify.

35. $\sqrt{\frac{9}{16}}$

36. $\sqrt{\frac{1}{25}}$

37. $\sqrt{\frac{20}{45}}$

38. $\sqrt{\frac{9}{32}}$

Divide.

39. $\frac{\sqrt{48}}{\sqrt{3}}$

40. $\frac{\sqrt{45x^4}}{\sqrt{9}}$

41. $\frac{\sqrt{100x^3}}{\sqrt{25x^3}}$

42. $\frac{\sqrt{80y^4}}{\sqrt{5y^4}}$

Rationalize the denominator.

43. $\frac{\sqrt{3}}{\sqrt{5}}$

44. $\frac{5}{\sqrt{3}}$

45. $\frac{\sqrt{8}}{\sqrt{x}}$

46. $\frac{\sqrt{64a^3}}{\sqrt{6}}$

47. $\sqrt{\frac{1}{8}}$

48. $\sqrt{\frac{5}{y}}$

11-6

To add or subtract real numbers with the same radicand, use the distributive property. You may need to simplify the radicals first.

Add or subtract.

49. $10\sqrt{5} + 3\sqrt{5}$

50. $\sqrt{80} - \sqrt{45}$

51. $\sqrt{x} + \sqrt{9x}$

52. $3\sqrt{2} - 5\sqrt{\frac{1}{2}}$

53. $\sqrt{9x + 9} + \sqrt{x + 1}$

54. $\sqrt{12x^2} + \sqrt{3x^2}$

11-7

The Pythagorean theorem, $c^2 = a^2 + b^2$, can be used to find the hypotenuse (c) or the legs (a and b) of a right triangle.

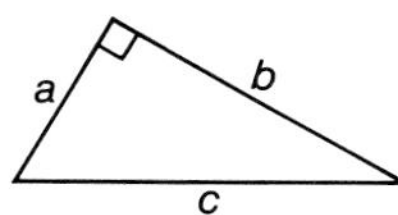

In a right triangle, find the length of the side not given.

55. $a = 15, b = 20$

56. $c = 5\sqrt{2}, b = 5$

57. $a = 6, c = 10$

58. $a = \sqrt{2}, b = \sqrt{5}$

59. $c = 18, b = 14$

60. $b = 6, a = 6\sqrt{3}$

11-8

Use the Pythagorean theorem and the Problem-Solving Guidelines to help you solve problems with right triangles.

Solve.

61. An 18-ft ladder leans against a house, reaching a point 14 ft above the ground. How far is the foot of the ladder from the bottom of the house?

62. How long must a wire be to reach from the top of a 12-ft pole to a point on the ground 8 ft from the pole?

11-9

To solve an equation with radicals, square both sides of the equation. You must always check for **extraneous solutions,** which are not solutions to the original equation.

Solve.

63. $\sqrt{x - 3} = 7$

64. $\sqrt{3x} - 8 = 13$

Solve. Use $V = 3.5\sqrt{h}$

65. A person can see 75.6 km to the horizon from the top of a mountain. How high is the mountain?

49. $13\sqrt{5}$
50. $\sqrt{5}$
51. $4\sqrt{x}$
52. $\frac{\sqrt{2}}{2}$
53. $4\sqrt{x + 1}$
54. $3x\sqrt{3}$
55. $c = 25$
56. $a = 5$
57. $b = 8$
58. $c = \sqrt{7}$
59. $a = 8\sqrt{2}$
60. $c = 12$
61. $\sqrt{128} \approx 11.3$ ft
62. $\sqrt{208} \approx 14.4$ ft
63. 52
64. 147
65. 466.56 m

ANSWERS

1. 8
2. -5
3. Rational
4. Irrational
5. $|a|$
6. $6|y|$
7. $|y + 2|$
8. $-2\sqrt{10}$
9. $3\sqrt{3}$
10. $5\sqrt{x - 1}$
11. x^3
12. $y^4\sqrt{y}$
13. $(y + 2)^2$
14. $\sqrt{33}$
15. $\sqrt{3xy}$
16. $\sqrt{\frac{10}{21}}$
17. $5\sqrt{2}$
18. $3ab^2\sqrt{2}$
19. $y\sqrt{xz}$
20. $\frac{3}{2}$
21. $\frac{12}{a}$
22. $\frac{1}{6}$
23. $\sqrt{3}$
24. $5x^2$
25. $y\sqrt{6}$
26. $\frac{\sqrt{2xy}}{y}$
27. $\frac{7\sqrt{2}}{2}$
28. $\frac{\sqrt{10}}{5}$
29. $-6\sqrt{2}$
30. $\frac{6}{5}\sqrt{5}$
31. $5x\sqrt{5}$
32. 35
33. ≈ 92 ft
34. 48
35. 38
36. 151.25 ft

Test Item Analysis

Item	Lesson
1–4	11-1
5–7	11-2
8–13	11-3
14–19	11-4
20–28	11-5
29–31	11-6
32	11-7
33	11-8
34–36	11-9

Chapter 11 Test

Simplify.

1. $\sqrt{64}$ **2.** $-\sqrt{25}$

Identify each number as rational or irrational.

3. $\sqrt{16}$ **4.** $-\sqrt{10}$

Simplify. The variables represent any real number.

5. $\sqrt{a^2}$ **6.** $\sqrt{36y^2}$ **7.** $\sqrt{(y + 2)^2}$

Simplify. Assume that all variables are nonnegative.

8. $-\sqrt{40}$ **9.** $\sqrt{27}$ **10.** $\sqrt{25x - 25}$

11. $\sqrt{x^6}$ **12.** $\sqrt{y^9}$ **13.** $\sqrt{(y + 2)^4}$

Multiply.

14. $\sqrt{3} \cdot \sqrt{11}$ **15.** $\sqrt{3x} \cdot \sqrt{y}$ **16.** $\sqrt{\frac{2}{3}} \cdot \sqrt{\frac{5}{7}}$

Multiply and simplify. Assume that all variables are nonnegative.

17. $\sqrt{5} \cdot \sqrt{10}$ **18.** $\sqrt{3ab} \cdot \sqrt{6ab^3}$ **19.** $\sqrt{xy} \cdot \sqrt{y^2}$

Simplify. Assume that all variables are nonnegative.

20. $\sqrt{\frac{27}{12}}$ **21.** $\sqrt{\frac{144}{a^2}}$ **22.** $\sqrt{\frac{1}{36}}$

Divide. Assume that all radicands are nonnegative.

23. $\frac{\sqrt{36}}{\sqrt{12}}$ **24.** $\frac{\sqrt{75x^4}}{\sqrt{3}}$ **25.** $\frac{\sqrt{96y^3}}{\sqrt{16y}}$

Rationalize the denominator.

26. $\frac{\sqrt{2x}}{\sqrt{y}}$ **27.** $\frac{7}{\sqrt{2}}$ **28.** $\sqrt{\frac{2}{5}}$

Add or subtract.

29. $3\sqrt{18} - 5\sqrt{18}$ **30.** $\sqrt{5} + \sqrt{\frac{1}{5}}$ **31.** $\sqrt{20x^2} + \sqrt{45x^2}$

32. In a right triangle, the length of the hypotenuse is 91 and the length of one of the legs is 84. Find the length of the missing leg.

33. A slow pitch softball diamond is a square 65 ft on a side. How far is it from home to second base?

Solve.

34. $\sqrt{3x} + 2 = 14$ **35.** $\sqrt{y - 2} + 3 = 9$

36. Use $r = 2\sqrt{5d}$. A car's rate (r) is 55 mi/h. How far (d) will it skid?

Chapters 1–11 Cumulative Review

1-4 Evaluate.

1. $x - (x - 1) + (x^2 + 1)$ for $x = 10$
2. $xy + (xy)^2 + x + y$ for $x = 5$ and $y = 2$

1-5 Factor.

3. $121a + 88b$
4. $36x + 24y + 12z$

1-6 Write as an algebraic expression.

5. the product of x and 4 less than y divided by the difference of x and 8 times y
6. 19 more than the fifth power of a

2-3, 2-4 Simplify.

7. $-12.1 + 100.6 - 18.5$
8. $\frac{11}{9} - \frac{4}{18} + \frac{1}{6} - \frac{2}{3} + \frac{1}{2}$

2-5 Multiply.

9. $6(-12)$
10. $(-2.3)(-4.4)$

2-6 Divide.

11. $\frac{-48}{-6}$
12. $\frac{18.6}{-6.2}$

2-7 Factor.

13. $-21x - 28w$
14. $144a^2 - 60b^2$

2-8 Simplify.

15. $-7(x - 1) + 2x$
16. $8[4 - (6x - 5)]$

3-4 Solve.

17. During the library marathon, Luis read twice as many books as Roger, but only half as many as Huong. If the three boys read 21 books, how many did Roger read?

3-5 Solve.

18. $5(a + 3) = 8a + 18$
19. $-3(m + 2) - 4 = -12 - (-2 + m)$

ANSWERS

1. 102
2. 117
3. $11(11a + 8b)$
4. $12(3x + 2y + z)$
5. $\frac{x(y - 4)}{x - 8y}$
6. $a^5 + 19$
7. 70
8. 1
9. -72
10. 10.12
11. 8
12. -3
13. $-7(3x + 4w)$
14. $12(12a^2 - 5b^2)$
15. $-5x + 7$
16. $72 - 48x$
17. 3 books
18. -1
19. 0

20. 50%
21. 250
22. 2.5
23. 770 oranges
24. $x \geq 7$
25. $x \leq -6$
26. $x > -6$
27. $x < 4$
28. 98
29. a^3b^9
30. x^{11}
31. a^3b
32. 1
33. $\frac{1}{7^4}$
34. 3^6
35. $-27x^{15}y^6$
36. $\frac{y^{12}}{8}$
37. 3.46×10^5
38. 6.28×10^{-5}
39. a
40. $9m - 28n$
41. $3c + 2bc + c^2 - 4 - 2b$
42. $6.25x^2 - 1.5xy + 0.09y^2$
43. $5x^2 + 4xy - 12y^2$
44. $a^2 + 4ac + 4c^2 - 1$
45. $h^2 - 8hk + 16k^2$
46. $4x^2 + 28xy + 49y^2$
47. $x^4 - 9$
48. $12x^2 + 2x - 2$

3-10 Translate to an equation and solve.

20. What percent of 1 is $\frac{1}{2}$?
21. 50 is 20% of what number?
22. 250% of what number is 6.25?

3-11 Translate to an equation and solve.

23. The ratio of apples to oranges sold in a local supermarket is 5 to 7. If 1320 pieces of fruit were sold in one week, how many were oranges?

4-4 Solve.

24. $8x - 2 \geq 7x + 5$
25. $-4x \geq 24$
26. $-3x < 30 + 2x$
27. $x + 3 > 6(x - 4) + 7$

4-5 Solve.

28. Amy received grades of 85, 87, 88, and 92 on her math tests. What must her grade be on her next test if her average is to be at least 90?

5-1, 5-2 Simplify.

29. $(a^2b^4)(ab^5)$
30. $x^4 \cdot x^6 \cdot x$
31. $\frac{a^8b^4}{a^5b^3}$
32. a^0
33. 7^{-4}
34. $(3^3)^2$
35. $(-3x^5y^2)^3$
36. $\left(\frac{y^4}{2}\right)^3$

5-4 Write using scientific notation.

37. 346,000
38. .0000628

5-5 Collect like terms.

39. $10a^2 + 6a - 8a^2 + 3a - 2a^2 - 8a$
40. $(8m + 6n) - (12n + 7m) + 2(4m - 11n)$

5-9, 5-10 Multiply.

41. $(4 + 2b + c)(c - 1)$
42. $(2.5x - 0.3y)^2$
43. $(5x - 6y)(x + 2y)$
44. $(a + 2c + 1)(a + 2c - 1)$
45. $(h - 4k)^2$
46. $(2x + 7y)^2$
47. $(x^2 + 3)(x^2 - 3)$
48. $(4x + 2)(3x - 1)$

6-1 to 6-7 Factor.

49. $x^3y^3 + x^2y^2 - 4xy$

50. $a^8 + a^7 - a^6$

51. $4 - 9m^4$

52. $9x^2 - 9b^2$

53. $x^2 - 4x - 12$

54. $s^2 - 16s + 15$

55. $t^3 - 5t^2 + 6t$

56. $7x^2 - 6x - 1$

57. $20y^2 + 19y + 3$

58. $6y^2 + 9y - 15$

6-8 Solve.

59. $x^2 - 3x - 10 = 0$

60. $y(3y - 2) = 0$

7-5, 7-6 Write an equation for the line that satisfies each condition.

61. slope is 5, passes through the origin

62. passes through (0, 3) and has x-intercept 6

63. slope is -1, y-intercept is -12

64. x-intercept is 7, y-intercept is -6

65. contains the points $(-1, 2)$ and $(2, 11)$

8-2, 8-3 Solve these systems.

66. $6x + 3y = -6$
$-2x + 5y = 14$

67. $2x + 3y = -3$
$y = 2x - 9$

8-4 to 8-6

68. Find two numbers such that their sum is 337 and their difference is 43.

69. The units digit of a certain number is one greater than twice the tens digit. If the digits are reversed, the new number is 36 more than the original number. Find the original number.

9-1

Let $A = \{0, 2, 4, 6, 8, 10, 12\}$ and $B = \{0, -2, -4, -6, -8, -10, -12\}$. Find the following.

70. $A \cup B$

71. $A \cap B$

9-3 Solve.

72. $|2x + 4| = 12$

73. $|2x - 5| = 7$

9-4 Solve and graph.

74. $|3y| < 12$

75. $|4x| \geq 20$

49. $xy(x^2y^2 + xy - 4)$
50. $a^6(a^2 + a - 1)$
51. $(2 - 3m^2)(2 + 3m^2)$
52. $9(x - b)(x + b)$
53. $(x - 6)(x + 2)$
54. $(s - 1)(s - 15)$
55. $t(t - 2)(t - 3)$
56. $(7x + 1)(x - 1)$
57. $(4y + 3)(5y + 1)$
58. $3(y - 1)(2y + 5)$
59. $-2, 5$
60. $0, \frac{2}{3}$
61. $y = 5x$
62. $y = -\frac{1}{2}x + 3$
63. $y = -x - 12$
64. $y = \frac{6}{7}x - 6$
65. $y = 3x + 5$
66. $(-2, 2)$
67. $(3, -3)$
68. 147, 190
69. 37
70. $\{-12, -10, -8, -6, -4, -2, 0, 2, 4, 6, 8, 10, 12\}$
71. $\{0\}$
72. $4, -8$
73. $6, -1$
74. $-4 < y < 4$

−4 0 4

75. $x \leq -5$ or $x \geq 5$

76. $\frac{3y}{2}$

77. $-\frac{2}{3}$

78. $\frac{6}{x + 3}$

79. x^3y^2

80. $\frac{8}{x + 4}$

81. $\frac{3y^2 - 5y - 6}{(y + 1)(y - 1)}$

82. $\frac{y^2 + 5 - 3x}{x - 2}$

83. -10

84. $-4, 3$

85. $26\frac{2}{3}$ h or 26 h 40 min

86. $x - 3 - \frac{4}{x + 8}$

87. $\frac{1 + 3x}{1 - 2x}$

10-2 Multiply. Simplify the product.

76. $\frac{3y}{y + 1} \cdot \frac{y + 1}{2}$

77. $\frac{-4}{3y + 3} \cdot \frac{y + 1}{2}$

10-3 Divide. Simplify the quotient.

78. $\frac{2x - 6}{5} \div \frac{x^2 - 9}{15}$

79. $\frac{x^2y + x^3y}{x} \div \frac{1 + x}{x^2y}$

10-4, 10-5 Add or subtract. Simplify.

80. $\frac{4}{2x + 8} + \frac{6}{x + 4}$

81. $\frac{3y}{y + 1} - \frac{2y + 6}{y^2 - 1}$

82. $\frac{y^2}{x - 2} + \frac{5}{x - 2} - \frac{3x}{x - 2}$

10-6 Solve.

83. $\frac{3}{x - 3} - \frac{2}{x + 3} = \frac{5}{x^2 - 9}$

84. $\frac{12}{y} - \frac{12}{y + 1} = 1$

10-7

85. It takes two computers working together 10 hours to solve problems about a tail design for an airplane. One computer working alone can do the job in 16 hours. How long does it take the other computer to do the job alone?

10-9 Divide.

86. $x^2 + 5x - 28$ by $x + 8$

10-10 Simplify.

87. $\frac{\frac{1}{x} + 3}{\frac{1}{x} - 2}$

11-1, 11-2 Simplify.

88. $\sqrt{49}$
89. $-\sqrt{121}$
90. $\sqrt{64p^2}$
91. $\sqrt{(-7c)^2}$
92. $\sqrt{(x-2)^2}$
93. $\sqrt{x^2 - 6x + 9}$

11-3, 11-4 Simplify.

94. $-\sqrt{56}$
95. $\sqrt{x^8}$
96. $\sqrt{36b^5}$
97. $\sqrt{20x^4y^5}$

Multiply. Simplify where possible.

98. $\sqrt{6} \cdot \sqrt{8}$
99. $\sqrt{6a}\sqrt{3a^2b^2}$
100. $\sqrt{2b} \cdot \sqrt{5a + 3b}$
101. $\sqrt{x + 4y} \cdot \sqrt{2x - 5y}$

11-5 Divide. Simplify where possible.

102. $\sqrt{\frac{1}{81}}$
103. $\frac{\sqrt{200x^3}}{\sqrt{25x}}$
104. $\frac{6}{\sqrt{2}}$
105. $\sqrt{\frac{1}{9}}$

11-6 Add or subtract.

106. $6\sqrt{2} - 8\sqrt{2}$
107. $\sqrt{200} - \sqrt{8}$
108. $\sqrt{7} + \sqrt{\frac{1}{7}}$
109. $\sqrt{\frac{3}{4}} - \sqrt{\frac{4}{3}}$

11-7

In a right triangle, find the length of the side not given.

110. $c = 15, a = 9$
111. $a = 16, b = 30$

11-8

112. Larry wants to fit a circular piece of glass, 86 in. in diameter, through a doorway measuring 30 in. by 80 in. Will the glass fit through the doorway? What is the maximum diameter that could fit through the doorway?

11-9 Solve.

113. $\sqrt{x - 5} = 3$
114. $\sqrt{2y - 3} = \sqrt{y + 6}$

88. 7
89. -11
90. $8|p|$
91. $7|c|$
92. $|x - 2|$
93. $|x - 3|$
94. $-2\sqrt{14}$
95. x^4
96. $6b^2\sqrt{b}$
97. $2x^2y^2\sqrt{5y}$
98. $4\sqrt{3}$
99. $3|ab|\sqrt{2a}$
100. $\sqrt{10ab + 6b^2}$
101. $\sqrt{2x^2 + 3xy - 20y^2}$
102. $\frac{1}{9}$
103. $2|x|\sqrt{2}$
104. $3\sqrt{2}$
105. $\frac{1}{3}$
106. $-2\sqrt{2}$
107. $8\sqrt{2}$
108. $\frac{8\sqrt{7}}{7}$
109. $\frac{-\sqrt{3}}{6}$
110. $b = 12$
111. $c = 34$
112. No; about 85 in.
113. 14
114. 9

CHAPTER 12 Relations and Functions

Chapter Overview

Relations and functions are defined and simple functions are graphed in this chapter. A relation is defined as a set of ordered pairs, and a function as a special kind of relation. The $f(x)$ notation and the terms domain and range are presented. Relations and functions are graphed in the plane, and the graphs of functions are distinguished from the graphs of nonfunctions. Absolute value functions are explored as a bonus topic. Interval graphs are introduced in Connections: Discrete Math. Quadratic equations of the form $y = ax^2 + bx + c$ are graphed and examined. Equations of direct, inverse, and joint variation are discussed.

The Problem-Solving Guidelines are used to solve word problems involving direct, inverse, and joint variation. As a culmination of all problem-solving strategy lessons presented in the book, the first of three situational problems, *Starting a Business,* is presented.

Objectives

☆ 3A, 3B	12-1	■ Determine whether a given relation is a function.
		■ Find the value of a function.
☆ 3A, 3N	12-2	■ Graph a function.
		■ Recognize the graph of a function.
☆ 3N	B.T.	■ Graph and compare absolute value functions.
☆ 3I	12-3	■ Solve problems involving linear functions.
☆ 4A, 4B	12-4	■ Graph quadratic functions.
☆ 2C, 3I	12-5	■ Give an equation of direct variation.
		■ Solve problems involving direct variation.
☆ 2C, 3I	12-6	■ Find an equation of inverse variation.
		■ Solve problems involving inverse variation.
☆ 2C, 3I	12-7	■ Solve problems involving joint variation.
		■ Solve problems involving combined variation.
		■ Solve problems involving joint variation.

TEACHING CHAPTER 12

Cooperative Learning Opportunities

The introductory **Explore** to Lesson 12-4 can be used in a cooperative setting. The activity can be done at the computer, on a graphing calculator, or the graphs can be done by hand.

Assign students in groups of 3 with the following roles: (1) suggest the equations, (2) input or draw the graph, (3) record how this graph fits into the family being considered.

Each group should begin with the graph of $y = x^2$ and then investigate the following families: (1) positive, whole numbers, and fractional coefficients of x^2; (2) positive and negative whole number coefficients of x^2; (3) positive and negative constants; (4) positive and negative x terms.

Have a representative of each group report to the class on how the changes affect the graph.

Multicultural Note: *Maria Agnesi*

Some mathematicians have expended a great deal of time and energy studying a single function or equation. Maria Agnesi, born in Italy in 1718, studied a curve that has been named after her.

Agnesi was highly gifted. As a child she was fluent in seven languages and gave talks on logic, chemistry, botany, and zoology. At the age of 20 she devoted herself to mathematics and later wrote a text that included original discoveries in topics from algebra to calculus. Agnesi studied the equation $x^2y = a^2(a - y)$ and its graph that now bears her name. Its mathematical properties and applications in physics have intrigued mathematicians ever since Agnesi's day.

At the age of 33, Maria Agnesi turned away from her mathematical and scientific work to care for her father and attend to the education of her brothers and sisters. Some years later she became the director of a home for the elderly.

For more information, see page 9 of **Multiculturalism in Mathematics, Science, and Technology**.

Alternative Assessment and Communication Ideas

Function is a difficult concept. Some students have difficulty grasping the meaning; others fail to see its importance. The **Writing to Learn** activity on page 541 and the Bonus Topic on page 546 reinforce the understanding of function.

Exercise 8 on page 546 gives students an opportunity to generalize their thinking and to explain the effects of different parameters.

As has been mentioned in earlier chapters, working backwards from graphs to equations can be a useful means to assess students' understanding. Have students write an equation for each of the following graphs.

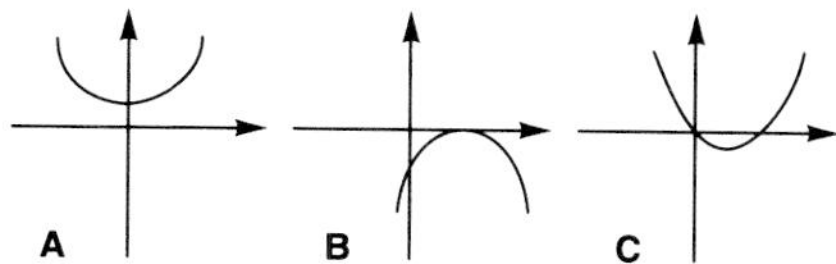

Answers will vary. Examples: (A) $f(x) = x^2 + 1$; (B) $f(x) = -x^2 - 3$; (C) $f(x) = x^2 - 2x$.

Investigations and Projects

Lessons 12-5 and 12-6 contain some geometric interpretations of direct and inverse variation. These and other geometric examples can be used as the basis for a project. Ask students to work on the following and then come up with general statements about variation.

(1) If the width of a rectangle remains 4 ft, what happens to its perimeter as its length increases? Make a table for the relationship, write an equation, and draw its graph.
(2) If the area of a rectangle remains 36 sq cm, write an equation for the area, and list some of the solutions.
(3) Draw the graph of the equation in (2). Use one axis for length and the other for width. What kind of variation is displayed?
(4) If the area of a triangle remains 24 sq in., what happens to the base as the height decreases? Write an equation for this relationship and draw its graph.

Ans. (1) increases, $y = 2x + 8$, line; (2) $xy = 36$; (6, 6), (4, 9), (18, 2), etc.; (3) joint variation (hyperbola); (4) $24 = \frac{1}{2}xy$, hyperbola.

MANAGING CHAPTER 12

Lesson	PACING CHART (DAYS) 2-Year* A for E	1-Year Minimum	1-Year Regular	1-Year Advanced	Opening Activity	Cooperative Activity	Seat or Group Work
12-1	2	1	2	2	First Five Minutes 12-1: ***FFMTM*** p. 35 or **TE** p. 536; Application: **SE** p. 536	Lesson Enrichment: **TE** p. 538; Calculator Worksheet 25: ***Technology*** p. 27	Try This a–f
12-2	2	1	1	1	First Five Minutes 12-2: ***FFMTM*** p. 35 or **TE** p. 542; ***Overhead Transparencies*** T25	Explore: **SE** p. 542; ✂ Manipulative Activity 12: ***Enrichment*** p. 45	Try This a–e
12-3	3	1	1	1	First Five Minutes 12-3: ***FFMTM*** p. 36 or **TE** p. 547	Connections: Discrete Math: **SE** pp. 550–551	Try This a
12-4	2	1	1	1	First Five Minutes 12-4: ***FFMTM*** p. 36 or **TE** p. 552; ***Overhead Transparencies*** T26, T27	Explore: **SE** p. 552; Connections: Geometry: **SE** p. 556	Try This a–c
12-5	2	1	1	1	First Five Minutes 12-5: ***FFMTM*** p. 36 or **TE** p. 557; Application: **SE** p. 557	Bonus Topic 12: ***Enrichment*** p. 13	Try This a–d
12-6	2	1	1	1	First Five Minutes 12-6: ***FFMTM*** p. 36 or **TE** p. 561; Application: **SE** p. 561	Spatial Relations: **SE** p. 564	Try This a–d
12-7	3	2	1	2	First Five Minutes 12-7: ***FFMTM*** p. 36 or **TE** p. 565	Problem Solving: Situational Problem Solving: **SE** p. 570	Try This a–c
Review	2	1	1	1			
Test	1	1	1	1			

*2-Year Management Guide can be found in *Algebra for Everyone*.

FFMTM: First Five Minutes Transparency Masters

MANAGING CHAPTER 12

Enrichment	Review/Assess	Reteach	Technology	Lesson
Lesson Enrichment: **TE** p. 538; Writing to Learn: **SE** p. 541	Mixed Review 23: ***SPMR*** p. 73; Lesson Quiz: **TE** p. 539		Evaluating Functions: **SE** p. 539; Calculator Worksheet 25: ***Technology*** p. 27	**12-1**
Biographical Note: Leonard Euler: **SE** p. 545; Bonus Topic: **SE** p. 546; ✂ Manipulative Activity 12: ***Enrichment*** p. 45	Lesson Quiz: **TE** p. 543		Problem for Programmers: **SE** p. 545; Computer Exploration 8: **SE** p. 720; Teacher Demonstration Lesson 2: ***Master Grapher*** pp. 9–10, 65–66, or 120–121; Worksheets 10, 11: ***Master Grapher*** pp. 40–46, 96–98, or 151–153; Worksheets 10, 11: ***TI-81 Activities*** pp. 35–42	**12-2**
Connections: Discrete Math: **SE** pp. 550–551	Mixed Review 24: ***SPMR*** p. 74; Lesson Quiz: **TE** p. 548; Quiz 23: ***Assessment*** p. 33	Skills Practice 33: ***SPMR*** p. 41; Problem Bank 23: ***Problem Bank*** p. 40		**12-3**
Critical Thinking 12: ***Enrichment*** p. 29 Teacher Demonstration Lesson 3: ***Master Grapher*** pp. 11–12, 67–68, or 122–123	Lesson Quiz: **TE** p. 554	Mixed Practice 23: **SE** p. 706	Computer Exploration 9: **SE** p. 721; Calculator Worksheet 26: ***Technology*** p. 28; Worksheets 12, 13: ***Master Grapher*** pp. 47–53, 103–109, or 158–164; Worksheets 12, 13: ***TI-81 Activities*** pp. 43–49	**12-4**
Bonus Topic 12: ***Enrichment*** p. 13	Lesson Quiz: **TE** p. 558	Problem Bank 24: ***Problem Bank*** p. 41	Calculator Worksheet 27: ***Technology*** p. 29	**12-5**
Looking for Errors 12: ***Enrichment*** p. 61	Lesson Quiz: **TE** p. 563; Quiz 24: ***Assessment*** p. 34	Problem Bank 25: ***Problem Bank*** p. 42	BASIC Computer Project 16: ***Technology*** p. 78	**12-6**
Lesson Enrichment: **TE** p. 567; Problem Solving: Situational Problem Solving: **SE** p. 570	Lesson Quiz: **TE** p. 567	Skills Practice 34: ***SPMR*** p. 42; Mixed Practice 24: **SE** p. 707		**12-7**
	Summary and Review: **SE** pp. 571–573; Test: **SE** p. 573	Strategy Problem Bank 12: ***Problem Bank*** p. 13		**Review**
	Chapter 12 Exam: ***A for E*** pp. 459–460; Chapter 12 Test: ***Assessment*** pp. 65–66 (min.), 137–142 (reg.), 185–186 (adv.)			**Test**

SPMR: Skills Practice Mixed Review

The solution to the problem posed on the facing page can be found on page 567.

Ready for Relations and Functions?

1-1, 1-3 Evaluate for $x = 5$ and $y = -3$.

1. $-\frac{2x}{y}$ $\frac{10}{3}$

2. $x^2 + 1$ 26

3. $y^3 - 4$ -31

1-9 Evaluate.

4. $A = \frac{1}{2}bh$ for $b = 7$ and $h = 6$. 21

5. $I = Prt$ for $P = 1500$, $r = 0.12$, and $t = 2$. 360

3-7

6. Solve $A = \frac{1}{2}h(b_1 + b_2)$ for h. $\frac{2A}{b_1 + b_2}$

7. Solve $C = 2\pi r$ for r. $\frac{C}{2\pi}$

3-9

8. The winner of an election won by a vote of 5 to 3, getting 1750 votes. How many votes did the loser get? 1050

7-1

9. Plot these points on a coordinate plane. See Teacher's Answer Section.
   a. $(-2, 5)$ **b.** $(2, 3)$ **c.** $(4, 0)$
   d. $(-5, -6)$ **e.** $(0, -3)$ **f.** $(6, -1)$

7-3 Graph each equation. See Teacher's Answer Section.

10. $5y - 4 = 2x$

11. $3x + y = 8$

CHAPTER

Relations and Functions 12

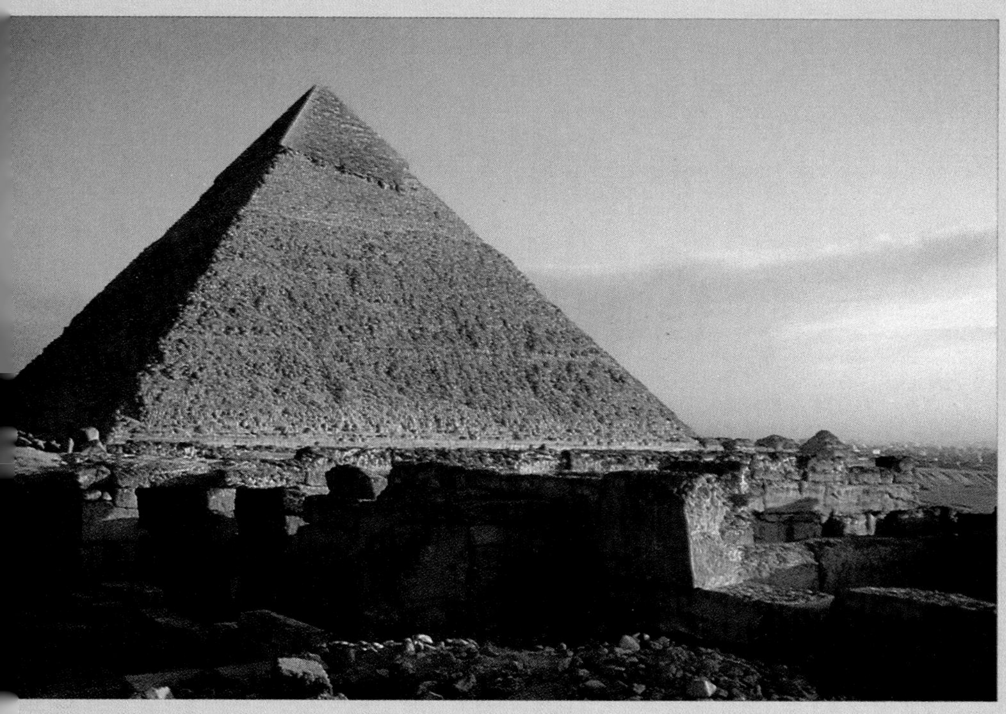

The volume of a pyramid varies jointly as the height of the pyramid and the area of its base. Find the volume of the Great Pyramid whose height is 147 m and whose base has an area of 50,000 m^2.

12-1

FIRST FIVE MINUTES

1. Write all the possible pairs of names such that the first name comes from the set {Ann, Beth} and the second name comes from the set {Smith, Wilson}.
   (Ann, Smith), (Ann, Wilson), (Beth, Smith), (Beth, Wilson)
2. Write all the possible pairs of numbers such that the first number comes from the set {0, 1} and the second number comes from the set {7, 8, 9}.
   (0, 7), (0, 8), (0, 9), (1, 7), (1, 8), (1, 9)

Identifying Functions

Emphasize that a function is a special kind of relation. That is, all functions are relations, but not all relations are functions.

When defining a function, emphasize that a member of the range may have more than one member of the domain assigned to it. However, each member of the domain is assigned to only one member of the range.

For example, two people have a height of 142 cm, but nobody has two heights.

Key Questions

If x is a member of the domain and y is a member of the range, which of the following relations are functions?

- x has English grade y
  This is a function. A person has only one grade.
- x is friends with y
  This is not a function. A person may be friends with more than one person.
- x is y feet tall
  This is a function. A person has only one height.
- x is the square of y
  This is not a function. A number is the square of two numbers.

12-1 Relations and Functions

Application

The diagram below shows that the size of a motion picture on the screen is related to the distance of the movie projector from the screen.

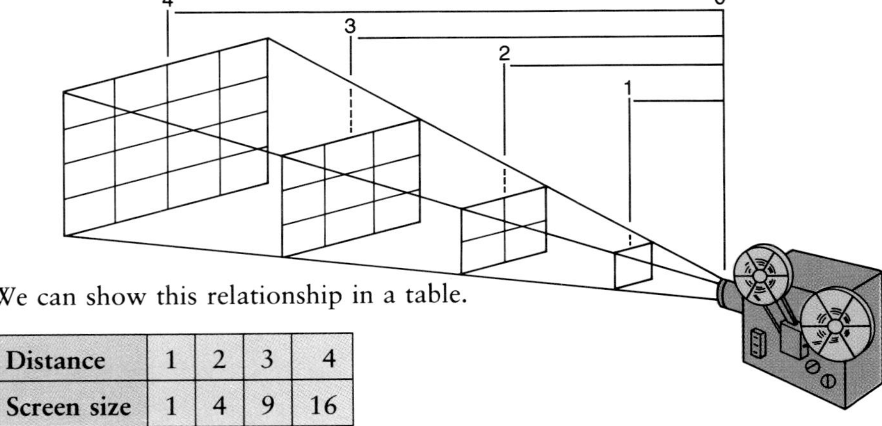

We can show this relationship in a table.

Distance	1	2	3	4
Screen size	1	4	9	16

We can also show this relationship using a formula. If d represents distance in units, and s represents screen size in squares, the formula $d = s^2$ shows the relationship between these quantities. We can see that for each value of s, we have one and only one value for d. In mathematics, this relationship is given a special name.

Identifying Functions

Objective: Determine whether a given relation is a function.

The numbers in the table above could be written as ordered pairs (x, y) where x is the first member or coordinate and y is the second coordinate. We can express these numbers as a set of ordered pairs.

$$\{(1, 1), (2, 4), (3, 9), (4, 16)\}$$

Definition

A **relation** is a set of ordered pairs. The **domain** of a relation is the set of first coordinates. The **range** is the set of second coordinates.

The list below shows a relation. Each person is paired with a number representing his or her height.

Person	Height (cm)
Lora	120
Jorge	202
Carolyn	142
Elaine	138
Saul	142

The domain is {Lora, Jorge, Carolyn, Elaine, Saul} and the range is {120, 202, 142, 138}. Notice that for each person there is exactly one height. This is a special kind of relation called a **function.**

Definition

A **function** is a relation that assigns to each member of the domain exactly one member of the range.

The members of the domain can be called **inputs** and the members of the range can be called **outputs.** Arrows can be used to describe the function.

Domain (Set of inputs) → **Range** (Set of outputs)

- Lora → 120
- Jorge → 202
- Carolyn → 142
- Elaine → 138
- Saul → 142

EXAMPLE 1 Are the following relations functions?

f: **Domain** → **Range**

- a → 4
- b → 0
- c → 0

g: **Domain** → **Range**

- 3 → 5
- 4 → 9
- 4 → −7
- 5 → −7
- 6 → −7

The relation f is a function, since each input is matched to only one output. The relation g is not a function, since the input 4 has more than one output.

EXAMPLE 2 Which of the following relations are functions?

h: **Domain** → **Range**

- 4 → 0
- 6 → 0
- 2 → 0

p: **Domain** → **Range**

- Cheese pizza → $9.75
- Cheese pizza → $7.25
- Tomato pizza → $8.50
- Meat pizza → $9.75

Chalkboard Examples

Are the following relations functions?

1.

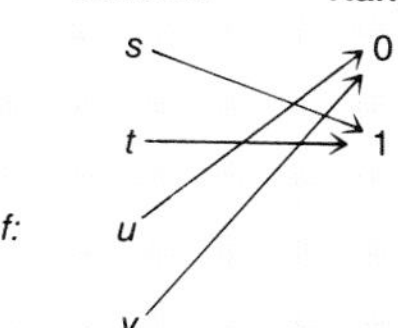

Relation f is a function, since each input is matched to only one output.

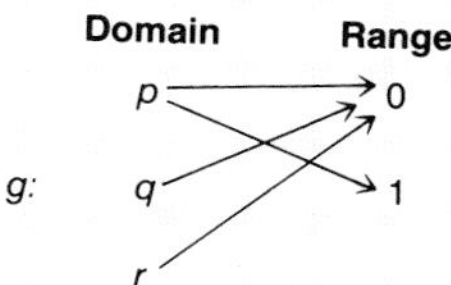

Relation g is not a function, since the input p has more than one output.

2.

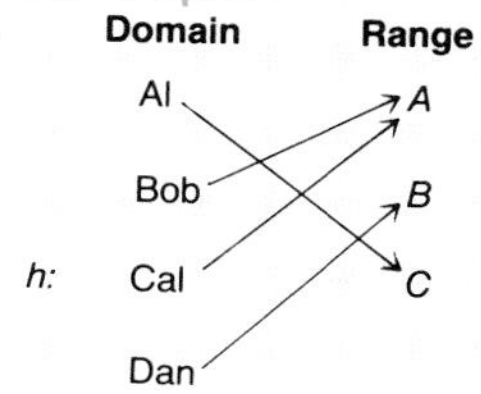

Relation h is a function.

3.

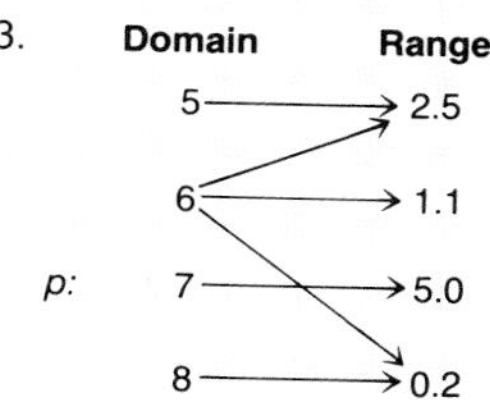

Relation p is not a function, since the input 6 has more than one output.

Function Notation

Emphasize that $f(x)$ does not mean "f times x." We read $f(x)$ as "f of x."

Chalkboard Example

1. Find the indicated outputs.
   $f(t) = 3t^2 - 1$; find $f(0)$, $f(-1)$, and $f(2)$.
   $f(0) = 3(0)^2 - 1 = -1$
   $f(-1) = 3(-1)^2 - 1 = 2$
   $f(2) = 3(2)^2 - 1 = 11$

LESSON ENRICHMENT

Let $f(x) = 3x - 1$ and $g(x) = \frac{x+1}{3}$.

Find $f(2)$, then find $g[f(2)]$. 5; 2
Find $f(3)$, then find $g[f(3)]$. 8; 3
Find $f(4)$, then find $g[f(4)]$. 11; 4
Find $g(5)$, then find $f[g(5)]$. 2; 5
Find $g(8)$, then find $f[g(8)]$. 3; 8
Find $g(11)$, then find $f[g(11)]$. 4; 11

$f(x)$ and $g(x)$ are called inverse functions. Ask students to find other pairs of inverse functions.

Relation h is a function. Relation p is not a function, since the input cheese pizza has two outputs. In a function, an element in the domain can be matched with only one element in the range.

Try This Are the following relations functions?

a.

Domain	Range
(12, 3) →	36
(5, 7) →	35
(6, 6) →	36

Yes

b.

Domain	Range
Tom →	18
Sue →	28
Jorge →	28
	12

No

Function Notation

Objective: Find the value of a function.

The input-output process can also be thought of in terms of a function machine. Inputs from the domain are put into the machine. The machine then gives the proper output.

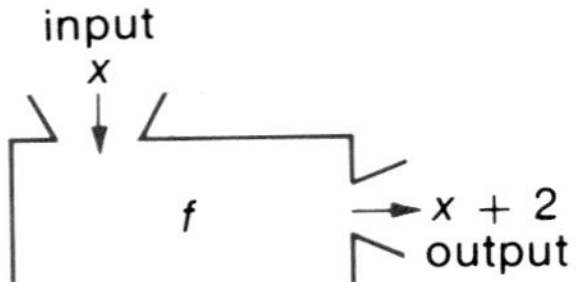

This function machine, for the relation f, assigns to each input x the output $x + 2$. It adds 2 to each input. The outputs for the inputs 8, -3, 0, and 5 are as follows.

$$8 \rightarrow 10 \qquad -3 \rightarrow -1 \qquad 0 \rightarrow 2 \qquad 5 \rightarrow 7$$

The symbol $f(x)$, read "f of x," denotes the number assigned to x by the relation f. If x is the input, $f(x)$ is the output. We can write the above results as follows where $f(x) = x + 2$.

$$f(8) = 8 + 2 = 10 \qquad f(-3) = -3 + 2 = -1$$
$$f(0) = 0 + 2 = 2 \qquad f(5) = 5 + 2 = 7$$

The outputs of a function are also called function values. For example, above we have $f(8) = 10$. We can say that "10 is the value of the function $f(x) = x + 2$ when $x = 8$."

EXAMPLE 3 Find the indicated outputs.

$f(t) = 2t^2 + 5$; find $f(-2)$, $f(0)$, and $f(3)$.

$$f(-2) = 2(-2)^2 + 5 = 2 \cdot 4 + 5 = 13$$

$$f(0) = 2(0)^2 + 5 = 5$$

$$f(3) = 2(3)^2 + 5 = 2 \cdot 9 + 5 = 23$$

Try This Find the indicated outputs.

c. $f(x) = x + 3$; find $f(5)$, $f(-8)$, and $f(-2)$. 8, −5, 1

d. $G(x) = 3x - x^2$; find $G(0)$, $G(-2)$, and $G(1)$. 0, −10, 2

e. $f(y) = 8y^2 + 3$; find $f(-1)$, $f(2)$, and $f\left(\frac{1}{2}\right)$. 11, 35, 5

f. $p(x) = 2x^2 + x - 1$; find $p(0)$, $p(-2)$, and $p(3)$. −1, 5, 20

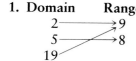

Evaluating Functions

We can use a calculator to evaluate functions. Suppose $f(x) = 2x^3$. Find $f(-4)$.

2 [×] 4 [y^x] 3 [=] 128 [+/−] -128

Note: Many calculators will not compute y^x if y is negative. In the example above, you must determine whether $(-4)^3$ will be positive or negative. Since it is negative, you must first compute 2^3 and then use the change sign key.

For additional calculator practice, see Calculator Worksheet 25.

Have students determine whether their calculators will compute −2 [y^x] 3. Stress that an error message does not mean that the student has made an error, only that the calculator will not compute powers of negative numbers. Remind these students that they must determine the sign of the expression.

LESSON QUIZ

1. Determine whether the following defines a function.

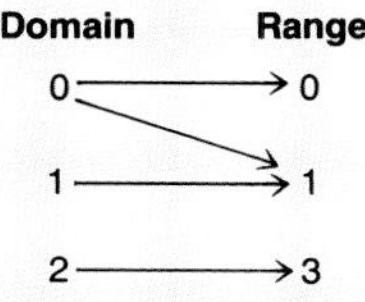

No

2. Find the indicated outputs. $f(x) = 3x - 1$; find $f(0)$, $f(-1)$, and $f(5)$.
   $f(0) = -1$
   $f(-1) = -4$
   $f(5) = 14$

Assignment Guide
Minimum: 1–20 e/o, MR

Regular: Day 1: 1–20 e/o, MR
Day 2: 21–32 e/o, 33
Advanced: Day 1: 1–20 e/o, MR
Day 2: 21–32 e/o, 33, 34–40 e/o

12-1 EXERCISES

A

Which of the following relations are functions? 1, 3, 4, 6

1. Domain → Range
2 → 9
5 → 8
19 → 9

2. Domain → Range

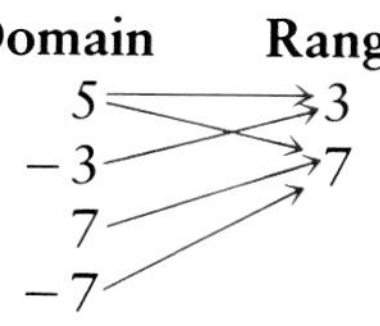

3. Domain → Range
−5 → 1
5 → 1
8 → 1

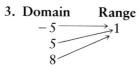

4. Domain → Range
6 → −6
7 → −7
3 → −3

5. Domain → Range
Los Angeles → Lakers
Los Angeles → Dodgers
New York → Mets
New York → Yankees

6. Domain → Range
(3, 4) → 12
(8, 10) → 18
(4, −2) → 2
(−3, −8) → −11

Find the indicated output for each function machine.

7.

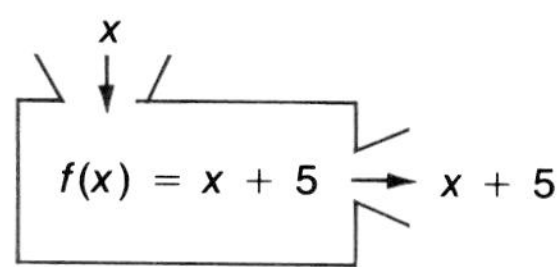

Find $f(3)$, $f(7)$, and $f(-9)$. 8, 12, −4

8.

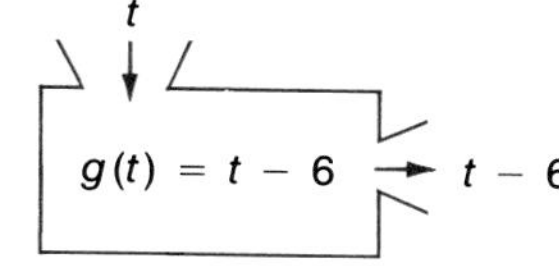

Find $g(0)$, $g(6)$, and $g(18)$. −6, 0, 12

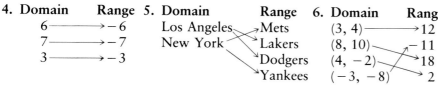

9. 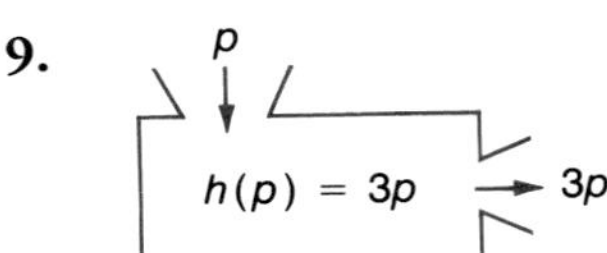

10. 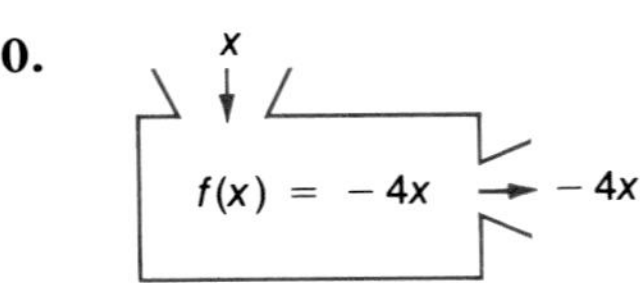

Find $h(-2)$, $h(5)$, and $h(24)$. $-6, 15, 72$ Find $f(6)$, $f\left(-\frac{1}{2}\right)$, and $f(20)$. $-24, 2, -80$

Find the indicated outputs for these functions.

11. $g(s) = 2s + 4$; find $g(1)$, $g(-7)$, and $g(6)$. $6, -10, 16$

12. $h(x) = 19$; find $h(4)$, $h(-6)$, and $h(12)$. $19, 19, 19$

13. $F(x) = 2x^2 - 3x + 2$; find $F(0)$, $F(-1)$, and $F(2)$. $2, 7, 4$

14. $P(x) = 3x^2 - 2x + 5$; find $P(0)$, $P(-2)$, and $P(3)$. $5, 21, 26$

15. $h(x) = |x|$; find $h(-4)$, $h(4)$, and $h(-3)$. $4, 4, 3$

16. $f(t) = |t| + 1$; find $f(-5)$, $f(0)$, and $f(-9)$. $6, 1, 10$

17. $f(x) = |x| - 2$; find $f(3)$, $f(93)$, and $f(-100)$. $1, 91, 98$

18. $g(t) = t^3 + 3$; find $g(1)$, $g(-5)$ and $g(0)$. $4, -122, 3$

19. $h(x) = x^4 - 3$; find $h(0)$, $h(-1)$, and $h(3)$. $-3, -2, 78$

20. $f(m) = 3m^2 - 5$; find $f(4)$, $f(-3)$, and $f(6)$. $43, 22, 103$

B

The cost of replacing a defective tire is a function of the tread depth. The chart below describes one such function. Refer to it for Exercises 21–24.

	Tread Depth in Millimeters								
	9	8	7	6	5	4	3	2	1
% charged	0%	20%	30%	40%	55%	70%	80%	90%	100%

21. Find the cost of replacing a tire whose regular price is \$64.50 and whose tread depth is 4 mm. \$45.15

22. Find the cost of replacing a tire whose regular price is \$78.50 and whose tread depth is 7 mm. \$23.55

23. Find the cost of replacing a tire whose regular price is \$67.80 and whose tread depth is 3 mm. \$54.24

24. Find the cost of replacing a tire whose regular price is \$72.40 and whose tread depth is 5 mm. \$39.82

25. The function $P(d) = 1 + \frac{d}{33}$ gives the pressure of salt water in atmospheres as a function of d, the depth in feet. Find the pressure at 20 feet, 30 feet, and 100 feet. $1\frac{20}{33}, 1\frac{30}{33}, 4\frac{1}{33}$

26. The function $R(t) = 33\frac{1}{3}t$ gives the number of revolutions of a $33\frac{1}{3}$ RPM record as a function of t, the time it is on the turntable. Find the number of revolutions at 5 minutes, 20 minutes, and 25 minutes. $166\frac{2}{3}, 666\frac{2}{3}, 833\frac{1}{3}$

27. The function $T(d) = 10d + 20$ gives the temperature in degrees Celsius inside the earth as a function of d, the depth in kilometers. Find the temperature at 5 km, 20 km, 1000 km. 70°, 220°, 10,020°

28. The function $W(d) = 0.112d$ gives the depth of water in centimeters as a function of d, the depth of snow in centimeters. Find the depth of water that results from these depths of snow: 16 cm, 25 cm, and 100 cm. 1.792 cm, 2.8 cm, 11.2 cm

Find the range of each function for the given domain.

29. $f(x) = 3x + 5$ when the domain is the set of whole numbers less than 4. 5, 8, 11, 14

30. $g(t) = t^2 - 5$ when the domain is the set of integers between -4 and 2. $-5, -4, -1, 4$

31. $h(x) = |x| - x$ when the domain is the set of integers between -2 and 20. 0, 2

32. $f(m) = m^3 + 1$ when the domain is the set of integers between -3 and 3. $-7, 0, 1, 2, 9$

33. ***Critical Thinking*** List all of the different relations between the elements in $\{a, b\}$ and $\{1, 2\}$.

Challenge

Suppose $f(x) = 3x$ and $g(x) = -4x^2$. Find the following.

34. $f(8) - g(2)$ 40

35. $f(0) - g(-5)$ 100

36. $2f(1) + 3g(4)$ -186

37. $g(-3) \cdot f(-8) + 16$ 880

38. $f[g(-2)]$ -48

39. $g[g(-1)]$ -64

40. If $f(-1) = -7$ and $f(3) = 8$, find a linear equation for $f(x)$. $f(x) = \frac{15}{4}x - \frac{13}{4}$

Mixed Review

Solve.

41. $x - y = -7$, $x + y = 5$

42. $2x + 3y = 11$, $5y - x = 1$

43. $2y + 5x = 4$, $4x = 13 - 3y$

Multiply.

44. $\sqrt{x}\sqrt{y}$

45. $\sqrt{y}\sqrt{y - 2}$

46. $\sqrt{a}\sqrt{a + 3}$

47. $\sqrt{m + n}\sqrt{m - n}$

48. $\sqrt{a + 3}\sqrt{2a + 1}$

49. $\sqrt{x - 4} \cdot \sqrt{3x + 2}$

Write an equation for the line that contains the given pair of points.

50. $(-2, 2)$ and $(3, 7)$

51. $(5, 1)$ and $(-7, 1)$

52. $(6, -1)$ and $(-2, -5)$

53. $(3, 3)$ and $(3, -1)$

Simplify.

54. $\sqrt{18}$

55. $\sqrt{144m^2}$

56. $\sqrt{20c^2}$

57. $\sqrt{32a^3}$

WRITING TO LEARN

Write a one-page paper on the different meanings of the word *function*. Your paper should include real-world situations so that someone not studying algebra will understand the meaning of a mathematical function.

ADDITIONAL ANSWERS

33.

a → 1, b → 2   a → 1, a → 2, b → 2

a → 1, b → 1, b → 2   a → 1, a → 2, b → 1, b → 2

a → 2, b → 1

Mixed Review

41. $(-1, 6)$
42. $(4, 1)$
43. $(-2, 7)$
44. $\sqrt{xy}$
45. $\sqrt{y^2 - 2y}$
46. $\sqrt{a^2 + 3a}$
47. $\sqrt{m^2 - n^2}$
48. $\sqrt{2a^2 + 7a + 3}$
49. $\sqrt{3x^2 - 10x - 8}$
50. $y = x + 4$
51. $y = 1$
52. $y = \frac{1}{2}x - 4$
53. $x = 3$
54. $3\sqrt{2}$
55. $12|m|$
56. $2|c|\sqrt{5}$
57. $4|a|\sqrt{2a}$

Writing to Learn

Students should express that a function is a relation between two sets—the domain and the range—that assigns one member of the range to each member of the domain. They should note that a relation that assigns more than one member of the range to any member of the domain is not a function, but that a member of the range may be assigned to more than one member of the domain.

12-2

FIRST FIVE MINUTES

Given that $f(x) = 2x^2 + 3$, find the following.

1. $f(1)$ 5
2. $f(-1)$ 5
3. $f(5)$ 53

EXPLORE

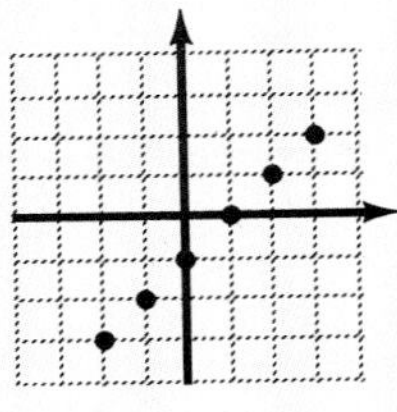

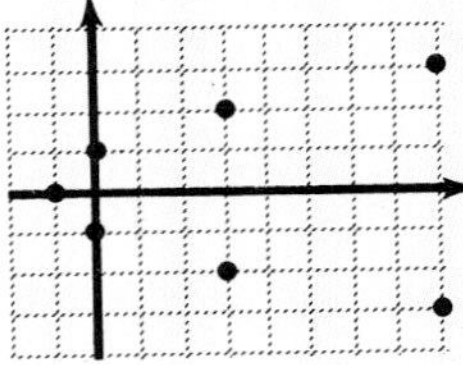

Only the first graph is a function. Students should realize that if any x-coordinate is associated with more than one y-coordinate, the graph is not a function.

Graphing Functions

Remind students that the *domain* of a function is the set of "input" values. The domain elements are the first coordinates of the ordered pairs that make up the function. The *range* of a function is the set of "output" values. The range elements are the second coordinates of the ordered pairs that make up the function.

Have students graph enough points to determine a pattern.

Key Questions

Here is a function defined by a table of ordered pairs.

x	0	1	2	3
f(x)	9	6	3	0

- What is the domain of this function? {0, 1, 2, 3}
- What is the range of this function? {9, 6, 3, 0}
- What is $f(3)$? 0

12-2 Functions and Graphs

Master Grapher Worksheets 10 and 11 can be used with this lesson.

Explore

Each equation below shows a relation between the variables x and y. Recall that a relation is a set of ordered pairs. Since we know how to graph ordered pairs, we know how to graph relations. Graph each of the following on separate coordinate axes.

- $y = x - 1$ for these replacements for x: $\{-2, -1, 0, 1, 2, 3\}$
- $y^2 = x + 1$ for these replacements for x: $\{-1, 0, 3, 8\}$ (Hint: Be sure to find all values of y for each value of x.)

Recall that a function is a relation where there is a unique output value for each input value. In the relations above, the replacements for x are the input values, and the replacements for y are the output values. Determine which of the relations above is a function and which is not. Can you determine from the graphs which is a function and which is not? How?

Graphing Functions

Objective: Graph a function.

We know that a relation is a set of ordered pairs, and that a function is a special type of relation. We already know how to graph ordered pairs, so we can graph functions.

EXAMPLE 1 Graph the function g described by $g(x) = |x|$ where the domain is the set of real numbers.

We cannot list all of the ordered pairs for this function, since there is an infinite number of real numbers. Thus we begin by listing some values of the function.

x	0	1	−1	2	−2	3	−3
g(x)	0	1	1	2	2	3	3

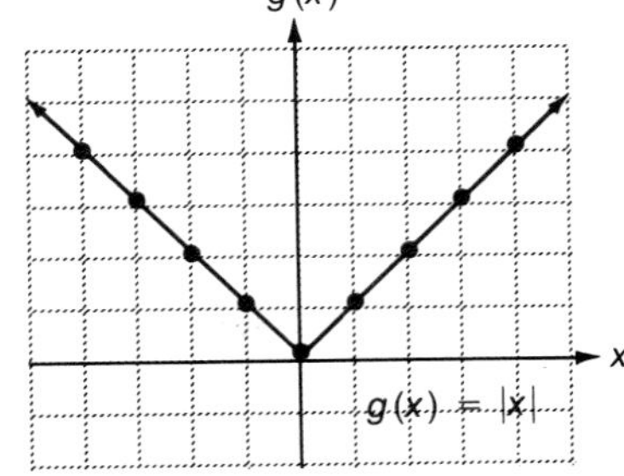

We can graph the ordered pairs. We connect the points to show all points whose coordinates are solutions of the equation $g(x) = |x|$.

Try This Graph the functions where the domain is the set of real numbers.

a. $f(x) = |x| - 1$ **b.** $h(x) = |x| + 1$ See Additional Answers.

Recognizing Graphs of Functions

Objective: Recognize the graph of a function.

We know that a function described by a set of ordered pairs in the form (x, y) has exactly one value for y for each value of x. Graphs A and B show the graphs of two relations. In Graph A, any vertical line that intersects the graph will intersect the graph in exactly one point. This means that there is only one y-value for each x-value. Therefore, Graph A is the graph of a function. The vertical dashed line in Graph B intersects the graph in two points. These points have the same x-coordinate but different y-coordinates. Graph B is *not* the graph of a function.

GRAPH *A*

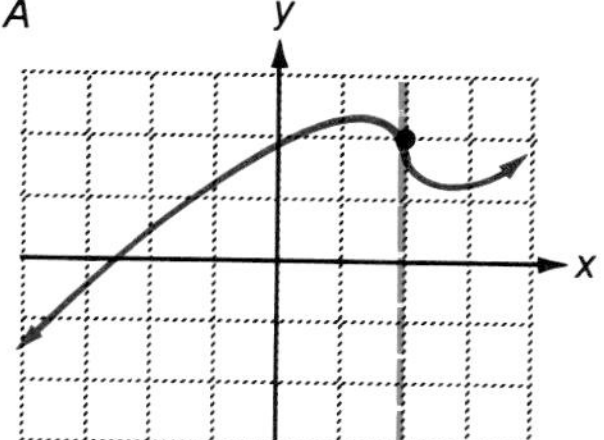

GRAPH *B*

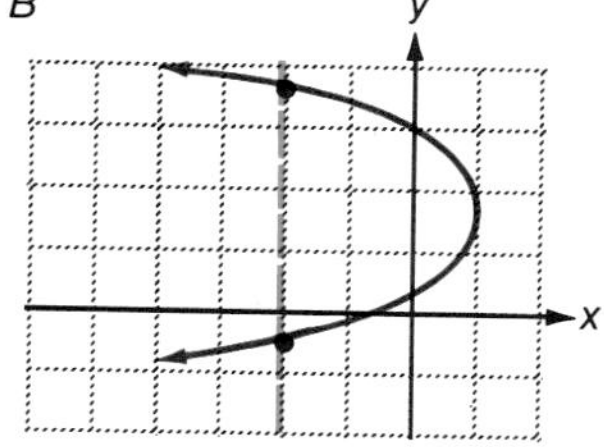

EXAMPLE 2 Which of the following are graphs of functions?

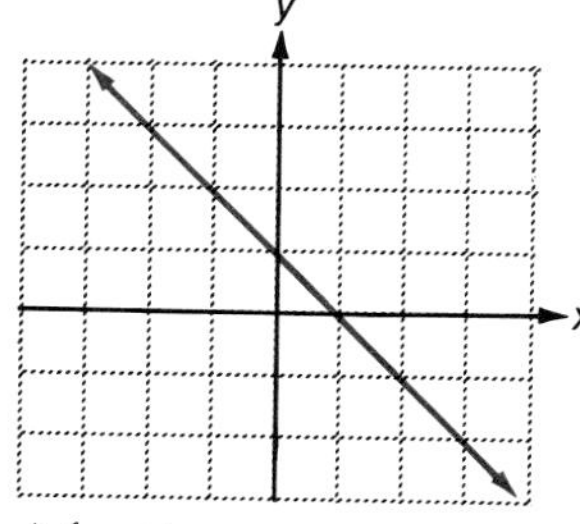

A function.
No vertical line crosses the graph more than once.

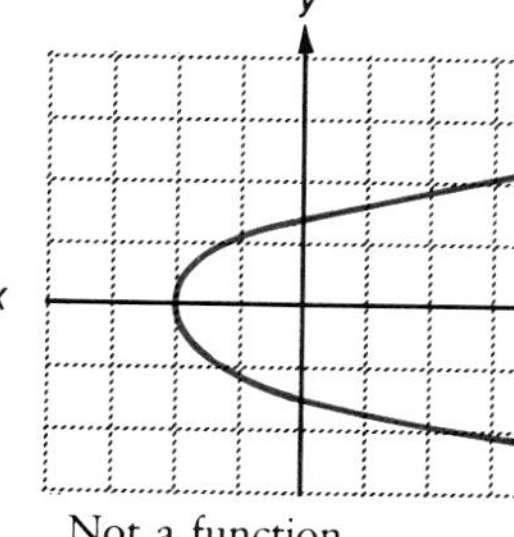

Not a function.
A vertical line crosses the graph more than once.

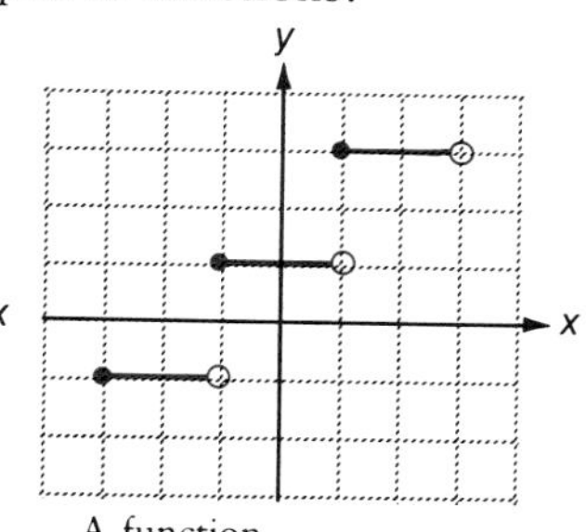

A function.
No vertical line crosses the graph more than once.

Try This Which of the following are graphs of functions?

c. Yes

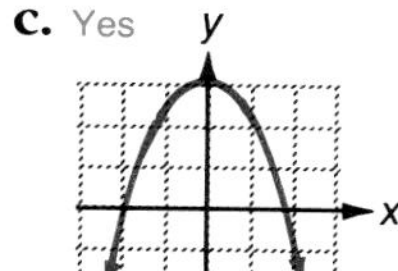

d. No

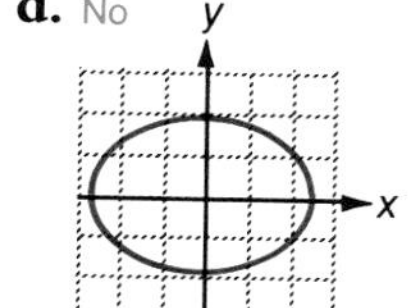

e. No

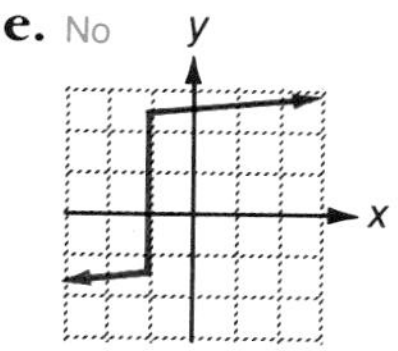

Chalkboard Example

1. Graph the function h described by $h(x) = |x + 1|$ where the domain is the set of real numbers between -2 and 3, inclusive.

x	−2	−1	0	1	2	3
h(x)	1	0	1	2	3	4

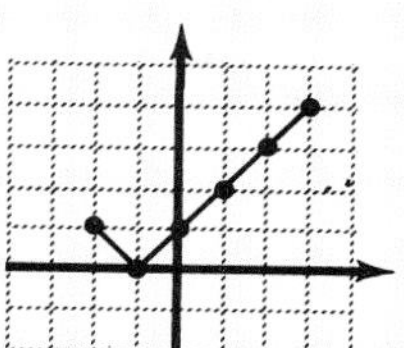

Recognizing Graphs of Functions

Chalkboard Example (*T25*)

1. Which of the following are graphs of functions?

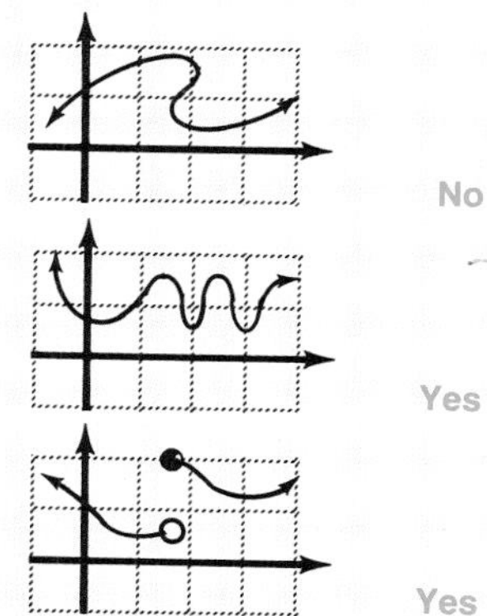

No

Yes

Yes

LESSON QUIZ

1. Graph the function $f(x) = 2x - 2$.

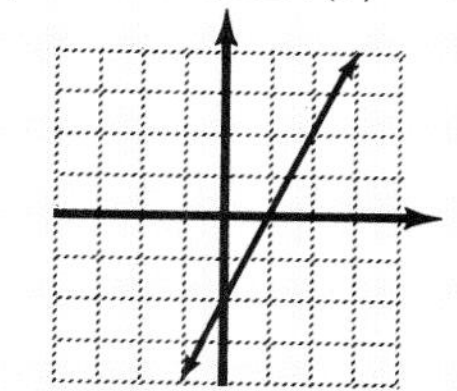

2. Graph the function $h(x) = |x - 1|$.

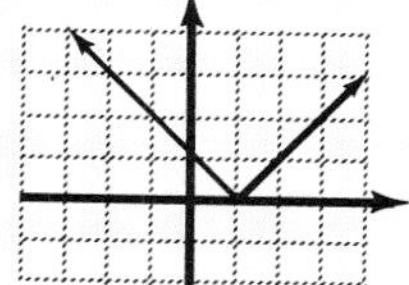

Assignment Guide
Minimum: 1–17 e/o, MR

Regular: 1–20 e/o, 21, MR

Advanced: 1–20 m3, 21–23, MR, assign w. Bonus Topic

ADDITIONAL ANSWERS

Try This

a.

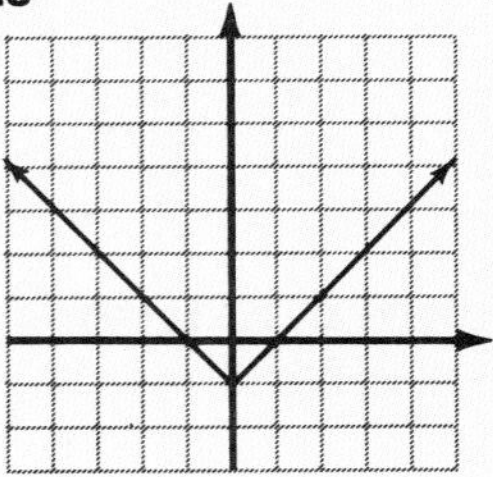

b.

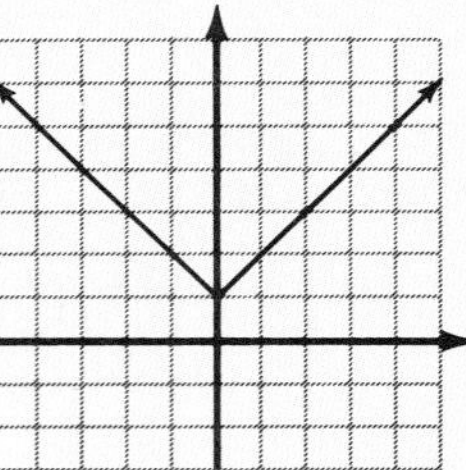

Exercises

1.

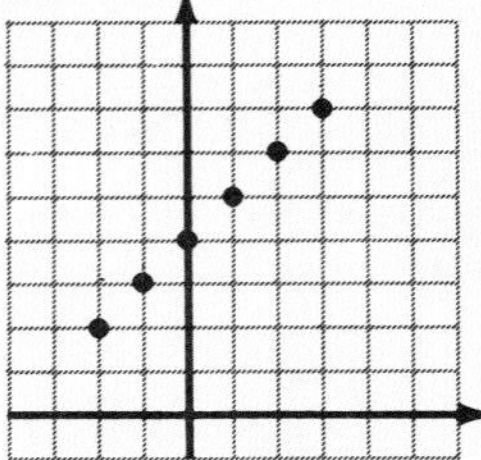

2.

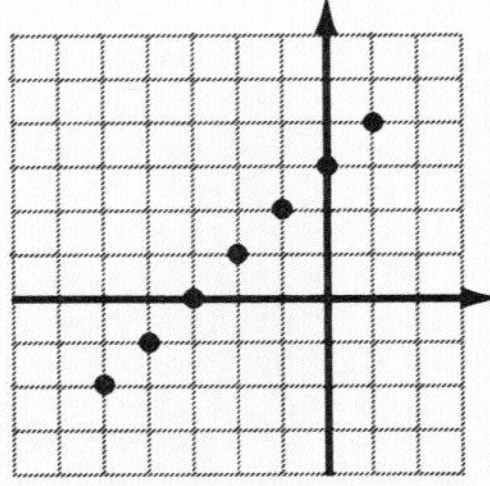

3–13. See Teacher's Answer Section.

18. Domain {0, 1, 2, 3}; Range {0, 2, 4, 6}; $f(x) = 2x$

12-2 EXERCISES

A

Graph each function.

1. $f(x) = x + 4$ where the domain is $\{-2, -1, 0, 1, 2, 3\}$.
2. $g(x) = x + 3$ where the domain is $\{-5, -4, -3, -2, -1, 0, 1\}$.
3. $h(x) = 2x - 3$ where the domain is $\{-3, -1, 1, 3\}$.
4. $f(x) = 3x - 1$ where the domain is $\{-1, 0, 2, 4, 6\}$.

Graph each function. The domain is all real numbers.

5. $g(x) = x - 6$
6. $h(x) = x - 5$
7. $f(x) = 2x - 7$
8. $g(x) = 4x - 13$
9. $f(x) = \frac{1}{2}x + 1$
10. $f(x) = -\frac{3}{4}x - 2$
11. $g(x) = 2|x|$
12. $h(x) = -|x|$
13. $g(x) = -2|x| + 2$

Which of the following are graphs of functions?

14. No

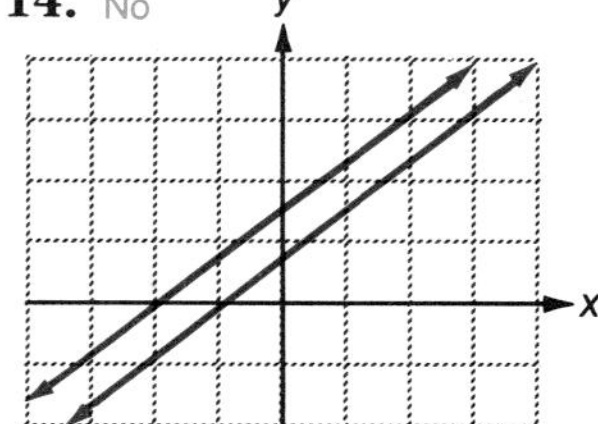

15. Yes

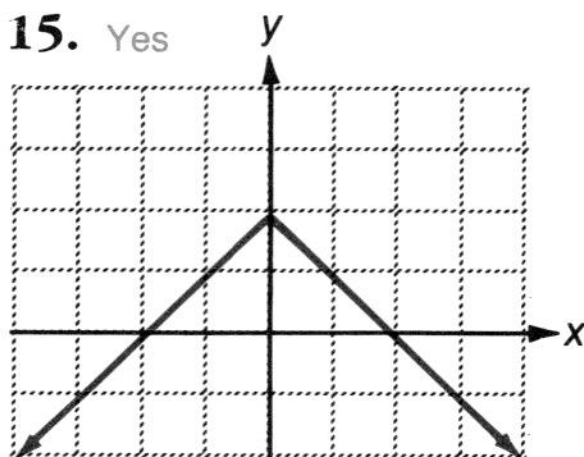

16. Yes

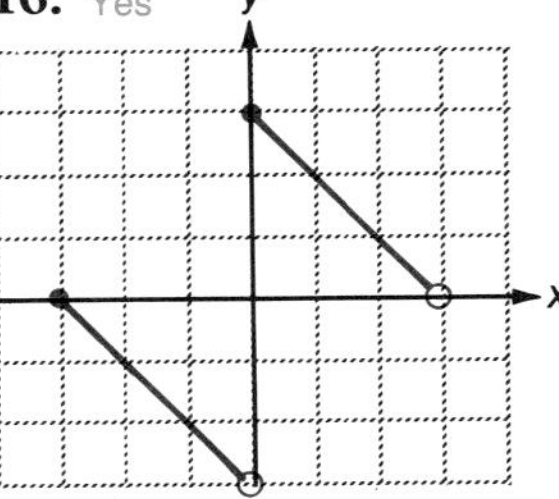

17. No

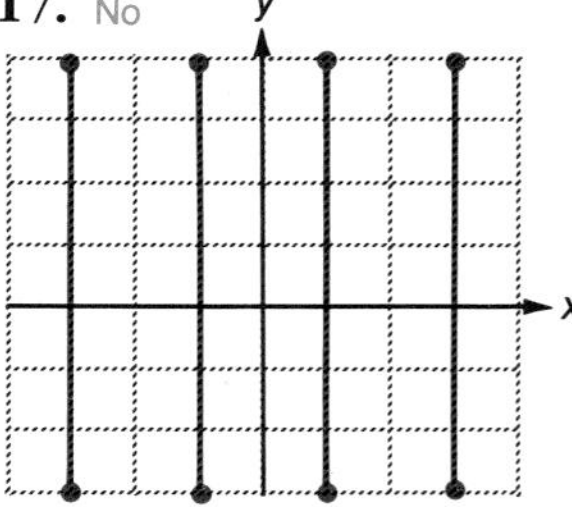

B

18. Here is the graph of a function. List the domain and the range of the function. Write an equation for this function.

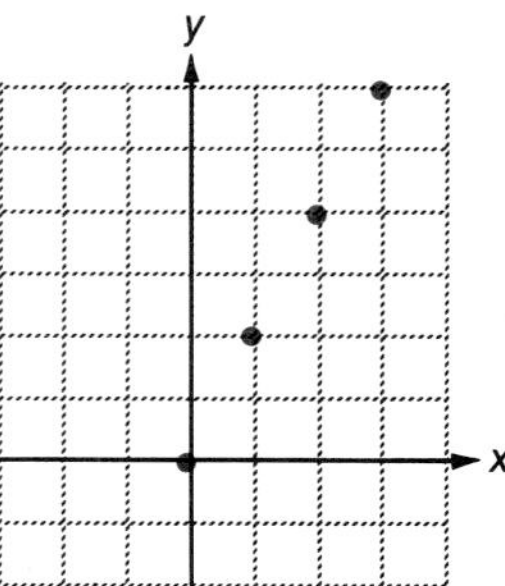

19. Draw the graph of $|y| = x$. Is this the graph of a function? No
20. Draw the graph of $g(x) = \frac{1}{x}$. Is this the graph of a function? Yes
21. ***Critical Thinking*** Sketch a graph involving absolute value that is not a function. Answers may vary. Ex: $|y| = x$

Challenge

22. Describe the graph of any function of the form $g(x) = a|x| + b$.

23. For the function defined by $g(x) = a|x| + b$, what effect does changing the value of a have on the graph? What effect does changing the value of b have on the graph?

Mixed Review

Simplify. **24.** $\frac{\sqrt{3}}{\sqrt{147}}$ **25.** $\frac{\sqrt{20}}{\sqrt{45}}$ **26.** $\frac{\sqrt{30}}{\sqrt{18}}$ **27.** $\frac{\sqrt{7}}{\sqrt{xy}}$

Divide. **28.** $(x^2 - 9x + 20) \div (x - 4)$ **29.** $(y^4 - 9) \div (y - 3)$

Simplify. **30.** $\frac{x^2 + 4x}{x + 3} - \frac{3x + 1}{x + 3} - \frac{5}{x + 3}$ **31.** $\frac{3y}{y^2 - 25} - \frac{2}{y + 5}$

Write using roster notation. **32.** the set A of positive integers whose squares are between 35 and 150

Problem for Programmers

Write a program that will find outputs for the function $f(x) = x^4 - x^3 - 11x^2 + 9x + 18$ for inputs from -4 to 4 in $\frac{1}{4}$ increments. Print the output as ordered pairs. Use the ordered pairs to graph this function.

Challenge. Include in this program a subroutine that will graph this function.

BIOGRAPHICAL NOTE: LEONARD EULER

Leonard Euler (1707–1783) was a Swiss mathematician with a phenomenal memory and prodigious powers of mental calculation. Although he spent the last 17 years of his life in total blindness, he continued to work complex calculations in his head.

Euler was perhaps one of the world's greatest algorists. An algorist is a mathematician who devises algorithms, or specific rules, for the solution of special types of problems. He was one of the first to use $f(x)$ to denote a function of x.

22. $\vee$ shaped, or $\wedge$ if a is negative, with "point" on the y-axis b units up or down from the origin

23. If $|a|$ increases, the graph gets thinner; if b increases, the graph is moved upwards.

Mixed Review

24. $\frac{1}{7}$

25. $\frac{2}{3}$

26. $\frac{\sqrt{15}}{3}$

27. $\frac{\sqrt{7xy}}{xy}$

28. $(x - 5)$

29. $y^3 + 3y^2 + 9y + 27 + \frac{72}{y - 3}$

30. $(x - 2)$

31. $\frac{y + 10}{y^2 - 25}$

32. $A = \{6, 7, 8, 9, 10, 11, 12\}$

Problem for Programmers

This program can be written using any programming language (BASIC, PASCAL, LOGO, etc.). Knowledge of graphics is necessary to write the program for the Challenge part of this program.

This program can also be written on a spreadsheet where the values of x are input in one column and the values of the function (y-values) are output in another column. The Challenge cannot be done on a spreadsheet.

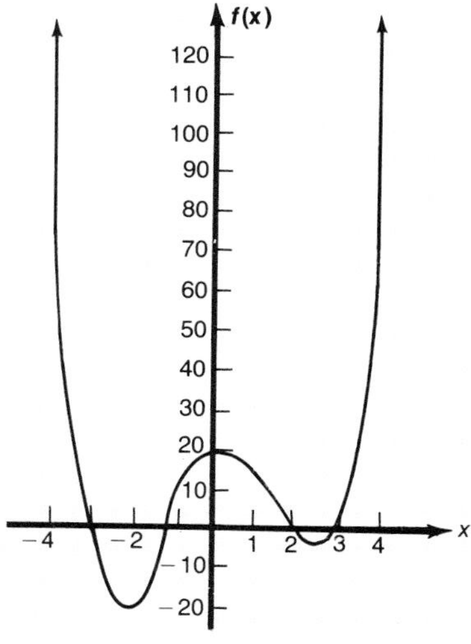

Bonus Topic

See Computer Exploration 8 on p. 720 for using a computer to explore absolute value functions.

ANSWERS

1. (0, 0); (−1, 0)

2. 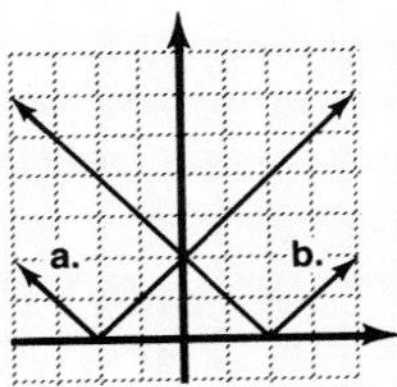

3. The constant b moves the vertex to $(-b, 0)$.

4. 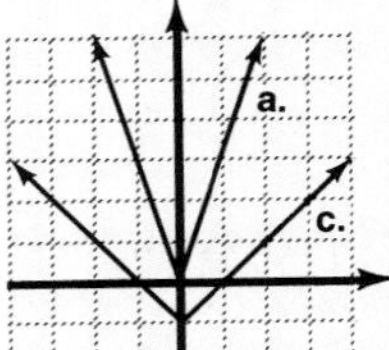

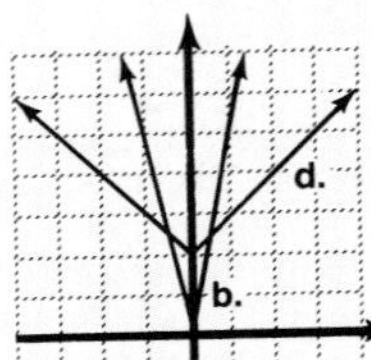

5. The constant a changes the slope of the legs of the graph to $\pm a$.
6. The constant c moves the vertex to $(0, c)$.

7. 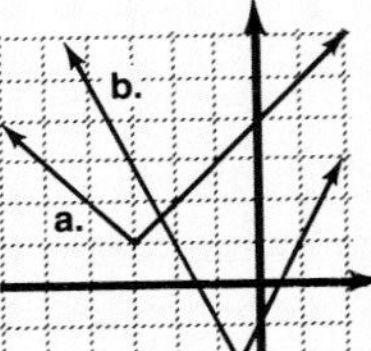

8. Answers may vary. Students should indicate that the graph of $|ax + b| + c$ will have a vertex at $\left(-\frac{b}{a}, c\right)$, and the legs will have slopes of $\pm a$.

Bonus Topic: Exploring Absolute Value Functions

Objective: Graph and compare absolute value functions.

The graph at the right shows the functions $f(x) = |x|$ and $f(x) = |x + 1|$.

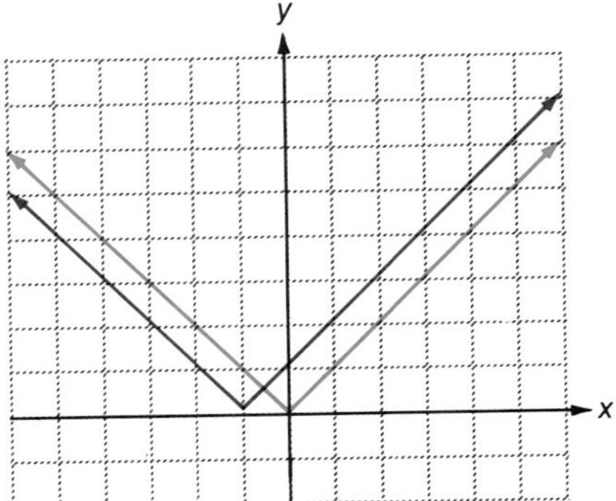

1. What are the coordinates of the point where the graph of $f(x) = |x|$ meets the x-axis? What are the coordinates of the point where the graph of $f(x) = |x + 1|$ meets the x-axis?
2. Graph these functions using a computer or graph paper.
   a. $f(x) = |x + 2|$
   b. $f(x) = |x - 2|$

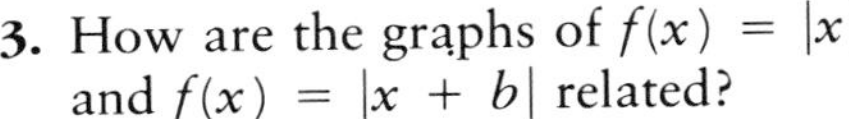

3. How are the graphs of $f(x) = |x|$ and $f(x) = |x + b|$ related?

The graph at the right shows the functions $f(x) = |2x|$ and $f(x) = |x| + 1$.

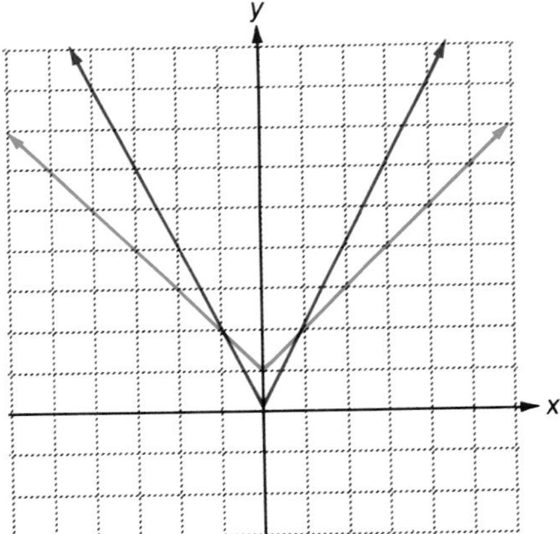

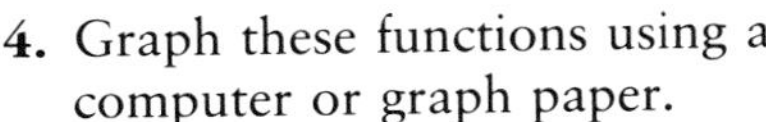

4. Graph these functions using a computer or graph paper.
   a. $f(x) = |-3x|$
   b. $f(x) = |5x|$
   c. $f(x) = |x| - 1$
   d. $f(x) = |x| + 2$
5. How are the graphs of $f(x) = |x|$ and $f(x) = |ax|$ related?
6. How are the graphs of $f(x) = |x|$ and $f(x) = |x| + c$ related?

The graph at the right shows the function $f(x) = |2x + 1| - 2$.

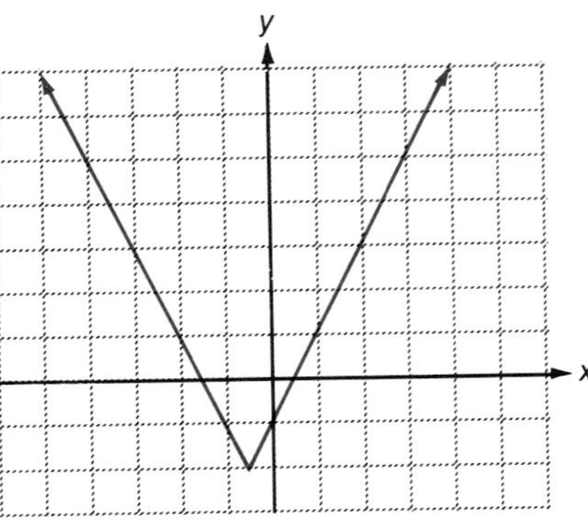

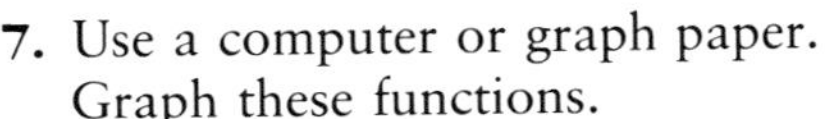

7. Use a computer or graph paper. Graph these functions.
   a. $f(x) = |x + 3| + 1$
   b. $f(x) = |-2x - 1| - 2$

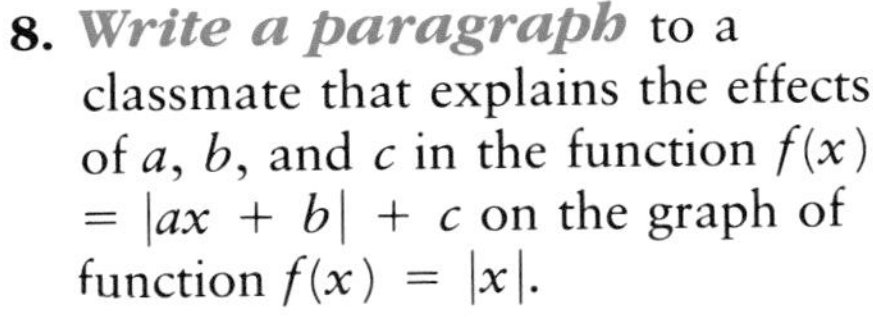

8. ***Write a paragraph*** to a classmate that explains the effects of a, b, and c in the function $f(x) = |ax + b| + c$ on the graph of function $f(x) = |x|$.

12-3 Problem Solving: Linear Functions

Objective: Solve problems involving linear functions.

The graph at the right is the graph of the equation $y = x + 3$. We can see that for each value of x on the graph there is only one value for y. Therefore, the equation $y = x + 3$ defines a function, which we call a **linear function.**

Since the equation $y = x + 3$ defines a function, we can write this equation using function notation as $f(x) = x + 3$.

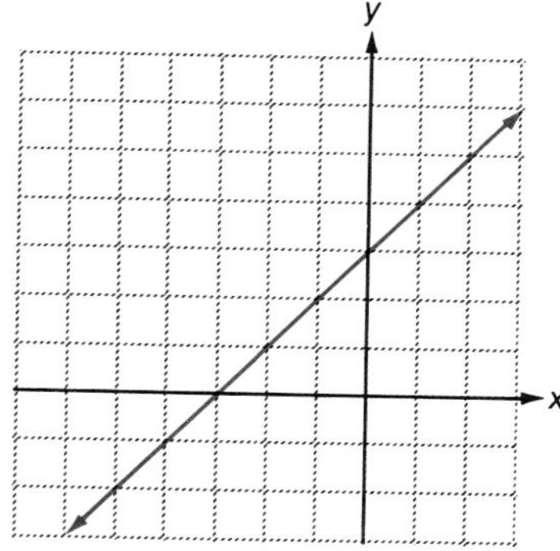

Definition

A function f defined by an equation of the form $y = mx + b$, where m and b are real numbers, is a **linear function** and can be written $f(x) = mx + b$.

We can see from the definition above that when the domain of a linear function is the set of real numbers, the graph is a line.

PROBLEM-SOLVING GUIDELINES
■ UNDERSTAND the problem
Develop and carry out a PLAN
Find the ANSWER and CHECK

We can use the Problem-Solving Guidelines to help us solve problems involving linear functions.

EXAMPLE 1

The amount of antifreeze needed to protect a radiator against freezing to a temperature of −18°C is about half the capacity of the radiator. How much antifreeze is needed to protect a radiator with a capacity of 15 L?

■ **UNDERSTAND the problem**

Question: What amount of antifreeze is needed for a 15-L radiator?
Data: The amount needed is half the capacity.

Develop and carry out a PLAN

Let x = the capacity of the radiator.
Let y = the amount of antifreeze needed.
We can now translate to an equation.

12-3

FIRST FIVE MINUTES

1. Graph $f(x) = 2|x|$.

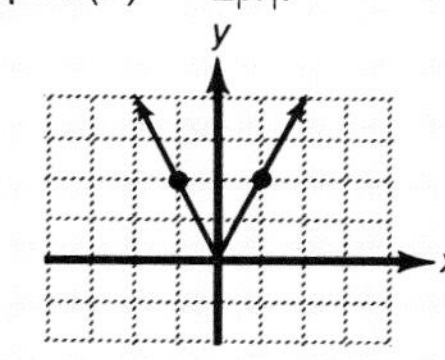

2. Graph $g(x) = 3x - 1$.

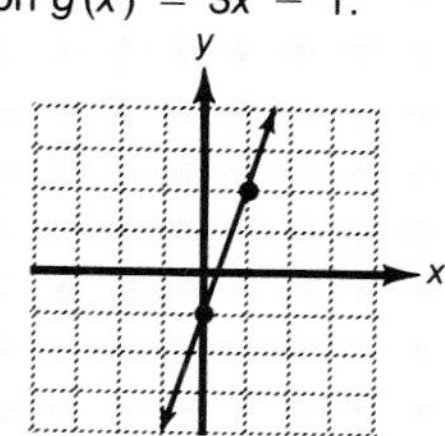

Point out that the graphs of linear functions, like those of linear equations, are always lines.

Key Questions

■ What is the equation that corresponds to the following table?

x	0	1	2	3	4	5
f(x)	0	3	6	9	12	15

$f(x) = 3x$

■ What is the equation that corresponds to the following table?

x	0	1	2	3	4	5
f(x)	2	5	8	11	14	17

$f(x) = 3x + 2$

Chalkboard Example

1. A recipe requires $\frac{1}{2}$ cup of flour for one dozen muffins. How many cups are required for three dozen muffins?
   Let d = number of dozen muffins.
   Let f = the amount of flour needed.
   $f = \frac{1}{2}d$ or $f(d) = \frac{1}{2}d$
   We can substitute 3 for d.
   $f(3) = \frac{1}{2} \cdot 3$
   $= \frac{3}{2}$
   $1\frac{1}{2}$ cups of flour are needed.

LESSON QUIZ

Translate the situation to an equation that describes a linear function. Then solve the problem.

1. A taxi ride costs $1 starting fee plus 75 cents per mile. How much does a 10-mile trip cost?
   $c(m) = 1 + 0.75m$
   $c(10) = \$8.50$
2. A phone costs $8 per month, plus 10 cents per message unit. How much is the monthly bill if 40 message units are used?
   $c(m) = 8.00 + 0.10m$
   $c(40) = \$12.00$

Assignment Guide
Minimum: 1–8, MR

Regular: 1–13 e/o, 14, MR

Advanced: 1–12 m3, 13–16, MR

ADDITIONAL ANSWERS

Exercises

1. $c(k) = 35 + 0.21k$; $c(340) = \$106.40$
2. $c(m) = 0.55 + 0.25m$; $c(12) = \$3.55$
3. $L(w) = \frac{1}{3}w + 40$; $L(15) = 45$ cm
4. $L(w) = \frac{1}{5}w + 60$; $L(20) = 64$ cm
5. $c(h) = 5.50 + 4.25h$; $c(4.5) = \$24.63$
6. $c(m) = 29 + 0.19m$; $c(280) = \$82.20$

Amount needed is half of the capacity.

$$\begin{array}{ccccc} \downarrow & \downarrow & \downarrow & \downarrow & \downarrow \\ y & = & \frac{1}{2} & \cdot & x \end{array}$$

This equation shows that for each value of x in the relation there is exactly one value for y. Therefore, the relation is a function. We can rewrite the equation to show this.

$$f(x) = \frac{1}{2}x$$

We can substitute 15 for x to find the amount of antifreeze needed.

$$\begin{aligned} f(15) &= \frac{1}{2} \cdot 15 \\ &= 7.5 \end{aligned}$$

Find the ANSWER and CHECK

The amount of antifreeze needed is 7.5 L.
This is half of 15 L. The answer is reasonable.

Try This Write a linear function. Then solve.

a. Frank's Baby-Sitting Service charges $3.50 plus $1.65 per hour. What is the cost of a nine-hour baby-sitting job? $c(h) = 3.50 + 1.65h$; $c(9) = \$18.35$

12-3 EXERCISES

A

Write a linear function describing each situation. Use the function to solve the problem.

1. The Triad Car Rental Company charges $35 per day plus 21¢ per mile. Find the cost of renting a car for a one-day trip of 340 miles.
2. The Dialum Phone Company charges 55¢ per long-distance call plus 25¢ per minute. Find the cost of a 12-minute long-distance call.
3. A 40-cm spring will stretch (in cm) one third the weight (in kg) attached to it. How long will the spring be if a 15-kg weight is attached?
4. A 60-cm spring will stretch (in cm) one fifth the weight (in kg) attached to it. How long will the spring be if a 20-kg weight is attached?
5. The cost of renting a floor waxer is $4.25 per hour plus $5.50 for the wax. Find the cost of waxing a floor if the time involved was 4.5 hours.
6. Sally rents a compact car for $29 per day plus 19¢ per mile. Compute the cost of a one-day trip of 280 miles.

7. The cost of renting a chain saw is \$3.90 per hour plus \$6.50 for a can of gas. Find the cost of using the chain saw for 7.5 hours.

8. The airport parking garage charges \$1.25 for the first hour and 70¢ for each additional hour. Find the cost of parking for 18 hours.

B

9. A woman's phone bill is based on 15¢ per message unit charge plus a base charge. Her July bill was \$18 and included 62 message units. Find the base charge. Her August bill included 76 message units. How much was her August bill? \$8.70; \$20.10

10. The city's water department charges 23¢ per kiloliter (kL) plus a fixed charge. Mr. Ahmed's water bill for the use of 70 kL was \$26.60. Find the fixed charge. The next month he used 85 kL. How much was his bill? \$10.50; \$30.05

11. A parking garage in the city charges \$2.00 for the first hour and \$1.50 for each additional hour. Saturday and Sunday, the rates are decreased by 50%. How much does it cost to park a car from 5 p.m. on Friday until 2 a.m. on Saturday? \$12.50

12. A car rental company charges \$41 per day plus 24¢ for each mile over 100 miles. Find the cost of renting a car for three days during which it is driven 150 miles. How far can you drive in three days and keep the cost under \$150? \$135.00; 212 miles

13. A constant function is any function that can be described by an equation of the form $y = k$. Sketch the graph of a constant function. A horizontal line

14. ***Critical Thinking*** Make up a real-world example of a constant function.

Challenge

15. Draw the graph of the function described by $f(t) = t^3$.

16. A restaurant has some fixed operating costs and some that vary with the number of people in attendance. If 4000 people visit the restaurant in one month, the operating costs are \$1300. If 2800 people visit the restaurant in one month, the operating costs are \$970. What would be the operating costs for this restaurant in a month where only 1500 people visit the restaurant?

Mixed Review

Add or subtract. **17.** $3\sqrt{8} + 2\sqrt{2}$ **18.** $\sqrt{24} - \sqrt{6}$

Write using scientific notation. **19.** 5,470,000 **20.** 0.0034709

Simplify. **21.** $\frac{6(x + 1)}{5x} \cdot \frac{35x}{21x + 21}$ **22.** $\frac{(y + 2)^3}{(y - 2)^2} \div \frac{(y + 2)^3}{(y - 2)^2}$

Solve and graph. **23.** $|3x| > 12$ **24.** $|2x| \geq 6$ **25.** $|x - 1| > 3$

7. $c(h) = 6.50 + 3.90h$; $c(7.5) = \$35.75$
8. $c(h) = 0.70(h - 1) + 1.25$; $c(18) = \$13.15$
14. Answers may vary. If you make a yearly salary, you are paid a constant amount each month regardless of the number of hours you work. Say you make \$600 a month, then $f(h) = 600$ no matter what h (hours worked) is. This of course differs from a job where you are paid by the hour, which is not a constant function.
15.

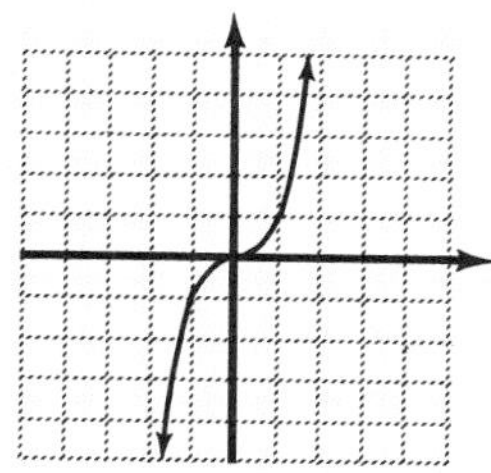

16. $c(p) = 200 + 0.275p$; $c(1500) = \$612.50$

Mixed Review

17. $8\sqrt{2}$
18. $\sqrt{6}$
19. 5.47×10^6
20. 3.4709×10^{-3}
21. 2
22. 1
23. $x > 4$ or $x < -4$

−4 0 4

24. $x \geq 3$ or $x \leq -3$

−3 0 3

25. $x > 4$ or $x < -2$

−2 0 4

CONNECTIONS: DISCRETE MATH

Interval Graphs

In Chapter 7 you learned how to graph data using the Cartesian coordinate system. There are many other ways to represent data using graphs. One kind of graph, called an **interval graph,** can be used to solve problems involving the intersection of various time intervals. Interval graphs are just a collection of points, called **vertices,** and line segments, called **edges,** connecting some of the vertices.

Interval graphs have been used to date artifacts from prehistoric sites in archeology, to identify genes, and to check the testimony of witnesses and suspects in crime investigations.

EXAMPLE

Several students spend Saturday morning at the library. It is a small library, and if two students are there at the same time, they are sure to see each other. Abdul arrives at 9 a.m. and stays for 2 hours. Becca arrives 45 minutes after 9. Carol arrives with Abdul and leaves with Becca, before Abdul is ready to leave. Doug arrives as Abdul is leaving and leaves at noon. Erik spends the shortest amount of time, but he sees Abdul, Becca, Carol, and Doug. Filipe sees Abdul but not Becca. How many students could Becca see at the library?

We represent each student with a vertex labeled by the first letter of his or her name. Whenever 2 students are at the library at the same time, we connect their vertices with an edge.

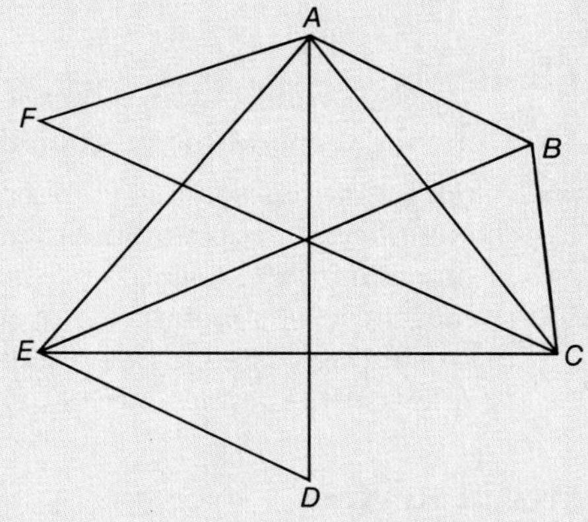

Since Abdul and Carol arrive at the same time, we connect their vertices. Becca arrives before Abdul leaves and leaves with Carol, so B should be connected with both A and C. Since Doug arrives as Abdul leaves, he misses Carol and Becca, so D is connected to A but not to C or B. Erik sees the first four students, so E is connected to A, B, C, and D. Filipe could arrive at 9 and leave before Becca arrives, in which case he would see Abdul and Carol.

The graph indicates that Becca sees 3 other students: Abdul, Carol, and Erik.

We can also represent these data using a time line. The places where the intervals overlap represent the edges of the interval graph on the previous page. We know some of the endpoints (Becca's, Abdul's, and Carol's arrivals) but not some others (Becca's and Carol's departure). We can tell that Erik spends less than an hour and that his interval must overlap Becca's and Doug's. Check to see if this time line agrees with the interval graph on the previous page.

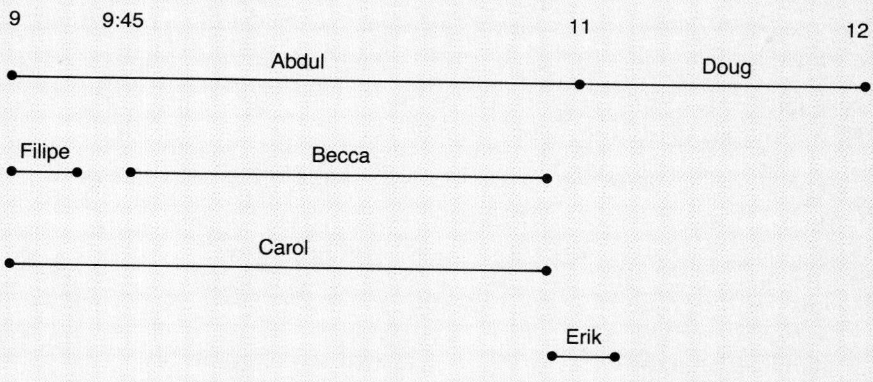

Problems

1. Check the information in the example and see if you can find another interval in which Filipe could visit the library. Draw a time line and an interval graph representing all the data if Filipe's interval is changed. Does your answer change the number of students Becca sees? Explain.
2. Six people are running the 1600-meter race in the Blackhawk conference. Below are the slow and fast times of each runner in minutes and seconds.

	Triggs	Carius	Nordvall	Oberle	Keller	Park
Slow	5:01	4:50	4:43	4:40	4:47	4:50
Fast	4:48	4:42	4:34	4:33	4:39	4:41

Assume that each runner's time is within his time interval.

a. Make an interval graph for the data. Remember that when the intervals of 2 runners intersect, you connect their vertices with an edge.

b. Make a time line representing the data.

c. Would it be possible for Triggs to beat Carius?

d. Would it be possible for Park to beat Oberle?

e. Would it be possible for Carius, Triggs, and Keller to finish first, second, and third?

f. Would it be possible for Nordvall to win?

ANSWERS

1. Filipe could also visit the library just after Becca leaves, while Abdul is still at the library. This would not change the number of students that Becca sees because she does not see Filipe in either case.

2. a.

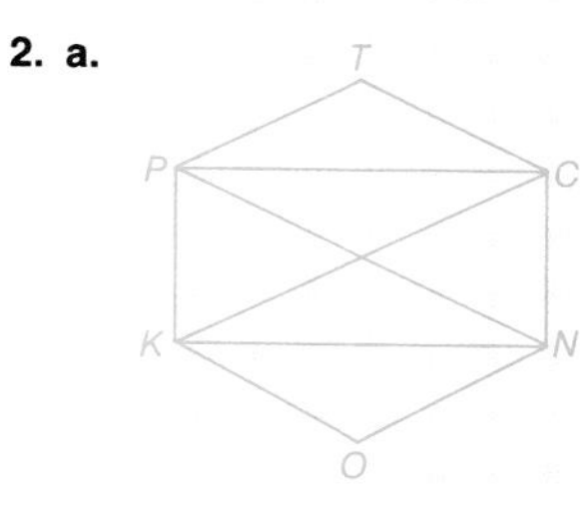

b.

4:33 :36 :39 :42 :45 :48 :51 :54 :57 5:00

Triggs

Carius

Nordvall

Oberle

Keller

Park

c. Yes

d. No

e. No

f. Yes

FIRST FIVE MINUTES

1. Find a linear function that describes the situation, and solve the problem. A tractor rents for \$50, plus \$5 per engine hour. How much does it cost to rent and run the tractor for 6 hours?
   $c(h) = 50 + 5h$
   $c(6) = \$80$

EXPLORE

The lowest point on the graph of $y = x^2$ is (0, 0). The graph is divided in half by the y-axis.

The graph of $y = 2x^2$ is narrower than the graph of $y = x^2$.

The graph of $y = 2x^2 + 1$ is the graph of $y = 2x^2$ moved up 1 unit.

The graph of $y = 2x^2 - 4x$ is the graph of $y = 2x^2$ moved to the right 1 unit and down 2 units.

The graph of $y = 2x^2 - 4x$ is the graph of $y = 2x^2 + 1$ moved to the right 1 unit and down 3 units.

Give examples where parabolas occur in the real world. The path of an object thrown up in the air and the shape of a satellite dish, for instance, are parabolic.

Ask students to give examples of line symmetry. For example, the capital letters A, H, I, M, O, T, U, V, W, X, and Y have a vertical line of symmetry.

Students may note that the graph in Example 1 opens upward, and the coefficient of x^2 is 1, which is positive. The graph in Example 2 opens downward and the coefficient of x^2 is -2, which is negative. In general, the graph of $f(x) = ax^2 + bx + c$ opens *upward* if $a > 0$ and *downward* if $a < 0$.

Key Questions

- Is $f(x) = 2 - 8x + 7x^2$ a quadratic function?
  Yes
- Which capital letters have a horizontal line of symmetry?
  B, C, D, E, H, I, O, and X
- How many vertices does a parabola have?
  1

12-4 Quadratic Functions

Objective: Graph quadratic functions.

Master Grapher Worksheets 12 and 13 can be used with this lesson.

Explore

Graph the function $y = x^2$. The domain is the set of all real numbers. Use values for x ranging from 3 to -3.

- What is the lowest point on the graph?
- Which axis divides the graph in half?

Graph each of the following equations on the same coordinate axes used above.

$$y = 2x^2 \qquad y = 2x^2 + 1 \qquad y = 2x^2 - 4x$$

- How is the graph of $y = 2x^2$ related to the graph of $y = x^2$?
- How is the graph of $y = 2x^2 + 1$ related to the graph of $y = 2x^2$?
- How is the graph of $y = 2x^2 - 4x$ related to the graph of $y = 2x^2$?
- How is the graph of $y = 2x^2 + 1$ related to the graph of $y = 2x^2 - 4x$?

The graph at the right is the graph of the equation $y = 2x^2 + 5x + 3$. We can see that for each value of x on the graph, there is exactly one value for y. Therefore, the equation $y = 2x^2 + 5x + 3$ defines a function. This equation is an example of a **quadratic function.** We can write $f(x) = 2x^2 + 5x + 3$.

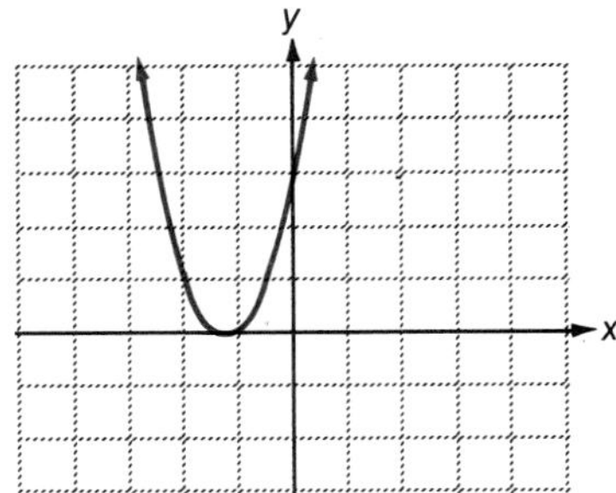

Definition

A function f defined by an equation of the form $y = ax^2 + bx + c$, where a, b, and c are real numbers and $a \neq 0$, is a **quadratic function** and can be written $f(x) = ax^2 + bx + c$.

We can graph a quadratic function by making a table of values and graphing the ordered pairs. When the domain of the function is the set of real numbers, the graph is a **parabola**.

EXAMPLE 1 Graph the quadratic function $f(x) = 2x^2$.

Graph the ordered pairs (x, y) or $(x, f(x))$.

x	$f(x)$
−3	18
−2	8
−1	2
0	0
1	2
2	8
3	18

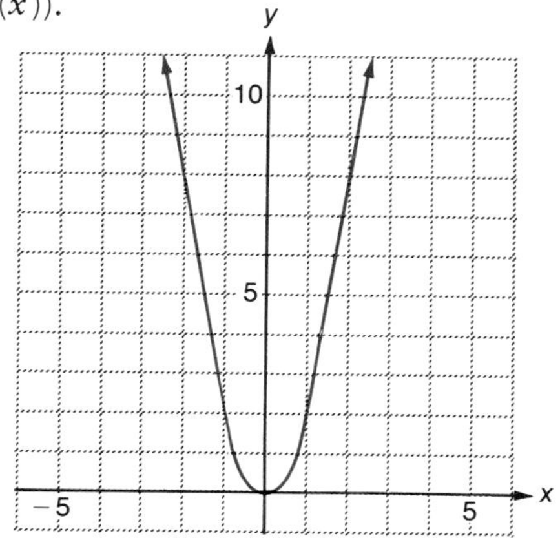

Try This

a. Graph the quadratic function $f(x) = 3x^2 - 5$. See Additional Answers.

In Example 1, the point (0, 0) on the graph is called the **vertex** of the parabola. The vertex is the maximum or the minimum point of a parabola. In Example 1, the vertex is the minimum point. The y-axis is the **axis of symmetry** for the graph in Example 1. Notice in Example 1, the points, other than the vertex, occur in pairs that have the same y-coordinate. If you fold the graph along the axis of symmetry, the two sides of the parabola coincide.

Parabolas defined by equations of the form $y = ax^2$ will always have the vertex at the origin and the axis of symmetry will be the y-axis. We can use the following to find the vertex and the axis of symmetry for quadratic functions of the form $y = f(x) = ax^2 + bx + c$.

Vertex and Axis of Symmetry

For a parabola defined by the equation $y = ax^2 + bx + c$,

1. the x-coordinate of the vertex is $-\frac{b}{2a}$.
2. the axis of symmetry is the line $x = -\frac{b}{2a}$.

EXAMPLE 2 Graph the function $f(x) = -2x^2 + 4x + 1$.

First find the vertex and the axis of symmetry.

x-coordinate of the vertex: $-\frac{b}{2a} = -\frac{4}{2(-2)} = 1$

Chalkboard Examples (*T26, T27*)

1. Graph the quadratic function $f(x) = -x^2$.

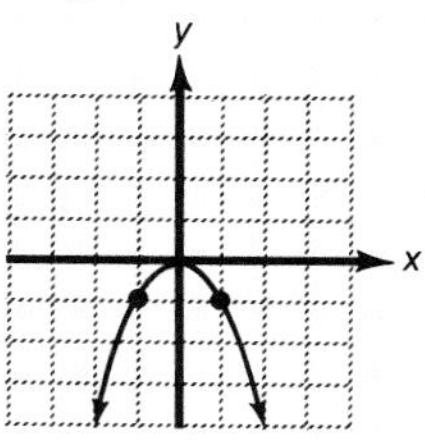

2. Find the vertex and the axis of symmetry. Then graph the function $f(x) = 2x^2 - 8x + 4$.
   x-coordinate of the vertex:
   $-\frac{b}{2a} = \frac{8}{4} = 2$
   y-coordinate of the vertex:
   $y = 2(2)^2 - 8(2) + 4$
   $y = -4$
   The axis of symmetry is the line $x = 2$.

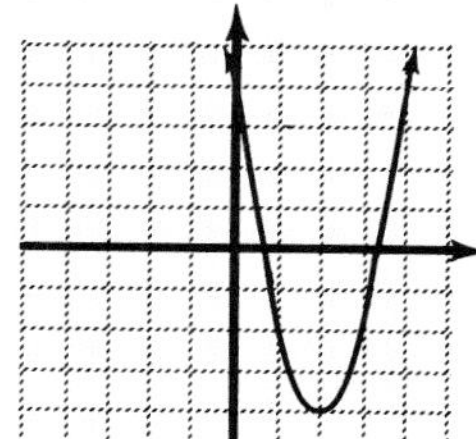

LESSON QUIZ

1. Find the vertex and the axis of symmetry. Then graph the function $f(x) = 3x^2 + 6x - 7$.
The vertex is $(-1, -10)$.
The axis of symmetry is the line $x = -1$.

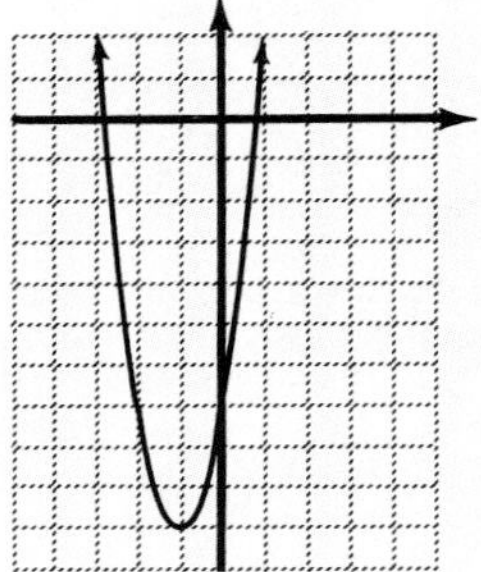

> ***Assignment Guide***
> Minimum: 1–18 e/o, MR
>
> Regular: 1–18 m3, 19–30 e/o, 31, MR
> Advanced: 1–30 m3, 31–34, MR

ADDITIONAL ANSWERS

Try This

a.

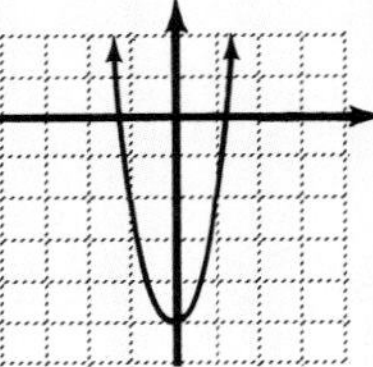

b.

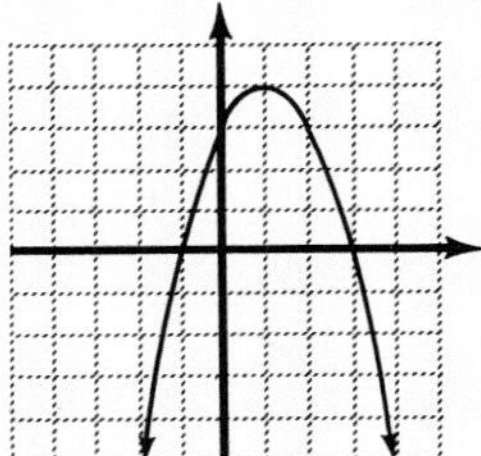

c.

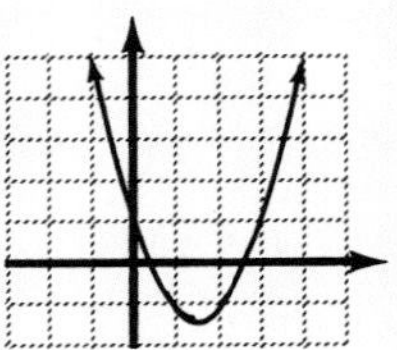

Substitute the x-coordinate into the original equation and solve for y.

$$\begin{aligned} y &= -2x^2 + 4x + 1 \\ &= -2(1)^2 + 4(1) + 1 \\ y &= 3 \end{aligned}$$

vertex: $(1, 3)$

The axis of symmetry is the line $x = 1$.
We choose points on both sides of the vertex and graph the parabola.

x	y
-1	-5
0	1
1	3
2	1
3	-5

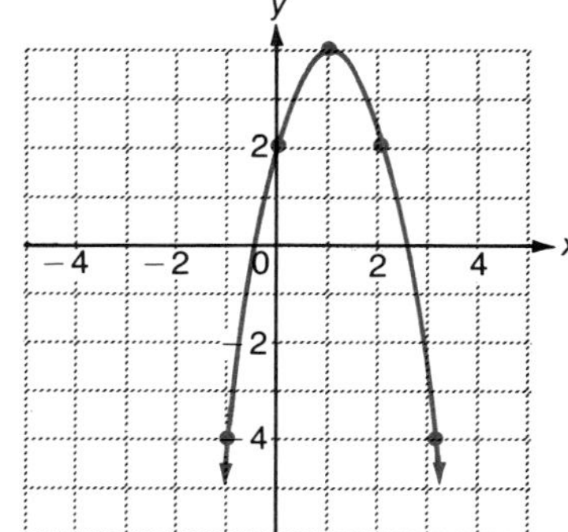

Try This Graph each function. See Additional Answers.

b. $f(x) = -x^2 + 2x + 3$ **c.** $g(x) = x^2 - 3x + 1$

12-4 EXERCISES

A

Graph each function.

1. $f(x) = -3x^2$
2. $f(x) = 3x^2$
3. $f(x) = 2x^2$
4. $f(x) = -2x^2$
5. $f(x) = \frac{1}{4}x^2$
6. $f(x) = 8x^2$

Graph each function.

7. $f(x) = x^2 - 3$
8. $f(x) = -x^2 + 3$
9. $f(x) = 2x^2 - 1$
10. $f(x) = x^2 + x - 6$
11. $f(x) = -x^2 + x - 1$
12. $f(x) = 8 - x - x^2$
13. $y = x^2 + 10x + 25$
14. $y = x^2 - 8x + 16$
15. $y = 2x^2 + 4x - 1$
16. $y = x^2 + 5$
17. $y = x^2 + 3$
18. $y = x^2 + 2x$

B

19. For the graph of a linear function $f(x) = mx + b$, we know the y-intercept is b. Examine the graphs of the functions in Exercises 7–18. Describe the y-intercept of the graph of a quadratic function.

20. The graph of a quadratic equation opens upward or opens downward. Examine the graphs in Exercises 7–18. What is true about equations whose graphs open upward? What is true about equations whose graphs open downward?

Determine if the graph of each equation opens upward or downward.

a. $y = 2x^2$ **b.** $y = -x^2 + 8$ **c.** $y = 5 + 3x - x^2$

21. The graph of each quadratic function has either a high point (maximum) or low point (minimum). Examine the graphs in Exercises 7–18. What types of graphs have a maximum or minimum?

22. Determine the minimum or maximum point for each equation. Indicate whether it is a minimum or maximum.

a. $y = 3x^2 - 4$ **b.** $y = -x^2 + 7$ **c.** $y = 2 + 3x - 6x^2$

23. Examine the parabolas graphed in Exercises 7–18. Describe the axis of symmetry for each.

When a projectile is thrown into the air with an initial vertical velocity of r feet per second, its distance (d), in feet, above its starting point t seconds after it is thrown is approximately

$$d = rt - 16t^2$$

For a projectile with an initial upward velocity of 96 feet per second, the function is

$$d = 96t - 16t^2$$

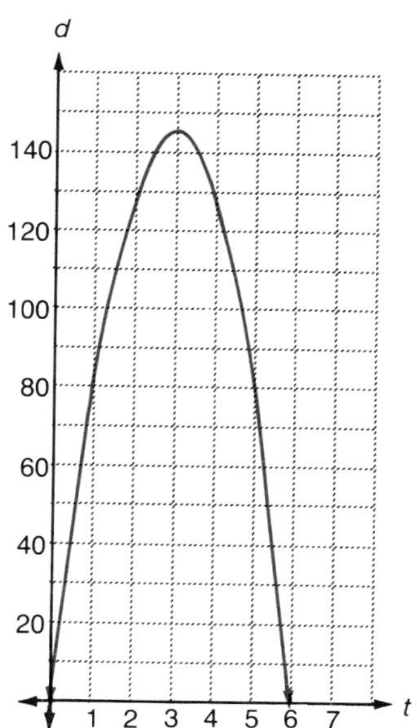

Use the graph of this quadratic function to answer Exercises 24–26.

24. How many seconds after launch is the projectile 128 feet above the ground? 2 s, 4 s

25. When does the projectile reach its maximum height? What is this height? 3 s; 144 ft

26. How many seconds after launch does the projectile return to the ground? 6 s

Exercises

1.

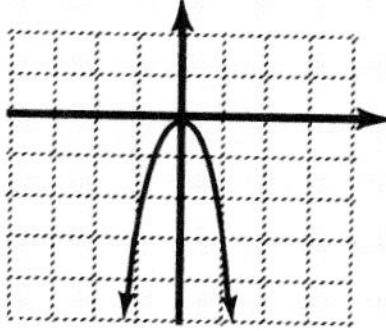

2.

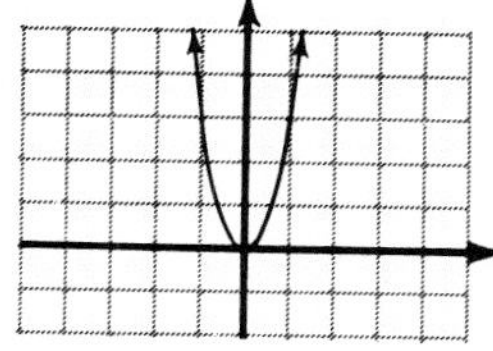

3.

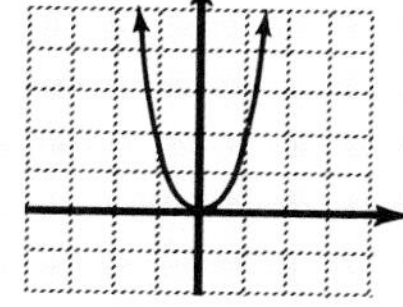

4–18. See Teacher's Answer Section.

19. When the function is in standard form, the y-intercept is the constant term.

20. $a > 0$; $a < 0$
a. upward
b. downward
c. downward

21. Graphs that open upward have a minimum point. Graphs that open downward have a maximum point.

22. a. $(0, -4)$ min. pt.
b. $(0, 7)$ max. pt.
c. $\left(\frac{1}{4}, \frac{19}{8}\right)$ max. pt.

23. Axis is parallel to y-axis and contains maximum or minimum point.

27.

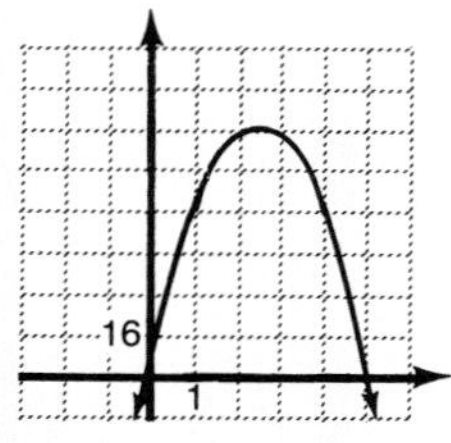

31. As $|a|$ increases, the graph narrows.
32. $-2.4, 3.4$
33. If the graph of the function does not cross the x-axis, then the equation has no real-number solution.
34. $A = lw$; $A = l(8 - l)$, $A = 8l - l^2$; maximum is at (4, 16); largest area is 4 by 4

Mixed Review

35. 0.0000005115 **36.** 479,330
37. 289 **38.** 41
39. 80 **40.** 50
41. 7 **42.** 5
43. $\frac{-2\sqrt{35}}{35}$ **44.** $x - \sqrt{x}$
45. $\frac{3\sqrt{10} + \sqrt{15}}{15}$
46. $-3, 7, 3, -23$
47. $-1, 11, 5, -10$
48. 6 **49.** $|x - 5|$
50. $5|y|$ **51.** $9|m|\sqrt{3m}$

Connections: Geometry

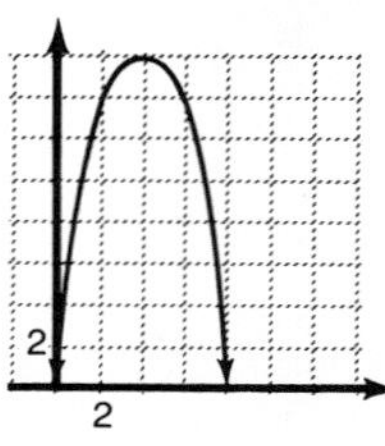

Maximum at (4, 16), so the largest area that can be enclosed is 16 ft^2.

Suppose a baseball player hits a long fly ball with an initial upward velocity of 80 feet per second.

27. Sketch the graph of the quadratic function for this situation.

28. How high will the ball be after 1 second? 2 seconds? 64 ft, 96 ft

29. After how many seconds will the ball be at its maximum height? 2.5 s

30. What is the approximate maximum height the ball will reach? 100 ft

31. ***Critical Thinking*** Use the same set of axes. Graph $y = x^2$, $y = 2x^2$, $y = 3x^2$, and $y = \frac{1}{2}x^2$. Describe the change in the graph of a quadratic function $y = ax^2$ as $|a|$ changes.

Challenge

32. Graph the equation $y = x^2 - x - 6$. Use your graph to approximate the solutions of $x^2 - x - 6 = 2$. (Hint: Graph $y = 2$ on the same set of axes as your graph of $y = x^2 - x - 6$.)

33. Graph $y = 2x^2 - 4x + 7$. Use the graph to approximate the solutions of $2x^2 - 4x + 7 = 0$. (Hint: Find the values of x when y is 0.)

34. What is the largest rectangular area that can be enclosed with 16 ft of fence?

Mixed Review

Write using decimal notation. **35.** 5.115×10^{-7} **36.** 4.7933×10^5

Solve. **37.** $\sqrt{x} = 17$ **38.** $\sqrt{2y - 1} = 9$ **39.** $11 - \sqrt{x + 1} = 2$

40. $2\sqrt{2x} = 20$ **41.** $\sqrt{3x + 4} = 5$ **42.** $5 + \sqrt{2x - 1} = 8$

Add or subtract. **43.** $\sqrt{\frac{5}{7}} - \sqrt{\frac{7}{5}}$ **44.** $x - \frac{x}{\sqrt{x}}$ **45.** $\sqrt{\frac{2}{5}} + \sqrt{\frac{1}{15}}$

Find the indicated outputs for these functions.

46. $f(m) = 2m - 1$; find $f(-1)$, $f(4)$, $f(2)$, and $f(-11)$

47. $g(x) = -3x + 5$; find $g(2)$, $g(-2)$, $g(0)$, and $g(5)$

Simplify. **48.** $\sqrt{36}$ **49.** $\sqrt{(x - 5)^2}$ **50.** $\sqrt{(-5y)^2}$ **51.** $\sqrt{243m^3}$

CONNECTIONS: GEOMETRY

What is the largest rectangular area that can be enclosed with 16 ft of fence?

$$2w + 2l = 16$$
$$w + l = 8$$
$$w = 8 - l$$

l

w

Substitute for w in the formula for the area of a rectangle: $A = lw$. Graph the resulting quadratic function and find its maximum.

12-5 Direct Variation

Application

The distance a bicycle travels varies as the rate of the bicycle and the time traveled. Suppose a bicycle travels at a constant rate of 10 km/h. Then the distance it travels will vary depending only on time. The table below shows the distance (d) a bicycle travels for several times (t) traveling at a rate of 10 km/h.

t (hours)	1	2	3	4
d (km)	10	20	30	40

We can see that the distance increases as the time increases. We can say that the distance "varies directly" as the time traveled. We can write

$$d = 10t$$

Equations of Direct Variation

Objective: Give an equation of direct variation.

When the value of one variable in an equation increases (or decreases) as another variable in the same equation increases (or decreases), the variables are said to vary directly.

Definition

An equation of the form $y = kx$, where k is a constant, expresses **direct variation.** k is called the **constant of variation.**

When there is direct variation, $y = kx$, the constant of variation can be found if one pair of values of x and y is known.

EXAMPLE 1

Find an equation of direct variation where y varies directly as x. One pair of values is $y = 7$ when $x = 25$.

We substitute to find k.

$$y = kx$$
$$7 = k \cdot 25$$

12-5

FIRST FIVE MINUTES

1. Graph $f(x) = x^2 + x - 2$.

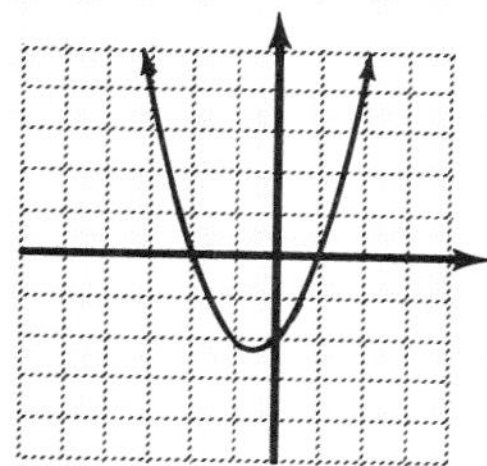

Equations of Direct Variation

Explain that the ratio, $\frac{y}{x}$, of the variables in a direct variation is constant and that this ratio is equal to the constant k. For instance, in the bicycle example, the ratio of distance to time, k, is 10.

Math Point
The graph of an equation of direct variation is a line through the origin with a slope equal to the constant of variation.

Key Question

- What are some common situations where one quantity varies directly as another?
  Gasoline and cost,
  Circumference and radius of a circle

Chalkboard Example

1. Find an equation of variation where y varies directly as x, and $y = 2$ when $x = 1$.
   $y = kx$
   $2 = k(1)$
   $k = 2$
   Thus the equation of variation is $y = 2x$.

Problem Solving

Chalkboard Example

1. The cost of the electricity used by a light bulb varies directly as the time the bulb is on. Three hours of use cost seven cents. How much will 11 hours of use cost?
   Let c be the cost, in cents, of the electricity.
   Let t be the time the bulb is used, in hours.
   $c = kt$
   $(7) = k(3)$
   $k = \frac{7}{3}$
   The equation of variation is
   $c = \frac{7}{3}t.$
   Substituting 11 for t,
   $\frac{7}{3}(11) = \frac{77}{3} \approx 26$
   11 hours will cost about 26 cents.

LESSON QUIZ

1. Find the equation of variation where y varies directly as x, and $y = 7$ when $x = 2$.
   $y = \frac{7}{2}x$
2. A salesman's income varies directly as the dollar amount of sales per month. The salesman made \$3000 of income on sales of \$12,000. How much will he make on sales of \$17,000?
   $I = \frac{1}{4}S$
   \$4250

$$\frac{7}{25} = k, \text{ or } k = 0.28$$

Then the equation of variation is $y = 0.28x$.

The relation given by $y = 0.28x$ is a function. Therefore, we can also write $f(x) = 0.28x$ as the equation of direct variation.

Try This Find an equation of variation where y varies directly as x. One pair of values is given.

a. $y = 84$ when $x = 12$ $y = 7x$ **b.** $y = 50$ when $x = 80$ $y = 0.625x$

Problem Solving

Objective: Solve problems involving direct variation.

EXAMPLE 2

The weight (J) of an object on Jupiter varies directly as its weight (E) on Earth. An object that weighs 225 lb on Earth has a weight of 594 lb on Jupiter. What is the weight on Jupiter of an object that has a weight of 115 lb on Earth?

First find an equation of direct variation. We substitute to find k. Then we can use our equation to find J for any value of E.

$$J = kE$$
$$594 = k \cdot 225$$
$$\frac{594}{225} = k$$
$$2.64 = k$$

The equation of variation is $J = 2.64E$.

Use the equation to find the weight on Jupiter of the 115 lb object.

$$J = 2.64E$$
$$J = 2.64(115)$$
$$J = 303.6$$

The object would have a weight of 303.6 lb on Jupiter.

Try This

c. The cost (c) of operating a TV varies directly as the number (n) of hours it is in operation. It costs \$14.00 to operate a standard size color TV continuously for 30 days. At this rate, about how much would it cost to operate the TV for 1 day? 1 hour? $46\frac{2}{3}$¢, $1\frac{17}{18}$¢

d. The weight (V) of an object on Venus varies directly as its weight (E) on Earth. A person weighing 120 lb on Earth would weigh 106 lb on Venus. How much would a person weighing 150 lb on Earth weigh on Venus? 132.5 lb

12-5 EXERCISES

A

Find an equation of variation where y varies directly as x, and the following are true.

1. $y = 28$ when $x = 7$ $y = 4x$

2. $y = 30$ when $x = 8$ $y = 3.75x$

3. $y = 0.7$ when $x = 0.4$ $y = 1.75x$

4. $y = 0.8$ when $x = 0.5$ $y = 1.6x$

5. $y = 400$ when $x = 125$ $y = 3.2x$

6. $y = 630$ when $x = 175$ $y = 3.6x$

7. $y = 200$ when $x = 300$ $y = \frac{2}{3}x$

8. $y = 500$ when $x = 60$ $y = \frac{25}{3}x$

Solve.

9. A person's paycheck (p) varies directly as the number (h) of hours worked. For working 15 hours, the pay is \$78.75. Find the pay for 35 hours of work.

10. The number (b) of bolts a machine can make varies directly as the time it operates. It can make 6578 bolts in 2 hours. How many can it make in 5 hours?

11. The number (n) of servings of meat that can be obtained from a turkey varies directly as its weight (w). From a turkey weighing 22 lb one can get 40 servings of meat. How many servings can be obtained from a 14-lb turkey?

12. The number (n) of servings of meat that can be obtained from round steak varies directly as the weight (w). From 9 kg of round steak one can get 70 servings of meat. How many servings can one get from 12 kg of round steak?

13. The weight (M) of an object on the moon varies directly as its weight (E) on Earth. A person who weighs 115 lb on Earth weighs 19 lb on the moon. How much would a person who weighs 150 lb on Earth weigh on the moon?

14. The weight (M) of an object on Mars varies directly as its weight (E) on Earth. A person who weighs 115 lb on Earth weighs 44 lb on Mars. How much would a person who weighs 150 lb on Earth weigh on Mars?

15. The number of kg of water (W) in a human body varies directly as the total body weight (B). A person who weighs 75 kg contains 54 kg of water. How many kilograms of water are in a person weighing 95 kg?

16. The amount (A) which a family gives to charity varies directly as its income (I). Last year, the family earned \$25,880 and gave \$4011 to charity. How much will they give if they make \$30,000 this year?

17. The distance between two cities is 1500 miles. They are shown to be 6 in. apart on a globe. What is the actual distance between two cities that are shown to be 10 inches apart on the globe?

18. The volume inside a balloon varies directly as the temperature. The volume of the balloon is 3 L at a temperature of 300° Kelvin. What is the volume if the temperature rises to 350° Kelvin?

Assignment Guide
Minimum: 1–18 e/o, MR

Regular: 1–18 m3, 19–27 e/o, 28, MR
Advanced: 1–27 m3, 28–32, MR

ADDITIONAL ANSWERS

Exercises

9. \$183.75
10. 16,445 bolts
11. Approx. 25 servings
12. Approx. 93 servings
13. Approx. 25 lb
14. Approx. 57 lb
15. 68.4 kg
16. Approx. \$4650
17. 2500 miles
18. 3.5 L

25. $C = kr\ (k = 2\pi)$
26. $B = kN$
27. $C = kA$
28. The graph of an equation of direct variation is a line through the origin with a slope equal to k.
31. $A = kr^2$
32. $V = kr^3$

Mixed Review

33. $t \geq 0$
34. Any real number
35. $a \geq 7$
36. $m \geq \frac{1}{3}$
37. Any real number
38. Any real number
39. Any real number
40. $\frac{\sqrt{x}}{x}$
41. $\sqrt{3xy}$
42. $\frac{3|m|\sqrt{2}}{4}$
43. $7\sqrt{3}$
44. $10\sqrt{2}$
45. 9
46. $-8, -2, 40, 22$
47. $-2, 2, 0, 4$

B

Which of the following vary directly?

19. the amount of a gas in a tank in liters and the amount in gallons Yes
20. the temperature in Fahrenheit degrees and in Celsius No
21. the price per pound of carrots and the number of pounds No
22. the total price of tomatoes and the number of pounds Yes
23. a number and its reciprocal No

Write an equation of direct variation for each situation.

24. The perimeter (P) of an equilateral polygon varies directly as the length of a side (S). $P = kS$ (k = number of sides)
25. The circumference of a circle (C) varies directly as the radius (r).
26. The number of bags (B) of peanuts sold at a baseball game varies directly as the number (N) of people in attendance.
27. The cost (C) of building a new house varies directly as the area (A) of the floor space of the house.
28. ***Critical Thinking*** Describe the graph of an equation of direct variation ($y = kx$). What is the relationship between k, the constant of variation and the graph of the equation?

Challenge

Write an equation of variation to describe these situations.

29. In a stream, the amount of salt (S) carried varies directly as the sixth power of the speed (V) of the stream. $S = kV^6$
30. The square of the pitch (P) of a vibrating string varies directly as the tension (t) on the string. $P^2 = kt$
31. The surface area (A) of a sphere varies directly as the square of the radius (r).
32. The volume (V) of a sphere varies directly as the cube of the radius (r).

Mixed Review

Determine the replacements for the variables that give real numbers.

33. $\sqrt{5t}$ **34.** $\sqrt{3x^2}$ **35.** $\sqrt{a - 7}$ **36.** $\sqrt{3m - 1}$
37. $\sqrt{y^2 + 3}$ **38.** $\sqrt{x^2 - 4x + 4}$ **39.** $\sqrt{a^2 + 6a + 9}$

Rationalize the denominator. **40.** $\frac{\sqrt{y}}{\sqrt{xy}}$ **41.** $\frac{\sqrt{15x^3y^2}}{\sqrt{5x^2y}}$ **42.** $\frac{\sqrt{18m^2n}}{\sqrt{16n}}$

In a right triangle, find the length of the side not given.

43. $a = 7, c = 14$ **44.** $a = 10, b = 10$ **45.** $b = 12, c = 15$

Find the indicated outputs for these functions.

46. $f(t) = 2t^2 - 10$; find $f(1), f(-2), f(5), f(-4)$
47. $g(c) = |c| - 3$; find $g(1), g(5), g(-3), g(-7)$

12-6 Inverse Variation

Application

The table below shows the time (t) needed for a trip of 10 km traveling at different rates (r).

r (km/h)	10	20	30	40
time (h)	1	$\frac{1}{2}$	$\frac{1}{3}$	$\frac{1}{4}$

We can see that the time decreases as the rate increases. We can say that the time "varies inversely" as the rate. We can write

$$t = \frac{10}{r}$$

Equations of Inverse Variation

Objective: Find an equation of inverse variation.

When the value of one variable in an equation increases (or decreases) as another variable in the same equation decreases (or increases), the variables are said to vary inversely.

Definition

An equation of the form $y = \frac{k}{x}$, where k is a constant, expresses **inverse variation.**

EXAMPLE 1 Find an equation of variation where y varies inversely as x. One pair of values is $y = 145$ when $x = 0.8$.

We substitute to find k.

$$y = \frac{k}{x}$$

$$145 = \frac{k}{0.8}$$

$$(0.8)145 = k$$

$$116 = k$$

The equation of variation is $y = \frac{116}{x}$.

The relation given by $y = \frac{116}{x}$ is a function. Therefore, we can also write $f(x) = \frac{116}{x}$ as the equation of inverse variation.

12-6

FIRST FIVE MINUTES

1. Find the equation of variation where y varies directly as x, and $y = 3$ when $x = 5$.

   $y = \frac{3}{5}x$

2. The cost (c), in dollars, of gasoline varies directly as the amount (a), in gallons purchased. The cost of 7 gallons is \$9.10. What is the cost of 13 gallons?

   $c = ka$
   $(9.10) = k(7)$
   $k = \frac{9.1}{7}$
   $k = 1.3$
   $c = 1.3a$ is the equation
   $c = 1.3(13)$
   $c = 16.9$
   13 gallons will cost \$16.90.

Equations of Inverse Variation

Point out that the product of the two variables, xy, in an inverse variation is the constant k. In the example of the trip, for instance, the product of each pair of entries is 10.

Key Question

- What are some common situations in which one quantity varies inversely as another?

  The time needed to complete a job tends to vary inversely as the number of people working.
  The time that a trip takes varies inversely as the speed.
  The pitch of a guitar string varies inversely as its length.

Chalkboard Example

1. Find the equation of variation where y varies inversely as x, and $y = 5$ when $x = 3$.

   $y = \frac{k}{x}$

   $5 = \frac{k}{3}$

   $k = 15$

   $y = \frac{15}{x}$

Problem Solving

Chalkboard Examples

1. The time (t), in days, required to build a house varies inversely as the number (n) of people at work. If three people can build a house in 20 days, how long will it take 8 people to build a house? First, find an equation of variation.

$$t = \frac{k}{n}$$
$$20 = \frac{k}{3}$$
$$k = 60$$
$$t = \frac{60}{n}$$
$$t = \frac{60}{8}$$
$$t = 7.5$$

It will take 7.5 days.

2. The pitch (P), in vibrations per second, of a guitar string varies inversely as its wavelength (W). A string of length 10 inches has a pitch of 1320 vibrations per second. First, find an equation of variation. What is the pitch of a string of length 11 inches?

$$P = \frac{k}{W}$$
$$1320 = \frac{k}{10}$$
$$k = 13200$$
$$P = \frac{13200}{W}$$
$$P = \frac{13200}{11}$$
$$P = 1200$$

The string has a pitch of 1200 vibrations per second.

Try This Find an equation of variation where y varies inversely as x. One pair of values is given.

a. $y = 105$ when $x = 0.6$ $y = \frac{63}{x}$ **b.** $y = 45$ when $x = 20$ $y = \frac{900}{x}$

Problem Solving

Objective: Solve problems involving inverse variation.

EXAMPLE 2

The pitch (P) of a musical tone varies inversely as its wavelength (W). One tone has a pitch of 660 vibrations per second and a wavelength of 1.6 feet. Find the wavelength of another tone which has a pitch of 440 vibrations per second.

Find an equation of variation.

$$P = \frac{k}{W}$$
$$660 = \frac{k}{1.6}$$
$$1.6(660) = k$$
$$1056 = k$$

The equation of variation is $P = \frac{1056}{W}$.

Use the equation to find the wavelength of the second tone.

$$P = \frac{1056}{W}$$
$$440 = \frac{1056}{W}$$
$$440W = 1056$$
$$W = 2.4$$

The wavelength is 2.4 feet.

Try This

c. The time (t) required to drive a fixed distance varies inversely as the speed (r). It takes 5 hours at 60 km/h to drive a fixed distance. How long would it take to drive the same distance at 40 km/h? $7\frac{1}{2}$ hr

d. The time (t) required to do a certain job varies inversely as the number of people (n) working (assuming all work at the same rate). It takes 4 hours for 20 people working together to wash and wax the floors in a building. How long would it take 25 people working together to complete the same job? 3.2 h or $3\frac{1}{5}$ h

12-6 EXERCISES

A

Find an equation of variation where y varies inversely as x. One pair of values is given.

1. $y = 25$ when $x = 3$ $y = \frac{75}{x}$
2. $y = 45$ when $x = 2$ $y = \frac{90}{x}$
3. $y = 8$ when $x = 10$ $y = \frac{80}{x}$
4. $y = 7$ when $x = 10$ $y = \frac{70}{x}$
5. $y = 0.125$ when $x = 8$ $y = \frac{1}{x}$
6. $y = 6.25$ when $x = 0.16$ $y = \frac{1}{x}$
7. $y = 42$ when $x = 25$ $y = \frac{1050}{x}$
8. $y = 42$ when $x = 50$ $y = \frac{2100}{x}$
9. $y = 0.2$ when $x = 0.3$ $y = \frac{0.06}{x}$
10. $y = 0.4$ when $x = 0.6$ $y = \frac{0.24}{x}$
11. $y = 0.8$ when $x = 4$ $y = \frac{3.2}{x}$
12. $y = 80$ when $x = 0.7$ $y = \frac{56}{x}$
13. $y = \frac{2}{5}$ when $x = \frac{5}{2}$ $y = \frac{1}{x}$
14. $y = \frac{4}{3}$ when $x = \frac{3}{2}$ $y = \frac{2}{x}$

Solve.

15. It takes 16 hours for 2 people to resurface a gym floor. How long would it take 6 people to do the job? $5\frac{1}{3}$ hr
16. It takes 4 hours for 9 cooks to prepare a school lunch. How long would it take 8 cooks to prepare the lunch? $4\frac{1}{2}$ hr
17. The volume (V) of a gas varies inversely as the pressure (P) upon it. The volume of a gas is 200 cubic centimeters (cm^3) under a pressure of 32 kg/cm^2. What will be its volume under a pressure of 20 kg/cm^2? 320 cm^3
18. The current (I) in an electrical conductor varies inversely as the resistance (r) of the conductor. The current is 2 amperes when the resistance is 960 ohms. What is the current when the resistance is 540 ohms? $3\frac{5}{9}$ amp
19. The time (t) required to empty a tank varies inversely as the rate (r) of pumping. A pump can empty a tank in 90 minutes at the rate of 1200 L/min. How long will it take the pump to empty the tank at 2000 L/min? 54 min
20. The height (H) of triangles of fixed area varies inversely as the base (B). Suppose the height is 50 cm when the base is 40 cm. Find the height when the base is 8 cm. What is the fixed area? 250 cm; 1000 cm^2

B

Write an equation of inverse variation for each situation.

21. The cost per person (C) of chartering a fishing boat varies inversely as the number (N) of persons sharing the cost. $C = \frac{k}{N}$
22. The number (N) of revolutions of a tire rolling over a given distance varies inversely as the circumference (C) of the tire. $N = \frac{k}{C}$
23. The amount of current (I) flowing in an electric circuit varies inversely with the resistance (R) of the circuit. $I = \frac{k}{R}$
24. The intensity of illumination (I) from a light source varies inversely as the square of the distance (d) from the source. $I = \frac{k}{d^2}$

LESSON QUIZ

1. Find the equation of variation where y varies inversely as x, and $y = 3$ when $x = 2$.

   $y = \frac{6}{x}$

2. It takes 3 people 5 hours to sort 100 pounds of coffee beans. How long will it take 8 people to do the job?

   $t = \frac{15}{p}$

   It will take 1.875 hours.

Assignment Guide

Minimum: 1–20 e/o, MR

Regular: 1–20 m3, 21–28 e/o, 29, MR

Advanced: 1–28 m3, 29–31, MR

ADDITIONAL ANSWERS

Exercises

29. It is halved; it is halved.

Mixed Review

32. $|x - 5|\sqrt{2}$
33. $|a|c^2\sqrt{a}$
34. 18
35. 33
36. No
37. Yes
38. Yes
39. No

40.

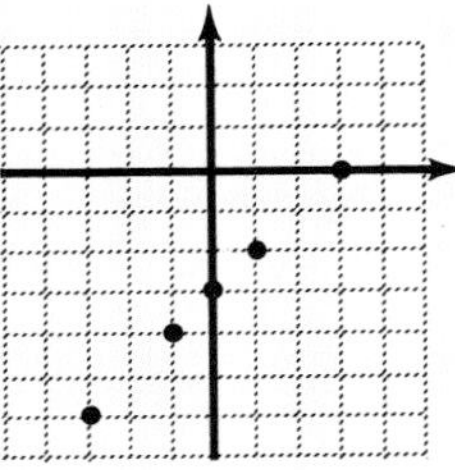

41.

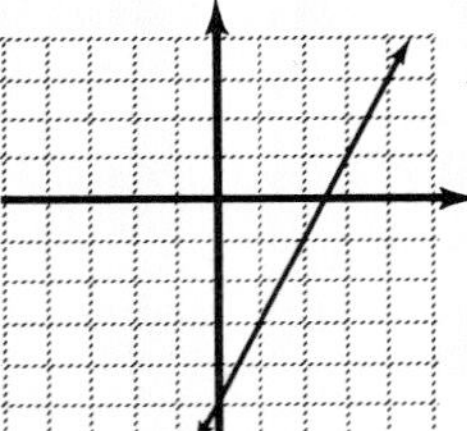

42.

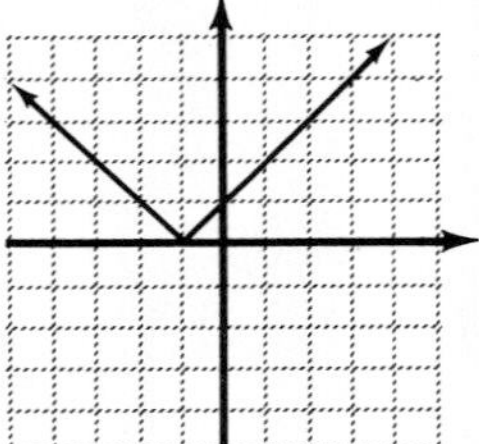

Spatial Relations

1. d
2. d
3. a

Which of the following vary inversely?

25. the cost of mailing a letter in the U.S. and the distance it travels No
26. a runner's speed in a race and the time it takes to run it Yes
27. the number of plays to go 80 yards for a touchdown and the average gain per play Yes
28. the weight of a turkey and the cooking time No
29. ***Critical Thinking*** Suppose y varies inversely as x. If the value of x is doubled, what happens to the value of y? If the value of y is doubled, what happens to the value of x?

Challenge

Write an equation of variation for each of the following.

30. The force (F) needed to keep a car from skidding on a curve varies directly as the square of the car's speed (S) and its mass (m) and inversely as the radius of the curve (r). $F = \frac{kS^2m}{r}$
31. For a horizontal beam supported at both ends, the maximum safe load (L) varies directly as its width (w) and the square of its thickness (t) and inversely as the distance (d) between the supports. $L = \frac{kwt^2}{d}$

Mixed Review

Simplify. **32.** $\sqrt{2x^2 - 20x + 50}$ **33.** $\sqrt{ac^3}\sqrt{a^2c}$

Solve. **34.** $\sqrt{x - 2} = 4$ **35.** $7 - \sqrt{x + 3} = 1$

Determine whether the given point is a solution of $3x + 4y > 2$.

36. $(-3, 1)$ **37.** $(2, 0)$ **38.** $(0, 1)$ **39.** $(-1, 1)$

Graph the function. **40.** $f(x) = x - 3$ where the domain is $\{-3, -1, 0, 1, 3\}$ **41.** $g(x) = 2x - 5$ **42.** $h(x) = |x + 1|$

SPATIAL RELATIONS

In each set of figures, the first two have a particular relationship. Which figure (a, b, c, or d) has the same relationship to the third figure?

1.

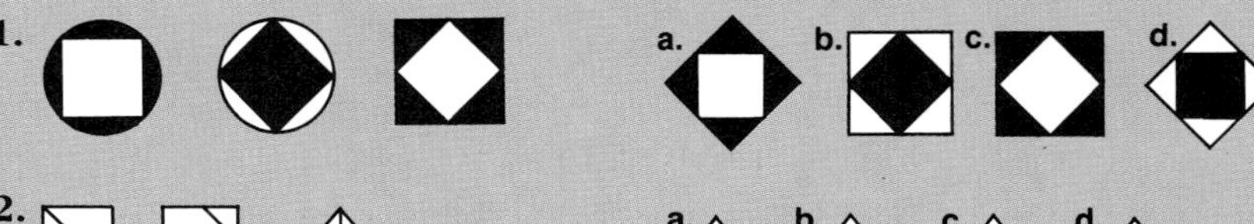

2.

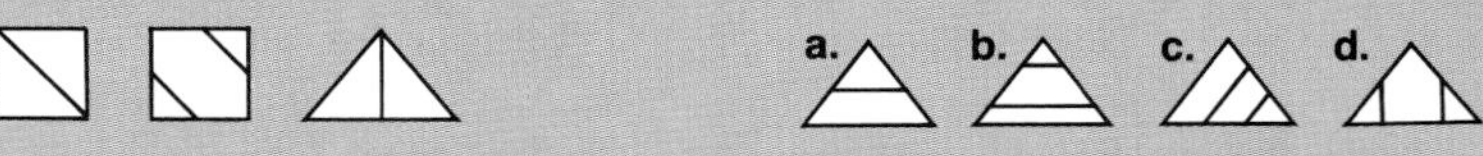

3.

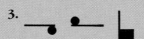

12-7 Joint and Combined Variation

Joint Variation

Objective: Find an equation of joint variation.

The formula for the area (A) of a triangle is $A = \frac{1}{2}bh$, where b is the base of the triangle and h is the height of the triangle. In this formula, the area varies directly as the base and the height of the triangle. We can say that the area of the triangle varies **jointly** as the base and the height.

Definition

An equation of the form $z = kxy$, where k is a nonzero constant, expresses **joint variation.**

EXAMPLE 1

Find an equation of joint variation where V varies jointly as B and h. One set of values for the relationship is $V = 35$, $B = 7$, and $h = 15$. Find V when $B = 18$ and $h = 6$.

We can write $V = kBh$ to show the joint variation.
Now we can substitute the given values to find the value of k.

$$V = k \cdot B \cdot h$$
$$35 = k \cdot 7 \cdot 15$$
$$35 = k \cdot 105$$
$$k = \frac{35}{105} = \frac{1}{3}$$

The equation for joint variation is $V = \frac{1}{3}Bh$.

We can now substitute the given values for B and h and solve for V.

$$V = \frac{1}{3}Bh$$
$$V = \frac{1}{3} \cdot 18 \cdot 6$$
$$V = 36$$

Try This

a. Find an equation of joint variation where w varies jointly as x, y, and z. One set of values is $w = 36$, $x = 3$, $y = 5$, and $z = 6$. Find the value of w when $x = 2$, $y = 8$, and $z = 5$. $w = 0.4xyz$; 32

12-7

FIRST FIVE MINUTES

1. Find the equation of variation where y varies directly as x, and $y = 6$ when $x = 5$.
   $y = kx$
   $6 = k5$
   $k = \frac{6}{5}$
   $y = \frac{6}{5}x$
2. Find the equation of variation where y varies inversely as x, and $y = 2$ when $x = 7$.
   $y = \frac{k}{x}$
   $2 = \frac{k}{7}$
   $k = 14$
   $y = \frac{14}{x}$

Joint Variation

Point out that joint variation relates three quantities.

Key Questions

- What are three common variables related by joint variation?
  Distance varies jointly as rate and time.
- How is total price related to the cost per item and the number of the items purchased?
  The total price varies jointly as the cost per item and the number of items purchased.

Chalkboard Example

1. Find an equation of joint variation where Q varies jointly as R and S, and $Q = 2$ when $R = 1$ and $S = 3$.
   $Q = kRS$
   $2 = k(1)(3)$
   $k = \frac{2}{3}$
   $Q = \frac{2}{3}RS$ is the equation.

Combined Variation

Chalkboard Example

1. Find an equation of combined variation where x varies directly as y and inversely as z, and $x = 7$ when $y = 3$ and $z = 6$. Find the value of x when $y = 9$ and $z = 12$.

   $x = \frac{ky}{z}$

   $(7) = \frac{k(3)}{6}$

   $k = 14$

   $x = \frac{14y}{z}$ is the equation for combined variation. When $y = 9$ and $z = 12$,

   $x = \frac{14(9)}{12} = \frac{21}{2}$

Combined Variation

Objective: Solve problems involving combined variation.

The formula $P = \frac{0.25W}{A}$ gives the recommended tire pressure for each tire for the total weight (W) of a car and the area (A) of the ground covered by each tire. The formula shows that the recommended tire pressure varies directly as the weight of the car and inversely as the area of the ground. The formula $P = \frac{0.25W}{A}$ expresses **combined variation.**

Definition

An equation of the form $z = \frac{kx}{y}$, where k is a nonzero constant, expresses **combined variation.**

EXAMPLE 2

Find an equation of combined variation where A varies directly as b and inversely as c. One set of values is $A = 4$, $b = 12$, and $c = 9$. Find A when $b = 7$ and $c = 3$.

We can write $A = \frac{kb}{c}$ to show the combined variation.

Now we can substitute to find the value of k.

$$A = \frac{kb}{c}$$

$$4 = k \cdot \frac{12}{9}$$

$$k = 3$$

The equation for combined variation is $A = \frac{3b}{c}$.

We can now substitute the given values for b and c and solve for A.

$$A = \frac{3b}{c}$$

$$A = 3 \cdot \frac{7}{3}$$

$$A = 7$$

Try This

b. Find an equation of combined variation where P varies directly as q and inversely as r. One set of values is $P = 0.064$, $q = 16$, and $r = 5$. Find P when $q = 12$ and $r = 10$. $P = \frac{0.02q}{r}$; 0.024

Problem Solving

Objective: Solve problems involving joint variation.

PROBLEM-SOLVING GUIDELINES
■ UNDERSTAND the problem
■ Develop and carry out a PLAN
■ Find the ANSWER and CHECK

Joint variation has many real-world applications.

EXAMPLE 3

The volume of a pyramid varies jointly as the height of the pyramid and the area of its base. The volume of a pyramid with height 12 cm and base 5 cm^2 is 20 cm^3. Find the volume of the Great Pyramid whose height is 147 m and whose base has an area of 50,000 m^2.

We can write $V = kBh$ to show the joint variation.
Now we can substitute the given values to find the value of k.

$$V = k \cdot B \cdot h$$
$$20 = k \cdot 5 \cdot 12$$
$$20 = k \cdot 60$$
$$k = \frac{20}{60} = \frac{1}{3}$$

The equation for the joint variation is $V = \frac{1}{3}Bh$.

We can now use this information to find the volume (in m^3) of the Great Pyramid. Substitute the values of B and h in the equation and solve for V.

$$V = \frac{1}{3}Bh$$
$$V = \frac{1}{3} \cdot 50{,}000 \cdot 147$$
$$V = 2{,}450{,}000$$

The volume of the Great Pyramid is 2,450,000 m^3.

Try This

c. The temperature inside the chamber of a piston varies jointly as the pressure and the volume. The temperature is 300 Kelvin when the volume is 200 in.^{3} and the pressure is 100 pounds per square inch (lb/in.^{2}). Find the temperature when the pressure is 70 lb/in.^{2} and the volume is 400 in.^{3} 420 K

Problem Solving

Chalkboard Example

1. The interest earned at Whole World Savings & Loan varies jointly as the amount deposited in the bank (the principal) and the time elapsed since the deposit. If a \$500 deposit earns \$120 interest after 3 years, how much does an \$800 deposit earn after 5 years?

$$120 = k \cdot 500 \cdot 3$$
$$120 = k \cdot 1500$$
$$k = \frac{2}{25}$$
$$I = \frac{2}{25} \cdot 800 \cdot 5$$
$$I = \$320$$

LESSON ENRICHMENT

Determine whether each situation is an example of direct variation, inverse variation, joint variation, or combined variation.

1. Your appetite varies ______ as the elapsed time from your last meal. Direct variation
2. The time it takes to type a theme paper varies ______ as the speed at which it is typed. Inverse variation
3. The distance a car travels varies ______ as the rate and the time. Joint variation
4. The time a car travels varies ______ as the distance and the rate. Combined variation

Write other situations that illustrate various types of variation.

LESSON QUIZ

1. Find the equation of joint variation where C varies jointly as a and b, and $C = 5$ when $a = 2$ and $b = 10$.

   $C = \frac{1}{4}ab$

2. Find the equation of combined variation where U varies directly as V and inversely as W, and $U = 3$ when $V = 2$ and $W = 5$.

   $U = \frac{15V}{2W}$

Assignment Guide
Minimum: 1–12 e/o, MR

Regular: 1–18 m3, 19, MR, assign w. Situational Problem Solving
Advanced: 1–18 m3, 19–23, MR

ADDITIONAL ANSWERS

Exercises

1. $r = \frac{1}{2}st$; 54
2. $m = 0.8np$; 104
3. $q = 5rs$; 0.8
4. $a = bc$; 0.024
5. $x = \frac{3}{10}wyz$; 54
6. $p = \frac{1}{3}qrs$; 70
7. $a = \frac{6b}{c}$; 3
8. $m = \frac{10n}{p}$; 2
9. $w = \frac{2x}{3y}$; 2
10. $p = \frac{0.7q}{r}$; 2.8
11. $u = \frac{1.5v}{w}$; 0.9375
12. $a = \frac{0.75b}{c}$; 19.2
13. 2.8
14. 14
15. 28 cm^3

12-7 EXERCISES

A

Find an equation of joint variation. Then solve for the missing value.

1. r varies directly as s and t. One set of values is $r = 28$, $s = 7$, $t = 8$. Find r when $s = 12$ and $t = 9$.
2. m varies jointly as n and p. One set of values is $m = 86.4$, $n = 9$, and $p = 12$. Find m when $n = 20$ and $p = 6.5$.
3. q varies jointly as r and s. One set of values is $q = 2.4$, $r = 0.6$, and $s = 0.8$. Find q when $r = 1.6$ and $s = 0.1$.
4. a varies jointly as b and c. One set of values is $a = 1$, $b = 5$, and $c = 0.2$. Find a when $b = 2.4$ and $c = 0.01$.
5. x varies jointly as w, y, and z. One set of values is $x = 18$, $w = 2$, $y = 6$, and $z = 5$. Find x when $w = 5$, $y = 12$, and $z = 3$.
6. p varies jointly as q, r, and s. One set of values is $p = 70$, $q = 7$, $r = 5$, and $s = 6$. Find p when $q = 2$, $r = 15$, and $s = 7$.

Find an equation of combined variation for each. Then solve for the missing value.

7. a varies directly as b and inversely as c. One set of values is $a = 14$, $b = 7$, and $c = 3$. Find a when $b = 4$ and $c = 8$.
8. m varies directly as n and inversely as p. One set of values is $m = 5$, $n = 2$, and $p = 4$. Find m when $n = 10$ and $p = 50$.
9. w varies directly as x and inversely as y. One set of values is $w = 3$, $x = 9$, and $y = 2$. Find w when $x = 15$ and $y = 5$.
10. p varies directly as q and inversely as r. One set of values is $p = 0.8$, $q = 8$, and $r = 7$. Find p when $q = 12$ and $r = 3$.
11. u varies directly as v and inversely as w. One set of values is $u = 5.75$, $v = 2.3$, and $w = 0.6$. Find u when $v = 0.5$ and $w = 0.8$.
12. a varies directly as b and inversely as c. One set of values is $a = 6.75$, $b = 1.8$, and $c = 0.2$. Find a when $b = 6.4$ and $c = 0.25$.

B

13. A varies jointly as b and c and inversely as d. One set of values is $A = 0.525$, $b = 6$, $c = 7$, and $d = 8$. Find A when $b = 12$, $c = 7$, and $d = 3$.
14. W varies jointly as x and y and inversely as z. One set of values is $W = 112$, $x = 4$, $y = 8$, and $z = 0.2$. Find W when $x = 8$, $y = 10$ and $z = 4$.
15. The volume of a cone varies jointly as the height of the cone and the area of the base. The volume of a cone with height 15 cm and base 28 cm^2 is 140 cm^3. Find the volume of a cone with height 7 cm and base 12 cm^2.

16. A pitcher's earned run average (a) varies directly as the number of earned runs (r) allowed and inversely as the number of innings (i) pitched. Joe Price had an earned run average of 2.55. He gave up 85 earned runs in 300 innings. About how many earned runs would he have given up had he pitched 353 innings with the same average?

Use the following relationship: The lateral surface area of a cylinder varies jointly as the radius and height of the cylinder. A cylinder with radius 0.8 in. and height 6 in. has a lateral surface area of 29.76 in^2.

17. Find the height of a cylinder with radius 1.5 in. and lateral surface area 74.4 in^2.

18. Find the radius of a cylinder with height 6 cm and lateral surface area 111.6 cm^2.

19. *Critical Thinking* The area of a circle varies directly as the square of the length of its diameter. What is the constant of variation?

Challenge

20. Suppose y varies directly as x. What happens to the value of y if the value of x is doubled?

21. Suppose y varies directly as the square of x. What happens to the value of y if the value of x is doubled?

22. The stopping distance (d) of a car after the brakes are applied varies directly as the square of the speed (r). A car traveling 35 mi/h will travel about 106 ft after braking. What is the rate of a car that needs about 228 ft to stop?

23. The force of attraction of a body varies directly as its mass and inversely as the square of the distance from the body. A body of mass 10 kg has a force of attraction of 7.8 newtons at a distance of 20 m. How far away is the force of attraction of a 10 kg mass equal to 31.2 newtons?

Mixed Review

Rationalize the denominator. 24. $\frac{\sqrt{16}}{\sqrt{3}}$ 25. $\frac{\sqrt{5}}{\sqrt{x}}$ 26. $\frac{\sqrt{x}}{\sqrt{xy}}$

27. $\frac{\sqrt{18}}{\sqrt{2y}}$ 28. $\frac{\sqrt{3x}}{\sqrt{12y}}$ 29. $\frac{\sqrt{x^4y}}{\sqrt{xy^2}}$ 30. $\frac{\sqrt{6c}}{\sqrt{8c^3}}$ 31. $\frac{\sqrt{12cd}}{\sqrt{3c^4d^4}}$

In a right triangle, find the length of the hypotenuse. 32. $a = 10$, $b = 24$ 33. $a = 5, b = 12$ 34. $a = 24, b = 32$

Solve. 35. $\sqrt{2x + 3} = \sqrt{5x - 6}$ 36. $-\sqrt{x} = 7$

37. $\sqrt{x + 7} = 2\sqrt{x - 5}$ 38. $\sqrt{x + 30} = 3\sqrt{x - 2}$

Graph. 39. $h(x) = 3x - 2$ 40. $f(x) = x^2 + 2$

16. 100
17. 8 in.
18. 3 cm
19. $\frac{\pi}{4}$
20. y is doubled
21. y is quadrupled
22. Approx. 51 mi/h
23. 10 m

Mixed Review

24. $\frac{4\sqrt{3}}{3}$
25. $\frac{\sqrt{5x}}{x}$
26. $\frac{\sqrt{y}}{y}$
27. $\frac{3\sqrt{y}}{y}$
28. $\frac{\sqrt{xy}}{2y}$
29. $\frac{x\sqrt{xy}}{y}$
30. $\frac{\sqrt{3}}{2c}$
31. $\frac{2\sqrt{cd}}{c^2d^2}$
32. 26
33. 13
34. 40
35. 3
36. No real-number solution
37. 9
38. 6
39.

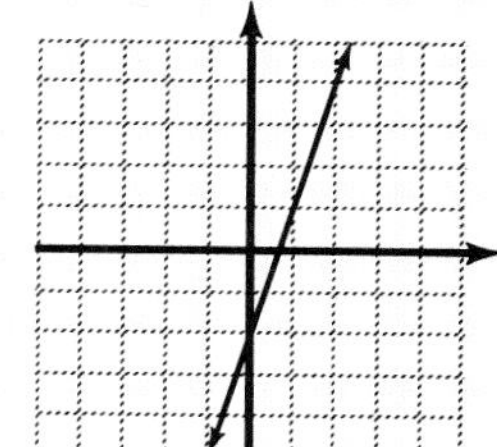

40.

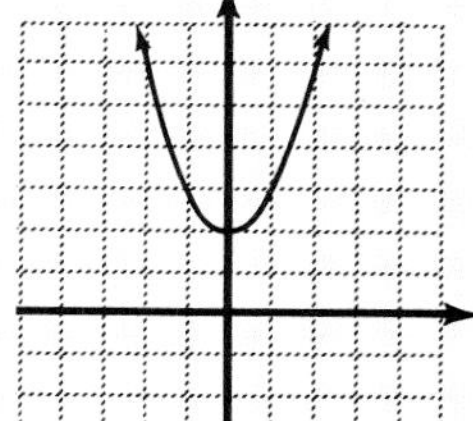

Problem Solving: Situational Problem Solving

Before students begin to work the situational problem, discuss possible modifications of the Problem-Solving Guideline subsections that can apply to situational problem solving.

For example,
Phase 1:
What am I trying to find?
What assumptions need to be made?
What data will I need?

Phase 2:
What subproblems need to be solved?
What strategies will I use to solve these problems?

Phase 3:
What is the answer to the problem?
Does the answer seem reasonable?
Have I stated the answer clearly?

You may wish to have students work in groups of four. After each group has completed its plan, have students present the plan to the class.

Extension

Let students choose a business and plan their business for the summer, developing their own assumptions.

Ask someone in the business community who owns a small business to share the organization of their business with the class.

Problem Solving: Situational Problem Solving

Starting a Business

In the problems you have seen so far in this book, the data needed to find a solution has been given, and the question needed to be answered has been easily identified. Many real-world problems are not presented in such a convenient manner.

In real-world situations you need to clarify, perhaps by asking many questions, exactly what you are being asked to do. You need to clarify the assumptions and collect the required data from a variety of sources. You may need to solve many subproblems before arriving at the final answer to the question. These problems are sometimes called **situational problems.**

PROBLEM-SOLVING GUIDELINES
■ UNDERSTAND the problem
■ Develop and carry out a PLAN
■ Find the ANSWER and CHECK

The Problem-Solving Guidelines can be used to solve situational problems.

Situational Problem

You and three friends decide to start a summer business cleaning houses. You each want to save $500 for a trip at the end of the summer. You estimate that you will spend half a day cleaning each house, and you will clean each house once a week. You will need to purchase your own supplies and pay for transportation. You also may want spending money for other things during the summer.

Possible Assumptions

1. You do not have to pay for insurance for your business.
2. You will not hire others to work with you.
3. You each want $50 spending money.
4. You will each be able to work for two months.
5. You can sell your extra supplies at the end of the summer.

Possible Subproblems

1. How much will your expenses be for supplies that are reusable?
2. How much will your expenses be for consumable supplies?
3. How much will you charge per hour?
4. How much will you make for cleaning each house?
5. How much profit will you make for cleaning each house?

How many houses will you need to have for your business, and how much will you charge for cleaning a house?

Chapter 12 Summary and Review

12-1

A **relation** is a set of ordered pairs; a **function** is a relation that assigns to each member of the **domain** (the set of first coordinates) exactly one member of the **range** (the set of second coordinates).

Are the following relations functions?

1. Domain → Range
- $-1 \to 3$
- $-1 \to 4$
- $0 \to 4$
- $1 \to 5$

2. Domain → Range
- $-2 \to 0$
- $5 \to 4$
- $7 \to 1$

Find the indicated outputs for these functions.

3. $f(x) = 3x - 4$; find $f(2)$, $f(0)$, and $f(-1)$

4. $g(t) = |t| - 3$; find $g(3)$, $g(-5)$, and $g(0)$

5. $h(x) = x^3 + 1$; find $h(-2)$, $h(0)$, and $h(-1)$

12-2

To graph a function, find some ordered pairs for the function, and plot the points. If the domain is the set of real numbers, then connect the points to show all the ordered pairs that belong to the function.

Graph each function with the given domain.

6. $f(x) = 2x + 3$ where the domain is $(-2, -1, 0, 1, 2)$

7. $g(x) = -3x$ where the domain is $(-4, -2, 0, 2, 4)$

Graph each function where the domain is the set of real numbers.

8. $g(x) = x + 7$ **9.** $f(x) = x^2 - 3$ **10.** $h(x) = 3|x|$

Which of the following are graphs of functions?

11. 

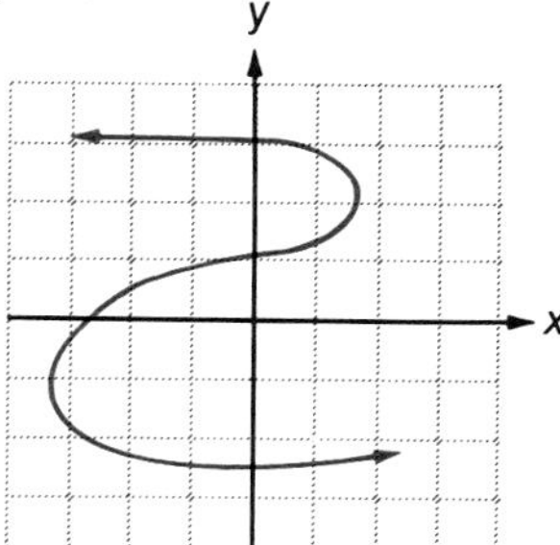

12. 

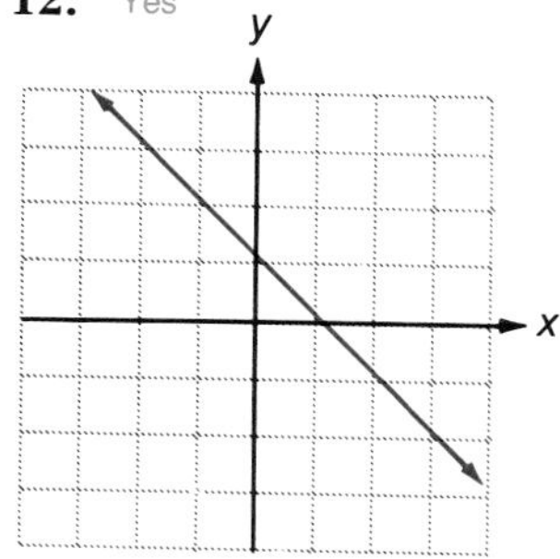

ANSWERS

1. No
2. Yes
3. 2; −4; −7
4. 0; 2; −3
5. −7; 1; 0
6. 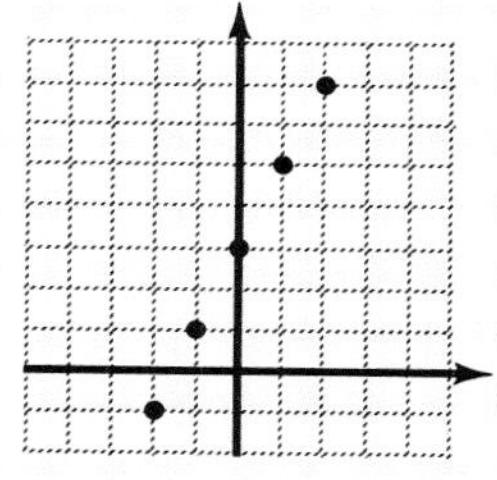
7. 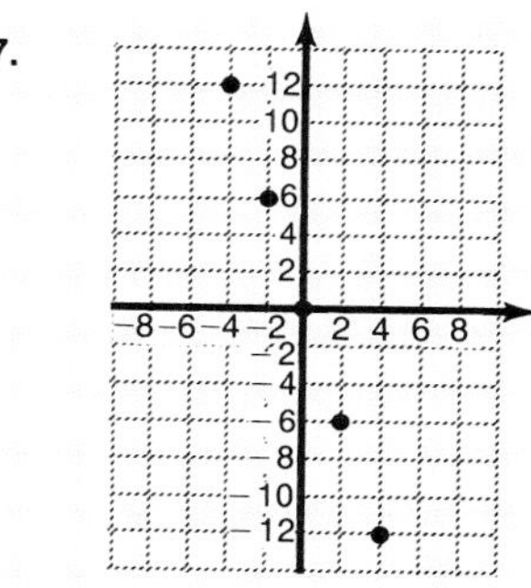

8. 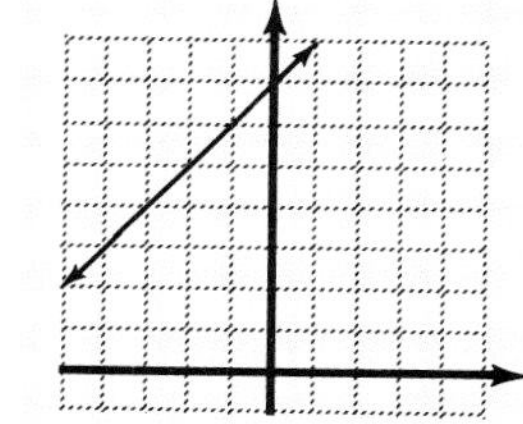
9. 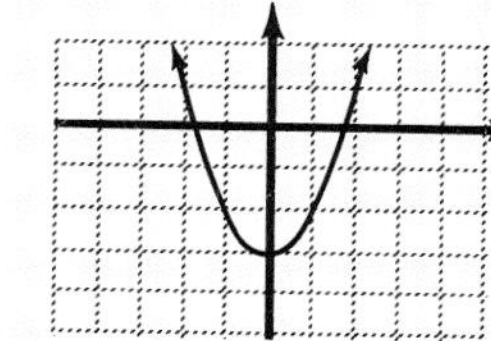
10. 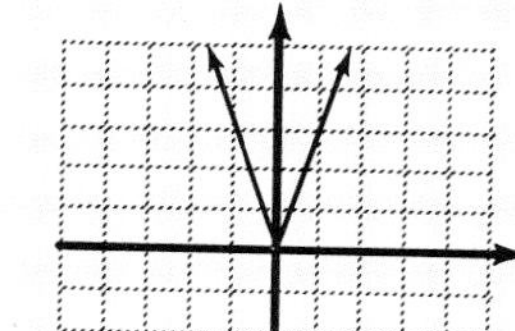

13. $c(m) = 0.35 + 0.25(m - 1)$; \$1.35

14.

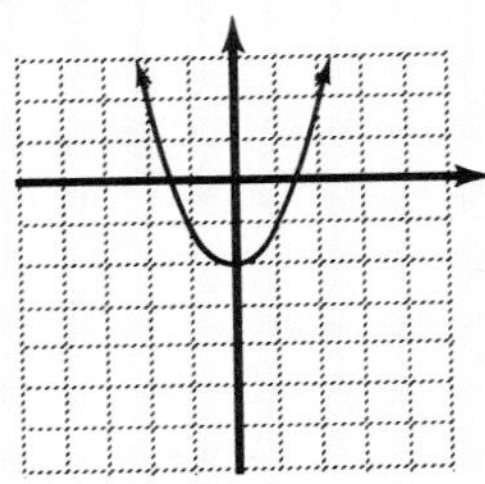

15.

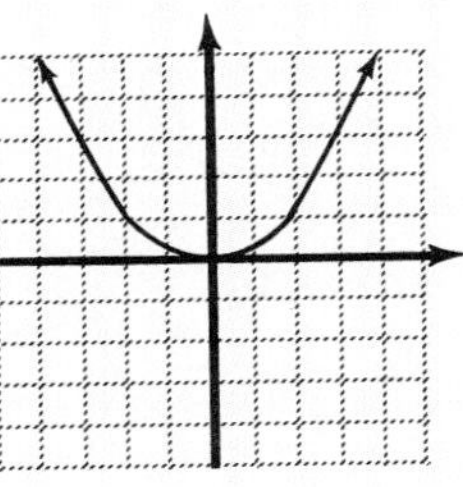

16. $y = 3x$

17. $y = \frac{1}{2}x$

18. \$247.50

19. $y = \frac{30}{x}$

20. $y = \frac{1}{x}$

21. 1 h

12-3

A function that can be described by $y = mx + b$ is a **linear function** and can be written $f(x) = mx + b$. You can use the Problem-Solving Guidelines to solve problems involving linear functions.

Solve.

13. A long-distance phone call from Houston to San Francisco costs \$0.35 for the first minute and \$0.25 for each additional minute. Find the cost of a five-minute call.

12-4

A function that can be described by $y = ax^2 + bx + c$ is a **quadratic function** and can be written $f(x) = ax^2 + bx + c$. If the domain of a quadratic function is the set of real numbers, then the graph of the function is a **parabola.** The x-coordinate of the **vertex,** the maximum or minimum point, is $-\frac{b}{2a}$.

Graph each function.

14. $f(x) = x^2 - 2$

15. $f(x) = \frac{1}{3}x^2$

12-5

An equation of the form $y = kx$, where k is constant, expresses **direct variation.** If one pair of values for x and y is known, substitute in the equation, $y = kx$, to find the value of k.

Find an equation of variation where y varies directly as x. One pair of values is given.

16. $y = 12$ when $x = 4$

17. $y = 4$ when $x = 8$

Solve.

18. A person's paycheck (P) varies directly as the number of hours (h) worked. The pay is \$165 for working 20 hours. Find the pay for 30 hours of work.

12-6

An equation of the form $y = \frac{k}{x}$, where k is constant, expresses **inverse variation.** If one pair of values for x and y is known, substitute in the equation to find k.

Find an equation of variation where y varies inversely as x. One pair of values is given.

19. $y = 5$ when $x = 6$

20. $y = 0.5$ when $x = 2$

Solve.

21. It takes five hours for two washing machines to wash a fixed amount. How long would it take for ten washing machines to wash the same amount of clothes?

12-7

An equation of the form $z = kxy$, where k is a constant, expresses joint variation. An equation of the form $z = \frac{kx}{y}$, where k is a nonzero constant, expresses combined variation.

22. The area of a trapezoid varies jointly as its altitude and the sum of the bases. $A = ka(b_1 + b_2)$. If $A = 120$ when $a = 8$, $b_1 = 12$, and $b_2 = 18$,
    a. find the constant of variation.
    b. find A when $a = 6$, $b_1 = 8$, and $b_2 = 12$.
23. W varies jointly as x and y and inversely as the square of z. If $W = 189$, $x = 28$, $y = 16$, and $z = 8$,
    a. find the constant of variation.
    b. find W when $x = 24$, $y = 4$, and $z = 6$.

Chapter 12 Test

1. $f(x) = \frac{1}{2}x + 1$; find $f(0)$, $f(1)$, and $f(2)$
2. $g(t) = -2|t| + 3$; find $g(-1)$, $g(0)$, and $g(3)$

Which of the following are graphs of functions?

3.
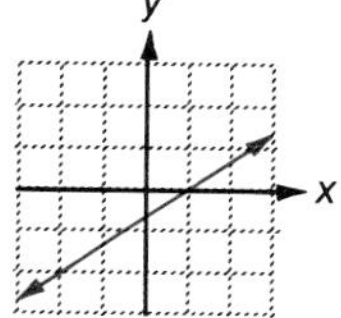

4.
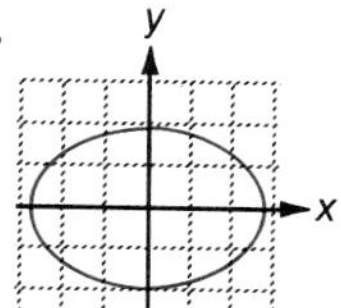

5. Elena rents a car for \$19 per day plus \$0.20 per mile. Compute the cost of a 2-day trip of 310 miles.

Graph.

6. $f(x) = x^2 + 4x + 4$
7. $f(x) = -x^2$
8. Find an equation of variation where y varies directly as x, and $y = 6$ when $x = 3$.
9. Find an equation of variation where y varies inversely with x and $y = 6$ when $x = 2$.
10. It takes 3 hours for 2 cement mixers to mix a certain amount. How long would it take 5 cement mixers to do the job?
11. y varies jointly with x and the square of z. One set of values is $y = 375$ when $x = 3$ and $z = 25$. Find y when $x = 8$ and $z = 6$.
12. x varies jointly with y and z and inversely with m. One set of values is $x = 2$ when $m = 3$, $y = 4$, and $z = 6$. Find x when $y = 7.5$, $m = 3$, and $z = 8$.

22. (a) $k = \frac{1}{2}$ **(b)** $A = 60$

23. (a) $k = 27$ **(b)** $W = 72$

ANSWERS

1. $1; \frac{3}{2}; 2$
2. $1; 3; -3$
3. Yes
4. No
5. \$100
6. 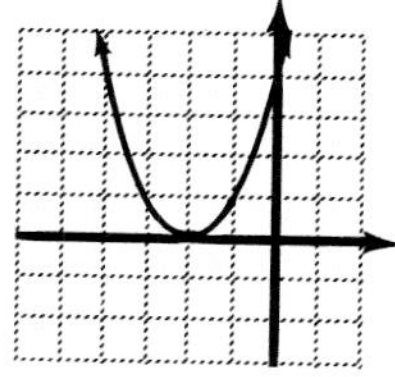
7. 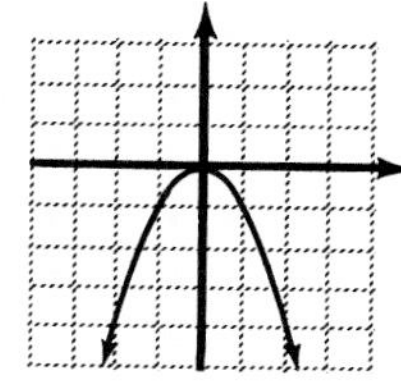
8. $y = 2x$
9. $y = \frac{12}{x}$
10. $1\frac{1}{5}$ h
11. $y = 0.2xz^2$; 57.6
12. $x = \frac{yz}{4m}$; $x = 5$

Test Item Analysis

Item	Lesson
1, 2	12-1
3, 4	12-2
5	12-3
6, 7	12-4
8	12-5
9, 10	12-6
11, 12	12-7

CHAPTER 13

Quadratic Equations

Chapter Overview

Quadratic equations and the quadratic formula are covered in this chapter. Quadratic equations are introduced and the simplest cases are considered first: where $ax^2 + bx = 0$; where the quadratic expression factors; and where $ax^2 = k$. *Completing the Square* is introduced as a method for solving quadratic equations and is used to develop the quadratic formula. The quadratic formula is then used to solve quadratic equations. The discriminant is defined and shown to characterize the solutions of a quadratic equation. Rational equations that reduce to quadratic equations are presented and solved. Equations involving radicals that reduce to quadratic equations are presented and solved. Formulas involving radicals and quadratic expressions are solved for a given variable.

A problem-solving section discusses tactics for solving problems that involve quadratic equations and provides an opportunity for students to use quadratic equations to make predictions. The second situational problem, *Designing a School Picnic,* is presented.

Objectives

13-1 ■ Write a quadratic equation in standard form.
■ Solve an equation of the form $ax^2 + bx = 0$.
■ Solve an equation of the form $ax^2 + bx + c = 0$.

13-2 ■ Solve a quadratic equation of the form $ax^2 = k$.
■ Solve a quadratic equation by factoring one expression into a binomial square.
■ Solve problems using quadratic equations.

13-3 ■ Complete a square for a quadratic equation.
■ Solve a quadratic equation by completing the square.

13-4 ■ Use the quadratic formula to solve quadratic equations.
■ Use discriminants to find the number of solutions for a quadratic equation.

13-5 ■ Solve rational equations involving quadratic equations.

13-6 ■ Solve radical equations involving quadratic equations.
■ Solve formulas for given variables.

13-7 ■ Solve problems involving quadratic equations.

Cooperative Learning Opportunities

Study pairs can be helpful in preventing the slowdown that sometimes accompanies the study of completing the square.

After a thorough explanation and review of the examples for Lesson 13-3, assign students in pairs to do the **Try This** exercises on page 587. Tell them that there are no roles but they should together talk their way through each step of the exercise and agree on the answer. Be sure to review the meaning of the "±" symbol.

Checking solutions with radicals is tedious but with a scientific calculator the process can be accelerated and made instructive. Again working in pairs, each student should watch the other do the check. For example, the solution to **Try This** Exercise f on page 587 can be approximated to 0.68614. When this is entered in the original quadratic the answer is −.038008 E–6. Show students that this number is very close to 0 but not exactly 0 because the replacement value was itself approximate.

Multicultural Note: *The Method of False Position*

The Egyptian papyrus referred to in the **Multicultural Note** for Chapter 2 contains linear and quadratic equations solved by a procedure called the method of false position. You first try any number as the solution. You then set up a proportion in which the answer desired is to the answer obtained as the desired number is to the number used. One papyrus problem, in our terminology, is $x + \frac{1}{4}x = 15$. We try 4 for x and this gives 5. The answer we want is 15 and so the proportion is $\frac{15}{5} = \frac{x}{4}$. The solution $x = 12$ solves the original equation.

The method can also be used in some quadratic equations. Suppose that 2 squares are given with sides x and $\frac{3}{4}x$, and the sum of the areas is 100 sq. in. We begin by trying 4 for x in the equation $x^2 + \frac{3}{4}x^2$, which gives 25. We want 100 as an answer. The value of x^2 must be increased by a factor of 4. This means increasing x by a factor of 2. The value 8 solves the equation.

For more information, see page 68 of **Multiculturalism in Mathematics, Science, and Technology**.

Alternative Assessment and Communication Ideas

Graphical representations of quadratics are shown several times in this chapter and can be used more extensively as a means of assessment. Pointing out natural points of contact among mathematical concepts will help break the barriers that compartmentalize knowledge.

In particular, assign students to solve the quadratics in Exercises 3, 5, 9, 11, and 15 on page 593. Then ask them to work together in groups of 5 to answer the following questions. Each student should answer a different question for each exercise, and 1 paper should be handed in for the group.

(1) Write the function related to this equation.
(2) Does the graph of the function open upward?
(3) Does the graph touch the x-axis in just one point? If so, what is the point?
(4) Does the graph cross the x-axis in two points?
(5) If yes to 4, what are the points?

If students have trouble getting started, suggest that they review page 591.

Investigations and Projects

Students might enjoy devising problems of their own. The student becomes the author, teacher, and test-giver.

For this project, students create number problems to be solved by factoring quadratic equations. Remind students that they may represent "any even number" by $2n$ and "any odd number" by $2n + 1$. Point out also that "the next consecutive even number" may be found by adding 2.

Have students make up number problems using products and sums of natural numbers. They should not multiply more than two numbers. This will result in an equation of degree higher than 2. They may use products, sums of squares, numbers multiplied by factors, and other relationships as long as they are clearly stated. Pairs of students can exchange problems as a challenge.

MANAGING CHAPTER 13

Lesson	PACING CHART (DAYS) 2-Year* A for E	1-Year Minimum	1-Year Regular	1-Year Advanced	Opening Activity	Cooperative Activity	Seat or Group Work
13-1	3	1.5	1.5	1.5	First Five Minutes 13-1: ***FFMTM*** p. 37 or **TE** p. 576; ***Overhead Transparencies*** T28	Critical Thinking 13 ***Enrichment*** p. 31	Try This a–g
13-2	3	1.5	1.5	1.5	First Five Minutes 13-2: ***FFMTM*** p. 37 or **TE** p. 580; ***Overhead Transparencies*** T29	Connections: Geometry: **TE** p. 585	Try This a–j
13-3	2	1	1	1	First Five Minutes 13-3: ***FFMTM*** p. 37 or **TE** p. 586	✂ Manipulative Activity 13: ***Enrichment*** p. 46	Try This a–g
13-4	3	1	1	1	First Five Minutes 13-4: ***FFMTM*** p. 38 or **TE** p. 589; ***Overhead Transparencies*** T30	Problem 73: **SE** p. 594; Calculator Worksheet 28: ***Technology*** p. 30	Try This a–g
13-5	2	0.5	1	1	First Five Minutes 13-5: ***FFMTM*** p. 38 or **TE** p. 595	Problem 34: **SE** p. 596	Try This a–c
13-6	2	1	1	1	First Five Minutes 13-6: ***FFMTM*** p. 38 or **TE** p. 598	Bonus Topic 13: ***Enrichment*** p. 14	Try This a–g
13-7	3	1.5	2	2	First Five Minutes 13-7: ***FFMTM*** p. 38 or **TE** p. 602	Problem Solving: Application: **SE** p. 607; Problem Solving: Situational Problem Solving: **SE** p. 608	Try This a–c
Review	2	1	1	1			
Test	1	1	1	1			
Cum. Review	0	1	0	0			
End-of Year Test	0	1	0	0			

*2-Year Management Guide can be found in *Algebra for Everyone*.

FFMTM: First Five Minutes Transparency Masters

Enrichment	Review/Assess	Reteach	Technology	Lesson
Critical Thinking 13 ***Enrichment*** p. 30	Lesson Quiz: **TE** p. 578		Computer Exploration 10: **SE** p. 721; Worksheet 14: ***Master Grapher*** pp. 54–56, 110–112, or 165–167; Worksheet 14: ***TI-81 Activities*** pp. 51–53	**13-1**
Lesson Enrichment: **TE** p. 582	Mixed Review 25: ***SPMR*** p. 75; Lesson Quiz: **TE** p. 582; Geometry Review 4: ***SPMR*** p. 88			**13-2**
✂ Manipulative Activity 13: ***Enrichment*** p. 46	Lesson Quiz: **TE** p. 587; Quiz 25: ***Assessment*** p. 35	Skills Practice 35: ***SPMR*** p. 43		**13-3**
Lesson Enrichment: **TE** p. 591; College Entrance Exam 4: ***Problem Bank*** pp. 62–66 Teacher Demonstration Lesson 4: ***Master Grapher*** pp. 13–14, 69–70, or 124–125	Mixed Review 25: **SE** p. 708; Lesson Quiz: **TE** p. 592		Approximating Solutions of Quadratic Equations: **SE** p. 592; Calculator Worksheet 28: ***Technology*** p. 30; TI-81 Investigation 3: **SE** pp. 728–729; Worksheet 15: ***Master Grapher*** pp. 57–58, 113–114, or 168–169; Worksheet 15: ***TI-81 Activities*** pp. 55–56	**13-4**
Problem for Programmers: **SE** p. 597	Mixed Review 26: ***SPMR*** p. 76; Lesson Quiz: **TE** p. 595		Problem for Programmers: **SE** p. 597	**13-5**
Bonus Topic 13: ***Enrichment*** p. 14; Looking for Errors 13: ***Enrichment*** p. 62	Lesson Quiz: **TE** p. 599; Quiz 26: ***Assessment*** p. 36		Worksheet 16: ***Master Grapher*** pp. 59–60, 115–116, or 170–171; Worksheet 16: ***TI-81 Activities*** pp. 57–58	**13-6**
Looking for Errors: **SE** p. 601; Problem Solving: Application: **SE** p. 607; Problem Solving: Situational Problem Solving: **SE** p. 608	Mixed Review 26: **SE** p. 709; Lesson Quiz: **TE** p. 605	Skills Practice 36: ***SPMR*** p. 44; Problem Bank 26: ***Problem Bank*** p. 43	Spreadsheet Activity 10: ***Technology*** pp. 55–56; BASIC Computer Project 17: ***Technology*** p. 79	**13-7**
	Summary and Review: **SE** pp. 609–610; Test: **SE** p. 611	Strategy Problem Bank 13: ***Problem Bank*** p. 14		**Review**
	Chapter 13 Exam: ***A for E*** pp. 491–492; Chapter 13 Test: ***Assessment*** pp. 67–68 (min.), 143–148 (reg.), 187–188 (adv.)			**Test**
	Cumulative Review: **SE** pp. 529–533; Strategy Problem Bank 13: ***Problem Bank*** p. 14			**Cum. Review**
	Assessing Strategies 8: ***Assessment*** pp. 209–210; End-of-Year Test: ***Assessment*** pp. 235–240			**End-of Year Test**

SPMR: Skills Practice Mixed Review

The solution to the problem posed on the facing page can be found on page 604.

Ready for Quadratic Equations?

5-10 Multiply.

1. $(x - 5)^2$ $x^2 - 10x + 25$

2. $(3x + 1)^2$ $9x^2 + 6x + 1$

6-8 Solve.

3. $x^2 - 6x = 0$ 0, 6

4. $x^2 - 5x + 6 = 0$ 2, 3

10-6 Solve.

5. $2x + \frac{8}{x} = 8$ 2

6. $\frac{x - 2}{x + 2} = \frac{1}{4}$ $\frac{10}{3}$

11-3 Simplify.

7. $\sqrt{88}$ $2\sqrt{22}$

8. $\sqrt{20}$ $2\sqrt{5}$

9. $\sqrt{44}$ $2\sqrt{11}$

10. $\sqrt{32}$ $4\sqrt{2}$

11-5 Rationalize the denominator.

11. $\sqrt{\frac{7}{3}}$ $\frac{\sqrt{21}}{3}$

12. $\sqrt{\frac{5}{2}}$ $\frac{\sqrt{10}}{2}$

13. $\sqrt{\frac{1}{5}}$ $\frac{\sqrt{5}}{5}$

14. $\sqrt{\frac{7}{8}}$ $\frac{\sqrt{14}}{4}$

12-7 Graph the following quadratic functions.

15. $f(x) = x^2 - 1$

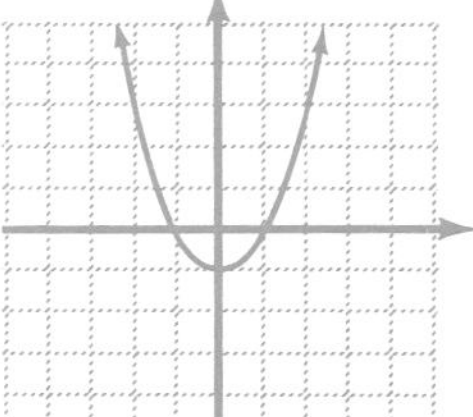

16. $y = -x^2 + 2$

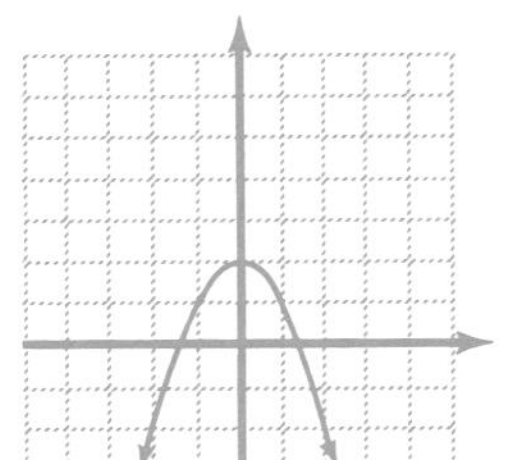

CHAPTER

Quadratic Equations 13

In testing the man powered Daedalus 88, *the craft was able to fly a three-mile course* with *the wind and fly back* against *the wind, in a total time of 25 minutes. If the speed of the wind was three miles per hour, what would be the speed of* Daedalus 88 *in still air?*

13-1

FIRST FIVE MINUTES

1. Solve for x where $(x - 1)(x - 2) = 0$.
   $x = 1$ or $x = 2$

Factor.

2. $x^2 - 3x$
   $x(x - 3)$
3. $6x^2 + 4x$
   $2x(3x + 2)$
4. $x^2 + 6x + 9$
   $(x + 3)^2$
5. $x^2 - x - 6$
   $(x + 2)(x - 3)$
6. $2x^2 + 5x - 3$
   $(2x - 1)(x + 3)$

Standard Form

Point out that in a quadratic equation of the form $ax^2 + bx + c = 0$, b and c can equal zero, but a cannot equal 0. For example, $x^2 = 0$ is a quadratic equation, but $0x^2 + x + 1 = 0$ is not.

See Computer Exploration 10 on p. 721 for using a computer to estimate the solution of a quadratic equation.

Key Questions

- What are a, b, and c in the quadratic equation $5x^2 + 3x + 1 = 0$?
  $a = 5, b = 3, c = 1$
- What are a, b, and c in the quadratic equation $7 + 8x = 9x^2$?
  $a = -9, b = 8, c = 7$ or $a = 9, b = -8, c = -7$
- What are a, b, and c in the quadratic equation $x^2 - x = 0$?
  $a = 1, b = -1, c = 0$

Chalkboard Examples

Write each in standard form and determine a, b, and c.

1. $5x^2 - x = 8$
   $5x^2 - x - 8 = 0$
   $a = 5, b = -1, c = -8$
2. $-7x^2 = 4x$
   $-7x^2 - 4x = 0$
   $a = -7, b = -4, c = 0$

13-1 Introduction to Quadratic Equations

Master Grapher Worksheet 14 can be used with this lesson.

You learned in Chapter 12 that a quadratic function is a function that can be defined by an equation of the form $ax^2 + bx + c = y$ and that the graph of a quadratic function is a parabola when the domain is the set of real numbers.

When $y = 0$ in the quadratic function $ax^2 + bx + c = y$, we have an equation of the form $ax^2 + bx + c = 0$. An equation that can be written in this form is called a **quadratic equation.**

Definition

An equation that can be written in the form $ax^2 + bx + c = 0$, where a, b, and c are real numbers and $a \neq 0$, is a **quadratic equation.**

We can graph the function $y = x^2 - 2x - 3$ as shown at the right. We can locate the points where $y = 0$.

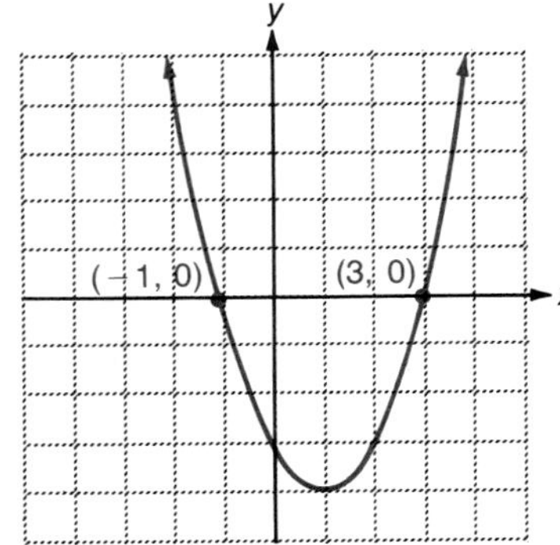

The x-values at these points are -1 and 3 and are the solutions of the quadratic equation $0 = x^2 - 2x - 3$.

Transparency 28 (*T28*) can be used with this illustration.

Standard Form

Objective: Write a quadratic equation in standard form.

Quadratic equations may be written in various forms.

$$4x^2 + 7x = 5 \qquad 3x^2 = 7 \qquad 5x^2 = -4x$$

Work with quadratic equations is usually simplified when a quadratic equation is written in **standard form,** $ax^2 + bx + c = 0$.

EXAMPLES Write in standard form and determine a, b, and c.

1. $4x^2 + 7x = 5$
   Standard form: $4x^2 + 7x - 5 = 0$; $a = 4, b = 7, c = -5$

2. $5x^2 = -4x$
Standard form: $5x^2 + 4x = 0$; $a = 5, b = 4, c = 0$

Try This Write in standard form and determine a, b, and c.

a. $x^2 = 7x$ **b.** $3 - x^2 = 9x$ **c.** $5x^2 = -4$ See Additional Answers.

Equations of the Form $ax^2 + bx = 0$

Objective: Solve an equation of the form $ax^2 + bx = 0$.

When $c = 0$ in the standard form equation $ax^2 + bx + c = 0$, we have an equation of the form $ax^2 + bx = 0$. We can factor this equation and use the principle of zero products to find its solutions.

EXAMPLE 3 Solve.

$$20x^2 - 15x = 0$$
$$5x(4x - 3) = 0 \quad \text{Factoring}$$
$$5x = 0 \text{ or } 4x - 3 = 0 \quad \text{Using the principle of zero products}$$
$$x = 0 \text{ or } x = \frac{3}{4}$$

Check:

$20x^2 - 15x$	$= 0$
$20(0)^2 - 15(0)$	0
$0 - 0$	0
0	0 ✓

$20x^2 - 15x$	$= 0$
$20\left(\frac{3}{4}\right)^2 - 15\left(\frac{3}{4}\right)$	0
$\frac{45}{4} - \frac{45}{4}$	0
0	0 ✓

The solutions are 0 and $\frac{3}{4}$.

A quadratic equation of this type will always have 0 as one solution and a nonzero number as the other solution.

Try This Solve.

d. $3x^2 + 5x = 0$ $\frac{-5}{3}, 0$ **e.** $10x^2 - 6x = 0$ $\frac{3}{5}, 0$

Equations of the Form $ax^2 + bx = 0$

This section reviews the principle of zero products presented in Chapter 6 and begins a series of techniques for solving quadratic equations, culminating with the quadratic formula in Lesson 13-4.

You may want occasionally to show the solutions graphically, as in the introduction to this chapter.

Chalkboard Examples

1. Solve $5x^2 + 7x = 0$.
$x(5x + 7) = 0$
$x = 0$ or $5x + 7 = 0$
$x = 0$ or $x = -\frac{7}{5}$

2. Solve $8x^2 = 2x$.
$8x^2 - 2x = 0$
$2x(4x - 1) = 0$
$2x = 0$ or $4x - 1 = 0$
$x = 0$ or $4x = 1$
$x = 0$ or $x = \frac{1}{4}$

Equations of the Form $ax^2 + bx + c = 0$

Chalkboard Example

1. Solve $x^2 - 4x = x - 6$.
   $x^2 - 5x + 6 = 0$
   $(x - 2)(x - 3) = 0$
   $x = 2$ or $x = 3$

LESSON QUIZ

1. Write in standard form and determine a, b, and c for $5x^2 = 9x + 3$.
   $5x^2 - 9x - 3 = 0$
   $a = 5, b = -9, c = -3$
2. Solve $3x^2 - 2x = 0$.
   $x = 0$ or $x = \frac{2}{3}$
3. Solve $x^2 = 7x - 10$.
   $x = 2$ or $x = 5$

Assignment Guide
Minimum: Day 1: 1–32 e/o, MR
Day 2: 33–48 e/o, assign w. 13-2
Regular: Day 1: 1–48 e/o, MR
Day 2: 49–64 e/o, 65, assign w. 13-2
Advanced: Day 1: 1–48 e/o, MR
Day 2: 49–64 e/o, 65–69, assign w. 13-2

ADDITIONAL ANSWERS

Try This

a. $x^2 - 7x = 0; a = 1, b = -7, c = 0$
b. $x^2 + 9x - 3 = 0; a = 1, b = 9, c = -3$
c. $5x^2 + 0x + 4 = 0; a = 5, b = 0, c = 4$

Exercises

1. $x^2 - 3x + 2 = 0$; $a = 1, b = -3, c = 2$
2. $x^2 - 8x - 5 = 0$; $a = 1, b = -8, c = -5$
3. $2x^2 - 3 = 0$; $a = 2, b = 0, c = -3$
4. $5x^2 - 9 = 0$; $a = 5, b = 0, c = -9$
5. $7x^2 - 4x + 3 = 0$; $a = 7, b = -4, c = 3$
6. $9x^2 - x - 5 = 0$; $a = 9, b = -1, c = -5$
7. $2x^2 - 3x + 5 = 0$; $a = 2, b = -3, c = 5$
8. $x^2 - 2x - 5 = 0$; $a = 1, b = -2; c = -5$
9. $3x^2 - 2x + 8 = 0$; $a = 3, b = -2, c = 8$

Equations of the Form $ax^2 + bx + c = 0$

Objective: Solve an equation of the form $ax^2 + bx + c = 0$.

We can also use the principle of zero products to solve equations of the form $ax^2 + bx + c = 0$, if $ax^2 + bx + c$ can be factored.

EXAMPLE 4 Solve.

$$y^2 - 5y + 6 = 6y - 18$$
$$y^2 - 11y + 24 = 0 \quad \text{Standard form}$$
$$(y - 8)(y - 3) = 0 \quad \text{Factoring}$$
$$y - 8 = 0 \text{ or } y - 3 = 0$$
$$y = 8 \text{ or } y = 3$$

Substitution will show that 8 and 3 check. The solutions are 8 and 3.

Try This Solve.

f. $3x^2 + x - 2 = 0$ $-1, \frac{2}{3}$ **g.** $x^2 + 4x + 8 = 8x + 29$ $7, -3$

13-1 EXERCISES

A

Write each equation in standard form and determine a, b, and c.

1. $x^2 - 3x + 2 = 0$ **2.** $x^2 - 8x - 5 = 0$ **3.** $2x^2 = 3$
4. $5x^2 = 9$ **5.** $7x^2 = 4x - 3$ **6.** $9x^2 = x + 5$
7. $5 = -2x^2 + 3x$ **8.** $2x = x^2 - 5$ **9.** $2x - 1 = 3x^2 + 7$

Solve.

10. $x^2 + 7x = 0$ $0, -7$ **11.** $x^2 + 5x = 0$ $0, -5$ **12.** $3x^2 + 6x = 0$ $0, -2$
13. $4p^2 + 8p = 0$ $0, -2$ **14.** $5x^2 - 2x = 0$ $0, \frac{2}{5}$ **15.** $3n^2 - 7n = 0$ $0, \frac{7}{3}$
16. $4x^2 + 4x = 0$ $0, -1$ **17.** $2t^2 - 2t = 0$ $0, 1$ **18.** $10x^2 - 30x = 0$ $0, 3$
19. $10x^2 - 50x = 0$ $0, 5$ **20.** $55x^2 - 11x = 0$ $0, \frac{1}{5}$ **21.** $33x^2 + 11x = 0$ $0, -\frac{1}{3}$
22. $14x^2 - 3x = 0$ $0, \frac{3}{14}$ **23.** $17x^2 - 8x = 0$ $0, \frac{8}{17}$ **24.** $3x^2 - 81x = 0$ $0, 27$

Solve.

25. $p^2 - 16p + 48 = 0$ $4, 12$ **26.** $x^2 + 8x - 48 = 0$ $4, -12$
27. $x^2 + 7x + 6 = 0$ $-1, -6$ **28.** $x^2 + 6x + 5 = 0$ $-1, -5$
29. $m^2 + 4m - 21 = 0$ $3, -7$ **30.** $x^2 + 7x - 18 = 0$ $2, -9$
31. $t^2 - 9t + 14 = 0$ $2, 7$ **32.** $x^2 - 8x + 15 = 0$ $3, 5$

33. $x^2 + 10x + 25 = 0$ -5

34. $x^2 + 6x + 9 = 0$ -3

35. $x^2 - 2x + 1 = 0$ 1

36. $x^2 - 8x + 16 = 0$ 4

37. $2x^2 - 13x + 15 = 0$ $\frac{3}{2}, 5$

38. $6x^2 + x - 2 = 0$ $-\frac{2}{3}, \frac{1}{2}$

39. $3a^2 - 10a - 8 = 0$ $4, -\frac{2}{3}$

40. $9b^2 - 15b + 4 = 0$ $\frac{4}{3}, \frac{1}{3}$

41. $3x^2 - 7x = 20$ $4, -\frac{5}{3}$

42. $6x^2 - 4x = 10$ $\frac{5}{3}, -1$

43. $2x^2 + 12x = -10$ $-1, -5$

44. $12x^2 - 5x = 2$ $\frac{2}{3}, -\frac{1}{4}$

45. $6x^2 + x - 1 = 0$ $\frac{1}{3}, -\frac{1}{2}$

46. $6x^2 + 13x + 6 = 0$ $-\frac{3}{2}, -\frac{2}{3}$

47. $2x^2 + 3x = 35$ $-5, \frac{7}{2}$

48. $12x^2 + 7x - 12 = 0$ $\frac{3}{4}, -\frac{4}{3}$

B

Solve.

49. $t(t - 5) = 14$

50. $m(3m + 1) = 2$

51. $3y^2 + 8y = 12y + 15$

52. $18 + 2z = z^2 - 5z$

53. $t(9 + t) = 4(2t + 5)$

54. $16(p - 1) = p(p + 8)$

55. $(2x - 3)(x + 1) = 4(2x - 3)$

56. $(3x - 1)(2x + 1) = 3(2x + 1)$

57. $(2m - 1)(m + 3) = -2(m + 4)$

58. $(m + 2)(2m + 3) = (m + 2)^2$

59. $1 = \frac{1}{3}x^2$

60. $x^2 + \sqrt{3}x = 0$

61. $\sqrt{5}y^2 - y = 0$

62. $\sqrt{7}x^2 + \sqrt{3}x = 0$

63. $\sqrt{5}y^2 + y = 0$

64. $\sqrt{3}x^2 - \sqrt{8}x = 0$

65. ***Critical Thinking*** Find a quadratic function, $f(x) = ax^2 + bx + c$, with a line of symmetry of $x = -\frac{3}{8}$ and whose value for c is 7.

Challenge

66. Find an equation of the form $ax^2 + bx = 0$ with solutions 0 and -6.

67. Find an equation of the form $ax^2 + bx + c = 0$ with solutions 4 and $\frac{3}{4}$.

68. Find an equation of the form $ax^2 + bx + c + 0$ with solutions $\frac{2}{5}, -5$.

69. Find an equation of the form $ax^3 + bx^2 + cx = 0$ with solutions $0, \frac{1}{2}$, and -3.

Mixed Review

Determine the replacements for the variables that give real numbers.

70. $\sqrt{5x^2}$ 71. $\sqrt{x - 3}$ 72. $\sqrt{x + 5}$ 73. $\sqrt{3x - 2}$

Factor. 74. $4m^2 - 10m - 6$ 75. $c^2 - c - 90$ 76. $y^2 - 121$

77. $9x^2 + 63x + 54$ 78. $x^2y + 4xy + 4y$

79. $2ab + 2bc + 3ad + 3dc$

Write roster notation for each set. 80. $G = \{x|x \text{ is a positive factor of } 6\}$

81. $H = \{y|y \text{ is a perfect square and } 20 < y < 50\}$

49. $-2, 7$
50. $\frac{2}{3}, -1$
51. $3, -\frac{5}{3}$
52. $-2, 9$
53. $4, -5$
54. 4
55. $\frac{3}{2}, 3$
56. $\frac{4}{3}, -\frac{1}{2}$
57. $-1, -\frac{5}{2}$
58. $-2, -1$
59. $\pm\sqrt{3}$
60. $-\sqrt{3}, 0$
61. $\frac{\sqrt{5}}{5}, 0$
62. $-\frac{\sqrt{21}}{7}, 0$
63. $-\frac{\sqrt{5}}{5}, 0$
64. $\frac{2\sqrt{6}}{3}, 0$
65–69. Answers may vary. Examples are given.
65. $f(x) = 4x^2 + 3x + 7$
66. $x^2 + 6x = 0$
67. $4x^2 - 19x + 12 = 0$
68. $5x^2 + 23x - 10 = 0$
69. $2x^3 + 5x^2 - 3x = 0$

Mixed Review

70. Any value
71. $x \geq 3$
72. $x \geq -5$
73. $x \geq \frac{2}{3}$
74. $2(2m + 1)(m - 3)$
75. $(c + 9)(c - 10)$
76. $(y - 11)(y + 11)$
77. $9(x + 1)(x + 6)$
78. $y(x + 2)^2$
79. $(2b + 3d)(a + c)$
80. $\{1, 2, 3, 6\}$
81. $\{25, 36, 49\}$

13-2

FIRST FIVE MINUTES

1. Write in standard form and identify a, b, and c.
   $9x^2 + 3x = 2x - 1$
   $9x^2 + x + 1 = 0$
   $a = 9, b = 1, c = 1$
2. Solve $7x^2 = 3x$.
   $x(7x - 3) = 0$
   $x = 0$ or $x = \frac{3}{7}$
3. Solve $3x^2 = 9x - 6$.
   $x^2 - 3x + 2 = 0$
   $(x - 1)(x - 2) = 0$
   $x = 1$ or $x = 2$

Equations of the Form $ax^2 = k$

Point out that the form $ax^2 = k$ is a special case of the standard form of a quadratic equation $ax^2 + bx + c = 0$, in which $b = 0$ and $c = -k$.

You may want to show a solution for an equation such as $x^2 - 16 = 0$ using the principle of zero products.

$$x^2 - 16 = 0$$
$$(x - 4)(x + 4) = 0$$
$$x - 4 = 0 \text{ or } x + 4 = 0$$
$$x = 4 \text{ or } x = -4$$

Then solve the same equation using the technique presented in this lesson.

$$x^2 - 16 = 0$$
$$x^2 = 16$$
$$x = \pm\sqrt{16}$$
$$x = \pm 4$$
$$x = 4 \text{ or } x = -4$$

Key Questions

- If $x^2 = 64$, what is x?
  $x = 8$ or $x = -8$
- What are a, b, and c in the equation $5x^2 = 4$?
  $a = 5, b = 0, c = -4$

Chalkboard Examples

Solve.

1. $6x^2 = 24$
   $x^2 = 4$
   $x = \pm 2$
2. $4x^2 - 7 = 0$
   $x^2 = \frac{7}{4}$
   $x = \pm\sqrt{\frac{7}{4}}$
   $x = \pm\frac{\sqrt{7}}{2}$

13-2 More Solving Quadratic Equations

Equations of the Form $ax^2 = k$

Objective: Solve a quadratic equation of the form $ax^2 = k$.

When b, the coefficient of the x-term, is 0 in the quadratic equation $ax^2 + bx + c = 0$, we have an equation of the form $ax^2 = k$. We first solve for x^2 and then find the square roots.

EXAMPLES Solve.

1. $3x^2 = 18$

$x^2 = 6$ Dividing both sides by 3

$x = \pm\sqrt{6}$ Finding the square roots

$x = \sqrt{6}$ or $x = -\sqrt{6}$

Check:

$3x^2$	$= 18$
$3(\sqrt{6})^2$	18
$3(6)$	18
18	18 ✓

$3x^2$	$= 18$
$3(-\sqrt{6})^2$	18
$3(6)$	18
18	18 ✓

The solutions are $\sqrt{6}$ and $-\sqrt{6}$.

2. $-3x^2 + 7 = 0$

$-3x^2 = -7$

$x^2 = \frac{7}{3}$

$x = \pm\sqrt{\frac{7}{3}}$ Finding the square roots

$x = \pm\sqrt{\frac{7}{3}\cdot\frac{3}{3}}$ Rationalizing the denominator

$x = \pm\frac{\sqrt{21}}{3}$

$x = \frac{\sqrt{21}}{3}$ or $x = -\frac{\sqrt{21}}{3}$

The solutions are $\frac{\sqrt{21}}{3}$ and $-\frac{\sqrt{21}}{3}$.

Try This Solve.

a. $2x^2 = 20$ $\pm\sqrt{10}$ **b.** $3y^2 = 5$ $\pm\frac{\sqrt{15}}{3}$ **c.** $4m^2 - 100 = 0$ ± 5
d. $9h^2 + 4 = 4$ 0

Squares of Binomials

Objective: Solve a quadratic equation by factoring one expression into a binomial square.

We can extend the square root method of solution to quadratic equations of the form $(x + a)^2 = k$.

EXAMPLES Solve.

3. $(x - 5)^2 = 9$
$$x - 5 = \pm\sqrt{9}$$
$$x = 5 \pm \sqrt{9}$$
$$x = 5 \pm 3$$
$x = 5 + 3$ or $x = 5 - 3$
$x = 8$ or $x = 2$
The solutions are 8 and 2.

4. $(x + 2)^2 = 7$
$$x + 2 = \pm\sqrt{7}$$
$$x = -2 \pm \sqrt{7}$$
The solutions are $-2 + \sqrt{7}$ and $-2 - \sqrt{7}$.

5. $x^2 + 16x + 64 = 17$
$$(x + 8)^2 = 17$$
$$x + 8 = \pm\sqrt{17}$$
$$x = -8 \pm \sqrt{17}$$
The solutions are $-8 + \sqrt{17}$ and $-8 - \sqrt{17}$.

Try This Solve.

e. $(x - 3)^2 = 16$ **f.** $(x + 3)^2 = 10$ **g.** $(m - 1)^2 = 5$
h. $x^2 - 14x + 49 = 3$ **i.** $z^2 + 22z + 121 = 169$

e. 7, −1
f. $-3 \pm \sqrt{10}$
g. $1 \pm \sqrt{5}$
h. $7 \pm \sqrt{3}$
i. 2, −24

Problem Solving

Objective: Solve problems using quadratic equations.

The sum of the first 6 natural numbers, $1 + 2 + 3 + 4 + 5 + 6$, can be found by making a table and looking for a pattern to complete the table.

n	1	2	3	4	5	6
S	1	3	6	10	15	21

+2 +3 +4 +5 +6

We can find the sum of the first n natural numbers using the formula

$$\frac{n^2 + n}{2} = S$$

where n is the number of consecutive natural numbers and S is their sum.

Squares of Binomials

Stress that an answer such as $5 \pm \sqrt{7}$ is an abbreviation for the two solutions, $5 + \sqrt{7}$ and $5 - \sqrt{7}$. A rational answer such as 5 ± 4 should always be computed and the answer given as 9 and 1.

Chalkboard Examples

Solve.

1. $x + 7 = \pm\sqrt{16}$.
$x + 7 = \pm\sqrt{16}$
$x + 7 = \pm 4$
$x = -7 \pm 4$
$x = -7 + 4$ or $x = -7 - 4$
$x = -3$ or $x = -11$
The solutions are −3 and −11.
2. $(x - 3)^2 = 2$
$x - 3 = \pm\sqrt{2}$
$x = 3 \pm \sqrt{2}$
$x = 3 + \sqrt{2}$ or $x = 3 - \sqrt{2}$
The solutions are $3 + \sqrt{2}$ and $3 - \sqrt{2}$.
3. $x^2 + 10x + 25 = 3$
$(x + 5)^2 = 3$
$x + 5 = \pm\sqrt{3}$
$x = -5 + \sqrt{3}$ or
$x = -5 - \sqrt{3}$
The solutions are $-5 + \sqrt{3}$ and $-5 - \sqrt{3}$.

Problem Solving

Math Point
When the great mathematician Carl Friedrich Gauss was a schoolboy, his teacher gave the class the problem of finding the sum of all the whole numbers from 1 to 100. Young Gauss had the answer almost immediately. He reasoned that there were 50 pairs of numbers and the sum of each pair was 101. Thus, the answer was $50 \cdot 101 = 5050$.

Chalkboard Examples

1. The sum of the first n numbers is 105. What is n?
$\frac{n^2 + n}{2} = 105$
$n^2 + n = 210$
$n^2 + n - 210 = 0$
$(n + 15)(n - 14) = 0$
Since the answer should be positive, n must be 14.

2. \$2000 invested at 8% annual interest rate, compounded annually for two years, will grow to what amount?

$A = P(1 + r)^t$
$= 2000(1 + 0.08)^2$
$= 2000(1.08)^2$
$\approx 2000(1.1664)$
≈ 2332.80

The amount will grow to \$2332.80.

3. \$1000 is invested at annual interest rate r, compounded annually. After two years, the amount grows to \$1210. What is the interest rate r?

$A = P(1 + r)^t$
$1210 = 1000(1 + r)^2$
$1.21 = (1 + r)^2$
$1.1 = 1 + r$
$r = 0.1$

The interest rate is 10 percent.

LESSON ENRICHMENT

1. What is the sum of the numbers from 13 to 92?

$\frac{92^2 + 92}{2} - \frac{13^2 + 13}{2} = 4187$

2. Find $\frac{n^2 + n}{4}$ for $n = 2, 4, 6$, and 8. Then compare with the sum of all even numbers through 2, 4, 6, and 8. Can you write a formula that will find the sum of all even numbers through n?

The sum of the even numbers through n is

$\frac{n^2 + n}{4} + \frac{n}{4}$ or $\frac{n^2 + 2n}{4}$.

LESSON QUIZ

Solve.

1. $25x^2 = 4$

$x = \pm\frac{2}{5}$

2. $(x - 5)^2 = 64$

$x = 13$ or $x = -3$

3. $x^2 - 6x + 9 = 4$

$x = 1$ or $x = 5$

EXAMPLE 6

Suppose 45 square blocks, each the same size, are used to build a staircase like the one shown at the right. How many steps are in the staircase?

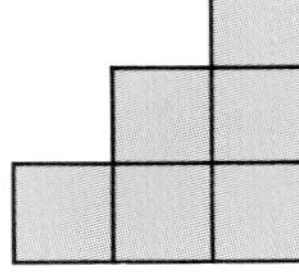

We substitute 45 for S and solve for n.

$$\frac{n^2 + n}{2} = S$$

$$\frac{n^2 + n}{2} = 45 \quad \text{Substituting 45 for } S$$

$$n^2 + n = 45 \cdot 2$$

$$n^2 + n - 90 = 0$$

$$(n + 10)(n - 9) = 0$$

$$n + 10 = 0 \quad \text{or} \quad n - 9 = 0$$

$$n = -10 \quad \text{or} \quad n = 9$$

Since the number of steps cannot be negative, -10 cannot be a solution. But 9 checks, so there are 9 steps in the staircase.

Interest problems may be solved using quadratic equations. If you put money in some savings accounts, you receive interest at the end of the year. At the end of the second year you receive interest on both the original amount and the interest. This is called **compounding** interest annually. An amount of money called principal P is invested at interest rate r. In t years it will grow to the amount A given by

$$A = P(1 + r)^t$$

EXAMPLE 7

Suppose \$256 is invested at interest rate r compounded annually. In two years it grows to \$289. What is the interest rate?

$$A = P(1 + r)^t$$

$$289 = 256(1 + r)^2 \quad \text{Substituting } A = 289,\ P = 256,\ t = 2$$

$$\frac{289}{256} = (1 + r)^2$$

$$\pm\sqrt{\frac{289}{256}} = 1 + r$$

$$-1 \pm \frac{17}{16} = r$$

$$\frac{1}{16} = r \quad \text{or} \quad -\frac{33}{16} = r$$

Since the interest rate cannot be negative, only $\frac{1}{16}$ is a solution. $\frac{1}{16} = 0.0625 = 6.25\%$. The interest rate must be 6.25% for \$256 to grow to \$289 in two years.

Try This

j. Suppose \$400 is invested at interest rate r compounded annually and grows to \$529 in two years. What is the interest rate? 15%

13-2 EXERCISES

A

Solve.

1. $x^2 = 121$
2. $x^2 = 10$
3. $5x^2 = 35$
4. $3x^2 = 30$
5. $5a^2 = 3$
6. $2x^2 = 5$
7. $4t^2 - 25 = 0$
8. $9x^2 - 4 = 0$
9. $3x^2 - 49 = 0$
10. $5x^2 - 16 = 0$
11. $4y^2 - 3 = 9$
12. $49m^2 - 16 = 0$
13. $25n^2 - 36 = 0$
14. $5d^2 - 100 = 0$
15. $100x^2 - 5 = 0$

Solve.

16. $(x - 2)^2 = 49$
17. $(x + 1)^2 = 6$
18. $(d + 3)^2 = 21$
19. $(b - 3)^2 = 6$
20. $(x + 13)^2 = 8$
21. $(x - 13)^2 = 64$
22. $(x - 7)^2 = 12$
23. $(n + 1)^2 = 14$
24. $(x + 9)^2 = 34$
25. $(y + 4)^2 = 36$
26. $(m + 10)^2 = 15$
27. $(y - 5)^2 = 20$

Solve.

28. $x^2 + 2x + 1 = 81$
29. $x^2 - 2x + 1 = 16$
30. $y^2 + 10y + 25 = 121$
31. $y^2 - 12y + 36 = 49$
32. $m^2 + 4m + 4 = 29$
33. $c^2 + 16c + 64 = 15$
34. $x^2 - 6x + 9 = 91$
35. $x^2 - 14x + 49 = 19$
36. $n^2 - 8n + 16 = 15$
37. $d^2 + 24d + 144 = 8$

For Exercises 38–40, use the formula $\frac{n^2 + n}{2} = S$.

38. Find the sum of the first 15 consecutive natural numbers.
39. The sum of the first n natural numbers is 210. What is n?
40. A total of 78 boxes are stacked following the pattern shown. How many boxes are in the bottom row of a stack of 78 boxes?

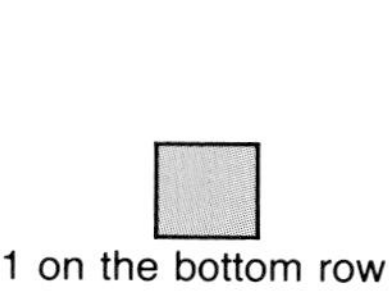
1 on the bottom row

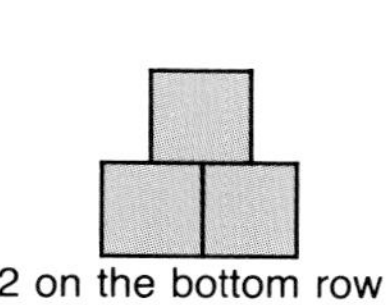
2 on the bottom row

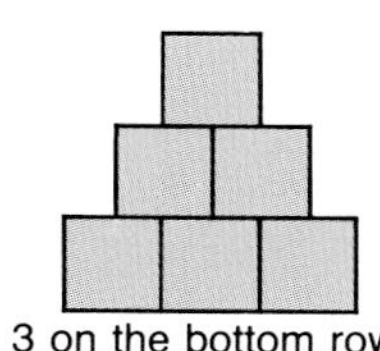
3 on the bottom row

Assignment Guide

Minimum: Day 1: 1–15 e/o, assign w. 13-1
Day 2: 16–48 e/o, MR

Regular: Day 1: 1–27 e/o, MR, assign w. 13-1
Day 2: 28–62 e/o, 63

Advanced: Day 1: 1–27 e/o, MR, assign w. 13-1
Day 2: 28–62 e/o, 63, 64–69 e/o

ADDITIONAL ANSWERS

Exercises

1. ± 11
2. $\pm\sqrt{10}$
3. $\pm\sqrt{7}$
4. $\pm\sqrt{10}$
5. $\pm\frac{\sqrt{15}}{5}$
6. $\pm\frac{\sqrt{10}}{2}$
7. $\pm\frac{5}{2}$
8. $\pm\frac{2}{3}$
9. $\pm\frac{7\sqrt{3}}{3}$
10. $\pm\frac{4\sqrt{5}}{5}$
11. $\pm\sqrt{3}$
12. $\pm\frac{4}{7}$
13. $\pm\frac{6}{5}$
14. $\pm 2\sqrt{5}$
15. $\pm\frac{\sqrt{5}}{10}$
16. $9, -5$
17. $-1 \pm \sqrt{6}$
18. $-3 \pm \sqrt{21}$
19. $3 \pm \sqrt{6}$
20. $-13 \pm 2\sqrt{2}$
21. 21, 5
22. $7 \pm 2\sqrt{3}$
23. $-1 \pm \sqrt{14}$
24. $-9 \pm \sqrt{34}$
25. $2, -10$
26. $-10 \pm \sqrt{15}$
27. $5 \pm 2\sqrt{5}$
28. $-10, 8$
29. $-3, 5$
30. $6, -16$
31. $13, -1$
32. $-2 \pm \sqrt{29}$
33. $-8 \pm \sqrt{15}$
34. $3 \pm \sqrt{91}$
35. $7 \pm \sqrt{19}$
36. $4 \pm \sqrt{15}$
37. $-12 \pm 2\sqrt{2}$
38. 120
39. 20
40. 12

41. 10%
42. 18.75%
43. 8%
44. 6.5%
45. 12.6%
46. 14.75%
47. 5.25%
48. 11%
49. $1, -\frac{1}{3}$
50. $3b, -b$
51. $\frac{1}{3}, -1$
52. $\frac{4}{5}, 0$
53. $\frac{1}{3}(4 \pm \sqrt{2})$
54. $-\frac{13}{8}, \frac{7}{8}$
55. $4, -2$
56. $1, -\frac{5}{2}$
57. ± 9
58. $\pm\sqrt{11}$
59. 7.81 s
60. ~0.3 s
61. $a = 1$
62. $a = 12$
63. $\frac{n^2 + n}{2} = \frac{n(n + 1)}{2} = \frac{n}{2}(n + 1)$
If $n = 6$, $\frac{n}{2} = 3$ and $n + 1 = 7$.
Therefore, $\frac{n^2 + n}{2} = 3(7)$.

The first amount is invested at interest rate r compounded annually and grows to the second amount in two years. Find the interest rate. Use $A = P(1 + r)^t$.

41. $P = \$100, A = \$121$

42. $P = \$2560, A = \$3610$

43. $P = \$6250, A = \$7290$

44. $P = \$400, A = \$453.69$

45. $P = \$1000, A = \$1267.88$

46. $P = \$4000, A = \$5267.03$

47. $P = \$1600, A = \$1772.41$

48. $P = \$1000, A = \$1232.10$

B

Solve for x.

49. $4x^2 - (x + 1)^2 = 0$

50. $(x - b)^2 = 4b^2$

51. $2(3x + 1)^2 = 8$

52. $5(5x - 2)^2 - 7 = 13$

53. $9x^2 - 24x + 16 = 2$

54. $64x^2 + 48x + 9 = 100$

55. $\frac{x - 1}{9} = \frac{1}{x - 1}$

56. $\frac{5}{x + 4} - \frac{3}{x - 2} = 4$

57. $\frac{x}{9} = \frac{36}{4x}$

58. $\frac{4}{x^2 - 7} = 1$

When an object is dropped or thrown downward with an initial velocity (v_0), the distance (d) in meters the object travels in t seconds is given by the formula $d = 5t^2 + v_0t$.

59. The Texas Commerce Center in Houston is 305 m high. How long would it take an object dropped from the top to reach the ground?

60. Two of the tallest buildings in San Francisco are the Transamerica Pyramid (260 m) and the Bank of America (237 m). How much longer would it take an object dropped from the Transamerica building to reach the ground than it would take for the same object to reach the ground from the top of the Bank of America?

61. The triangle shown is a right triangle. Use the Pythagorean theorem to find the missing length, a.

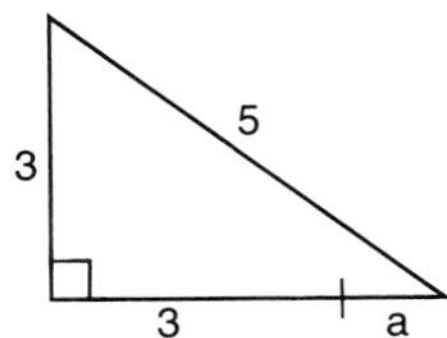

62. The triangle shown is a right triangle. Use the Pythagorean theorem to find the value of a.

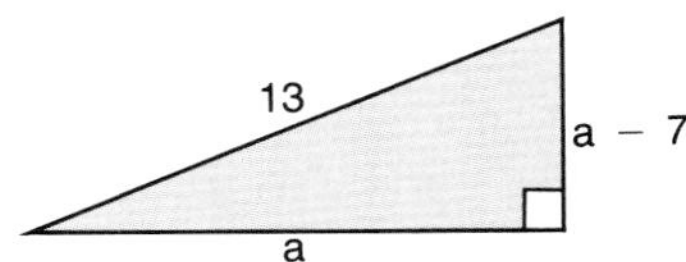

63. ***Critical Thinking*** The sum of the first 6 natural numbers can be found by adding $(1 + 6) + (2 + 5) + (3 + 4)$, which simplifies to 3(7) or 21. Compare this to the formula $\frac{n^2 + n}{2}$. (Hint: $\frac{n^2 + n}{2} = \frac{n(n + 1)}{2}$.)

Challenge

64. For \$2000 to double itself in two years, what would the interest rate have to be? $2P = P(1 + r)^2$, $(1 + r)^2 = 2$, $r = \sqrt{2} - 1 = 0.4142$ or 41.42%

65. In two years you want to have \$3000. How much do you need to invest now if you can get an interest rate of 5.75% compounded annually? \$2682.63

66. Solve $y^4 - 4y^2 + 4 = 0$. (Hint: Let $x = y^2$. Solve for x, then solve for y after finding x.) $x = 2$, $y = \pm\sqrt{2}$

67. The amount of \$1000 is invested at a quarterly interest rate of 2% compounded quarterly. What is the total amount in the account at the end of two years?

68. The amount of \$2000 is invested at an annual interest rate of 12% compounded quarterly. What is the total amount in the account at the end of two years? (Hint: First calculate the quarterly interest rate.)

69. Write a formula relating amount A to principal P invested at rate r for t years compounded q times per year.

Mixed Review

Graph each function. **70.** $f(x) = x^2 - 3$ **71.** $g(x) = 3 - x^2$

Divide and simplify. **72.** $\frac{\sqrt{10}}{\sqrt{5}}$ **73.** $\frac{\sqrt{45y^3}}{\sqrt{5y}}$ **74.** $\frac{\sqrt{27a^2}}{\sqrt{9a^2}}$ **75.** $\frac{\sqrt{16}}{\sqrt{3}}$

Find the indicated outputs for these functions. **76.** $f(t) = 2t^2 - 4t + 1$; find $f(-2)$, $f(1)$, and $f(3)$. **77.** $g(x) = |x| - 5$; find $g(-7)$, $g(-2)$, and $g(1)$. **78.** $h(s) = s^3 - 5$; find $h(-3)$, $h(1)$, and $h(3)$. **79.** $f(x) = x^4 + 2$; find $f(-2)$, $f(0)$, and $f(3)$.

CONNECTIONS: GEOMETRY (T29)

A **diagonal** of a polygon is a line segment that connects two nonadjacent vertices. The diagrams below show the number of diagonals in several polygons.

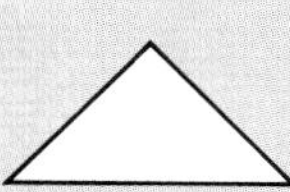

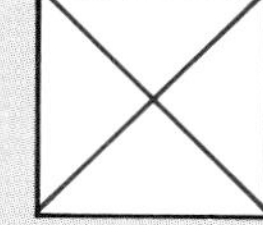

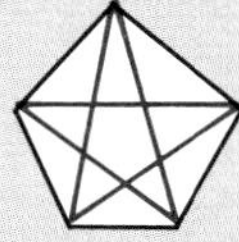

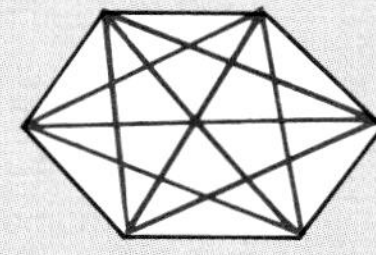

In general, the number of diagonals, d, of a polygon of n sides is given by

$$d = \frac{n^2 - 3n}{2}$$

Suppose we know that a polygon has 27 diagonals. How many sides does it have? 9

67. \$1171.66 **68.** \$2533.54

69. $A = P\left(1 + \frac{r}{q}\right)^{qt}$

Mixed Review

70.

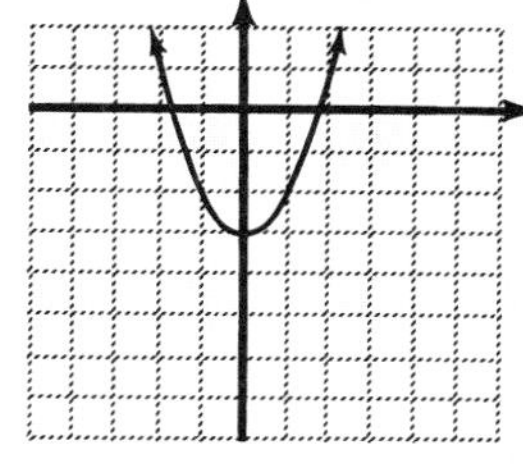

71.

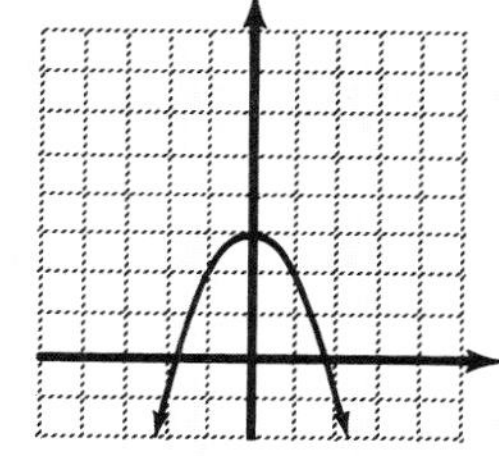

72. $\sqrt{2}$ **73.** $3|y|$

74. $\sqrt{3}$ **75.** $\frac{4\sqrt{3}}{3}$

76. 17, −1, 7 **77.** 2, −3, −4

78. 18, 2, 83 **79.** −32, −4, 22

Connections: Geometry

You may want to review some of the terminology used here.

Line segment—a set of points containing two points and all the points between them in a line.

Vertex—the point at which two sides intersect. (pl. vertices)

Nonadjacent vertices—two vertices that do not share a common side.

13-3

FIRST FIVE MINUTES

Solve.

1. $5x^2 = 20$
   $x^2 = 4$
   $x = \pm 2$
2. $(x - 1)^2 = 16$
   $x - 1 = \pm 4$
   $x = 1 \pm 4$
   $x = 5$ or $x = -3$
3. $x^2 - 10x + 25 = 81$
   $(x - 5)^2 = 81$
   $x - 5 = \pm 9$
   $x = 5 \pm 9$
   $x = 14$ or $x = -4$

Completing the Square

Emphasize that the expression after completing the square is not equivalent to the original expression.

Key Questions

- For what value of c is $x^2 + 2x + c$ a perfect square?
  1
- For what value of c is $x^2 + 6x + c$ a perfect square?
  9

Chalkboard Examples

1. Complete the square.
   $x^2 + 18x$
   $\left(\frac{18}{2}\right)^2 = 81$
   $x^2 + 18x + 81 = (x + 9)^2$
2. Complete the square.
   $x^2 - 3x$
   $\left(-\frac{3}{2}\right)^2 = \frac{9}{4}$
   $x^2 - 3x + \frac{9}{4} = \left(x - \frac{3}{2}\right)^2$

13-3 Solving by Completing the Square

Completing the Square

Objective: Complete a square for a quadratic equation.

We have seen that a quadratic equation of the form $(x + h)^2 = d$ can be solved by finding the square roots of both sides. Thus if we can write a quadratic equation in this form, we can solve as before.

In the illustration below, look at the relationship between the constant in the binomial and the coefficients in the trinomial square.

$$(x + 3)^2 = x^2 + 2(3)x + 9$$
$$= x^2 + 6x + 9$$
$$\frac{6}{2} = 3 \rightarrow 3^2$$

This suggests a process for changing an expression like $x^2 + 10x$ to a trinomial square of the form $x^2 + 10x + c$. The process is called **completing the square.**

$$x^2 + 10x$$
$$\downarrow$$
$$\frac{10}{2} = 5 \qquad \text{Taking half the } x\text{-coefficient}$$
$$\downarrow$$
$$5^2 = 25 \qquad \text{Squaring}$$
$$\downarrow$$
$$x^2 + 10x + 25 \qquad \text{Adding 25 to complete the square}$$

The trinomial $x^2 + 10x + 25$ is the square of $x + 5$.

EXAMPLE 1 Complete the square.

$$x^2 - 5x$$
$$\downarrow$$
$$\left(\frac{-5}{2}\right)^2 = \frac{25}{4}$$
$$\downarrow$$
$$x^2 - 5x + \frac{25}{4}$$

The trinomial $x^2 - 5x + \frac{25}{4}$ is the square of $x - \frac{5}{2}$.

Try This Complete the square.

a. $x^2 - 8x$ **b.** $x^2 + 12x$ **c.** $y^2 + 7y$ **d.** $m^2 - 3m$

a. $x^2 - 8x + 16 = (x - 4)^2$
b. $x^2 + 12x + 36 = (x + 6)^2$
c. $y^2 + 7y + \frac{49}{4} = \left(y + \frac{7}{2}\right)^2$
d. $m^2 - 3m + \frac{9}{4} = \left(m - \frac{3}{2}\right)^2$

Solving Quadratic Equations

Objective: Solve a quadratic equation by completing the square.

We can use the technique of completing the square to solve quadratic equations. Recall that the addition property allows us to add a number to both sides of the equation.

EXAMPLE 2 Solve by completing the square.

$$x^2 - 4x - 7 = 0$$
$$x^2 - 4x = 7 \quad \text{Adding 7 to both sides}$$
$$x^2 - 4x + 4 = 7 + 4 \quad \text{Adding 4 to both sides to complete the square}$$
$$(x - 2)^2 = 11$$
$$x - 2 = \pm\sqrt{11}$$
$$x = 2 \pm \sqrt{11}$$

The solutions are $2 + \sqrt{11}$ and $2 - \sqrt{11}$.

To use the technique of completing the square to solve a quadratic equation, the coefficient of the leading term (the second-degree term) must be 1. If the leading coefficient is not 1, we can use the multiplication property to make it 1.

EXAMPLE 3 Solve by completing the square.

$$2x^2 - 3x - 1 = 0$$
$$x^2 - \frac{3}{2}x - \frac{1}{2} = 0 \quad \text{Multiplying by } \tfrac{1}{2} \text{ to make the } x^2\text{-coefficient 1}$$
$$x^2 - \frac{3}{2}x = \frac{1}{2}$$
$$x^2 - \frac{3}{2}x + \frac{9}{16} = \frac{1}{2} + \frac{9}{16} \quad \text{Adding } \left(-\tfrac{3}{4}\right)^2 \text{ to both sides}$$
$$\left(x - \frac{3}{4}\right)^2 = \frac{8}{16} + \frac{9}{16}$$
$$\left(x - \frac{3}{4}\right)^2 = \frac{17}{16}$$
$$x - \frac{3}{4} = \pm\sqrt{\frac{17}{16}} = \pm\frac{\sqrt{17}}{4}$$
$$x = \frac{3}{4} \pm \frac{\sqrt{17}}{4} = \frac{3 \pm \sqrt{17}}{4}$$

The solutions are $\frac{3 + \sqrt{17}}{4}$ and $\frac{3 - \sqrt{17}}{4}$.

Try This Solve by completing the square.

e. $x^2 + 8x + 12 = 0$ **f.** $2x^2 + 3x - 3 = 0$ **g.** $3x^2 - 2x - 3 = 0$

e. $-2, -6$
f. $\frac{-3 \pm \sqrt{33}}{4}$
g. $\frac{1 \pm \sqrt{10}}{3}$

Solving Quadratic Equations

Solving quadratic equations by completing the square can be difficult for some students, and it is often forgotten by both teachers and students once the quadratic formula has been presented. Note, however, that this technique for solving quadratic equations is the basis for the quadratic formula.

Chalkboard Examples

1. Solve by completing the square.
$x^2 - 6x + 4 = 0$
$x^2 - 6x = -4$
$x^2 - 6x + 9 = 5$
$(x - 3)^2 = 5$
$x - 3 = \pm\sqrt{5}$
$x = 3 \pm \sqrt{5}$
The solutions are
$x = 3 + \sqrt{5}$ or $3 - \sqrt{5}$.
2. Solve by completing the square.
$3x^2 - 12x + 1 = 0$
$x^2 - 4x + \frac{1}{3} = 0$
$x^2 - 4x = -\frac{1}{3}$
$x^2 - 4x + 4 = 4 - \frac{1}{3}$
$(x - 2)^2 = \frac{11}{3}$
$x - 2 = \pm\sqrt{\frac{11}{3}}$
$x = 2 \pm \sqrt{\frac{11}{3}}$
$x = 2 \pm \frac{\sqrt{33}}{3}$

LESSON QUIZ

Solve by completing the square.

1. $x^2 - 8x = 3$
$x = 4 \pm \sqrt{19}$
2. $2x^2 - 4x + 1 = 0$
$x = 1 \pm \frac{\sqrt{2}}{2}$

Assignment Guide
Minimum: 1–29 e/o, MR

Regular: 1–35 e/o, 36, MR

Advanced: 1–35 e/o, 36, 37–42 e/o, MR

ADDITIONAL ANSWERS

Exercises

1. $x^2 - 6x + 9$
2. $y^2 + 8y + 16$
3. $m^2 + 7m + \frac{49}{4}$
4. $t^2 - 5t + \frac{25}{4}$
5. $x^2 + 4x + 4$
6. $n^2 - 12n + 36$
7. $z^2 - 20z + 100$
8. $y^2 + 9y + \frac{81}{4}$
9. $x^2 + 15x + \frac{225}{4}$
10. $-2, 8$
11. $-5, -3$
12. $-21, -1$
13. $-15, 1$
14. $1 \pm \sqrt{6}$
15. $2 \pm \sqrt{15}$
16. $11 \pm \sqrt{19}$
17. $9 \pm \sqrt{7}$
18. $-5 \pm \sqrt{29}$
19. $5 \pm \sqrt{29}$
20. $\frac{7 \pm \sqrt{57}}{2}$
21. $\frac{-7 \pm \sqrt{57}}{2}$
22. $-7, 4$
23. $-4, 7$
24. $\frac{-3 \pm \sqrt{145}}{4}$
25. $\frac{3 \pm \sqrt{17}}{4}$
26. $\frac{-2 \pm \sqrt{7}}{3}$
27. $\frac{2 \pm \sqrt{13}}{3}$
28. $-\frac{1}{2}, 5$
29. $-\frac{3}{2}, 4$
30. $\pm 12x$
31. $\pm 2x\sqrt{55}$
32. $\pm 16x\sqrt{2}$
33. $\pm 16x$
34. $\pm 2x\sqrt{c}$
35. $\pm 2x\sqrt{ac}$
36. $\frac{-b \pm \sqrt{b^2 - 4ac}}{2a}$; $a \neq 0$, $b^2 \geq 4ac$
37. $3a, -2a$
38. $-2b \pm \sqrt{2b(2b - 1)}$
39. $c + 1, -c$
40. $\frac{b \pm \sqrt{b^2 - 12}}{6}$
41. $\frac{-m \pm \sqrt{m^2 - 4nk}}{2k}$
42. $\frac{1 \pm \sqrt{1 - c^2}}{b}$

Mixed Review

43. $y = \frac{11}{4}x$
44. $y = 2x$
45. Irrational
46. Rational
47. Rational
48. 11
49. No real-number solution

13-3 EXERCISES

A

Complete the square.

1. $x^2 - 6x$
2. $y^2 + 8y$
3. $m^2 + 7m$
4. $t^2 - 5t$
5. $x^2 + 4x$
6. $n^2 - 12n$
7. $z^2 - 20z$
8. $y^2 + 9y$
9. $x^2 + 15x$

Solve by completing the square.

10. $x^2 - 6x - 16 = 0$
11. $m^2 + 8m + 15 = 0$
12. $x^2 + 22x + 21 = 0$
13. $x^2 + 14x - 15 = 0$
14. $x^2 - 2x - 5 = 0$
15. $x^2 - 4x - 11 = 0$
16. $n^2 - 22n + 102 = 0$
17. $x^2 - 18x + 74 = 0$
18. $x^2 + 10x - 4 = 0$
19. $x^2 - 10x - 4 = 0$
20. $n^2 - 7n - 2 = 0$
21. $t^2 + 7t - 2 = 0$
22. $x^2 + 3x - 28 = 0$
23. $x^2 - 3x - 28 = 0$
24. $2x^2 + 3x - 17 = 0$
25. $2r^2 - 3r - 1 = 0$
26. $3x^2 + 4x - 1 = 0$
27. $3x^2 - 4x - 3 = 0$
28. $2x^2 - 9x - 5 = 0$
29. $2x^2 - 5x - 12 = 0$

B

Complete the square.

30. $x^2 - ax$
31. $x^2 - (2b - 4)x$
32. $4x^2 + 20x$
33. $4x^2 + ? + 16$
34. $x^2 + ? + c$
35. $ax^2 + ? + c$
36. ***Critical Thinking*** Solve $ax^2 + bx + c = 0$ by completing the square. Express your answer in terms of a, b, and c. If the equation has real-number solutions, what restrictions are there on a, b, and c?

Challenge

Solve for x by completing the square.

37. $x^2 - ax - 6a^2 = 0$
38. $x^2 + 4bx + 2b = 0$
39. $x^2 - x - c^2 - c = 0$
40. $3x^2 - bx + 1 = 0$
41. $kx^2 + mx + n = 0$
42. $b^2x^2 - 2bx + c^2 = 0$

Mixed Review

Find an equation of variation where y varies directly as x, and the following are true. **43.** $y = 11$ when $x = 4$ **44.** $y = 16$ when $x = 8$

Identify as rational or irrational. **45.** $\sqrt{15}$ **46.** $\sqrt{225}$ **47.** $\sqrt{144}$

Solve. **48.** $\sqrt{2x + 3} = 5$ **49.** $-\sqrt{4x} = 4$

13-4 The Quadratic Formula

Master Grapher Worksheet 15 can be used with this lesson.

TI-81 Investigation 3 (page 728) can be used with this lesson.

Using the Quadratic Formula

Objective: Use the quadratic formula to solve quadratic equations.

Each time you solve quadratic equations by completing the square you follow the same steps. By looking at these steps we can find a formula for solving them.

Solve $ax^2 + bx + c = 0, a \neq 0$, for x.

We solve by completing the square.

$$x^2 + \frac{b}{a}x + \frac{c}{a} = 0 \qquad \text{Multiplying by } \frac{1}{a}$$

$$x^2 + \frac{b}{a}x = -\frac{c}{a} \qquad \text{Adding } -\frac{c}{a}$$

Half of $\frac{b}{a}$ is $\frac{b}{2a}$. The square is $\frac{b^2}{4a^2}$. We add $\frac{b^2}{4a^2}$ to both sides.

$$x^2 + \frac{b}{a}x + \frac{b^2}{4a^2} = -\frac{c}{a} + \frac{b^2}{4a^2}$$

$$\left(x + \frac{b}{2a}\right)^2 = \frac{b^2 - 4ac}{4a^2}$$

$$x + \frac{b}{2a} = \pm\sqrt{\frac{b^2 - 4ac}{4a^2}}$$

$$x = -\frac{b}{2a} \pm \frac{\sqrt{b^2 - 4ac}}{2a}$$

$$x = -\frac{b \pm \sqrt{b^2 - 4ac}}{2a}$$

$$x = \frac{-b + \sqrt{b^2 - 4ac}}{2a} \quad \text{or} \quad x = \frac{-b - \sqrt{b^2 - 4ac}}{2a}$$

Quadratic Formula

If $ax^2 + bx + c = 0, a \neq 0$, then

$$x = \frac{-b \pm \sqrt{b^2 - 4ac}}{2a}$$

gives the solutions of the quadratic equation.

13-4

FIRST FIVE MINUTES

Solve by completing the square.

1. $x^2 - 10x + 23 = 0$
$x^2 - 10x + 25 = 2$
$(x - 5)^2 = 2$
$x - 5 = \pm\sqrt{2}$
$x = 5 \pm \sqrt{2}$
2. $5x^2 - 10x - 10 = 0$
$x^2 - 2x - 2 = 0$
$x^2 - 2x + 1 = 3$
$(x - 1)^2 = 3$
$x - 1 = \pm\sqrt{3}$
$x = 1 \pm \sqrt{3}$

Using the Quadratic Formula

The quadratic formula is developed and used in this lesson. Note that the formula is obtained by completing the square of the general quadratic equation $ax^2 + bx + c = 0$.

Point out that the quadratic formula can be used to solve any of the special cases that have been presented. You may want to illustrate this using equations from previous lessons. The quadratic formula, however, is best used when the other methods cannot be used.

You may want students to check their solutions. Checking a radical solution can be a good review of radicals. When checking approximate solutions, students should realize that the answers will not check exactly.

Math Point

The quadratic formula is used to solve second-degree equations. We can use algebraic formulas to solve equations of up to fifth degree. Mathematicians tried for 300 years to solve higher-degree equations until Niels Abel, at the age of 22, showed that no formula can be derived that can solve all fifth-degree equations. Evariste Galois then showed that this is true of all equations of more than fourth degree. When Galois was 21, he wrote in one night the basis for a new theory of solving equations. He was killed in a duel the next day.

Key Questions

- What do you add to complete the square for $x^2 + bx$?
  $\left(\frac{b}{2}\right)^2$
- What do you add to complete the square for $x^2 + \frac{b}{a}x$?
  $\left(\frac{b}{2a}\right)^2$

Chalkboard Examples

1. Solve using the quadratic formula.
   $3x^2 - 7x + 2 = 0$
   $a = 3, b = -7, c = 2$
   $x = \frac{7 \pm \sqrt{7^2 - 4 \cdot 3 \cdot 2}}{2 \cdot 3}$
   $= \frac{7 \pm \sqrt{25}}{6}$
   $= \frac{7 \pm 5}{6}$
   $x = 2$ or $x = \frac{1}{3}$
2. Solve using the quadratic formula.
   $-x^2 + x + 1 = 0$
   $a = -1, b = 1, c = 1$
   $x = \frac{-1 \pm \sqrt{1 - 4 \cdot (-1) \cdot 1}}{2 \cdot (-1)}$
   $= \frac{-1 \pm \sqrt{5}}{-2}$
   $x = \frac{1 - \sqrt{5}}{2}$ or $x = \frac{1 + \sqrt{5}}{2}$

EXAMPLE 1 Solve $5x^2 - 8x = -3$ using the quadratic formula.

First find standard form and determine a, b, and c.

$5x^2 - 8x + 3 = 0$ Standard form
$a = 5, b = -8, c = 3$

Then use the quadratic formula.

$$x = \frac{-b \pm \sqrt{b^2 - 4ac}}{2a}$$

$$x = \frac{-(-8) \pm \sqrt{(-8)^2 - 4 \cdot 5 \cdot 3}}{2 \cdot 5}$$ Substituting for a, b, and c

$$x = \frac{8 \pm \sqrt{64 - 60}}{10}$$ Simplifying the radicand

$$x = \frac{8 \pm \sqrt{4}}{10} = \frac{8 \pm 2}{10}$$

$$x = \frac{8 + 2}{10} \quad \text{or} \quad x = \frac{8 - 2}{10}$$

$$x = \frac{10}{10} = 1 \quad \text{or} \quad x = \frac{6}{10} = \frac{3}{5}$$

The solutions are 1 and $\frac{3}{5}$.

Try This Solve using the quadratic formula.

a. $2x^2 = 4 - 7x$ $\frac{1}{2}, -4$ **b.** $3m^2 - 8 = 10m$ $4, -\frac{2}{3}$

EXAMPLE 2 Solve $3x^2 = 7 - 2x$ using the quadratic formula.

Approximate the solutions to the nearest tenth.

$3x^2 + 2x - 7 = 0$ Standard form
$a = 3, b = 2, c = -7$

$$x = \frac{-2 \pm \sqrt{88}}{6}$$ Substituting into the quadratic formula

$$x = \frac{-2 \pm 2\sqrt{22}}{6}$$

$$x = \frac{-1 \pm \sqrt{22}}{3}$$

The solutions are $\frac{-1 + \sqrt{22}}{3}$ and $\frac{-1 - \sqrt{22}}{3}$.

Substituting 4.690 for $\sqrt{22}$, we find the solutions are $\frac{-1 + 4.690}{3} = 1.2$ and $\frac{-1 - 4.690}{3} = -1.9$, each to the nearest tenth.

Try This Solve using the quadratic formula. Approximate the solutions to the nearest tenth.

c. $2x^2 - 4x = 5$ 2.9, −0.9 **d.** $x^2 + 5x = -3$ −0.7, −4.3

Discriminant

Objective: Use discriminants to find the number of solutions for a quadratic equation.

The quadratic equations you have solved so far have had two real-number solutions. Some quadratic equations have one or no real-number solutions. The expression under the radical in the quadratic formula, $b^2 - 4ac$, is called the **discriminant**. We can use the discriminant to determine the number of real-number solutions there are for the quadratic equation.

This chart illustrates the three possible cases.

Solutions to $0 = ax^2 + bx + c$	Discriminant $b^2 - 4ac$	Graph of the Function
$0 = x^2 + 2x - 3$ $x = \frac{-2 \pm \sqrt{16}}{2}$ $x = 1$ or $x = -3$ 2 real-number solutions	$2^2 - 4(1)(-3) = 16$	$y = x^2 + 2x - 3$
$0 = x^2 + 4x + 4$ $x = \frac{-4 \pm \sqrt{0}}{2}$ $x = -2$ 1 real-number solution	$4^2 - 4(1)(4) = 0$	$y = x^2 + 4x + 4$
$0 = x^2 + x + 5$ $x = \frac{-1 \pm \sqrt{-19}}{2}$ 0 real-number solutions	$1^2 - 4(1)(5) = -19$	$y = x^2 + x + 5$

When the value of the discriminant is positive, there are two real-number solutions. When the discriminant is 0, there is one real-number solution. When the discriminant is negative, there are no real-number solutions.

EXAMPLES Find the value of the discriminant to determine the number of real-number solutions.

3. $x^2 - x + 2 = 0$
$b^2 - 4ac = (-1)^2 - 4 \cdot 1 \cdot 2 = -7$
Since the discriminant is negative, there are no real-number solutions.

Discriminant (T30)

Note that the y-coordinate of the point where the graph crosses the x-axis is 0. Thus, this is where the function $ax^2 + bx + c$ equals 0. The x-coordinate of any point where the graph crosses the x-axis is, therefore, a solution to this quadratic equation. Point out that the graph crosses the x-axis twice when there are two real-number solutions, the graph crosses the x-axis once when there is one real-number solution, and the graph does not cross the x-axis at all when there are no real-number solutions.

Chalkboard Example

1. Find the discriminant and determine the nature of the solutions for the quadratic equation.
$4x^2 - 7x + 2 = 0$
$b^2 - 4ac = 49 - 4 \cdot 4 \cdot 2 = 17$
Since the discriminant is positive, there are two real-number solutions.

LESSON ENRICHMENT

Using the quadratic formula to solve a particular quadratic equation yields $x = \frac{1 \pm \sqrt{55}}{6}$. Find the original equation.

$\left(x - \frac{1 + \sqrt{55}}{6}\right)\left(x - \frac{1 - \sqrt{55}}{6}\right)$

$= x^2 - \frac{1 + \sqrt{55}}{6}x - \frac{1 - \sqrt{55}}{6}x + \left(\frac{1 + \sqrt{55}}{6}\right)\left(\frac{1 - \sqrt{55}}{6}\right)$

$= x^2 - \frac{1}{3}x - \frac{3}{2}$ or $6x^2 - 2x - 9$

Remind students that the fraction bar is a grouping symbol and that they must complete the operations above and below before dividing. You may wish to have students use a calculator for Exercises 35–50.

LESSON QUIZ

Solve using the quadratic formula.

1. $2x^2 - 5x + 2 = 0$

   $x = 2$ or $x = \frac{1}{2}$

2. $3x^2 + 4x + 1 = 0$

   $x = -1$ or $x = -\frac{1}{3}$

3. Find the discriminant and determine the nature of the solutions for the following equation.
   $3x^2 - 4x + 8 = 0$
   −80, no real-number solutions

4. $3x^2 = 7 - 2x$

   First rewrite the equation in standard form: $3x^2 + 2x - 7 = 0$

   $b^2 - 4ac = 2^2 - 4(3)(-7) = 88$

   Since the discriminant is positive, there are two real-number solutions.

Try This Find the value of the discriminant to determine the number of real-number solutions.

e. $2x^2 - 4x = 5$ 56, two real-number solutions **f.** $x^2 + 5x = -8$ −7, no real-number solutions **g.** $4x^2 = 8x - 4$ 0, one real-number solution

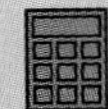

Approximating Solutions of Quadratic Equations

We can use a calculator to obtain rational approximations for solutions of quadratic equations.

EXAMPLE Solve $56.9x^2 - 77.4x = 33.2$ using the quadratic formula and a calculator. Round your answer to the nearest hundredth.

$$56.9x^2 - 77.4x - 33.2 = 0$$

$$a = 56.9 \quad b = -77.4 \quad c = -33.2$$

$$x = \frac{77.4 \pm \sqrt{77.4^2 - 4 \cdot 56.9(-33.2)}}{2 \cdot 56.9}$$

We can follow these steps using a calculator:

1. Find the discriminant. Store it in memory.

77.4 [x^2] [−] 4 [×] 56.9 [×] 33.2

[+/−] [=] 13547.08

[2nd] [x^2] 116.39192 [STO]

2. Find the first solution.

[CE/C] [(] 77.4 [+] [RCL] [)] [÷]

[(] 2 [×] 56.9 [)] [=] 1.7029167

3. Find the second solution.

[CE/C] [(] 77.4 [−] [RCL] [)] [÷]

[(] 2 [×] 56.9 [)] [=] -0.3426355

4. Round decimals to the nearest hundredth.

$x = 1.70$ and $x = -0.34$

For additional calculator practice, see Calculator Worksheet 28.

13-4 EXERCISES

A

Solve using the quadratic formula.

1. $x^2 - 4x = 21$ **2.** $x^2 + 7x = 18$
3. $x^2 = 6x - 9$ **4.** $x^2 = 8x - 16$
5. $3y^2 - 2y - 8 = 0$ **6.** $3y^2 - 7y + 4 = 0$
7. $4x^2 + 12x = 7$ **8.** $4x^2 + 4x = 15$
9. $x^2 - 9 = 0$ **10.** $x^2 - 4 = 0$
11. $x^2 - 2x + 1 = 0$ **12.** $x^2 - 4x - 7 = 0$
13. $y^2 - 10y + 22 = 0$ **14.** $y^2 + 6y - 9 = 0$
15. $x^2 + 4x + 4 = 7$ **16.** $x^2 - 2x + 1 = 5$
17. $3x^2 + 8x + 2 = 0$ **18.** $3x^2 - 4x - 2 = 0$
19. $2x^2 - 5x = 1$ **20.** $2x^2 + 2x = 3$
21. $4y^2 - 4y - 1 = 0$ **22.** $4y^2 + 4y - 1 = 0$
23. $3x^2 + 5x = 0$ **24.** $5x^2 - 2x = 0$
25. $2t^2 + 6t + 5 = 0$ **26.** $4y^2 + 3y + 2 = 0$
27. $4x^2 = 100$ **28.** $5t^2 = 80$
29. $3x^2 = 5x + 4$ **30.** $2x^2 + 3x = 1$
31. $2y^2 - 6y = 10$ **32.** $5m^2 = 3 + 11m$
33. $3p^2 + 2p = 3$ **34.** $3n^2 - 8n + 2 = 0$

Solve using the quadratic formula. Approximate solutions to the nearest tenth.

35. $x^2 - 4x - 7 = 0$ **36.** $x^2 + 2x - 2 = 0$
37. $y^2 - 6y - 1 = 0$ **38.** $y^2 + 10y + 22 = 0$
39. $4x^2 + 4x = 1$ **40.** $4x^2 = 4x + 1$
41. $3x^2 + 4x - 2 = 0$ **42.** $3x^2 - 8x + 2 = 0$
43. $2y^2 + 2y - 3 = 0$ **44.** $2y^2 + 6y - 2 = 0$
45. $x^2 + 8x + 16 = 5$ **46.** $x^2 - 3x + 1 = 3$
47. $2x^2 - 10x + 9 = 0$ **48.** $3x^2 + 12x + 8 = 0$
49. $5x^2 = 6 + 2x$ **50.** $7x^2 = 3$

Find the value of the discriminant and determine the number of real-number solutions for each quadratic equation.

51. $x^2 - 5x + 7 = 0$ **52.** $x^2 - 8x + 3 = 0$
53. $a^2 + 12a + 36 = 0$ **54.** $2m^2 - m - 6 = 0$
55. $4t^2 - 3t + 3 = 0$ **56.** $2x^2 - 4x - 6 = 0$
57. $3x^2 - 3x + 4 = 0$ **58.** $-3q^2 + 4q + 2 = 0$

Assignment Guide
Minimum: 1–58 m3, MR

Regular: 1–72 m3, 73, MR

Advanced: 1–50 m4, 51–72 m3, 73–75, MR

ADDITIONAL ANSWERS

Exercises

1. $-3, 7$ **2.** $-9, 2$
3. 3 **4.** 4
5. $-\frac{4}{3}, 2$ **6.** $1, \frac{4}{3}$
7. $-\frac{7}{2}, \frac{1}{2}$ **8.** $-\frac{5}{2}, \frac{3}{2}$
9. $-3, 3$ **10.** $-2, 2$
11. 1 **12.** $2 \pm \sqrt{11}$
13. $5 \pm \sqrt{3}$ **14.** $-3 \pm 3\sqrt{2}$
15. $-2 \pm \sqrt{7}$ **16.** $1 \pm \sqrt{5}$
17. $\frac{-4 \pm \sqrt{10}}{3}$ **18.** $\frac{2 \pm \sqrt{10}}{3}$
19. $\frac{5 \pm \sqrt{33}}{4}$ **20.** $\frac{-1 \pm \sqrt{7}}{2}$
21. $\frac{1 \pm \sqrt{2}}{2}$ **22.** $\frac{-1 \pm \sqrt{2}}{2}$
23. $-\frac{5}{3}, 0$ **24.** $0, \frac{2}{5}$
25. No real-number solutions
26. No real-number solutions
27. $-5, 5$ **28.** $-4, 4$
29. $\frac{5 \pm \sqrt{73}}{6}$ **30.** $\frac{-3 \pm \sqrt{17}}{4}$
31. $\frac{3 \pm \sqrt{29}}{2}$ **32.** $\frac{11 \pm \sqrt{181}}{10}$
33. $\frac{-1 \pm \sqrt{10}}{3}$ **34.** $\frac{4 \pm \sqrt{10}}{3}$
35. $-1.3, 5.3$ **36.** $-2.7, 0.7$
37. $-0.2, 6.2$ **38.** $-6.7, -3.3$
39. $-1.2, 0.2$ **40.** $-0.2, 1.2$
41. $-1.7, 0.4$ **42.** $0.3, 2.4$
43. $-1.8, 0.8$ **44.** $-3.3, 0.3$
45. $-1.7, -6.2$ **46.** $-0.6, 3.6$
47. $1.2, 3.8$ **48.** $-3.2, -0.8$
49. $-0.9, 1.3$ **50.** $0.7, -0.7$
51. -3, no real-number solutions
52. 52, two real-number solutions
53. 0, one real-number solution
54. 49, two real-number solutions
55. -39, no real-number solutions
56. 64, two real-number solutions
57. -39, no real-number solutions
58. 40, two real-number solutions

59. 0, 2
60. $-\frac{4}{3}$, 0
61. $\frac{3 \pm \sqrt{5}}{2}$
62. $\frac{7 \pm \sqrt{69}}{10}$
63. $\frac{-7 \pm \sqrt{61}}{2}$
64. −8, 4
65. $\frac{-2 \pm \sqrt{10}}{2}$
66. −2, 1
67. No real-number solutions
68. No real-number solutions
69. $\frac{-1 \pm \sqrt{3a+1}}{a}$
70. $\frac{5 \pm \sqrt{25 - 24b^2}}{4b}$
71. $\frac{c \pm d\sqrt{3}}{2}$
72. 0.25, −0.45

Mixed Review

76. $x^2 + 7x - 8 = 0$; $a = 1, b = 7, c = -8$
77. $4x^2 + 5x + 16 = 0$; $a = 4, b = 5, c = 16$
78. $3x^2 - 8x - 22 = 0$; $a = 3, b = -8, c = -22$
79. $y = \frac{64}{x}$
80. $y = \frac{0.1}{x}$
81. 6
82. 5
83. $5(m - 3)^2$
84. $(c - 1)^2(c + 1)$
85. 120 adults, 65 children
86. $3\frac{3}{4}$ h

B

Solve.

59. $5x + x(x - 7) = 0$
60. $x(3x + 7) - 3x = 0$
61. $3 - x(x - 3) = 4$
62. $x(5x - 7) = 1$
63. $(y + 4)(y + 3) = 15$
64. $(y + 5)(y - 1) = 27$
65. $x^2 + (x + 2)^2 = 7$
66. $x^2 + (x + 1)^2 = 5$
67. $(x + 2)^2 + (x + 1)^2 = 0$
68. $(x + 3)^2 + (x + 1)^2 = 0$
69. $ax^2 + 2x = 3$
70. $2bx^2 - 5x + 3b = 0$
71. $4x^2 - 4cx + c^2 - 3d^2 = 0$
72. $0.8x^2 + 0.16x - 0.09 = 0$

73. ***Critical Thinking***
   a. In $ax^2 + bx + c = 0$, suppose $b^2 > 4ac$. Will the equation have real-number solutions? Does it make any difference whether b is positive, negative, or zero? Yes; no
   b. In $ax^2 + bx + c = 0$, suppose $ac < 0$. Will the equation have real-number solutions? Does the value of b make any difference? Yes; no
   c. In $ax^2 + bx + c = 0$, suppose a and c are both positive. When will the equation have real-number solutions? When $b^2 \geq 4ac$

Challenge

74. Use the two roots given by the quadratic formula to find a formula for the sum of the solutions for any quadratic equation. What is the product of the solutions? Without solving, tell the sum and product of the solutions for $2x^2 + 5x - 3 = 0$. Sum: $\frac{-b}{a} = \frac{-5}{2}$; product: $\frac{c}{a} = \frac{-3}{2}$

75. One solution to the equation $2x^2 + bx - 3 = 0$ is known to be -5. Use the results of the preceding problem to find the other solution. $b = 9.4$, so $x = 0.3$

Mixed Review

Write in standard form and determine a, b, and c. **76.** $x^2 + 7x = 8$ **77.** $4x^2 + 16 = -5x$ **78.** $3x^2 - 12 = 8x + 10$

Find an equation of variation where y varies inversely as x. One pair of values is given. **79.** $y = 16$ when $x = 4$ **80.** $y = 0.1$ when $x = 1$

Solve. **81.** $11 - \sqrt{30 + x} = 5$ **82.** $\sqrt{2x + 2} = \sqrt{5x - 13}$

Factor. **83.** $5m^2 - 30m + 45$ **84.** $c^3 - c^2 - c + 1$

85. There were 185 sports fans at the game. Admission was \$2.50 for adults and \$1.50 for children. The receipts were \$397.50. How many adults and how many children attended the game?

86. It takes Sondra 6 hours to complete a certain job at the office. Tad needs 10 hours to do the same job. How long would it take them, working together, to do the job?

13-5 Solving Rational Equations

Objective: Solve rational equations involving quadratic equations.

Recall that we solve rational equations by multiplying both sides by the LCM of all the denominators. This can result in a quadratic equation. Remember that multiplying both sides of an equation by a variable can result in extraneous solutions. Therefore, you must check all possible solutions in the original equation.

EXAMPLES Solve.

1.

$$\frac{a+1}{2} = \frac{1}{a}$$
$$\frac{a+1}{2}(2a) = \frac{1}{a}(2a)$$
$$(a+1)a = 2$$
$$a^2 + a = 2$$
$$a^2 + a - 2 = 0$$
$$(a+2)(a-1) = 0$$
$$a + 2 = 0 \quad \text{or} \quad a - 1 = 0$$
$$a = -2 \quad \text{or} \quad a = 1$$

Check:

$\frac{a+1}{2}$	$= \frac{1}{a}$
$\frac{-2+1}{2}$	$\frac{1}{-2}$
$-\frac{1}{2}$	$-\frac{1}{2}$ ✓

$\frac{a+1}{2}$	$= \frac{1}{a}$
$\frac{1+1}{2}$	$\frac{1}{1}$
1	1 ✓

2.

$$\frac{3}{x-1} + \frac{5}{x+1} = 2 \quad \text{LCM is } (x-1)(x+1).$$
$$(x-1)(x+1)\left(\frac{3}{x-1} + \frac{5}{x+1}\right) = 2(x-1)(x+1)$$
$$(x-1)(x+1)\frac{3}{x-1} + (x-1)(x+1)\frac{5}{x+1} = 2(x-1)(x+1)$$
$$3(x+1) + 5(x-1) = 2(x-1)(x+1)$$
$$3x + 3 + 5x - 5 = 2(x^2 - 1)$$
$$8x - 2 = 2x^2 - 2$$
$$-2x^2 + 8x = 0$$
$$-2x(x-4) = 0 \quad \text{Factoring}$$
$$-2x = 0 \quad \text{or} \quad x - 4 = 0$$
$$x = 0 \quad \text{or} \quad x = 4$$

Substitution will show that both numbers check. The solutions are 0 and 4.

Try This Solve.

a. $x + 3 = \frac{10}{x}$ $-5, 2$ **b.** $1 = \frac{1}{a} + \frac{12}{a^2}$ $-3, 4$ **c.** $\frac{2}{x+2} + \frac{3}{x-2} = 1$ $6, -1$

13-5

FIRST FIVE MINUTES

1. Solve using the quadratic formula.
   $4x^2 + 5x + 1 = 0$
   $x = -\frac{1}{4}$ or $x = -1$
2. Solve using the quadratic formula.
   $x^2 - 2x - 2 = 0$
   $x = 1 \pm \sqrt{3}$

Remind students to check possible answers in the original equation. If they do not satisfy the original equation, they may be extraneous roots.

Avoiding Common Errors

Students may check wrong answers, find that they do not check, and assume that they are extraneous solutions. Point out that extraneous solutions for rational equations will give a zero in the denominator of the original equations. If an answer does not check and does not cause a zero in the denominator, students should examine their work for possible errors.

Key Questions

- For what values of x is the expression $2(x - 1)$ equal to 0?
  1
- For what values of x is the expression $\frac{3}{x-5}$ undefined?
  5

Chalkboard Example

Solve.

1. $\frac{18}{x+1} = x - 6$

$$(x+1)\frac{18}{x+1} = (x-6)(x+1)$$
$$18 = x^2 - 5x - 6$$
$$0 = x^2 - 5x - 24$$
$$0 = (x-8)(x+3)$$
$$x - 8 = 0 \quad \text{or} \quad x + 3 = 0$$
$$x = 8 \quad \text{or} \quad x = -3$$

Both numbers check.

LESSON QUIZ

Solve.

1. $\frac{6}{x-2} - \frac{2}{x-3} = 1$
   $x = 4$ or $x = 5$
2. $\frac{6}{x+1} - \frac{16}{x+3} = -1$
   $x = 5$ or $x = 1$

Assignment Guide
Minimum: 1–21 e/o, MR, assign w. Application
Regular: 1–21 m3, 22–33 e/o, 34, MR
Advanced: 1–33 m3, 34, 35–40 e/o, MR

ADDITIONAL ANSWERS

Exercises

22. No real-number solutions
23. $\frac{3 \pm \sqrt{33}}{2}$
24. $\frac{9 \pm \sqrt{73}}{2}$
25. $-1, 6$
26. $-3 \pm \sqrt{10}$
27. $4 \pm 2\sqrt{5}$
28. No real-number solutions
29. 0
30. 0
31. $\frac{1}{2}$
32. $-2 \pm 2\sqrt{3}$
33. $\frac{7 \pm \sqrt{13}}{2}$
35. $\frac{3}{4}$
36. 7
37. $3 \pm \sqrt{13}$
38. $\frac{-7 \pm \sqrt{145}}{4}$
39. $9 \pm \sqrt{59}$
40. $\frac{-3 \pm \sqrt{61}}{2}$

Mixed Review

41. $-3, 0$
42. $\pm\sqrt{15}$
43. $7, -2$
44. $0, -\frac{4}{7}$
45. $\pm\frac{2\sqrt{5}}{3}$
46. $5, -\frac{3}{2}$

13-5 EXERCISES

A

Solve each rational equation.

1. $\frac{7}{x+3} = x - 3$ 4, −4
2. $\frac{5}{y-2} = y + 2$ 3, −3
3. $\frac{x-2}{3} = \frac{1}{x}$ 3, −1
4. $\frac{a-1}{2} = \frac{3}{a}$ 3, −2
5. $\frac{5}{n^2} + \frac{4}{n} = 1$ 5, −1
6. $\frac{4}{a^2} - \frac{2}{a} = 2$ −2, 1
7. $x - 3 = \frac{5}{x-3}$ $3 \pm \sqrt{5}$
8. $x + 2 = \frac{3}{x+2}$ $-2 \pm \sqrt{3}$
9. $\frac{x^2}{x-4} - \frac{7}{x-4} = 0$ $\pm\sqrt{7}$
10. $\frac{x^2}{x+3} - \frac{5}{x+3} = 0$ $\pm\sqrt{5}$
11. $\frac{y+2}{y} = \frac{1}{y+2}$ No real solution
12. $\frac{8}{x-2} + \frac{8}{x+2} = 3$ 6, $-\frac{2}{3}$
13. $\frac{24}{x-2} + \frac{24}{x+2} = 5$ 10, $-\frac{2}{5}$
14. $1 + \frac{12}{x^2-4} = \frac{3}{x-2}$ 1
15. $\frac{5}{t-3} - \frac{30}{t^2-9} = 1$ 2
16. $\frac{4}{x+2} - \frac{5}{x-3} = 2$ No real solution
17. $\frac{2}{y-1} + \frac{3}{y+1} = 1$ 0, 5
18. $\frac{1}{t+2} + \frac{5}{t} = 1$ $2 \pm \sqrt{14}$
19. $\frac{2}{a+1} - \frac{3}{a} = 2$ No real solution
20. $\frac{x}{x+1} - \frac{x}{x-2} = 1$ $-1 \pm \sqrt{3}$
21. $\frac{y}{y+3} - \frac{y}{y-1} = 1$ $-3 \pm 2\sqrt{3}$

B

Solve each rational equation.

22. $\frac{2x-1}{5} - \frac{2}{x} = \frac{x}{2}$
23. $\frac{n-1}{2} - \frac{1}{n} = \frac{n}{3}$
24. $\frac{6}{a+1} - \frac{1}{a} = \frac{1}{2}$
25. $\frac{2}{x-2} - \frac{1}{x} = \frac{1}{3}$
26. $\frac{x}{x+1} - \frac{x}{x-1} = \frac{1}{3}$
27. $\frac{y}{y-2} - \frac{y}{y+2} = \frac{1}{2}$
28. $\frac{1}{a-1} + \frac{2}{1-a} = 3a$
29. $\frac{1}{2x-1} + \frac{1}{1-2x} = x$
30. $\frac{1}{x-2} - \frac{2}{x^2-4} = 0$
31. $\frac{2}{x+3} + \frac{5}{x^2-9} = 0$
32. $\frac{1}{x+2} - \frac{2}{x^2-4} = \frac{2}{x}$
33. $\frac{2}{y+3} - \frac{1}{y^2-9} = \frac{1}{y}$
34. ***Critical Thinking*** The sum of an integer, one more than its reciprocal, and $\frac{1}{2}$ its reciprocal is $4\frac{1}{2}$. What is the number? 3

Challenge

Solve.

35. $\frac{1}{x} - \frac{3}{1 - x} = \frac{2}{x^2 - x}$

36. $\frac{2}{y} + \frac{1}{1 - y} = \frac{5}{y^2 - y}$

37. $\frac{2}{x^2 - x - 6} + \frac{3}{x^2 - 7x + 12} = \frac{1}{x - 4}$

38. $\frac{-1}{x^2 + 4x - 5} + \frac{2}{x^2 + x - 20} = \frac{2}{x - 4}$

39. $\frac{1}{x^2 + 3x - 4} + \frac{1}{x^2 + 2x - 8} = \frac{1}{x^2 - 8x + 12}$

40. $\frac{1}{x^2 - 2x - 15} + \frac{1}{x^2 + x - 6} = \frac{1}{x^2 + 2x - 8}$

Mixed Review

Solve. **41.** $x^2 + 3x = 0$ **42.** $a^2 = 15$ **43.** $y^2 - 5y - 14 = 0$ **44.** $7x^2 + 4x = 0$ **45.** $9x^2 - 20 = 0$ **46.** $2x^2 - 7x - 15 = 0$

Graph. **47.** $f(x) = 2x^2 - 5$ **48.** $g(x) = \frac{1}{2}x^2 + 1$

49. $h(x) = -2x^2 + 7$ **50.** $f(x) = -\frac{1}{2}x^2 - 4$

Find an equation of variation. **51.** y varies directly as x, and $y = 0.6$ when $x = 0.4$ **52.** y varies inversely as x, and $y = 2$ when $x = 3$
53. y varies inversely as x, and $y = 5$ when $x = 2$
54. y varies directly as x and inversely as z, and $y = 4$ when $x = 8$ and $z = 6$

Write using scientific notation. **55.** 3,485,117 **56.** 0.0070023

57. Find the slope of the line containing the points $(-5, -9)$, $(1, 1)$.

Problem for Programmers

Write a program that will use the quadratic formula to approximate the real solutions for any equation of the form $ax^2 + bx + c = 0$. The inputs will be a, b, and c. The program should output the real-number solutions. (Hint: The program should use the discriminant to determine the number of real-number solutions.) Test your program using some of the exercises in this lesson.

47.

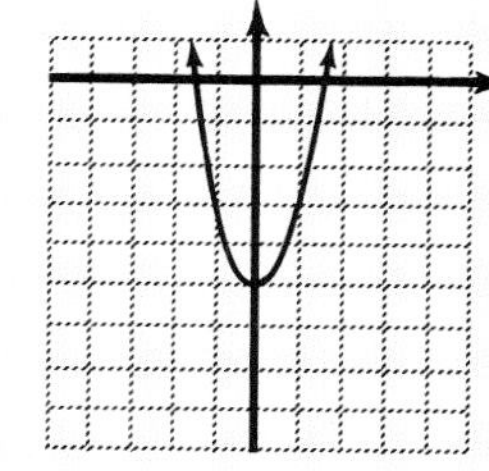

48.

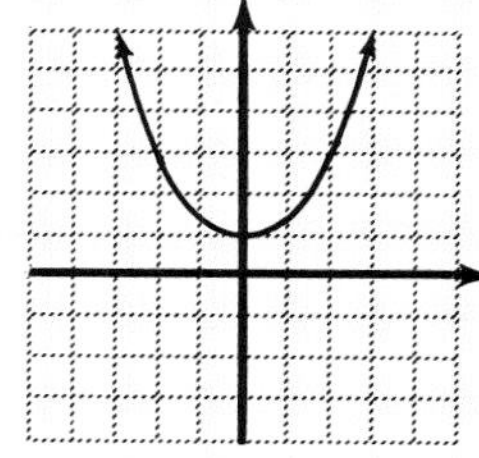

49.

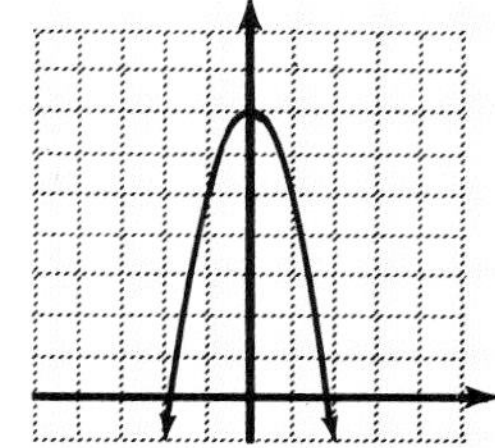

50.

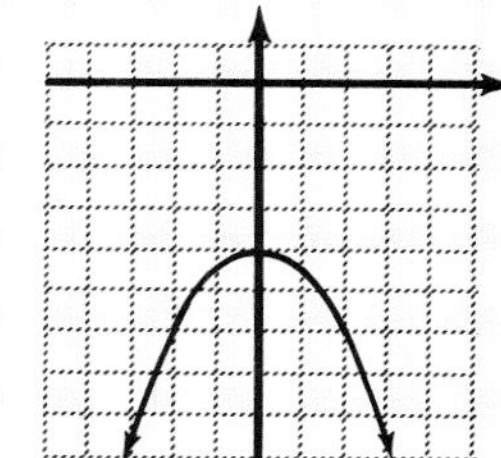

51. $y = 1.5x$
52. $y = \frac{6}{x}$
53. $y = \frac{10}{x}$
54. $y = \frac{3x}{z}$
55. 3.485117×10^6
56. 7.0023×10^{-3}
57. $m = \frac{5}{3}$

13-6

FIRST FIVE MINUTES

Solve.

1. $\frac{3}{3+x} + \frac{3}{9-x} = 1$

$3(9-x) + 3(3+x)$
$= (9-x)(3+x)$
$27 - 3x + 9 + 3x$
$= 27 + 6x - x^2$
$x^2 - 6x + 9 = 0$
$(x-3)(x-3) = 0$
$x = 3$

2. $\sqrt{x} + 6 = 11$

$\sqrt{x} = 5$
$x = 25$

Radical Equations

Emphasize that squaring both sides of an equation may introduce extraneous solutions. Therefore it is important to check all possible solutions. Note that square roots of negative numbers do not exist in the real-number system.

This would be a good time to summarize the procedures that can cause extraneous solutions. Extraneous roots occur when

1. the multiplication property is used to multiply by a variable.
2. the principle of squaring is used.

Emphasize that a solution that does not check, but does not cause an undefined term, indicates that an error may have been made.

Key Questions

Possible solutions for the equation $\sqrt{x+2} = x - 4$ were found to be 2 and 7.

- Does 2 check? No. $\sqrt{4} = +2$, not -2. The answer is extraneous.
- Does 7 check? Yes
- What is the solution to the equation? The solution is 7.

Chalkboard Examples

Solve.

1. $x - 4 = \sqrt{x+2}$

$(x-4)^2 = x + 2$
$x^2 - 8x + 16 = x + 2$
$x^2 - 9x + 14 = 0$
$(x-2)(x-7) = 0$
$x = 2$ or $x = 7$

The answer $x = 2$ is an extraneous root. The solution is $x = 7$.

13-6 Solving Radical Equations

Master Grapher Worksheet 16 can be used with this lesson.

Radical Equations

Objective: Solve radical equations involving quadratic equations.

We can solve some radical equations by first using the principle of squaring to find a quadratic equation. When we do this we must be sure to check.

EXAMPLE 1 Solve.

$$x - 5 = \sqrt{x+7}$$
$$(x-5)^2 = (\sqrt{x+7})^2 \quad \text{Using the principle of squaring}$$
$$x^2 - 10x + 25 = x + 7$$
$$x^2 - 11x + 18 = 0$$
$$(x-9)(x-2) = 0$$
$$x = 9 \text{ or } x = 2$$

Check:

$x - 5$	$\sqrt{x+7}$
$9 - 5$	$\sqrt{9+7}$
4	4 ✓

$x - 5$	$\sqrt{x+7}$
$2 - 5$	$\sqrt{2+7}$
-3	3

The number 9 checks, but 2 does not. Thus the only solution is 9.

EXAMPLE 2 Solve.

$$\sqrt{27-3x} + 3 = x$$
$$\sqrt{27-3x} = x - 3 \quad \text{Adding } -3 \text{ to get the radical alone on one side}$$
$$(\sqrt{27-3x})^2 = (x-3)^2 \quad \text{Using the principle of squaring}$$
$$27 - 3x = x^2 - 6x + 9$$
$$0 = x^2 - 3x - 18$$
$$0 = (x-6)(x+3)$$
$$x = 6 \text{ or } x = -3$$

Check:

$\sqrt{27-3x} + 3$	x
$\sqrt{27 - 3\cdot 6} + 3$	6
$\sqrt{9} + 3$	6
6	6 ✓

$\sqrt{27-3x} + 3$	x
$\sqrt{27 - 3\cdot(-3)} + 3$	-3
$\sqrt{27+9} + 3$	-3
$\sqrt{36} + 3$	-3
9	-3

There is only one solution, 6.

Try This Solve.

a. $\sqrt{x+2} = 4 - x$ 2 **b.** $\sqrt{30-3x} + 4 = x$ 7

Formulas

Objective: Solve formulas for given variables.

EXAMPLES Solve each formula for the given variable.

3. Solve $V = 3.5\sqrt{h}$ for h.

$$V = 3.5\sqrt{h}$$
$$V^2 = (3.5)^2(\sqrt{h})^2 \quad \text{Squaring both sides}$$
$$V^2 = 12.25h$$
$$\frac{V^2}{12.25} = h \quad \text{Multiplying by } \frac{1}{12.25} \text{ to get } h \text{ alone}$$

4. Solve $T = 2\pi\sqrt{\frac{L}{g}}$ for g.

$$T = 2\pi\sqrt{\frac{L}{g}}$$
$$T^2 = \left(2\pi\sqrt{\frac{L}{g}}\right)^2 \quad \text{Squaring both sides}$$
$$T^2 = (2\pi)^2\left(\sqrt{\frac{L}{g}}\right)^2$$
$$T^2 = \frac{4\pi^2 L}{g}$$
$$gT^2 = 4\pi^2 L$$
$$g = \frac{4\pi^2 L}{T^2} \quad \text{Multiplying by } \frac{1}{T^2}$$

5. Solve $A = P(1 + r)^2$ for r.

$$A = P(1 + r)^2$$
$$\frac{A}{P} = (1 + r)^2 \quad \text{Multiplying by } \frac{1}{P}$$
$$\sqrt{\frac{A}{P}} = 1 + r \quad \text{Taking the square root on both sides}$$
$$-1 + \sqrt{\frac{A}{P}} = r$$

Since the interest rate (r) can only be positive, we do not need to find the negative square root, as it would lead to a negative solution.

Try This Solve for the given variable.

c. $r = 2\sqrt{5L}$; L $\frac{r^2}{20}$ **d.** $T = 2\pi\sqrt{\frac{L}{g}}$; L $\frac{T^2 g}{4\pi^2}$ **e.** $c = \sqrt{\frac{E}{m}}$; m $\frac{E}{c^2}$

f. $A = \pi r^2$; r $\sqrt{\frac{A}{\pi}}$ **g.** $C = P(d - 1)^2$; d $1 \pm \sqrt{\frac{C}{P}}$

2. $\sqrt{x - 4} + 6 = x$

$x - 4 = (x - 6)^2$
$x - 4 = x^2 - 12x + 36$
$0 = x^2 - 13x + 40$
$0 = (x - 5)(x - 8)$
$x = 5$ or $x = 8$
The answer 5 does not check.
The solution is 8.

Formulas

You may want to point out that the formula in Example 5 gives the amount of money A in an account after two years at interest rate r with original investment P.

Chalkboard Examples

1. Solve $r = \sqrt{\frac{k}{F}}$ for F.

$r^2 = \frac{k}{F}$

$F = \frac{k}{r^2}$

2. Solve $\frac{\sqrt{A}}{\sqrt{\pi}} = 2r$ for A.

$\sqrt{\frac{A}{\pi}} = 2r$

$\frac{A}{\pi} = 4r^2$

$A = 4\pi r^2$

3. Solve $E = \frac{1}{2}mv^2$ for v.

$\frac{2E}{m} = v^2$

$v = \sqrt{\frac{2E}{m}}$

LESSON QUIZ

1. Solve $x + 1 = \sqrt{x + 7}$.
The solution is 2.
2. Solve $\sqrt{\frac{3V}{h\pi}} = r$ for V.

$V = \frac{1}{3}\pi r^2 h$

Assignment Guide
Minimum: 1–36 e/o, MR

Regular: 1–44 e/o, 45, MR

Advanced: 1–44 m3, 45, 46–53 e/o, MR

ADDITIONAL ANSWERS

Exercises

23. $a = \sqrt{c^2 - b^2}$
24. $c = \sqrt{\frac{E}{m}}$
25. $b = \sqrt{c^2 - a^2}$
26. $A = \frac{N^2}{6.25}$
27. $r = \sqrt{\frac{V}{\pi h}}$ or $\frac{\sqrt{V\pi h}}{\pi h}$
28. $t = \sqrt{\frac{2s}{g}}$ or $\frac{\sqrt{2sg}}{g}$
29. $\sqrt{r^2 - y^2 - z^2}$
30. $\sqrt{PR}$
31. $\sqrt{\frac{GmM}{F}}$
32. $\frac{t^2a}{2}$
33. $\frac{P}{I^2}$
34. $\sqrt{\frac{x - 2V}{a}}$
35. $\sqrt{\frac{P}{R}} - 4$
36. $\frac{4\pi^2 l}{T^2}$
37. 13
38. 2
39. $\sqrt{\frac{3}{5}}$ or $\frac{\sqrt{15}}{5}$
40. 2
41. 63
42. $\frac{125}{2}$
43. 0
44. −1
45. $C = 2\sqrt{\pi A}$, $A = \frac{C^2}{4\pi}$

13-6 EXERCISES

A

Solve each radical equation.

1. $\sqrt{2a} = 6$ 18 **2.** $\sqrt{3x} = 9$ 27 **3.** $\sqrt{x + 2} = 3$ 7

4. $\sqrt{m} - 4 = 5$ 29 **5.** $\sqrt{\frac{x}{3}} = 2$ 12 **6.** $\sqrt{\frac{m}{2}} = 5$ 50

7. $\sqrt{2x} + 3 = 7$ 8 **8.** $\sqrt{5t} - 2 = 1$ $\frac{9}{5}$ **9.** $\sqrt{2x + 3} = 3$ 3

10. $\sqrt{4m} - 1 = 5$ $\frac{13}{2}$ **11.** $\sqrt{\frac{x + 2}{3}} = 6$ 106 **12.** $\sqrt{\frac{a - 3}{4}} = 2$ 19

13. $x - 7 = \sqrt{x - 5}$ 9 **14.** $\sqrt{x + 7} = x - 5$ 9

15. $\sqrt{x + 18} = x - 2$ 7 **16.** $x - 9 = \sqrt{x - 3}$ 12

17. $\sqrt{5x + 21} = x + 3$ 3 **18.** $\sqrt{2x + 3} = 6 - x$ 3

19. $x = 1 + 6\sqrt{x - 9}$ 13, 25 **20.** $\sqrt{2x - 1} + 2 = x$ 5

21. $x + 4 = 4\sqrt{x + 1}$ 0, 8 **22.** $x + 1 = 3\sqrt{x + 5}$ 11

Solve each formula for the given variable.

23. $c^2 = a^2 + b^2$; a **24.** $E = mc^2$; c **25.** $c = \sqrt{a^2 + b^2}$; b

26. $N = 2.5\sqrt{A}$; A **27.** $V = \pi r^2 h$; r **28.** $s = \frac{gt^2}{2}$; t

29. $x^2 + y^2 + z^2 = r^2$; x **30.** $P = \frac{V^2}{R}$; V

31. $F = \frac{GmM}{r^2}$; r **32.** $\sqrt{\frac{2s}{a}} = t$; s

33. $\sqrt{\frac{P}{R}} = I$; R **34.** $x = 2V + at^2$; t

35. $P = R(4 + I)^2$; I **36.** $T = 2\pi\sqrt{\frac{l}{g}}$; g

B

Solve.

37. $\sqrt{x + 3} = \frac{8}{\sqrt{x - 9}}$ **38.** $\frac{12}{\sqrt{5x + 6}} = \sqrt{2x + 5}$

39. $\sqrt{4x^2 + 3} = 3x$ **40.** $\sqrt{2y^2 - 4} = y$

41. $6\sqrt{a} = 18\sqrt{7}$ **42.** $2\sqrt{x} = 5\sqrt{10}$

43. $\sqrt{t^2 + 1} = 1 - t$ **44.** $\sqrt{a^2 - 1} = 1 + a$

45. ***Critical Thinking*** Find a formula for the circumference of a circle in terms of the area of a circle. Then use the formula to express the area of the circle in terms of the circumference of the circle.

Challenge

46. Solve. $2\sqrt{x - 1} - \sqrt{3x - 5} = \sqrt{x - 9}$ 10

47. Solve. $\sqrt{y + 1} - \sqrt{2y - 5} = \sqrt{y - 2}$ 3

48. Solve $x + 1 + 3\sqrt{x + 1} - 28 = 0$ using two methods. First use the principle of squaring. Second, let $y = \sqrt{x + 1}$. (Then $y^2 = x + 1$.) Solve for y, then substitute to find x. 15

49. Solve $h = vt + 8t^2$ for t. $\frac{-v \pm \sqrt{v^2 + 32h}}{16}$

Solve the following systems of equations.

50. $2\sqrt{a} + 3\sqrt{b} = 21$
$\sqrt{a} - \sqrt{b} = -2$

51. $5\sqrt{m} + 2\sqrt{n} = 39$
$3\sqrt{m} - \sqrt{n} = 19$

52. $3r^2 + 2s^2 = 11$
$r^2 - 2s^2 = -7$

53. $5x^2 - 3y^2 = -7$
$-x^2 + 3y^2 = 23$

Mixed Review

Complete the square. 54. $x^2 + 4x$ 55. $m^2 - 5m$ 56. $a^2 - a$

Solve. 57. $9a^2 - 18a = 0$ 58. $3x^2 - 13x + 4 = 0$

59. $2m^2 - 25 = 0$ 60. $(x - 3)^2 = 36$ 61. $(c - 5)^2 = 17$

Simplify. 62. $\frac{\sqrt{1}}{\sqrt{81}}$ 63. $-\frac{\sqrt{4}}{\sqrt{121}}$ 64. $\frac{\sqrt{11}}{\sqrt{22}}$ 65. $\frac{\sqrt{56}}{\sqrt{8}}$ 66. $\frac{\sqrt{64}}{\sqrt{4}}$

Solve by graphing. 67. $y = x - 1$, $y = -x + 5$ 68. $y = 2x$, $x + y = 0$ 69. $y = 1 - x$, $x - y = 7$

70. The numerical value for the area of a square is 32 more than the perimeter. Find the length of a side.

LOOKING FOR ERRORS

Each exercise has an error commonly made by algebra students. Can you find and correct the error?

1. $\sqrt{3x + 7} = x + 3$
$3x + 7 = x^2 + 9$
$0 = x^2 - 3x + 2$
$0 = (x - 2)(x - 1)$
$x - 2 = 0$ or $x - 1 = 0$
$x = 2$ or $x = 1$
The solutions are 2 and 1.

2. $\sqrt{x + 1} = x - 5$
$x + 1 = x^2 - 10x + 25$
$0 = x^2 - 11x + 24$
$0 = (x - 8)(x - 3)$
$x - 8 = 0$ or $x - 3 = 0$
$x = 8$ or $x = 3$
The solutions are 8 and 3.

50. $a = 9, b = 25$
51. $m = 49, n = 4$
52. $(-1, -2), (1, -2), (-1, 2), (1, 2)$
53. $(-2, -3), (2, -3), (-2, 3), (2, 3)$

Mixed Review

54. $x^2 + 4x + 4$
55. $m^2 - 5m + \frac{25}{4}$
56. $a^2 - a + \frac{1}{4}$
57. 2, 0
58. $\frac{1}{3}$, 4
59. $\pm\frac{5\sqrt{2}}{2}$
60. 9, −3
61. $5 \pm \sqrt{17}$
62. $\frac{1}{9}$
63. $-\frac{2}{11}$
64. $\frac{\sqrt{2}}{2}$
65. $\sqrt{7}$
66. 4
67. (3, 2)
68. (0, 0)
69. (4, −3)
70. 8 units

Looking for Errors

1. The student squared $x + 3$ incorrectly. $(x + 3)^2 = x^2 + 6x + 9$. The correct solutions are −2 and −1.
2. The student forgot to check. The correct solution is just 8.

13-7

FIRST FIVE MINUTES

Solve.

1. $\frac{4}{x} + \frac{1}{x-6} = 1$

$4(x - 6) + x = x(x - 6)$
$4x - 24 + x = x^2 - 6x$
$0 = x^2 - 11x + 24$
$0 = (x - 3)(x - 8)$
$x = 3$ or $x = 8$
The solution is 3 or 8.

2. $\sqrt{x + 1} = x - 5$

$x + 1 = (x - 5)^2$
$x + 1 = x^2 - 10x + 25$
$0 = x^2 - 11x + 24$
$0 = (x - 3)(x - 8)$
$x = 3$ or $x = 8$
$x = 3$ does not check.
The solution is 8.

Remind students that *drawing a diagram* is an important part of understanding the problem when the problem involves some type of geometric shape. A carefully drawn diagram can also help students determine if the answer is reasonable.

Key Questions

- In Example 1, if the width of the frame is x, what is the width of the picture?
  $20 - 2x$
- What is the height of the picture?
  $14 - 2x$
- Write an expression for the area of the picture.
  $(20 - 2x)(14 - 2x)$

13-7 Problem Solving: Quadratic Equations

Objective: Solve problems involving quadratic equations.

PROBLEM-SOLVING GUIDELINES
■ UNDERSTAND the problem
□ Develop and carry out a PLAN
■ Find the ANSWER and CHECK

We can use Problem-Solving Guidelines to help solve problems involving quadratic equations.

EXAMPLE 1

A picture frame measures 20 cm by 14 cm. The picture, inside the frame, takes up 160 square centimeters. Find the width of the frame.

■ **UNDERSTAND the problem**

Question: What is the width of the frame?
Data: Picture frame is 20 cm × 14 cm; picture has area 160 cm^2.

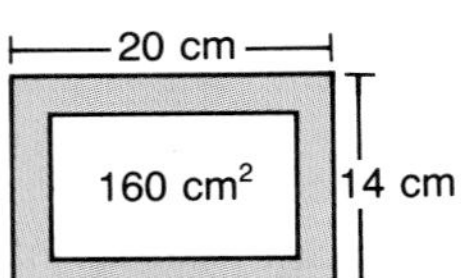

□ **Develop and carry out a PLAN**

Let x = width of the picture frame.
We can use the picture to help us express the other dimensions of the picture in terms of the width, x, of the picture frame. Also, recall that area can be found by multiplying the length by the width.

$$\begin{aligned} lw &= A \\ lw &= 160 \\ (20 - 2x)(14 - 2x) &= 160 \\ 280 - 68x + 4x^2 &= 160 \\ 4x^2 - 68x + 120 &= 0 \\ x^2 - 17x + 30 &= 0 \\ (x - 15)(x - 2) &= 0 \quad \text{Factoring} \\ x = 15 \quad &\text{or} \quad x = 2 \end{aligned}$$

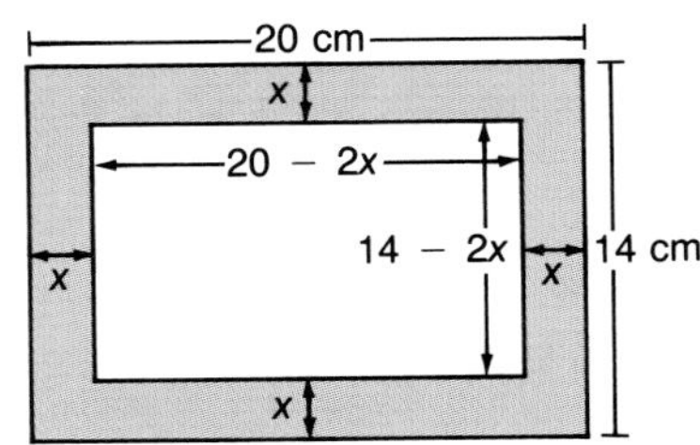

■ **Find the ANSWER and CHECK**

When $x = 15$, $20 - 2x = -10$, and $14 - 2x = -16$. Since the length and width of the picture cannot be negative, 15 is not an answer.
When $x = 2$, $20 - 2x = 16$, and $14 - 2x = 10$. A 10×16 picture has an area of 160 cm^2. This answer is reasonable and checks.
The width of the picture frame is 2 cm.

Try This Solve.

a. A rectangular garden is 80 m by 60 m. Part of the garden is torn up to install a strip of lawn of equal width around the garden. The new area of the garden is 800 m^2. How wide is the strip of lawn? 20 m

EXAMPLE 2

The hypotenuse of a right triangle is 6 m long. One leg is 1 m longer than the other. Find the lengths of the legs. Round to the nearest hundredth.

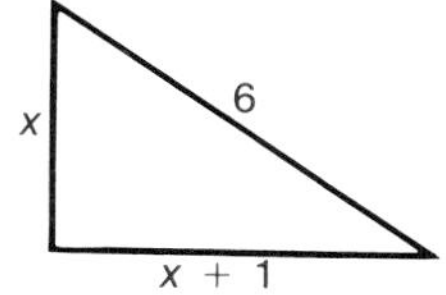

We first make a drawing. Let x = the length of one leg. Then $x + 1$ is the length of the other leg. To translate we use the Pythagorean theorem.

$$\begin{aligned} x^2 + (x+1)^2 &= 6^2 \\ x^2 + x^2 + 2x + 1 &= 36 \\ 2x^2 + 2x - 35 &= 0 \end{aligned}$$

Since we cannot factor, we use the quadratic formula.

$$a = 2,\ b = 2,\ c = -35, \text{ so } b^2 - 4ac = 284$$

$$\begin{aligned} x &= \frac{-b \pm \sqrt{b^2 - 4ac}}{2a} \\ &= \frac{-2 \pm \sqrt{284}}{4} \\ &= \frac{-2 \pm \sqrt{4 \cdot 71}}{4} \\ &= \frac{-2 \pm 2 \cdot \sqrt{71}}{2 \cdot 2} \\ &= \frac{-1 \pm \sqrt{71}}{2} \end{aligned}$$

$$x = \frac{-1 + \sqrt{71}}{2} \approx 3.72 \quad \text{or} \quad x = \frac{-1 - \sqrt{71}}{2} \approx -4.72$$

Since the length of a leg cannot be negative, -4.72 does not check. 3.72 does check. Thus one leg is about 3.72 m and the other is about $3.72 + 1 = 4.72$ m long. These lengths are reasonable, as the hypotenuse is greater than each leg.

Try This Solve.

b. The hypotenuse of a right triangle is 4 cm long. One leg is 1 cm longer than the other. Find the lengths of the legs. Round to the nearest tenth. 2.3 cm, 3.3 cm

Chalkboard Examples

1. A tennis court has an area of 312 square yards. It is surrounded by a border of constant width whose outer dimensions are 32 yards long by 18 yards wide. What is the width of the border?
   Let x be the width of the border, in yards. The length of the tennis court is $32 - 2x$. The width of the tennis court is $18 - 2x$. The length of the court times the width of the court equals the area, 312 square yards.
   $$\begin{aligned} (32 - 2x)(18 - 2x) &= 312 \\ 576 - 100x + 4x^2 &= 312 \\ 144 - 25x + x^2 &= 78 \\ x^2 - 25x + 66 &= 0 \\ (x - 22)(x - 3) &= 0 \end{aligned}$$
   $x = 22$ or $x = 3$
   $x = 22$ leads to negative lengths and thus does not check.
   The border is 3 yards wide.
2. The hypotenuse of a right triangle is 13 feet long. One leg is 7 feet longer than the other leg. Find the lengths of the legs.
   Let x be the length, in feet, of the shorter leg. The longer leg is $x + 7$.
   $$\begin{aligned} x^2 + (x+7)^2 &= 13^2 \\ x^2 + x^2 + 14x + 49 &= 169 \\ 2x^2 + 14x - 120 &= 0 \\ x^2 + 7x - 60 &= 0 \end{aligned}$$
   $$\begin{aligned} x &= \frac{-7 \pm \sqrt{49 - 4 \cdot 1 \cdot (-60)}}{2} \\ &= \frac{-7 \pm \sqrt{289}}{2} \\ &= \frac{-7 \pm 17}{2} \end{aligned}$$
   $x = 5$ or $x = -12$
   The negative answer does not check.
   The legs are of lengths 5 and 12.

3. The speed of a boat in still water is 8 miles per hour. The boat travels 3 miles upriver and 3 miles back in 1 hour. What is the speed of the river?

Let s be the speed of the river, in miles per hour. The boat's speed upriver is $8 - s$. The time of the trip upriver, using $t = \frac{d}{r}$, is $\frac{3}{8 - s}$. The boat's speed downriver is $8 + s$. The time of the trip downriver, using $t = \frac{d}{r}$, is $\frac{3}{8 + s}$. We summarize in a chart.

	Distance	Rate	Time
Upstream	3	$8 - s$	$\frac{3}{8 - s}$
Downstream	3	$8 + s$	$\frac{3}{8 + s}$

The total time is

$$\frac{3}{8 - s} + \frac{3}{8 + s} = 1$$
$$3(8 + s) + 3(8 - s) = (8 - s)(8 + s)$$
$$24 + 3s + 24 - 3s = 64 - s^2$$
$$s^2 - 16 = 0$$
$$s = 4 \quad \text{or} \quad s = -4$$

The negative answer does not make sense. The speed of the river is 4 miles per hour.

EXAMPLE 3

In April, 1988, *Daedalus 88*, a man-powered aircraft weighing 70 pounds, made a historic 74-mile crossing from Crete to the Greek Isle of Santorini. In testing, the craft was able to fly a three-mile course *with* the wind and fly back *against* the wind in a total time of 25 minutes. If the speed of the wind was three miles per hour, what would be the speed of the *Daedalus 88* in still air?

Let d represent the distance for both directions, as the distances are the same. Let r represent the speed of *Daedalus 88* in still air.

When traveling with the wind, the speed of the plane is $r + 3$, and when traveling against the wind, the speed of the plane is $r - 3$. Since $d = rt$, we know that $t = \frac{d}{r}$. Thus the time to travel against the wind is $\frac{3}{r + 3}$. We summarize this in a chart.

	d	r (mi/h)	t (h)
With the wind	3	$r + 3$	$\frac{3}{r + 3}$
Against the wind	3	$r - 3$	$\frac{3}{r - 3}$

Since the total time is 25 minutes, or $\frac{5}{12}$ hours, we add the time *with* the wind and the time *against* the wind to get an equation for the total time.

$$\frac{3}{r + 3} + \frac{3}{r - 3} = \frac{5}{12} \qquad \text{LCM} = 12(r + 3)(r - 3)$$

$$12(r + 3)(r - 3)\left(\frac{3}{r + 3} + \frac{3}{r - 3}\right) = 12(r + 3)(r - 3)\frac{5}{12} \qquad \text{Multiplying by the LCM}$$

$$36(r - 3) + 36(r + 3) = 5r^2 - 45$$

$$5r^2 - 72r - 45 = 0$$

$$(5r + 3)(r - 15) = 0 \qquad \text{Factoring}$$

$$5r + 3 = 0 \quad \text{or} \quad r - 15 = 0 \qquad \text{Using the principle of zero products}$$

$$5r = -3 \quad \text{or} \quad r = 15$$

$$r = -\frac{3}{5} \quad \text{or} \quad r = 15$$

Since speed cannot be negative, $-\frac{3}{5}$ cannot be a solution. However, 15 checks, so the speed of the plane in still air must be 15 miles per hour.

Try This Solve.

c. The speed of a boat in still water is 12 km/h. The boat travels 45 km upstream and 45 km downstream in a total time of 8 hours. What is the speed of the stream? (Hint: Let s = the speed of the stream. Then $12 - s$ is the speed upstream and $12 + s$ is the speed downstream.) 3 km/h

13-7 EXERCISES

A

Solve.

1. A picture frame is 20 cm by 12 cm. There are 84 cm^2 of picture showing. Find the width of the frame. 3 cm
2. A picture frame is 18 cm by 14 cm. There are 192 cm^2 of picture showing. Find the width of the frame. 1 cm
3. The hypotenuse of a right triangle is 25 ft long. One leg is 17 ft longer than the other. Find the lengths of the legs. 7 ft, 24 ft
4. The hypotenuse of a right triangle is 26 yd long. One leg is 14 yd longer than the other. Find the lengths of the legs. 10 yd, 24 yd
5. The length of a rectangle is 2 cm greater than the width. The area is 80 cm^2. Find the length and width. 8 cm, 10 cm
6. The width of a rectangle is 4 cm less than the length. The area is 320 cm^2. Find the length and width. 20 cm, 16 cm

For Exercises 7 and 8, round your answer to the nearest tenth.

7. The hypotenuse of a right triangle is 8 m long. One leg is 2 m longer than the other. Find the lengths of the legs. 4.6 m, 6.6 m
8. The hypotenuse of a right triangle is 5 cm long. One leg is 2 cm longer than the other. Find the lengths of the legs. 2.4 cm, 4.4 cm
9. The current in a stream moves at a speed of 3 km/h. A boat travels 40 km upstream and 40 km downstream in a total time of 14 hours. What is the speed of the boat in still water? 7 km/h
10. The current in a stream moves at a speed of 4 mi/h. A boat travels 4 mi upstream and 12 mi downstream in a total time of 2 hours. What is the speed of the boat in still water? 8 mi/h
11. The speed of a boat in still water is 10 km/h. The boat travels 12 km upstream and 28 km downstream in a total time of 4 hours. What is the speed of the stream? 4 km/h
12. An airplane flies 738 mi against the wind and 1062 mi with the wind in a total time of 9 hours. The speed of the airplane in still air is 200 mi/h. What is the speed of the wind? 36 mi/h

B

13. Find the side of a square whose diagonal is 3 cm longer than a side.

LESSON QUIZ

1. The hypotenuse of a right triangle is 15 feet long. The short leg is 3 feet less than the long leg. How long are the legs? 9 feet and 12 feet

Assignment Guide

Minimum: 1–12 e/o, MR

Regular: 1–17 e/o, 18, MR

Advanced: 1–17 m3, 18–21, MR

ADDITIONAL ANSWERS

Exercises

13. $3 + 3\sqrt{2}$ or 7.243 cm

14. 2.41 cm
15. 14.14 in.; a 15-in. pizza
16. 5.33 cm
17. 15 mi/h, 20 mi/h
18. 2 ft
19. 100 m
20. 1 second (it will also be at a height of 50 in 10 seconds.)
21. −25 or 25 m below the starting point

Mixed Review

22. 103
23. 3
24. −7, −3
25. 3, −5
26. 5
27. $\frac{-5 \pm \sqrt{17}}{2}$
28. 3, 4
29. $y = -\frac{2}{5}x - \frac{16}{5}$

14. Find r in this figure. Round to the nearest hundredth.

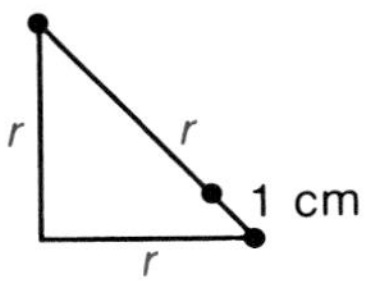

15. What should the diameter (d) of a pizza be so that it has the same area as two 10-in. pizzas? Do you get more to eat with a 15-in. pizza or two 10-in. pizzas?

16. In this figure, the area of the shaded region is 24 cm^2. Find r if R = 6 cm. Round to the nearest hundredth.

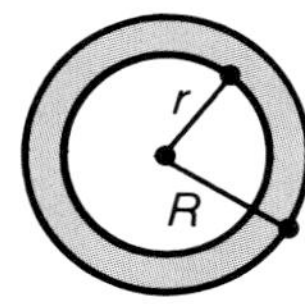

17. Trains A and B leave the same city at the same time. Train A heads north and train B heads east. Train B travels 5 mi/h faster than train A. After 2 hours they are 50 mi apart. Find the speed of each train.

18. ***Write a Convincing Argument*** Solve the problem below. Then write an argument to convince a classmate that your solution is correct.

A 10-ft long ladder leans against a wall. The bottom of the ladder is 6 ft from the wall. How much would the lower end have to be pulled away so that the top end would be pulled down the same amount?

Challenge

The formula $d = rt - 5t^2$ gives the approximate distance in meters of an object above its starting point t seconds after it was thrown with an initial upward velocity of r meters per second. Use this formula to solve the following problems.

19. How high would a ball be in 5 seconds if it was thrown up at an initial velocity of 45 meters per second?

20. How long would it take a ball thrown up at an initial velocity of 55 meters per second to reach a height of 50 meters?

21. Where would a rock be in 5 seconds if it was thrown as shown at the right with an initial upward velocity of 20 meters per second?

Mixed Review

Solve. **22.** $\sqrt{m - 3} = 10$ **23.** $\sqrt{\frac{a}{3}} = 1$ **24.** $x + 7 = 2\sqrt{x + 7}$

Solve. **25.** $x^2 + 2x - 15 = 0$ **26.** $x^2 - 10x + 25 = 0$

27. $x^2 + 5x + 2 = 0$ **28.** $x^2 - 7x + 12 = 0$

29. Find an equation of the line containing the points (2, −4) and (−3, −2).

Problem Solving: Application

Annual Percentage Rate

Banks often advertise interest rates by giving a compound percentage rate followed by a second rate labeled **APR.**

5.5% compounded daily,
5.65% APR

Which rate is correct?

The first is the actual rate used to compute the interest at any given time. Banks call this the **nominal rate.** The second, APR, is the **annual percentage rate,** and is sometimes called the **effective annual yield.** This rate is the equivalent simple interest for one year. You can use the APR as simple interest to quickly determine the amount of interest you will pay or receive in one year. If you invested \$1000 at the rates above, you would earn $\$1000 \times 0.0565 = \$56.50$. The APR gives an efficient way of comparing interest rates. If the APR is not given, you can use the following formula to find it.

Where E = effective annual yield or APR, r is the interest rate, and n is the number of compounding periods per year,

$$E = \left(1 + \frac{r}{n}\right)^n - 1.$$

Find the APR if the advertised interest rate is 7% compounded quarterly.

$$\begin{aligned} E &= \left(1 + \frac{r}{n}\right)^n - 1 \\ &= \left(1 + \frac{0.07}{4}\right)^4 - 1 = (1.035)^4 - 1 \approx 7.19\% \end{aligned}$$

Find the APR if the advertised interest rate is $7\frac{1}{4}\%$ compounded yearly. Compare the results with the rate above.

Problems

1. How much interest will you receive on an investment of \$2100 for 1 year in an account that has an APR of 6.2%?
2. Find the APR if the advertised interest rate is 6.2% compounded monthly.
3. Find the APR if the advertised interest rate is 4.1% compounded daily.
4. Which rate will yield more in one year, one that pays 8.1% compounded monthly or one that pays 8% compounded daily?

Problem Solving: Application

The formula for the APR, or effective yield, can be derived from the simple interest formula, $A = P + Prt$, and the compound interest formula, $A = P\left(1 + \frac{r}{n}\right)^{nt}$.

If we let $t = 1$, the above formulas become $A = P + Pr$, or $A = P(1 + r)$, and $A = P\left(1 + \frac{r}{n}\right)^n$ Since the effective yield is the simple interest for a one year period, we will replace the r in the simple interest formula with E. The amounts will be the same, so we have

$$P(1 + E) = P\left(1 + \frac{r}{n}\right)^n$$

We can simplify

$$\begin{aligned} (1 + E) &= \left(1 + \frac{r}{n}\right)^n \\ E &= \left(1 + \frac{r}{n}\right)^n - 1 \end{aligned}$$

ANSWERS

1. \$130.20
2. 6.38%
3. 4.18%
4. 8.1% compounded monthly

Problem Solving: Situational Problem Solving

You may want to have students work in small groups and prepare several plans. Then have the class decide which plan would be the most practical.

Extension

You may wish to have students change the assumptions. For example, assume that only 250 students will attend if the cost per student is over $5 and that only 150 students will attend if the cost per student is over $10.

Problem Solving: Situational Problem Solving

Designing a School Picnic

Some schools have end-of-the-year picnics for their students. These picnics usually involve games and, of course, food. It takes careful planning to assure that all the expenses can be paid (and that everyone gets enough to eat). You can use the Problem-Solving Guidelines to help organize a plan for a school picnic.

PROBLEM-SOLVING GUIDELINES
■ UNDERSTAND the problem
Develop and carry out a PLAN
■ Find the ANSWER and CHECK

You can use the Problem-Solving Guidelines to help you solve the situational problem about planning a picnic.

Use the Problem-Solving Guidelines to solve the following.

Situational Problem

Lincoln High School has 350 students in the sophomore class. The class has decided to plan an all-day class picnic. They plan to go to a state park that is 30 miles away. They have $200 in the class treasury to spend for the picnic. The students must share the additional expenses. Plan the expenses for this trip and the cost for each student to attend.

Possible Assumptions

1. You will have to buy 1 paper cup and 1 paper plate for each student.
2. There is no cost for supplies for games and activities that you select.
3. All the students in the class will attend the picnic.

How will you design your picnic? What will be the cost per person?

Possible Subproblems

1. What type of food will you have at the picnic and how much of each type will you need?
2. How much will it cost for supplies for the picnic?
3. How much will it cost for transportation?
4. How much more than $200 will your class need for the picnic?

Chapter 13 Summary and Review

13-1

To solve a quadratic equation in standard form, $ax^2 + bx + c = 0$, you may be able to factor the equation and use the principle of zero products to find the solutions.

Write in standard form.

1. $3x^2 + 6x = -4$
2. $5x^2 = 2x$

Solve.

3. $5x^2 - 7x = 0$
4. $3x^2 - 4x = 0$
5. $5x^2 - 8x + 3 = 0$
6. $3y^2 + 5y = 2$

13-2

To solve a quadratic equation of the form $ax^2 = k$ or $(x + a)^2 = k$, first solve for x^2 or $(x + a)^2$, and then find the square roots of each side.

Solve.

7. $5x^2 = 40$
8. $8x^2 = 24$
9. $(x + 8)^2 = 13$
10. $(x + 6)^2 = 49$
11. $4y^2 + 20y + 25 = 16$
12. Suppose we know a polygon has 35 diagonals. Use the formula $d = \frac{n^2 - 3n}{2}$ to find the number of sides.
13. The sum of \$1000 is invested at interest rate r. In 2 years the total grows to \$1690. Use the formula $A = P(1 + r)^t$ to find the annual interest rate.
14. The sum of \$4000, invested at 8% for 2 years, compounded annually, will grow to what amount?

13-3

To complete the square for an expression like $x^2 + 8x$, take half of the coefficient of x and square it. Add this new term to the binomial $x^2 + 8x$ to make a trinomial square, $x^2 + 8x + 16$. You can use the technique of completing the square to solve quadratic equations.

Complete the square.

15. $c^2 + 22c$
16. $w^2 - 7w$

Solve by completing the square.

17. $x^2 - 2x - 10 = 0$
18. $9x^2 - 6x - 9 = 0$
19. $3x^2 - 2x - 5 = 0$
20. $2x^2 + 7x - 1 = 0$

ANSWERS

1. $3x^2 + 6x + 4 = 0$
2. $5x^2 - 2x = 0$
3. $0, \frac{7}{5}$
4. $0, \frac{4}{3}$
5. $\frac{3}{5}, 1$
6. $\frac{1}{3}, -2$
7. $2\sqrt{2}, -2\sqrt{2}$
8. $\sqrt{3}, -\sqrt{3}$
9. $-8 \pm \sqrt{13}$
10. $1, -13$
11. $-\frac{1}{2}, -\frac{9}{2}$
12. $n = 10$
13. 30%
14. \$4665.60
15. $c^2 + 22c + 121$
16. $w^2 - 7w + \frac{49}{4}$
17. $1 \pm \sqrt{11}$
18. $\frac{1 \pm \sqrt{10}}{3}$
19. $\frac{5}{3}, -1$
20. $\frac{-7 \pm \sqrt{57}}{4}$

21. $3 \pm 3\sqrt{2}$
22. $\frac{1 \pm \sqrt{61}}{6}$
23. $\frac{3 \pm \sqrt{33}}{2}$
24. $\frac{-3 \pm \sqrt{89}}{10}$
25. $-3 \pm \sqrt{2}$
26. 7
27. 24, two real-number solutions
28. −8, no real-number solutions
29. 3, −5
30. 1
31. 52
32. 10
33. $F = \frac{mV^2}{qr}$
34. $\sqrt{\frac{3A}{\pi}}$
35. 10 m, 7 m
36. 4 mi/h
37. 10 in., 24 in. or 2 ft

13-4

You can use the **quadratic formula** $x = \frac{-b \pm \sqrt{b^2 - 4ac}}{2a}$ to solve quadratic equations. The expression under the radical, $b^2 - 4ac$, is called the **discriminant.** When the discriminant is positive, there are two real-number solutions to the quadratic equation. When the discriminant is 0, there is only one real-number solution, and when the discriminant is negative, there are no real-number solutions.

Solve using the quadratic formula.

21. $x^2 - 6x - 9 = 0$

22. $3x^2 - x - 5 = 0$

23. $x^2 - 3x - 6 = 0$

24. $5x^2 + 3x - 4 = 0$

25. $x^2 + 6x + 7 = 0$

26. $x^2 - 14x + 49 = 0$

Compute the discriminant and determine how many real-number solutions there are.

27. $5x^2 - 8x + 2 = 0$

28. $x^2 - 18x + 83 = 0$

13-5

When you multiply both sides of a rational equation by the LCM, you may get a quadratic equation. Be sure to check all possible solutions in the original equation.

Solve.

29. $\frac{15}{x} - \frac{15}{x + 2} = 2$

30. $x + \frac{1}{x} = 2$

13-6

To solve a radical equation, first square both sides to find a quadratic equation. Then solve by factoring or using the quadratic equation.

31. $\sqrt{x - 3} = 7$

32. $\sqrt{3x + 4} = \sqrt{2x + 14}$

33. Solve for F: $V = \sqrt{\frac{Fqr}{m}}$

34. Solve for r: $A = \frac{1}{3}\pi r^2$

13-7

You can use the Problem-Solving Guidelines to solve problems involving quadratic equations.

35. The length of a rectangle is 3 m greater than the width. The area is 70 m^2. Find the length and the width.

36. You can row upstream 5 miles and then row back downstream all in 3 hours and 20 minutes. If the river has an average current of 2 mi/h, at what rate are you able to row in still water?

37. One side of a right triangle is 1 ft, 4 in. shorter than the hypotenuse. The other side is 2 in. shorter than the hypotenuse. Find the lengths of the two legs.

Chapter 13 Test

Write in standard form.

1. $6x^2 = 3x + 4$
2. $3y = 2y^2$

Solve.

3. $4a^2 + 4a = 0$
4. $7x^2 + 8x = 0$
5. $x^2 + 2x - 48 = 0$
6. $3y^2 + 5y = 2$
7. $16b^2 - 25b = 0$
8. $7x^2 = 35$
9. $(x + 8)^2 = 13$
10. $(x - 1)^2 = 8$

Complete the square.

11. $x^2 + 8x$
12. $y^2 + 9y$

Solve.

13. $x^2 + 4x - 10 = 0$
14. $x^2 - 3x - 7 = 0$
15. $x^2 - x - 3 = 0$
16. $3x^2 - 7x + 1 = 0$
17. $x - \frac{2}{x} = 1$
18. $\frac{4}{x} - \frac{4}{x + 2} = 1$

Compute the value of the discriminant and use it to determine how many real-number solutions each quadratic equation has.

19. $3x^2 + 12x + 13 = 0$
20. $5x^2 + 17x + 14 = 0$

Solve.

21. $\sqrt{x + 1} = 6$
22. $\sqrt{6x + 1} = \sqrt{5x + 13}$
23. Solve $g = 2\sqrt{\frac{v}{kh}}$ for h.
24. The sum of \$2000 is invested at interest rate r. In 4 years it grows to \$2621.59. Use the formula $A = P(1 + r)^t$ to find the interest rate r.
25. The width of a rectangle is 4 m less than the length. The area is 16.25 m^2. Find the length and the width.
26. An airplane flies between two cities that are 700 miles apart, traveling with a wind of 25 mi/h when going, and traveling against it when returning. The trip out takes 15 minutes less time than the return flight. What is the speed of the plane in still air?

ANSWERS

1. $6x^2 - 3x - 4 = 0$
2. $2y^2 - 3y = 0$
3. $0, -1$
4. $0, -\frac{8}{7}$
5. $-8, 6$
6. $\frac{1}{3}, -2$
7. $0, \frac{25}{16}$
8. $\pm\sqrt{5}$
9. $-8 \pm \sqrt{13}$
10. $1 \pm 2\sqrt{2}$
11. $x^2 + 8x + 16$
12. $y^2 + 9y + \frac{81}{4}$
13. $-2 \pm \sqrt{14}$
14. $\frac{3 \pm \sqrt{37}}{2}$
15. $\frac{1 \pm \sqrt{13}}{2}$
16. $\frac{7 \pm \sqrt{37}}{6}$
17. $2, -1$
18. $2, -4$
19. -12, no real-number solutions
20. 9, two real-number solutions
21. 35
22. 12
23. $\frac{4V}{kg^2}$
24. 7%
25. $l = 6.5$ m, $w = 2.5$ m
26. 375 mi/h

Test Item Analysis

Item	Lesson
1–6	13-1
7–10	13-2
11–12	13-3
13–16	13-4
17–18	13-5
19–20	13-4
21–23	13-6
24	13-2
25–26	13-7

CHAPTER **14**

Trigonometry

Chapter Overview

A review of geometry needed for trigonometry is presented early in this chapter. Similar triangles are introduced, and the proportionality of corresponding sides in similar triangles is presented. Proportionality is used to find the missing sides in similar triangles. (For further geometry review, use *Geometry Review* worksheets in the **Skills Practice and Mixed Review** supplement.)

The sine, cosine, and tangent of an angle are defined as ratios of lengths of sides in a right triangle. The use of trigonometric tables and calculators is discussed. Measures of angles and lengths of sides are found from the values of the trigonometric ratios.

A problem-solving section suggests a strategy for solving problems involving the trigonometric ratios. The situational problem presented is *Designing a Park*.

Objectives

14-1
- Write true proportions for similar right triangles.
- Find a missing side in a pair of similar right triangles.

14-2
- Find the sine ratio of an angle.
- Find the cosine ratio of an angle.
- Find the tangent ratio of an angle.

14-3
- Find the value of a trigonometric ratio by reading a table or using a calculator.
- Find an angle given the value of a trigonometric ratio.

14-4
- Solve problems involving trigonometric functions.

TEACHING CHAPTER 14

Cooperative Learning Opportunities

Measurement activities can help teach the concept of similarity as used in the basic right-triangle trigonometric functions. As an introductory activity to Lesson 14-2, assign students in pairs and distribute to each student a sheet with right triangles as shown here. Make the triangles as large as possible.

Ask the groups to identify the three similar triangles. Then have students measure the sides of the triangles and compute, to the nearest hundredth, the sine and cosine of $\angle A$ in each triangle. Partners should work together reading measurements. They will have 3 numbers for each angle. Have the students use a protractor to measure $\angle A$ to the nearest degree. Review the function values found by different groups and compare them with the values in the trig tables.

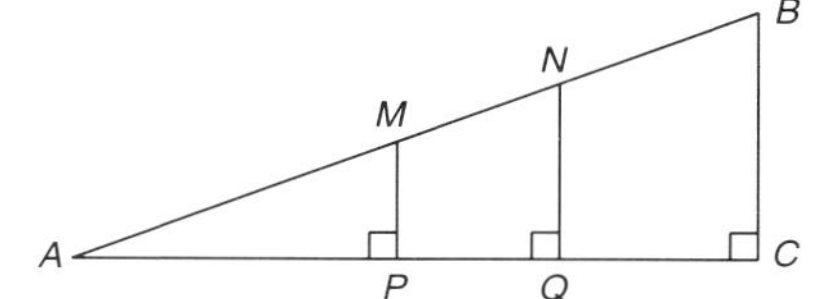

Multicultural Note: *The Origins of Trigonometry*

The various measurements, ratios and tables that have been collected under the name trigonometry originated in different places and circumstances.

The Greek historian Herodotus wrote that, after each flood, the rulers in Egypt would send out surveyors to measure the land, discover the area that was lost and then rectify the situation. It is also said that the Egyptians used a cord with 12 equally spaced knots to form a right triangle that might be used as the corner of a plot.

The Babylonians created the 360-degree circle, a figure that has come to be universally accepted. The Babylonians also made accurate astronomical measurements and were able to predict eclipses.

Ptolemy, a Greek mathematician and astronomer of the second century A.D., made discoveries about quadrilaterals inscribed in circles that led to formulas for the sums and differences of trig functions. These, in turn, permitted Ptolemy to construct accurate trigonometric tables.

Alternative Assessment and Communication Ideas

You can sometimes evaluate students' grasp of concepts by their ability to extend ideas.

Have students rewrite, in their own words, the definition of similar triangles. Then ask them to write a definition of similar rectangles and similar pentagons. Have them draw figures corresponding to the definitions. Point out, if necessary, that two polygons need not be regular in order to be similar.

Next ask students to write about similarity of two squares or two circles, and then about similarity of regular polygons with the same number of sides. Finally, ask students if they can write a definition of similarity for two n-gons, that is two n-sided polygons.

If your students are working with scientific calculators, have them do some of the exercises in Lesson 14-3 using the calculator and some using the tables.

Investigations and Projects

Have students investigate the trig functions as defined within a circle. The tables in the back of the book, by giving values for 0 and 90, already take a small step beyond the right–triangle definitions. Show the diagram below and ask students how to define the trigonometric functions for values from 90 to 180.

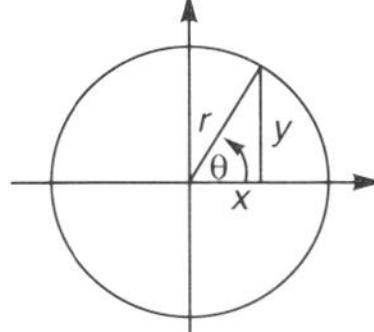

As they develop hypotheses and suggest results you can ask leading questions about relationships: How are the values from 0 to 90 related to those from 90 to 180? How are sine and cosine values related to each other? What can you say about values at 0, 90 and 180?

MANAGING CHAPTER 14

Lesson	PACING CHART (DAYS) 2-Year* A for E	1-Year Minimum	1-Year Regular**	1-Year Advanced	Opening Activity	Cooperative Activity	Seat or Group Work
14-1	2	0	1	1	First Five Minutes 14-1: ***FFMTM*** p. 39 or **TE** p. 614; ***Overhead Transparencies*** T31; Application: **SE** p. 614	Lesson Enrichment: **SE** p. 616	Try This a–b
14-2	3	0	1	1	First Five Minutes 14-2: ***FFMTM*** p. 39 or **TE** p. 619; ***Overhead Transparencies*** T32	✂ Manipulative Activity 14: ***Enrichment*** p. 47	Try This a–c
14-3	2	0	1	1	First Five Minutes 14-3: ***FFMTM*** p. 40 or **TE** p. 625	Problem 38: **SE** p. 627	Try This a–g
14-4	3	0	4	3	First Five Minutes 14-4: ***FFMTM*** p. 40 or **TE** p. 628	Problem Solving: Application: **SE** p. 633; Problem Solving: Situational Problem Solving: **SE** p. 634	Try This a–c
Review	2	0	1	1			
Test	1	0	1	1			
Cum. Review	0	0	1	0			
End-of-Year Test	0	0	1	0			

*2-Year Management Guide can be found in *Algebra for Everyone*.

**Either Chapter 14 or Chapter 15 can be covered.

FFMTM: First Five Minutes Transparency Masters

Enrichment	Review/Assess	Reteach	Technology	Lesson
Lesson Enrichment: **SE** p. 616; Looking for Errors 14: ***Enrichment*** p. 63	Lesson Quiz: **TE** p. 616		BASIC Computer Project 18: ***Technology*** p. 80	**14-1**
Calculator Investigation: **SE** p. 624; ✂ Manipulative Activity 14: ***Enrichment*** p. 47	Mixed Review 27: ***SPMR*** p. 77; Mixed Practice 27: **SE** p. 710; Lesson Quiz: **TE** p. 621; Quiz 27: ***Assessment*** p. 37	Skills Practice 37: ***SPMR*** p. 45	Calculator Investigation: **SE** p. 624	**14-2**
Bonus Topic 14: ***Enrichment*** p. 15	Lesson Quiz: **TE** p. 626		Finding Trigonometric Values: **SE** p. 625; Finding Angles: **SE** p. 626; Calculator Worksheets 29, 30: ***Technology*** pp. 31, 32	**14-3**
Lesson Enrichment: **SE** p. 629; Problem Solving: Application: **SE** p. 633; Problem Solving: Situational Problem Solving: **SE** p. 634; Critical Thinking 14: ***Enrichment*** p. 31	Mixed Review 28: ***SPMR*** p. 78; Mixed Practice 28: **SE** p. 711; Lesson Quiz: **TE** p. 630; Quiz 28: ***Assessment*** p. 38	Skills Practice 38: ***SPMR*** p. 46; Problem Bank 27: ***Problem Bank*** p. 44; Strategy Problem Bank 14: ***Problem Bank*** p. 15	Problem for Programmers: **SE** p. 632; Calculator Worksheet 31: ***Technology*** p. 33; Spreadsheet Activity 11: ***Technology*** pp. 57–58; BASIC Computer Project 19: ***Technology*** p. 81	**14-4**
	Summary and Review: **SE** pp. 635–636; Test: **SE** p. 637			**Review**
	Chapter 14 Exam: ***A for E*** pp. 511–512; Chapter 14 Test: ***Assessment*** pp. 149–154 (reg.), 189–190 (adv.)			**Test**
	Cumulative Review: **SE** pp. 677–683			**Cum. Review**
	End-of-Year Test: ***Assessment*** pp. 241–258 (reg.); Assessing Strategies 8: ***Assessment*** pp. 209–210			**End-of Year Test**

SPMR: Skills Practice Mixed Review

The solution to the problem posed on the facing page can be found on page 633.

Ready for Trigonometry?

2-6 Write using decimal notation. Approximate to four decimal places.

1. $\frac{15}{16}$ 0.9375 **2.** $\frac{13}{12}$ 1.0833 **3.** $\frac{5}{17}$ 0.2941 **4.** $\frac{24}{25}$ 0.9600 **5.** $\frac{8}{13}$ 0.6154 **6.** $\frac{15}{39}$ 0.3846

3-9 Solve.

7. $\frac{4}{5} = \frac{x}{20}$ 16 **8.** $\frac{9}{10} = \frac{2}{t}$ $2\frac{2}{9}$ **9.** $\frac{14}{20} = \frac{3}{m}$ $4\frac{2}{7}$ **10.** $\frac{5}{9} = \frac{y}{11}$ $6\frac{1}{9}$

3-11 Translate to an equation. Then solve and check.

11. One angle of a triangle is three times as large as another. The third angle is twice the sum of the other two angles. What are the measures of the three angles? 15°, 45°, 120°

12. One angle of a triangle is six times as large as another. The measure of the third angle is 84° greater than that of the smallest angle. What are the measures of the three angles? 12°, 72°, 96°

CHAPTER

Trigonometry 14

When surveyors are working on maps of land that has a slope, they have to measure the surface distance and also find the horizontal distance that will be shown on a map. What is the horizontal distance that will underlie a surface distance of 138 m where the land slopes upward at 32°?

14-1

FIRST FIVE MINUTES

1. What is the degree measure of a right angle? 90°
2. If the triangle ABC is a right triangle with legs of length 6 and 8, what is the length of the hypotenuse?
   $c = 10$
3. If a triangle is not a right triangle, does it have a hypotenuse?
   No, the hypotenuse is the side opposite the right angle.

Similar Triangles

Develop the idea of similar triangles by constructing several triangles with the same angle measurement. Many students are surprised that the angle measurement of a large triangle can be the same as for a small triangle.

Point out that angles are often labeled with capital letters, and sides are labeled with lowercase letters. We use a for the side opposite angle A, b for the side opposite angle B, etc.

Remind students that the symbol ~ means *is similar to.*

Emphasize that only the corresponding sides of similar triangles are proportional, not just any pair.

Key Questions

- Is a triangle with sides 3, 5, and 7 similar to a triangle with sides 6, 10, and 14?
  Yes
- Find a triangle that is similar to a triangle with sides 2, 4, and 6.
  A triangle with sides 1, 2, and 3 or any multiples of 1, 2, and 3

Chalkboard Example (*T31*)

1. $\triangle PQR$ is similar to $\triangle XYZ$. Write several true proportions.

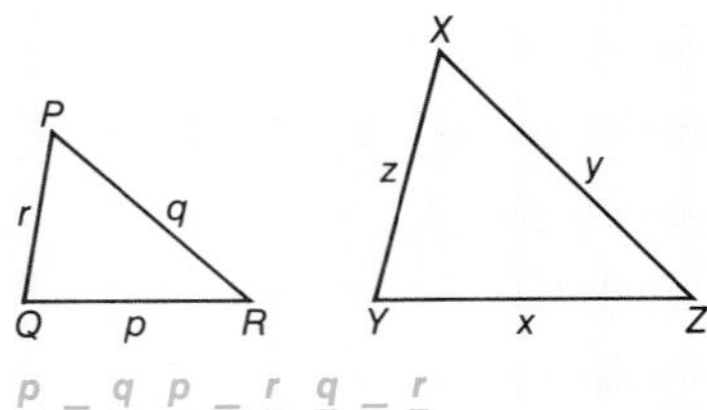

$\frac{p}{x} = \frac{q}{y}, \frac{p}{x} = \frac{r}{z}, \frac{q}{y} = \frac{r}{z}$

14-1 Similar Right Triangles

Application

Similar triangles have the same shape, but do not need to be the same size or positioned the same way. The distance across the river can be found using similar triangles.

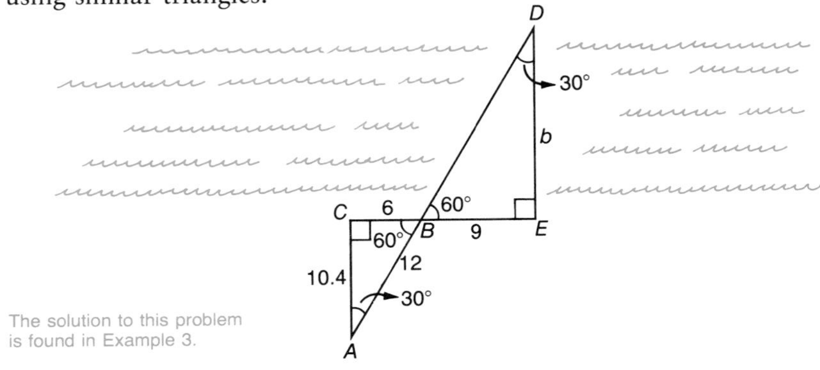

The solution to this problem is found in Example 3.

Similar Triangles

Objective: Write true proportions for similar right triangles.

In similar triangles, we identify corresponding angles and sides. Notice that angle B is the same in both triangles, angles C and E have the same measure, and angles A and D have the same measure.

Corresponding Angles	Corresponding Sides
$\angle B$ and $\angle B$	$\overline{AC}$ and $\overline{DE}$
$\angle C$ and $\angle E$	$\overline{AB}$ and $\overline{BD}$
$\angle A$ and $\angle D$	$\overline{BC}$ and $\overline{BE}$

When writing a statement such as $\triangle ACB \sim \triangle DEB$, we always list the vertices in corresponding order. For the triangles above, we could also write $\triangle BCA \sim \triangle BED$ or $\triangle CBA \sim \triangle EBD$.

Similar Triangles

Similar triangles have the following properties:

1. The lengths of the corresponding sides of a pair of similar triangles are proportional.
2. Corresponding angles are the same size.

EXAMPLE 1 $\triangle ABC \sim \triangle RST$. Write three true proportions.

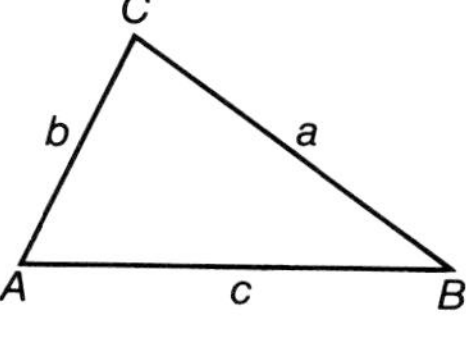

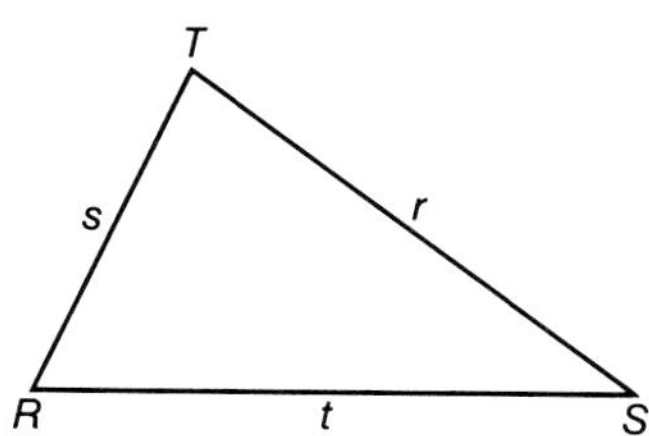

The small letters are the lengths of the sides.

These proportions are true.

$$\frac{a}{r} = \frac{b}{s}, \frac{c}{t} = \frac{a}{r}, \text{ and } \frac{b}{s} = \frac{c}{t}$$

There are others.

Try This

a. $\triangle PQR \sim \triangle XYZ$. Write three true proportions.

$\frac{p}{x} = \frac{q}{y}, \frac{r}{z} = \frac{p}{x}, \frac{q}{y} = \frac{r}{z}$; there are others.

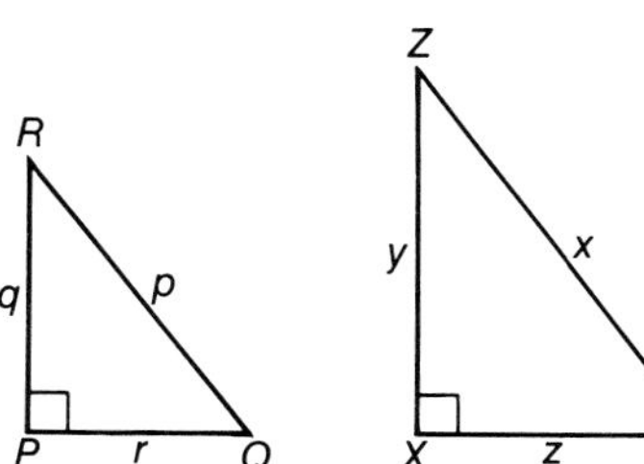

Right Triangles

Objective: Find a missing side in a pair of similar right triangles.

A right triangle has one angle of 90°, often marked with a small square. The other two angles must each be less than 90°, since the sum of the interior angles of a triangle is 180°. Angles whose measures are less than 90° are called **acute angles.** If two angles of any triangle have the same measures as two angles of another triangle, then the third angles must also be equal. Therefore, two right triangles are similar if an acute angle of one triangle has the same measure as the acute angle of the other.

Right Triangles

You may want to demonstrate the fact that the sum of the angles of a triangle is 180°. Cut out a triangle and tear off each corner. Place the three corners together to show that they form a line, which is 180°.

Chalkboard Examples

1. Which triangles are similar?

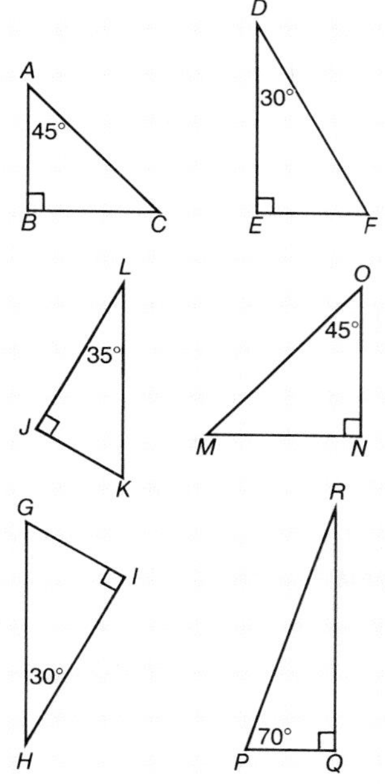

$\triangle ABC \sim \triangle MNO$, $\triangle DEF \sim \triangle HIG$

2. Suppose $\triangle UVW$ is similar to $\triangle RST$. Find the length of r.

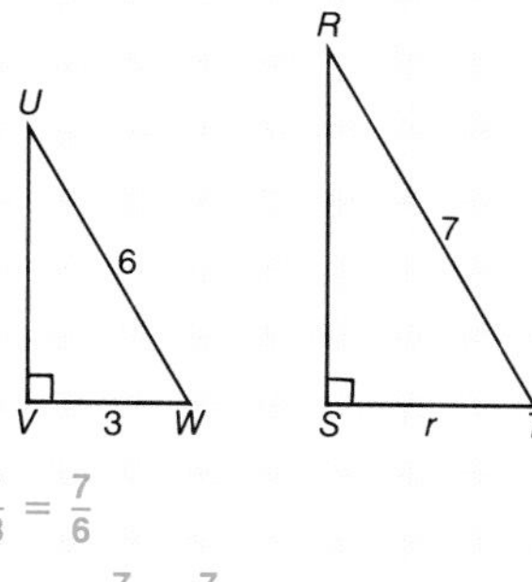

$\frac{r}{3} = \frac{7}{6}$

$r = 3 \cdot \frac{7}{6} = \frac{7}{2}$

LESSON ENRICHMENT

Right triangles ABC and ADC are inscribed in a circle with diameter AC as shown.

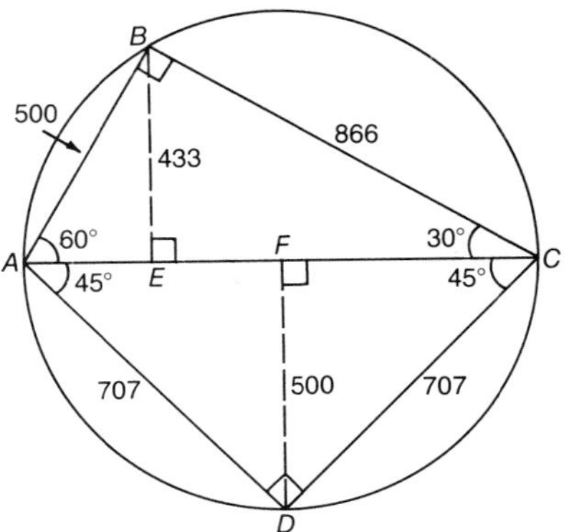

Find pairs of similar triangles.

$\triangle ABE \sim \triangle BCE$ $\triangle ADF \sim \triangle CDF$
$\triangle ABC \sim \triangle BEC$ $\triangle ADF \sim \triangle ACD$
$\triangle ABE \sim \triangle ACB$ $\triangle CDF \sim \triangle ACD$

Find the lengths of AE, EC, AF, and AC.

250, 750, 500, 1000

LESSON QUIZ

1. $\triangle ABC$ is similar to $\triangle XYZ$. Write three true proportions.

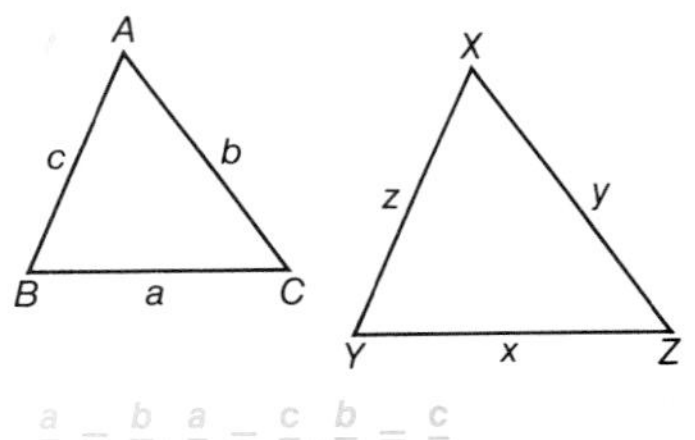

$\frac{a}{x} = \frac{b}{y}, \frac{a}{x} = \frac{c}{z}, \frac{b}{y} = \frac{c}{z}$

2. $\triangle ABC$ is similar to $\triangle XYZ$. Find length y.

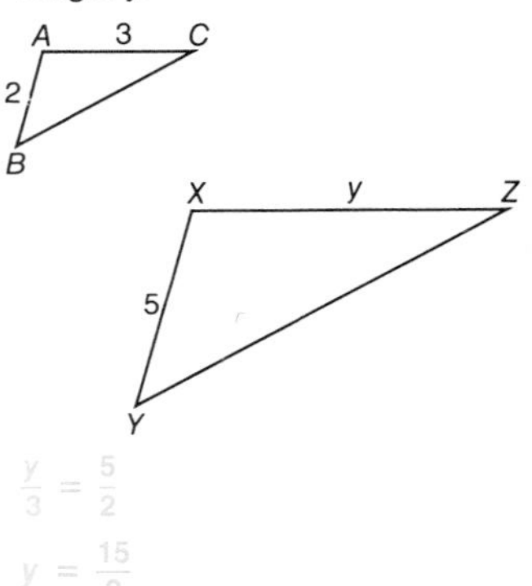

$\frac{y}{3} = \frac{5}{2}$

$y = \frac{15}{2}$

EXAMPLE 2 Which right triangles are similar?

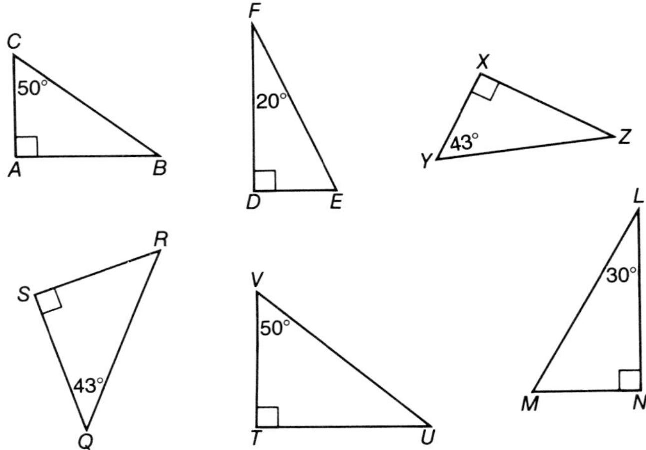

$\triangle ABC \sim \triangle TUV$ and $\triangle XYZ \sim \triangle SQR$.

When triangles are similar, the corresponding sides are proportional. We can use this relationship to find the length of a side whose length is not known.

EXAMPLE 3 $\triangle ACB \sim \triangle DEB$.
Find length b.

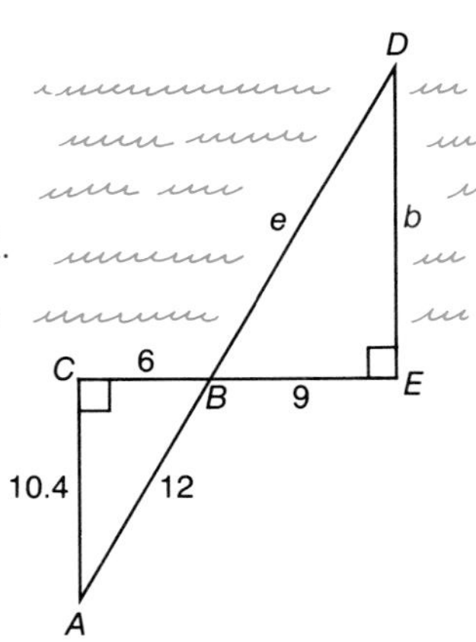

$$\frac{b}{10.4} = \frac{9}{6}$$ The corresponding sides are proportional.

$$10.4 \cdot \frac{b}{10.4} = \frac{9}{6} \cdot 10.4$$ Multiplying each side by 10.4

$$b = 15.6$$

The length b is 15.6.

Try This

b. $\triangle RST \sim \triangle WXY$. Find length x. 75

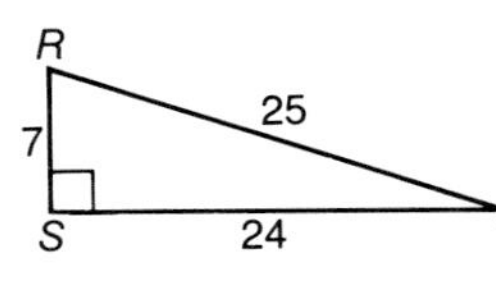

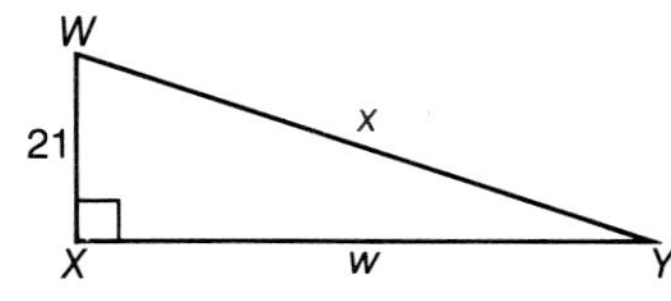

14-1 EXERCISES

A

1. $\triangle ABC \sim \triangle DEF$. Name the corresponding sides and angles.

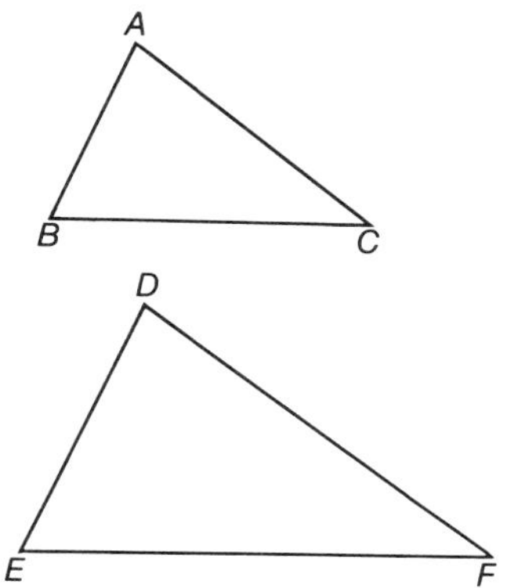

2. $\triangle PQR \sim \triangle WXY$. Name the corresponding sides and angles.

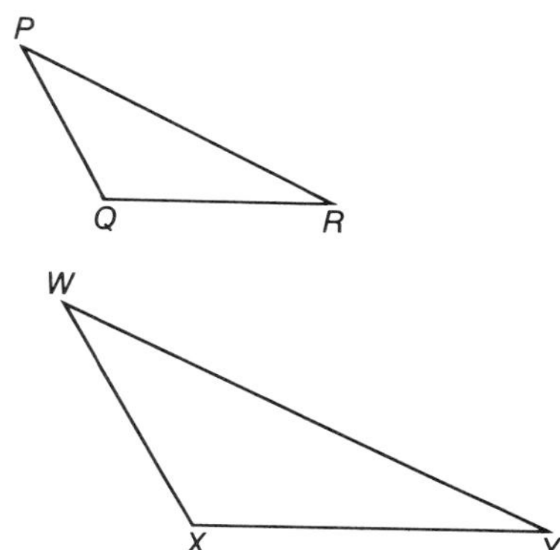

3. $\triangle STU \sim \triangle LMN$. Write three true proportions.

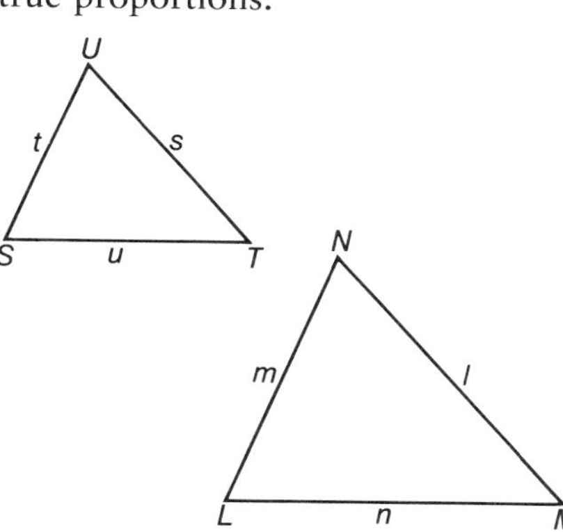

4. $\triangle FGH \sim \triangle JKL$. Write three true proportions.

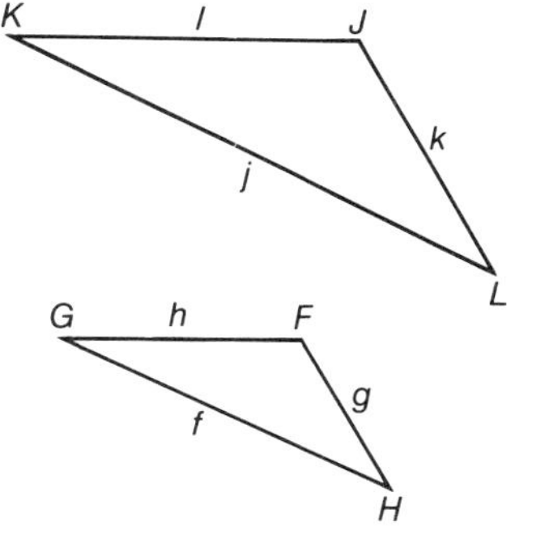

5. $\triangle ABC \sim \triangle DEF$. Find length f. 16

C 9 15 A 12 B

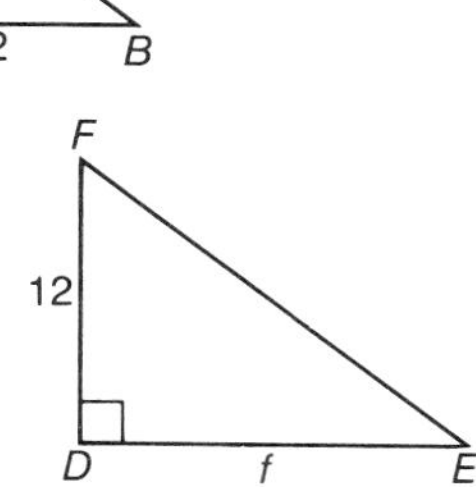

6. $\triangle LMN \sim \triangle HJK$. Find length h. $3\sqrt{89}$

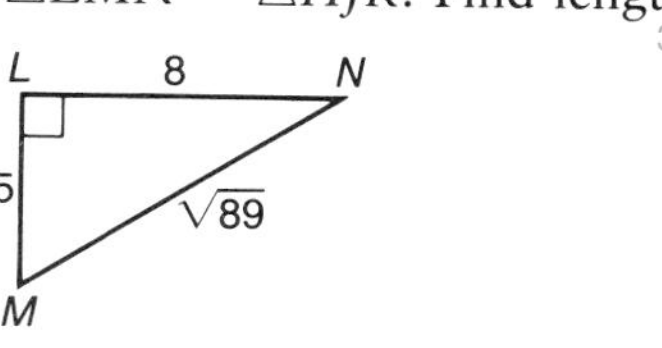

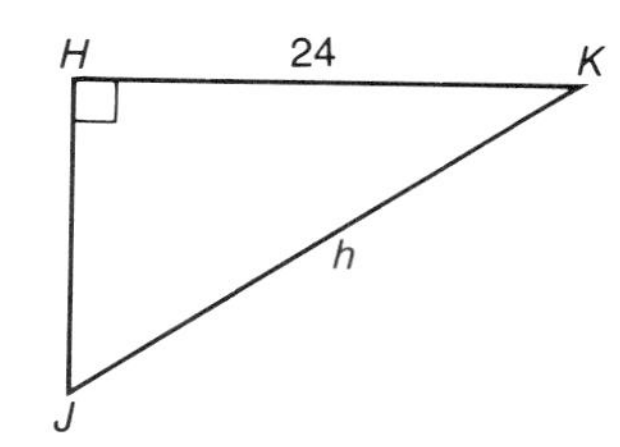

Assignment Guide
Minimum: omit

Regular: 1–10, MR

Advanced: 1–9 e/o, 10–14, MR

ADDITIONAL ANSWERS

Exercises

1. Corresponding angles: $\angle B$ and $\angle E$, $\angle C$ and $\angle F$, $\angle A$ and $\angle D$; corresponding sides: $\overline{BC}$ and $\overline{EF}$, $\overline{CA}$ and $\overline{FD}$, $\overline{AB}$ and $\overline{DE}$
2. Corresponding angles: $\angle Q$ and $\angle X$, $\angle R$ and $\angle Y$, $\angle P$ and $\angle W$; corresponding sides: $\overline{QR}$ and $\overline{XY}$, $\overline{RP}$ and $\overline{YW}$, $\overline{PQ}$ and $\overline{WX}$
3. Answers may vary. $\frac{t}{m} = \frac{u}{n}, \frac{s}{u} = \frac{l}{n}, \frac{u}{t} = \frac{n}{m}$
4. Answers may vary. $\frac{g}{k} = \frac{f}{j}, \frac{h}{l} = \frac{g}{k}, \frac{j}{l} = \frac{f}{h}$

Mixed Review
15. $-3 \pm \sqrt{14}$
16. $2 \pm 2\sqrt{5}$
17. 1 real-number solution
18. No real-number solution
19. $y = \frac{21}{x}$
20. $x = \frac{1}{4}yz$
21. $y = 0.3x$
22. $2m(m - 2)^2$
23. $(a - 6)^2(a + 6)^2$
24. $(x + 5)(x - 5)$

7. A rod 3 m tall casts a shadow 5 m long. At the same time, the shadow of a tower is 110 m long. How tall is the tower? 66 m

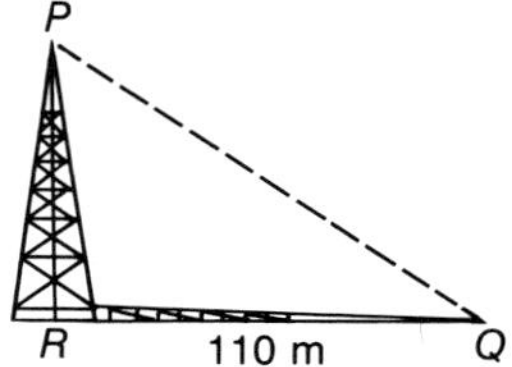

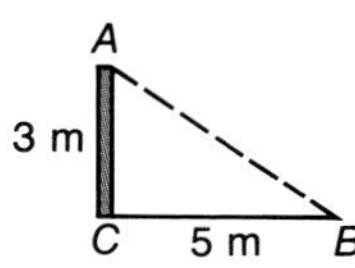

B

Assume that the three sides of $\triangle RST$ are 12, 16, and 20.

8. If $\triangle DEF$ is similar to $\triangle RST$ and the longest side of $\triangle DEF$ is 30, what are the lengths of the other two sides? 18, 24

9. If $\triangle XYZ \sim \triangle RST$ and the shortest side of $\triangle XYZ$ is 6, what are the lengths of the other two sides? 8, 10

10. ***Critical Thinking*** What relationship holds between the area of $\triangle ABC$ and $\triangle DEF$ if the triangles are similar and $\frac{AB}{DE} = k$? Area $\triangle ABC = k^2 \cdot$ Area $\triangle DEF$

Challenge

11. There are three right triangles in the figure below. Name them, writing the right angle first. $\triangle BAC$, $\triangle DAB$, $\triangle DBC$

12. Which of these proportions are true?

$\frac{AB}{BC} = \frac{AC}{DB}$ No

$\frac{AC}{AB} = \frac{BC}{BD}$ Yes

$\frac{BD}{BC} = \frac{AB}{BC}$ No

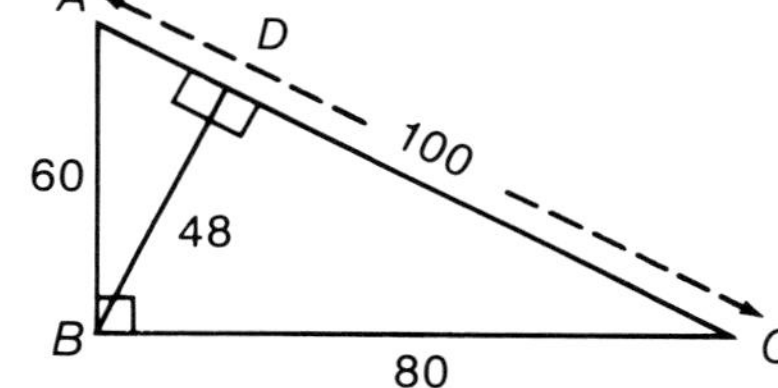

13. If $\frac{AD}{AB} = \frac{AB}{AC}$, find the length of $\overline{AD}$. 36

14. If $\frac{AD}{BD} = \frac{BD}{DC}$, find the length of $\overline{DC}$. 64

Mixed Review

Solve. **15.** $x^2 + 6x - 5 = 0$ **16.** $x^2 - 4x - 16 = 0$

Find the number of real-number solutions.

17. $x^2 - 10x + 25 = 0$ **18.** $y^2 - y + 1 = 0$

Write an equation of variation. **19.** y varies inversely as x, and $y = 3$ when $x = 7$. **20.** x varies jointly with y and z, and $x = 9$ when $y = 4$ and $z = 9$. **21.** y varies directly as x, and $y = 1.2$ when $x = 4$.

Factor. **22.** $2m^3 - 8m^2 + 8m$ **23.** $a^4 - 72a^2 + 1296$

24. $x^2 - 25$

14-2 Trigonometric Ratios

For any right triangle six ratios of pairs of sides are possible. For the triangle at the right, we have these six ratios.

$$\frac{a}{c}, \frac{b}{c}, \frac{a}{b}, \frac{b}{a}, \frac{c}{a}, \frac{c}{b}$$

These six ratios are called *trigonometric ratios.*

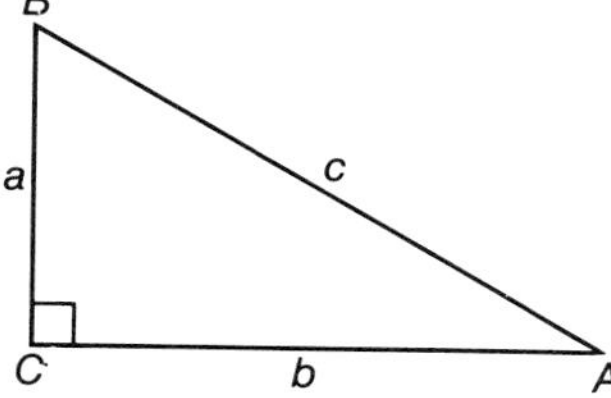

Sine

Objective: Find the sine ratio of an angle.

Each of these six ratios has a name. First we discuss the **sine** ratio. We define the sine ratio as follows.

$$\text{The sine of } A \text{ (or } \sin A) = \frac{\text{length of side opposite } \angle A}{\text{length of hypotenuse}} = \frac{a}{c}$$

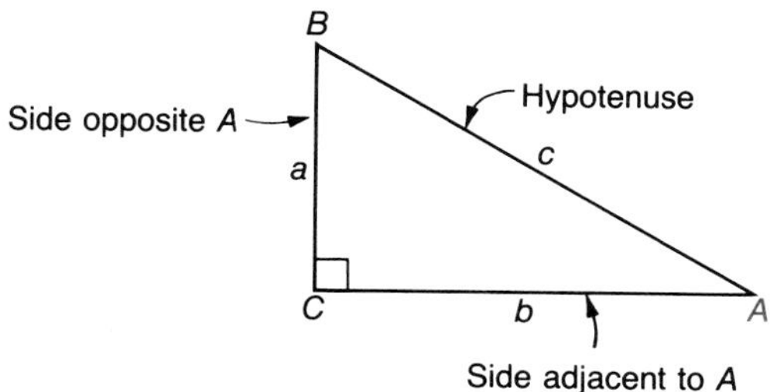

EXAMPLE 1

In $\triangle ABC$, find $\sin B$. Write this value to four decimal places.

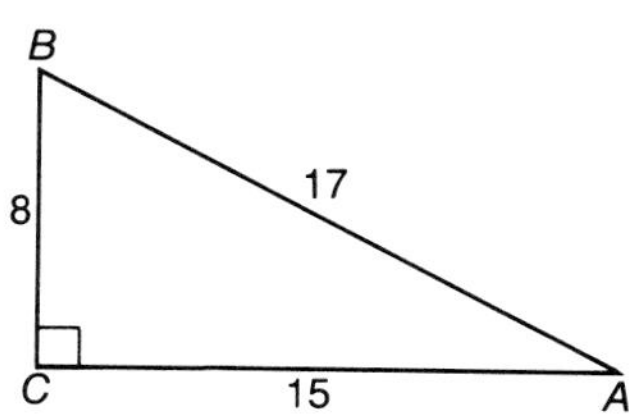

$$\sin B = \frac{\text{length of side opposite } \angle B}{\text{length of hypotenuse}} = \frac{15}{17} \approx 0.8824$$

14-2

FIRST FIVE MINUTES

1. $\triangle ABC$ is similar to $\triangle XYZ$. Find x and y.

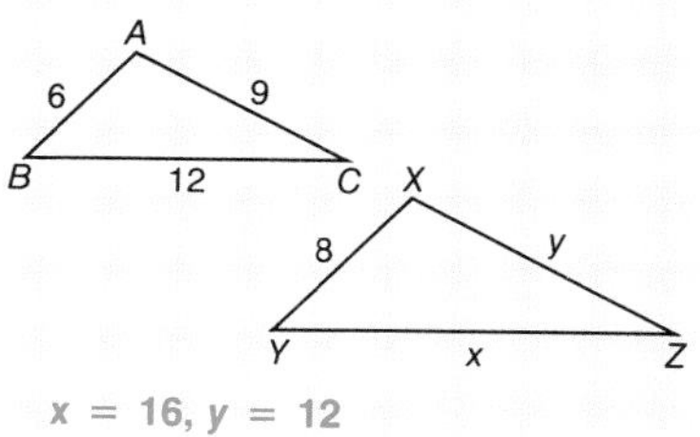

$x = 16, y = 12$

Sine

Draw a right triangle and ask students to identify the hypotenuse and the opposite and adjacent sides, for each angle. Emphasize that the adjacent side of one acute angle is the opposite side of another.

Point out that trigonometric ratios can only be formed for the acute angles in a right triangle, not the right angle.

The definition of the sine function is often shortened to opposite/hypotenuse. It is important, however, for students to understand that "opposite" is short for "the length of the side opposite the angle."

Key Questions

- What happens to the sine ratio when each side of the triangle is doubled in length?
  The sine remains constant.
- How is the sine ratio computed?
  The *opposite* over the *hypotenuse*

Chalkboard Examples (*T32*)

1. Find $\sin A$.

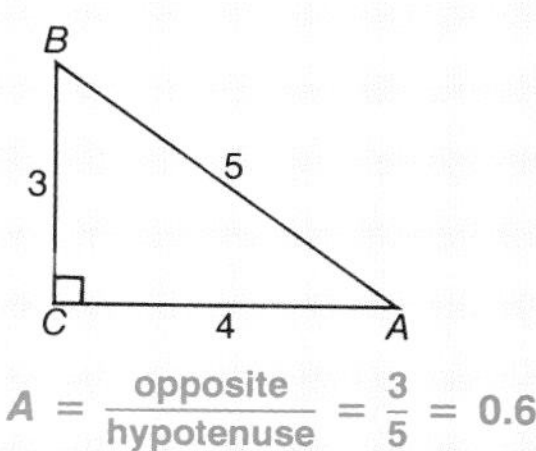

$\sin A = \frac{\text{opposite}}{\text{hypotenuse}} = \frac{3}{5} = 0.6$

2. Find $\sin B$.

$\sin B = \frac{4}{5} = 0.8$

Cosine

Point out that the word *adjacent* means "near" or "close to." Note that the sine of angle *A* is the cosine of angle *B* in the triangle below.

Chalkboard Examples (*T32*)

1. Find cos *A*.

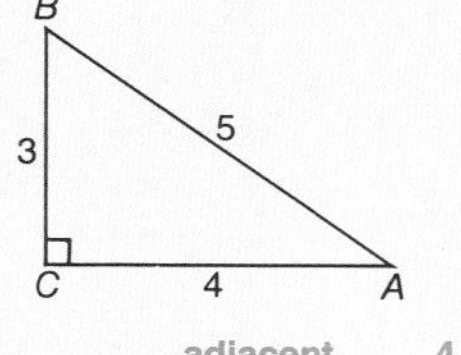

$\cos A = \frac{\text{adjacent}}{\text{hypotenuse}} = \frac{4}{5} = 0.8$

2. Find cos *B*.

$\cos B = \frac{3}{5} = 0.6$

3. Find sin *A*.

$\sin A = \frac{3}{5} = 0.6$

Try This

a. In $\triangle PQR$, find $\sin R$ to four decimal places.

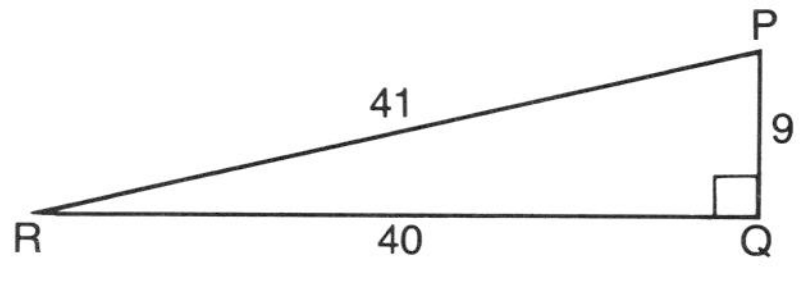

$\frac{9}{41} \approx 0.2195$

Cosine

Objective: Find the cosine ratio of an angle.

For any acute angle *A* of a right triangle, we define the **cosine** ratio as follows.

$$\text{The cosine of } A \text{ (or } \cos A) = \frac{\text{length of side adjacent to } \angle A}{\text{length of hypotenuse}} = \frac{b}{c}.$$

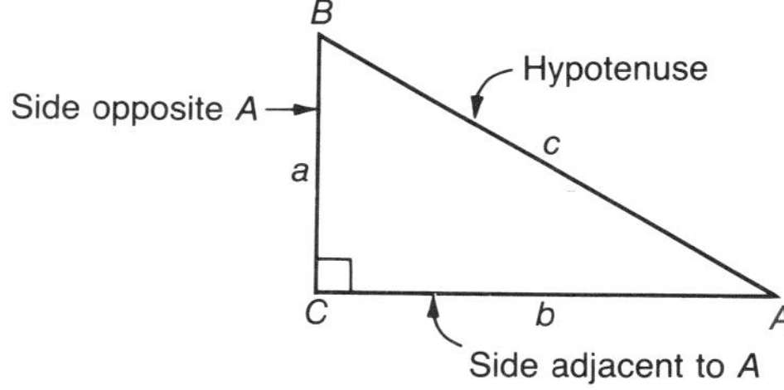

EXAMPLE 2

In $\triangle CLF$, find $\cos F$. Write this value to four decimal places.

$$\cos F = \frac{\text{length of side adjacent to } \angle F}{\text{length of hypotenuse}} = \frac{32}{40}$$

$$= \frac{4}{5} = 0.8000$$

$$\cos F = 0.8000$$

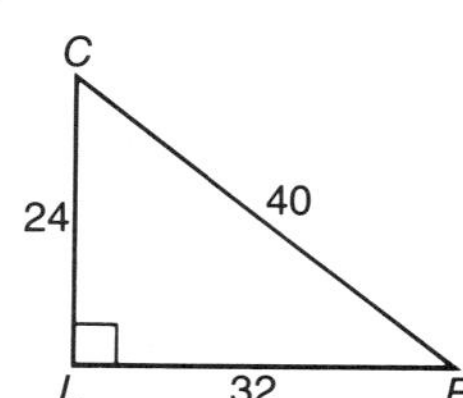

Try This

b. In $\triangle DEF$, find $\cos D$ to four decimal places. $\frac{15}{39} \approx 0.3846$

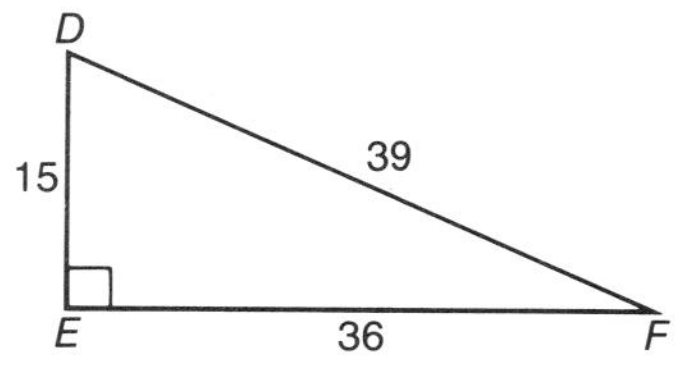

Tangent

Objective: Find the tangent ratio of an angle.

For any acute angle A of a right triangle, we define the **tangent** ratio as follows.

The tangent of A:

$$\tan A = \frac{\text{length of opposite side}}{\text{length of adjacent side}} = \frac{a}{b}$$

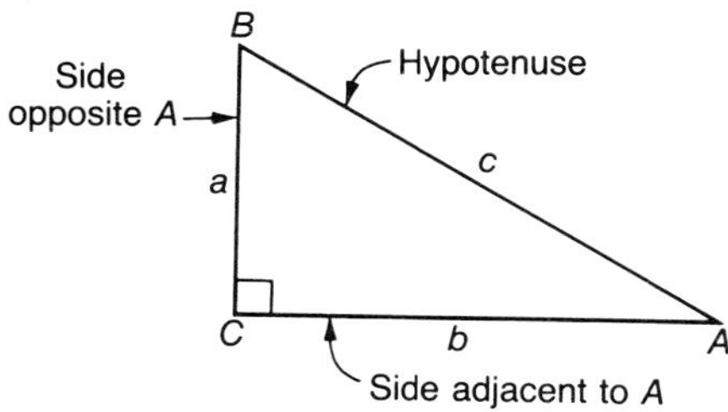

EXAMPLE 3

In $\triangle RST$, find $\tan S$. Write this value to four decimal places.

$$\tan S = \frac{\text{length of opposite side}}{\text{length of adjacent side}} = \frac{25}{60}$$

$$= \frac{5}{12} \approx 0.4167$$

$$\tan S \approx 0.4167$$

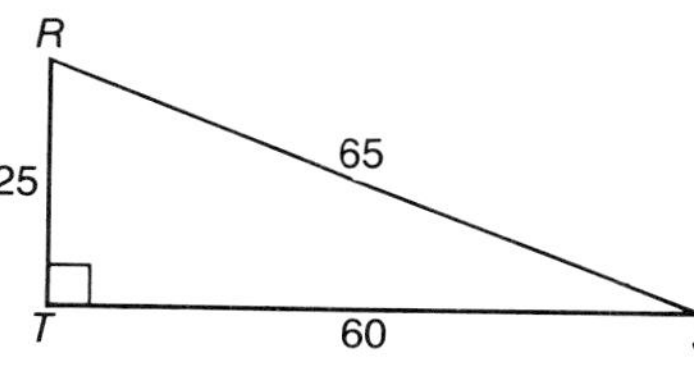

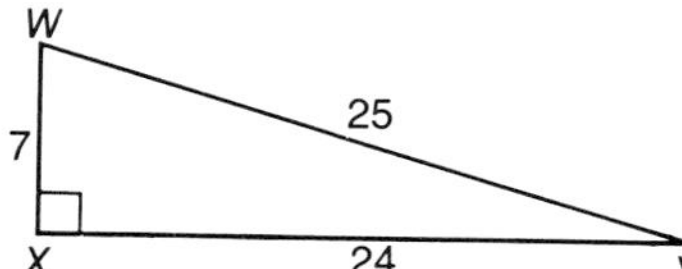

Try This

c. In $\triangle WXY$, find $\tan Y$. $\frac{7}{24} \approx 0.2917$

14-2 EXERCISES

A

Find the sine ratio for each triangle.

1. In $\triangle DEF$, find $\sin F$.

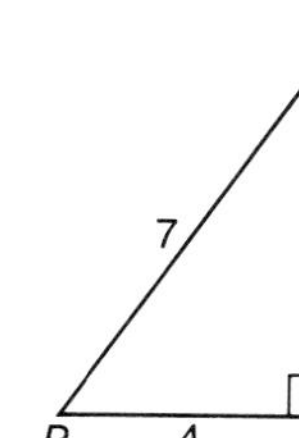

2. In $\triangle PQR$, find $\sin P$.

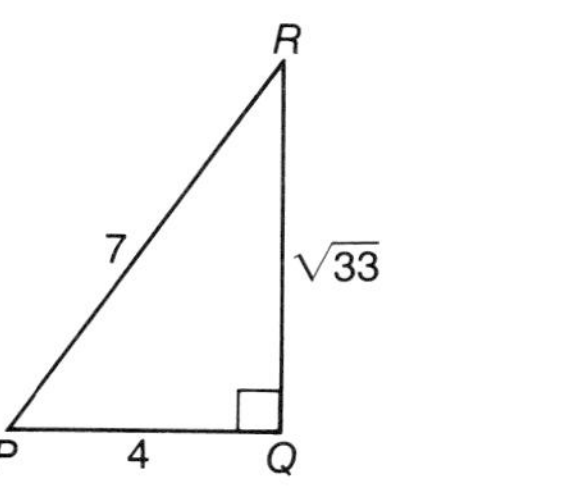

Tangent

You may want to point out the relationship between tangent and slope.

For a particular right triangle, have students compute sine, cosine, sine/cosine and tangent for an acute angle.

Math Point

The other three trigonometric ratios also have names.

cosecant A or

$$\csc A = \frac{\text{length of hypotenuse}}{\text{length of opposite side}}$$

secant A or

$$\sec A = \frac{\text{length of hypotenuse}}{\text{length of adjacent side}}$$

cotangent A or

$$\cot A = \frac{\text{length of adjacent side}}{\text{length of opposite side}}$$

These are the reciprocals of the three trigonometric functions sine, cosine, and tangent.

Chalkboard Examples (*T32*)

1. Find $\tan A$.

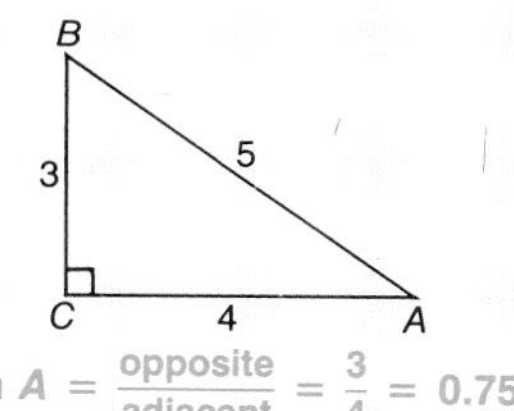

$\tan A = \frac{\text{opposite}}{\text{adjacent}} = \frac{3}{4} = 0.75$

2. Find $\tan B$.

$\tan B = \frac{4}{3} \approx 1.3$

LESSON QUIZ

Given the following right triangle, find the required ratios to the nearest hundredth.

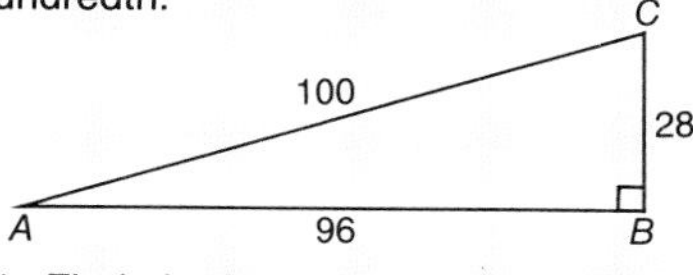

1. Find $\sin A$.

$\sin A = \frac{28}{100} = 0.28$

2. Find $\cos A$.

$\cos A = \frac{96}{100} = 0.96$

3. Find $\tan A$.

$\tan A = \frac{28}{96} \approx 0.29$

Assignment Guide
Minimum: omit

Regular: 1–26 e/o, 27, MR

Advanced: 1–26 e/o, 27–29, MR

ADDITIONAL ANSWERS
Exercises

1. $\frac{\sqrt{3}}{2}$ or 0.8660
2. $\frac{\sqrt{33}}{7}$ or 0.8207
3. $\frac{4}{5} = 0.8$
4. $\frac{8}{17} \approx 0.4706$
5. $\frac{8}{17} \approx 0.4706$
6. $\frac{48}{52} \approx 0.9231$
7. $\frac{44}{55} = 0.8$
8. $\frac{9}{15} = 0.6$
9. $\frac{20}{52} \approx 0.3846$
10. $\frac{40}{58} \approx 0.6897$
11. $\frac{36}{39} \approx 0.9231$
12. $\frac{126}{130} \approx 0.9692$

3. In $\triangle ABC$, find $\sin A$.

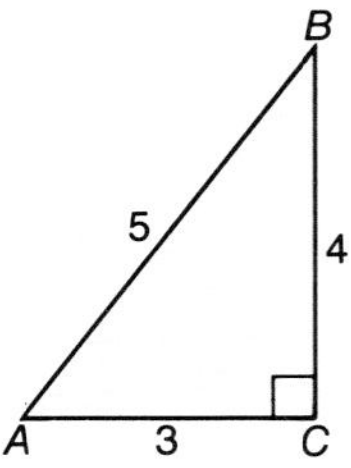

4. In $\triangle PQR$, find $\sin R$.

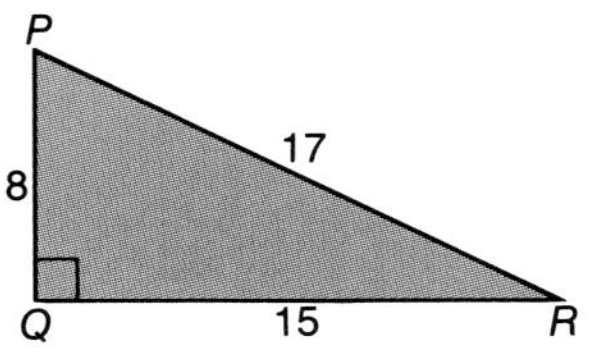

5. In $\triangle RST$, find $\sin T$.

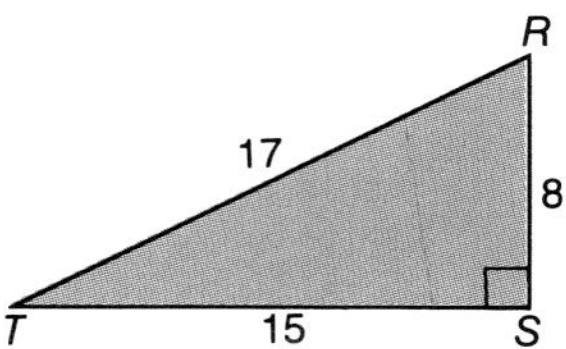

6. In $\triangle PQR$, find $\sin Q$.

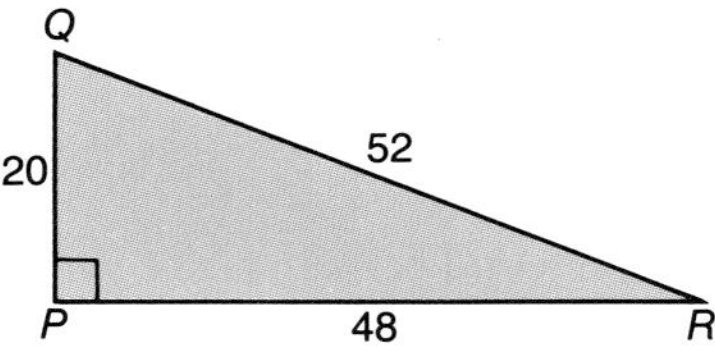

Find the cosine for each triangle.

7. Find $\cos S$.

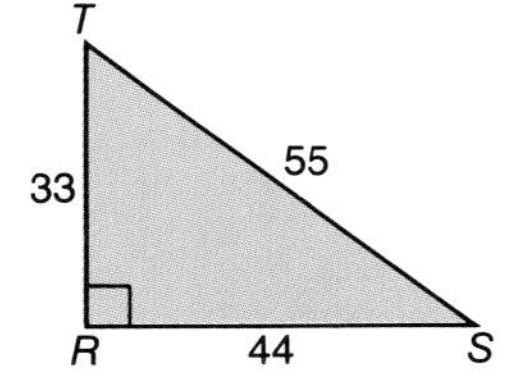

8. Find $\cos B$.

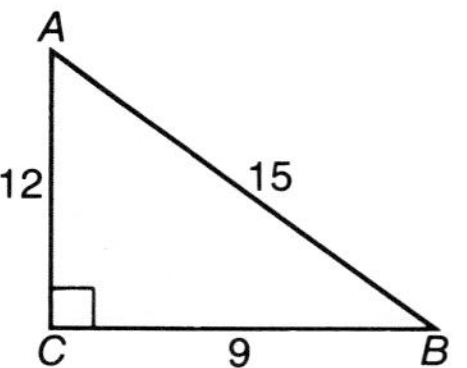

9. Find $\cos F$.

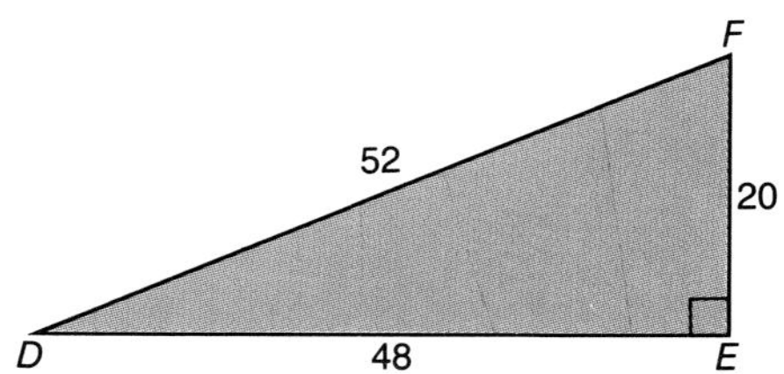

10. Find $\cos Z$.

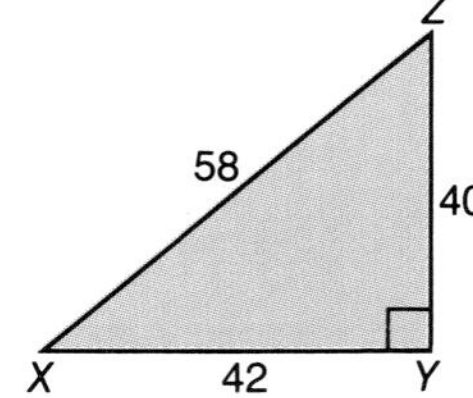

Find the cosine for each triangle.

11. Find $\cos S$.

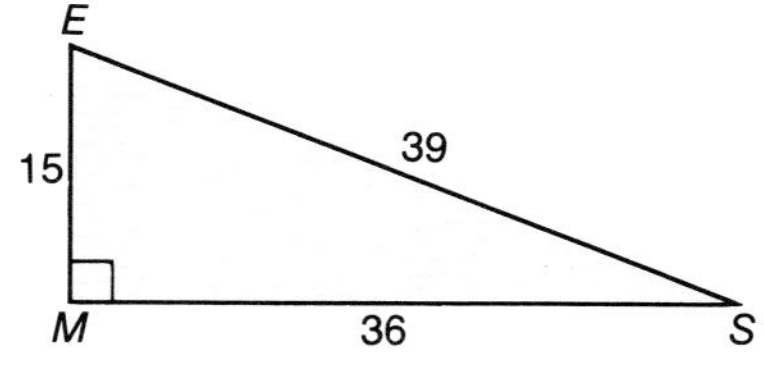

12. Find $\cos R$.

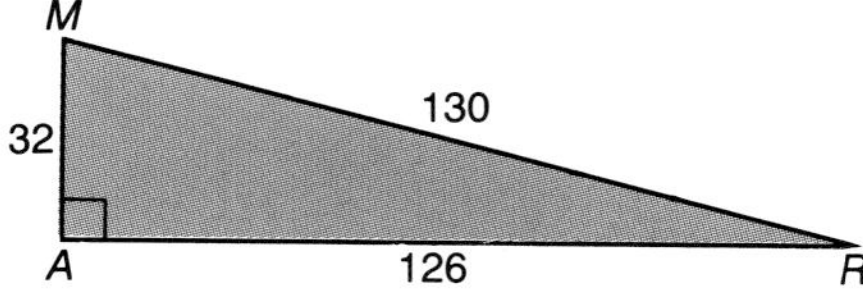

Find the tangent for each triangle.

13. Find tan R.

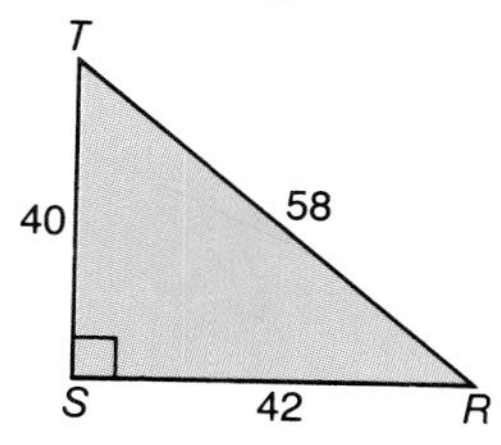

14. Find tan T.

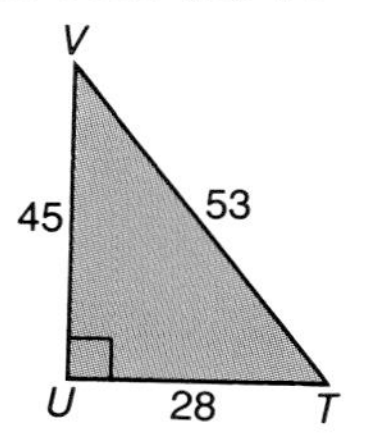

15. Find tan P.

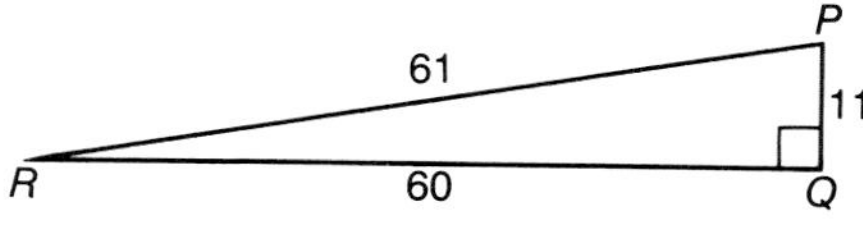

16. Find tan A.

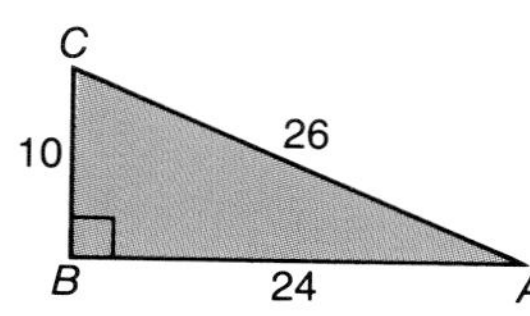

Find the tangent for each triangle.

17. Find tan P.

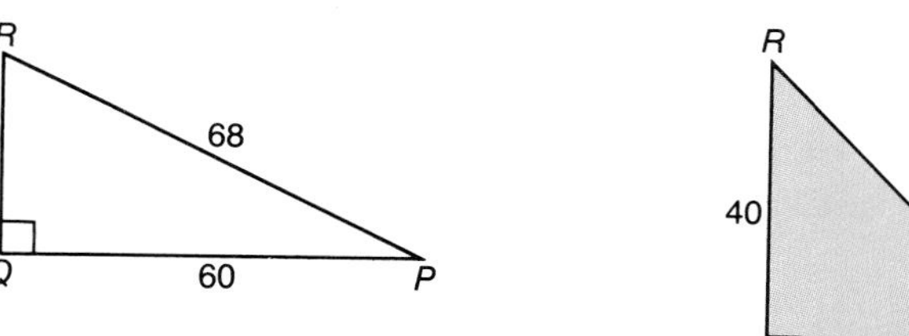

18. Find tan S.

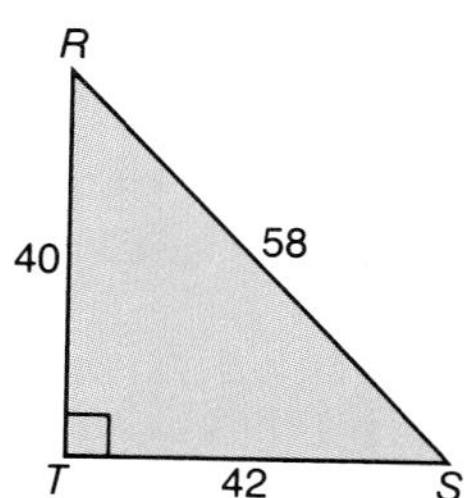

B

Use a calculator to solve.

19. In $\triangle PQR$, find cos R to four decimal places. 0.2925

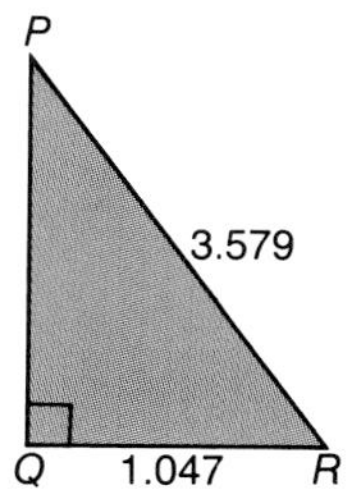

20. In $\triangle ABC$, find tan B to four decimal places. 1.0961

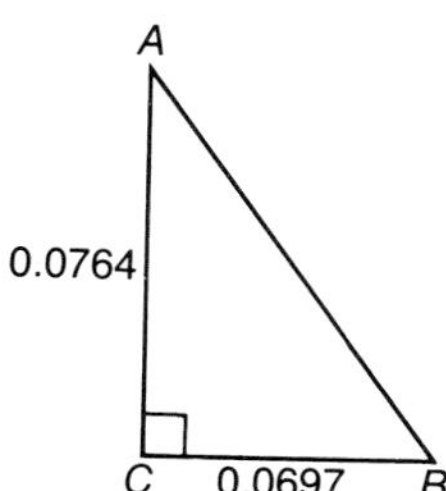

Use the Pythagorean theorem to find the length, to the nearest tenth, of the hypotenuse of a triangle with legs of the given lengths. Then find the sine ratio for each acute angle.

21. 9 and 12 **22.** 4 and 6 **23.** 5 and 13

24. 16 and 30 **25.** 24 and 32 **26.** 18 and 36

13. $\frac{40}{42} \approx 0.9524$

14. $\frac{45}{28} \approx 1.6071$

15. $\frac{60}{11} \approx 5.4545$

16. $\frac{10}{24} \approx 0.4167$

17. $\frac{32}{60} \approx 0.5333$

18. $\frac{40}{42} \approx 0.9524$

21. 15; 0.6; 0.8
22. 7.2; 0.6; 0.8
23. 13.9; 0.4; 0.9
24. 34; 0.5; 0.9
25. 40; 0.6; 0.8
26. 40.2; 0.4; 0.9

27. $\dfrac{\frac{\text{opp}}{\text{hyp}}}{\frac{\text{adj}}{\text{hyp}}} = \dfrac{\text{opp}}{\text{hyp}} \cdot \dfrac{\text{hyp}}{\text{adj}} = \dfrac{\text{opp}}{\text{adj}}$

Mixed Review

30. 0, -4
31. -2, 4
32. $\pm\frac{3}{2}$
33. $3 \pm \sqrt{3}$
34. No real-number solution
35. ± 5
36.

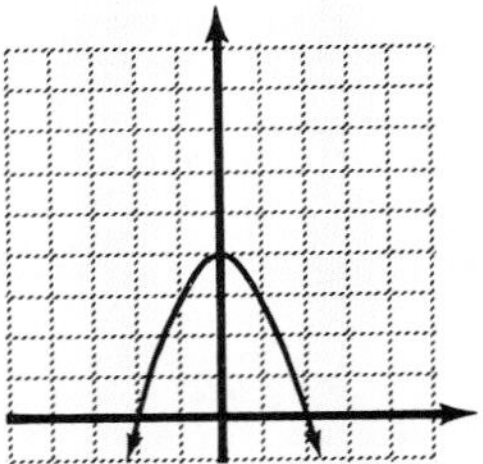

37.

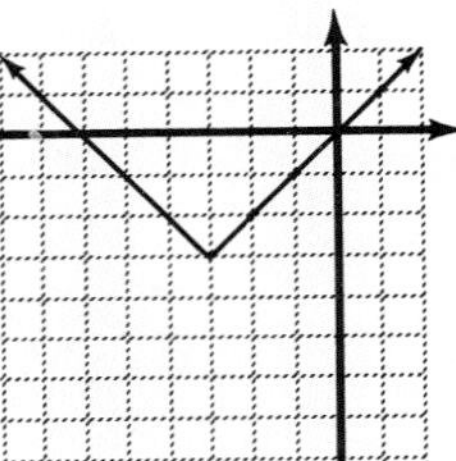

38. $\left|\frac{x}{y}\right|$
39. $|a|\sqrt{6a}$
40. $|x - 3|$
41. $\frac{2\sqrt{3}}{9}$
42. \$30.00
43. After 6 h

Calculator Investigation

$(\sin R)^2 = 0.18$, $(\cos R)^2 = 0.82$
1. They equal 1.
2. Yes; $\sin^2 a + \cos^2 a$ always equals 1.

27. ***Critical Thinking*** Show that the sine of an angle divided by the cosine of the same angle gives the tangent of the angle.

Challenge

28. Find sin T. 0.85

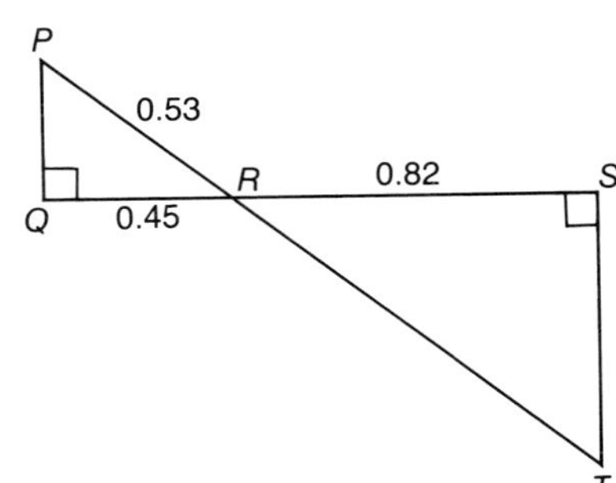

29. Find sin $(\angle BCD)$. 0.88

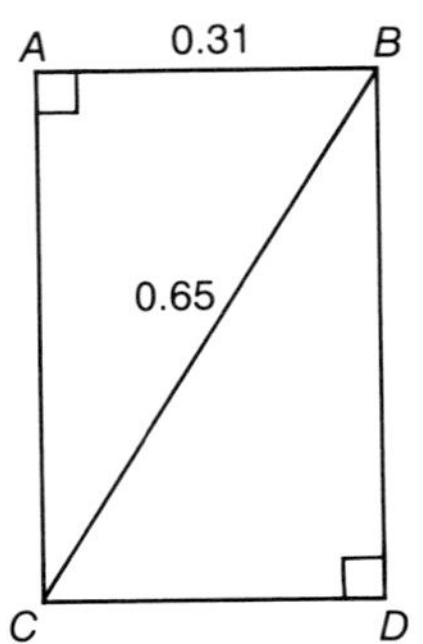

Mixed Review

Solve. **30.** $3x^2 + 12x = 0$ **31.** $y^2 - 2y = 8$ **32.** $4a^2 = 9$

33. $m^2 - 6m + 6 = 0$ **34.** $2x^2 - 7x + 15 = 0$ **35.** $3c^2 = 75$

Graph. **36.** $f(x) = -x^2 + 4$ **37.** $g(x) = |x + 3| - 3$

Simplify. **38.** $\dfrac{\sqrt{x^3y}}{\sqrt{xy^3}}$ **39.** $\dfrac{\sqrt{12a^5}}{\sqrt{2a^2}}$ **40.** $\dfrac{\sqrt{(x-3)^3}}{\sqrt{(x-3)}}$ **41.** $\dfrac{1}{\sqrt{3}} - \dfrac{1}{\sqrt{27}}$

42. The cost of renting a paint sprayer is \$12.50 plus \$3.50 per hour. Find the cost of renting a paint sprayer for 5 hours.

43. A car leaves town and travels north at 36 mi/h. Two hours later a second car leaves town and travels north on the same road at 48 mi/h. When will the second car overtake the first?

Calculator Investigation

Find $(\sin R)^2$ and $(\cos R)^2$ for the triangle at the right.

1. What do you notice about the sum of these values?
2. Test other triangles to see if this relationship seems to be true for any acute angle in a right triangle.

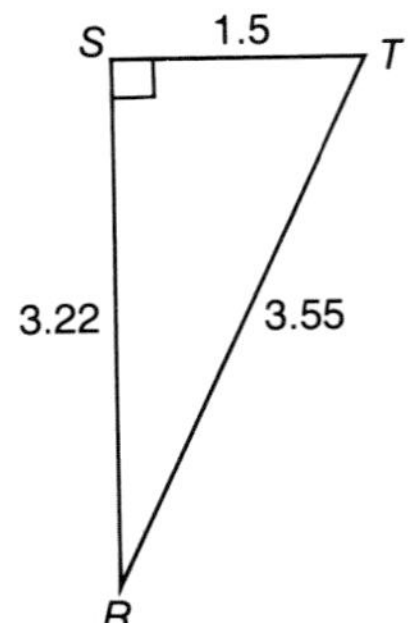

14-3 Trigonometric Values

Since corresponding sides of similar triangles are proportional, the sine ratio of 30° is the same in any right triangle. This is true for any trigonometric value of an angle in a right triangle. The values for angle measures can be found using a table, a calculator, or a computer.

Finding Trigonometric Values

Objective: Find the value of a trigonometric ratio by reading a table or using a calculator.

The values of trigonometric ratios have been computed for angle measures between 0° and 90°. Table 2 in the Appendix shows these values computed to four decimal places. Part of that table is shown below.

Degrees	Sin	Cos	Tan
56°	0.8290	0.5592	1.4826
57°	0.8387	0.5446	1.5399
58°	0.8480	0.5299	1.6003
59°	0.8572	0.5150	1.6643

EXAMPLE 1 Find tan 59°.

The entry in the Tan column opposite 59° is 1.6643. Thus, tan 59° ≈ 1.6643.

Try This Use Table 2 to find the trigonometric values.

a. sin 57° 0.8387 **b.** cos 77° 0.2250 **c.** tan 46° 1.0355

Many calculators are programmed to give the sine, cosine, or tangent of an angle.

Finding Trigonometric Values

Here is the key sequence to find the approximate value for the sine, cosine, and tangent of a 56° angle.

56 sin → 0.8290376

56 cos → 0.5591929

56 tan → 1.4825609

For additional calculator practice, see Calculator Worksheet 29.

14-3

FIRST FIVE MINUTES

Given $\triangle ABC$, find each ratio to two decimal places.

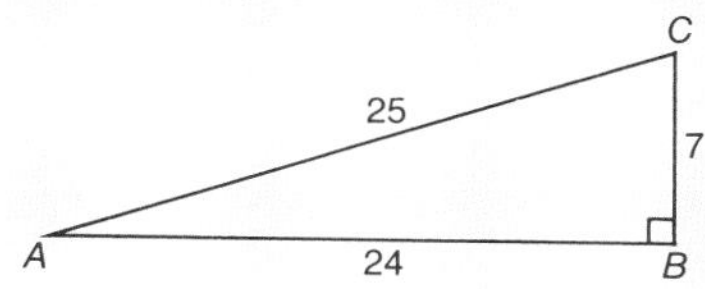

1. Find sin *A*.
   sin *A* = 0.28
2. Find cos *A*.
   cos *A* = 0.96
3. Find tan *A*.
   tan *A* ≈ 0.29

Finding Trigonometric Values

Emphasize that most of the trigonometric values given in the table are approximations. Note that the table can be used in two ways. First, given any angle, we can find the trigonometric ratios that correspond to the angle. Second, given a trigonometric ratio, we can find an angle that corresponds to the ratio.

You may want to have students compare the columns for sine and cosine. Students should notice that the sine of one angle is the same as the cosine of a second angle. The sum of these two angles is 90°.

Key Questions

- Can we use the table to find the sine of an acute angle in a right triangle for any size right triangle? Yes
- Does sin 60° ≈ 0.8660 using the table? Yes
- What is sin 60° using a calculator? Answers may vary. 0.8660254
- Which is correct? They are both approximations for sin 60°.

Chalkboard Examples

Use Table 2 on p. 654 or a calculator.

1. Find sin 59°.
   sin 59° ≈ 0.8572
2. Find cos 57°.
   cos 57° ≈ 0.5446

Finding Angles

Chalkboard Examples

Use Table 2 on p. 654 or a calculator.

1. Suppose tan A = 1.4826. Find A.
   $A \approx 56°$
2. Suppose cos A = 0.5592. Find A.
   $A \approx 56°$

There are three different ways of measuring angles: in degrees, radians, and grads. In a right angle there are 90°, $\frac{\pi}{2}$ radians, and 100 grads. Many calculators will find trigonometric values for any of these measures. Students whose calculators include more than one measure should make sure that their calculator is in the degree mode when they do these calculations ("deg" should appear on the display).

LESSON QUIZ

Use Table 2 to find the following.

1. sin 42°
   0.6691
2. cos 12°
   0.9781
3. tan 37°
   0.7536
4. Find A, given that tan A = 0.2867.
   $A \approx 16°$
5. Find A, given that cos A = 0.8910.
   $A \approx 27°$

Finding Angles

Objective: Find an angle given the value of a trigonometric ratio.

The trigonometric table can also be used to approximate the measure of an angle if one of its trigonometric values is known.

EXAMPLES Use Table 2 to find the angle.

2. Suppose cos A = 0.5592. Find A.
In the Cos column find the entry 0.5592. Find the entry opposite 0.5592 in the Degree column. This is 56°, so A = 56°.

There are many trigonometric values that are not listed in the table. We can approximate the measure of the angle to the nearest degree by determining which value in the table is closest.

3. Suppose sin B = 0.8391. Find B to the nearest degree.
In the Sin column the value 0.8391 is between two values.

$$0.8387 = \sin 57° \text{ and } 0.8480 = \sin 58°$$

Therefore, sin B is between 57° and 58°. Since 0.8391 is closer to 0.8387, sin B = 57° to the nearest degree.

Try This Use Table 2 to find the angle.

d. Suppose cos A = 0.6947. Find A. 46°
e. Suppose sin B = 0.3584. Find B. 21°
f. Suppose sin A = 0.8293. Find A to the nearest degree. 56°
g. Suppose tan B = 3.0771. Find B to the nearest degree. 72°

You can also find the angle value on a calculator if you know the trigonometric value by using the inverse key.

Finding Angles

Here is the key sequence to find the approximate angle for a given trigonometric value.

0.8290	2nd	sin	→	55.99615	≈ 56°
0.9613	2nd	cos	→	15.99204	≈ 16°
3.7321	2nd	tan	→	75.00019	≈ 75°

For additional calculator practice, see Calculator Worksheet 30.

14-3 EXERCISES

A

Find these trigonometric values.

1. sin 38° **2.** sin 47° **3.** tan 56° **4.** tan 84° **5.** cos 9°
6. cos 31° **7.** sin 60° **8.** sin 30° **9.** tan 45° **10.** tan 55°
11. cos 1° **12.** cos 89° **13.** sin 71° **14.** sin 45° **15.** sin 15°

Find angle A.

16. $\sin A = 0.2588$ 15° **17.** $\sin A = 0.9397$ 70° **18.** $\cos A = 0.8572$ 31°
19. $\cos A = 0.1564$ 81° **20.** $\tan A = 0.4877$ 26° **21.** $\tan A = 2.2460$ 66°
22. $\cos A = 0.7547$ 41° **23.** $\cos A = 0.9816$ 11° **24.** $\tan A = 9.5144$ 84°
25. $\tan A = 1.1918$ 50° **26.** $\sin A = 0.7193$ 46° **27.** $\sin A = 0.0872$ 5°

Find angle A to the nearest degree.

28. $\sin A = 0.1746$ 10° **29.** $\sin A = 0.8753$ 61° **30.** $\tan A = 2.9064$ 71°
31. $\tan A = 0.7824$ 38° **32.** $\cos A = 0.8749$ 29° **33.** $\cos A = 0.4234$ 65°
34. $\tan A = 9.5234$ 84° **35.** $\tan A = 2.8011$ 70° **36.** $\sin A = 0.9948$ 84°

B

37. One degree is 60 minutes (60′). The value of the trigonometric ratio of an angle measured in degrees and minutes can be approximated using the idea of proportion. For example, sin 37°10′ must lie between sin 37° and 38°. It is reasonable to assume that sin 37°10′ would be about $\frac{10}{60}$ of the difference between sin 37° and sin 38°. Find sin 37°10′, sin 37°20′, and sin 37°50′.

38. *Critical Thinking* Find an angle that has the same sine and cosine.

Challenge

39. Find an angle B such that $\sin 2B = \cos B$.

40. Find an angle B such that $B = \frac{A}{2}$ and $2 \cos A = \sin A$. (Hint: First show that $\tan A = \frac{\sin A}{\cos A}$.)

Mixed Review

Solve. **41.** $x - 7 = \frac{4}{x - 7}$ **42.** $\frac{y^2}{y + 1} - \frac{7}{y + 1} = 0$

43. $\frac{4}{a - 2} + \frac{6}{a + 2} = 1$ **44.** $5c^2 = 65$ **45.** $(m + 2)^2 = 16$

46. $x^2 + 4x - 16 = 0$ **47.** $x^2 + 20x + 91 = 0$

Determine whether the given point is a solution of the equation.

48. $(1, -2)$, $2y = x - 5$ **49.** $(3, -1)$, $2y = 3x - 7$

50. $(-2, 1)$, $5y - 2x = x + 11$ **51.** $(-2, 3)$, $|x + y| - 3 = x$

Assignment Guide
Minimum: omit

Regular: 1–36 e/o, 37, 38, MR

Advanced: 1–36 e/o, 37–40, MR

ADDITIONAL ANSWERS

Exercises

1. 0.6157
2. 0.7314
3. 1.4826
4. 9.5144
5. 0.9877
6. 0.8572
7. 0.8660
8. 0.5000
9. 1.0000
10. 1.4281
11. 0.9998
12. 0.0175
13. 0.9455
14. 0.7071
15. 0.2588

37. 0.6041, 0.6064, 0.6134
38. 45°
39. 30°
40. 31.7°

Mixed Review

41. 5, 9
42. $\pm\sqrt{7}$
43. 0, 10
44. $\pm\sqrt{13}$
45. 2, −6
46. $-2 \pm 2\sqrt{5}$
47. −7, −13
48. Yes
49. No
50. Yes
51. Yes

14-4

FIRST FIVE MINUTES

1. Find cos 31°.
   0.8572
2. Find tan 14°.
   0.2493
3. Find A, given that $\tan A = 0.9325$.
   43°
4. Find A, given that $\sin A = 0.6157$.
   38°

Emphasize the importance of drawing a diagram.

Illustrate the difference between the angle of elevation and the angle of depression, as shown below.

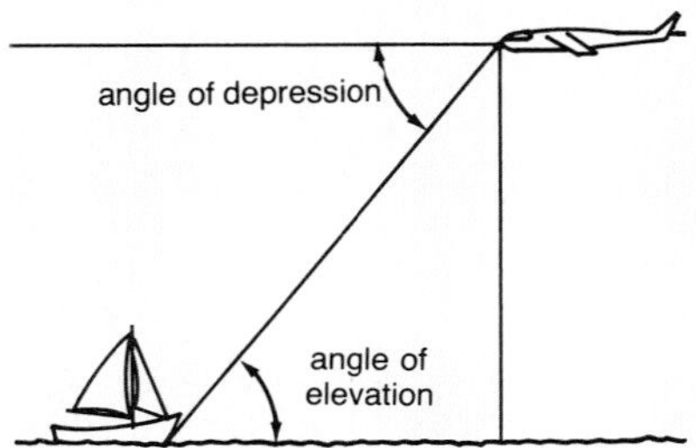

Key Questions

- How can you tell which side is the hypotenuse? It is always opposite the right angle.
- How can you tell what side is the adjacent side? It is the side *next to* the angle of reference.

14-4 Problem Solving: Right Triangle Problems

Objective: Solve problems involving trigonometric functions.

PROBLEM-SOLVING GUIDELINES
■ UNDERSTAND the problem
■ Develop and carry out a PLAN
■ Find the ANSWER and CHECK

You can use the Problem-Solving Guidelines to help you solve problems where your plan involves the use of a trigonometric ratio.

EXAMPLE 1 In the right triangle ABC, $B = 61°$ and $c = 20$ cm. Find b.

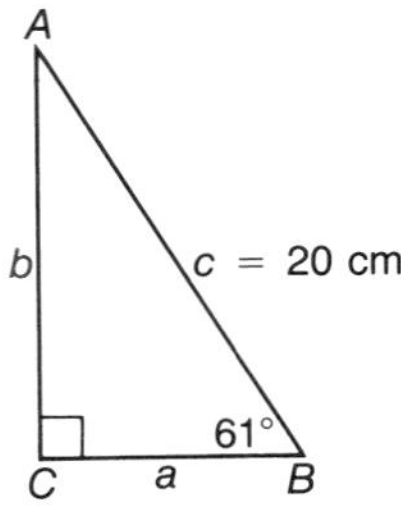

■ **UNDERSTAND the problem**

Question: What is the length of side b?

Data: $\angle B$ is 61°.

c is 20 cm and is the hypotenuse of a right triangle.

Drawing a diagram helps organize the data.

■ **Develop and carry out a PLAN**

We will use the sine ratio, since it relates the side opposite the given angle and the hypotenuse.

$$\sin B = \frac{b}{c}$$

$$\sin 61° = \frac{b}{20}$$

$$0.8746 \approx \frac{b}{20} \quad \text{Finding sin } 61°$$

$$20(0.8746) \approx b$$

$$17.492 \approx b$$

■ **Find the ANSWER and CHECK**

b is about 17.5 cm. If the drawing is accurate, we can see that 17.5 cm seems reasonable.

Try This

a. In right triangle ABC, $B = 42°$ and $c = 10$ cm. Find b.

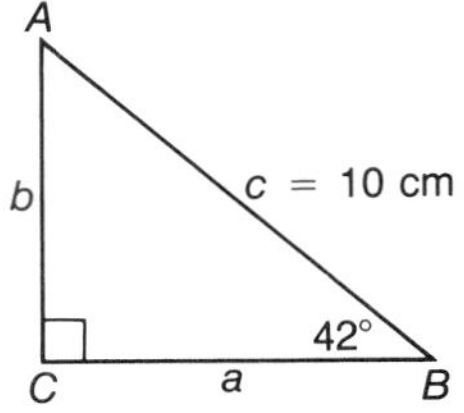

6.7 cm

EXAMPLE 2 In right triangle DEF, $D = 25°$ and $f = 18$ km. Find e.

$$\cos D = \frac{f}{e}$$

$$\cos 25° = \frac{18}{e}$$

$$0.9063 \approx \frac{18}{e} \quad \text{Finding } \cos 25°$$

$$0.9063e \approx 18$$

$$e \approx \frac{18}{0.9063}$$

$$e \approx 19.8609$$

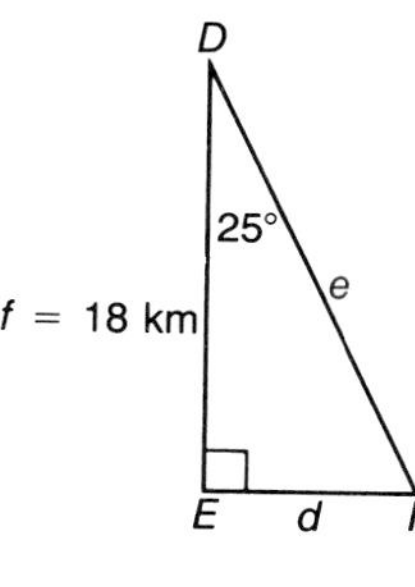

e is about 19.9 km.

Try This

b. In right triangle DEF, $D = 36°$ and $f = 30$ m. Find e to the nearest tenth. 37.1 m

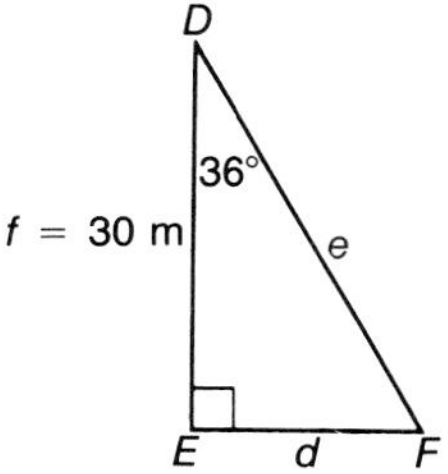

Trigonometric ratios can sometimes be used to help solve problems. We translate the information into a right triangle diagram.

EXAMPLE 3

The angle of elevation of an airplane is 12°. The distance to the plane is 16 km. How high is the plane?

Let the height of the plane be h.

16 km
Angle of elevation
12°
h

$$\sin 12° = \frac{h}{16}$$

$$0.2079 \approx \frac{h}{16} \quad \text{Finding } \sin 12°$$

$$16(0.2079) \approx h$$

$$3.3264 \approx h$$

The height of the airplane is about 3.3 km.

Chalkboard Examples

1. Find a.

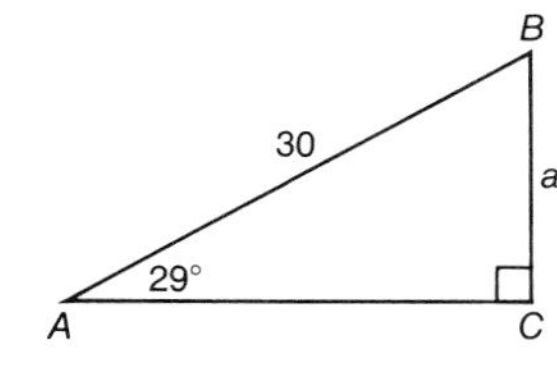

$\sin 29° = \frac{a}{30}$

$a = 30 \cdot \sin 29°$

$a \approx 30 \cdot 0.4848$

$a \approx 14.54$

2. Find b.

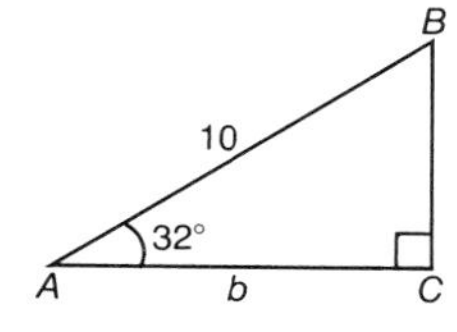

$\cos 32° = \frac{b}{10}$

$b = 10 \cdot \cos 32°$

$b \approx 10 \cdot 0.8480 \approx 8.480$

3. A mountain trail slopes upward at an angle of 5°. A hiker hikes four miles up the trail. How much altitude does the hiker gain?

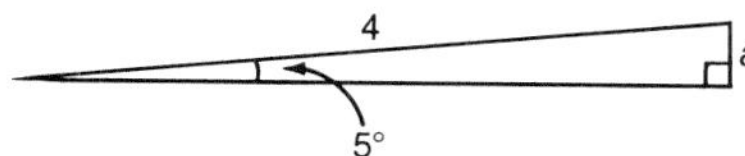

Let a be the gain in altitude.

$\sin 5° = \frac{a}{4}$

$a = 4 \cdot \sin 5°$

$a \approx 4 \cdot 0.0872 \approx 0.35$

The hiker gains 0.35 miles of altitude.

LESSON ENRICHMENT

Ask students to make up problems involving buildings, or other objects with which everyone is familiar, that can be solved using the methods of this chapter. If measurements aren't known, estimate them.

LESSON QUIZ

Find the following to the nearest tenth.

1. Find *a*.

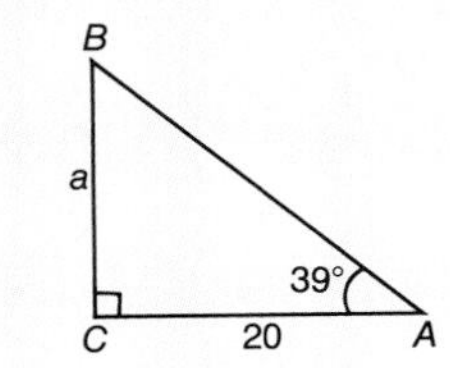

$a = 16.2$

2. Find *b*.

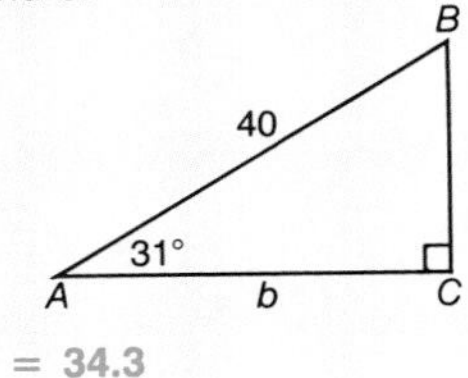

$b = 34.3$

Assignment Guide
Minimum: Omit

Regular: Day 1: 1–16
Day 2: 17–21, MR
Advanced: Day 1: 1–16 e/o, assign w. Application
Day 2: 17–23, MR

EXAMPLE 4

A fire warden's tower is 43 m tall. The angle of depression from the window of the tower to a fire in the woods is 5°. How far away from the base of the tower is the fire?

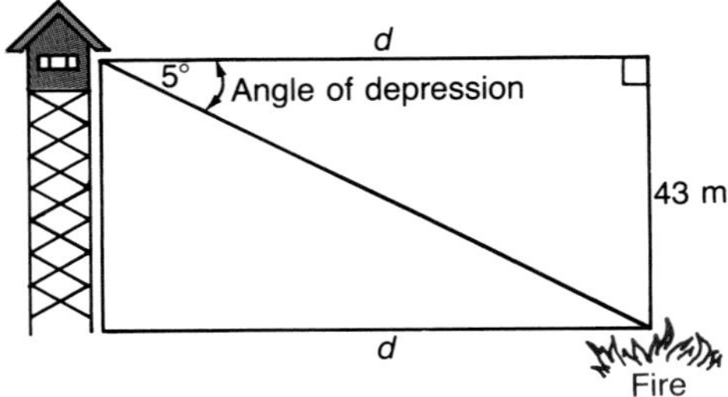

Let d be the distance from the fire to the base of the tower.

$$\tan 5° = \frac{43}{d}$$

$$0.0875 \approx \frac{43}{d} \qquad \text{Finding } \tan 5°$$

$$0.0875d \approx 43$$

$$d \approx 491.4$$

The distance to the fire is about 491 m.

Try This

c. A kite is flown with 180 m of string. The angle of elevation of the kite is 58°. How high is the kite? Round to the nearest tenth. 152.6 m

14-4 EXERCISES

A

Solve the following triangle problems. Round answers to the nearest tenth.

1. $B = 38°$ and $c = 37$ cm. Find b. 22.8 cm

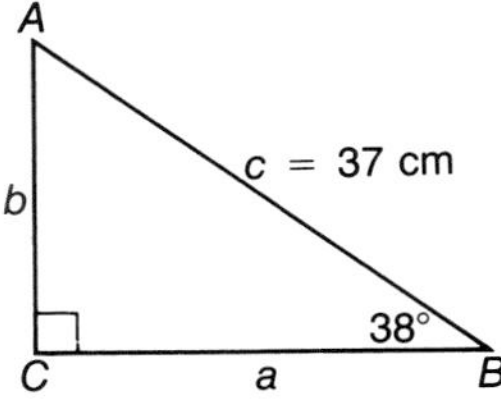

2. $B = 57°$ and $c = 24$ cm. Find b. 20.1 cm

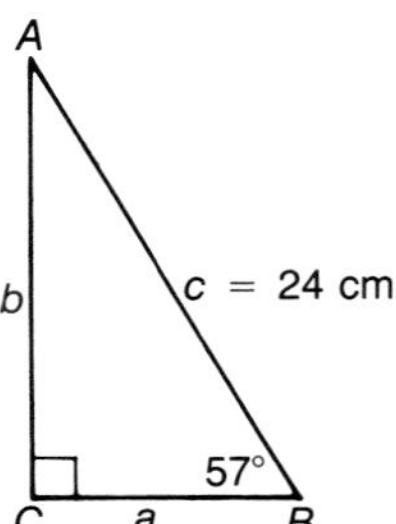

3. $D = 39°$ and $f = 42$ cm.
Find e. 54.0 cm

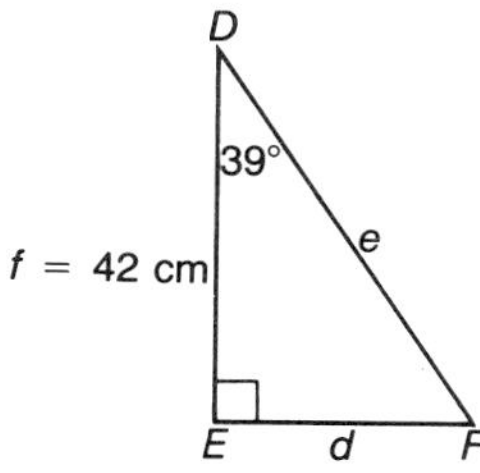

4. $D = 18°$ and $f = 16$ cm.
Find e. 16.8 cm

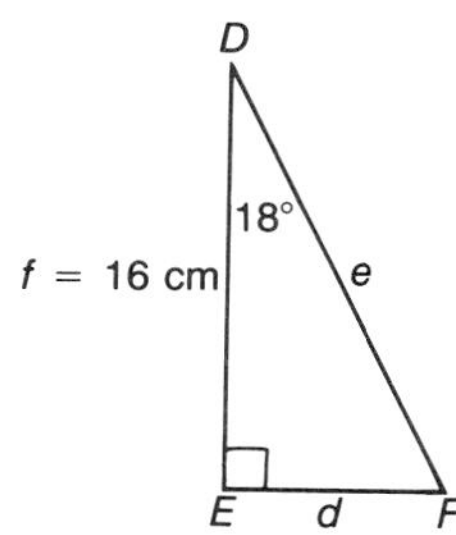

5. $k = 18$ cm and $g = 26$ cm.
Find K to the nearest degree. 35°

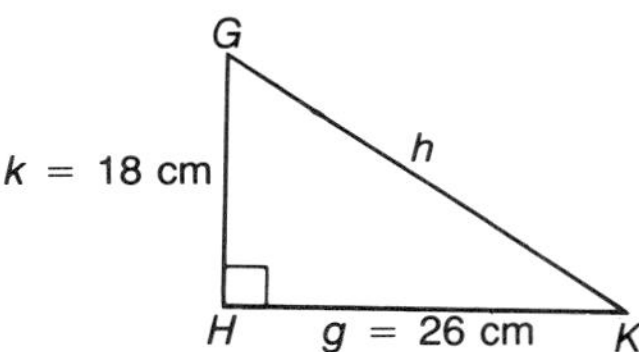

6. $k = 29$ cm and $g = 41$ cm.
Find K to the nearest degree. 35°

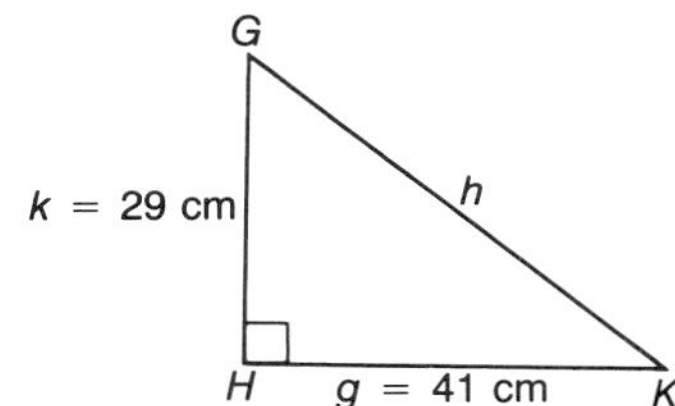

Solve. Draw a diagram first. Round answers to the nearest tenth.

7. The angle of elevation of an airplane is 9°. The distance to the plane is 21 km. How high is the plane? 3.3 km

8. A kite is flown with 210 m of string. The angle of elevation of the kite is 61°. How high is the kite? 183.7 m

9. The top of a lighthouse is 110 m above the level of the water. The angle of depression from the top of the lighthouse to a fishing boat is 18°. How far from the base of the lighthouse is the fishing boat? 338.6 m

10. An observation tower is 98 m tall. The angle of depression from the top of the tower to a historical marker is 23°. How far from the base of the tower is the marker? 230.9 m

11. A flagpole casts a shadow 4.6 m long. The angle of elevation of the sun is 49°. How high is the flagpole? 5.3 m

12. A water tower casts a shadow 23 m long. The angle of elevation of the sun is 52°. How tall is the water tower? 29.4 m

13. The firing angle of a missile is 28°. About how high is it after it has traveled 450 m? 211.3 m

14. A rocket is launched at an angle of 34°. About how high is it after it has traveled 670 m? 374.7 m

15. A pilot in a plane 3 km above the ground estimates that the angle of depression to a runway is 51°. What is the horizontal distance to the runway? 2.4 km

ADDITIONAL ANSWERS

Exercises

21. Using the tan of 7°, Lynnette has 8161 ft, or 1.5 mi to walk. At 4 mi/h, it will take her 0.4 h, or 22.5 minutes.

22. Draw h so that it makes a right angle with side b. Then

$\sin A = \frac{h}{c}$, so area $= \frac{1}{2}bh$

$= \frac{1}{2}bc\left(\frac{h}{c}\right) = \frac{1}{2}bc \sin A.$

23.

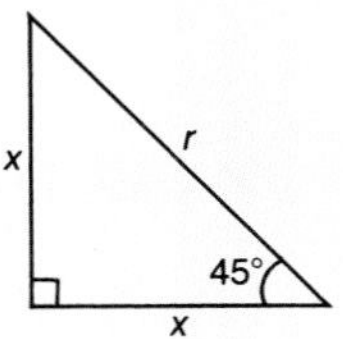

$x^2 + x^2 = r^2$

$r = \sqrt{x^2 + x^2}$

$= \sqrt{2x^2}$

$= x\sqrt{2}$

$\sin 45° = \frac{x}{x\sqrt{2}}$

$= \frac{1}{\sqrt{2}}$

$= \frac{\sqrt{2}}{2}$

Mixed Review

24. $y = x + 4$
25. $x = 3$
26. $y = \frac{2}{3}x - \frac{5}{3}$
27. (4, 2)
28. (−1, −3)
29. (−2, 3) and (0, 7)
30. $\frac{5}{2}, -\frac{3}{4}$
31. 16

Problem for Programmers

This program can be written using any programming language (BASIC, PASCAL, LOGO, etc.).

16. A balloonist 1.4 km above the ground estimates the angle of depression to a highway intersection to be 37°. How far is the balloonist horizontally from the intersection? 1.9 km

B

It can be shown that the area of a triangle equals one half the product of two adjacent sides times the sine of the angle between them. Use this formula, area of $\triangle ABC = \frac{1}{2}bc \sin \angle A$, to find the area of the following triangles to the nearest tenth.

17. $\triangle ABC$ where $A = 50°$, $b = 12$, and $c = 8$. 36.8

18. $\triangle MNP$ where $N = 67°$, $m = 40$, $p = 52$. 957.3

19. $\triangle XYZ$ where $Z = 12°$, $x = 18$, and $y = 18$. 33.7

20. $\triangle GHJ$ where $J = 24°$, $g = 6$, and $h = 6$. 7.3

21. ***Critical Thinking*** Lynnette is behind schedule. She is going to be late for an appointment in twenty minutes at the Texas Commerce Center. She knows that the building is 1002 ft tall, the angle to the building is 7°, and she is walking at a steady pace of 4 mi/h. How does she know that she will be late for her appointment? (5280 ft = 1 mi)

Challenge

22. Draw an acute triangle, ABC, with side a opposite $\angle A$, b opposite $\angle B$, and so on. Prove that $\frac{1}{2}bc \sin A$ is the area of the triangle. (Hint: Draw an altitude h.)

23. An equilateral isosceles triangle has two equal sides and two 45° angles. Use the Pythagorean theorem to find sin 45°.

Mixed Review

Write an equation for the line that contains the given pair of points.

24. (−2, 2), (3, 7) **25.** (3, 5), (3, −1) **26.** (4, 1), (−2, −3)

Solve. **27.** $y = 3x - 10$, $x = 2y$ **28.** $5x + 2y = -11$, $3x - 2y = 3$ **29.** $x^2 + y = 7$, $y - 2x = 7$

Solve. **30.** $8c^2 - 14c = 15$ **31.** $\sqrt{x - 7} = x - 13$

Problem for Programmers

Write a program that will find the desired length of a side of a right triangle. The input will include one of the acute angles, the length of one side, and information indicating the position of the side given and the side desired relative to the input angle (opposite, adjacent, or hypotenuse). Use Exercises 1–4 in Lesson 14-4 to test your program.

Problem Solving: Application

Surveying

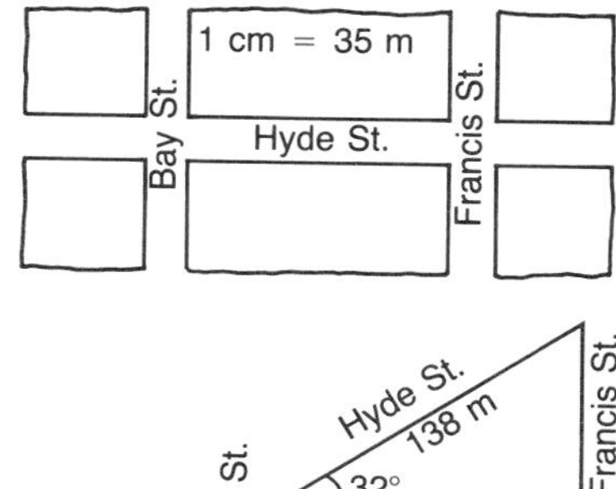

Have you ever chosen a walking route on a map and then found, when you got to a hill, that the distance seems longer than it looked on the map? This is because maps show horizontal distance not elevation. So the sloping distance of the land surface really is longer, as shown in the sketch at the right.

When surveyors are working on maps of land that has a slope, they have to measure the surface distance and also find the horizontal distance that will be shown on the map. In the sketch, the surface distance is 138 meters, and the land slopes upward at 32°. The surveyor would use trigonometric ratios to find the horizontal distance as follows:

$$\cos 32° = \frac{a}{138}$$

$$a = 138 \cos 32°$$

$$a \approx 117$$

The distance is 117 m.

Problems

1. A surveyor has found that the surface distance from the top of the riverbed to the edge of the river is 27.3 meters. She has found that the angle at which the land slopes downward is 15°. Find horizontal distance a.
2. The surface distance down the straight ski slope shown at right is 520 meters. The slope is 28°. Find horizontal distance a.
3. A surveyor has found that the slope of the hill at right is 11°, and the surface distance up the hill is 2578 feet. Find horizontal distance a.

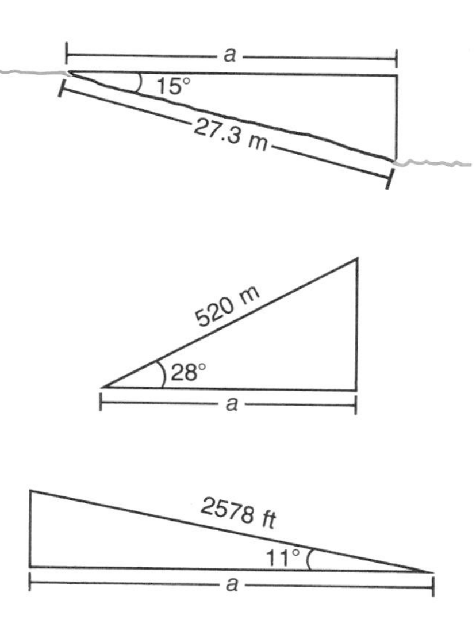

Problem Solving: Application

ANSWERS

1. 26.4 m
2. 459 m
3. 2531 ft

Problem Solving: Situational Problem Solving

You may want to have students work in small groups to develop their plans. Then have them submit the plan to you or to another class as if they were submitting the plan to a city council.

Extension

Have someone from your city planning commission review the plans and discuss the plans with the class.

Problem Solving: Situational Problem Solving

Designing a Park

Most communities have parks for people to enjoy. Parks can have picnic areas, softball or baseball fields, play areas, paths, and grassy areas.

PROBLEM-SOLVING GUIDELINES
■ UNDERSTAND the problem
■ Develop and carry out a PLAN
■ Find the ANSWER and CHECK

You can use the Problem-Solving Guidelines to help you solve the situational problem about designing a park.

Situational Problem

A rectangular lot, 375 ft by 500 ft, has been donated to your city to be used as a park. The park is to have one tennis court, a softball field, and at least one picnic area. Volunteers will build the park, but materials must be purchased. Your job is to suggest a layout for the park, make a scale drawing of the park, and propose a budget for the project.

Possible Assumptions

1. You will use all of the donated area for the park.
2. You have to keep the costs as low as possible.

How will you design your park? What will be the total cost for its development?

Possible Subproblems

1. What are the dimensions of a tennis court and a softball field?
2. How much space will you allow for each activity?
3. What will be the scale of your drawing?
4. What will the materials for each picnic area cost?
5. What will the materials for a tennis court cost?
6. What will the materials for the softball field cost?

Chapter 14 Summary and Review

14-1

In **similar triangles,** the lengths of the corresponding sides are proportional and the corresponding angles are the same size.

1. $\triangle PQR \sim \triangle STV$. Name the corresponding sides and angles.

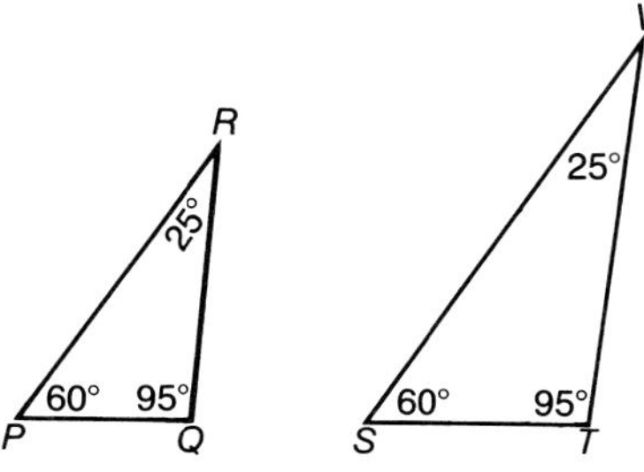

2. $\triangle ABC \sim \triangle DEF$. Find d and f.

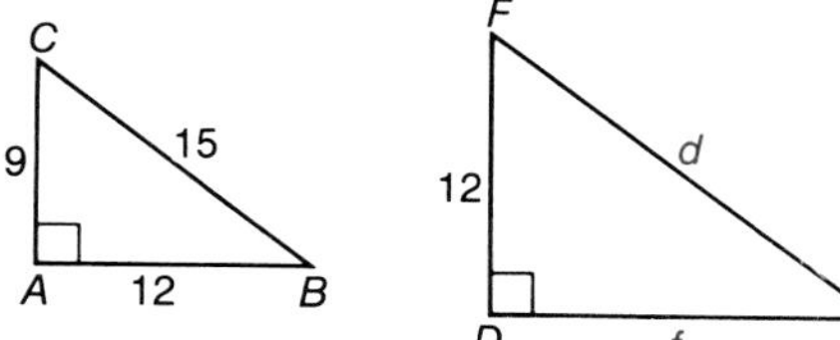

14-2

We studied these three trigonometric ratios:

$$\sin A = \frac{\text{length of opposite side}}{\text{length of hypotenuse}} = \frac{a}{c}$$

$$\cos A = \frac{\text{length of adjacent side}}{\text{length of hypotenuse}} = \frac{b}{c}$$

$$\tan A = \frac{\text{length of opposite side}}{\text{length of adjacent side}} = \frac{a}{b}$$

3. In $\triangle XYZ$, find $\sin Z$ rounded to four decimal places.

4. In $\triangle PQR$, find $\cos R$ rounded to four decimal places.

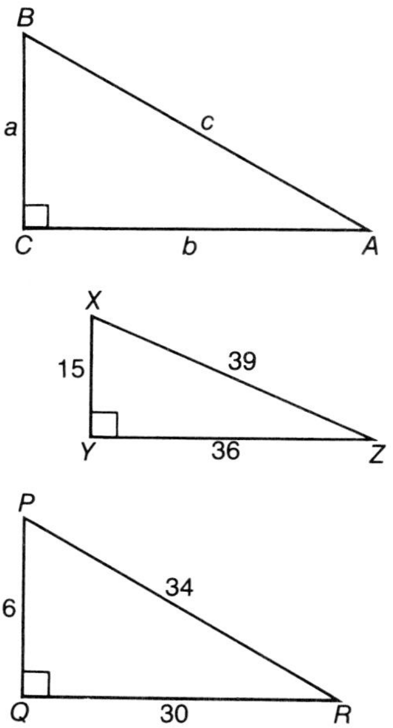

ANSWERS

1. $\overline{PQ}$ and $\overline{ST}$, $\overline{QR}$ and $\overline{TV}$, $\overline{RP}$ and $\overline{VS}$, $\angle P$ and $\angle S$, $\angle Q$ and $\angle T$, $\angle R$ and $\angle V$
2. $d = 20$, $f = 16$
3. 0.3846
4. 0.8824

5. 0.2250
6. 0.9231
7. 0.4540
8. 0.4226
9. 28.6363
10. 0.7660
11. 44°
12. 31°
13. 45°
14. 76°
15. 28.8 cm
16. 27.6 cm
17. 30°
18. 186.5 m
19. 329.7 m
20. ≈567 ft

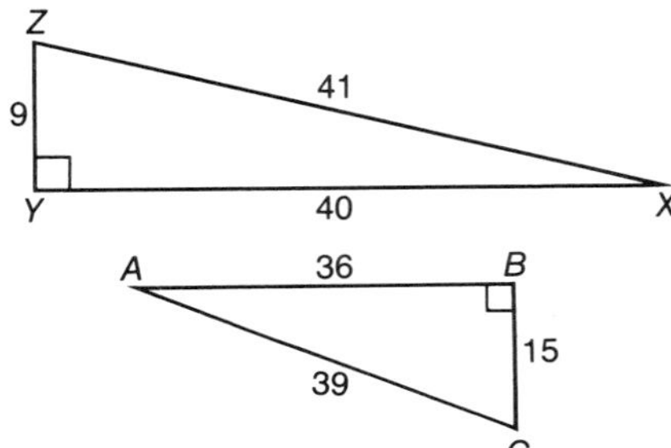

5. In $\triangle XYZ$, find tan X rounded to four decimal places.

6. In $\triangle ABC$, find cos A rounded to four decimal places.

14-3

You can find an approximate value of a trigonometric ratio from a table or a calculator.

Use Table 2 for Exercises 7–14.

7. Find sin 27°.
8. Find cos 65°.
9. Find tan 88°.
10. Find sin 50°.

You can find the angle if you know the approximate decimal value of a trigonometric ratio. To use the table, first find the decimal numeral in the appropriate column, then read the entry in the degrees column.

11. Suppose sin $A = 0.6947$. Find A.
12. Suppose cos $B = 0.8572$. Find B.
13. Suppose tan $X = 1.0000$. Find X.
14. Suppose tan $C = 4.1034$. Find C to the nearest degree.

14-4

You can use the Problem-Solving Guidelines to help you solve problems involving trigonometric ratios. Always draw a diagram.

15. In right triangle CLF, L is the right angle, $C = 46°$, and $l = 40$ cm. Find c.
16. In right triangle XYZ, Z is the right angle, $X = 23°$, and $z = 30$ cm. Find y.
17. In right triangle ABC, C is the right angle, $b = 70$ km, and $a = 120$ km. Find B to the nearest degree.
18. A kite is flown with 225 m of string. The angle of elevation of the kite is 56°. How high is the kite?
19. The top of the lighthouse is 120 m above the water level. The angle of depression from the top of the lighthouse to a motorboat is 20°. How far from the base of the lighthouse is the motorboat?
20. A model rocket is launched upward. An observer stands 100 ft from the launch and finds that the angle of elevation to the apogee (highest point) is 80°. How high did the rocket fly?

Chapter 14 Test

1. $\triangle PQR \sim \triangle SZW$. If $q = 25$, $r = 65$, $p = 60$, and $z = 75$, find w and s.
2. In $\triangle ABC$, find sin A to four decimal places.

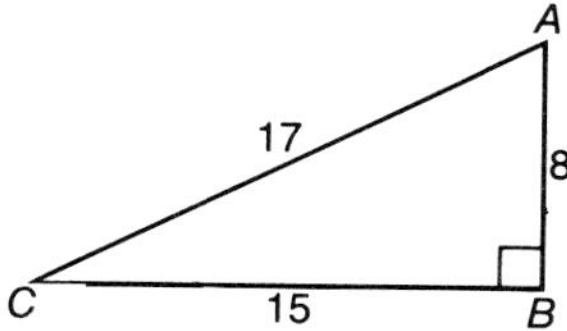

3. In $\triangle DEF$, find cos F to four decimal places.

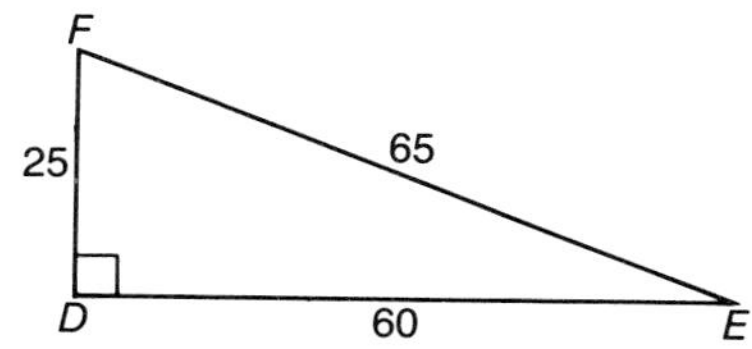

4. In $\triangle RST$, find tan R to four decimal places.

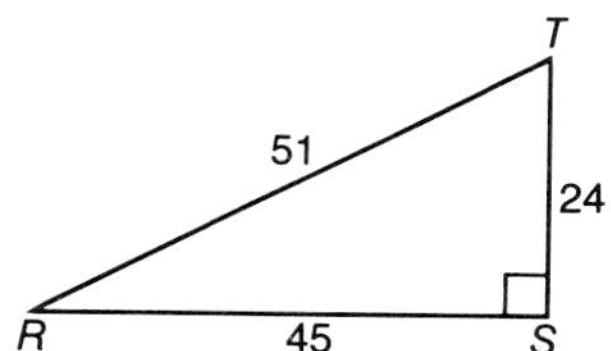

Use Table 2 for Exercises 5–8.

5. Find sin 13°.
6. Find cos 52°.
7. Suppose sin $A = 0.9659$. Find A.
8. Suppose tan $B = 0.6009$. Find B.
9. In right triangle GHK, K is the right angle, $H = 41°$, and $k = 60$ cm. Find h.
10. In right triangle MNQ, N is the right angle, $M = 18°$, and $n = 60$ m. Find q.
11. In right triangle PQR, R is the right angle, $q = 85$ km, and $p = 140$ km. Find Q to the nearest degree.
12. The angle of elevation of a hang glider is 15°. The distance to the hang glider is 2 km. How high is the hang glider?
13. An observation tower is 95 m tall. The angle of depression from the top of the tower to a monument is 26°. How far from the base of the tower is the monument?

ANSWERS

1. $w = 195$, $s = 180$
2. 0.8824
3. 0.3846
4. 0.5333
5. 0.225
6. 0.6157
7. 75°
8. 31°
9. ≈39.4 cm
10. ≈57.1 m
11. 31°
12. ≈0.5 km
13. ≈194.8 m

Test Item Analysis

Item	Lesson
1	14-1
2–4	14-2
5–8	14-3
9–13	14-4

CHAPTER **15**

Introduction to Probability and Statistics

Chapter Overview

Although Introduction to Probability and Statistics is the last chapter in this book, it is not necessary to teach it last. An optional Management Guide is presented on page 638C for teaching this chapter in four sections following chapters 4, 6, 8, and 12 respectively. You may also teach Probability and Statistics in its entirety anytime after Chapter 7.

The fundamental concepts of probability are covered in this chapter. Simulation is introduced as a method for finding experimental probability. Distribution techniques for organizing data are presented. These techniques include frequency distributions, stem-and-leaf diagrams, line plots, histograms, and scatter plots. Measures of central tendency, mean, median, and mode are discussed.

Problem Solving: College Entrance Exams take the mean one step further by introducing weighted averages.

Two TI-81 Investigations on matrices can be found in the Appendix. Matrices could be introduced with this chapter by using Investigations 5 and 6 (pages 732 and 736). Matrices provide an efficient method for displaying data.

Objectives

15-1 ■ Find the probability of a simple event.
15-2 ■ Find the theoretical probability of a complementary event.
■ Find the theoretical probability of two mutually exclusive events.
■ Find the theoretical probability of two events.
15-3 ■ Use simulation to find the experimental probability of an event.
15-4 ■ Construct a frequency distribution for a set of data.
■ Construct a stem-and-leaf diagram for a set of data.
15-5 ■ Construct a line plot for a set of data.
■ Construct a histogram for a set of data.
■ Construct a frequency polygon for a set of data.
15-6 ■ Find the mean, median, and mode of a set of data.
15-7 ■ Make scatter plots and determine data relationships.

Cooperative Learning Opportunities

The manufacturing of shoes, discussed in the **Multicultural Note**, can be used in a paired cooperative learning activity about scatter plots, discussed in Lesson 15-7. Distribute this table and have each student rank the factors based on importance, to him or her, when buying a pair of shoes.

Factor	Your Rank (x)	Partner's Rank (y)
Fit		
Brand Name		
Color		
Durability		
Style		
Price		
Place Made		
Weight		

After the ranking, assign students to pairs. Each pair should draw an 8–by–8 first–quadrant graph and plot points determined by the x– and y–values above. Show students the different graphs and point out how the scatter plots indicate an agreement or disagreement between the rankings.

Multicultural Note: *Jan Matzeliger*

Jan Matzeliger (1852–1889) was an African-American inventor who was born in Surinam, South America, and immigrated to the United States at the age of 19.

The sewing machine, invented in 1846, led to the invention of special machines for sewing shoes. Matzeliger invented a machine to last the shoe, that is, to attach the upper portion to the sole.

In 1883 Matzeliger obtained a patent for the machine and with two investors formed the Hand Method Lasting Machine Company in Lynn, Massachusetts. Using this machine, 700 shoes could be lasted in a day whereas previously only 50 shoes could be lasted by hand. Manufacturing standardized products requires a number of statistical considerations, some of which are listed in the **Cooperative Learning Opportunities**.

For more information, see page 107 of **Multiculturalism in Mathematics, Science, and Technology**.

Alternative Assessment and Communication Ideas

The ideas associated with probability and statistics are particularly suited to verbal explanations. Many of the exercises in Chapter 15 can be used, as written, as the basis of alternative assessment.

When covering Exercises 5–8 in Lesson 15-2, ask students to write a reason or explanation for each answer. In Lesson 15-3, students should explain, either orally or in writing, how to develop an experimental model.

Exercise 10 in Lesson 15-4 asks for a paragraph explaining the advantages and disadvantages of different statistical methods. In a similar way, for Lesson 15-6, ask for a short written piece exploring situations that might lead to the use of mean, median, and mode.

In Lesson 15-7 you can ask for examples of research in which scatter plots might arise.

Investigations and Projects

The news media offer a variety of statistics and suggest that we should consider them in making decisions. Invite your students to do a research project on one of the following areas, gathering data from the library and other sources. Students should explain the information and express their views about how statistics affect people's decisions, including their own.

Heart Disease. Factors such as diet, smoking, exercise, and certain genetic dispositions are considered when placing a person in a certain category of risk. Ask students to review the statistics in each category and discuss how they might be interrelated. Ask also what they perceive as the lesson to be learned.

Automobile Accidents. Some of the factors affecting injury in automobile accidents include alcohol consumption, car speed, and safety devices in the car. Have students gather information about these factors and ask what decisions they will make based on the statistics.

MANAGING CHAPTER 15

Lesson	PACING CHART (DAYS) 2-Year* A for E	1-Year Minimum	1-Year Regular**	1-Year Advanced	Opening Activity	Cooperative Activity	Seat or Group Work
15-1	2	0	1	1	First Five Minutes 15-1: ***FFMTM*** p. 41 or **TE** p. 640	Probability/Statistics 1, 2: ***Enrichment*** pp. 66–67; ✂ Manipulative Activity 15: ***Enrichment*** p. 48	Try This a–e
15-2	3	0	1	1	First Five Minutes 15-2: ***FFMTM*** p. 41 or **TE** p. 644	Probability/Statistics 3: ***Enrichment*** p. 68	Try This a–f
15-3	2	0	1	1	First Five Minutes 15-3: ***FFMTM*** p. 41 or **TE** p. 649	Probability/Statistics 4: ***Enrichment*** p. 69; Critical Thinking 15: ***Enrichment*** p. 32	Try This a–b
15-4	2	0	1	1	First Five Minutes 15-4: ***FFMTM*** p. 42 or **TE** p. 653	Lesson Enrichment: **TE** p. 654	Try This a–c
15-5	3	0	1	1	First Five Minutes 15-5: ***FFMTM*** p. 42 or **TE** p. 657; ***Overhead Transparencies*** T33, T34	Problem 13: **SE** p. 660	Try This a–c
15-6	2	0	1	1	First Five Minutes 15-6: ***FFMTM*** p. 42 or **TE** p. 661	Probability/Statistics 5, 6, 7: ***Enrichment*** pp. 70–72	Try This a–c
15-7	3	0	1	2.5	First Five Minutes 15-7: ***FFMTM*** p. 42 or **TE** p. 665; Application: **SE** p. 665	Problem Solving: Application: **SE** pp. 669–670	Try This a–d
Review	2	0	1	0.5			
Test	1	0	1	1			
Cum. Review	4	0	1	1			
End-of Year Test	1	0	1	1			

*2-Year Management Guide can be found in *Algebra for Everyone*.
**Either Chapter 14 or Chapter 15 can be covered.

FFMTM: First Five Minutes Transparency Masters

Enrichment	Review/Assess	Reteach	Technology	Lesson
Probability/Statistics 1, 2: ***Enrichment*** pp. 66–67; Probability: It's a Small World: **SE** p. 643; ✂ Manipulative Activity 15: ***Enrichment*** p. 48	Lesson Quiz: **TE** p. 642		Computer Exploration 11: **SE** p. 722	**15-1**
Probability/Statistics 3: ***Enrichment*** p. 68	Lesson Quiz: **TE** p. 646; Mixed Review 29: ***SPMR*** p. 79		Computer Exploration 12: **SE** p. 723	**15-2**
Probability/Statistics 4: ***Enrichment*** p. 69; Critical Thinking 15: ***Enrichment*** p. 32	Mixed Practice 29: **SE** p. 712; Lesson Quiz: **TE** p. 651; Quiz 29: ***Assessment*** p. 39	Skills Practice 39: ***SPMR*** p. 47	BASIC Computer Project 20: ***Technology*** p. 82	**15-3**
Lesson Enrichment: **TE** p. 654	Lesson Quiz: **TE** p. 655		TI-81 Investigation 5: **SE** pp. 732–735	**15-4**
Bonus Topic 15: ***Enrichment*** p. 16	Lesson Quiz: **TE** p. 659; Quiz 30: ***Assessment*** p. 40			**15-5**
Probability/Statistics 5, 6, 7: ***Enrichment*** pp. 70–72	Mixed Practice 30: **SE** p. 713; Lesson Quiz: **TE** p. 662; Mixed Review 30: ***SPMR*** p. 80		Problem for Programmers: **SE** p. 664; TI-81 Investigation 4: **SE** pp. 730–731	**15-6**
Problem Solving: Application: **SE** pp. 669–670; Problem Solving: College Entrance Exams: **SE** pp. 671–672; Looking for Errors 15: ***Enrichment*** p. 64	Lesson Quiz: **TE** p. 666	Skills Practice 40: ***SPMR*** p. 48; Strategy Problem Bank 15: ***Problem Bank*** p. 16	TI-81 Investigation 6: **SE** pp. 736–739; Calculator Worksheet 32: ***Technology*** p. 34; Spreadsheet Activity 12: ***Technology*** pp. 59–60	**15-7**
	Summary and Review: **SE** pp. 673–675; Test: **SE** pp. 675–676			**Review**
	Chapter 15 Exam: ***A for E*** pp. 545–546; Chapter 15 Test: ***Assessment*** pp. 155–160 (reg.), 191–192 (adv.)			**Test**
	Cumulative Review: **SE** pp. 677–683			**Cum. Review**
	Assessing Strategies 8: ***Assessment*** pp. 209–210; Cumulative Exam: ***A for E*** pp. T71–T76; End-of-Year Test: ***Assessment*** pp. 241–258 (reg.), 259–265 (adv.)			**End-of Year Test**

SPMR: Skills Practice Mixed Review

1. 0 4

2. −5 0

The solution to the problem posed on the facing page can be found on pages 650 and 651.

Ready for Introduction to Probability and Statistics?

2-1 Graph each rational number on a number line.

1. 4

2. -5

4-1 Determine whether the given number is a solution of $y < 6$.

3. 5 Yes

4. 8 No

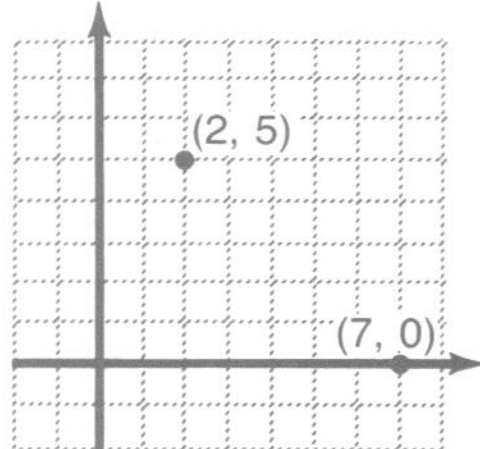

7-1 Plot these points on graph paper.

5. (2, 5)

6. (7, 0)

9-1 Write roster notation.

7. $A = \{x|x \text{ is an integer and } 1 < x < 6\}$ {2, 3, 4, 5}

8. $B = \{x|x \text{ is an odd natural number less than } 10\}$ {1, 3, 5, 7, 9}

Let $A = \{2, 3, 4, 5, 6, 7, 8, 9\}$ and let $B = \{x|x \text{ is an even integer}\}$

9. Find $A \cap B$. {2, 4, 6, 8}

CHAPTER 15

Introduction to Probability and Statistics

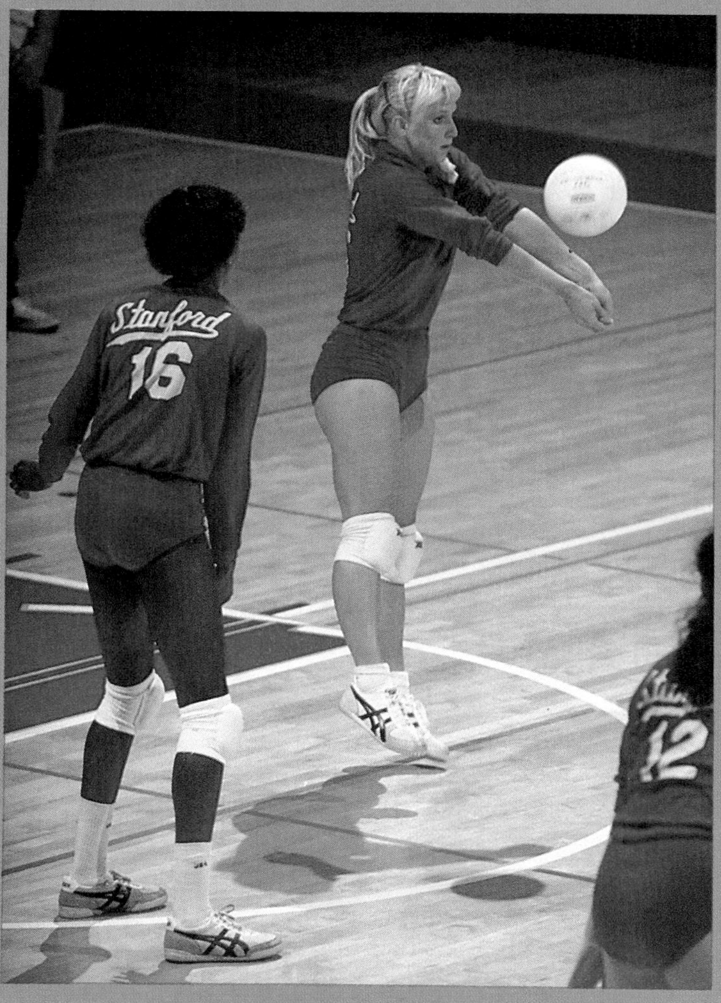

Two volleyball teams, the Hurricanes and the Tigers, are involved in a five-game play-off series. The outcome of any one game does not depend on what has happened in previous games. If the teams are evenly matched, find the probability that each team will win at least two games in a row.

15-1

FIRST FIVE MINUTES

1. What is the ratio of 1's to all the digits in the following sequence? 001011010111

   $\frac{7}{12}$
2. If you flip a coin 100 times, how many times do you expect heads to occur?

   About 50
3. A coin is tossed twice. One outcome is HT. Write down all the possible outcomes.

   HH, HT, TH, TT

Point out that a *fair* die is one whose sides are each *equally likely* to land up when tossed. No one side is more likely to be rolled than is another.

You may wish to point out some equivalent probability situations, for example, throwing a fair die, spinning a spinner with 6 positions of equal size, or drawing a tag at random from a bag of tags, numbered 1 through 6, each tag being the same size. Experiments show that these situations do yield indistinguishable outcomes.

Emphasize that $P(E)$ means "the probability of event E," not "P times E."

Key Questions

- What is the sample space for Example 2?

  {1, 2, 3, 4, 5, 6}
- What is the set for the event $\{n < 4\}$ in Example 4?

  {2H, 2D, 2C, 2S, 3H, 3D, 3C, 3S}

15-1 Probability

Objective: Find the theoretical probability of a simple event.

Math History

The study of probability is less than 400 years old. Many consider the birth of this branch of mathematics to stem from the work of the French mathematician Blaise Pascal (1623–1662). His early work dealt with the calculation of probabilities for dice games. The development of sound foundations for the subject did not come until the early 1900s with the work of the Russian mathematician Andrei Kolmogoroff (1902–1987). Today, probability plays an important role in many careers.

If we toss a coin 1000 times and it comes up heads 503 times, we can say that the probability of getting a head is $\frac{503}{1000}$. This is **experimental probability.**

We could reason that there are only two ways a coin can fall, heads or tails. If the coin is fair, each outcome is equally likely, so we can say that the probability of getting a head is $\frac{1}{2}$. This is **theoretical probability.**

You can see that experimental probability and theoretical probability can differ. If an experiment is repeated many times, however, the two probabilities will become very close. In this chapter we will consider theoretical probability.

The set of all possible outcomes of an experiment such as tossing a coin, rolling a die, or picking a card from a deck is called a **sample space.** An **event** is a set of outcomes that is a subset of the sample space.

Definition

If an event E can occur m ways out of n possible equally likely ways, the **probability** of that event is

$$P(E) = \frac{m}{n}$$

A cube with six faces, each containing a number of dots from one to six, is called a **die** (plural, dice). We will consider the die to be fair. In other words, each face is equally likely to land up when tossed.

EXAMPLE 1 What is the probability of rolling a 4 on a die?

The sample space for rolling a die is {1, 2, 3, 4, 5, 6}. The event is {4}. Therefore, there is 1 way out of 6 possible ways that a 4 can be rolled. By the definition of probability, $P(4) = \frac{1}{6}$.

EXAMPLE 2 What is the probability of rolling an odd number on a die?

The event (odd) can occur in three ways {1, 3, 5}. The number of possible outcomes is 6. Thus, $P(\text{odd}) = \frac{3}{6} = \frac{1}{2}$.

Try This A fair die is tossed.

a. What is the probability of rolling a factor of 6? $\frac{4}{6}$ or $\frac{2}{3}$

b. What is the probability of rolling a multiple of 2? $\frac{3}{6}$ or $\frac{1}{2}$

A standard deck of 52 cards consists of 13 black spades, 13 black clubs, 13 red hearts, and 13 red diamonds. Each suit has an ace, a king, a queen, a jack, and the numbers from 2 to 10.

EXAMPLES A card is drawn from a well-shuffled deck of 52 cards.

3. What is the probability of drawing a queen?

The event (queen) can occur in 4 ways, namely, hearts, diamonds, spades, and clubs. There are 52 possible outcomes, so

$$P(\text{queen}) = \frac{4}{52} = \frac{1}{13}$$

4. What is the probability of drawing a card with a number printed on it that is less than 4?

The event ($n < 4$) can occur in 8 ways, namely, 2 and 3 in each of the four suits, hearts, diamonds, clubs, and spades. There are 52 possible outcomes, so

$$P(n < 4) = \frac{8}{52} = \frac{2}{13}$$

5. What is the probability of drawing a green card?

There are no green cards in a standard deck of cards. The event is the empty set, so

$$P(\text{green card}) = \frac{0}{52} = 0$$

These examples illustrate the following basic property of probability.

Basic Property of Probability

For any event E with a sample space S,

$P(E)$ is a number between 0 and 1, or
$P(E) = 0$ if the event cannot occur, or
$P(E) = 1$ if the event is certain to occur.

Chalkboard Examples

1. What is the probability of rolling a 3 on a fair die?
   $P(3) = \frac{1}{6}$
2. What is the probability of rolling a multiple of 3 on a die?
   $P(3, 6) = \frac{2}{6} = \frac{1}{3}$
3. What is the probability of drawing a 7 from a well-shuffled deck of cards?
   There are four sevens among the 52 possible outcomes.
   $P(7) = \frac{4}{52} = \frac{1}{13}$
4. What is the probability of drawing a face card (king, queen, or jack) from a deck of cards?
   There are four of each type of card, for a total of 12 outcomes of the desired type out of the 52 possible outcomes.
   $P(\text{face}) = \frac{12}{52} = \frac{3}{13}$
5. What is the probability of drawing either a red card or a black card?
   Every card is either a red card or a black card. The probability is $\frac{52}{52} = 1$.

LESSON QUIZ

1. What is the probability of rolling a number 3 or greater on a die?

   $P(3, 4, 5, 6) = \frac{4}{6} = \frac{2}{3}$

2. What is the probability of drawing a 10 from a well-shuffled deck of cards?

   $P(10) = \frac{4}{52} = \frac{1}{13}$

3. What is the probability of drawing either an ace or a king?

   $P(\text{ace or king}) = \frac{8}{52} = \frac{2}{13}$

Assignment Guide

Minimum: omit

Regular: 1–16 e/o, 17, MR

Advanced: 1–14 m3, 15–17, 18–22 e/o, MR

Try This A card is drawn from a well-shuffled deck of 52 cards.

c. What is the probability of drawing a red card? $\frac{26}{52}$ or $\frac{1}{2}$

d. What is the probability of drawing a card with an even number? $\frac{20}{52}$ or $\frac{5}{13}$

e. What is the probability of drawing a blue card? $\frac{0}{52}$ or 0

15-1 EXERCISES

A

A spinner numbered 1 to 8 is spun.

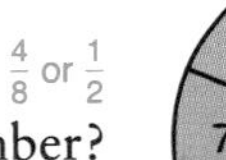

1. What is the probability of spinning an even number? $\frac{4}{8}$ or $\frac{1}{2}$

2. What is the probability of spinning a divisor of 12? $\frac{5}{8}$

3. What is the probability of spinning a multiple of 3? $\frac{2}{8}$ or $\frac{1}{4}$

4. What is the probability of spinning a multiple of 4? $\frac{2}{8}$ or $\frac{1}{4}$

5. What is the probability of spinning a prime number? $\frac{4}{8}$ or $\frac{1}{2}$

6. What is the probability of spinning a factor of 10? $\frac{3}{8}$

7. What is the probability of spinning a 9? $\frac{0}{8}$ or 0

One card is drawn from a well-shuffled deck of 52 cards.

8. What is the probability of drawing an ace? $\frac{4}{52}$ or $\frac{1}{13}$

9. What is the probability of drawing a card with an odd number? $\frac{16}{52}$ or $\frac{4}{13}$

10. What is the probability of drawing a card with a number greater than 8? $\frac{8}{52}$ or $\frac{2}{13}$

11. What is the probability of drawing a face card? $\frac{12}{52}$ or $\frac{3}{13}$

12. What is the probability of drawing a card with the number 0? $\frac{0}{52}$ or 0

13. What is the probability of drawing a card with a number that is divisible by 3? $\frac{12}{52}$ or $\frac{3}{13}$

14. What is the probability of drawing a card with a prime number? $\frac{16}{52}$ or $\frac{4}{13}$

B

15. Obtain a 3 × 5 file card and fold it in half widthwise. Toss the folded card 100 times and determine experimental probabilities for the card falling "flat," "on edge," or "as a tent." Answers may vary.

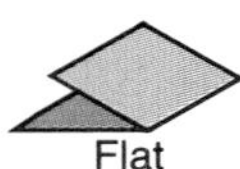

Flat

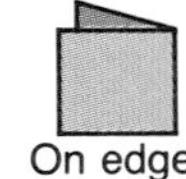

On edge

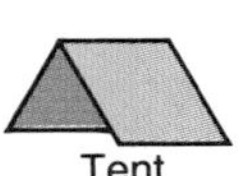

Tent

16. Obtain the cap from a tube of toothpaste. Determine the various possibilities that can occur when the cap is tossed. Toss the cap 100 times, and determine experimental probabilities for the various events. Answers may vary.

17. *Critical Thinking* Suppose a fair coin has come up tails for the last 10 tosses. What is the probability of getting a head on the next toss? Why?

Challenge

Two dice are tossed.

18. What is the probability that the numbers on the dice will total 7? $\frac{6}{36}$ or $\frac{1}{6}$
19. What is the probability that the numbers on the dice will total 1? $\frac{0}{36}$ or 0
20. What is the probability that the numbers on the dice will total 9? $\frac{4}{36}$ or $\frac{1}{9}$
21. What is the probability that the total will be greater than 10? $\frac{3}{36}$ or $\frac{1}{12}$
22. What total on the dice is most likely to be rolled? Why? The total of 7 is most likely to be rolled as it has the highest probability, $\frac{6}{36}$ or $\frac{1}{6}$.

Mixed Review

Solve. **23.** $m^2 - 8m = 0$ **24.** $y^2 - 5y = 6$ **25.** $12x^2 + 7x + 1 = 0$
26. $3a^2 - 5 = 16$ **27.** $(c + 7)^2 = 20$ **28.** $y^2 - 10y + 25 = 11$

Determine the nature of the solutions to these equations.

29. $x^2 - 121 = 0$ **30.** $y^2 - 3y + 9 = 0$ **31.** $a^2 - 4a + 4 = 0$

Use the figure to find the following.

32. the length of RT
33. $\tan R$ **34.** $\sin R$ **35.** $\sin T$
36. $\cos R$ **37.** $\cos T$ **38.** $\tan T$

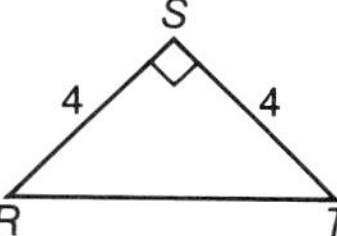

PROBABILITY: IT'S A SMALL WORLD

Have you ever struck up a conversation with a total stranger and been amazed to find out that the two of you had a common acquaintance?

There is a very good reason why such coincidences occur so often. Most of us have at least a casual acquaintance with about 1000 other people. That means that there is about 1 chance in 100,000 that two people selected at random in the United States will know each other.

That isn't much of a chance. There is, however, 1 chance in 100 that, like you and the stranger, any two people will have a friend in common. And it is virtually certain that any two people will have a friend of a friend in common.

In other words, if you were to pick two names out of two phone books in two different parts of the country, the chances would be better than 99 percent that the first person would know someone who knows someone who knows the second person.

ADDITIONAL ANSWERS

Exercises

17. The probability of a head on the next toss is $\frac{1}{2}$. The probability of getting a head when tossing a fair coin is not affected by previous tosses.

Mixed Review

23. 0, 8
24. 6, −1
25. $-\frac{1}{4}, -\frac{1}{3}$
26. $\pm\sqrt{7}$
27. $-7 \pm 2\sqrt{5}$
28. $5 \pm \sqrt{11}$
29. 2 real-number solutions
30. No real-number solution
31. 1 real-number solution
32. $4\sqrt{2}$
33. 1
34. $\frac{\sqrt{2}}{2}$
35. $\frac{\sqrt{2}}{2}$
36. $\frac{\sqrt{2}}{2}$
37. $\frac{\sqrt{2}}{2}$
38. 1

15-2

FIRST FIVE MINUTES

1. What is the probability of rolling a 3 on a fair die?

$\frac{1}{6}$

2. What is the probability of drawing an ace from a well-shuffled deck of 52 cards?

$\frac{4}{52} = \frac{1}{13}$

3. What is the probability of drawing a card numbered 2 through 10 from a well-shuffled deck of cards?

$\frac{36}{52} = \frac{9}{13}$

Complementary Events

Point out that E' is read as "E prime" and means *the complement of E.*

You may want to show these examples of complementary events.

P(rolling a 1 on a die) $= \frac{1}{6}$

P(not rolling a 1 on a die) $= \frac{5}{6}$

P(rolling a 2, 3, 4, 5, or 6) $= \frac{5}{6}$

P(rolling a 1 on a die) $+$ P(not rolling a 1 on a die) $=$ $\frac{1}{6} + \frac{5}{6} = 1$

Key Questions

The sample space for a certain experiment is 0, 1, 2, 3, 4, 5, 6, 7, 8, 9.

- What is the complement of the outcome set {0, 2, 4, 6, 8}?
  {1, 3, 5, 7, 9}
- What is the complement of the empty set?
  {0, 1, 2, 3, 4, 5, 6, 7, 8, 9}
- What is the complement of {0, 1, 2, 3, 4, 5, 6, 7, 8, 9}?
  The empty set

Chalkboard Examples

1. Suppose an event A has probability $\frac{5}{7}$. What is $P(A')$?

   $P(A') = 1 - \frac{5}{7} = \frac{2}{7}$

2. Suppose the event A has probability 0.12. What is the probability of A'?

   $P(A') = 1 - 0.12 = 0.88$

15-2 More on Probability

Complementary Events

Objective: Find the theoretical probability of a complementary event.

Rolling a 1 on a die is an event, say E. *Not* rolling a 1 on a die is also an event, which we call the **complement of E,** or E'. E and E' are called complementary events.

Rolling an even number is the event {2, 4, 6}. The complement of this event, *not* rolling an even number (rolling an odd number), is $E' = \{1, 3, 5\}$. We can see that $P(E) = \frac{1}{2}$ and $P(E') = \frac{1}{2}$, and that

$$P(E) + P(E') = \frac{1}{2} + \frac{1}{2} = 1.$$

Complementary Events

For any event A, $P(A) + P(A') = 1.$

Since $P(A) + P(A') = 1$, we know that $P(A') = 1 - P(A)$.

EXAMPLE 1 Suppose that an event A has a probability of $\frac{2}{9}$.

What is $P(A')$?

$$P(A') = 1 - P(A)$$
$$= 1 - \frac{2}{9} = \frac{7}{9}$$

EXAMPLE 2 Suppose that the probability of rain today is 0.36.

What is the probability that it will not rain today?

Let the probability of rain be event R. Then the probability that it will *not* rain is R'.

$$P(R') = 1 - P(R)$$
$$= 1 - 0.36 = 0.64$$

Try This

a. Suppose that an event A has a probability of $\frac{4}{7}$. What is $P(A')$? $\frac{3}{7}$

b. Suppose that the probability of sitting next to your best friend is 0.08. What is the probability that you will *not* sit next to your best friend? 0.92

Mutually Exclusive Events

Objective: Find the theoretical probability of two mutually exclusive events.

Two events that cannot both happen at the same time are called **mutually exclusive events.** An event and its complement are examples of mutually exclusive events.

Suppose there are 5 red marbles, 7 green marbles, and 11 blue marbles in a bag. Let us consider the mutually exclusive events *draw a green marble G* and *draw a red marble R*. We know that $P(R) = \frac{5}{23}$ and $P(G) = \frac{7}{23}$. We can easily see that $P(R \text{ or } G) = \frac{12}{23}$, since there are twelve marbles that are red or green. Note that $P(R \text{ or } G) = \frac{5}{23} + \frac{7}{23} = \frac{12}{23}$. The idea of adding probabilities when working with mutually exclusive events is true in general.

> **$P(A \text{ or } B)$ for Mutually Exclusive Events**
>
> If A and B are mutually exclusive events then
>
> $$P(A \text{ or } B) = P(A) + P(B)$$

EXAMPLE 3 One die is tossed.

What is the probability that a 3 or a 5 will be rolled?

$P(3)$ and $P(5)$ are mutually exclusive events, so

$$\begin{aligned} P(3 \text{ or } 5) &= P(3) + P(5) \\ &= \frac{1}{6} + \frac{1}{6} \\ &= \frac{2}{6} \text{ or } \frac{1}{3} \end{aligned}$$

EXAMPLE 4 A block is chosen at random from a bag containing 6 white blocks, 4 black blocks, and 12 red blocks.

What is the probability that it will be a red block or a white block?

Choosing a red block and choosing a white block are mutually exclusive events, so

$$\begin{aligned} P(R \text{ or } W) &= P(R) + P(W) \\ &= \frac{12}{22} + \frac{6}{22} \\ &= \frac{18}{22} \text{ or } \frac{9}{11} \end{aligned}$$

Mutually Exclusive Events

It may be easier for students to understand mutually exclusive events by first discussing events that are not mutually exclusive, such as *rolling an even number* or *rolling a prime number.* The event *rolling an even number* is {2, 4, 6} and the event *rolling a prime number* is {2, 3, 5}. The intersections of these two sets is {2}. Therefore they are *not* mutually exclusive events.

Key Questions

The outcomes of an experiment are {0, 1, 2, 3, 4, 5}.

- Are the outcome sets {0, 1, 2} and {5, 2} mutually exclusive?
  No
- Are the outcome sets {1, 3, 5} and {0, 4} mutually exclusive?
  Yes
- Are drawing a black card and drawing a red king mutually exclusive outcome sets?
  Yes

Chalkboard Examples

1. What is the probability that a 5 or a 6 will occur in the toss of a fair die?
   The events are mutually exclusive.
   $$\begin{aligned} P(5 \text{ or } 6) &= P(5) + P(6) \\ &= \frac{1}{6} + \frac{1}{6} \\ &= \frac{2}{6} = \frac{1}{3} \end{aligned}$$
2. What is the probability of drawing a black card or a red ace from a well-shuffled deck of cards?
   The events are mutually exclusive.
   $$\begin{aligned} &P(\text{black card or red ace}) \\ &= P(\text{black card}) + P(\text{red ace}) \\ &= \frac{26}{52} + \frac{2}{52} \\ &= \frac{28}{52} = \frac{7}{13} \end{aligned}$$

The Probability of A or B

Point out that the rule in this section applies to mutually exclusive events as well as those that are not mutually exclusive. Since mutually exclusive events have no elements in their intersection, $P(A \cap B) = 0$. Thus, in this case $P(A \text{ or } B) = P(A) + P(B) + 0 = P(A) + P(B)$.

Chalkboard Example

1. What is the probability of drawing a black card or an ace?
   $P(\text{black or ace})$
   $= P(\text{black}) + P(\text{ace}) - P(\text{black} \cap \text{ace})$
   $= \frac{26}{52} + \frac{4}{52} - \frac{2}{52}$
   $= \frac{28}{52}$
   $= \frac{7}{13}$

LESSON QUIZ

1. Suppose that event A has probability $\frac{2}{5}$. What is the probability of A'?
   $P(A') = \frac{3}{5}$
2. A card is chosen from a well-shuffled deck. What is the probability of drawing an ace or a two?
   $P(\text{ace or } 2) = \frac{2}{13}$
3. What is the probability of drawing a black card or a red jack?
   $\frac{7}{13}$
4. What is the probability of drawing a red card or any face card (jack, queen, or king)?
   $\frac{8}{13}$

Try This

c. What is the probability of rolling a 1 or a 6 on one toss of a die? $\frac{2}{6}$ or $\frac{1}{3}$

d. What is the probability that a block selected from the bag described in Example 4 will be black or white? $\frac{10}{22}$ or $\frac{5}{11}$

The Probability of A or B

Objective: Find the theoretical probability of two events.

Mutually exclusive events do not occur at the same time. There are, however, events that can occur at the same time. The sample space for one spin on the spinner shown is $S = \{1, 2, 3, 4, 5, 6, 7, 8\}$. What is the probability of spinning an even number or a number less than 5?

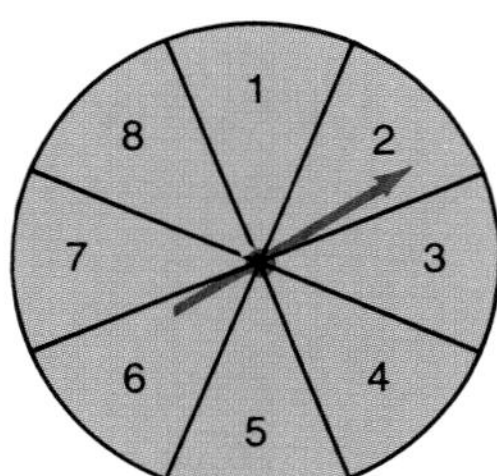

These two events can be represented by the sets $A = \{2, 4, 6, 8\}$ and $B = \{1, 2, 3, 4\}$. They are not mutually exclusive as shown in the diagram below.

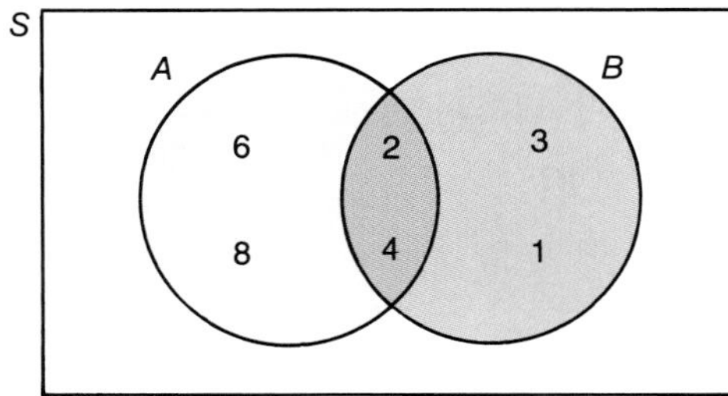

If we add the probabilities of event A and event B, we will count the probabilities of the intersection of these events twice. If we subtract $P(A \cap B)$ from $P(A) + P(B)$, however, we will eliminate this problem.

$$P(A \text{ or } B) = P(A) + P(B) - P(A \cap B) = \frac{4}{8} + \frac{4}{8} - \frac{2}{8} = \frac{6}{8} = \frac{3}{4}$$

The Probability of A or B

If A and B are events from a sample space S, then

$$P(A \text{ or } B) = P(A) + P(B) - P(A \cap B)$$

EXAMPLE 5 What is the probability of spinning a prime number or an odd number on a spinner numbered 1 to 8?

Let A be the event of spinning a prime number; $A = \{2, 3, 5, 7\}$, $P(A) = \frac{4}{8}$

Let B be the event of spinning an odd number; $B = \{1, 3, 5, 7\}$, $P(B) = \frac{4}{8}$

$$A \cap B = \{3, 5, 7\}, \text{ so } P(A \cap B) = \frac{3}{8}$$

$$\begin{aligned} P(A \text{ or } B) &= P(A) + P(B) - P(A \cap B) \\ &= \frac{4}{8} + \frac{4}{8} - \frac{3}{8} \\ &= \frac{5}{8} \end{aligned}$$

Try This

e. What is the probability of spinning an even number or a divisor of 8 on the spinner used for Example 5? $\frac{5}{8}$

f. What is the probability of drawing a king or a black card from a well-shuffled deck of 52 cards? $\frac{28}{52}$ or $\frac{7}{13}$

15-2 EXERCISES

A

1. Suppose that an event A has probability of $\frac{3}{8}$. What is $P(A')$? $\frac{5}{8}$
2. Suppose that an event B has probability of $\frac{7}{19}$. What is $P(B')$? $\frac{12}{19}$
3. Suppose that the probability of snow is 0.58. What is the probability that it will *not* snow? 0.42
4. Suppose that the probability that you will win a contest is 0.001. What is the probability that you will *not* win the contest? 0.999

A card is chosen from a well-shuffled deck of 52 cards.

5. What is the probability that the card will be a king or a queen?
6. What is the probability that the card will be an ace or a card with a number less than 5?
7. What is the probability that the card will be a red jack or a black king?
8. What is the probability that the card will be a face card or a card with a prime number?

A spinner numbered 1 to 10 is spun. Each number is equally likely to be spun.

9. What is the probability of spinning an odd number or a power of 3?
10. What is the probability of spinning an even number or a multiple of 4?
11. What is the probability of spinning a number less than 8 or a divisor of 15?

Assignment Guide
Minimum: omit

Regular: 1–18 e/o, 19, MR

Advanced: 1–15 m3, 16–19, 20–23 e/o, MR

ADDITIONAL ANSWERS

Exercises

5. $\frac{8}{52}$ or $\frac{2}{13}$

6. $\frac{16}{52}$ or $\frac{4}{13}$

7. $\frac{4}{52}$ or $\frac{1}{13}$

8. $\frac{28}{52}$ or $\frac{7}{13}$

9. $\frac{5}{10}$ or $\frac{1}{2}$

10. $\frac{5}{10}$ or $\frac{1}{2}$

11. $\frac{7}{10}$

12. $\frac{16}{52}$ or $\frac{4}{13}$

13. $\frac{14}{52}$ or $\frac{7}{26}$

14. $\frac{38}{52}$ or $\frac{19}{26}$

15. $\frac{26}{52}$ or $\frac{1}{2}$

19. Answers may vary. For example, the probability of tossing a coin and getting either a head or a tail is 1, and the probability of rolling a standard die and getting a 13 is 0.

20. $P(\text{sum of 3}) = \frac{2}{36}$ or $\frac{1}{18}$

$P(\text{sum not 3}) = \frac{17}{18}$

21. $\frac{15}{36}$

22. $P(A \text{ or } B \text{ or } C) = P(A) + P(B) + P(C) - P(A \cap B) - P(A \cap C) - P(B \cap C) + P(A \cap B \cap C)$

Mixed Review

24. $r = \sqrt{\frac{A}{\pi}}$
25. $b = \sqrt{c^2 - a^2}$
26. $y = \sqrt{z^2 - w^2 - x^2}$
27. $b = \frac{2A}{h}$
28. $-5 \pm \sqrt{6}$
29. $\pm\sqrt{5}$
30. 1, 6
31. $-3 \pm \sqrt{5}$
32. $3, \frac{1}{3}$
33. $\pm\sqrt{2}$
34. 0.2756
35. 0.9397
36. 5.6713
37. 0.6018
38. 0.7660
39. 0.0875

A card is drawn from a well-shuffled deck of 52 cards.

12. What is the probability of drawing a diamond or a queen?

13. What is the probability of drawing a heart or a red jack?

14. What is the probability of drawing a black card or a card with a number less than 8?

15. What is the probability of drawing a spade or a black card?

B

16. If the set of whole numbers {0, 1, 2, 3, 4, 5, . . .} is the sample space, describe the complement of the set of even numbers. The set of odd numbers

17. A card is chosen from a well-shuffled deck of 52 cards. What is the probability that it will be a face card or an ace or a card with a number less than 4? $\frac{24}{52}$ or $\frac{6}{13}$

18. Two dice are tossed. What is the probability that a three will show face up? $\frac{11}{36}$

19. ***Critical Thinking*** Describe two easily understood events that can be confidently expected to have probabilities of 0 and 1, respectively.

Challenge

20. Two dice are tossed. What is the probability that the sum is three? What is the complement of this event?

21. Two dice are tossed. What is the probability that a four will show face up or that the sum of the two dice will be eight?

22. How can $P(A \text{ or } B \text{ or } C)$ be determined if events A, B, and C are *not* mutually exclusive?

23. Two events A and B are called independent if and only if $P(A \cap B) = P(A) \cdot P(B)$. A nickel and a die are tossed. What is the probability that the nickel shows tails and the die comes up even? $\frac{1}{4}$

Mixed Review

Solve each formula for the given positive variable. **24.** $A = \pi r^2; r$

25. $a^2 + b^2 = c^2; b$ **26.** $w^2 + x^2 + y^2 = z^2; y$ **27.** $A = \frac{1}{2}bh; b$

Solve. **28.** $x + 5 = \frac{6}{x + 5}$ **29.** $\frac{y^2}{y - 2} - \frac{5}{y - 2} = 0$

30. $\frac{12}{a + 3} + \frac{2}{a - 3} = 2$ **31.** $x^2 + 6x + 4 = 0$

32. $3y^2 - 10y + 3 = 0$ **33.** $4m^2 - 1 = 7$

Find these trigonometric function values. **34.** sin 16° **35.** cos 20° **36.** tan 80° **37.** sin 37° **38.** cos 40° **39.** tan 5°

15-3 Experimental Probability and Simulation

Objective: Use simulation to find the experimental probability of an event.

Probabilities associated with events can be difficult to determine using theoretical probability. Because it is not always possible to actually perform an experiment, we can **simulate** the event in order to determine the desired probability. Simulations are also used to verify theoretical probabilities.

PROBLEM-SOLVING GUIDELINES
■ UNDERSTAND the problem
■ Develop and carry out a PLAN
■ Find the ANSWER and CHECK

We can use the Problem-Solving Guidelines to solve problems using simulation.

When developing and carrying out a plan for a simulation, you should **select an appropriate model** and **define a trial.** Then you are ready to **collect data** and **run a sufficient number of trials.**

EXAMPLE 1 A sock manufacturer makes an equal number of socks with red and blue stripes. Three pairs of socks are selected randomly to be packaged in each box. What is the probability that any box will have two pairs of socks with blue stripes and one pair of socks with red stripes?

■ **UNDERSTAND the problem**

The problem is to determine the probability that a given box contains two pairs of socks with blue stripes and one pair with red stripes.

■ **Develop and carry out a PLAN**

Since we are dealing with two color choices, we can simulate the color of a pair of stripes with a coin toss. A head stands for blue stripes and a tail for red stripes. Thus the **model** for our simulation is a coin toss.

Three successive tosses of a coin determine the colors of the socks in a given box. Hence, a **trial** for this simulation consists of three tosses of a coin, which provides data that we can **collect,** for instance HHT for two heads (blue) and one tail (red).

Finally, we need to run a fairly large number of trials to determine the frequency of the boxes with two pairs of socks with blue stripes and one pair with red stripes. Here are some sample results of 50 trials.

```
HHH  TTT  THH  TTH  HTH  HHT  THH  TTT  HTT  HHH
THT  TTT  HHT  HHT  THH  THT  TTH  THH  THH  HHH
HHH  THH  HHH  HTT  THT  TTH  TTH  THT  THH  TTT
HHT  HHT  HTT  TTT  HHT  HHH  THT  HHT  HHT  HTT
TTT  HHT  HTH  HHH  HHH  THT  TTH  THT  TTH  HTH
```

15-3

FIRST FIVE MINUTES

1. What is the probability of drawing a red ace from a deck of cards?
   $\frac{2}{52} = \frac{1}{26}$
2. What is the probability of drawing a red 7 or any black card?
   $\frac{2}{52} + \frac{26}{52} = \frac{28}{52} = \frac{7}{13}$
3. What is the probability of drawing any numbered card, or a red card?
   $\frac{36}{52} + \frac{26}{52} - \frac{18}{52} = \frac{44}{52} = \frac{11}{13}$

Emphasize the importance of selecting an appropriate model. Point out that flipping a coin would not be an appropriate model if the sock manufacturer made more socks with red stripes than socks with blue stripes.

Key Questions

- What are the combinations of socks that could occur in Example 1?
  3 red, 3 blue, 2 red and 1 blue, or 2 blue and 1 red
- Do you think each of these outcomes is equally likely?
  No
- If the teams in Example 2 are evenly matched, what do you think the probability is that the Hurricanes will win the series?
  $\frac{1}{2}$

Chalkboard Example

1. The probability that it will rain on each of the next four days is $\frac{1}{2}$. What is the probability that it will not rain over the next four days? Toss a coin 4 times to simulate the event, letting heads represent rain and tails represent no rain. You may wish to have each student in your class toss a coin 4 times. The number of trials will be the same as the number of students. Ask students who tossed 4 tails to raise their hands. The experimental probability that it will not rain is the number of students with raised hands divided by the total number of students. (The theoretical probability is $\frac{1}{16}$.)

Find the ANSWER and CHECK

An examination of the trials shows that 19 of 50 result in exactly two heads (blue) and one tail (red) in them. So we would estimate that the probability of getting a box with two pairs of socks with blue stripes and one pair of socks with red stripes is $\frac{19}{50}$. The probability of $\frac{19}{50}$ is an estimate derived from experimentation. The reliability of this estimate improves as the number of trials increases.

Try This

a. Use a simulation to find the probability that a box will have three pairs of socks with blue stripes. Answers may vary. Theoretical probability is $\frac{1}{8}$.

How many trials should you run to find an accurate probability? This question does not have an easy answer. A famous theorem in probability called the **Law of Large Numbers** says that the more trials you run, the closer your simulation will come to the theoretical probability. So, the best answer to this question is to run as many trials as time will allow.

EXAMPLE 2

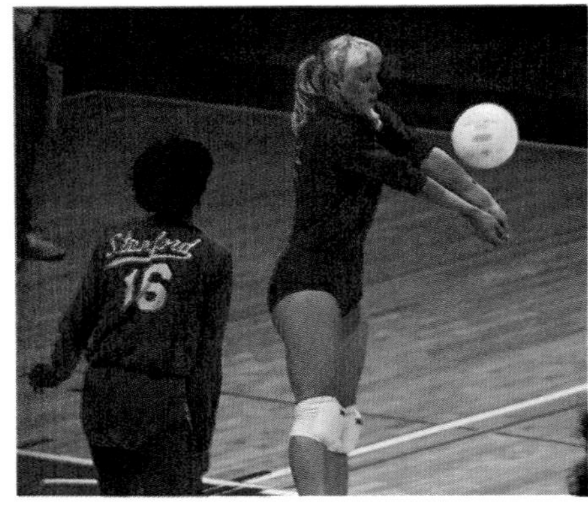

Two volleyball teams, the Hurricanes and the Tigers, are involved in a five-game play-off series. The outcome of any one game does not depend on what has happened in previous games. The Hurricanes and the Tigers are evenly matched.

a. Find the probability that the Hurricanes will win three or more games.

b. Find the probability that the Hurricanes will win exactly two games.

c. Find the probability that each team will win at least two games in a row.

These probabilities can be found if the simulation is carefully designed. Since the Hurricanes and the Tigers are evenly matched, we can assume that the probability of either team's winning a given game is $\frac{1}{2}$. So the toss of a coin is a good model. A head represents a victory for the Hurricanes and a tail, a victory for the Tigers. We need to conduct a large number of five-toss trials to simulate the five-game series. Each toss in the trial indicates the outcome of one game. A trial like HTTHT indicates victories for the Hurricanes in the first and fourth games and victories for the Tigers in the other games.

To answer the questions, we run 50 trials. Sample results are as follows:

HHTTH	HTTHT	THTTH	HTHHT	HTTHH
HHTHH	HTTHT	HHTHH	THTTH	TTHHH
HTTTH	HTHTT	HTHTH	HTTTT	HHTTT
THTHH	HHHHT	HTTHH	HHTTT	TTHTT
TTTHT	THTTT	HHHTH	HTHHH	TTHTH
HTTTT	THTTH	HTTHT	HTTTT	HHTHT
TTHTT	THTTT	HHHHH	THHTH	THHTH
HTTHT	TTHHH	HTTHH	TTTHT	TTHHT
HHHTH	THTHT	TTTHH	TTHTT	HHHHT
THTTH	TTTHH	HTTTH	HHHTT	HTTHT

We can use these results to answer the questions.

a. An examination of the trials shows that we can expect the Hurricanes to win the series 21 out of 50 times. This is equivalent to a probability of $\frac{21}{50}$.

b. To find the probability that the Hurricanes will win exactly two games, we look for trials with two tails. There are 18 such trials, so we can expect a probability of $\frac{18}{50}$ or $\frac{9}{25}$.

c. To find the number of series in which each team will win at least two games in a row, we look for series in which each team has at least two successive wins. There are 12 trials out of 50, so we can expect a probability of $\frac{12}{50}$ or $\frac{6}{25}$.

Try This

b. Find the probability that the winner of the five-game series will be decided in the fifth game of the series. $\frac{20}{50}$ or $\frac{2}{5}$

15-3 EXERCISES

A

1. What is the probability that a family with three children will have two boys and one girl?
   - **a.** What are you being asked to find?
   - **b.** What model can you use to simulate the event?
   - **c.** Define the trial for this simulation.
   - **d.** Run 20 trials and find the probability.
2. What is the probability that a family with three children will have at least two boys?
   - **a.** What are you being asked to find?
   - **b.** What model can you use to simulate the event?
   - **c.** Define the trial for this simulation.
   - **d.** Run 20 trials and find the probability.

LESSON QUIZ

1. A bicycle manufacturer makes an equal number of red, black, and yellow bikes. If he ships 3 at random to a store, what is the probability that the store will receive 1 of each color?
   Answers may vary. The theoretical probability is $\frac{6}{27}$.

Assignment Guide
Minimum: Omit

Regular: 1–10 e/o, 11, 12, MR

Advanced: 1–10 e/o, 11–14, MR

ADDITIONAL ANSWERS

Exercises

1. a. The probability that out of 3 children, 2 will be boys
b. A coin toss
c. A trial is 3 tosses of a coin. Heads can represent either boys or girls.
d. Answers may vary. The theoretical probability is $\frac{3}{8}$.

2. a. The probability that out of 3 children, either 2 or 3 will be boys.
b. A coin toss
c. A trial is 3 tosses of a coin. Heads can represent either boys or girls.
d. Answers may vary. The theoretical probability is $\frac{1}{2}$.

3–10. Answers may vary. The theoretical probability for each problem is given.

3. $\frac{4}{27}$ **4.** $\frac{2}{27}$

5. $\frac{4}{27}$ **6.** $\frac{16}{81}$

7. $\frac{1}{2}$ **8.** $\frac{35}{127}$

9. $\frac{1}{2}$ **10.** $\frac{1}{127}$

11. Answers may vary. The theoretical probabilities for Example 2 are (a) $\frac{1}{2}$, (b) $\frac{5}{32}$, and (c) $\frac{1}{4}$. Students should find that the more trials they run, the closer the results are to the theoretical values. They should also recognize that an experiment with 100 trials should be more reliable than one with 50 trials.

12. Yes. Each toss of a coin is an independent event. Therefore, either model is acceptable.

13. Answers may vary. The theoretical probability is 0.1001.

14. Answers may vary. The theoretical probability is 0.088.

Mixed Review

15. $2x^2 + 3x - 10 = 0$; 2, 3, −10
16. $x^2 - 2x - 15 = 0$; 1, −2, −15
17. $5x^2 - 3x - 39 = 0$; 5, −3, −39
18. 17 m, 11 m

For Exercises 3–6, use a die and 30 trials for your simulation. A tennis ball manufacturer packages four tennis balls to a tournament pack with white, orange, and yellow tennis balls equally likely. What is the probability that an individual pack has

3. two white, one orange, and one yellow tennis ball?

4. two white and two orange tennis balls?

5. two white and two other tennis balls of the same color?

6. no white tennis balls?

Suppose the freshman class sponsor told the class president that she would drive her van to the game if four of the seven officers wanted to go. If the probability that any one officer will want to go is $\frac{1}{2}$, answer the following questions.

7. What is the probability that at least four officers will want to go to the game?

8. What is the probability that only four officers will want to go to the game?

9. What is the probability that less than four officers will want to go to the game?

10. What is the probability that all seven officers will want to go to the game?

B

11. Repeat the simulation in Example 2, this time collecting data from 100 trials. What probabilities did you get for the three questions? How did they change from the values obtained from only 50 trials? Which set of data do you think would give more reliable results?

12. ***Critical Thinking*** In Example 1, a trial consisted of tossing a coin three times to simulate the color of the stripes on three pairs of socks. Instead, could we have tossed three coins for each trial? Explain.

Challenge

Six students travel to a speech contest. Suppose that the probability of each student getting laryngitis is $\frac{1}{3}$.

13. What is the probability that at least four (4, 5, or 6) of the students will become ill?

14. What is the probability that none of the six students will become ill?

Mixed Review

Write in standard form and determine a, b, and c. **15.** $3x = 10 - 2x^2$

16. $2x + 6 = x^2 - 9$ **17.** $8 - 3x = 47 - 5x^2$

18. The length of a rectangle is 6 m greater than its width. The area of the rectangle is 187 m^2. Find the length and the width.

15-4 Statistics: Organizing Data

The branch of mathematics that deals with the collection, organization, display, and interpretion of data is called **statistics.** Statistics is used to solve many problems and to help in making decisions.

Frequency Distributions

Objective: Construct a frequency distribution for a set of data.

When a set of data is collected it is often disorganized. We can organize data by using charts or tables. A **frequency distribution** is a type of table that is often used in statistics.

EXAMPLE 1 Here is a set of temperatures, in degrees Fahrenheit, recorded at noon each day during the month of April. Construct a frequency distribution.

49, 50, 49, 50, 50, 51, 49, 49, 51, 52, 51, 56, 53, 54, 50,
49, 53, 53, 55, 54, 50, 57, 49, 55, 56, 58, 54, 59, 55, 54

The temperatures range from a low of 49 to a high of 59. We make our frequency distribution as follows.

Temperatures	Tally	Frequency
49	~~IIII~~ I	6
50	~~IIII~~	5
51	III	3
52	I	1
53	III	3
54	IIII	4
55	III	3
56	II	2
57	I	1
58	I	1
59	I	1

Try This

a. Here is a set of pulse rates on 25 patients. Construct a frequency distribution. See Additional Answers.
72, 70, 74, 72, 69, 68, 69, 72, 75, 74, 73, 70, 68,
69, 73, 75, 72, 76, 73, 73, 72, 68, 70, 71, 74

15-4

FIRST FIVE MINUTES

Here are the speeds, in miles per hour, of 14 cars that passed a particular intersection at noon.

34 27 41 43 39 29 45
33 41 51 44 36 42 29

1. How many cars were going between 20 and 30 mi/h? 3
2. How many cars were going between 30 and 40 mi/h? 4
3. How many cars were going between 40 and 50 mi/h? 6
4. Were any cars going the same speed? Yes; 2 cars were going 41 mi/h and 2 were going 29 mi/h.

Frequency Distributions

For Try This Exercise b, you may want to suggest that students use intervals of 100 starting with 900 − 999.

Key Questions

The results of a certain experiment are the numbers 73, 56, 19, 32, 87, 68, 12, 44, 13, 82, 84, 44.

- What is the smallest outcome? 12
- What is the largest outcome? 87
- Which outcome occurs the most often? 44

Chalkboard Examples

1. Here are the weights, in ounces, of 20 turnips, rounded off to the nearest ounce. Construct a frequency distribution.
3, 1, 2, 4, 7, 3, 4, 6, 3, 4, 5, 7, 2, 3, 5, 4, 8, 2, 5, 4

Weights	Tally	Frequency
1	I	1
2	III	3
3	IIII	4
4	IIII	5
5	III	3
6	I	1
7	II	2
8	I	1

2. Below are the times, in hours, between arrivals of ships at a certain port. Construct a frequency distribution using intervals of length 50.
53, 157, 43, 51, 112, 223, 72, 49, 128, 65, 38, 159, 82, 31, 140, 263

Interval	Tally	Frequency
0–49	IIII	4
50–99	IIII	5
100–149	III	3
150–199	II	2
200–249	I	1
250–299	I	1

Stem-and-leaf Diagrams

Note that in Example 3 we could have chosen the first stem to be 1 rather than 16. However, this would have led to only two stems, the first of which would have 12 leaves.

Chalkboard Example

1. The table below contains the weights, in pounds, of the members of a high school class. Construct a stem-and-leaf diagram.
98, 182, 114, 124, 145, 164, 121, 139, 84, 137, 118, 126, 155

Stem	Leaf
8	4
9	8
10	
11	4, 8
12	4, 1, 6
13	9, 7
14	5
15	5
16	4
17	
18	2

LESSON ENRICHMENT

Students may be interested in statistics about the class or school. For example, height, age, number of children in the family, and so on. Have small groups collect data, then compile the data into one large frequency distribution.

If the data are spread over a large range of numbers, we may group the data into intervals. We usually try to have from 10 to 15 intervals.

EXAMPLE 2 Construct a frequency distribution using intervals.

Here is a set of times, in hours, showing how long it took each of 24 light bulbs to burn out.

979, 986, 1134, 1213, 1097, 1089, 897, 1219, 1093, 992, 1228, 1298, 1226, 947, 1007, 1167, 1214, 895, 996, 1043, 1152, 982, 1231, 1099

Suppose that we want about 9 intervals. The smallest value is 895 and the largest value is 1298. We find the difference, $1298 - 895 = 403$, and divide 403 by 9. This is approximately 45, which suggests that a convenient interval length is 50. Thus the intervals can be $850 - 899$, $900 - 949$, $950 - 999$, and so on.

Hours	Tally	Frequency
850–899	II	2
900–949	I	1
950–999	~~IIII~~	5
1000–1049	II	2
1050–1099	IIII	4
1100–1149	I	1
1150–1199	II	2
1200–1249	~~IIII~~ I	6
1250–1299	I	1

Try This Construct a frequency distribution. See Additional Answers.

b. Here is a set of 33 monthly salaries. Use 8 intervals.
1120, 1200, 1150, 1400, 1550, 1475, 995, 1100, 1250, 1195, 1400, 1650, 1500, 1225, 1190, 980, 1650, 1425, 1320, 1119, 1235, 1545, 1399, 986, 1675, 1330, 1256, 1175, 1298, 1187, 1298, 1200, 1145

Stem-and-Leaf Diagrams

Objective: Construct a stem-and-leaf diagram for a set of data.

Another useful way of organizing data is to construct a **stem-and-leaf diagram.**

EXAMPLE 3 Construct a stem-and-leaf diagram.

Here is a set of heights, in centimeters, of players on a high school basketball team.

172, 169, 183, 201, 203, 178, 183, 196, 198, 184, 195, 201, 199, 190, 186

As we look at these heights, we see that there are some that are in the 160s, some in the 170s, and so on. We use this idea to construct a stem-and-leaf diagram. We split each numeral into two parts, a stem and a leaf. The first value, 172, is split into 17 and 2. We write the stem, 17, in the first column and the leaf, 2, in the second column.

Stem	Leaf
16	9
17	2, 8
18	3, 3, 4, 6
19	6, 8, 5, 9, 0
20	1, 3, 1

We can see that the stem-and-leaf diagram has organized the data. It is easy to find the shortest height, 169, and the tallest height, 203. Also, it is obvious that many of the players have heights in the 190s.

Try This Construct a stem-and-leaf diagram. See Additional Answers.

c. Here is a set of weights, in pounds, of people in a fitness class.
108, 112, 124, 106, 124, 148, 132, 129, 152, 132, 121, 118, 106, 109, 118, 114, 130, 126, 116, 113, 141, 137, 150, 127, 116, 134, 118, 129

15-4 EXERCISES

A

Construct a frequency distribution for each set of data.

1. The ages of the children in a nursery school class.
3, 4, 2, 2, 4, 3, 5, 4, 2, 2, 2, 4, 4, 3, 2, 3, 4, 4, 3, 3, 4, 4, 4, 3, 2, 2, 5
2. The numbers of "no-shows" on 30 regularly-scheduled airline flights.
23, 25, 22, 17, 23, 22, 19, 21, 20, 19, 18, 25, 21, 22, 25, 24, 20, 21, 20, 18, 23, 20, 17, 19, 20, 20, 18, 24, 21, 19

Construct a frequency distribution using intervals.

3. The heights, in meters, of the 25 highest mountain peaks in the world. Use 10 intervals.
8750, 8156, 7885, 7937, 8126, 8068, 7902, 8033, 7897, 7925, 8598, 8470, 8048, 8047, 8172, 8078, 8013, 7893, 7852, 7821, 7952, 8501, 8153, 7852, 7829
4. The lengths, in feet, of 19 of the world's longest suspension bridges. Use 11 intervals.
2190, 2150, 2000, 3500, 2800, 2310, 3300, 4200, 2336, 3240, 2000, 2300, 2336, 3254, 4626, 3323, 4260, 2150, 3800

LESSON QUIZ

1. Construct a frequency distribution for the following set of numbers. Use intervals of length 10.
47, 73, 24, 35, 58, 53, 82, 91, 54, 63, 87, 66, 71, 68, 77, 78

Interval	Tally	Frequency
20–29	I	1
30–39	I	1
40–49	I	1
50–59	III	3
60–69	III	3
70–79	IIII	4
80–89	II	2
90–99	I	1

Assignment Guide
Minimum: omit

Regular: 1–8 e/o, 9, 10, MR

Advanced: 1–8 m3, 9–11, MR

ADDITIONAL ANSWERS

Try This

a.

Pulse Rates	Frequency
68	3
69	3
70	3
71	1
72	5
73	4
74	3
75	2
76	1

b.

Salaries	Frequency
900 – 999	3
1000–1099	0
1100–1199	9
1200–1299	8
1300–1399	3
1400–1499	4
1500–1599	3
1600–1699	3

c.

Stem	Leaf
10	8, 6, 6, 9
11	2, 8, 8, 4, 6, 3, 6, 8
12	4, 4, 9, 1, 6, 7, 9
13	2, 2, 0, 7, 4
14	8, 1
15	2, 0

Exercises

1–6. See Teacher's Answer Section.

7.

Stem	Leaf
40	2, 9, 3, 0
41	7, 6, 2
42	3, 6, 9, 7
43	9, 8, 9
44	8
45	6, 6
46	7, 3, 7
47	8, 6, 6, 1
48	9, 7
49	8, 9

8.

Stem	Leaf
0	9
1	8, 3, 6, 1, 7, 9, 8, 9, 8, 0, 9
2	7, 8, 1, 5, 8, 8, 4, 9, 7
3	6, 2, 2, 3, 4, 9
4	0, 5, 7, 6, 0, 8
5	1, 2, 0

9. Answers may vary.

10. Answers may vary. A stem-and-leaf diagram gives a visual picture of each interval; a frequency distribution chart gives the total sum for each interval.

11. $P(1) = \frac{12}{120} = \frac{1}{10}$

$P(3) = \frac{15}{120} = \frac{1}{8}$

$P(6) = \frac{30}{120} = \frac{1}{4}$

It appears that the die may not be fair as 6 is rolled ten more times than would be expected. However, this is not conclusive evidence to prove that the die is not fair. The die would need to be rolled 120 more times to see if this pattern continues.

Mixed Review

12. 4, 5

13. $\frac{-5 \pm \sqrt{37}}{2}$

14. $\frac{12}{13}$

15. $\frac{12}{13}$

16. $\frac{12}{5}$

17. $\frac{5}{13}$

18. $\frac{5}{12}$

19. $\frac{5}{13}$

20. $y = -\frac{1}{2}x + \frac{9}{2}$

21. $y = 6$

22. $y = -\frac{1}{3}x + 2$

23. {1, 2, 3, 4, 6, 8, 12, 24}

24. {7, 11, 13, 17, 19, 23, 29, 31, 37, 41, 43, 47}

Construct a stem-and-leaf diagram for each set of data.

5. The distances, to the nearest centimeter, jumped by a class of middle-school girls.
177, 180, 172, 168, 172, 165, 159, 165, 176, 181, 166, 174, 169, 170, 174, 165, 179, 180, 167, 178, 174, 167, 175, 164, 179, 176, 163, 158

6. The weight gains, in pounds, of a group of cattle eating a new brand of cattle feed.
103, 107, 111, 108, 102, 103, 123, 143, 125, 132, 143, 135, 127, 119, 106, 154, 123, 165, 154, 138, 139, 146, 132, 128, 119, 129, 162, 152

7. The average verbal SAT scores for 28 high schools.
402, 478, 417, 416, 467, 456, 463, 498, 476, 489, 476, 409, 429, 423, 471, 467, 438, 400, 439, 456, 448, 499, 439, 403, 427, 412, 487, 426

8. The weights, in pounds, of carry-on luggage as determined by a survey of 36 passengers at an airline check-in desk.
27, 18, 28, 40, 36, 21, 13, 25, 45, 28, 16, 9, 11, 47, 32, 17, 32, 19, 51, 28, 46, 24, 18, 19, 33, 29, 40, 18, 10, 52, 34, 39, 50, 48, 19, 27

B

9. A **ranked** stem-and-leaf diagram has the values arranged in order from least to greatest. Choose any stem-and-leaf diagram that you have constructed for Exercises 5 to 8 and rank it.

10. ***Critical Thinking*** Write a paragraph describing the advantages and disadvantages of frequency distributions compared with stem-and-leaf diagrams. Illustrate your response with an example.

Challenge

11. A die was rolled 120 times. A frequency distribution was made and shown at the right. Find the experimental probabilities $P(1)$, $P(3)$, and $P(6)$. Do you think that this die is fair? Why or why not?

Side	Frequency
1	12
2	21
3	15
4	18
5	24
6	30

Mixed Review

Solve. **12.** $x^2 - 9x + 20 = 0$ **13.** $y^2 + 5y = 3$

In $\triangle ABC$, find the following.

14. $\sin B$ **15.** $\cos C$ **16.** $\tan B$

17. $\cos B$ **18.** $\tan C$ **19.** $\sin C$

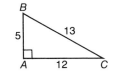

Find the equation of the line containing the given pair of points.

20. (5, 2), (−1, 5) **21.** (2, 6), (−7, 6) **22.** (3, 1), (−3, 3)

Write roster notation for each. **23.** $A = \{x \mid x \text{ is a positive factor of } 24\}$

24. $B = \{y \mid y \text{ is a prime number and } 6 < y < 50\}$

15-5 Graphs of Data

In statistics it is often helpful to give a pictorial representation of a set of data. Graphs are used for this purpose.

Line Plots

Objective: Construct a line plot for a set of data.

One type of graph that can be constructed quickly is a **line plot.** To construct a line plot, we draw a portion of a number line and place a dot above the line for each occurrence of a value.

EXAMPLE 1 Construct a line plot.

Here is a set of morning temperatures, in degrees Celsius, for the month of March in a northeastern town.

5, 7, 4, 5, 3, 2, 0, 3, 2, 4, 5, 5, 4, 5, 6, 4, 7, 7, 9, 10, 9, 11, 12, 11, 13, 11, 10, 9, 10, 11, 13

The lowest temperature is 0° and the highest temperature is 13°. We draw a number line that includes these values and the values between. We place a dot above the line for each temperature.

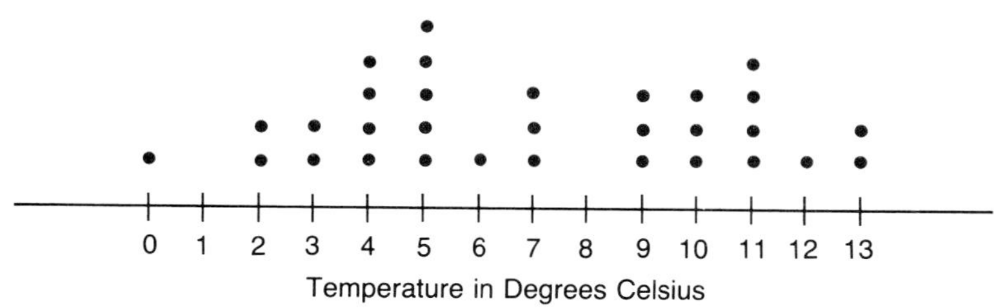

Try This Construct a line plot. See Additional Answers.

a. Here is a set of scores on an algebra test.
76, 80, 78, 68, 74, 69, 78, 80, 81, 80, 76, 65, 90, 88, 78, 81, 80, 76, 90, 73, 78

15-5

FIRST FIVE MINUTES

1. Construct a frequency distribution.
   8, 2, 0, 7, 9, 8, 0, 1, 9, 0, 1, 9, 1, 0, 7, 9, 2, 6, 8, 3

Number	Tally	Frequency
0	IIII	4
1	III	3
2	II	2
3	I	1
4		0
5		0
6	I	1
7	II	2
8	III	3
9	IIII	4

Line Plots

Emphasize that equal spacing is used between the vertical dots on a line plot. If the spacing is not consistent, the visual information will be lost.

Key Question

The results of a certain experiment are 11, 8, 14, 7, 18, 6, 9, 11, 13, 12, 17, 15.

■ What are the upper and lower numbers that will be used to label the x-axis for the line plot?
6 and 18

Chalkboard Example

1. Below are the numbers of days absent for the members of a high school class. Construct a line plot.
   0, 1, 2, 1, 4, 6, 1, 3, 0, 2, 1, 8, 1, 3, 4, 2, 6, 2

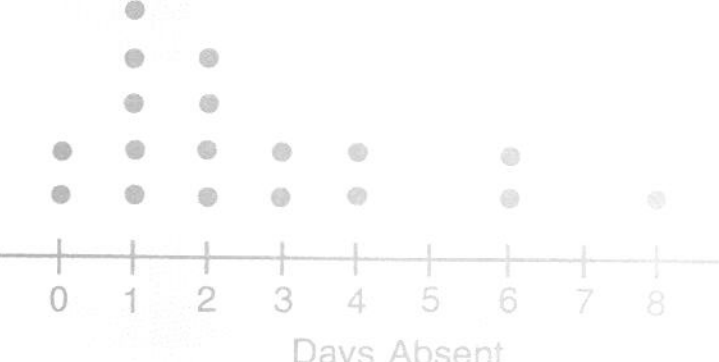

Histograms

Point out that if each stem-and-leaf diagram is rotated 90°, it will have the general shape of a histogram.

Chalkboard Example (*T33*)

1. Below is the stem-and-leaf diagram of the weights, in pounds, of the members of a high school marching band. Construct a histogram.

Stem	Leaf
10	2
11	3, 4
12	8, 1, 3, 5
13	2, 4, 2
14	8, 4, 1, 5
15	3, 9
16	0, 3
17	4

Histograms

Objective: Construct a histogram for a set of data.

A bar graph, called a **histogram**, is useful for comparing data. A histogram always has a title and clearly labeled horizontal and vertical scales.

EXAMPLE 2 Construct a histogram.

Here is a stem-and-leaf diagram of the set of heights, in centimeters, of players on the high school basketball team from Example 3, page 654.

Stem	Leaf
16	9
17	2, 8
18	3, 3, 4, 6
19	6, 8, 5, 9, 0
20	1, 3, 1

For the histogram we let the horizontal scale represent the heights (160s, 170s, etc.) and the vertical scale represent the frequency (how many players had heights in the 160s, 170s, etc.).

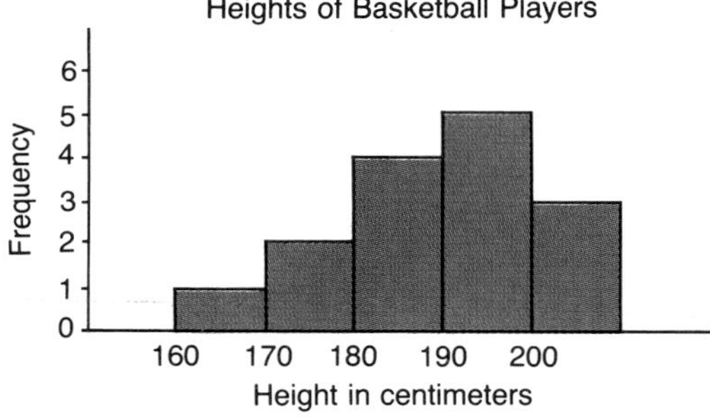

We can see from the histogram that there are two players whose heights are between 170 and 180, while four players have heights from 180 to 190.

Try This Construct a histogram. See Additional Answers.

b. Here is a stem-and-leaf diagram of the numbers of games won by the great pitcher Cy Young each year from 1890 to 1911.

Stem	Leaf
0	9, 7, 7
1	8, 3, 9
2	7, 5, 9, 1, 5, 6, 0, 8, 6, 2, 1
3	6, 2, 5, 3, 2

Frequency Polygons

Objective: Construct a frequency polygon for a set of data.

Another type of graph often used in statistics is the **frequency polygon.** An easy way to construct a frequency polygon is to connect the midpoints of the bars of a histogram with line segments. Here is a frequency polygon for the height data on the basketball players.

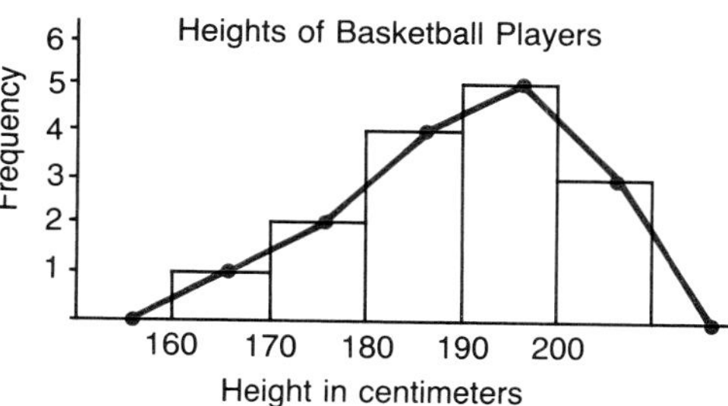

EXAMPLE 3 Construct a frequency polygon.

Here is the set of data from Try This **b.** concerning the number of games won by Cy Young.

Stem	Leaf
0	9, 7, 7
1	8, 3, 9
2	7, 5, 9, 1, 5, 6, 0, 8, 6, 2, 1
3	6, 2, 5, 3, 2

We first construct a histogram. We let the horizontal scale be the number of games won and the vertical scale be the frequency. We then connect the midpoints of the bars of the histogram.

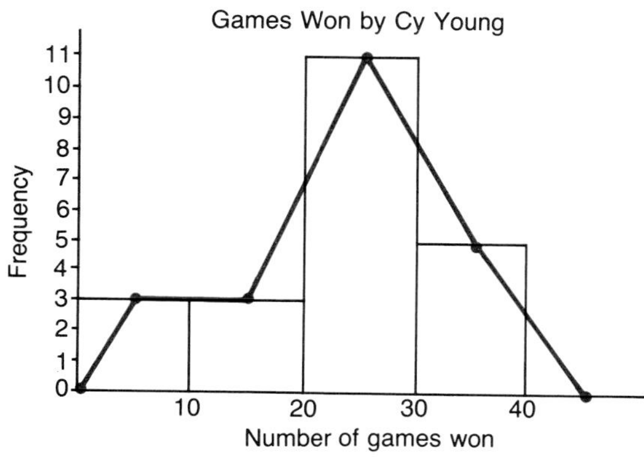

Try This Construct a frequency polygon. See Additional Answers.

c. Here are the heights, in feet, of some of the world's highest dams.
764, 761, 892, 777, 932, 770, 858, 778, 794, 932, 1017

Frequency Polygons

Chalkboard Example (*T34*)

1. Here is the stem-and-leaf diagram for the cost of motor scooters in the local want ads. Construct a frequency polygon.

Stem	Leaf
0	95, 75
1	20, 75, 50
2	50, 20, 30, 75
3	00, 20
4	00
5	20

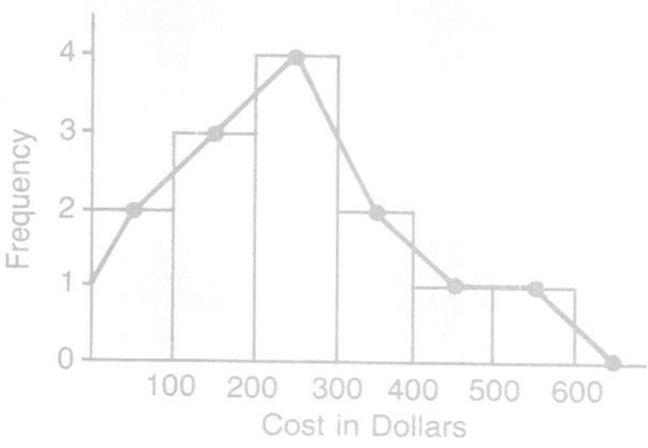

LESSON QUIZ

1. Construct a line plot for the test scores below.
2, 5, 3, 2, 6, 5, 4, 5, 3, 2, 1, 2, 2

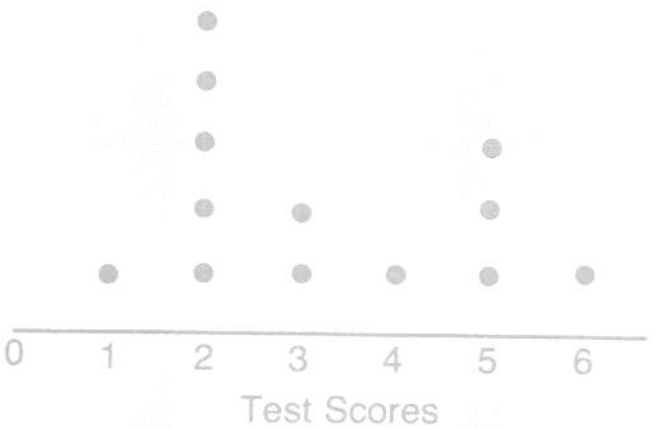

2. Construct a histogram for the scores below.
94, 83, 72, 45, 67, 76, 81, 73, 84, 78, 71, 65

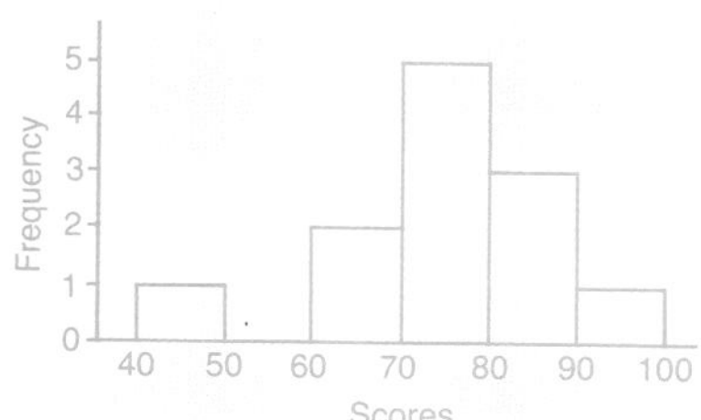

Assignment Guide
Minimum: omit

Regular: 1–12 e/o, 13, 14, MR

Advanced:1–12 m4, 13–15, MR

ADDITIONAL ANSWERS

Try This

a.

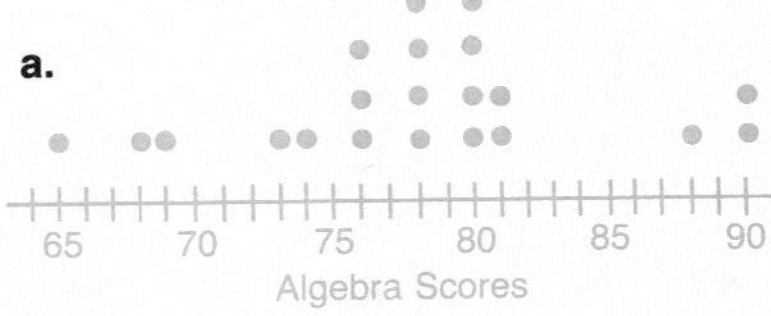

b.

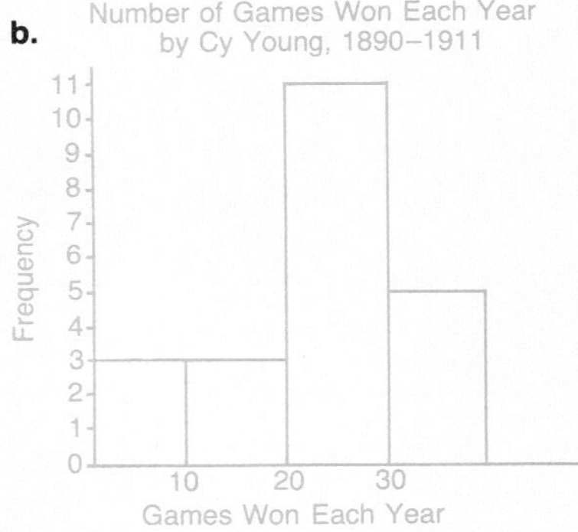

c.

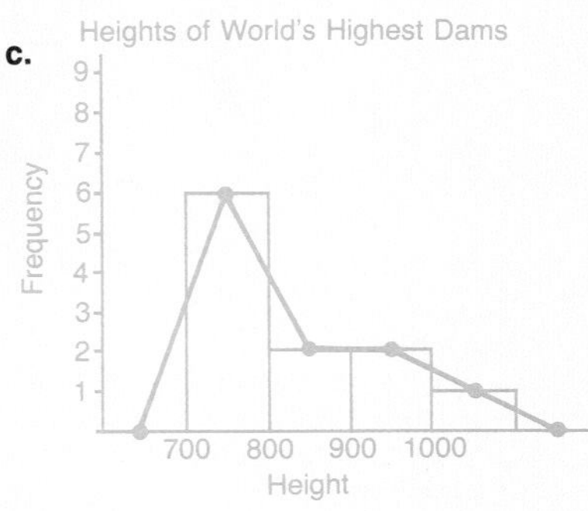

Exercises

1–15. See Teacher's Answer Section.

Mixed Review

16. 12 **17.** $11\sqrt{2}$ **18.** 24 **19.** 0, 4 **20.** $\frac{1}{2}, \frac{1}{4}$ **21.** 73° **22.** 37° **23.** 69° **24.** $\frac{1}{13}$ **25.** $\frac{1}{2}$ **26.** $\frac{1}{4}$

15-5 EXERCISES

A

Construct a line plot for each set of data.

1. The pulse rates of 30 patients.
76, 78, 68, 73, 80, 78, 67, 76, 75, 78, 74, 75, 81, 75, 72, 73, 81, 67, 68, 72, 70, 78, 76, 81, 69, 71, 68, 70, 74, 76

2. The golf scores of 25 high-school golfers.
86, 79, 69, 74, 78, 87, 83, 81, 76, 80, 88, 79, 86, 90, 86, 75, 78, 79, 80, 87, 78, 74, 87, 80, 79

3. The systolic blood pressure of 28 patients.
120, 132, 127, 132, 137, 127, 123, 133, 133, 128, 133, 137, 129, 138, 128, 120, 128, 139, 140, 132, 136, 126, 128, 133, 137, 121, 139, 141

4. The scores of 35 students on a ten-point biology quiz.
7, 9, 4, 6, 5, 8, 8, 10, 5, 10, 4, 8, 7, 9, 10, 3, 9, 5, 3, 0, 9, 10, 2, 5, 7, 8, 6, 9, 10, 7, 7, 5, 10, 9, 7

5–8. Construct a histogram for each set of data in Exercises 1–4.

9–12. Construct a frequency polygon for each set of data in Exercises 1–4.

B

13. Collect a set of data on a topic of interest to you. Construct a line plot, a histogram, and a frequency polygon for your set of data.

14. ***Critical Thinking*** How can a histogram be quickly sketched if you have a stem-and-leaf diagram for a set of data?

Challenge

15. Construct a frequency distribution for the biology quiz scores in Exercise 4. Add another column to the frequency distribution entitled **cumulative frequency.** In this column, opposite any score n, indicate the number of students that had a score of n or a score less than n. Use the frequency distribution to construct a new graph called a **cumulative frequency polygon.** Let the vertical scale represent the cumulative frequency and the horizontal scale represent scores.

Mixed Review

In a right triangle, find the length of the side not given.

16. $a = 5, c = 13$ **17.** $a = 11, b = 11$ **18.** $c = 25, b = 7$

Solve. **19.** $2x^2 - 8x = 0$ **20.** $8a^2 - 6a + 1 = 0$

Use Table 2 or a calculator to find A for the following function values of A.

21. $\sin A = 0.956$ **22.** $\cos A = 0.799$ **23.** $\tan A = 2.605$

Find the probability of drawing each of the following from a well-shuffled deck of 52 cards. **24.** a king **25.** a black card **26.** a heart

15-6 Measures of Central Tendency

Objective: Find the mean, median, and mode of a set of data.

TI-81 Investigation 4 (page 730) can be used with this lesson.

A question often asked when analyzing a set of data is, "What single number best represents the set of data as a whole?" The *mean*, *median*, and *mode* are numbers that are used to answer this question. The mean, median, and mode are called **measures of central tendency** because they represent the center of a set of data.

The **mean** is the *average* of a set of values. To find the mean we find the sum of all the values and divide by the number of values.

EXAMPLE 1 Find the mean to the nearest tenth.

Here is a set of diameters, in miles, of the first ten asteroids discovered. Find the mean diameter.

485, 304, 118, 243, 50, 121, 121, 56, 78, 40

There are ten values. We find the sum and divide by 10.

The sum is 1616; $\frac{1616}{10} = 161.6$

The mean diameter is 161.6 miles.

Try This Find the mean to the nearest tenth.

a. Here is a set of radar-recorded speeds, in miles per hour, of automobiles traveling on an interstate highway. Find the mean speed. 58.7 mi/h

54, 58, 61, 65, 59, 60, 68, 55, 58, 49

The **median** of a set of data is the middle value when all the values are arranged in order.

EXAMPLE 2 Find the median.

Here is the number of children per family for the 25 families of the students in an algebra class. Find the median number of children per family.

2, 1, 5, 3, 4, 3, 3, 5, 2, 1, 3, 2, 1, 5, 3, 3, 6, 2, 6, 1, 2, 7, 3, 2, 4

We arrange the numbers in order from least to greatest.

1, 1, 1, 1, 2, 2, 2, 2, 2, 2, 3, 3, 3, 3, 3, 3, 3, 4, 4, 5, 5, 5, 6, 6, 7

There are 25 numbers. Thus the 13th number, 3, is the middle value. The median number of children per family is 3.

15-6

FIRST FIVE MINUTES

1. Make a line plot for the following data.
   5, 7, 3, 8, 6, 9, 7, 8, 9, 6, 5, 4, 8

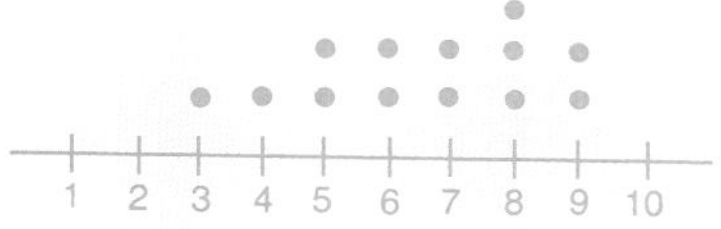

Compare the three measures of central tendency. You may wish to use Exercise 12 as an oral discussion.

The mean can be visualized as the balance point of the histogram, the mode is the highest column of a histogram, and the median is the halfway point of the histogram.

The mean of a set of data can be affected by any extreme values. For instance, in Example 1, the 485 mile diameter asteroid has a tendency to make the mean larger than it otherwise would be.

Key Questions

Below is a list of 5 scores and the histogram for the scores.
2, 3, 2, 1, 2

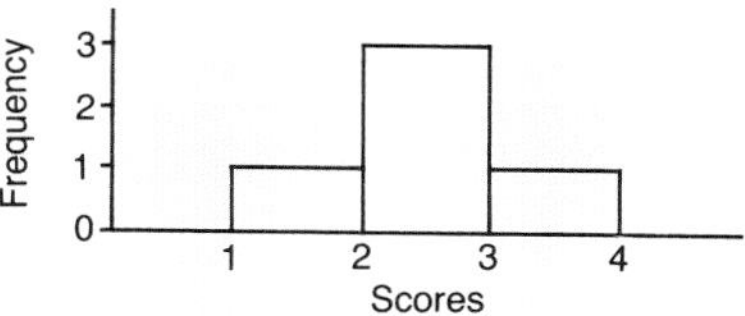

- Where, approximately, is the center of the histogram? 2
- What is the mean of the scores? 2

Chalkboard Examples

1. Here is the set of numbers of words per page in a certain book. What is the mean number of words per page?
   121, 115, 134, 127, 118
   121 + 115 + 134 + 127 + 118 = 615
   $\frac{615}{5} = 123$
   The mean number of words per page is 123.
2. Find the median of the set 2, 5, 6, 3, 7, 8, 1, 3, 9.
   Order the set.
   1, 2, 3, 3, 5, 6, 7, 8, 9
   The median is 5.

3. Here is the stem-and-leaf diagram showing the telephone calls each day at a certain business. Find the median number of calls.

Stem	Leaf
0	5, 7
1	2, 4
2	7, 3, 5, 6
3	2, 4, 1
4	5, 8
5	2

Order the numbers.
5, 7, 12, 14, 23, 25, 26, 27, 31, 32, 34, 45, 48, 52
The median is between 26 and 27. The median is 26.5.

4. Find the mode of the following set of numbers.
4, 3, 2, 6, 5, 4, 7, 8, 6, 7, 5, 4, 6, 5, 3, 4, 7, 1
The number 4 occurs four times. The mode is 4.

LESSON QUIZ

1. Find the mean of the set of numbers 5, 4, 7, 2, 8, 4.
5
2. Find the median of the set of scores 6, 3, 5, 3, 8, 2, 8, 9, 1.
5
3. Find the mode of the numbers 5, 3, 2, 4, 6, 5, 4, 5, 2, 5, 6.
5

There is always a middle value when there is an odd number of values. If the number of values is even, then we use the average of the two middle values as the median.

EXAMPLE 3 Find the median.

This stem-and-leaf diagram shows the number of home runs hit by Babe Ruth each year from 1914 to 1935. Find the median number of home runs.

Stem	Leaf
0	0, 4, 3, 2, 6
1	1
2	9, 5, 2
3	5, 4
4	1, 6, 7, 6, 9, 6, 1
5	4, 9, 4
6	0

The stem-and-leaf diagram makes it easy for us to arrange the numbers in order from least to greatest.

0, 2, 3, 4, 6, 11, 22, 25, 29, 34, 35, 41,
41, 46, 46, 46, 47, 49, 54, 54, 59, 60

We find the average of the two middle values, 35 and 41. $\frac{35 + 41}{2} = 38$

The median number of home runs hit by Babe Ruth is 38.

Try This Find the median.

b. Here is a set of evacuation times, in minutes, for a series of fire drills in a school. Find the median evacuation time. 2.75 min
3.0, 2.7, 3.5, 2.7, 3.0, 2.6, 2.9, 3.2, 2.6, 2.7, 2.6, 2.8, 2.7, 2.9

The **mode** of a set is the value that occurs most often. Some sets of data have more than one mode, and some sets of data have no mode.

EXAMPLE 4 Find the mode.

Here is a set of shoe sizes of shoes sold one evening at a shoe store.

7A, 6B, 8AA, 7A, 8AA, 6D, 7½D, 6AA, 8AA, 7B, 6C, 8AA

The size 8AA occurs four times. It is the mode.

Try This Find the mode.

c. Here are the number of games won per year by the major-league pitcher Don Drysdale. 13
5, 17, 12, 17, 15, 13, 25, 19, 18, 23, 13, 13, 14, 5

15-6 EXERCISES

A

Find the mean (to the nearest tenth), median, and mode for each set of data.

1. The number of home runs hit each year from 1954 to 1976 by Hank Aaron.

Stem	Leaf
1	3, 2, 0
2	7, 6, 4, 9, 0
3	0, 9, 4, 2, 9, 8, 4
4	4, 0, 4, 5, 4, 4, 7, 0

2. The scores of a high school gymnast on the floor exercise in 11 successive gymnastic meets.
6.7, 7.4, 8.1, 8.0, 7.9, 8.2, 7.9, 8.4, 9.0, 7.3, 8.8
3. The number of years served by the Chief Justices of the United States from John Jay in 1789 to Warren Burger in 1986.

Stem	Leaf
0	5, 0, 4, 8, 8, 4, 7
1	4, 0, 1, 5, 8
2	8, 1
3	4

4. The ages at the first inauguration of the first 40 Presidents of the United States.
57, 61, 57, 57, 58, 57, 61, 54, 68, 51, 49, 64, 50, 48, 65, 52, 56, 46, 54, 49, 50, 47, 55, 55, 54, 42, 51, 56, 55, 51, 54, 51, 60, 62, 43, 55, 56, 61, 52, 69
5. The lengths, in feet, of nine of the major U.S. 3-engine jet transport planes.
133.1, 133.1, 153.1, 153.1, 177.5, 164.2, 182.2, 181.6, 182.3
6. The depths, in meters, of certain points of the oceans and seas of the world.
10918, 9219, 7455, 5625, 4632, 5016, 4773, 3787, 3658, 2782, 3742, 3777, 660, 2211, 421, 6946, 183

B

7. Collect a set of data on some topic of interest to you. Find the mean, median, and mode of your set of data. Answers may vary.
8. Extreme values can affect the mean. Recalculate the mean for Exercise 6 after deleting the highest and lowest value. Which mean is a better measure of central tendency? 4313.6; Answers may vary.
9. If a set of data has two modes it is said to be **bimodal.** Are any of the six sets of data above bimodal? Exercise 3 and Exercise 5

Assignment Guide
Minimum: omit

Regular: 1–9 e/o, 10, MR

Advanced: 1–9 m3, 10–14, MR

ADDITIONAL ANSWERS

Exercises

1. Mean: 32.8, median: 34, mode: 44
2. Mean: 8.0, median: 8.0, mode: 7.9
3. Mean: 12.5, median: 10, mode: 8, 4
4. Mean: 54.8, median: 55, mode: 51, 54, 55, 57
5. Mean: 162.2, median: 164.2, mode: 133.1, 153.1
6. Mean: 4459.1, median: 3787, mode: none

10. The median is the most affected and the mode the least.

12. Opinions may vary.
13. The mean takes every value into account, but may be overly influenced by extreme values. The median is not influenced by extreme values, but does not represent every value. The mode is easy to find, but does not represent every value, and some data do not have a mode.

Mixed Review

15. $y = -x + 5$ 16. $x = -3$
17. $y = \frac{5}{2}x - 3$ 18. 8, 9
19. 3 20. 0, 3
21. $-3, -5$ 22. $5, -3$
23. $0, -4$ 24. $b = \pm\frac{7}{5}$
25. $x = \frac{2}{3}, -5$

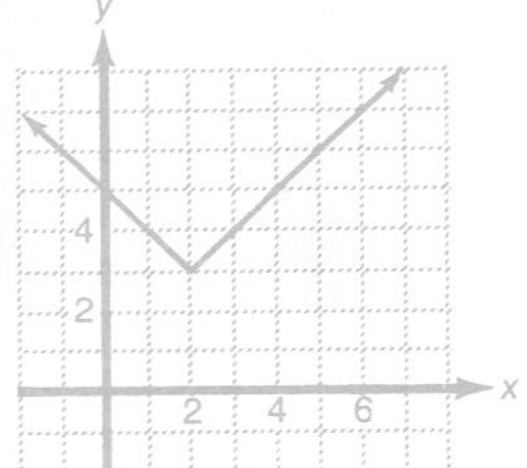

27.

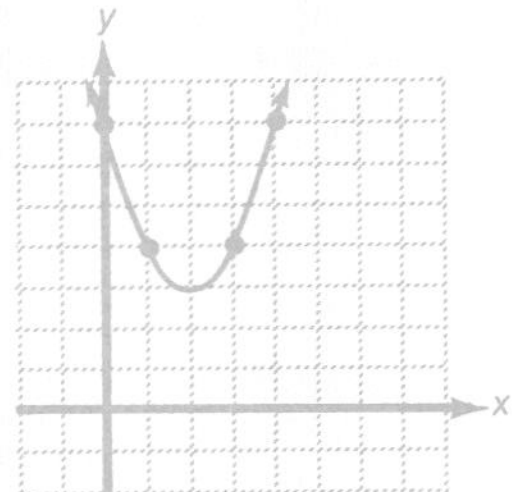

28. $\frac{1}{2}$ 29. $\frac{1}{2}$
30. $\frac{1}{2}$ 31. $\frac{1}{4}, -\frac{1}{4}$

Problem for Programmers

This program can be written using any programming language (BASIC, PASCAL, LOGO, etc.) and on most spreadsheets.

10. *Critical Thinking* Which of the measures of central tendency in a set of 10 scores with 1 duplicate is most affected by the addition of another unique score? Which is least affected?

Challenge

11. A measure of how much a set of data varies from the mean of the data is called *variance.* The variance is the average of the squares of the differences of each data element from the mean of the data.
a. Find the variance for the data in Exercise 2. 0.40
b. Find the variance for the data in Exercise 4. 36.7
c. Which set of data is clustered closer to its mean? Ex. 2

12. Compare the sets of home-run data for Babe Ruth (Example 3) and Hank Aaron (Exercise 1) with respect to the mean, median, and mode of each set. In your opinion, who was the greater home-run hitter? Defend your opinion with the data.

13. What are the advantages and disadvantages of the mean, median, and mode as measures of central tendency?

14. Roll three dice 10 times and record the sum for each toss. Find the mean, median, and mode for the set of data generated. Repeat the experiment with 50 rolls. Explain any differences between the two experiments. Which set of data most closely approximates the theoretical values (mean: 10.5, median: 10.5, mode: 10, 11)?
Answers may vary; the second experiment is a better approximation of the theoretical values.

Mixed Review

Write an equation for the line that contains the given pair of points.
15. (4, 1), (−1, 6) **16.** (−3, 4), (−3, 0) **17.** (2, 2), (−4, −13)
Solve. **18.** $\sqrt{x - 8} = x - 8$ **19.** $\sqrt{x + 6} = x$
20. $5y^2 - 15y = 0$ **21.** $m^2 + 8m + 15 = 0$ **22.** $a^2 - 2a = 15$
23. $3w^2 = -12w$ **24.** $25b^2 - 49 = 0$ **25.** $3x^2 + 13x - 10 = 0$
Graph these functions. **26.** $y = |x - 2| + 3$ **27.** $y = (x - 2)^2 + 3$
Find the probability that each of the following will appear when a single die is tossed. **28.** a factor of 4 **29.** an odd number **30.** a prime number

31. The reciprocal of a number divided by eight is the same as two times the number. Find the number.

Problem for Programmers

Write a program that will find the mean of any group of input data. The program should count the number of input data for you. Test your program using the data in Exercises 1–6 in Lesson 15-6.

☆ 3G

15-7 Scatter Plots and Data Relationships

Objective: Make scatter plots and determine data relationships.

Application

The table below shows the number of hours a student studied and the grade received on eight separate exams.

Hours	0	0	1	2	2	4	5	5
Grade	30	40	60	60	70	80	90	95

Is there a relationship between hours studied and the grade received on each exam? An examination of the data shows that there is some relationship, but statisticians use a more objective method of analysis.

In Chapter 7 you learned how to find an equation for the line of best fit. In this lesson we will concentrate on using the line of best fit to determine whether a relationship exists between two variables. Statisticians spend a great deal of their time analyzing data from surveys and experiments, trying to find patterns of behavior or relationships between different pieces of information. They use a variety of techniques to do this, one of which is the **scatter plot.**

A scatter plot is a graph that shows the relationship between two variables. A scatter plot of the above data is shown at the right. If you draw the line of best fit, the line will have a positive slope. This is an indication that there is a **positive** relationship between x and y.

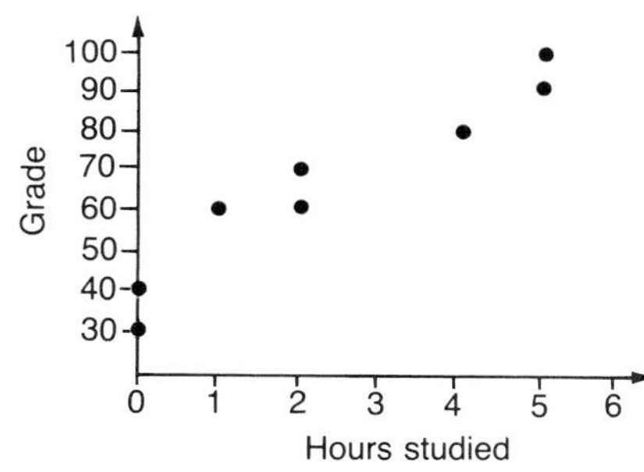

The following graphs show two other relationships that occur.

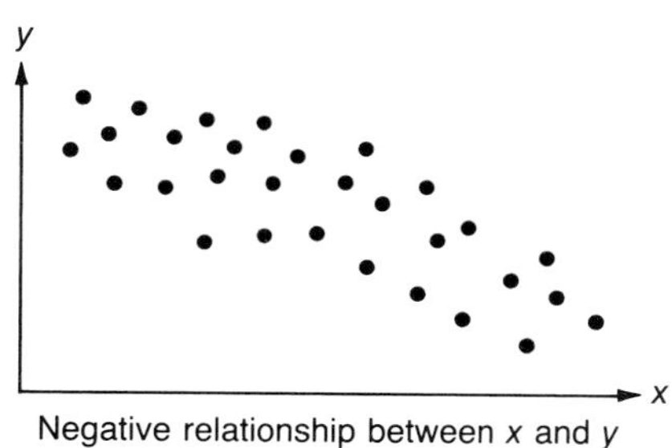

Negative relationship between x and y

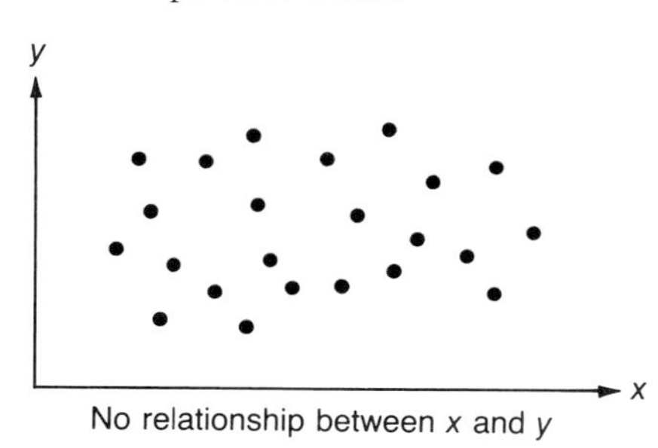

No relationship between x and y

15-7

FIRST FIVE MINUTES

1. Find the mean, median, and mode of the following set of data.
   17, 12, 14, 10, 9, 12, 16, 17, 12
   Mean: 13.2; median: 12; mode: 12

Emphasize that a positive relationship means that as one variable increases, so does the other; and that a negative relationship means that as one variable increases, the other decreases. You may wish to explain that these relationships are often called positive and negative correlations.

You may wish to point out that the fact that a relationship exists between two sets of data does not necessarily mean that one causes the other. For example, hemlines tend to go up when the stock market goes up, but it is unlikely that one of these events directly causes the other.

Key Questions

- Do you expect the grade to increase or decrease when the number of hours studied increases?
  Increase
- Do you expect the amount of pounds a man can lift to increase or decrease with age?
  Decrease

Chalkboard Examples

1. Below are data for 20 U.S. cities. Construct a scatter plot and determine what type of relationship exists between a city's latitude and its average high temperature in January.

	Latitude	Temperature
Mobile	31°	61°
Omaha	41°	30°
New Orleans	30°	62°
Boston	42°	36°
Houston	30°	62°
Milwaukee	43°	26°
Portland, Ore	46°	44°
Jackson, Miss	32°	57°
Albuquerque	35°	47°
Hartford	42°	34°
Little Rock	35°	50°
San Francisco	38°	55°
Charlotte	35°	50°
Spokane	48°	31°
Nashville	36°	46°
Chicago	42°	29°
Miami	26°	75°
Juneau	58°	27°
San Juan	18°	83°
Cleveland	41°	33°

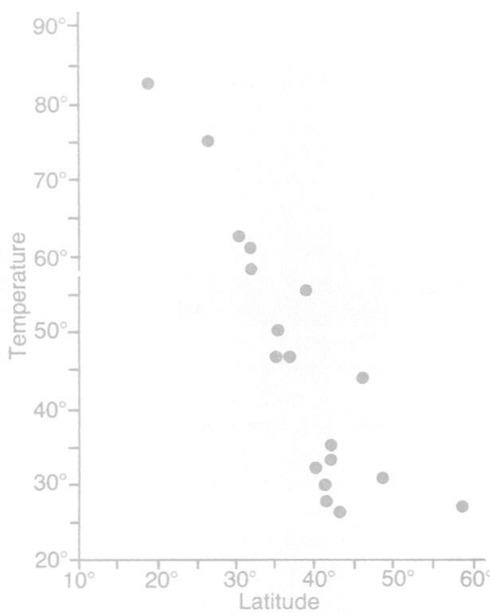

There appears to be a negative relationship between a city's latitude and its average high temperature in January.

LESSON QUIZ

1. Use the data below to construct a scatter plot. What relationships exist between an animal's fastest speed and its average life expectancy?

	Speed	Life Expectancy
Lion	50	15
Horse	47.5	20
Elk	45	15
Zebra	40	15
Rabbit	35	5
Giraffe	32	10
Deer	30	8
Grizzly bear	30	25
Cat	30	12
Elephant	25	37.5
Squirrel	12	10
Pig	6	10

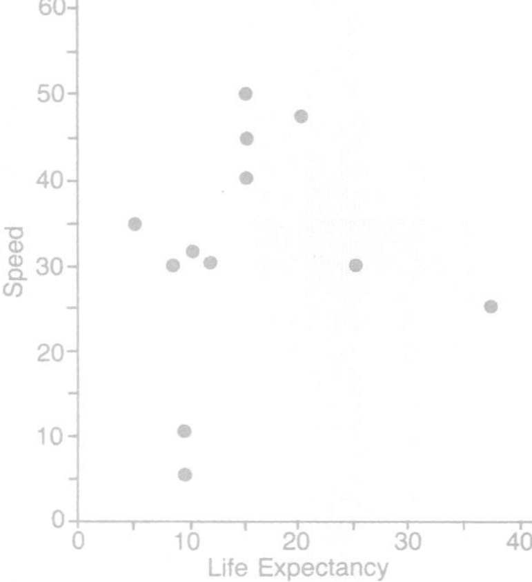

EXAMPLE 1

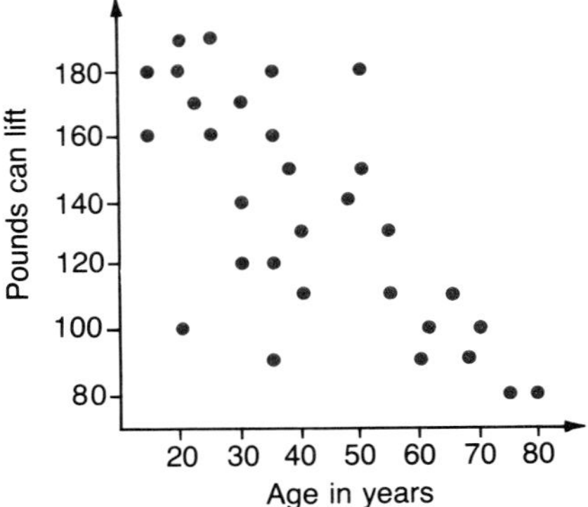

The graph at the right represents data collected from a group of 30 adult males. Mentally draw the line of best fit and determine what type of relationship exists between a man's age and the amount he can lift.

The line of best fit has a negative slope, which indicates a negative relationship between the two variables.

Try This What type of relationship exists between the variables in each graph?

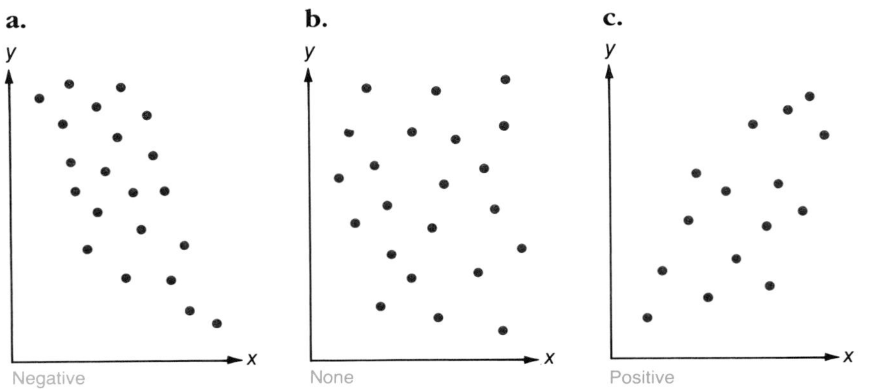

EXAMPLE 2

Use the data from the box score for a game from the 1988 National Basketball Association Championship series to make a scatter plot representing the field goals attempted (fga) and the total points (total). What type of relationship exists?

Los Angeles

	fga	fg	fta	ft	total
Green	2	2	8	6	10
Worthy	22	12	6	4	28
Abdul-Jabbar	14	3	8	8	14
E. Johnson	12	3	13	12	22
Scott	12	7	4	2	16
Thompson	6	3	2	1	7
Rambis	1	1	0	0	2
Cooper	3	1	2	2	4
Totals	72	32	43	35	103

Detroit

	fga	fg	fta	ft	total
Dantley	10	3	8	8	14
Mahorn	3	2	0	0	4
Laimbeer	5	0	2	2	2
Dumars	12	7	2	2	16
Thomas	32	18	7	5	43
Salley	2	1	1	1	3
V. Johnson	7	2	2	1	5
Rodman	2	2	5	3	7
Edwards	6	4	0	0	8
Totals	79	39	27	22	102

We plot field goals attempted on the horizontal axis and total points on the vertical axis. We can plot each point using an L if it represents a player for Los Angeles and a D if it represents a player for Detroit. The graph shows that players who attempt more field goals usually score more total points and players who attempt fewer field goals have fewer total points. Thus, there is a positive relationship between field goals attempted and total points scored.

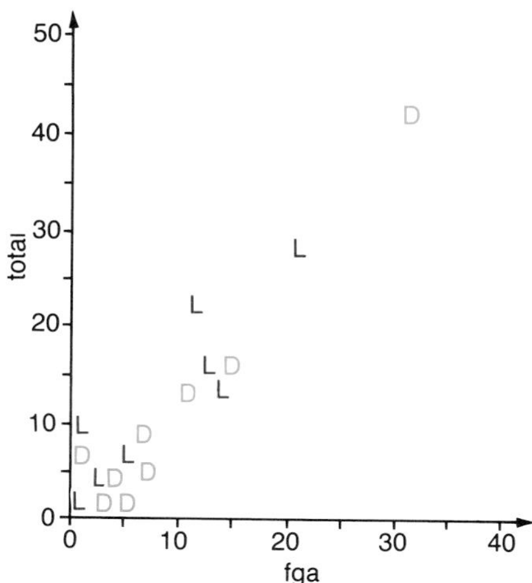

There appears to be no relationship between an animal's speed and its life expectancy.

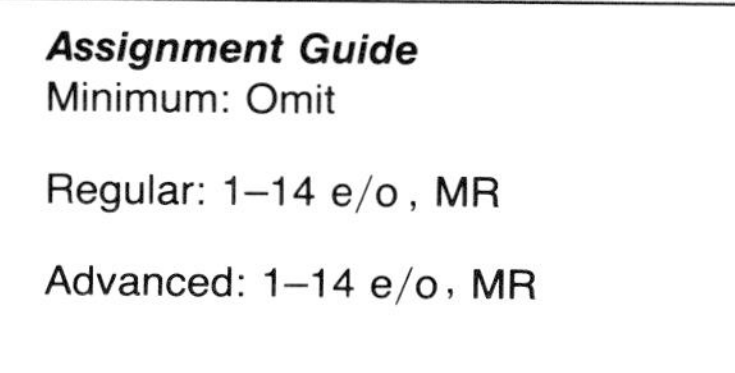

Assignment Guide
Minimum: Omit
Regular: 1–14 e/o, MR
Advanced: 1–14 e/o, MR

ADDITIONAL ANSWERS

Try This

d.

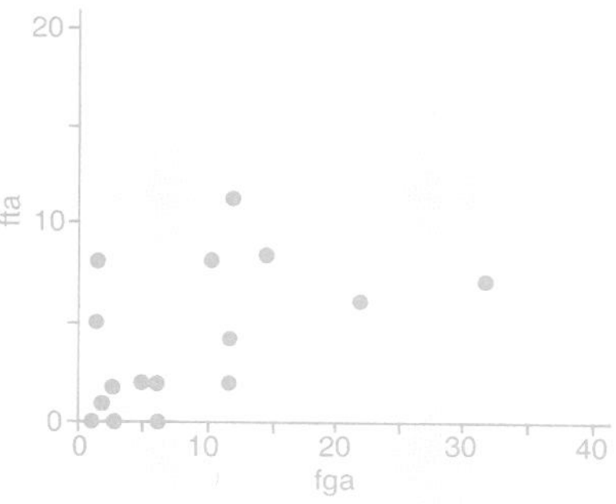

There appears to be no relationship between field goals attempted and free throws attempted.

Try This

d. Use the box score to make a scatter plot representing the field goals attempted (fga) and the free throws attempted (fta). What type of relationship exists? See Additional Answers.

15-7 PROBLEMS

What type of relationship exists between the variables in each graph?

1.

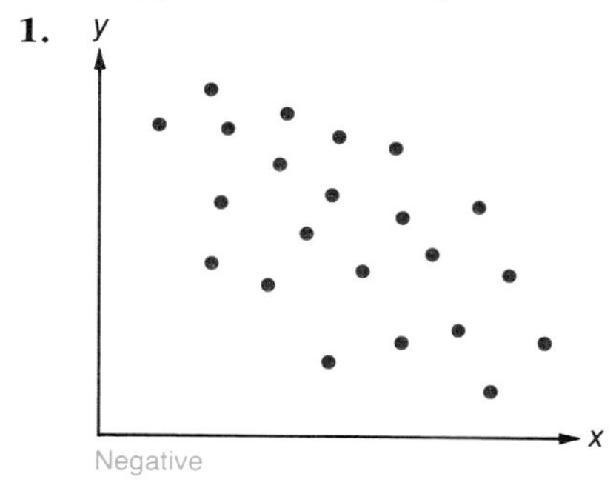

Negative

2.

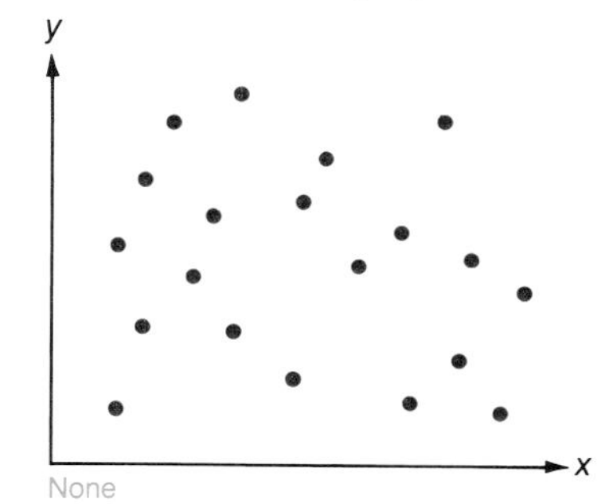

None

3.

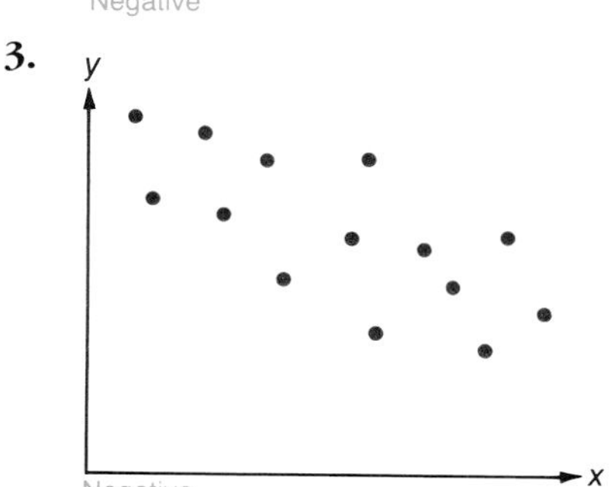

Negative

4.

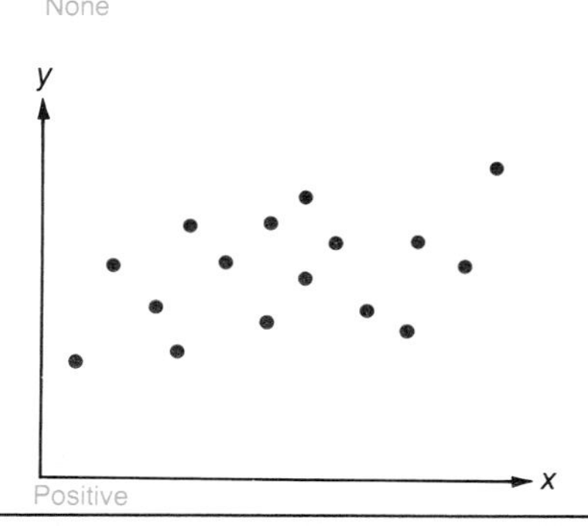

Positive

Problems

11.

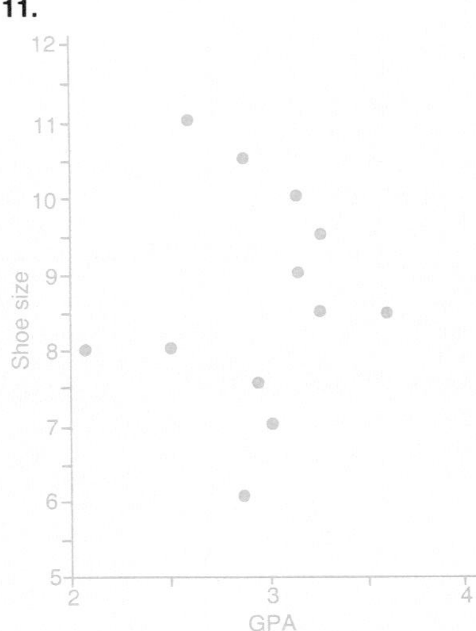

There appears to be no relationship between grade point average and shoe size.

12.

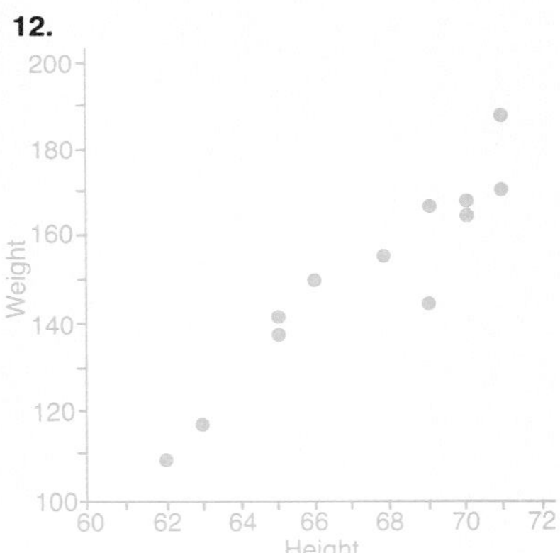

There appears to be a positive relationship between height and weight.

13. Answers may vary. Students should find a positive relationship between height and arm length.

14. Answers may vary.

Mixed Review

15. 24 **16.** 5
17. 26 **18.** 0.3249
19. 0.5592 **20.** 0.1045
21. 0.9205 **22.** 0.9986
23. 4.3315 **24.** 0

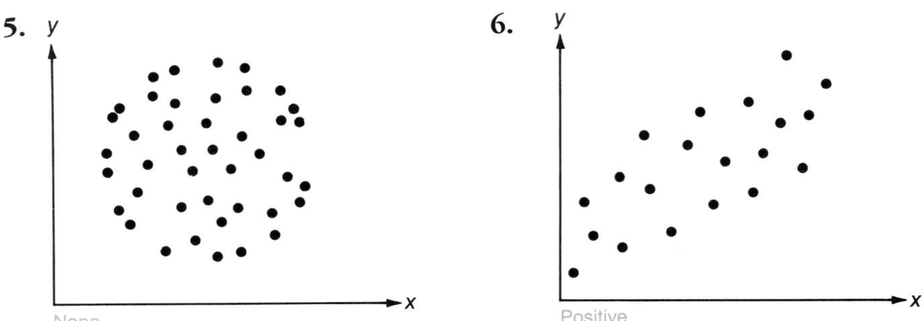

For each of the following sets of data, what type of relationship might you expect?

7. the weight of a sirloin steak and the selling price Positive

8. the number of problems assigned for homework and the amount of time spent doing homework assignments Positive

9. athletic ability and musical ability None

10. math anxiety and score on a math exam Negative

For Exercises 11 and 12, use the information shown in the following table.

Student	**1**	**2**	**3**	**4**	**5**	**6**	**7**	**8**	**9**	**10**	**11**	**12**
GPA	3.6	2.9	3.2	2.6	2.8	2.1	3.3	3.0	3.2	3.3	2.5	2.8
Shoe size	8.5	7.5	9	11	6	8	8.5	7	10	9.5	8	10.5
Height (in.)	65	69	70	71	62	66	68	65	69	70	63	71
Weight (lb)	141	145	163	170	109	150	156	138	166	168	118	188

11. Make a scatter plot for the data consisting of grade point average (GPA) and shoe size. Based on the scatter plot, what type of relationship exists between a student's grade point average and shoe size?

12. Make a scatter plot for the data consisting of height and weight. Based on the scatter plot, what type of relationship exists between a student's height and weight?

For Exercises 13 and 14, make a questionnaire and collect the needed data from approximately 20 students. Make a scatter plot and write a paragraph describing your results. Try to explain any trends or patterns.

13. Investigate whether there is a relationship between a person's height and the length of a person's arm from the elbow to the hand.

14. Investigate whether there is a relationship between the circumferences of a person's head and a person's neck.

Mixed Review

In a right triangle, find the length of the side not given.

15. $b = 18, c = 30$ **16.** $c = 5\sqrt{2}, a = 5$ **17.** $a = 10, b = 24$

Find these trigonometric function values. **18.** tan 18° **19.** sin 34°

20. cos 84° **21.** sin 67° **22.** cos 3° **23.** tan 77° **24.** cos 90°

Problem Solving: Application

Weather Vane Plot

In ancient Egypt, picture writing, or hieroglyphics, was the key to communication. Five thousand years later, scientists once again are turning to picture writing. In medicine, astronomy, geology, meteorology, social studies, and other disciplines, pictorial representations known as **glyphs** are being used to display complex data. The word *glyph* means "pictograph" or "symbolic representation."

Scientists are familiar with representing two variables on a graph. But the new pictorial methods can represent three or more variables in a simpler way. A **weather vane plot** using glyphs can be used by a meteorologist to display daily air pollution data. The position of each glyph in the plot's Cartesian (x-y) coordinate system is determined by weather conditions, and so is the shape and size of each glyph. Each of the circle-ray glyphs in the weather vane plot below represents five variables for a day at a specific site.

- **solar radiation level:** the distance from the center of each glyph to the y-axis
- **ozone level:** the distance from the center of each glyph to the x-axis
- **minimum daily temperature:** the diameter of the circle (hot day = large circle)
- **average wind speed:** the length of the ray is the inverse of the speed (high wind = short ray)
- **average wind direction:** the direction of the ray (up = north, left = west, right = east, down = south)

The day shown by glyph D had an ozone level of about 0.07, a solar radiation level of about 60, moderate temperature, and high northeasterly winds.

The day shown by glyph F had an ozone level of about 0.065, a solar radiation level of about 120, a cool temperature, and high southwesterly winds.

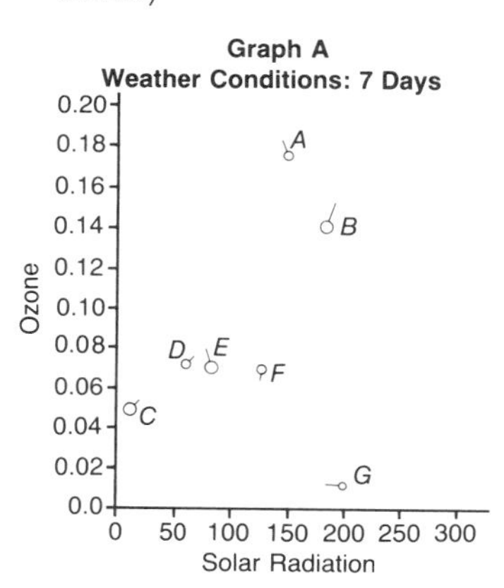

Problem Solving: Application

Point out that the wind's direction is the direction the wind is coming from. For example, a northeasterly wind comes from the northeast.

You may wish to review the concept of plotting data with the following example.

A scientist performs an experiment with a piston that contains some gas. She has a pressure gauge, which will tell how much pressure is in the piston when she compresses the gas to different volumes. She tries changing the volume in the piston and records the pressures for several different volumes in a table like the one below.

Plot the data on a graph. Explain that graphs organize information. Scientists often use graphs to study trends and make conjectures about data. Sometimes there are more than just two variables that are related. The weather vane example illustrates one way that scientists graph data with more than two variables.

Volume (L)	2	6	3	4	8	12
Pressure (atm)	12	4	8	6	3	2

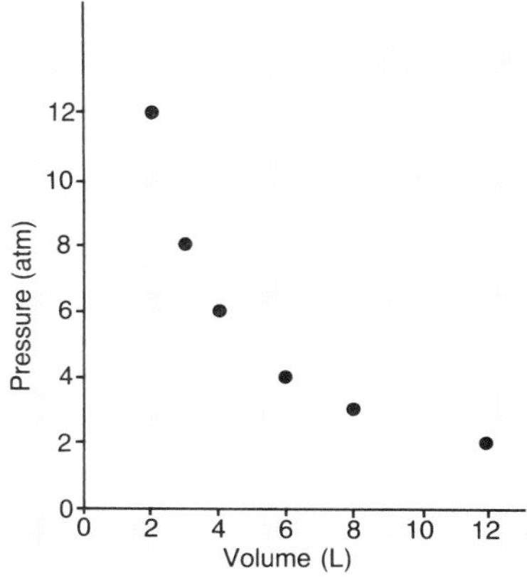

ANSWERS

1. Solar radiation level of about 150, moderate temperature, low winds in northwesterly direction
2. Day shown by glyph G; lower temperature than C
3. Days shown by glyphs D, E, and F; solar radiation level ranges from about 50 to about 120; similar temperatures

4–5.

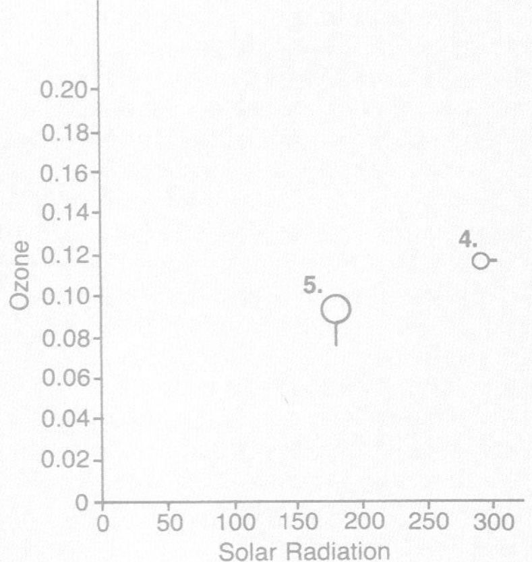

6. Low solar radiation levels seem to be linked with low ozone levels.
7. Not necessarily
8. Moderate wind speeds, low temperatures

Problems

Examine the graph above.

1. For the day with the highest ozone level, give the solar radiation level and describe the temperature, wind speed, and direction.
2. Which day has the highest solar radiation? How does its temperature compare to the day with the lowest solar radiation?
3. Which days have about the same ozone levels? How do their solar radiation levels and temperatures compare?

Make a weather vane plot with appropriate scales.

4. Plot a glyph that you think would represent a cold day with easterly winds for which the solar radiation was about 300 and the ozone level was about 0.12.
5. Plot a glyph that you think would represent a hot day, with light winds in a southerly direction, having an ozone level of 0.09 and a solar radiation level of about 170.

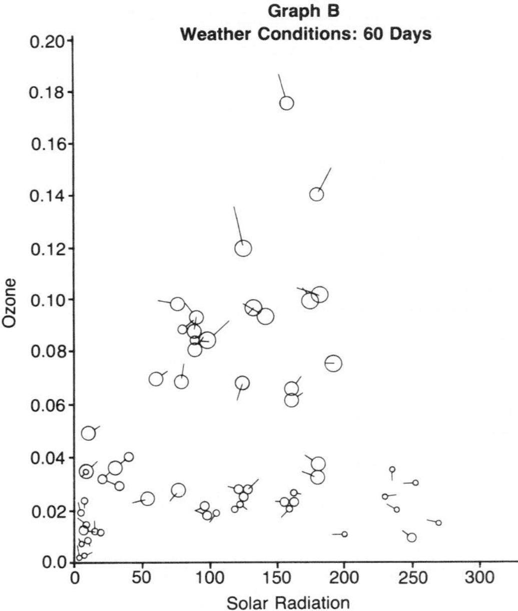

Examine the 60-day graph.

6. For this site, what relationship seems to hold between low solar radiation levels and ozone levels?
7. On days with high solar radiation levels, is the ozone level necessarily high?
8. What kinds of temperatures and wind speeds generally accompany days with high solar radiation levels and low ozone levels?

Problem Solving: College Entrance Exams

Averages

College entrance exams often require that the average, or mean, of a set of numbers be found. These problems can be solved using the definition of average and the equation-solving skills you have learned.

EXAMPLE 1

Larry's marks on five tests are 70, 90, 65, 85, and 75. What must his mark be on the next test to raise his average to 80?

Since we know the average we want is 80, and the number of tests is 6, we can write the following equation.

$$80 = \frac{\text{(sum of the 6 numbers)}}{6}$$

$$80 = \frac{70 + 90 + 65 + 85 + 75 + n}{6}$$

$$480 = 385 + n$$

$$480 - 385 = n$$

$$95 = n$$

He needs 95 points on the last exam to get an average of 80.

Example 2 involves a weighted average. It is weighted because the groups are of different sizes.

EXAMPLE 2

If the average of 3 numbers is 5, and the average of 7 other numbers is 15, then the average of all the numbers is

(A) 9 (B) 10 (C) 11 (D) 12 (E) 13

Using the formula for average we know the following are true.

The sum of the first three numbers, sum A, is 15, since

$$\frac{\text{sum } A}{3} = 5$$

$$\text{sum } A = 15$$

The sum of the other seven numbers, sum B, is 105, since

$$\frac{\text{sum } B}{7} = 15$$

$$\text{sum } B = 105$$

Therefore, the sum of all ten numbers is $15 + 105 = 120$, and the average of these ten numbers is $\frac{120}{10} = 12$.

Problem Solving: College Entrance Exams

It may be helpful for students to practice using a variety of strategies for working these problems. They can be worked using the strategies *Guess, Check, Revise* or *Look for a Pattern.*

ANSWERS

1. (A)
2. (B)
3. (E)
4. (D)
5. (A)
6. (E)
7. (C)
8. (D)
9. (D)

Problems

1. If Margie's first two test grades are 90 and 81, what grade must she get on her third test for the average of the three to be 80?

   (A) 69 (B) 68 (C) 67 (D) 66 (E) 65

2. If Tito's first three test grades are 89, 95, and 100, what grade does he need on the next test to average 95?

   (A) 97 (B) 96 (C) 95 (D) 94 (E) 93

3. The average of three numbers is greater than 70. If two of them are 67 and 68, then the third number could be

   (A) 72 (B) 73 (C) 74 (D) 75 (E) 76

4. The average of two numbers is A and one number is N. The other number is

   (A) $2N$ (B) $2A$ (C) $2A - 2$ (D) $2A - N$ (E) $A - N$

5. If the average of 3 numbers is between 7 and 10, then the sum of the 3 numbers could be any one of the following except

   (A) $20\frac{1}{2}$ (B) $22\frac{1}{2}$ (C) 23 (D) 26 (E) 29

6. The average (mean) of five positive numbers is 16. If three of the numbers are 15, 18, and 12, which of the following could *not* be one of the other two numbers?

   (A) 17 (B) 20 (C) 26 (D) 33 (E) 36

7. If the average of the first 5 numbers on a list is equal to the average of the first 4 numbers on the list, then the fifth number must be equal to

   (A) a number greater than the average of the first 4 numbers
   (B) a number less than the average of the first 4 numbers
   (C) the average of the first 4 numbers
   (D) an odd number
   (E) a negative number

8. A class of 30 students took a test that was scored from 0 to 90. Exactly 10 students received scores less than or equal to 60. If A is the class average score, which of the following is the *highest* possible value of A?

   (A) 60 (B) 70 (C) 75 (D) 80 (E) 85

9. The average of M numbers is A, and the average of N numbers is B. What is the average of all the numbers?

   (A) $A + B$ (B) $\frac{A + B}{2}$ (C) $\frac{AM + BN}{2}$

   (D) $\frac{AM + BN}{M + N}$ (E) $\frac{AM + BN}{A + B}$

Chapter 15 Summary and Review

15-1

To find the **theoretical probability** of an event, you must know how many ways the event can occur (m), and the number of possible outcomes (n). Then the probability is $\frac{m}{n}$.

A spinner numbered 1 to 8 is spun.

1. What is the probability of spinning a 6?
2. What is the probability of spinning an odd number?
3. What is the probability of spinning a multiple of two?

One card is drawn from a well-shuffled deck of 52 cards.

4. What is the probability of drawing a jack?
5. What is the probability of drawing a red card?
6. What is the probability of drawing a card with a number that is divisible by 4?

15-2

The sum of the probabilities of two **complementary events** is 1. If two events, A and B, are **mutually exclusive,** then $P(A \text{ or } B) = P(A) + P(B)$. In general, $P(A \text{ or } B) = P(A) + P(B) - P(A \cap B)$.

7. Suppose that an event C has a probability of $\frac{5}{16}$. What is $P(C')$?
8. Suppose that an event A has a probability of 0.46. What is $P(A')$?
9. A spinner numbered 1 to 6 is spun. What is the probability of spinning a 1 or a 2?
10. A box contains 4 red marbles, 6 white marbles, and 8 blue marbles. A marble is chosen at random. What is the probability that it will be a red marble or a blue marble?
11. When spinning a spinner numbered 1 to 8, what is the probability of spinning an even number or a multiple of 3?
12. A card is drawn from a well-shuffled deck of 52 cards. What is the probability of drawing a spade or a king?
13. A card is drawn from a well-shuffled deck of 52 cards. What is the probability of drawing a red card or a face card?

15-3

It is not always reasonable to perform an experiment, so we can **simulate** an event to find the desired probability. When developing and carrying out a plan for a simulation, you should select an appropriate model and define a trial. Then you must collect data and run a sufficient number of trials.

ANSWERS

1. $\frac{1}{8}$
2. $\frac{4}{8}$ or $\frac{1}{2}$
3. $\frac{4}{8}$ or $\frac{1}{2}$
4. $\frac{4}{52}$ or $\frac{1}{13}$
5. $\frac{26}{52}$ or $\frac{1}{2}$
6. $\frac{8}{52}$ or $\frac{2}{13}$
7. $\frac{11}{16}$
8. 0.54
9. $\frac{2}{6}$ or $\frac{1}{3}$
10. $\frac{12}{18}$ or $\frac{2}{3}$
11. $\frac{5}{8}$
12. $\frac{16}{52}$ or $\frac{4}{13}$
13. $\frac{32}{52}$ or $\frac{8}{13}$

14. Four tosses of a coin

15.

Stem	Leaf
42	.0, .5
43	.5
44	
45	
46	.5
47	.5
48	.0
49	.5, .0, .5, .0
50	.0, .5, .0
51	.0, .0

16.

Miles	Frequency
24,000–24,499	3
24,500–24,999	1
25,000–25,499	5
25,500–25,999	1
26,000–26,499	5
26,500–26,999	4
27,000–27,499	5

17.

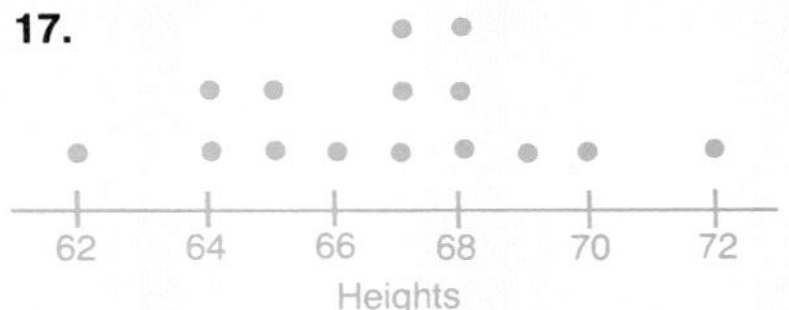

18.

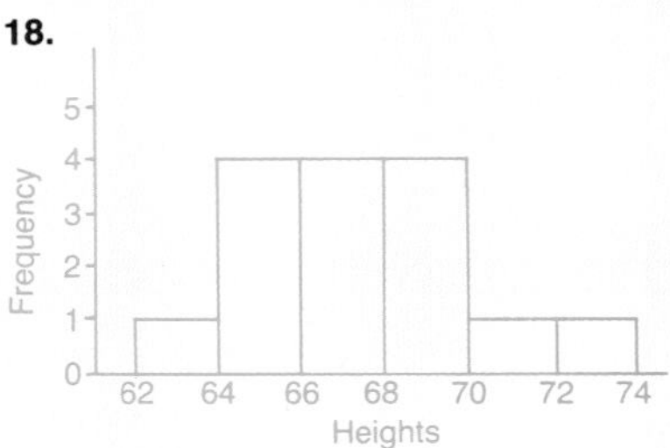

19.

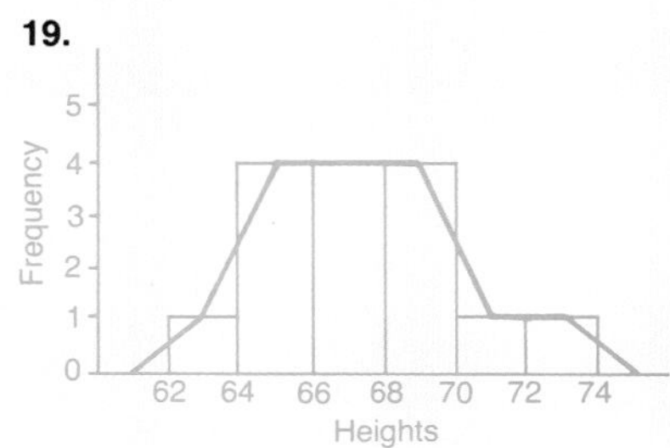

14. Define a trial for the simulation used to find the probability that a cat with four kittens will have two male and two female kittens.

15-4

Often data is best organized in a table or diagram. A **frequency distribution** table shows the frequency, or number of occurrences, of a particular measurement, date, interval, or other set of data. A **stem-and-leaf** diagram splits each value in the data into two parts, a stem and a leaf.

15. Construct a stem-and-leaf diagram for the following heights, in inches, of girls in a third-grade class.

49.5, 42, 43.5, 48, 42.5, 51, 46.5, 49, 49.5,
50, 50.5, 49, 51, 50, 47.5

16. Construct a frequency distribution using 7 intervals for the following set of numbers showing how many miles each of 24 automobile tires lasted.

24,242	25,201	24,004	26,051
24,284	25,268	25,841	26,284
26,053	27,499	26,842	24,986
26,820	27,005	27,233	26,241
25,382	26,911	27,048	25,411
25,484	27,084	26,921	26,048

15-5

A set of data can be presented in pictorial representation. A **line plot** is constructed by drawing part of a number line and placing dots above the line for each occurrence of a value. A **histogram** is a type of bar graph with horizontal and vertical scales and no spaces between the bars. A **frequency polygon** is a line graph that connects the midpoints of the bars of a histogram.

Here are heights, in inches, of boys in an algebra class.

68	65	64	67	68
62	69	67	67	66
65	72	68	70	64

17. Construct a line plot for this data.

18. Construct a histogram for this data.

19. Construct a frequency polygon for this data.

15-6

Three **measures of central tendency**, the mean, the median, and the mode, often represent a set of data. The **mean,** or average, is found by adding all the values and dividing by the number of values. The **median** is the middle value of a set of data. The **mode** is the value that occurs most often.

The top ten times in the boys' 15-to-18-year-old 50-yd freestyle in the championship meet were

26.00	25.02	26.05	25.60	24.70
23.92	24.20	22.28	28.46	24.70

20. Find the mean to the nearest hundredth for this data.
21. Find the median for this data.
22. Find the mode for this data.

15-7

A **scatter plot** is a graph that shows the relationship between two variables. You can use the line of best fit to determine whether there is a **positive** relationship, a **negative** relationship, or no relationship between the two variables.

23. What type of relationship would you expect between the number of field goals attempted and the number of field goals made?

The table shows the top 10 times paired with the ages of the female 30-to-39-year-old racers in the Five-Mile Classic.

Age	32	30	31	33	37	39	35	37	36	38
Time	37.4	37.9	39.9	41.0	42.3	43.1	43.8	45.3	46.0	47.5

24. Make a scatter plot for these data. What type of relationship seems to exist between a runner's age and time?

20. 25.09 **21.** 24.86
22. 24.70
23. Positive
24.

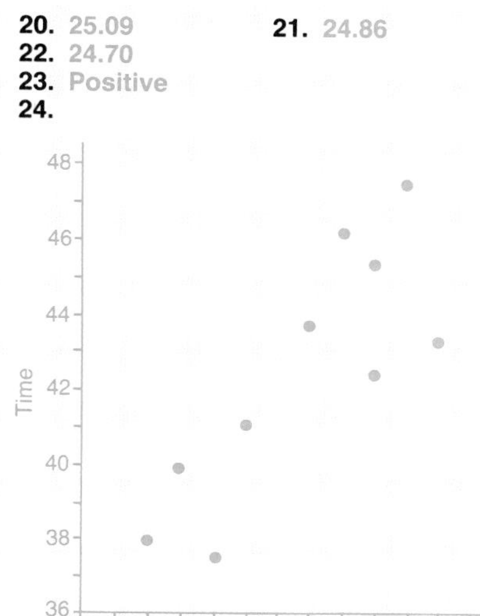

A positive relationship

Chapter 15 Test

A spinner numbered 1 through 12 is spun.

1. What is the probability of spinning a multiple of 4? $\frac{3}{12}$ or $\frac{1}{4}$
2. What is the probability of spinning a factor of 12? $\frac{6}{12}$ or $\frac{1}{2}$
3. What is the probability of spinning a prime number? $\frac{5}{12}$

ANSWERS

13.

Stem	Leaf
14	8, 4, 9, 9, 8, 9
15	0, 2, 2, 4, 9
16	7, 1, 3
17	2, 7

14.

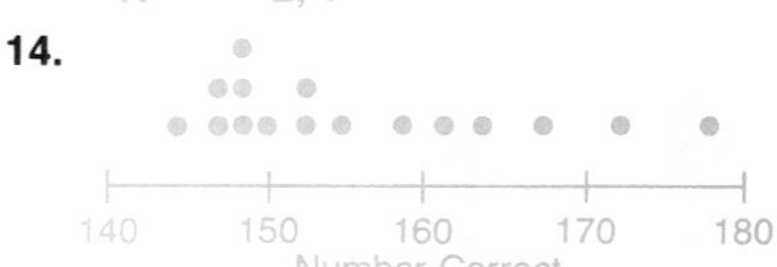

15.

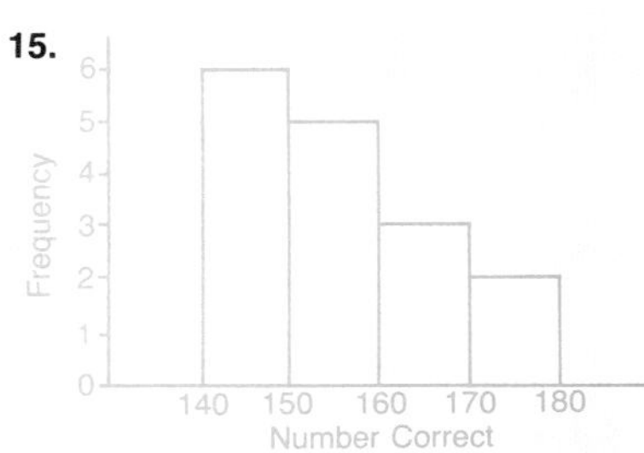

16.

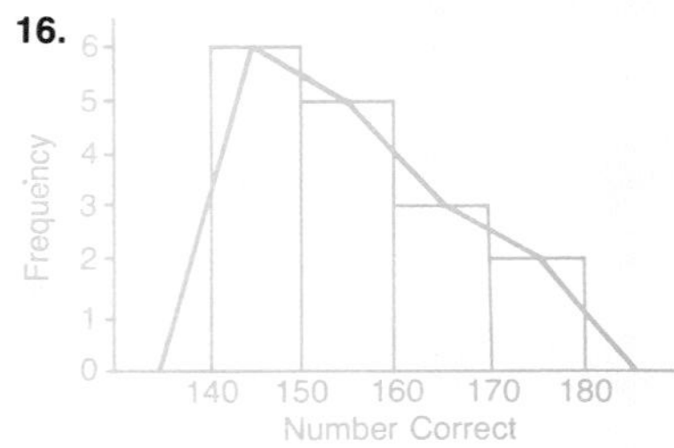

21.

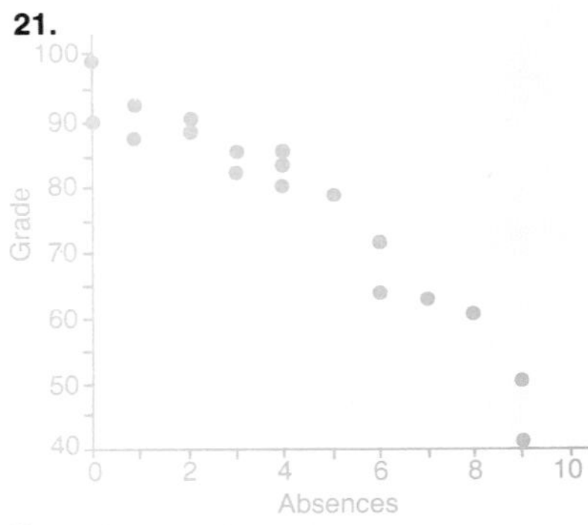

Negative relationship

Test Item Analysis

Item	Lesson
1–6	15-1
7–11	15-2
12	15-3
13	15-4
14–16	15-5
17–19	15-6
20, 21	15-7

A card is drawn at random from a well-shuffled deck of 52 cards. What is the probability that

4. the card is the seven of hearts? $\frac{1}{52}$

5. the card is an eight? $\frac{4}{52}$ or $\frac{1}{13}$

6. the card is a number less than six? $\frac{16}{52}$ or $\frac{4}{13}$

7. the card is a five or a six? $\frac{8}{52}$ or $\frac{2}{13}$

8. the card is black or a six? $\frac{28}{52}$ or $\frac{7}{13}$

9. the card is red or a multiple of three? $\frac{32}{52}$ or $\frac{8}{13}$

10. Suppose that event B has a probability of $\frac{7}{8}$. What is $P(B')$? $\frac{1}{8}$

11. Suppose that the probability of rain today is 0.43. What is the probability that it will not rain today? 0.57

12. Define a trial for the simulation used to find the probability that a family with four children has at least three girls. Four tosses of a coin

The number of problems Laurel Nissan answered correctly on successive computer games was

148	172	144	167	149	150	149	148
152	161	149	152	154	177	159	163

13. Construct a stem-and-leaf diagram for this data.

14. Construct a line plot for this data.

15. Construct a histogram for this data.

16. Construct a frequency polygon for this data.

The temperature in San Francisco reached these highs over a one-week period in August.

85 83 79 72 68 71 72

17. Find the mean to the nearest tenth for this data. 75.7

18. Find the median for this data. 72

19. Find the mode for this data. 72

20. What type of relationship would you expect between the number of dogs in 30 California cities and the number of cats in 30 Texas cities? None

The table shows the number of absences and the final exam grades for a class of 18 students.

Absences	3	6	0	9	4	2	5	8	3	9	0	2	4	6	1	1	4	7
Grade	85	64	90	41	83	88	78	60	82	50	98	90	85	71	93	87	79	63

21. Make a scatter plot for these data. What type of relationship seems to exist between absences and final exam grades?

Chapters 1–15 Cumulative Review

1-4 Evaluate.

1. $(x - 3)^2 + 5$ for $x = 10$ 54
2. $(y - 1)^2 + (y + 6)^2$ for $y = 4$ 109
3. $(x - y)^2 + 2(x + y)$ for $x = 10$ and $y = 2$ 88

1-5 Use the associative property to write an equivalent expression.

4. $(7 + 6) + 4$ $7 + (6 + 4)$
5. $a \cdot (b \cdot c)$ $(a \cdot b) \cdot c$

2-3, 2-4 Add.

6. $-12.8 + 2.6 + (-11.9) + 6.2 + 0.9$ -15
7. $-\frac{1}{8} - 4 - \frac{3}{4} + 2\frac{1}{2} - 6\frac{1}{4}$ $-8\frac{5}{8}$
8. $2 + 6x - 14 - 5x$ $x - 12$
9. $18a + 16b + 2a - 10b$ $20a + 6b$

2-5 Multiply.

10. $(-8)(-5)$ 40
11. $(-11.2)(3.1)$ -34.72

2-6 Divide.

12. $-\frac{4}{7} \div \frac{1}{14}$ -8
13. $-\frac{8}{9} \div -\frac{1}{3}$ $\frac{8}{3}$

3-3 to 3-5 Solve.

14. $3x - 12 = 2x$ 12
15. $-\frac{7}{8}x + 7 = \frac{3}{8}x - 3$ 8
16. $0.6x - 1.8 = 1.2x$ -3
17. Three fifths of the automobiles entering the city each morning will be parked in city parking lots. These cars fill 3654 parking spaces. How many cars enter the city each morning? 6090 cars

3-7

18. Solve $A = \pi r^2$ for r.
19. Solve $A = 2\pi r^2 + 2\pi rh$ for h.

3-9

20. After election results of 378 votes were tallied, the new student-body president won by a margin of 5 to 4. How many votes did she get?

ANSWERS

18. $r = \sqrt{\frac{A}{\pi}}$ or $\frac{\sqrt{A \cdot \pi}}{\pi}$

19. $h = \frac{A}{2\pi r} - r$ or $\frac{A - 2\pi r^2}{2\pi r}$

20. 210

ANSWERS

27. $x < 21$
28. $a \geq -13$
29. $y \leq \frac{1}{2}$
30. $c > -3$
31. $y > -5$
32. $x \leq \frac{17}{5}$
33. $l \geq 15$
34. a^{10}
35. $4m^2$
36. $\frac{1}{y^3}$
37. $8y^{18}$
38. $\frac{x^2}{y^6}$
39. $27x^{15}y^{12}$
40. $-6y^3$
41. $12ab^4c^5$
42. $-\frac{5x^3}{2}$
43. $6xy^2$
44. $7m^3 - 10m^2 + 1$
45. $-a^3 + 4a^2 - 2a$
46. $16b^2 + 8b - 3$
47. $2m^2 - 9m - 18$
48. $49y^2 - 36$
49. $a^2 + 4a + 4$
50. $a^2 - 6a + 9$
51. $9m^2 + 30m + 25$

3-10 Solve.

21. What percent of 52 is 13? 25%
22. What percent of 86 is 129? 150%
23. 60 is what percent of 720? $8\frac{1}{3}\%$
24. 12 is what percent of 0.5? 2400%
25. 110% of what number is 11? 10
26. What is 25% of 16? 4

4-2 to 4-4 Solve.

27. $x - 9 < 12$
28. $3a + 8 \geq -5 + 2a$
29. $6y \leq 3$
30. $3c - 6 < 5c$
31. $7y + 2 > 5y - 8$
32. $23 - 7x - 3x \geq -11$

4-5

33. The width of a rectangle is 15 cm. What length will make the area at least 225 cm^2?

5-1, 5-2 Simplify.

34. $a^4 \cdot a^6$
35. $\frac{4m^5}{m^3}$
36. y^{-3}
37. $(2y^6)^3$
38. $\left(\frac{x}{y^3}\right)^2$
39. $(3x^5y^4)^3$

5-3, 5-4 Multiply.

40. $(-3y)(2y^2)$
41. $(-3ab^2c)(-4b^2c^4)$

Divide.

42. $\frac{-25x^4}{10x}$
43. $\frac{-18x^2y^3z}{-3xyz}$

5-7, 5-8 Add or subtract.

44. $(2m^3 - 9) + (5m^3 - 10m^2 + 10)$
45. $(-6a^2 - a + 3) - (a^3 - 10a^2 + a + 3)$

5-10 Multiply.

46. $(4b - 1)(4b + 3)$
47. $(2m + 3)(m - 6)$
48. $(7y + 6)(7y - 6)$
49. $(a + 2)^2$
50. $(a - 3)^2$
51. $(3m + 5)^2$

6-1 to 6-5 Factor.

52. $m^3 - m$
53. $49x^2 - 64$
54. $m^4 - 1$
55. $2x^2 + 13x - 99$
56. $7m^2 - 8m + 1$
57. $9x^2 - 24x + 16$
58. $9x^4 - 30x^2y + 25y^2$
59. $100x^3 + 60x^2 + 9x$

7-3 Graph each equation.

60. $x + y = 5$
61. $2x + 3y = -1$
62. $-y = 7$

7-5 Find the slope and y-intercept of each line.

63. $10x = 125 - 20y$
64. $2y - 3x + 1 = 0$

7-6 Write an equation for each line.

65. the line containing (0, 10) and parallel to the x-axis
66. the line containing the origin and $(-3, 3)$
67. the line with slope of $-\frac{2}{3}$ that crosses the x-axis at -7
68. the line with x-intercept 6 and y-intercept -1

8-1

Which of these pairs are solutions of the systems of equations in Exercises 69–71? (0, 0), $(-2, 1)$, (4, 3), (1, 1)

69. $5x - 2y = -12$
$3x + 8y = 2$ $(-2, 1)$

70. $2y = 6$
$-3x = -12$ (4, 3)

71. $x + 8y = 6$
$3x + 6y = 0$ $(-2, 1)$

8-2, 8-3 Solve these systems of equations.

72. $y = x - 6$
$x + y = -2$ $(2, -4)$

73. $\frac{1}{2}x + 2y = 9$
$4x + 3y = 7$ $(-2, 5)$

8-4 to 8-6

74. The difference of two numbers is 14. Three times the larger number is 45 less than four times the smaller. What are the two numbers?
75. In 15 years Dorothy will be three times as old as Stan. Five years ago the difference in their ages was 50. How old are Dorothy and Stan?
76. An airplane whose speed in still air is 530 mi/h carries enough air gas for 10 hours of flight. On a certain flight it flies against a wind of 30 mi/h. On the return flight it travels with a wind of 30 mi/h. How far can the plane fly without refueling?
77. For the school festival, 600 tickets were sold. Student tickets sold for \$1.60, and adult tickets sold for \$2.25. If the total amount received was \$1122.50, how many tickets of each kind were sold?

52. $m(m + 1)(m - 1)$
53. $(7x + 8)(7x - 8)$
54. $(m^2 + 1)(m + 1)(m - 1)$
55. $(2x - 9)(x + 11)$
56. $(m - 1)(7m - 1)$
57. $(3x - 4)^2$
58. $(3x^2 - 5y)^2$
59. $x(10x + 3)^2$

60.
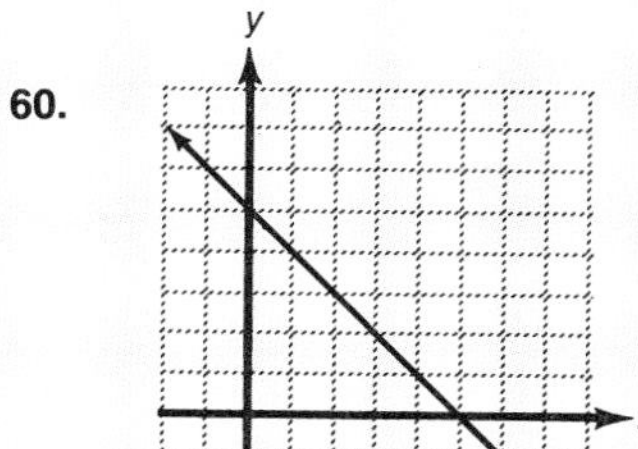

61.
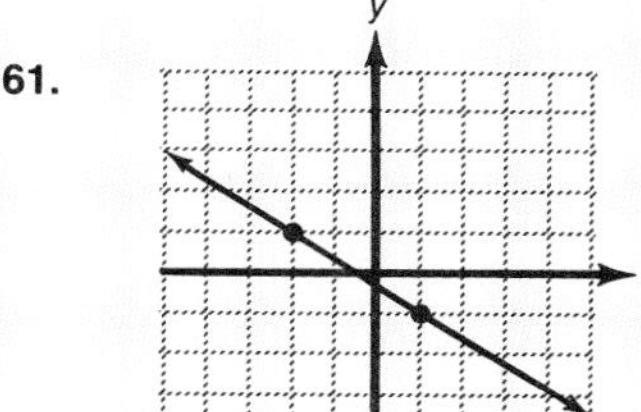

62.
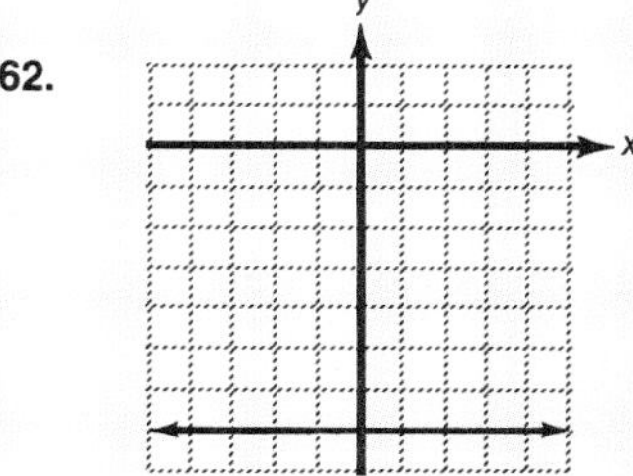

63. $m = -\frac{1}{2}, b = \frac{25}{4}$
64. $m = \frac{3}{2}, b = -\frac{1}{2}$
65. $y = 10$
66. $y = -x$
67. $y = -\frac{2}{3}x - \frac{14}{3}$
68. $y = \frac{1}{6}x - 1$
74. 87, 101
75. Dorothy is 60 years old; Stan is 10 years old.
76. Approximately 2641.5 mi each way or 5283 mi
77. 350 student tickets, 250 adult tickets

78. {100, 102, 104, 105, 106, 108, 110, 112, 115, 120}
79. {99, 100, 102, 105, 108, 110, 111, 115, 120}
80. {99, 100, 102, 104, 105, 106, 108, 110, 111, 112}
81. {100, 110}
82. {105}
83. {102, 108}
84. $-4 < x < 4$

85. $x < -5$ or $x > 5$

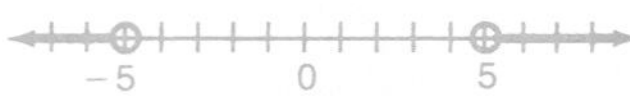

86. $-4 \le x \le 16$

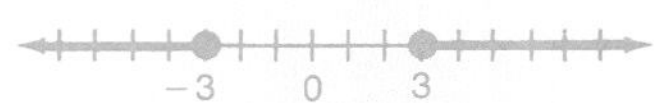

87. $x \le -3$ or $x \ge 3$

88. $\frac{30}{15x^2 - 2x - 24}$
89. $\frac{x^2 + 6x + 9}{x^4 - 4x^2 + 4}$
90. $x + 3$
91. $\frac{10}{a + 1}$
92. $\frac{1}{(y - 1)(y - 3)}$
93. $\frac{28}{3}$
94. $x + 1$
95. $x + 3$
96. $\frac{-10x + 25}{x(x - 5)}$
97. $\frac{-5x + 17}{(x - 4)(x + 3)(x - 3)}$
98. $\frac{2}{9}$
99. -5
100. $4\frac{4}{9}$ h
101. 17 km/h, 22 km/h
102. \$6250, \$4750

9-1

Let $A = \{100, 105, 110, 115, 120\}$, $B = \{100, 102, 104, 106, 108, 110, 112\}$, and $C = \{99, 102, 105, 108, 111\}$.

Find the following.

78. $A \cup B$ **79.** $A \cup C$ **80.** $B \cup C$

81. $A \cap B$ **82.** $A \cap C$ **83.** $B \cap C$

9-4 Solve and graph.

84. $|x| < 4$ **85.** $|x| > 5$

86. $|x - 6| \le 10$ **87.** $2|x| \ge 6$

10-2 Multiply. Simplify the product when possible.

88. $\frac{-5}{3x - 4} \cdot \frac{-6}{5x + 6}$ **89.** $\frac{x + 3}{x^2 - 2} \cdot \frac{x + 3}{x^2 - 2}$

90. $\frac{x^2 - 6x}{x - 6} \cdot \frac{x + 3}{x}$ **91.** $\frac{5a + 5}{a + 3} \cdot \frac{2a + 6}{a^2 + 2a + 1}$

10-3 Divide. Simplify the quotient.

92. $\frac{y + 4}{y^2 - 1} \div \frac{y^2 + y - 12}{y + 1}$ **93.** $\frac{8x - 12}{5} \div \frac{6x - 9}{35}$

10-4, 10-5 Add or subtract. Simplify.

94. $\frac{2x^2}{2x - 1} - \frac{1 - x}{2x - 1}$ **95.** $\frac{x^2}{x - 3} + \frac{9}{3 - x}$

96. $\frac{x - 5}{x} - \frac{x}{x - 5}$ **97.** $\frac{3}{12 + x - x^2} - \frac{2}{x^2 - 9}$

10-6, 10-7 Solve.

98. $\frac{6x - 2}{2x - 1} = \frac{9x}{3x + 1}$ **99.** $\frac{2}{x + 1} = \frac{5}{2x}$

100. In checking records a contractor finds that crew A can pave a certain length of highway in 8 hours. Crew B can do the same job in 10 hours. How long would it take if they worked together?

101. One boat travels 5 km/h slower than another. While one boat travels 85 km, the other travels 110 km. Find their speeds.

102. Two women were partners in a store, one investing \$50,000 and the other \$38,000. They agreed to share the profits in the ratio of the amount invested. The profits for the first year were \$11,000. How much should each receive?

11-1 Simplify.

103. $\sqrt{49}$ 7 **104.** $-\sqrt{81}$ -9

11-2

Determine the replacements for the variable that will make each expression a real number.

105. $\sqrt{x + 4}$ $x \geq -4$ **106.** $\sqrt{x - 6}$ $x \geq 6$

Simplify.

107. $\sqrt{c^2d^2}$ $|cd|$ **108.** $\sqrt{(x + 1)^2}$ $|x + 1|$ **109.** $\sqrt{64x^2}$ $8|x|$

11-3 Simplify. Assume all variables are nonnegative.

110. $\sqrt{150}$ $5\sqrt{6}$ **111.** $\sqrt{9y}$ $3\sqrt{y}$ **112.** $\sqrt{16x - 16}$ $4\sqrt{x - 1}$

113. $\sqrt{y^7}$ $y^3\sqrt{y}$ **114.** $\sqrt{8x^4y^4}$ $2x^2y^2\sqrt{2}$ **115.** $\sqrt{9(a + 4)^2}$ $3(a + 4)$

11-4, 11-5 Multiply and simplify. Assume all variables are nonnegative.

116. $\sqrt{4xy^2} \cdot \sqrt{8x^2y}$ $4xy\sqrt{2xy}$ **117.** $\sqrt{32ab} \cdot \sqrt{6a^4b^2}$ $8a^2b\sqrt{3ab}$

Rationalize the denominator. Assume all variables are nonnegative.

118. $\sqrt{\frac{1}{6}}$ $\frac{\sqrt{6}}{6}$ **119.** $\frac{\sqrt{5}}{\sqrt{18}}$ $\frac{\sqrt{10}}{6}$ **120.** $\sqrt{\frac{x^2}{27}}$ $\frac{x\sqrt{3}}{9}$

11-6 Add or subtract.

121. $6\sqrt{a} + 7\sqrt{a}$ $13\sqrt{a}$ **122.** $\sqrt{81y^3} - \sqrt{4y}$ $(9y - 2)\sqrt{y}$

123. $3x\sqrt{x^2y} - x\sqrt{x^2y^3} - 2\sqrt{y^3}$ $(3x^2 - x^2y - 2y)\sqrt{y}$

11-7

124. In a right triangle with hypotenuse c, $a = 9$ and $c = 41$. Find the length of side b. 40

12-1 Find the indicated output for the function $f(x) = 2x^2 + 7x - 4$.

125. $f(0)$ -4 **126.** $f\left(\frac{1}{2}\right)$ 0 **127.** $f(-2)$ -10

12-4 Graph each function.

128. $g(x) = x^2 - 1$ **129.** $f(x) = \frac{1}{4}x^2$

128.

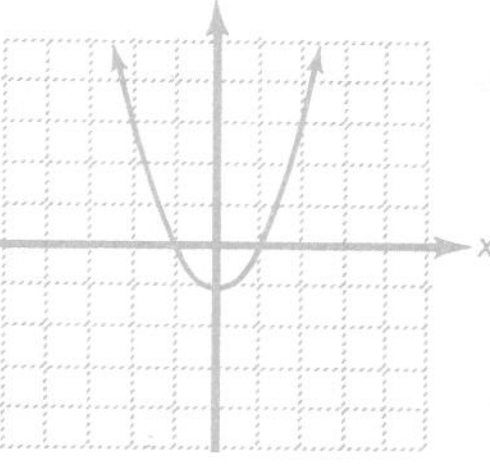

129.

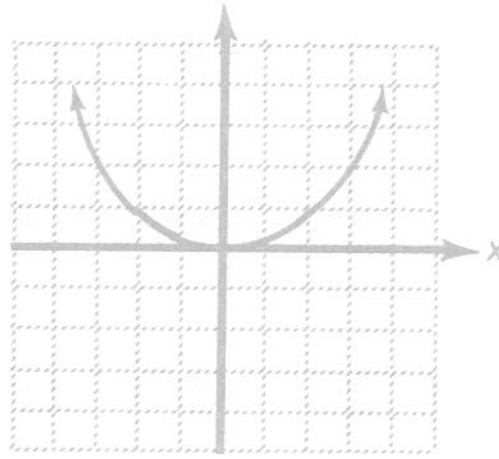

133. $\sqrt{10}, -\sqrt{10}$
134. $0, \frac{7}{3}$
135. 2
136. $\frac{1}{2}, -\frac{2}{3}$
137. $3 \pm \sqrt{6}$
138. $5 \pm \sqrt{29}$
139. $\frac{2 \pm \sqrt{6}}{3}$
140. $\frac{7 \pm 3\sqrt{5}}{2}$
141. $\frac{\pm 2\sqrt{6}}{3}$
142. $-3, 2$
143. 1, 3
144. 1
145. 2 km/h
146. $l = 8m, w = 4m$

12-5 to 12-7

130. When you swim underwater, the pressure in your ears varies directly as the depth at which you swim. At 50 ft the pressure is about 21.5 pounds per square inch (psi). Find the pressure at 20 ft. 8.6 psi

131. The volume of a certain quantity of gas varies inversely as its pressure. If its pressure is 15 psi when its volume is 3 cubic feet, what will the pressure be when the gas is expanded to a volume of 5 cubic feet? 9 psi

132. Assume that p varies directly as r and inversely as s where p is 10 when r is 8 and s is 4. Find p when r is 10 and s is 2. 25

13-1 to 13-4 Solve.

133. $3x^2 = 30$

134. $3x^2 - 7x = 0$

135. $x^2 + 4 = 4x$

136. $6x^2 + x - 2 = 0$

137. $(x - 3)^2 = 6$

138. $x^2 - 10x - 4 = 0$

139. $9x^2 - 12x - 2 = 0$

140. $x^2 = 7x - 1$

13-5 Solve.

141. $\frac{x + 2}{x^2 - 2} = \frac{2}{2 - x}$

142. $1 + \frac{1}{x} = \frac{6}{x^2}$

13-6 Solve.

143. $p = \sqrt{4p - 3}$

144. $2\sqrt{x^2 - 1} = x - 1$

13-7

145. The speed of a boat in still water is 8 km/h. It travels 60 km upstream and 60 km downstream in a total time of 16 hours. What is the speed of the stream?

146. The width of a rectangle is half its length. The area is 32 m^2. Find the length and the width.

14-1

147. $\triangle RST \sim \triangle ABC$. Find the length c. $\frac{1}{2}\sqrt{33} \approx 2.9$

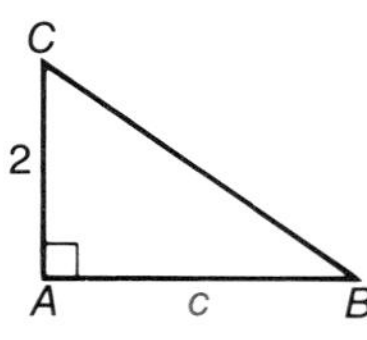

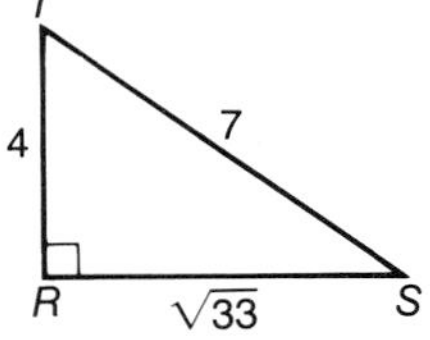

14-2

148. In $\triangle RST$ (above), find sin S, cos S, and tan S rounded to 4 decimal places. $\frac{4}{7} \approx 0.5714, \frac{\sqrt{33}}{7} \approx 0.8207, \frac{4}{\sqrt{33}} \approx 0.6963$

14-4

149. In $\triangle XYZ$, $X = 29°$ and $y = 18$ m. Find z. 15.7 m

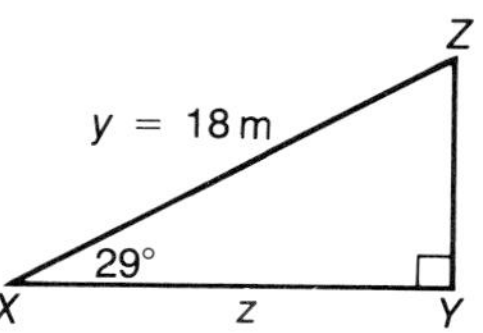

15-1

Cards are drawn from a well-shuffled deck of 52 cards.

150. What is the probability of drawing a face card?

151. What is the probability of drawing a card with an even number?

15-2

152. A bag contains 10 black marbles, 6 white marbles, and 2 red marbles. A marble is chosen at random. What is the probability that it will be a red marble or a white marble?

153. When spinning a spinner numbered 1 to 8, what is the probability of spinning an odd number or a multiple of 3?

15-4

Here is a set of weights, in pounds, of men in a body-building class.

195, 182, 186, 218, 240, 196,
225, 210, 189, 192, 237,
198, 187, 204, 201, 187,
206, 239, 204, 194, 243

154. Construct a stem-and-leaf diagram for this data.

155. Construct a frequency distribution using 7 intervals for this data.

15-5

Here is a set of test scores on a geometry final.

92, 85, 73, 98, 75, 78, 84,
96, 99, 79, 88, 92, 87,
86, 75, 85, 94, 86, 81

156. Construct a histogram for this data.

157. Construct a frequency polygon for this data.

15-6

Here is a set of math scores for one student.

75, 90, 95, 75, 80, 95,
85, 80, 90, 85, 80

158. Find the mean for this data. 84.5

159. Find the median for this data. 85

160. Find the mode for this data. 80

150. $\frac{12}{52}$ or $\frac{3}{13}$

151. $\frac{20}{52}$ or $\frac{5}{13}$

152. $\frac{8}{18}$ or $\frac{4}{9}$

153. $\frac{5}{8}$

154.

Stem	Leaf
18	2, 6, 9, 7, 7
19	5, 6, 2, 8, 4
20	4, 1, 6, 4
21	8, 0
22	5
23	7, 9
24	0, 3

155.

Data	Frequency
180–189	5
190–199	5
200–209	4
210–219	2
220–229	1
230–239	2
240–249	2

156.

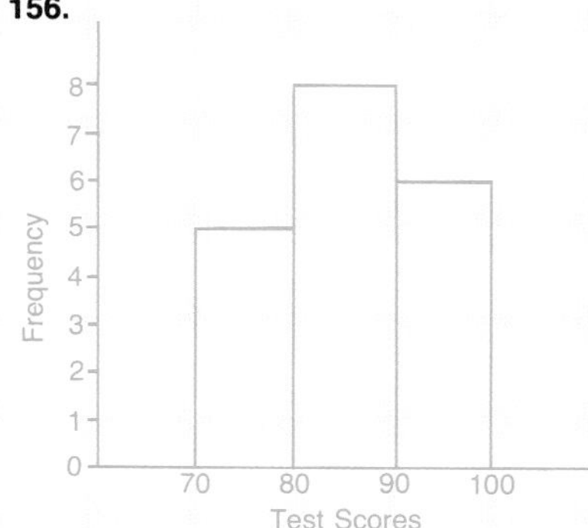

157.

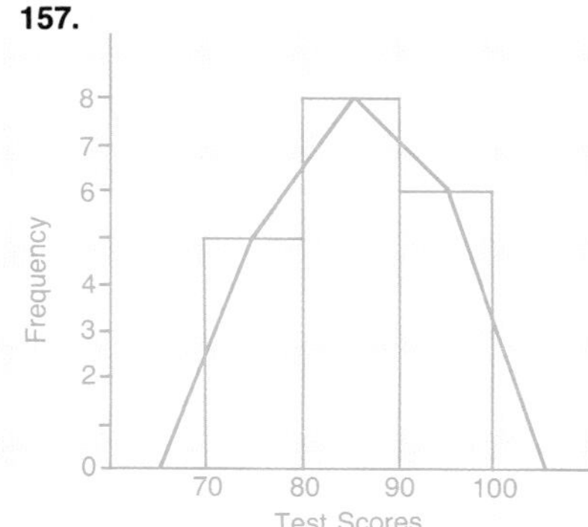

Answers

1. $\frac{2a}{6}$
2. $\frac{3m}{4m}$
3. $\frac{xy}{7y}$
4. answers will vary
5. answers will vary
6. answers will vary
7. answers will vary
8. answers will vary
9. answers will vary
10. 13
11. 41
12. 3
13. 6
14. 8
15. 49
16. 1089
17. 5
18. 48
19. 21
20. 4
21. 1
22. 32
23. 2
24. 0
25. 225
26. 216
27. 0
28. 1
29. 14
30. 16
31. 30
32. 60
33. $\frac{20}{9}$
34. 1
35. 3^4
36. $7n^4$
37. w^1
38. no
39. no
40. no
41. yes
42. no
43. yes
44. 12
45. 4
46. 24
47. $\frac{1}{5}$
48. $4n$
49. $\frac{11v}{2}$
50. $4d$
51. $\frac{4t}{r}$
52. $\frac{5t}{7y}$
53. 49
54. 9
55. 27
56. 9
57. 23
58. 1
59. 20
60. 100
61. 100

Item Analysis

Item	Lesson
1–3	1-2
4–9	1-4
10–15	1-1
16–28	1-3
29–34	1-4
35–37	1-3
38–43	1-2
44–46	1-1
47–52	1-2
53–61	1-3, 1-4

MIXED PRACTICE 1 For use after Lesson 1-4

Write an equivalent expression.

1. $\frac{a}{3}$ Use $\frac{2}{2}$ for 1. **2.** $\frac{3}{4}$ Use $\frac{m}{m}$ for 1. **3.** $\frac{x}{7}$ Use $\frac{y}{y}$ for 1.

4. $5 \cdot (m \cdot n)$ **5.** $(s + 3) + t$ **6.** $a \cdot b \cdot 11$

7. $r(2 + s)t$ **8.** $1 + (2m^2 + n)$ **9.** $(xy)z + w$

Evaluate.

10. $9 + y + y$ for $y = 2$ **11.** $2a + 5b$ for $a = 3$ and $b = 7$

12. $\frac{3x}{5y}$ for $x = 10$ and $y = 2$ **13.** $\frac{2m + n}{3}$ for $m = 7$ and $n = 4$

14. $h + 3k$ for $h = 5$ and $k = 1$ **15.** $4(r + 6) - 3$ for $r = 7$

16. $(3a)^2$ for $a = 11$ **17.** $5y^2$ for $y = 1$ **18.** $6a^3$ for $a = 2$

19. $5r^2 + 1$ for $r = 2$ **20.** $m^3 + 4$ for $m = 0$ **21.** $x^3 - 7$ for $x = 2$

22. $(2c)^5$ for $c = 1$ **23.** $2c^2$ for $c = 1$ **24.** $5y^8$ for $y = 0$

25. $(3xy)^2$ for $x = 5$ and $y = 1$ **26.** $(ab)^3$ for $a = 2$ and $b = 3$

27. $(2mn)^4$ for $m = 0$ and $n = 2$ **28.** $(st)^5$ for $s = 1$ and $t = 1$

29. $(m - 4)(m + 1)$ for $m = 6$ **30.** $(9 - w)^2$ for $w = 5$

31. $y(11 - y)$ for $y = 5$ **32.** $5(a + 3)$ for $a = 9$

33. $\frac{a^2 + 4}{3a}$ for $a = 6$ **34.** $\frac{m^2 + 3m}{7m}$ for $m = 4$

Write using exponential notation.

35. $3 \cdot 3 \cdot 3 \cdot 3$ **36.** $7 \cdot n \cdot n \cdot n \cdot n$ **37.** w

Tell whether each pair of expressions is equivalent.

38. $3t + 5t$ and $8 + 2t$ **39.** $xy + yz$ and $xz + yy$

40. $mn + pq$ and $n \cdot p \cdot m \cdot q$ **41.** $a \cdot b + xyz$ and $xzy + ba$

42. $rs + tu$ and $r + s + t + u$ **43.** $hj + lm$ and $ml + jh$

Simplify.

44. $18 - 6 \times 8 - 2$ **45.** $19 - 2 \times 8 + 1$ **46.** $3 \times 8 - 6 \times 0$

47. $\frac{3w}{15w}$ **48.** $\frac{24mn}{6m}$ **49.** $\frac{11uvw}{2uw}$

50. $\frac{8ced}{2ec}$ **51.** $\frac{12st}{3rs}$ **52.** $\frac{5xtv}{7vxy}$

Calculate.

53. $(5 + 2)^2$ **54.** $5 + 2^2$ **55.** $5^2 + 2$

56. $(5 - 2)^2$ **57.** $5^2 - 2$ **58.** $5 - 2^2$

59. $5 \cdot 2^2$ **60.** $(5 \cdot 2)^2$ **61.** $5^2 \cdot 2^2$

MIXED PRACTICE 2 For use after Lesson 1-9

Factor and check by multiplying.

1. $12a + 42b + 18$ **2.** $25x + 60y + 40z$ **3.** $14m + 10n + 6$

Simplify each expression. Factor and collect like terms as needed.

4. $xy + 3x + 6xy + 4x$ **5.** $6a^2 + 3ab + 2ab + 4a^2$

6. $8xy + 9xz + 4xy + 3xz$ **7.** $27c + 5 + 8c$

Write as an algebraic expression.

8. a number n divided among 5 **9.** a number y increased by 17

10. Let p be the number of problems Lonnie completed. Ray completed 8 more than Lonnie. Write an expression for the problems Ray completed.

11. Let b be the number of books Victor read. Donna read half as many books as Victor. Write an expression for the number of books Donna read.

12. Let w be Barbara's weight. Laurel weighs 6 pounds less than Barbara. Write an expression for Laurel's weight.

Evaluate.

13. $\frac{12m}{18n}$ for $m = 12$ and $n = 8$ **14.** $\frac{x \cdot y}{6} + \frac{x + 2}{2}$ for $x = 8$ and $y = 3$

Evaluate $\frac{2a + c}{5}$ when

15. a is 3 and c is 4. **16.** c is 1 and a is twice c.

17. a is 15 and c is twice a. **18.** c is 25 and a is half c.

Solve for the given replacement set.

19. $3m^2 - 1 = 47$ $\{2, 4, 6\}$ **20.** $y + 3 = 5y - 25$ $\{5, 6, 7\}$

Simplify, then solve mentally.

21. $6x + 3x = 36$ **22.** $n + 7n = 16$ **23.** $3t + 2t = 35$

24. $\frac{32m}{8} = 12$ **25.** $5a^2 = 5$ **26.** $\frac{15k}{3} = 20$

Determine whether each pair of equations is equivalent.

27. $3a + 6 = 12$
$3a + 6 - 6 = 12 + 6$

28. $10 + 3x = 12x - 4$
$10 + 3x - 3x = 12x - 4 + 4$

29. $2y - 5 = 19 - 4y$
$2y - 5 + 4y = 19 - 4y + 4y$

30. $17 - 5t = 2t - 4$
$17 - 5t + 5t = 2t - 4 - 5t$

31. Find the area (A) of a playing field with length (l) of 25 yd and width (w) of 50 ft using the formula $A = lw$.

32. Find the sales tax (T) paid on an item selling for a price (p) of \$12.50 using the formula $T = 0.06p$ (6% tax rate).

Answers

1. $6(2a + 7b + 3)$
2. $5(5x + 12y + 8z)$
3. $2(7m + 5n + 3)$
4. $7x(y + 1)$ **5.** $5a(2a + b)$
6. $12x(y + z)$ **7.** $5(7c + 1)$
8. $\frac{n}{5}$ **9.** $y + 17$
10. $p + 8$ **11.** $\frac{b}{2}$
12. $w - 6$ **13.** 1
14. 9 **15.** 2
16. 1 **17.** 12
18. 10 **19.** (4)
20. (7) **21.** 4
22. 2 **23.** 7
24. 3 **25.** ± 1
26. 4 **27.** no
28. no **29.** yes
30. no **31.** 3750 ft²
32. \$0.75

Item Analysis

Item	Lesson
1–3	1-5
4–7	1-5
8–12	1-6
13–18	1-6
19, 20	1-7
21–26	1-7
27–30	1-7
31, 32	1-8

Answers

1. $+3$	2. -1073
3. 22	4. 15
5. 0.6	6. 1.295
7. $<$	8. $<$
9. $>$	10. $>$
11. $<$	12. $<$
13. $>$	14. $>$
15. $>$	16. $>$
17. $<$	18. $>$
19. -11	20. -13
21. 2	22. $\frac{1}{8}$
23. $-\frac{2}{5}$	24. $-\frac{13}{16}$
25. -18.5	26. 77
27. $\frac{11}{12}$	28. $\frac{32}{15}$
29. 0	30. 40
31. -9.75	32. -12.2
33. 2.15	34. -3.9
35. 11	36. 15
37. 3	38. 6
39. -1	40. 24
41. 1	42. 0
43. -105	44. -7
45. $19 - 12a$	46. $-5x + 32$
47. $1 - 3y$	48. 5
49. $34.90	50. 51°

Item Analysis

Item	Lesson
1, 2	2-1
3–6	2-1
7–10	2-1
11–18	2-2
19–28	2-3
29–34	2-4
35–41	2-1
42–47	2-4
48	2-3
49, 50	2-4

MIXED PRACTICE 3 For use after Lesson 2-4

Name the integer that is suggested by each situation.

1. Letitia gained 3 pounds. **2.** Lost Canyon is 1073 ft deep.

Find the absolute value.

3. $|22|$ **4.** $|-15|$ **5.** $|0.6|$ **6.** $|-1.295|$

Write a true sentence using $<$ or $>$.

7. $-9 \quad 7$ **8.** $3 \quad 4$ **9.** $5 \quad -8$ **10.** $-2 \quad -3$

11. $-63 \quad -51$ **12.** $0.01 \quad 0.011$ **13.** $4.12 \quad -4.13$ **14.** $7.52 \quad 7.25$

15. $\frac{2}{3} \quad \frac{1}{2}$ **16.** $-\frac{1}{8} \quad -\frac{3}{16}$ **17.** $-\frac{2}{5} \quad \frac{1}{3}$ **18.** $\frac{4}{5} \quad \frac{7}{10}$

Add.

19. $-9 + (-2)$ **20.** $5 + (-18)$ **21.** $-6 + 8$

22. $-\frac{3}{8} + \frac{1}{2}$ **23.** $\frac{2}{5} + -\frac{4}{5}$ **24.** $-\frac{3}{4} + -\frac{1}{16}$

25. $17 + (-39) + 3.5$ **26.** $-21 + (-5) + 103$

27. $-\frac{2}{3} + \frac{5}{6} + -\frac{1}{4} + 1$ **28.** $3 + -\frac{1}{5} + -\frac{2}{3}$

Subtract.

29. $-7 - (-7)$ **30.** $19 - (-21)$ **31.** $-8 - 1.75$

32. $23 - (35.2)$ **33.** $-1.25 - (-3.4)$ **34.** $-9 - (-5.1)$

Evaluate.

35. $|2| + |-9|$ **36.** $|-4| \cdot |2| + |-7|$ **37.** $|3| + |-4| \cdot |0|$

38. $|a| - 17$ for $a = -23$ **39.** $|n| - |m|$ for $n = -5$ and $m = 6$

40. $2|x| \cdot |y|$ for $x = -3$ and $y = -4$ **41.** $16 - 3|t|$ for $t = -5$

Simplify.

42. $19 + (-27) - 5 - (-13)$ **43.** $-53 + (-19) - 41 - (-8)$

44. $-7 - (16) + (-9) - (-25)$ **45.** $11 - (3a) - 26a + 8 - (-17a)$

46. $21x - (17x) - (-32) + (-9x)$

47. $10 - (-5y) + (-9) + (-8y)$

Solve.

48. Bob entered the elevator on the eighth floor. The elevator went up 4 floors. Next it went down 10 floors. Then the elevator went up three floors and Bob got off. What floor was he on?

49. Cheryl's checking account was overdrawn by $102.75. After she made a deposit, she was overdrawn by $67.85. How much did she deposit?

50. At 4 a.m. the temperature at Anchorage was -12°F. By noon, the temperature was 39°F. How many degrees did the temperature rise?

MIXED PRACTICE 4 For use after Lesson 2-9

Simplify.

1. $2[5(6-4)+(-3)^2]$
2. $(-2)^3-(-1)^8+(-3)^2$
3. $3(-2)^3\cdot(-1)^{21}$
4. $5[-3(2^3)+(-2)^2(7)]$
5. $\frac{5(-11)+(-1)}{7}$
6. $3\frac{1}{8} \div 5\frac{1}{2}$
7. $\frac{4^3}{(-2)^6}$
8. $2\frac{1}{3} \div 5\frac{1}{4}$
9. $\frac{(-6)^3}{-(3^2)}$
10. $\frac{4+(-8)5}{-9}$
11. $\frac{(-8)^2}{(-2)^2}$
12. $\frac{10+2(-5)^2}{(2^2)(3)}$
13. $-4\frac{2}{5} \div 2\frac{5}{8}$
14. $45-(-21)+(-7)-9+3-(-5)+(-12)-37$
15. $-11+(-36)+27-(-8)-15+(-2)+21-6$
16. $[3(x+5)-7]+[-5(x-2)+11]$
17. $[4(x-3)+18]-[3(x+1)+2]$
18. $[4(x+1)+11]-[7(x-3)-1]$
19. $[9(3-x)+7]+[4(5+x)-2]$

Evaluate for $x=-4$, $y=2$, $z=3$.

20. $(-2x)yz$
21. $5y^2+2xz$
22. $y(x^2)-5z$
23. $5(2y-x)+z$
24. $2[(x-y)+z]$
25. $z(9y+4x)$
26. $3|x|-yz$
27. $5x-2|y|$
28. $4|x|+7|z|-5y$
29. $|x|\cdot|y|+|z|$
30. $|x|\cdot|-y|\cdot|z|$
31. $|x|-|y|+|z|$

Multiply or divide.

32. $3(-5)(1.2)(1)(-2.5)(0.08)(-10)$
33. $-2(5)(1.4)(-0.25)(20)(0.5)$
34. $-\frac{1}{3}\left(\frac{2}{5}\right)\left(\frac{5}{7}\right)\left(-\frac{7}{8}\right)\left(-\frac{3}{8}\right)$
35. $\left(-\frac{2}{9}\right)\left(\frac{6}{5}\right)\left(-\frac{4}{7}\right)\left(-\frac{1}{8}\right)\left(\frac{3}{20}\right)$
36. $\frac{3}{8}\left(\frac{1}{5}x-\frac{2}{3}y+4\right)$
37. $-\frac{2}{5}\left(-\frac{3}{8}x+\frac{1}{2}y-\frac{2}{3}\right)$
38. $1.2(2x+4y-7)$
39. $-2.25(-5x+2.4y)$
40. $-\frac{2}{3} \div \frac{3}{8}$
41. $\frac{5}{6} \div \left(-\frac{3}{4}\right)$
42. $-\frac{3}{16} \div \left(-\frac{3}{4}\right)$
43. $107.25 \div (-5.5)$
44. $-69.3 \div (4.2)$
45. $-48.16 \div (-8.6)$

Factor.

46. $256-80y$
47. $21x-56y+14$
48. $12x+12y-36z$
49. $-\frac{2}{3}x+y-\frac{1}{3}z$
50. $\frac{5}{24}x-\frac{5}{4}y$
51. $\frac{24}{5}x-\frac{4}{5}y+\frac{8}{15}$

Answers

1. 38 **2.** 0
3. 24 **4.** 20
5. -8 **6.** $\frac{25}{44}$
7. 1 **8.** $\frac{4}{9}$
9. 24 **10.** 4
11. 16 **12.** 5
13. $-1\frac{71}{105}$ **14.** 9
15. -14 **16.** $-2x+29$
17. $x+1$ **18.** $-3x+37$
19. $-5x+52$ **20.** 48
21. -4 **22.** 17
23. 43 **24.** -6
25. 6 **26.** 6
27. -24 **28.** 27
29. 11 **30.** 24
31. 5 **32.** -36
33. 35 **34.** $-\frac{1}{32}$
35. $-\frac{1}{350}$ **36.** $\frac{3}{40}x-\frac{1}{4}y+\frac{3}{2}$
37. $\frac{3}{20}x-\frac{1}{5}y+\frac{4}{15}$
38. $2.4x+4.8y-8.4$
39. $11.25x-5.4y$
40. $-\frac{16}{9}$ **41.** $-\frac{10}{9}$
42. $\frac{1}{4}$ **43.** -19.5
44. -16.5 **45.** 5.6
46. $16(16-5y)$
47. $7(3x-8y+2)$
48. $12(x+y-3z)$
49. $-\frac{1}{3}(2x-3y+z)$
50. $\frac{5}{4}\left(\frac{1}{6}x-y\right)$
51. $-\frac{4}{5}\left(-6x+y-\frac{2}{3}\right)$

Item Analysis

Item	Lesson
1–4	2-5
5–13	2-6
14, 15	2-4
16–19	2-8
20–25	2-5
26–31	2-1
32–35	2-5
36–39	2-7
40–45	2-6
46–51	2-7

Answers

1. −5	**2.** −21.5
3. 9	**4.** −6
5. $-\frac{3}{10}$	**6.** $-\frac{1}{6}$
7. $-\frac{9}{10}$	**8.** $-\frac{3}{8}$
9. $\frac{11}{24}$	**10.** 4.8
11. 9.5	**12.** −3.6
13. 1	**14.** 9
15. −2	**16.** 3
17. −5	**18.** 4
19. 6	**20.** −3
21. 4	**22.** 10
23. 3	**24.** −3
25. −17	**26.** 5
27. 1	**28.** −3
29. −2	**30.** −4
31. $\frac{x}{2} - 24$	**32.** $3\left(x + \frac{1}{x}\right)$
33. $4(x - 3)$	**34.** $\frac{1}{2}(x \cdot 5)$
35. −62	**36.** 43
37. 27	**38.** 48 min
39. 4 hrs	**40.** 11

Item Analysis

Item	Lesson
1–6	3-2
7–12	3-1
13–20	3-5
21, 22	3-1
23–30	3-3
31–34	3-4
35	3-1
36, 37	3-4
38	3-5
39	3-3
40	3-2

MIXED PRACTICE 5 For use after Lesson 3-5

Solve.

1. $-17.4t = 87$ **2.** $-9y = 193.5$ **3.** $-14x = -126$

4. $-\frac{2}{3}x = 4$ **5.** $\frac{5}{8}x = -\frac{3}{16}$ **6.** $-\frac{3}{4}y = \frac{1}{8}$

7. $m + \frac{2}{5} = -\frac{1}{2}$ **8.** $x + \frac{5}{8} = \frac{1}{4}$ **9.** $y - \frac{5}{6} = -\frac{3}{8}$

10. $x - 7.3 = -2.5$

11. $3.4 = r - 6.1$

12. $y + 9 = 5.4$

13. $10 - x - 7 = 3x - 1$

14. $18 + 3x - 5 = 7x - 14 - x$

15. $4a - (5a + 3) = -1$

16. $7y - 5 = 8(5 - y)$

17. $6(m + 3) = 2(m - 1)$

18. $7(a - 7) = -3(a + 3)$

19. $2(5t - 3) = 3(2t + 6)$

20. $4(2m + 1) = 2(3m - 1)$

21. $x + 5 = x + (9 - x)$

22. $20 - (4 - y) = 26$

23. $5x + 6 = 7x$

24. $4t + 5t = -27$

25. $3y - 9y = 102$

26. $4.3x - 7.9x = -18$

27. $4(5x - 7) - 8x = -16$

28. $2(9 - 6x) - 49 = 5$

29. $-2(4x + 5) - 11 = -5$

30. $6x - 5(3 + 2x) = 1$

Write as an algebraic expression.

31. 24 less than half a number

32. 3 times the sum of a number and its reciprocal

33. 4 times the difference of a number and 3

34. one-half of the product of a number and 5

Translate to an equation and solve.

35. Nine more than a number is −53. Find the number.

36. There are 64 members in the History Club. 11 less than half of the members are girls. How many members are boys?

37. The number of girls in Mrs. Busbee's class is 3 more than twice the number of boys. There are 19 girls. What is the total number of boys and girls in the class?

38. Mara read an average of 0.75 pages a minute. At that rate, in how many minutes will she read 36 pages?

39. Rico spent $18.50 to rent a lawn mower. The fee for the first hour was $8.00. Each additional hour cost $3.50. For how many hours did he rent the mower?

40. Twelve times a number is 132. Find the number.

MIXED PRACTICE 6 For use after Lesson 3-11

Write as a decimal.

1. 23% **2.** 0.04% **3.** 13.5% **4.** 160% **5.** 6.7%

Express as a percent. Round to the nearest tenth of a percent if necessary.

6. $\frac{3}{5}$ **7.** $\frac{1}{25}$ **8.** $\frac{5}{8}$ **9.** $\frac{2}{3}$ **10.** $\frac{37}{100}$

Solve.

11. $\frac{3}{2}x + \frac{3}{4}x + \frac{3}{8}x = 21$

12. $\frac{3}{4}n - \frac{1}{8}n = 6 + \frac{1}{8}n$

13. $\frac{1}{4} - x = \frac{1}{2}x + \frac{9}{4}$

14. $5|x| + 7 = 32$

15. $|y| + 7 = 3|y| - 9$

16. $|-x| = 14$

17. $A = \frac{1}{2}bh$, for h

18. $V = \frac{s}{t + r}$, for t

19. $B = 2(x + y)$, for x

20. What is 4% of 65?

21. 15 is 6% of what number?

22. 28 is what percent of 35?

Translate to an equation and solve.

23. The ratio of right-handed students to left-handed students in Mr. Duggan's class is 7 to 2. There are 27 students in the class. How many are right-handed?

24. The sum of three consecutive integers is 108. What are the integers?

25. At the end of the week, Lori had $440.28 in her account. She had written checks for $57.34, $19.09, and $30.77, and had made deposits of $42.00 and $15.85. How much was in her account at the beginning of the week?

26. Darrell bought a box of 36 ball point pens for $20.88. Find the cost of a single pen.

27. Raoul bought some $3 rolls of film and an $8 photo album. The total cost was $35. How many rolls of film did he buy?

28. Carl's age, 32, is 25 less than one-third his weight. How much does Carl weigh?

29. A movie theater had 46 more occupied seats than empty seats. It had a total of 320 seats. How many seats were occupied?

30. Alondra worked 5 hours and was paid $28.75. At that rate, how long will it take Alondra to earn $69?

Answers

1. 0.23 **2.** 0.0004
3. 0.135 **4.** 1.6
5. 0.067 **6.** 60%
7. 4% **8.** 62.5%
9. 66.7% **10.** 37%
11. 8 **12.** 12
13. $-\frac{4}{3}$ **14.** 5 and −5
15. 8 and −8 **16.** 14 and −14
17. $h = \frac{2A}{b}$ **18.** $t = \frac{s}{V} - r$
19. $x = \frac{B}{2} - y$ **20.** 2.6
21. 250 **22.** 80%
23. 21 **24.** 35, 36, 37
25. $489.63 **26.** $0.58
27. 9 **28.** 171
29. 183 **30.** 12 hours

Item Analysis

Item	Lesson
1–10	3-10
11–13	3-6
14–16	3-8
17–19	3-7
20–22	3-10
23	3-9
24	3-11
25	3-1
26	3-2
27	3-3
28	3-4
29	3-5
30	3-11

Answers

1. no, yes, yes, no
2. yes, yes, no, no
3. yes, no, yes, no
4. yes, yes, no, no
5. yes, no, yes, yes
6. $x \le -1$
7. $x > -2$
8. $x \ge 2$
9. $x < -3$
10. $x \ge -3$
11. $x < -\frac{3}{8}$
12. $y > \frac{11}{12}$
13. $x \le \frac{13}{15}$
14. $x > \frac{1}{8}$
15. $a < \frac{1}{10}$
16. $x \ge \frac{5}{8}$
17. $m > -17$
18. $y \ge 3.5$
19. $x \le -15$
20. $y \le -14$
21. $x \le 3$
22. $y \ge -11$
23. $x < 2$
24. $y > 10$
25. $x > 7$
26. $m < -2$
27. $x > 15$
28. $x \le -7$
29. false
30. false
31. true
32. true
33. false
34. true
35. true
36. true
37. true

38–43. For graphs, see Teacher's Answer Section.

38. $x \le \frac{3}{10}$
39. $m > -2\frac{1}{3}$
40. $x \le \frac{7}{2}$
41. $y < -\frac{3}{2}$
42. $m > -\frac{1}{2}$
43. $x \ge -3$

Item Analysis

Item	Lesson
1–5	4-1
6–10	4-1
11–16	4-2
17–22	4-3
23–28	4-2
29–37	4-1
38–42	4-3
43	4-2

MIXED PRACTICE 7 For use after Lesson 4-3

Determine whether the given number is a solution of the inequality.

	a.	b.	c.	d.
1. $x \le -1$	**a.** 2	**b.** -4	**c.** -1	**d.** 0
2. $y > -3$	**a.** 0	**b.** -2	**c.** -4	**d.** -3
3. $x < 4$	**a.** 3	**b.** 4	**c.** -1	**d.** 7
4. $x \le \frac{1}{3}$	**a.** $\frac{1}{8}$	**b.** $-\frac{1}{2}$	**c.** $\frac{1}{2}$	**d.** 0.5
5. $y \ge -\frac{3}{8}$	**a.** $\frac{3}{8}$	**b.** $-\frac{3}{5}$	**c.** -0.2	**d.** $-\frac{1}{8}$

Write the inequality shown by each graph.

6.

7.

8.

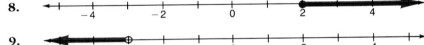

9.

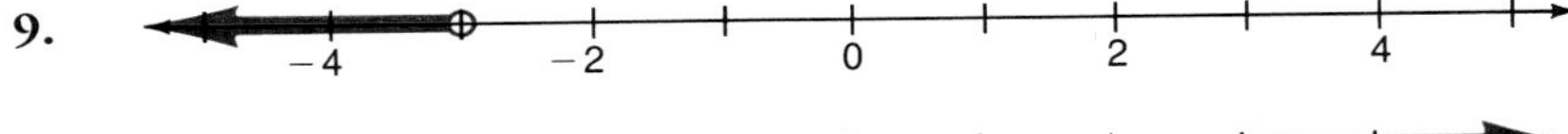

10.

Solve.

11. $x + \frac{1}{2} < \frac{1}{8}$ **12.** $y - \frac{2}{3} > \frac{1}{4}$ **13.** $x - \frac{1}{5} \le \frac{2}{3}$

14. $x - \frac{1}{8} > 0$ **15.** $\frac{2}{5} + a < \frac{1}{2}$ **16.** $x + \frac{1}{8} \ge \frac{3}{4}$

17. $-6m < 102$ **18.** $9y \ge 31.5$ **19.** $-15x \ge 225$

20. $7y \le -98$ **21.** $9x - 7x \le 6$ **22.** $66 \ge 2y - 8y$

23. $5(x + 3) - 4x < 17$ **24.** $3y - 2(y + 4) > 2$

25. $-3(x + 5) + 4(x + 8) > 24$ **26.** $-5m + 4 + 6m < 2$

27. $5(x - 2) - 4x > 5$ **28.** $-2(x - 4) + 3x \le 1$

Classify each statement as true or false.

29. $-4 \le -5$ **30.** $7 \le -7$ **31.** $4.5 \ge 4.5$

32. $|-0.3| \ge 0$ **33.** $|-2| < |1|$ **34.** $3.01 < 3.10$

35. $|x| \ge x$ **36.** $|x| \ge 0$ **37.** $|x + 1| > x$

Solve and graph the solution.

38. $t + \frac{3}{5} \le \frac{9}{10}$ **39.** $m + \frac{1}{3} > -2$ **40.** $\frac{1}{3}x \le \frac{7}{6}$

41. $-6y > 9$ **42.** $8m > -4$ **43.** $5x + 4 - 7x \le 10$

MIXED PRACTICE 8 For use after Lesson 4-6

Solve using the addition and multiplication properties.

1. $3(5 - x) \leq 2(x - 9)$
2. $4(x + 5) \leq 3(6 + x)$
3. $10 + 3y - 3 \geq 5y - 7$
4. $4x - 3 < 10x - 5$
5. $12 - 9c > 38 + 4c$
6. $2(x - 6) + 5 \geq 9$
7. $\frac{3}{8}y - 5 > \frac{7}{8}y$
8. $\frac{3}{4}x + 3 \leq x + \frac{1}{2}$
9. $1.6x - 0.5 \leq 1.2x + 1.5$
10. $2.2y + 3.2 < 3.4y - 1.6$
11. $6(1.5 - x) + 3x < 4(3 - x)$
12. $5(x + 2) - 4 > 3x$

Translate to an inequality.

13. 6 more than half a number is less than 7
14. 9 less than twice a number is less than 2
15. 15 is greater than or equal to half a number
16. 7 more than 5 times a number is at most 31
17. 6 less than 4 times a number is at least 40
18. 3 more than half a number is at least 15

Solve.

19. Find the greatest possible pair of integers such that one integer is 4 less than twice the other and their sum is at most 50.
20. Find all numbers such that the sum of the number and 24 is greater than 4 times the number.
21. The sum of four consecutive even integers is less than or equal to 116. Find the greatest possible values of the integers.
22. Roberta wants to buy a scarf and sweater and must not spend more than $36.00 for both. If the scarf costs $13.80, how much can she pay for the sweater?
23. Mitch scored 25 points in the first basketball game, 18 in the second, and 35 in the third. How many points must he score in the fourth game to maintain an average of at least 28 points scored for the four games?
24. The length of a rectangle is 22.5 cm. What width will make the area at least 405 cm^2?
25. Find the greatest possible pair of integers such that one integer is 2 less than three times the other and the sum is less than 42.

Answers

1. $x \geq 6.6$
2. $x \leq -2$
3. $y \leq 7$
4. $x > \frac{1}{3}$
5. $c < -2$
6. $x \geq 8$
7. $y < -10$
8. $x \geq 10$
9. $x \leq 5$
10. $y > 4$
11. $x < 3$
12. $x > -3$
13. $\frac{n}{2} + 6 < 7$
14. $(2n - 9) < 2$
15. $15 \geq \frac{n}{2}$
16. $5n + 7 \leq 31$
17. $4n - 6 \geq 40$
18. $\frac{n}{2} + 3 \geq 15$
19. 18, 32
20. $x < 8$
21. 26, 28, 30, 32
22. $22.20
23. 34 pts
24. $w \geq 18$ cm
25. 11, 31

Item Analysis

Item	Lesson
1–12	4-4
13–18	4-5
19–25	4-5

Answers

1. 1
2. x^5y^2
3. 3^{-4}
4. $32w^{45}$
5. $-8x^{27}$
6. $-27m^{12}$
7. $2y^{12}$
8. x^{12}
9. 2^{-3}
10. $(-2)^{-7}$
11. xy^3
12. $\frac{2^{10}}{3}$
13. $\frac{y^3}{2}$
14. $\frac{y^3}{3}$
15. $\frac{4m^3}{n}$
16. $-\frac{b^2}{9a}$
17. 1.224×10^{-1}, 0.1224
18. 3.3×10^{-7}, 0.00000033
19. 9.0×10^{-4}, 0.0009
20. 5.0×10^{1}, 50
21. 6.0×10^{3}, $6{,}000$
22. 8.0×10^{-7}, 0.0000008
23. $1{,}000$
24. 32
25. 1
26. $1{,}000{,}000$
27. $400{,}300$
28. 0.00096
29. $1{,}392$
30. 0.0014
31. $38{,}000$
32. 0.00003752
33. 4, 4, 0; 4
34. 8, 13, 22, 0; 22
35. 2, 0, 3, 1; 3
36. 5, 6, 3, 0; 6
37. 9.475001×10^6
38. 3.7×10^{-4}
39. 6.5×10^1
40. 1.0×10^{-6}
41. 9.39×10^{-2}
42. 4.63×10^4
43. $-3a^3c, 11a^2c^2, 5c^3; -3, 11, 5$
44. $4x^2, -6xy, -8y^2; 4, -6, -8$
45. $-3x^3yz, 4x^2y^2z, -19xy^2z^3, 15; -3, 4, -19, 15$
46. $7xy^3 - 3x^2y$
47. $2m^2 + 4m$
48. $-\frac{2}{5}x^2 - 2x + 4$
49. $\frac{2}{3}x^2 - \frac{1}{2}x + 3$
50. $\frac{1}{6}x^3 - 2x + 2$
51. $-\frac{3}{10}x^4 - 2x^2 + \frac{4}{5}x$

Item Analysis

Item	Lesson
1–3	5-1
4–6	5-2
7, 8	5-3
9–11	5-1
12, 13	5-2
14–16	5-3
17–22	5-4
23–26	5-1
27–32	5-4
33–36	5-5
37–42	5-4
43–45	5-5
46–51	5-5

MIXED PRACTICE 9

For use after Lesson 5-5

Simplify.

1. $(-8)^0$ **2.** $(x^3y)(x^2y)$ **3.** $(3^{-1})^4$ **4.** $(2w^9)^5$

5. $[2(-x^9)]^3$ **6.** $(-3m^4)^3$ **7.** $(2y^2)(y^5)^2$ **8.** $(x^2)^3(x^3)^2$

9. $\frac{2^5}{2^8}$ **10.** $\frac{(-2)^2}{(-2)^9}$ **11.** $\frac{x^3 \cdot y^4}{x^2y}$ **12.** $\frac{(4 \cdot 2^3)^2}{3}$

13. $\frac{(-y)^4}{2y}$ **14.** $\frac{(3y^4)^2}{27y^5}$ **15.** $\frac{-16m^5}{-4m^2n}$ **16.** $\frac{-3ab^2}{27a^2}$

Multiply or divide. Express the result using scientific and standard notation.

17. $(5.1 \times 10^3)(2.4 \times 10^{-5})$ **18.** $(1.1 \times 10^{-4})(3.0 \times 10^{-3})$

19. $\frac{1.8 \times 10^4}{2 \times 10^7}$ **20.** $\frac{3.5 \times 10^{-3}}{7 \times 10^{-5}}$

21. $\frac{(4.0 \times 10^3)(9.0 \times 10^5)}{(6.0 \times 10^5)}$ **22.** $\frac{(1.2 \times 10^4)(4.0 \times 10^{-3})}{(6.0 \times 10^7)}$

Evaluate each expression.

23. $x^2 \cdot x^1$ for $x = 10$ **24.** $2^a \cdot 2^b \cdot 2^c$ for $a = 1, b = 4, c = 0$

25. $7^a \cdot 5^a \cdot 3^a$ for $a = 0$ **26.** $10^x \cdot 10^y \cdot 10^z$ for $x = 3, y = 2, z = 1$

Write using standard notation.

27. 4.003×10^5 **28.** 9.6×10^{-4} **29.** 1.392×10^3

30. 1.4×10^{-3} **31.** 3.8×10^4 **32.** 3.752×10^{-5}

Identify the degree of each term and the degree of the polynomial.

33. $4x^3y - 19x^2y^2 + 21$ **34.** $-3x^5y^3 - 5x^4y^9 + 8xy^{21} + 15$

35. $4x^2 + 15 - 8x^3 + 11x$ **36.** $9x^2y^3 + 4x^5y - 2xy^2 - 1$

Write using scientific notation.

37. 9,475,001 **38.** 0.00037 **39.** 65

40. 0.000001 **41.** 0.0939 **42.** 46,300

Identify the terms. Give the coefficient of each term.

43. $-3a^3c + 11a^2c^2 + 5c^3$ **44.** $4x^2 - 6xy - 8y^2$

45. $-3x^3yz + 4x^2y^2z - 19xy^2z^3 + 15$

Collect like terms.

46. $9xy^3 - 3x^2y - 2xy^3$ **47.** $3m^2 - m^2 + 3m + m$

48. $\frac{3}{5}x^2 + 4 - 2x - x^2$ **49.** $\frac{1}{2}x + \frac{2}{3}x^2 - x + 3$

50. $2 - \frac{1}{2}x^3 - 2x + \frac{2}{3}x^3$ **51.** $\frac{1}{2}x^4 - 2x^2 - \frac{4}{5}x^4 + \frac{4}{5}x$

MIXED PRACTICE 10 For use after Lesson 5-12

Collect like terms and then arrange in descending order for the variable x.

1. $5x^3 + 6x - 4x^2 - x + 4$
2. $xy - 7x^2 + 5xy + 21 - 3$
3. $3x - 3x^2 + 4x - x^2$
4. $5y^5 - x^2 + 4xy + 7x^2$
5. $-xy + 5x^2y^3 - 5 + 7xy - x^3 + 4xy + x^2y^3 - 2$

Add or subtract.

6. $(-3x^2 + 4x - 19) + (9x + 11 + 4x^2y - 5y)$
7. $(3m^2n + mn - 25) - (6m^2n - 5m + 9)$
8. $(4x^3 + 8x^2 - x + 4) - (3x^2 - 5x^3 + 1)$
9. $(2x^5y^2 - 4x^3 - 2x + 4) + (x^3 - 4x^5y^2 - 9x + 6)$

Simplify.

10. $(x^2 - x) + (x - 8) - (x + 5x^2) + (2x^2 - 9x + 1)$
11. $(5x^2 - 2x + 1) - (3x + 4) + (25 - 4x^2) - (9x + 7)$
12. $(4x^2y - 5x + 1) + (3y^2 - 4) - (7x + 4y^2 + 2x^2y)$
13. $(-4x^4 + 2xy) - (x^2 - 5xy + x^4) + (3x^4 + 2xy)$

Evaluate each polynomial for $x = -2$ and $y = 3$.

14. $4x^2 - 5xy$
15. $10 - 3x^2 - 5y$
16. $3x^2 + 10xy + 2y^2$
17. $x^3y^2 + 9x - 2y + 10$
18. $x^2y^3 + 15x - 20$
19. $2y^3 - 2y^2x + 4x^2 + 1$

Add or subtract using columns.

20. $(7y^5 + 4y^2 - 9) - (5y^3 - 7y^2 + 6y - 3)$
21. $(3x^5 - 9x^3y + 15 - 9x) + (14x^3y + 6x - y + 4 - 11x^5)$
22. $(4x^5y + 3x^3y^3 - 9xy + 4) - (2x^5y + 4x^4y^2 - 10xy - 3)$
23. $(-4mn^2 + 3m^4 + 6n - m^3) + (15n + 7m^3 - m^2 + 6mn^2 - 4)$

Multiply.

24. $(0.5x^3)(4x^5)$
25. $4x^2(x^3 - 5x + 16)$
26. $(5a^3 - 7)(-2a^2 + a)$
27. $(4x + 3)(3x - 4)$
28. $(4m + 0.5)(4m - 0.5)$
29. $(7 - 5x)^2$
30. $(3y + 2)^2$
31. $(2x^3 - 11)(2x^3 + 11)$
32. $(x^2 - 5)(x^3 - 2x^2 - 2)$
33. $(-2x^3 + 5x + 1)(x + 1)$
34. Find the area of a rectangle with length $= (a + 5)$ and width $= (a - 7)$.
35. Find the area of a square with each side $= (x + y)$.
36. Find three consecutive numbers, the sum of whose squares is 29 more than three times the square of the smallest.

Answers

1. $5x^3 - 4x^2 + 5x + 4$
2. $-7x^2 + 6xy + 18$
3. $-4x^2 + 7x$
4. $6x^2 + 4xy + 5y^5$
5. $-x^3 + 6x^2y^3 + 10xy - 7$
6. $x^2y + 13x - 5y - 8$
7. $-3m^2n + 5m + mn - 34$
8. $9x^3 + 5x^2 - x + 3$
9. $-2x^5y^2 - 3x^3 - 11x + 10$
10. $-2x^2 - 10x - 7$
11. $x^2 - 14x + 15$
12. $2x^2y - 12x - y^2 - 3$
13. $-2x^4 - x^2 + 9xy$
14. 46
15. -17
16. -30
17. -86
18. 58
19. 107
20. $7y^5 - 5y^3 + 11y^2 - 6y - 6$
21. $-8x^5 + 5x^3y - 3x - y + 19$
22. $2x^5y - 4x^4y^2 + 3x^3y^3 + xy + 7$
23. $3m^4 + 6m^3 - m^2 + 2mn^2 + 21n - 4$
24. $2x^8$
25. $4x^5 - 20x^3 + 64x^2$
26. $-10a^5 + 5a^4 + 14a^2 - 7a$
27. $12x^2 - 7x - 12$
28. $16m^2 - 0.25$
29. $25x^2 - 70x + 49$
30. $9y^2 + 12y + 4$
31. $4x^6 - 121$
32. $x^5 - 2x^4 - 5x^3 + 8x^2 + 10$
33. $-2x^4 - 2x^3 + 5x^2 + 6x + 1$
34. $a^2 - 2a - 35$
35. $x^2 + 2xy + y^2$
36. 4, 5, 6

Item Analysis

Item	Lesson
1–5	5-6
6	5-7
7, 8	5-8
9	5-7
10–13	5-8
14–19	5-6
20	5-8
21	5-7
22	5-8
23	5-7
24–27	5-9
28–31	5-10
32, 33	5-11
34, 35	5-9
36	5-10

Answers

1. $(m^2 + 5)(m^2 - 5)$
2. $(9t + 10s^2)(9t - 10s^2)$
3. $(2y + 3)(2y - 3)$
4. $(7 - w^3)(7 + w^3)$
5. $x^2(x^2 - 5x + 1)$
6. $(x - 5)(x + 2)$
7. $(t + 3)(t + 1)$
8. $(c - 7)(c - 1)$
9. no 10. yes 11. no
12. no 13. yes 14. no
15. $(c - 2)(c + 2)$
16. $(9m - 5)(9m + 5)$
17. $(y^5 - z^5)(y^5 + z^5)$
18. $(7 - n^4)(7 + n^4)$
19. $2a^2b(a^2 + ab - b)$
20. $5x(x^3y + xy - 2)$
21. $2(x + 1)(x - 5)$
22. $(2x + 1)(x - 5)$
23. $(x - 1)(2x + 5)$
24. $(x + 1)(2x - 5)$
25. no 26. yes 27. yes
28. yes 29. no 30. no
31. yes 32. no 33. no
34. no
35. $(m^2 - 3)(m^2 + 3)$
36. $(2y - 1)(2y + 1)$
37. $3(2x + 3)(x - 1)$
38. $(5x + 3)(2x - 1)$
39. $(x - 9)(x + 5)$
40. $(t - 4)(t - 3)$
41. $(3 - x)(x + 4)$
42. $(2y + 1)(y - 5)$
43–46. answers will vary
47. $x(x + 1)(x - 1)(x^2 - 3)$
48. $(x - 2)(3 - 2x)$
49. $4y(y^2 - 3y + 1)$
50. $2(3a^2 - a + 5)$
51. $(x + 5)(x - y)$
52. $(2t + 1)(3t + 1)$
53. $(x - 4)(2x - 1)$
54. $(3x - 2)(x + 4)$

Item Analysis

Item	Lesson
1–4	6-2
5	6-1
6–8	6-4
9–14	6-3
15–18	6-2
19–21	6-1
22–24	6-5
25–34	6-2
35, 36	6-2
37, 38	6-5
39, 40	6-4
41, 42	6-5
43–46	6-1
47, 48	6-5
49, 50	6-1
51–54	6-4

MIXED PRACTICE 11 For use after Lesson 6-5

Factor.

1. $m^4 - 25$
2. $81t^2 - 100s^4$
3. $-9 + 4y^2$
4. $49 - w^6$
5. $x^4 - 5x^3 + x^2$
6. $x^2 - 3x - 10$
7. $t^2 + 4t + 3$
8. $c^2 - 8c + 7$

State whether each expression is a difference of two squares.

9. $4y^2 - x$
10. $9x^2 - 25$
11. $m^2 + n^2$
12. $4a^3 - b^2$
13. $36 - 49t^2$
14. $12m^2 - 4n^2$

Factor.

15. $c^2 - 4$
16. $81m^2 - 25$
17. $y^{10} - z^{10}$
18. $49 - n^8$
19. $2a^4b + 2a^3b^2 - 2a^2b^2$
20. $5x^4y + 5x^2y - 10x$
21. $2x^2 - 8x - 10$
22. $2x^2 - 9x - 5$
23. $2x^2 + 3x - 5$
24. $2x^2 - 3x - 5$

State whether each expression is a trinomial square.

25. $x^2 - 2xy - y^2$
26. $4x^2 + 4xy + y^2$
27. $x^2 - 10xy + 25y^2$
28. $9x^2 - 18xy + 9y^2$
29. $2v^2 + 4vw + 4w^2$
30. $24x^2 + 20xy + 4y^2$
31. $x^2 + 2x + 1$
32. $y^2 - 6y - 9$
33. $c^4 + 4c + 4$
34. $7m^2 + 14m + 49$

Factor.

35. $m^4 - 9$
36. $4y^2 - 1$
37. $6x^2 + 3x - 9$
38. $10x^2 + x - 3$
39. $x^2 - 4x - 45$
40. $t^2 - 7t + 12$
41. $12 - x - x^2$
42. $2y^2 - 9y - 5$

Find three factorizations for each monomial.

43. $4x^2y$
44. $-9m^3n$
45. $15t^23$
46. $-12pq^2$

Factor.

47. $x^5 - 4x^3 + 3x$
48. $7x - 6 - 2x^2$
49. $4y^3 - 12y^2 + 4y$
50. $6a^2 - 2a + 10$
51. $x^2 + 5x - xy - 5y$
52. $6t^2 + 5t + 1$
53. $2x^2 - 9x + 4$
54. $3x^2 + 10x - 8$

MIXED PRACTICE 12

Factor.

1. $2y^2 - 9y - 5$
2. $2t^2 + 25t + 12$
3. $4m^2 - 1$
4. $3y^2 + y - 10$
5. $x^2 + 4x - 21$
6. $y^2 - 12y + 36$
7. $10 + 3x - x^2$
8. $t^2 + 8t + 16$
9. $3x^3 + 3x^2 - 15x$
10. $x^3 + 3x^2 - x$

Solve.

11. $t^2 - 25 = 0$
12. $x^2 - x = 20$
13. $x^2 + 49 = 14x$
14. $3x^2 + x = 0$
15. $(2y - 1)(y - 5) = 0$
16. $t(t + 7) = 4(3 + 2t)$
17. $t^2 + 3t - 4 = 36$
18. $3y^2 + 17y + 10 = 0$
19. $t^2 - \frac{25}{4} = 0$
20. $\frac{3x^2}{4} = 27$

Factor by grouping.

21. $x^3 + 3x^2 - x - 3$
22. $2x^4 + 5x^3 + 2x + 5$
23. $6y^3 - 10y^2 + 9y - 15$
24. $x^3 + 2x^2 - 7x - 14$

Translate to an equation and solve.

25. Find two consecutive even integers whose product is 288.
26. Twelve more than the square of a number is seven times the number. Find the number.
27. The width of a rectangle is 7 ft less than the length. The area of the rectangle is 228 ft^2. Find the length and width.
28. If the sides of a square are lengthened by 4 in., the area becomes 256 in^2. Find the length of a side of the original square.
29. Find two consecutive integers whose product is 182.
30. The sum of squares of two consecutive odd positive integers is 202. Find the integers.
31. The height of a triangle is 6 m more than the base. The area is 216 m^2. Find the base and height.
32. If a number is subtracted from its square, the result is 2. Find the number.
33. Four times the square of a number is 9. Find the number.

Answers

1. $(2y + 1)(y - 5)$
2. $(t + 12)(2t + 1)$
3. $(2m + 1)(2m - 1)$
4. $(3y - 5)(y + 2)$
5. $(x + 7)(x - 3)$
6. $(y - 6)^2$
7. $(x + 2)(5 - x)$
8. $(t + 4)^2$
9. $3x(x^2 + x - 5)$
10. $x(x^2 + 3x - 1)$
11. $5, -5$
12. $5, -4$
13. 7
14. $0, -\frac{1}{3}$
15. $\frac{1}{2}, 5$
16. $4, -3$
17. $5, -8$
18. $-\frac{2}{3}, -5$
19. $\frac{5}{2}, -\frac{5}{2}$
20. $6, -6$
21. $(x + 1)(x - 1)(x + 3)$
22. $(x + 1)(x^2 - x + 1)(2x + 5)$
23. $(2y^2 + 3)(3y - 5)$
24. $(x^2 - 7)(x + 2)$
25. 16, 18 or −16, −18
26. 3, 4
27. 19 ft, 12 ft
28. 12 in.
29. 13, 14 or −13, −14
30. 9, 11
31. 18, 24
32. 2, −1
33. $\frac{3}{2}, -\frac{3}{2}$

Item Analysis

Item	Lesson
1, 2	6-5
3–10	6-7
11–20	6-8
21–24	6-6
25–33	6-9

Answers

1. (3, 4)
2. (−4, 4)
3. (4, −3)
4. (−3, −1)
5. (2, 1)
6. (3, −2)
7. *a*
8. *e*
9. *b*
10. *c*
11. *d*
12. $-\frac{2}{3}$
13. $\frac{5}{8}$
14. $\frac{1}{2}$
15. 1
16. no
17. yes
18. yes
19. yes
20. answers may vary
21. answers may vary
22. answers may vary
23. 2
24. 3
25. −6
26. $mAB = -4$, $mBC = -\frac{1}{5}$, $mCA = \frac{3}{4}$
27. $x = -3$
28. $y = -2.5$
29. Quadrant IV
30. Quadrant III
31. not in a quadrant
32. Quadrant I

Item Analysis

Item	Lesson
1–6	7-1
7–11	7-3
12–15	7-4
16–19	7-2
20–22	7-1
23–26	7-4
27, 28	7-3
29–32	7-1

MIXED PRACTICE 13 For use after Lesson 7-4

Find the coordinates of each point.

1. Q **2.** R **3.** S

4. T **5.** U **6.** V

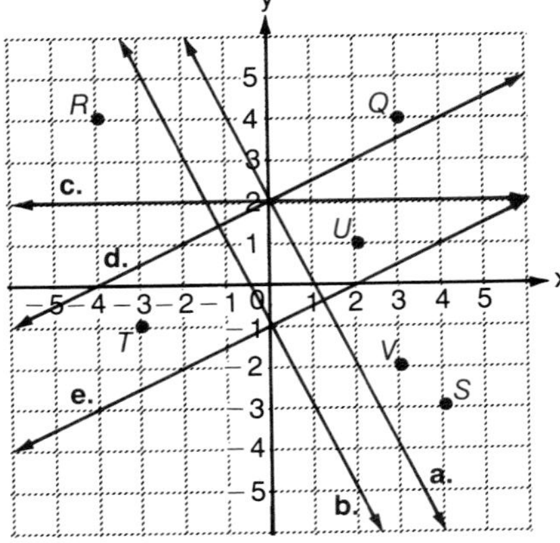

Match each equation with its corresponding graph at the right.

7. $y = -2x + 2$

8. $y = \frac{1}{2}x - 1$

9. $y = -2x - 1$

10. $y = 2$

11. $y = \frac{1}{2}x + 2$

Find the slopes of the lines containing these points.

12. (3, 7) (6, 5)

13. (10, 9) (2, 4)

14. (2, −2) (10, 2)

15. (4, 13) (7, 16)

Determine whether the given point is a solution of the equation.

16. (4, 1), $y = \frac{1}{2}x - 3$

17. $\left(-\frac{1}{2}, \frac{9}{8}\right)$, $y = -\frac{1}{4}x + 1$

18. (0, 2), $5y = 2x + 10$

19. (4, −4), $2y + 3x = 4$

Find three points that satisfy the following conditions.

20. The x-coordinate is half of the y-coordinate.

21. The x-coordinate is 3 less than the y-coordinate.

22. The x-coordinate is five less than twice the y-coordinate.

Solve.

23. A line contains (−3, 10) and (x, −5). It has slope −3. Find x.

24. A line contains (−2, −17) and (x, 8). It has slope 5. Find x.

25. A line contains (2, 7) and (x, −9). It has slope 2. Find x.

26. The vertices of a triangle are $A(3, 2)$, $B(4, -2)$ and $C(-1, -1)$. Find the slope of each side of the triangle.

27. Write an equation of a line that is parallel to the y-axis and 3 units to the left of it.

28. Write an equation of a line that is parallel to the x-axis and intersects the y-axis at (0, −2.5).

In which quadrant is each point located?

29. (27, −4) **30.** (−6, −53) **31.** (0, 4) **32.** (2, 17)

MIXED PRACTICE 14 For use after Lesson 7-9

Write an equation for each line that contains the given pair of points.

1. $(1, 5)$ $(-4, -5)$

2. $(-3, 1)$ $(0, -1)$

3. $(2, 6)$ $(-4, -24)$

4. $(0, 5)$ $(3, -13)$

Graph each line using the slope and y-intercept.

5. $4y + 8x = -12$

6. $2y - 10 = 6x$

7. $5y + 20x = 5$

8. $x - y = 2$

Write an equation for each line.

9. the line containing $(-3, 1)$ and parallel to the line $y + 2x = 3$

10. the line containing $(2, 6)$ and perpendicular to the line $4y = x - 4$

11. the line containing $(3, 5)$ and parallel to the line $3y = 15x - 7$

12. the line containing $(2, -4)$ and perpendicular to the line $y = -3x + 5$

13. the line that has the same slope as the line described by $5y + 15 = 2x$ and contains the point $(-5, -1)$

14. the line that has the same slope as the line described by $2y + 4x = 6$ and contains the point $(-6, 5)$

15. the line that is perpendicular to the y-axis and intersects the y-axis at $(0, 3)$

Graph using intercepts.

16. $2x + 2y = 6$

17. $2y + 1 = x$

18. $3y + 6 = 15x$

19. $3y - 2x = 12$

Find the slope of each line by solving for y.

20. $8y + 3x = 16$

21. $-9x = -1 - y$

22. $2y + 4 = x - 2$

23. $2y + 8x = 14$

Write an equation for each line given the slope and y-intercept. Express the equation in slope-intercept form.

24. $m = -\frac{1}{3}, b = 2$

25. $m = \frac{4}{3}, b = \frac{1}{8}$

26. $m = 2, b = 0$

27. $m = 0, b = -1$

Solve. Assume a linear relationship fits the data.

28. A catering company advertised the following rates: "Complete Texas-style barbeque lunch just $277.50 ($d$) for 50 people ($p$), or $526.00 for 120 people." Use the ordered pairs (p, d).

a. Find a linear equation for the data points.

b. Use this linear equation to find the cost of lunch for 65 people.

Answers

1. $y = 2x + 3$

2. $y = -\frac{2}{3}x - 1$

3. $y = 5x - 4$

4. $y = -6x + 5$

5–8. For graphs, see Teacher's Answer Section.

5. $y = -2x - 3$

6. $y = 3x + 5$

7. $y = -4x + 1$

8. $y = x - 2$

9. $y = -2x - 5$

10. $y = -4x - 14$

11. $y = 5x - 10$

12. $y = \frac{1}{3}x - \frac{14}{3}$

13. $y = \frac{2}{5}x + 1$

14. $y = -2x - 7$

15. $y = 3$

16–19. See Teacher's Answer Section.

20. $-\frac{3}{8}$

21. 9

22. $\frac{1}{2}$

23. -4

24. $y = -\frac{1}{3}x + 2$

25. $y = \frac{4}{3}x + \frac{1}{8}$

26. $y = 2x$

27. $y = -1$

28. $d = 3.55p + \$100, \$330.75$

Item Analysis

Item	Lesson
1–4	7-6
5–8	7-5
9–12	7-8
13, 14	7-6
15	7-3
16–19	7-3
20–23	7-5
24–27	7-5
28	7-7

Answers

1. no
2. yes
3. yes
4. yes
5. yes
6. no
7. (7, 5)
8. (−4, −2)
9. (−5, 8)
10. (−3, 2)
11. (5, 1)
12. (−2, 7)
13. (−4, −1)
14. (3, −5)

15–18. See Teacher's Answer

19. 18 m, 12.5 m
20. 73, 28
21. 66, 30
22. 10, 16

Item Analysis

Item	Lesson
1–4	8-1
5, 6	8-2
7–10	8-3
11–14	8-2
15–18	8-1
19	8-3
20	8-2
21, 22	8-3

MIXED PRACTICE 15 For use after Lesson 8-3

Determine whether the given ordered pair is a solution of the system of equations.

1. (4, 5); $2y - x = 6$, $y + x = 7$

2. (−8, −8); $8y + 40 = 3x$, $y - x = 0$

3. (4, 3); $4y + 8 = 5x$, $2x - y = 5$

4. (2, −7); $3x + y = -1$, $y + 5 = -x$

5. (−2, 3); $2x - y = -7$, $-y + x = -5$, $y = 3$

6. (7, −2); $x + 2y = 3$, $-y + 9 = x$, $-x - y = -5$

Solve using the addition method.

7. $3x - 4y = 1$, $-x + 2y = 3$

8. $3x - 5y = -2$, $5y - 2x = -2$

9. $3x + 2y = 1$, $5x + 3y = -1$

10. $4x + 9y = 6$, $5y + 3x = 1$

Solve using the substitution method.

11. $3y = x - 2$, $y - x = -4$

12. $2y + 5x = 4$, $x + y = 5$

13. $5y - x = -1$, $3y - 2x = 5$

14. $5x + 2y = 5$, $2x - y = 11$

Solve these systems graphically.

15. $2y = -x + 4$, $x - y = 1$

16. $y - x = 5$, $x + y = -1$

17. $x + y = -4$, $3y = x - 4$

18. $y + 1 = -x$, $y = x - 7$

Translate to a system of equations and solve.

19. The perimeter of a rectangle is 61 m. The length of the rectangle is 7 less than twice the width. Find the length and width of the rectangle.

20. Find two numbers whose sum is 101 and whose difference is 45.

21. The difference between two numbers is 36. Five times the larger is 11 times the smaller. What are the numbers?

22. The sum of two numbers is 26. Two-fifths of the first number plus three-eighths of the second number is 10. Find the numbers.

MIXED PRACTICE 16 For use after Lesson 8-6

Solve.

1. $2x - 5y = 7$
   $2y - 3x = 6$
2. $2x - 3y = 4$
   $5y - 3x = -5$
3. $6x + 12y = 5$
   $6y - 10x = 9$
4. $x - 3y = 7$
   $3x + 2y = 10$
5. $x + 2y = 15$
   $5x - y = -2$
6. $4x + 7y = -3$
   $2y - 3x = 24$

Solve by graphing.

7. $3y + 2x = 6$
   $6y = 3x - 2$
8. $y = x + 5$
   $2y + x = -2$

Translate to a system of equations and solve.

9. A collection of nickels and dimes totals $22.40. There are 304 coins in all. How many nickels are there?
10. The sum of the digits of a two-digit number is 11. When the number is reversed, the new sum is 27 less than the original number. Find the original number.
11. A fishing boat broke down after travelling 2 hours against a 4 km/h current. The boat was carried back to its starting point by the current. The whole trip took 5.5 hours. Find the speed of the boat in still water before the motor failed.
12. Admission to the gymnastics meet was $2.40 for adults and $1.25 for students. If 540 tickets were sold for a total of $934.90, how many tickets of each kind were sold?
13. The sum of two numbers is 248. Their difference is 64. Find the numbers.
14. Two cars leave town at the same time travelling in opposite directions. One travels 51 mi/h and the other travels 45 mi/h. In how many hours will they be 432 miles apart?
15. A two-digit number is four times the sum of its digits. The ones digit is 4 more than the tens digit. Find the original number.
16. Two cars leave town at the same time going in the same direction on the same road. One travels 28 mi/h and the other travels 46 mi/h. In how many hours will they be 63 miles apart?

Answers

1. $(-4, -3)$
2. $(5, 2)$
3. $\left(-\frac{1}{2}, \frac{2}{3}\right)$
4. $(4, -1)$
5. $(1, 7)$
6. $(-6, 3)$

7–8. See Teacher's Answer Section.

9. 160
10. 74
11. 11 km/h
12. 226 adults, 314 students
13. 156, 92
14. 4.5 hr
15. 48
16. 3.5 hr

Item Analysis

Item	Lesson
1–3	8-3
4, 5	8-2
6	8-3
7, 8	8-1
9	8-6
10	8-6
11	8-5
12	8-6
13	8-3
14	8-5
15	8-6
16	8-5

MIXED PRACTICE 17

For use after Lesson 9-3

Solve.

1. $2x + 1 > 5$ or $x - 2 \leq -1$
2. $2x + 1 < 5$ and $x - 2 \geq -1$
3. $|3x - 7| = 11$
4. $-|x - 3| = -5$
5. $-5 \leq 2x + 3 < 21$
6. $-x + 1 > 3$ or $2x - 5 > 3$
7. $2|5x - 3| = 26$
8. $7 + |2x + 3| = 11$

Write the inequality shown by each group.

9. 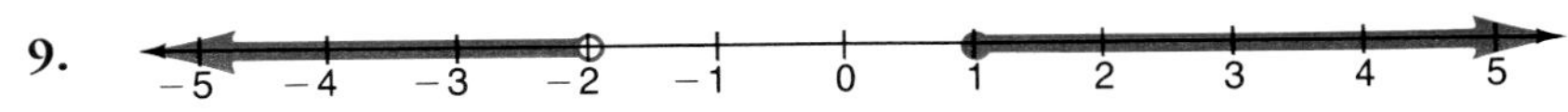

10. 

11. −5 −4 −3 −2 −1 0 1 2 3 4 5

12. 

Write using (**a**) roster notation and (**b**) set-builder notation.

13. the set W of positive multiples of 5 less than 38
14. the set P of prime numbers between 15 and 25
15. the set F of positive integers that are factors of 24
16. the set N of integers whose absolute values are less than 6

Write a compound sentence for each situation.

17. Water must be more than 0°C but less than 100°C to be in liquid form.
18. Special classes were created for students who scored less than 58 or more than 97 on the placement test.
19. Each crate of melons weighed at least 40 pounds and less than 45 pounds.

Let $A = \{2, 3, 5, 7\}$, $B = \{0, 3, 6, 9\}$, $C = \{1, 3, 5, 7, 9\}$, and $D = \{0, 1, 2, 3, 4, 5, 6\}$.

Find each of the following.

20. $A \cup B$
21. $C \cap D$
22. $A \cup C$
23. $B \cap C$
24. $A \cap D$
25. $B \cup C$
26. $A \cap C$
27. $B \cup D$

Solve and graph.

28. $-2 < x - 3 < 3$
29. $-2 > x + 3$ or $x + 6 \geq 7$
30. $-3x > 9$ or $2x - 5 > -3$
31. $-7 < 2x + 3 \leq 7$

Answers

1. $x > 2$ or $x \leq 1$
2. $1 \leq x < 2$
3. $6, -\frac{4}{3}$
4. $8, -2$
5. $-4 \leq x < 9$
6. $x < -2$ or $x > 4$
7. $\frac{16}{5}, -2$
8. $\frac{1}{2}, -\frac{7}{2}$
9. $x < -2$ or $x \geq 1$
10. $-1 \leq x < 2$
11. $-4 \leq x \leq 3$
12. $x \leq 1$ or $x > 3$
13. (a) $W = \{5, 10, 15, 20, 25, 30, 35\}$ (b) $W = \{x | x$ is a multiple of 5 and $0 < x < 38\}$
14. (a) $P = \{17, 19, 23\}$ (b) $P = \{x | x$ is prime and $15 < x < 25\}$
15. (a) $F = \{1, 2, 3, 4, 6, 8, 12, 24\}$ (b) $F = \{x | x$ is an integer factor of 24 and $0 < x\}$
16. (a) $N = \{-5, -4, -3, -2, -1, 0, 1, 2, 3, 4, 5\}$ (b) $N = \{x | x$ is an integer and $|x| < 6\}$
17. $0°C < w < 100°C$
18. $x < 58$ or $x > 97$
19. $40 \leq x < 45$
20. $\{0, 2, 3, 5, 6, 7, 9\}$
21. $\{1, 3, 5\}$
22. $\{1, 2, 3, 5, 7, 9\}$
23. $\{3, 9\}$
24. $\{2, 3, 5\}$
25. $\{0, 1, 3, 5, 6, 7, 9\}$
26. $\{3, 5, 7\}$
27. $\{0, 1, 2, 3, 4, 5, 6, 9\}$

28–31. For graphs, see Teacher's Answer Section.

28. $1 < x < 6$
29. $x < -5$ or $x \geq 1$
30. $x < -3$ or $x > 1$
31. $-5 < x \leq 2$

Item Analysis

Item	Lesson
1, 2	9-2
3, 4	9-3
5, 6	9-2
7, 8	9-3
9–12	9-2
13–16	9-1
17–19	9-2
20–27	9-1
28–31	9-2

MIXED PRACTICE 18 For use after Lesson 9-6

Graph on a number line.

1. $|y + 1| < 6$ **2.** $|3x| > 6$ **3.** $|x - 4| > 2$

Solve.

4. $|y + 4| = 6$ **5.** $|2x + 1| = -5$ **6.** $|2x + 1| > 3$

7. $4|3y| > 20$ **8.** $2|3x| < 20$ **9.** $|3y - 2| < 7$

10. $|3x + 2| < -3$ **11.** $2|-3x| = 24$ **12.** $|2x - 7| = 21$

13. $-2|x - 3| < -8$ **14.** $|2a + 5| < 1$ **15.** $|3x + 1.5| = 5.7$

Graph on a coordinate plane.

16. $-x < y$ **17.** $y < x - 1$ **18.** $2y < x + 4$

Determine whether the given point is a solution of the inequality.

19. $(1, 3)$; $2x - y > 5$ **20.** $(-2, 3)$; $2x + 3y \geq 5$

21. $(4, -1)$; $2x - 4y < 16$ **22.** $(-2, -7)$; $y + 5x \leq 2$

Solve by graphing.

23. $y < 2x$, $y < 4$ **24.** $y - x < 0$, $3y + 2x > 1$ **25.** $x + y > 1$, $x < 2$

Write an inequality for each graph.

26.

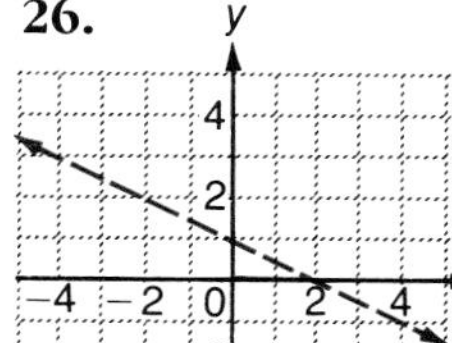

27.

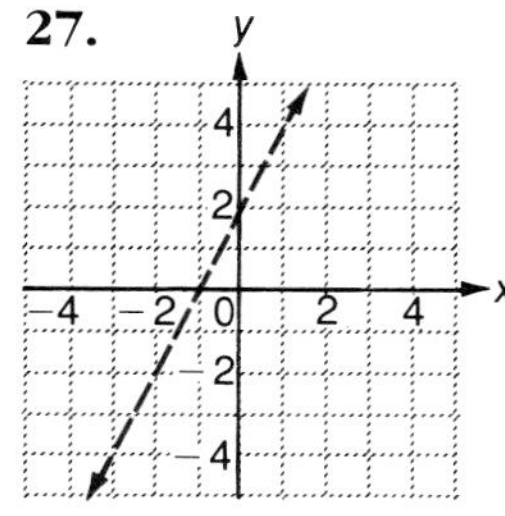

28.

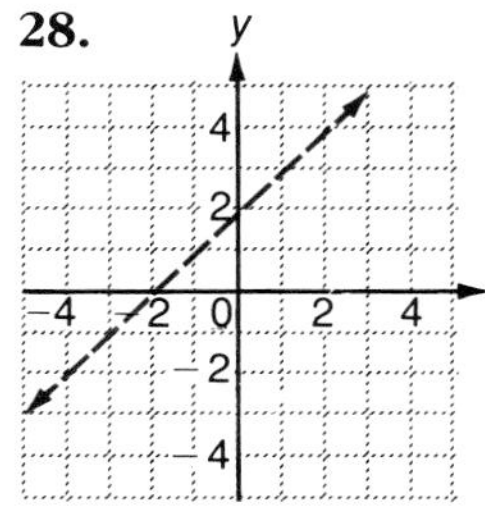

Write a system of inequalities whose solution is shown by each graph.

29.

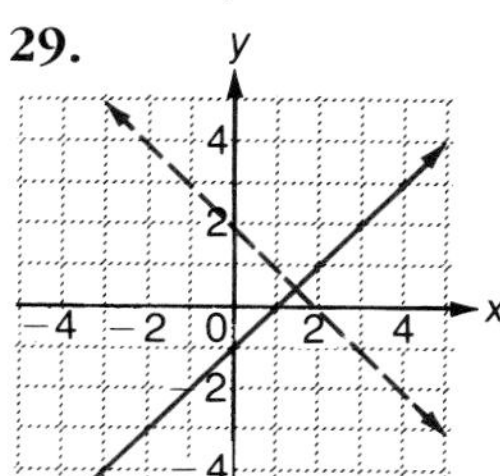

30.

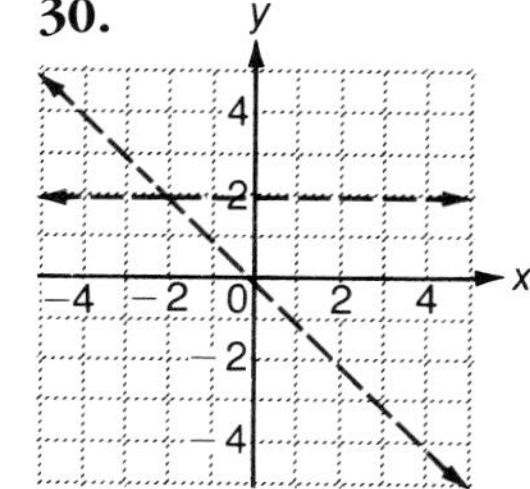

31.

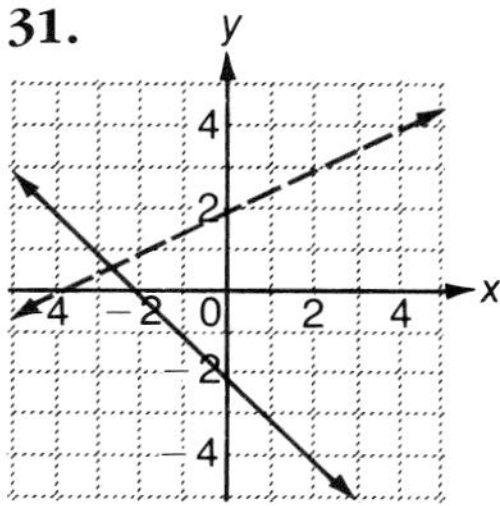

Answers

1–3. See Teacher's Answer Section.
4. $\{2, -10\}$
5. no solution
6. $\{x \mid x < -2 \text{ or } x > 1\}$
7. $\left\{y \mid y < -\frac{5}{3} \text{ or } y > \frac{5}{3}\right\}$
8. $\left\{x \mid -\frac{10}{3} < x < \frac{10}{3}\right\}$
9. $\left\{y \mid -\frac{5}{3} < y < 3\right\}$
10. no solution
11. $\{-4, 4\}$
12. $\{-7, 14\}$
13. $\{x \mid x > 7 \text{ or } x < -1\}$
14. $\{a \mid -3 < a < -2\}$
15. $\{-2.4, 1.4\}$
16–18. See Teacher's Answer Section.
19. no
20. yes
21. yes
22. yes
23–25. See Teacher's Answer Section.
26. $y > -\frac{1}{2}x + 1$
27. $y < 3x + 3$
28. $y > x + 2$
29. $y \geq x - 1$, $y > -x + 2$
30. $y < 2$, $y > -x$
31. $y < \frac{1}{2}x + 2$, $y \leq -x - 2$

Item Analysis

Item	Lesson
1–3	9-4
4, 5	9-3
6–10	9-4
11, 12	9-3
13, 14	9-4
15	9-3
16–18	9-5
19–22	9-5
23–25	9-6
26–28	9-5
29–31	9-6

Answers

1. $\frac{x+1}{x-2}$ 2. $5x - 3$
3. $\frac{1}{2}$ 4. $y - 1$
5. -1 6. $\frac{x-3}{x+1}$
7. 3 8. $\frac{3}{3x+2}$
9. $\frac{y+5}{y-3}$ 10. $\frac{2(y-2)}{y^2}$
11. $\frac{3a}{a-2}$ 12. $\frac{2m+3}{8m}$
13. 1 14. $\frac{x^2-2x-1}{x^2-1}$
15. $\frac{2x+5}{x^2}$ 16. $\frac{x^2-x+1}{x^2-1}$
17. $\frac{(x+2)(x+4)}{2x}$ 18. $\frac{2(a^2+1)}{a^2-1}$
19. $\frac{2}{(x-1)^2}$ 20. $\frac{x-1}{x-2}$
21. $\frac{m-2}{m+1}$ 22. $\frac{3x}{x+1}$
23. $\frac{n^3}{m-n}$ 24. $\frac{x+3}{x-4}$
25. $\frac{(x+2)(x+3)}{(x-2)(x-3)}$ 26. $\frac{x(x-1)}{x+4}$
27. $(x-3)^2$ 28. $\frac{a+3}{a-3}$
29. $\frac{(x-2)^2}{x+1}$ 30. $\frac{m+3}{5}$
31. $\frac{2}{x^2-4}$
32. $(2x+3)(2x-3)$
33. $(x-3)^2(x-2)$
34. $2(x+4)(x-4)$
35. $2(a+5)(a-5)$
36. $72a^3bc$
37. $(x-1)(x-2)(x+1)(x+3)$

Item Analysis

Item	Lesson
1–6	10-1
7–9	10-4
10–18	10-5
19–22	10-2
23, 24	10-3
25	10-2
26–30	10-3
31	10-2
32–37	10-5

MIXED PRACTICE 19

For use after Lesson 10-5

Simplify.

1. $\frac{x^2-2x-3}{x^2-5x+6}$
2. $\frac{25x^2-9}{5x+3}$
3. $\frac{5x^2-5}{10x^2-10}$
4. $\frac{2y^2+5y-7}{2y+7}$
5. $\frac{16-a}{a-16}$
6. $\frac{2x^2-6x}{2x^2+2x}$

Add or subtract and simplify.

7. $\frac{2x+9}{x+7} + \frac{x+12}{x+7}$
8. $\frac{7x+9}{3x+2} - \frac{7x+6}{3x+2}$
9. $\frac{3y+1}{y-3} - \frac{2y-4}{y-3}$
10. $\frac{3}{y} - \frac{y+4}{y^2}$
11. $\frac{3a}{a+2} + \frac{12a}{a^2-4}$
12. $\frac{3m+7}{4m} - \frac{4m+11}{8m}$
13. $\frac{2-x}{x^2-7x+10} + \frac{x-4}{x-5}$
14. $\frac{x}{x+1} - \frac{1}{x-1}$
15. $\frac{1}{x} + \frac{x+5}{x^2}$
16. $\frac{x^2}{x^2-1} - \frac{1}{x+1}$
17. $\frac{x+4}{2} + \frac{x+4}{x}$
18. $\frac{a+1}{a-1} + \frac{a-1}{a+1}$

Multiply or divide and simplify.

19. $\frac{3}{2(x-1)} \cdot \frac{4}{3(x-1)}$
20. $\frac{x^2-1}{x^2-4} \cdot \frac{x+2}{x+1}$
21. $\frac{m}{m+1} \cdot \frac{m^2-m-2}{m^2+m}$
22. $\frac{6x^2}{6x^2+9x+3} \cdot \frac{6x+3}{2x}$
23. $\frac{mn+n^2}{m} \div \frac{m^2-n^2}{mn^2}$
24. $\frac{x^2-x-12}{x+2} \div \frac{(x-4)^2}{x+2}$
25. $\frac{x^2-3x-10}{x^2+2x-15} \cdot \frac{x^2+8x+15}{x^2-7x+10}$
26. $\frac{x^2-4x}{x+1} \div \frac{x^2-16}{x^2-1}$
27. $\frac{x^2-9}{x+5} \div \frac{x+3}{x^2+2x-15}$
28. $\frac{a^2+6a+9}{a-3} \div \frac{a^2+4a+3}{a+1}$
29. $\frac{x^2-4}{x+1} \div \frac{x+2}{x-2}$
30. $\frac{m-1}{5} \div \frac{m^2-2m+1}{m^2+2m-3}$
31. $\frac{2}{x^2+4x+4} \cdot \frac{x+2}{x-2}$

Find the LCM.

32. $2x-3,\ 4x^2-9$
33. $x^2-5x+6,\ x^2-6x+9$
34. $x^2-16,\ 2x+8$
35. $10-2a,\ a^2-25$
36. $24a^3b,\ 18abc$
37. $x^2-1,\ x^2-3x+2,$
x^2+x-6

MIXED PRACTICE 20   For use after Lesson 10-10

Solve.

1. $\dfrac{x+2}{x-2} = x - 1$

2. $\dfrac{x+6}{x+2} = \dfrac{x}{x-1}$

3. $\dfrac{4x-5}{2x+1} + \dfrac{x+1}{x-1} = 3$

4. $2a - 1 = \dfrac{8a+3}{a+1}$

Write and solve an equation.

5. The Highway Department has purchased wildflower seed mixtures from two companies. Mixture A is 28% bluebonnets, and Mixture B is 48% bluebonnets. How much of each mix should be used to create 250 pounds of blended seed that is 35% bluebonnets?
6. The reciprocal of two more than a number is three-fourths of the reciprocal of the number itself. What is the number?
7. It takes Sylvia 8 hours to assemble a carton of widgets. Joe can do the same job in 12 hours. How long would it take them to assemble a carton of widgets if they worked together?
8. Marty drove his fully-loaded moving van 270 miles to Memphis. With his van empty, Marty drove 15 mi/h faster and made the return trip in 1.5 hours less. Find the speed going.
9. The reciprocal of 5 less than a number is 4 times the reciprocal of twice the number. Find the number.

Divide.

10. $\dfrac{3x^4 - 27x^3 + 3x^2}{3x^2}$

11. $\dfrac{16x^3 + 4x^2 - 4x - 1}{4x + 1}$

12. $x^2 + 4x - 24 \div x - 3$

13. $10a^2 + 7a - 12 \div (2a + 3)$

14. $2x^4 - x^2 - 15 \div x^2 - 3$

15. $y^4 - 4y^2 + 3 \div y - 1$

Simplify.

16. $\dfrac{\dfrac{x}{(3x-1)(x-y)}}{\dfrac{y}{x-y}}$

17. $\dfrac{\dfrac{x(y-3)}{y}}{\dfrac{y-3}{x}}$

18. $\dfrac{\dfrac{1}{m} + \dfrac{1}{n}}{\dfrac{1}{m} - \dfrac{1}{n}}$

19. $\dfrac{1 - \dfrac{1}{a^2}}{1 - \dfrac{1}{a}}$

20. $\dfrac{\dfrac{x^2}{x^2 - y^2}}{\dfrac{x}{x+y}}$

21. $\dfrac{\dfrac{x}{2} - \dfrac{y}{3}}{\dfrac{2}{x} - \dfrac{3}{y}}$

Answers

1. 0, 4
2. 2
3. 3
4. 4, $-\frac{1}{2}$
5. 162.5 lb A, 87.5 lb B
6. 6
7. 4.8 hours
8. 45 mi/h
9. 10
10. $x^2 - 9x + 1$
11. $4x^2 - 1$
12. $x + 7 - \frac{3}{x-3}$
13. $5a - 4$
14. $2x^2 + 5$
15. $y^3 + y^2 - 3y - 3$
16. $\frac{x}{y(3x-1)}$
17. $\frac{x^2}{y}$
18. $\frac{n+m}{n-m}$
19. $\frac{a+1}{a}$
20. $\frac{x}{x-y}$
21. $\frac{-xy}{6}$

Item Analysis

Item	Lesson
1–4	10-6
5	10-8
6	10-7
7	10-8
8, 9	10-7
10–15	10-9
16–21	10-10

Answers

1. 13
2. -7
3. 10
4. 14
5. mn
6. $5y^2$
7. $2x$
8. $x - 3$
9. $3y\sqrt{y}$
10. $(x - 2)^2\sqrt{x - 2}$
11. $14m\sqrt{m}$
12. $5x^2y\sqrt{3x}$
13. $\frac{y}{10}$
14. $\frac{3m^2}{5n^3}$
15. $\frac{6x}{7}$
16. $\frac{x - 4}{x - 1}$
17. $y \geq 0$
18. $x \geq \frac{1}{2}$
19. $x \geq 5$
20. any value
21. any value
22. $x \geq -5$
23. $20\sqrt{2}$
24. $2\sqrt{7}$
25. $5a\sqrt{b}$
26. $3\sqrt{3}$
27. $2x\sqrt{y}$
28. $4m$
29. $2b\sqrt{15c}$
30. $2 - 2\sqrt{2}$
31. $15a\sqrt{3a}$
32. $6xy\sqrt{6z}$
33. $10x^{15}\sqrt{x}$
34. $8y^7\sqrt{3}$
35. $16x^{157}\sqrt{2x}$
36. $10(x + 1)\sqrt{15(x + 1)}$
37. $5(x^4 - 1)$
38. $3w^{16}$
39. $3m^2n^2\sqrt{2n}$
40. $9a^2\sqrt{2a}$
41. $2(x - 5)$
42. $2(x + 1)\sqrt{2}$
43. $5(x + y)$
44. $\frac{3}{4}$
45. 2
46. $\frac{5\sqrt{3}}{3}$
47. $\frac{y^3\sqrt{x}}{x}$
48. $\frac{x\sqrt{7y}}{14}$
49. $\frac{y^3\sqrt{xy}}{x^2}$
50. $\frac{2\sqrt{7}}{7}$
51. $\frac{1}{16}$
52. $\frac{5\sqrt{21}}{21}$
53. $x\sqrt{6}$
54. $2m\sqrt{m}$
55. $\frac{3}{5}$
56. $\frac{1}{6}$
57. $5x$
58. $\frac{y^2\sqrt{3}}{3}$
59. $\frac{\sqrt{mn}}{n}$
60. $\frac{mn}{5}$
61. $\frac{\sqrt{(a^2 - b^2)}}{a + b}$

Item Analysis

Item	Lesson
1–4	11-1
5–8	11-2
9–12	11-3
13–16	11-2
17–22	11-2
23–34	11-4
35–43	11-3
44–52	11-5
53–61	11-5

MIXED PRACTICE 21 For use after Lesson 11-5

Simplify. Assume that all radicands are nonnegative.

1. $\sqrt{169}$ **2.** $-\sqrt{49}$ **3.** $\sqrt{6^2 + 8^2}$ **4.** $\sqrt{(6 + 8)^2}$

5. $\sqrt{m^2n^2}$ **6.** $\sqrt{25y^4}$ **7.** $\sqrt{(-2x)^2}$ **8.** $\sqrt{x^2 - 6x + 9}$

9. $\sqrt{9y^3}$ **10.** $\sqrt{(x - 2)^5}$ **11.** $2\sqrt{49m^3}$ **12.** $\sqrt{75x^5y^2}$

13. $\sqrt{\frac{y^2}{100}}$ **14.** $\sqrt{\frac{9m^4}{25n^6}}$ **15.** $\sqrt{\frac{36x^2}{49}}$ **16.** $\sqrt{\frac{x^2 - 8x + 16}{x^2 - 2x + 1}}$

Determine the values for the variable that will make each expression a real number.

17. $\sqrt{5y}$ **18.** $\sqrt{2x - 1}$ **19.** $\sqrt{2x - 10}$

20. $\sqrt{2x^2}$ **21.** $\sqrt{x^2 + 17}$ **22.** $\sqrt{x + 5}$

Multiply and simplify.

23. $\sqrt{25} \cdot \sqrt{32}$ **24.** $\sqrt{14} \cdot \sqrt{2}$ **25.** $\sqrt{5a} \cdot \sqrt{5ab}$

26. $\sqrt{3} \cdot \sqrt{3} \cdot \sqrt{3}$ **27.** $\sqrt{2x^2} \cdot \sqrt{2y}$ **28.** $\sqrt{8m} \cdot \sqrt{2m}$

29. $\sqrt{30b} \cdot \sqrt{2bc}$ **30.** $\sqrt{2}(\sqrt{2} - 2)$ **31.** $\sqrt{15} \cdot \sqrt{45a^3}$

32. $\sqrt{12xy} \cdot \sqrt{18xyz}$ **33.** $\sqrt{10^2} \cdot \sqrt{x^{31}}$ **34.** $\sqrt{8y^2} \cdot \sqrt{2y^3} \cdot \sqrt{12y^9}$

Simplify.

35. $\sqrt{512x^{315}}$ **36.** $\sqrt{1500(x + 1)^3}$ **37.** $\sqrt{25(x^4 - 1)^2}$

38. $\sqrt{9w^{32}}$ **39.** $\sqrt{18m^4n^5}$ **40.** $3a\sqrt{18a^3}$

41. $\sqrt{4x^2 - 40x + 100}$ **42.** $\sqrt{8x^2 + 16x + 8}$

43. $\sqrt{25x^2 + 50xy + 25y^2}$ **44.** $\sqrt{\frac{9}{16}}$

45. $\sqrt{\frac{100}{25}}$ **46.** $\sqrt{\frac{50}{6}}$ **47.** $\sqrt{\frac{y^7}{xy}}$ **48.** $\sqrt{\frac{x^2y}{28}}$

49. $\sqrt{\frac{y^7}{x^3}}$ **50.** $\sqrt{\frac{48}{84}}$ **51.** $\sqrt{\frac{1}{256}}$ **52.** $\sqrt{\frac{75}{63}}$

Divide and simplify.

53. $\frac{\sqrt{36x^3}}{\sqrt{6x}}$ **54.** $\frac{\sqrt{48m^5}}{\sqrt{12m^2}}$ **55.** $\frac{\sqrt{72}}{\sqrt{200}}$

56. $\frac{\sqrt{7}}{\sqrt{252}}$ **57.** $\frac{\sqrt{50x^3}}{\sqrt{2x}}$ **58.** $\frac{\sqrt{7y^5}}{\sqrt{21y}}$

59. $\frac{\sqrt{m^2n}}{\sqrt{n^2m}}$ **60.** $\frac{\sqrt{m^2n^2}}{\sqrt{25}}$ **61.** $\frac{\sqrt{a - b}}{\sqrt{a + b}}$

MIXED PRACTICE 22 For use after Lesson 11-9

Add or subtract.

1. $\sqrt{25x} - 3\sqrt{x}$
2. $\sqrt{54} - \sqrt{20}$
3. $\sqrt{18x + 9} + \sqrt{2x + 1}$
4. $3\sqrt{18} + 5\sqrt{12} - 3\sqrt{2}$
5. $2\sqrt{108} - 6\sqrt{3} + \sqrt{75}$
6. $2\sqrt{147} + \sqrt{12} - \sqrt{432}$
7. $\sqrt{18x^5y} + \sqrt{32xy^3} - \sqrt{128xy}$
8. $\sqrt{7x^4} - \sqrt{28x^2y^2} + \sqrt{7y^4}$
9. $\sqrt{\frac{3}{8}} + \sqrt{\frac{2}{3}} + \sqrt{\frac{8}{12}}$
10. $\sqrt{\frac{1}{12}} - \sqrt{\frac{1}{8}} + \sqrt{\frac{3}{4}}$

Rationalize the denominator.

11. $\frac{5\sqrt{7}}{7\sqrt{5}}$
12. $\frac{3\sqrt{8}}{2\sqrt{2}}$
13. $\frac{14}{\sqrt{7}}$
14. $\frac{24\sqrt{3}}{18\sqrt{2}}$
15. $\frac{10}{\sqrt{20}}$
16. $\frac{3\sqrt{21}}{5\sqrt{15}}$
17. $\frac{6\sqrt{27}}{4\sqrt{3}}$
18. $\frac{5\sqrt{338}}{8\sqrt{2}}$
19. $\frac{2\sqrt{\frac{3}{5}}}{3\sqrt{\frac{1}{20}}}$
20. $\frac{\sqrt{\frac{3}{5}}}{\sqrt{\frac{5}{8}}}$
21. $\frac{\sqrt{\frac{x}{y}}}{\sqrt{\frac{y}{x}}}$
22. $\frac{\frac{3\sqrt{15}}{2}}{\frac{2\sqrt{5}}{3}}$

Find the length of the side not given for a right triangle with hypotenuse c and legs a and b.

23. $a = 12, c = 20$
24. $a = 8, b = 15$
25. $c = 13, b = 12$
26. $b = 4, c = 5$
27. $a = 6, c = 10$
28. $a = 16, b = 30$

Simplify.

29. $7mn\sqrt{32m^3n^2}$
30. $-5\sqrt{24}$
31. $2x^2\sqrt{75xy}$
32. $\sqrt{27x} \cdot \sqrt{8x}$
33. $\sqrt{10}\sqrt{3a}\sqrt{5a^3}$
34. $\sqrt{x^{35}}\sqrt{10^{15}}\sqrt{10^4x^{21}}$
35. $\frac{\sqrt{18x^3}}{\sqrt{24x}}$
36. $\frac{\sqrt{27x^3y}}{\sqrt{48x}}$
37. $\frac{\sqrt{65xy}}{\sqrt{5xy}}$

Solve.

38. $3\sqrt{2x - 1} = 9$
39. $2\sqrt{3y - 2} = \sqrt{10y + 4}$
40. $\sqrt{2x + 20} = \sqrt{x + 8}$
41. $5\sqrt{3x + 7} = 2\sqrt{32x + 4}$
42. How long must a wire be to reach from the top of a 30 ft flag pole to a point on the ground 16 ft from the foot of the pole?
43. Find a number such that twice its square root is one fifth of the number itself.
44. Find a number such that nine times the inverse of its square root is -72.

Answers

1. $2\sqrt{x}$
2. $3\sqrt{6} - 2\sqrt{5}$
3. $4\sqrt{2x + 1}$
4. $6\sqrt{2} + 10\sqrt{3}$
5. $11\sqrt{3}$
6. $4\sqrt{3}$
7. $(3x^3 + 4y - 8)\sqrt{2xy}$
8. $(x - y)^2\sqrt{7}$
9. $\frac{11}{12}\sqrt{6}$
10. $\frac{8\sqrt{3} - 3\sqrt{2}}{12}$
11. $\frac{\sqrt{35}}{7}$
12. 3
13. $2\sqrt{7}$
14. $\frac{2\sqrt{6}}{3}$
15. $\sqrt{5}$
16. $\frac{3\sqrt{35}}{25}$
17. $\frac{9}{2}$
18. $\frac{65}{8}$
19. $\frac{4\sqrt{3}}{3}$
20. $\frac{2\sqrt{6}}{5}$
21. $\frac{x}{y}$
22. $\frac{9\sqrt{3}}{4}$
23. 16
24. 17
25. 5
26. 3
27. 8
28. 34
29. $28m^2n^2\sqrt{2m}$
30. $-10\sqrt{6}$
31. $10x^2\sqrt{3xy}$
32. $6x\sqrt{6}$
33. $5a^2\sqrt{6}$
34. $10^9x^{28}\sqrt{10}$
35. $\frac{x\sqrt{3}}{2}$
36. $\frac{3x\sqrt{y}}{4}$
37. $\sqrt{13}$
38. 5
39. 6
40. no value
41. 3
42. 34 ft
43. 100
44. 64

Item Analysis

Item	Lesson
1–10	11-6
11–22	11-5
23–28	11-7
29–31	11-3
32–34	11-4
35–37	11-5
38–41	11-9
42	11-8
43, 44	11-9

Answers

1. yes
2. no
3. yes
4. 16, 8, 0, −4, −8
5. −11, −2, −5, 4, 7
6. 21, 5, −3, −3, −4
7. −64, 125, 1, −1, 8
8. 6, 0, 4, 0, 0

9–12. See Teacher's Answer

13. $y = \$0.85x + \$3.00$, \$14.90
14. $\$1035 = 12(\$80) + r$, \$75; $y = \$80x + \$75$, \$1195
15. $C = \$40(c) + \$5.50(l)$; \$208; $\$40(2) + \$5.50(l) < \$125$, 8 letters

16–18. For graphs, see Teacher's Answer Section.

16. $\left(-\frac{1}{2}, -\frac{1}{4}\right)$, $x = -\frac{1}{2}$
17. $\left(\frac{3}{2}, -\frac{1}{4}\right)$, $x = \frac{3}{2}$
18. $(0, 4)$, $x = 0$

Item Analysis

Item	Lesson
1–3	12-2
4–8	12-1
9–12	12-2
13–15	12-3
16–18	12-4

MIXED PRACTICE 23 For use after Lesson 12-4

Which of the following are graphs of functions?

1.

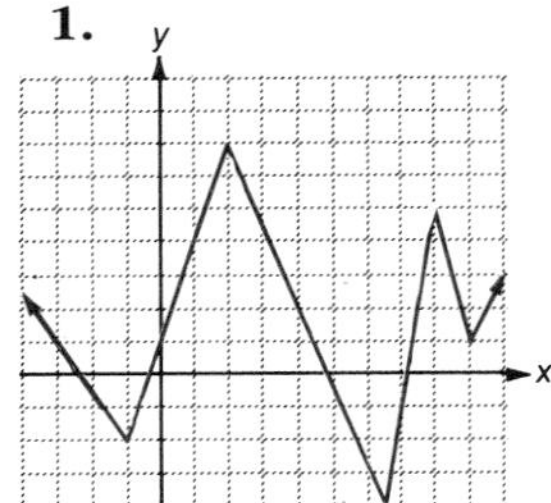

2.

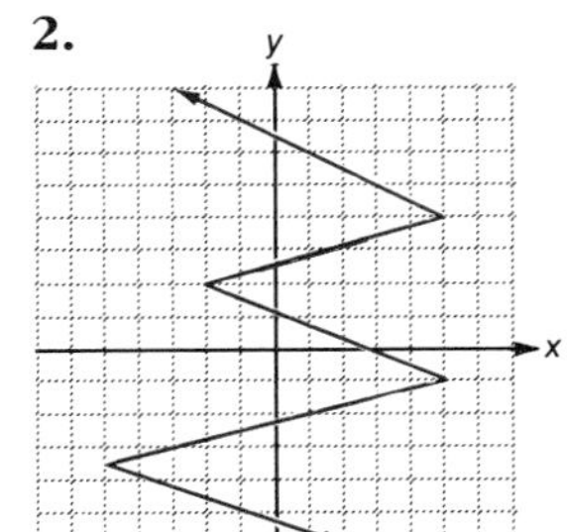

3.

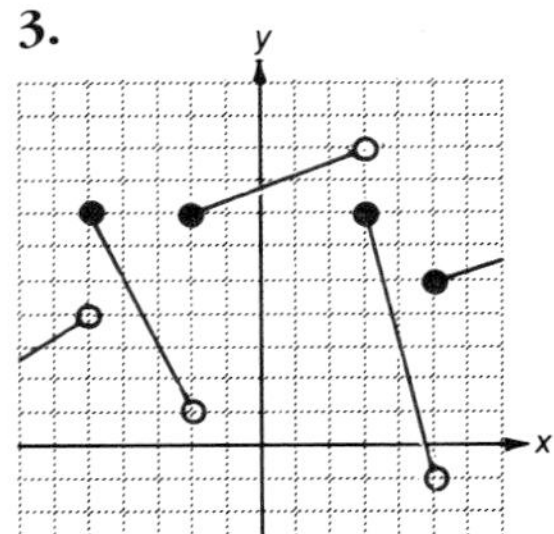

Find the indicated outputs for these functions.

4. $M(s) = |s| - 3s$; find $M(-4)$, $M(-2)$, $M(0)$, $M(2)$, $M(4)$
5. $W(x) = 3x - 2$; find $W(-3)$, $W(0)$, $W(-1)$, $W(2)$, $W(3)$
6. $h(x) = x^2 - 4$; find $h(-5)$, $h(3)$, $h(1)$, $h(-1)$, $h(0)$
7. $f(t) = t^3$; find $f(-4)$, $f(5)$, $f(1)$, $f(-1)$, $f(2)$
8. $g(a) = |a| - a$; find $g(-3)$, $g(10)$, $g(-2)$, $g(0)$, $g(4)$

Graph each function.

9. $f(x) = -x + 4$ where the domain is $\{-3, -1, 0, 2, 5\}$
10. $h(x) = |x| - 1$ where the domain is all real numbers
11. $f(x) = 2x - 5$ where the domain is all real numbers
12. $g(x) = 2x - 1$ where the domain is $\{-3, -1, 0, 2, 3\}$

Write a linear function describing each situation. Use the function to solve the problem.

13. A fabric store sells flannel for \$0.85 a yard plus a \$3.00 cutting fee. Find the cost of 14 yards of flannel.
14. Each semester, Maria's college charges \$80 per class unit plus a registration fee. Last semester Maria paid \$1035 for 12 class units. Find the registration fee. Next semester, Maria will be taking 14 class units. How much will she have to pay?
15. Thi Tran makes advertising banners. He charges \$40 per color plus \$5.50 per letter. Find the cost of a three-color banner with 16 letters. How many letters can you have on a two-color banner and keep the cost under \$125?

Graph each function. Find the vertex and axis of symmetry.

16. $y = x^2 + x$ 17. $y = x^2 - 3x + 2$ 18. $y = -x^2 + 4$

MIXED PRACTICE 24 For use after Lesson 12-7

Find an equation of variation where y varies directly as x, and the following are true.

1. $y = 150$ when $x = 0.75$ **2.** $y = 128$ when $x = 16$

3. $y = 12$ when $x = 30$ **4.** $y = 0.36$ when $x = 45$

Find an equation of variation where y varies inversely as x. One pair of values is given.

5. $y = 26$ when $x = 18$ **6.** $y = 0.2$ when $x = 15$

7. $y = 1$ when $x = 100$ **8.** $y = 32$ when $x = 150$

Find an equation of joint or combined variation for each. Then solve for the missing value.

9. x varies jointly as y and z. One set of values is $x = 67.5$, $y = 6$, $z = 9$. Find x when $y = 4$ and $z = 10$.

10. w varies directly as y and inversely as z. One set of values is $w = 12$, $y = 8$ and $z = 5$. Find x when $y = 9$ and $z = 15$.

11. a varies jointly as b, c, and d. One set of values is $a = 24$, $b = 3$, $c = 2$, and $d = 8$. Find a when $b = 10$, $c = 1$, and $d = 5$.

12. r varies directly as s and inversely as t. One set of values is $r = 2.7$, $s = 18$ and $t = 16$. Find r when $s = 10$ and $t = 4$.

Determine whether the following vary directly or inversely.

13. the amount of interest earned and the balance in a standard savings account

14. the amount of time required to do a job and the number of people working on the job

15. the size of a room and the amount of paint required to cover its walls

16. the distance a string is stretched by a hanging object and the weight of the object

17. the number of people that share a pizza and the size of each share

Solve.

18. The amount Tyler earns varies directly with the number of hours he works. He earns $101.25 in 15 hours. How much does he earn in 40 hours?

19. The time required to set up the chairs for a school assembly varies inversely as the number of people working. It takes 5 hours for 3 people to do the job. How long will it take 20 people to set up the chairs?

Answers

1. $y = 200x$
2. $y = 8x$
3. $y = 0.4x$
4. $y = 0.008x$
5. $y = \frac{468}{x}$
6. $y = \frac{3}{x}$
7. $y = \frac{100}{x}$
8. $y = \frac{4800}{x}$
9. $x = 1.25yz$; 50
10. $w = \frac{7.5y}{z}$; 4.5
11. $a = 0.5bcd$; 25
12. $r = \frac{2.4s}{t}$; 6
13. directly
14. inversely
15. directly
16. directly
17. inversely
18. $270
19. $\frac{3}{4}$ hr

Item Analysis

Item	Lesson
1–4	12-5
5–8	12-6
9–12	12-7
13	12-5
14	12-6
15, 16	12-5
17	12-6
18	12-5
19	12-6

Answers

1. $a^2 + 18a + 81$
2. $x^2 - 7x + \frac{49}{4}$
3. $x^2 - 20x + 100$
4. $y^2 + 100y + 2500$
5. $x^2 - 12x + 36$
6. $m^2 - 6m + 9$
7. $3x^2 - 15 = 0$; 3, 0, −15
8. $x^2 - 6x + 4 = 0$; 1, −6, 4
9. $5y^2 + 3y - 91 = 0$; 5, 3, −91
10. $t^2 - 8t + 9 = 0$; 1, −8, 9
11. $x^2 - 11x + 9 = 0$; 1, −11, 9
12. $x^2 - 10x + 35 = 0$; 1, −10, 35
13. 16; 2 real number solutions
14. 0; 1 real number solution
15. −16; no real number solutions
16. 121; 2 real number solutions
17. 0, 3
18. 0, 5
19. −1, 0
20. −2, 2
21. $-\frac{8}{3}, \frac{8}{3}$
22. −9, 9
23. 16, −6
24. $-3 \pm \sqrt{7}$
25. −9, 1
26. 5, −3
27. $\frac{4}{3}$
28. −8, 5
29. 10, −8
30. −9, 3
31. $\frac{7}{2}, -4$
32. 8, −2
33. $2 \pm \sqrt{7}$
34. −15, 12
35. 2, 4
36. 3, 4
37. 16, −1
38. 4, 1
39. $\frac{3}{2}, -\frac{2}{3}$
40. $\frac{\pm\sqrt{30}}{2}$
41. $3, -\frac{5}{2}$
42. 3, −8
43. 11, −7
44. $\frac{1 \pm \sqrt{97}}{4}$
45. $-\frac{4}{3}, \frac{1}{5}$
46. $\pm 18x$
47. $\pm 2x\sqrt{30}$
48. $\pm 4x\sqrt{6}$
49. $0, \frac{1}{21}$
50. $-\frac{1}{2}, -\frac{5}{2}$
51. $\frac{5}{2}, -\frac{3}{4}$
52. 3, 1
53. $\frac{3 \pm 3\sqrt{5}}{2}$
54. −9, 3

Item Analysis

Item	Lesson
1–6	13-3
7–12	13-1
13–16	13-4
17–19	13-1
20–25	13-2
26–29	13-1
30, 31	13-2
32–37	13-3
38–45	13-4
46–48	13-3
49–54	13-4

MIXED PRACTICE 25

For use after Lesson 13-4

Complete the square.

1. $a^2 + 18a$
2. $x^2 - 7x$
3. $x^2 - 20x$
4. $y^2 + 100y$
5. $x^2 - 12x$
6. $m^2 - 6m$

Write each equation in standard form and determine a, b, and c.

7. $3x^2 - 15 = 0$
8. $x^2 + 4 = 6x$
9. $5y^2 + 3y = 91$
10. $8t - 9 = t^2$
11. $x^2 + 4 = 11x - 5$
12. $35 + x^2 = 10x$

Find the value of the discriminant and determine the number of real-number solutions for each quadratic equation.

13. $x^2 + 12x + 32 = 0$
14. $y^2 - 10y + 25 = 0$
15. $x^2 - 2x + 5 = 0$
16. $x^2 = 11x$

Solve.

17. $3x^2 - 9x = 0$
18. $2x^2 - 10x = 0$
19. $4y^2 + 4y = 0$
20. $5x^2 = 20$
21. $9y^2 - 64 = 0$
22. $3x^2 - 243 = 0$
23. $(x - 5)^2 = 121$
24. $(y + 3)^2 = 7$
25. $(x + 4)^2 = 25$
26. $x(x - 2) = 15$
27. $9y^2 - 14y = 10y - 16$
28. $x^2 + 3x - 10 = 30$
29. $(y - 1)^2 - 81 = 0$
30. $m^2 + 6m - 6 = 21$
31. $x(2x + 1) = 28$

Solve by completing the square.

32. $x^2 - 6x - 16 = 0$
33. $y^2 - 4y = 3$
34. $x^2 + 3x - 180 = 0$
35. $x^2 - 6x + 8 = 0$
36. $a^2 - 7a + 12 = 0$
37. $x^2 - 15x - 15 = 1$

Solve using the quadratic formula.

38. $x^2 - 5x + 4 = 0$
39. $6t^2 - 5t - 6 = 0$
40. $8x^2 = 60$
41. $2x^2 - x - 15 = 0$
42. $m^2 + 5m - 24 = 0$
43. $x^2 - 4x - 77 = 0$
44. $2x(x - 2) = 3(4 - x)$
45. $(3x + 4)(5x - 1) = 0$

Find all middle terms which complete the square.

46. $x^2 + ? + 81$
47. $x^2 + ? + 30$
48. $x^2 + ? + 24$

Solve.

49. $21x^2 = x$
50. $4x^2 + 12x + 5 = 0$
51. $8x^2 = 14x + 15$
52. $m^2 - 4m + 3 = 0$
53. $x^2 - 9 = 3x$
54. $x^2 + 6x = 27$

MIXED PRACTICE 26

For use after Lesson 13-7

Solve each rational equation.

1. $\frac{9}{x-3} - \frac{x-4}{x-3} = \frac{1}{4}$

2. $\frac{1}{x-1} + \frac{2}{x} = 0$

3. $\frac{y^2}{6} = \frac{y}{3} + \frac{1}{2}$

4. $\frac{m}{m-3} + \frac{6}{m+3} = 1$

5. $x - 3 = \frac{1}{x-3}$

6. $x - 6 = \frac{x}{x-6}$

7. $x + \frac{x}{x+1} = \frac{4x+3}{x+1}$

8. $\frac{1}{x+5} + \frac{5}{x^2-25} = 0$

Solve each radical equation.

9. $\sqrt{3x-5} = 4$

10. $\sqrt{x+5} = \sqrt{2x-3}$

11. $2\sqrt{x-3} = 6 - x$

12. $\sqrt{y-5} = y - 7$

13. $\sqrt{x} + \sqrt{7} = \sqrt{x+7}$

14. $m + \sqrt{2m-6} = 3$

Solve.

15. $2x^2 - 5x + 3 = 0$

16. $(x+2)(x-1) = 10$

17. $6x^2 - x = 1$

18. $3t^2 + 5t = 28$

19. $(3y-10)^2 = 0$

20. $10x - 19 = x^2$

Solve.

21. Quentin deposited \$500 in his savings account. In two years it grew to \$561.80. What is the interest rate? (Use $A = P(1+r)^t$.)

22. A picture frame is 30 cm by 24 cm. There are 520 cm^2 of picture showing. Find the width of the frame.

23. The hypotenuse of a right triangle is 13 m long. One leg is 7 m shorter than the other. Find the lengths of the legs.

24. The length of a rectangle is 15 ft greater than the width. The area is 1000 ft^2. Find the length and width.

25. The current in a stream moves at a speed of 5 km/h. A boat travels 20 km upstream and 20 km downstream in a total of 3 hrs. Find the speed of the boat in still water.

26. Marla can type a 24 page report in 3 hours. If Marla and Gene work together, they can type the same report in 2 hours. How long would it take Gene alone to type the report?

27. Find the side of a square whose diagonal is 5 cm longer than a side.

Answers

1. 11
2. $\frac{2}{3}$
3. $-1, 3$
4. 1
5. 2, 4
6. 9, 4
7. 3
8. 0
9. 7
10. 8
11. 4
12. 9
13. 0
14. 3
15. $1, \frac{3}{2}$
16. $3, -4$
17. $-\frac{1}{3}, \frac{1}{2}$
18. $-4, \frac{7}{3}$
19. $\frac{10}{3}$
20. $5 \pm \sqrt{6}$
21. 6%
22. 2 cm
23. 5 m, 12 m
24. 40 ft, 25 ft
25. 15 km/h
26. 6 hr
27. $5 + 5\sqrt{2}$ cm

Item Analysis

Item	Lesson
1–8	13-5
9–14	13-6
15–20	13-4
21	13-2
22–27	13-7

Answers

1. Corresponding angles: $\angle A$ and $\angle D$, $\angle B$ and $\angle E$, $\angle C$ and $\angle F$; corresponding sides $\overline{AB}$ and $\overline{DE}$, $\overline{BC}$ and $\overline{EF}$, $\overline{CA}$ and $\overline{FD}$
2. $2\sqrt{117}$
3. Answers will vary.
4. 8
5. 0.6, 0.8, 0.75
6. 0.3846, 0.9231, 0.4167
7. 0.96, 0.28, 3.429
8. 0.8, 0.6, 1.333
9. 0.9231, 0.3846, 2.4
10. 0.28, 0.96, 0.292
11. 30, 0.6, 0.8
12. 34, 0.5, 0.9
13. 75, 0.6, 0.8

Item Analysis

Item	Lesson
1–4	14-1
5–10	14-2
11–13	14-2

MIXED PRACTICE 27

For use after Lesson 14-2

1. $\triangle ABC \sim \triangle DEF$. Name the corresponding sides and angles.

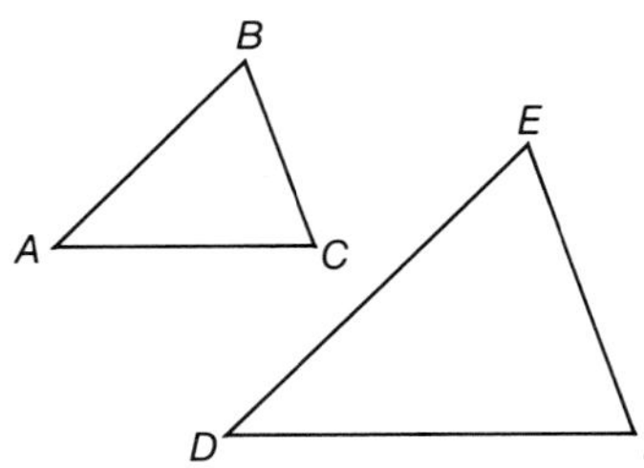

2. $\triangle LMN \sim \triangle HJK$. Find the length j.

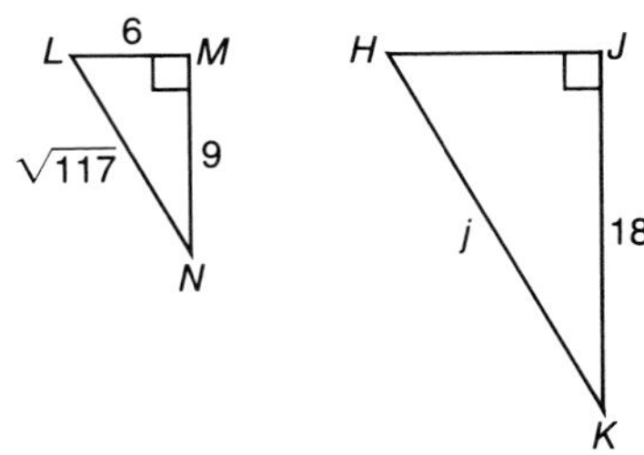

3. $\triangle RST \sim \triangle UVW$. Write three true proportions.

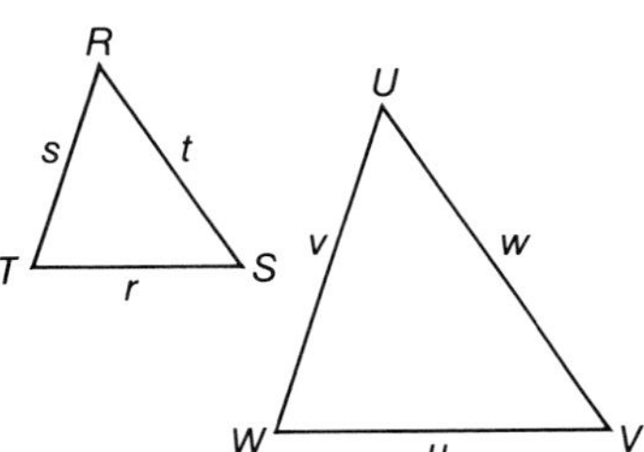

4. $\triangle BCD \sim \triangle XYZ$. Find length z.

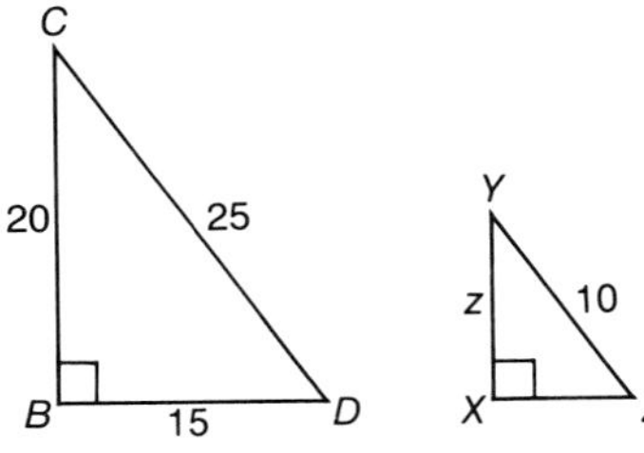

Find the trigonometric ratios for each triangle.

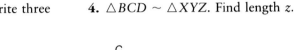

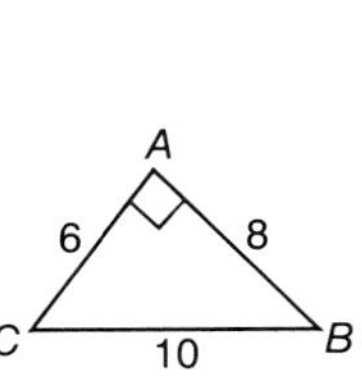

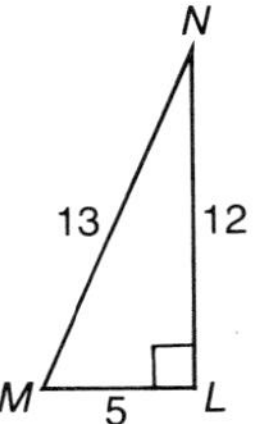

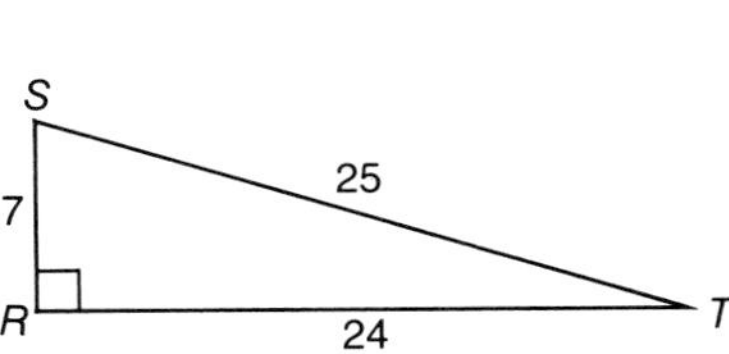

5. In $\triangle ABC$, find sin B, cos B, and tan B.

6. In $\triangle LMN$, find sin N, cos N, and tan N.

7. In $\triangle RST$, find sin S, cos S, and tan S.

8. In $\triangle ABC$, find sin C, cos C, and tan C.

9. In $\triangle LMN$, find sin M, cos M, and tan M.

10. In $\triangle RST$, find sin T, cos T, and tan T.

Use the Pythagorean theorem to find the lengths, to the nearest tenth, of the hypotenuse of a triangle with legs of the given lengths. Then find the sine ratio for each acute angle.

11. 18 and 24 **12.** 16 and 30 **13.** 45 and 60

MIXED PRACTICE 28 For use after Lesson 14-4

Find these trigonometric values.

1. sin 82° **2.** cos 82° **3.** cos 8° **4.** tan 48°

5. sin 20° **6.** cos 63° **7.** tan 20° **8.** tan 81°

Find angle A to the nearest degree.

9. $\tan A = 0.5090$ **10.** $\cos A = 0.2590$ **11.** $\sin A = 0.6300$

12. $\cos A = 0.9950$ **13.** $\sin A = 0.1904$ **14.** $\tan A = 1.0217$

Assume that the sides of $\triangle ABC$ are 9, 12, 15.

15. If $\triangle ABC \sim \triangle DEF$ and the longest side of $\triangle DEF$ is 40, what are the lengths of the other two sides?

16. If $\triangle ABC \sim \triangle GHJ$ and the shortest side of $\triangle GHJ$ is 6, what are the lengths of the other two sides?

17. Find the sine ratios for the acute angles of $\triangle ABC$.

Solve the following triangle problems. Round answers to the nearest tenth.

18. $A = 62°$ and $c = 17$. Find a.

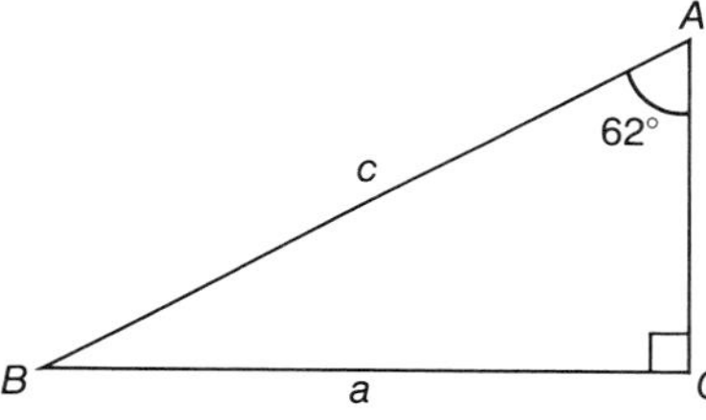

19. $J = 14$ and $K = 48$. Find $LKJH$ to the nearest degree.

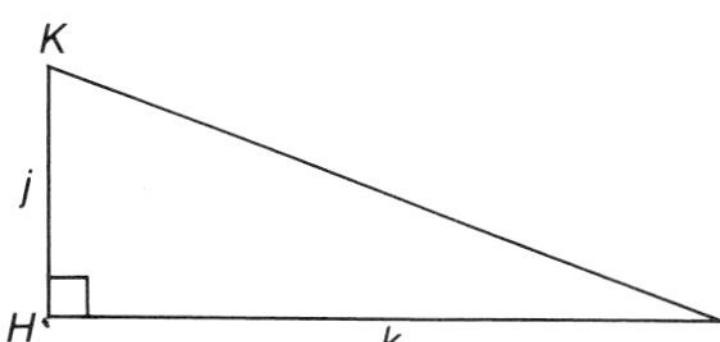

Solve. Draw a picture first. Round answers to the nearest tenth.

20. Lynette is flying a kite on 300 ft of string. The angle of elevation of the kite is 40°. How high is the kite?

21. A 24 ft ladder is placed against a wall so that its angle of elevation is 61°. How far from the ground is the top of the ladder?

22. Jack stands in an observation deck at the top of a 200 ft building and looks down at his car in the parking lot. The angle of depression from the observation deck to the car is 55°. How far is Jack's car from the base of the building?

23. A 12 ft ladder leans against a wall. The foot of the ladder is 3 ft from the wall. What is the ladder's angle of elevation?

Answers

1. 0.9903
2. 0.1392
3. 0.9903
4. 1.1106
5. 0.3420
6. 0.4540
7. 0.3640
8. 6.3138
9. 27°
10. 75°
11. 39°
12. 6°
13. 11°
14. 46°
15. 24, 32
16. 8, 10
17. 0.8, 0.6
18. 15
19. 16.3°
20. 193 ft
21. 21 ft
22. 140 ft
23. 75.5°

Item Analysis

Item	Lesson
1–8	14-3
9–14	14-3
15, 16	14-1
17	14-2
18–19	14-4
20–23	14-4

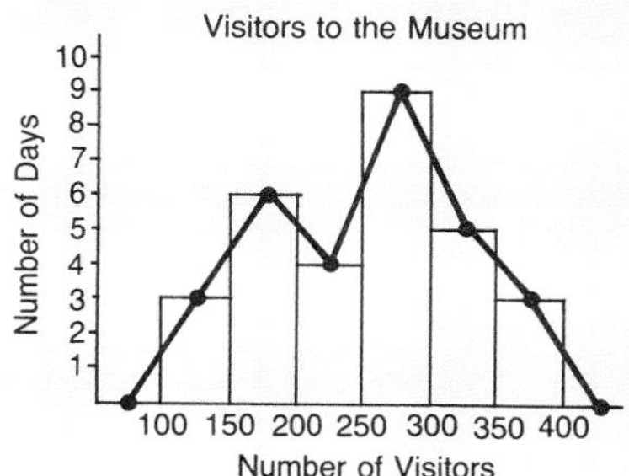

Answers

1. $\frac{1}{12}$
2. $\frac{11}{12}$
3. $\frac{6}{12}$ or $\frac{1}{2}$
4. $\frac{4}{12}$ or $\frac{1}{3}$
5. $\frac{4}{12}$ or $\frac{1}{3}$
6. $\frac{5}{12}$
7. $\frac{2}{12}$ or $\frac{1}{6}$
8. $\frac{5}{12}$
9. $\frac{8}{12}$ or $\frac{2}{3}$
10. $\frac{5}{20}$ or $\frac{1}{4}$
11. $\frac{15}{20}$ or $\frac{3}{4}$
12. $\frac{14}{20}$ or $\frac{7}{10}$
13. $\frac{4}{20}$ or $\frac{1}{5}$
14. Answers will vary.
15. Answers will vary.
16. Answers will vary.
17. $\frac{13}{52}$ or $\frac{1}{4}$
18. $\frac{4}{52}$ or $\frac{1}{13}$
19. 0
20. $\frac{27}{52}$

Item Analysis

Item	Lesson
1, 2	15-2
3–6	15-1
7–12	15-2
13	15-1
14–16	15-3
17–20	15-1

MIXED PRACTICE 29 For use after Lesson 15-3

A spinner numbered 1–12 is spun.

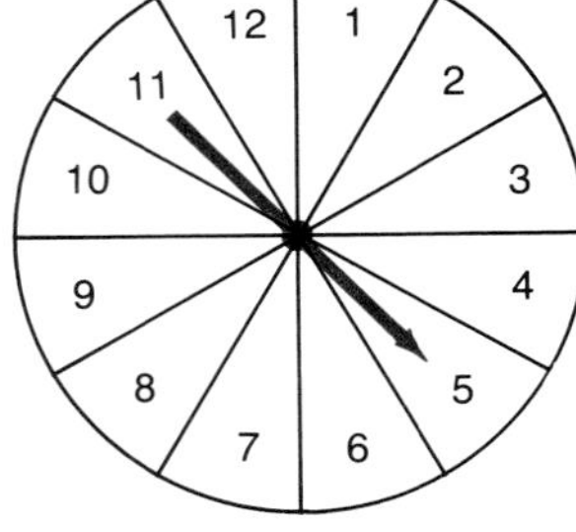

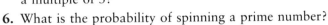

1. What is the probability of spinning a 5?
2. What is the probability of not spinning a 5?
3. What is the probability of spinning an odd number?
4. What is the probability of spinning a factor of 8?
5. What is the probability of spinning a multiple of 3?
6. What is the probability of spinning a prime number?
7. What is the probability of spinning a 7 or a 12?
8. What is the probability of spinning a multiple of 3 or a 5?
9. What is the probability of spinning an odd number or a multiple of 3?

Randy has 20 cans of food: 3 cans of soup, 1 can of tuna, 4 cans of corn, 3 cans of peaches, 5 cans of beans, 2 cans of peas, and 2 cans of pears. Randy's little brother has taken all the labels off the cans. Randy selects one can and opens it.

10. What is the probability the can contains fruit?
11. What is the probability the can does not contain fruit?
12. What is the probability the can does not contain peas or corn?
13. What is the probability the can contains soup or tuna?

The most popular ride at the Amusement Park is the rollercoaster. Each car on this attraction will hold 4 people. Use 30 tosses of a coin for your simulation to answer the following questions.

14. What is the probability that a car will hold a boy and three girls?
15. What is the probability that all four riders in a car will be boys?
16. What is the probability that the first rider in a car will be a girl?

One card is drawn from a well-shuffled deck of 52 cards.

17. What is the probability the card will be a diamond?
18. What is the probability the card will be a red 3 or a black 5?
19. What is the probability the card will be a green card?
20. What is the probability the card will be a black card or the 2 of hearts?

MIXED PRACTICE 30 For use after Lesson 15-6

Construct a frequency distribution for this set of data.

1. The number of loaves of french bread used at the deli each day in June

   12, 15, 13, 12, 12, 13, 14, 12, 15, 15, 12, 14, 13, 12, 13,
   12, 13, 11, 13, 12, 12, 15, 12, 11, 13, 14, 14, 13, 15, 14

Construct a frequency distribution using intervals.

2. The attendance at each of the Jackson High basketball team's home games. Use ten intervals.

   228, 225, 178, 204, 227, 114, 210, 230, 194, 248,
   127, 156, 293, 338, 230, 321, 280, 232, 222, 181,
   230, 211, 245, 147, 215, 217, 345, 208, 249, 290

Construct a ranked stem-and-leaf diagram.

3. The number of sit-ups performed in three minutes by a seventh grade physical education class

   83, 70, 63, 53, 85, 83, 72, 116, 107, 59, 64, 70, 81, 107,
   88, 93, 57, 76, 68, 80, 108, 61, 77, 64, 92, 112, 103, 95

Construct a line plot for this set of data.

4. The scores of 30 students on the history pop-quiz

   7, 6, 9, 8, 9, 9, 7, 5, 4, 0, 8, 6, 5, 9, 8,
   5, 8, 8, 7, 8, 6, 9, 7, 6, 7, 8, 2, 6, 9, 6

Construct a histogram for this set of data.

5. The number of miles driven in a day by each of 24 trucks from the Delivery Company

   159, 45, 220, 165, 190, 140, 238, 80, 35, 160, 95, 235,
   120, 240, 172, 94, 188, 112, 178, 91, 142, 60, 168, 87

Construct a frequency polygon for this set of data.

6. The number of visitors to the State Railroad Museum each day in November

   260, 272, 210, 165, 265, 380, 308, 144, 162, 270,
   368, 330, 210, 216, 177, 390, 255, 291, 180, 309,
   312, 288, 295, 184, 111, 147, 330, 284, 235, 164

Find the mean (to the nearest tenth), median and mode.

7. The weight, in pounds, of the frozen turkeys at Simoni's Market

   11.8, 20.7, 12.4, 14.3, 17.4, 18.2, 12.7, 14.3, 15.1, 18.1

Answers

1.

Loaves	Frequency
11	2
12	10
13	8
14	5
15	5

2.

Attendance	Frequency
100–124	1
125–149	2
150–174	1
175–199	3
200–224	7
225–249	10
250–274	0
275–299	3
300–324	1
325–349	2

3.

Stem	Leaf
05	3, 7, 9
06	1, 3, 4, 4, 8
07	0, 0, 2, 6, 7
08	0, 1, 3, 3, 5, 8
09	2, 3, 5
10	3, 7, 7, 8
11	2, 6

4.

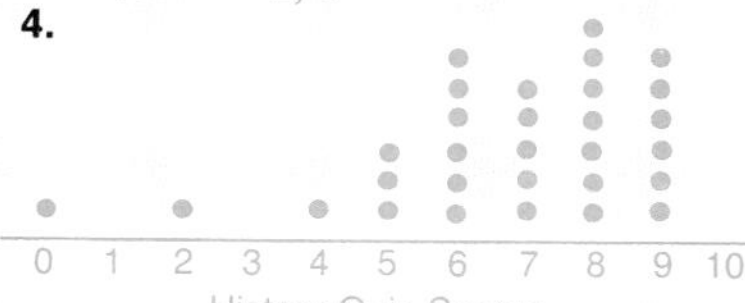

5.

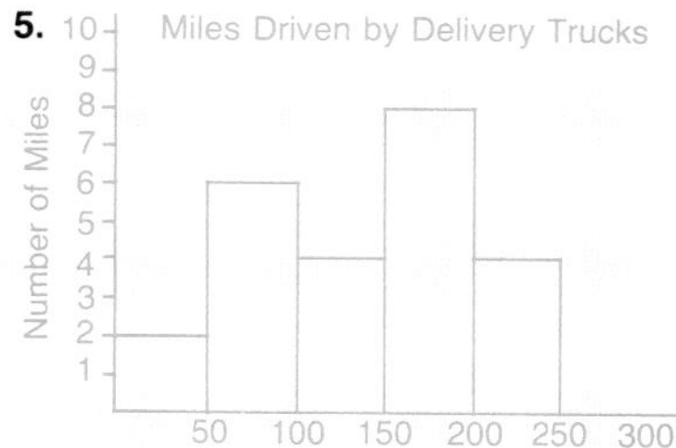

7. mean 15.5
   median 14.7
   mode 14.3

Item Analysis

Item	Lesson
1 – 3	15-4
4–6	15-5
7	15-6

Computer Exploration contains programs that allow students to use a computer to explore algebraic concepts taught in the book. The student tries to solve problems or make generalizations about mathematical concepts using data and graphs generated by the computer.

A complete BASIC program is provided for each exploration, except those that involve graphing. These programs contain many of the most common BASIC statements. Note that programs can be written in many ways. Ours are designed so that a student can easily understand the program as a whole as well as each line of the program. At first you may want to go over each line, discussing the procedure the program uses to produce a solution or a graph. Mention that the programs contain REM lines that make the program more readable but are ignored by the computer.

Explorations involving graphing can be done using *Master Grapher,* the program provided in *Management and Teaching Aids,* or any program that graphs functions.

Show students the symbols, such as +, −, /, *, and ^, used by the computer to perform arithmetic operations.

Computer Exploration

Some problems encountered in algebra require higher mathematics, such as calculus, to solve. Many of these problems, however, can be translated from algebra into computer programs in order to find a solution. While many languages exist for this purpose, the easiest to understand is BASIC (Beginner's All-purpose Symbolic Instruction Code). This appendix shows how problems that require tedious calculations to find an answer can be solved quickly using a computer.

As you input each program, look at the codes used in each line. These codes, often written as English words, give the computer instructions. Notice the FOR and NEXT statements in the programs. These allow the computer to make many repetitions of the lines in between.

The following hints will assist you in using the programs to solve each problem. Before typing in a program, first type NEW <cr>*. This will erase any program that exists in the computer's memory. If a mistake is noticed in a line after it is typed, simply retype the line. After inputting the program, type LIST <cr>. This will display the program on the screen. Compare it carefully with the program in the book. Any mistakes may cause an erroneous answer. If you type SAVE ANYNAME <cr>, the program you just typed will be saved on the disk under the name ANYNAME. A file already on the disk with the name ANYNAME will be erased, so be careful. If you wish to use the program at a later date, simply type LOAD ANYNAME <cr> at that time.

*<cr> means press carriage return or return

Computer Exploration 1: Guess, Check, Revise

(for use with Lesson 1-10)

Computers can be programmed to use a form of *Guess, Check, Revise* to solve problems very efficiently. Since many checks can be done very quickly on a computer the program is written to check all possible solutions.

The following program finds all three-digit whole numbers that are divisible by the product of their digits. The program is written to test every possible three-digit number to see if the number is divisible by the product of the digits.

Program

```
10  REM THREEDIGITS PROBLEM
15  REM FIRST, SCND, AND THIRD REPRESENT
    THE DIGITS LEFT TO RIGHT
20  FOR FIRST = 1 TO 9
30  FOR SCND = 1 TO 9
40  FOR THIRD = 1 TO 9
45  REM PRODUCT REPRESENTS THE PRODUCT OF
    THE DIGITS
50  PRODUCT = FIRST * SCND * THIRD
55  REM NMBR REPRESENTS THE VALUE OF THE
    NUMBER
60  NMBR = 100 * FIRST + 10 * SCND + THIRD
70  IF NMBR / PRODUCT = INT (NMBR / PRODUCT)
    THEN PRINT NMBR;"   ";
80  NEXT THIRD
90  NEXT SCND
100 NEXT FIRST
110 END
```

PROBLEMS

1. RUN the program above, and use a watch to see how long it takes your computer to find all three-digit whole numbers that are divisible by the product of their digits.
2. Add lines 17, 62, and 65 to view the computer process. The left number counts the numbers tested. How many numbers are tested?

```
17 LET N = 0
62 LET N = N + 1
75 PRINT N;" TESTING THE NUMBER
   ";FIRST;SCND;THIRD
```

Guess, Check, Revise

We exclude 0 as a second or third digit, since we cannot divide by 0. Line 70 checks to see if the quotient is an integer.

Answers

```
RUN
111   112   115   128
132   135   144   175
212   216   224   312
315   384   432   612
624   672   735   816
```

20 numbers work.

The number of numbers per row may vary. For a 40-character screen, 8 will print out on each line.

1. Answers will vary; approximately 20 seconds.
2. 729 numbers are tested.

Multiplication with Negative Numbers

Answers

1.
```
RUN
5 × 8 = 40
4 × 8 = 32
3 × 8 = 24
2 × 8 = 16
1 × 8 = 8
0 × 8 = 0
-1 × 8 = -8
-2 × 8 = -16
-3 × 8 = -24
-4 × 8 = -32
-5 × 8 = -40
```
The product of a negative number and a positive number is negative.

2.
```
RUN
-8 × 5 = -40
-8 × 4 = -32
-8 × 3 = -24
-8 × 2 = -16
-8 × 1 = -8
-8 × 0 = 0
-8 × -1 = 8
-8 × -2 = 16
-8 × -3 = 24
-8 × -4 = 32
-8 × -5 = 40
```
The product of a positive number and a negative number is negative.

3.
```
RUN
5 × -8 = -40
4 × -8 = -32
3 × -8 = -24
2 × -8 = -16
1 × -8 = -8
0 × -8 = 0
-1 × -8 = 8
-2 × -8 = 16
-3 × -8 = 24
-4 × -8 = 32
-5 × -8 = 40
```
The product of two negative numbers is positive.

4. The product of two numbers with the same sign is positive. The product of two numbers with opposite signs is negative.

Computer Exploration 2: Multiplication with Negative Numbers

(for use with Lesson 2-5)

Multiplying negative numbers is much like multiplying positive numbers except we must determine whether an answer is positive or negative.

Program

```
10 REM MULT NEGATIVE
20 FOR N = 5 TO -5 STEP -1
30 LET P = 8
40 LET Q = P * N
50 PRINT N;
55 PRINT " X ";
60 PRINT P;
65 PRINT " = ";Q
70 NEXT N
80 END
```

PROBLEMS

1. RUN the program above and look for a pattern. From the pattern you see, do you think that the product of a negative number and a positive number will be positive or negative? Will this always be true?
2. Change the following lines in the above program.
```
40 LET Q = N*P
50 PRINT P;
60 PRINT N;
```
RUN the program and look for a pattern. From the pattern you see, do you think that the product of a positive number and a negative number will be positive or negative? Will this always be true?
3. Change the following lines in the program in Problem 1.
```
30 LET P = -8
```
RUN the program above and look for a pattern. From the pattern you see, do you think that the product of two negative numbers will be positive or negative? Will this always be true?
4. Write a paragraph that states how you determine whether a product of two numbers will be positive or negative.

Computer Exploration 3: Scientific Notation

(for use with Lesson 5-4)

Computers, like calculators, are programmed to convert very large and very small numbers to scientific notation. On many microcomputers, large numbers are printed out like this:

1,234,000,000 will be printed out as `1.234E+9` which is 1.234×10^9.

The following program can be used to determine how your computer uses scientific notation for large numbers.

Program

```
10 REM SCIENTIFIC NOTATION
20 LET X = 1.234
30 FOR N = 1 TO 20
40 LET X = 10 * X
50 PRINT X
60 NEXT N
80 END
```

PROBLEMS

1. Enter the program above and RUN the program on your computer.
  a. How many decimal places does your computer print out before converting to scientific notation?
  b. How does your computer print the number 12,340,000?
  c. How does your computer print the number 1,234,000,000,000?
  d. How do you think that your computer would print the number 43,200,000,000?

2. Change line 40 to `LET X = X/10`.
  a. How many decimal places does your computer print out before converting to scientific notation?
  b. How does your computer print the number 0.0001234?
  c. How does your computer print the number 0.0000001234?
  d. How do you think that your computer would print the number 0.000003445?

3. Change line 30 to `FOR N = 1 to 100`, and line 40 `LET X = 10 * X`. What is the largest number that your computer prints before it prints "`OVERFLOW ERROR`"?

Scientific Notation

Answers

1.
```
RUN
12.34
123.4
1234
12340
123400
1234000
12340000
123400000
1.234E+09
1.234E+10
1.234E+11
1.234E+12
1.234E+13
1.234E+14
1.234E+15
1.234E+16
1.234E+17
1.234E+18
1.234E+19
1.234E+20
```
a. 9
b. 12340000
c. 1.234E+12
d. 4.32E+10

2.
```
RUN
.1234
.01234
1.234E-03
1.234E-04
1.234E-05
1.234E-06
1.234E-07
1.234E-08
1.234E-09
1.234E-10
1.234E-11
1.234E-12
1.234E-13
1.234E-14
1.234E-15
1.234E-16
1.234E-17
1.234E-18
1.234E-19
1.234E-20
```
a. 5
b. 1.234E-04
c. 1.234E-07
d. 1.234E-08

3. 1.234×10^{37}

Linear and Non-Linear Equations

Students can use any function grapher, such as *Master Grapher,* or input the program listed in the *Management and Teaching Aids* supplement.

You may want students to try to determine before graphing whether each equation is linear or non-linear. They can then check their answers with the graph.

You may need to explain that different notation is often used in computer programs. Some common differences are:

- * and / are used for multiplication and division.
- ^ is used for exponentiation.
- $f(x)$ notation may be used for the dependent variable. You may need to introduce this notation.

Be aware that some students may confuse asymptotes lines for graph lines.

Slope and Intercept

Students can use any function grapher, such as *Master Grapher,* or input the program listed in the *Management and Teaching Aids* supplement.

Students may choose to represent fractions with equivalent decimals.

Answers

1. As the coefficient of x gets larger, the slope of the graph becomes steeper.
2. As the coefficient of x gets smaller, the slope of the graph becomes closer to horizontal.
3. Looking from left to right, a line with negative slope slopes downward. A line with positive slope slopes upward.
4. Changing b, the y-intercept, shifts the line up or down. As b increases, the graph is shifted upward. As b decreases, it is shifted downward.

Computer Exploration 4: Linear and Non-Linear Equations

(for use with Lesson 7-3)

1. Graph the following equations, and determine whether each is a linear equation or a non-linear equation.

a. $y = x - 2$ Linear **b.** $y = 3 - 4x$ Linear **c.** $y = \frac{3}{14}x + 5$ Linear

d. $y = 3x + 10$ Linear **e.** $y = 7 - x^2$ Non-linear **f.** $y = \frac{5}{1 + x}$ Non-linear

g. $y = x^2 - 1$ Non-linear **h.** $y = \frac{2}{x}$ Non-linear **i.** $y = \frac{3x + 4}{7}$ Linear

j. $y = 3x^4 + 8$ Non-linear **k.** $y = \frac{x}{2}$ Linear **l.** $y = \frac{x^2}{8}$ Non-linear

2. Write a paragraph explaining how can you determine whether an equation is linear or non-linear from the equation. Linear equations can be written in the form $y = mx + b$.

Computer Exploration 5: Slope and Intercept

(for use with Lesson 7-5)

1. Graph the following equations. Describe how the slope of the graph changes as the coefficient of x gets larger.

a. $y = x + 2$ **b.** $y = 2x + 2$ **c.** $y = 3x + 2$

d. $y = 10x + 2$ **e.** $y = 30x + 2$ **f.** $y = 100x + 2$

2. Graph the following equations. Describe how the slope of the graph changes as the coefficient of x gets smaller.

a. $y = x + 2$ **b.** $y = \frac{1}{2}x + 2$ **c.** $y = \frac{1}{3}x + 2$

d. $y = \frac{1}{4}x + 2$ **e.** $y = \frac{1}{10}x + 2$ **f.** $y = \frac{1}{50}x + 2$

3. Graph the following equations. Describe how the slope of graphs with a positive slope differ from those with negative slopes.

a. $y = 3x + 4$ **b.** $y = -3x + 4$ **c.** $y = 2x - 1$

d. $y = -2x - 1$ **e.** $y = \frac{1}{2}x - 2$ **f.** $y = -\frac{1}{2}x - 2$

4. Graph the following equations. Describe how the constant term affects the graph of the equation.

a. $y = 3x$ **b.** $y = 3x + 1$ **c.** $y = 3x + 2$

d. $y = 3x + 10$ **e.** $y = 3x - 10$ **f.** $y = 3x - 2$

Computer Exploration 6: Finding the Line of Best Fit

(for use with Lesson 7-7)

This program will determine an equation for the line of best fit for input data. Although this program will determine an equation for any set of data, it should be used for data that appears to cluster around a straight line.

Program

```
10  REM LINE OF BEST FIT
20  INPUT "NUMBER OF KNOWN POINTS? ";N
30  PRINT "ENTER THE COORDINATES OF THE
    POINTS LIKE THIS: 8,16"
40  FOR I = 1 TO N
50  INPUT "ENTER A DATA POINT: ";X,Y
55  LET XS = X + XS:YS = Y + YS
60  LET P = P + X ^ 2:R = R + X * Y
70  NEXT I
80  MX = XS / N:MY = YS / N
90  A = (R - (XS * YS / N)) /
    (P - (XS ^ 2) / N)
100 B = MY - A * MX
110 PRINT "Y = ";A;"X + ";B
120 END
```

PROBLEMS

1. Use the program to determine the equation for the line of best fit for Exercises 7–10 on pp. 336–337. Compare your answers to those that you got using two data points.
2. Some economists believe that demand inflation (the annual percent of increase or decrease in demand for labor) depends on the civilian unemployment rate (the percent of the labor force out of work). Find the equation for the line of best fit for the following data points.

Year	Civilian Unemployment	Demand Inflation	Year	Civilian Unemployment	Demand Inflation
1962	5.9%	0.6%	1976	7.4%	−2.7%
1964	5.2%	0.2%	1978	5.9%	1.3%
1966	3.8%	1.3%	1980	7.1%	−0.2%
1968	3.6%	1.1%	1982	9.5%	−2.5%
1970	5.1%	−1.2%	1984	7.4%	0.0%
1972	5.4%	−0.3%	1986	6.9%	−1.1%
1974	5.4%	1.6%			

Finding the Line of Best Fit

When a scatterplot of observations on two variables x, y shows an approximately linear pattern, fitting a straight line to the data is useful for predicting y from x. Such a "best-fit" line can be found by the technique of least-squares regression. This technique finds the line that has the smallest sum of the squares of the vertical distances of the data points from the line.

Answers

1. **7.** $y = 0.430041151d + 1.90329221$
   8. $c = 1.50802752m + 0.925779825$
   9. $h = -7.65000004x + 81.3500001$
   10. $c = 7.26930442d + 1893.28545$
2. $y = -0.620383724x + 3.60478159$

Parallel and Perpendicular Lines

Students can use any function grapher, such as *Master Grapher,* or input the program listed in the *Management and Teaching Aids* supplement.

Answers

1. a. perpend. b. parallel c. neither d. perpend. e. parallel f. perpend. g. neither h. parallel i. perpend.
2. When two linear equations are written in $y = mx + b$ form, the lines are parallel if their x coefficients are equal. The lines are perpendicular if the product of their x coefficients is -1.

Absolute Value Graphs

Students can use any function grapher, such as *Master Grapher,* or input the program listed in the *Management and Teaching Aids* supplement.

If possible, graph several exercises on the same set of axes so that students can make immediate comparisons. However, too many graphs may become confusing.

Note that a common notation for $|x|$ is *ABS*(*X*), but individual programs may differ.

Students may need to be reminded to use parentheses to group quantities such as fraction parts correctly. Grouping errors will result in incorrect graphs.

Answers

1. As b increases, the graph shifts further left. As b decreases, it shifts right.
2. As the magnitude of $|a|$ increases the V becomes narrower. As it decreases, the V becomes wider.
3. As c increases, the graph shifts upward. As c decreases, it shifts downward.

Computer Exploration 7: Parallel and Perpendicular Lines

(for use with Lesson 7-8)

1. Graph the following pairs of equations, and determine which are parallel, which are perpendicular, and which are neither.

a. $y = 2x + 4$, $y = -\frac{1}{2}x$ **b.** $y = 5x - 2$, $y = 5x + 3$ **c.** $y = 2x - 1$, $y = -2x - 3$

d. $y = \frac{1}{3}x$, $y = -3x + 5$ **e.** $y = -5x + 3$, $y = -5x - 4$ **f.** $y = -8x - 3$, $y = \frac{1}{8}x + 2$

g. $y = \frac{1}{4}x + 1$, $y = 4x + 4$ **h.** $y = -0.5x$, $y = -0.5x - 2$ **i.** $y = -\frac{1}{7}x + 5$, $y = 7x + 3$

2. Write a paragraph explaining how can you determine whether two equations are parallel or perpendicular from the equation.

Computer Exploration 8: Absolute Value Graphs

(for use with Lesson 12-2 Bonus Topic)

1. Graph the following equations of the form $y = |x + b|$. Determine how the graph changes as the value of b increases or decreases.

a. $y = |x + 4|$ **b.** $y = |x - 3|$ **c.** $y = |x + 1|$

d. $y = |x + 6|$ **e.** $y = |x|$ **f.** $y = \left|x - \frac{2}{3}\right|$

2. Graph the following equations of the form $y = |ax|$. Determine how the graph changes as the value of a increases or decreases.

a. $y = |3x|$ **b.** $y = |7x|$ **c.** $y = |-0.3x|$

d. $y = |-2x|$ **e.** $y = |5x|$ **f.** $y = |-5x|$

3. Graph the following equations of the form $y = |ax + b| + c$. Determine how the graph changes as the value of c increases or decreases.

a. $y = |3x + 2| + 1$ **b.** $y = |3x + 2| - 3$ **c.** $y = |3x + 2| + 4$

d. $y = |2x - 1| + 3$ **e.** $y = |2x - 1|$ **f.** $y = |2x - 1| - 5$

Computer Exploration 9: Graphs of Parabolas

(for use with Lesson 12-4)

1. Graph the following equations of the form $y = ax^2$. Determine how the graph changes as the value of a increases or decreases.

   a. $y = 2x^2$ **b.** $y = 6x^2$ **c.** $y = x^2$

   d. $y = \frac{1}{3}x^2$ **e.** $y = -2x^2$ **f.** $y = -8x^2$

2. Graph the following equations of the form $y = ax^2 + c$. Determine how the graph changes as the value of c increases or decreases.

   a. $y = 3x^2 + 1$ **b.** $y = 3x^2 + 5$ **c.** $y = 3x^2 - 3$

   d. $y = -4x^2 + 1$ **e.** $y = -4x^2$ **f.** $y = -4x^2 + 3.5$

3. Graph the following equations of the form $y = ax^2 + bx$. Determine how the graph changes as the value of b increases or decreases.

   a. $y = 2x^2 + 8x$ **b.** $y = 2x^2 + 2x$ **c.** $y = 2x^2 - 5x$

   d. $y = 2x^2$ **e.** $y = 2x^2 + x$ **f.** $y = 2x^2 + 4x$

Graphs of Parabolas

Students can use any function grapher, such as *Master Grapher,* or input the program listed in the *Management and Teaching Aids* supplement.

If possible, graph several exercises on the same set of axes so that students can make immediate comparisons. However, too many graphs may become confusing.

Answers

1. As the absolute value of a increases, the parabola becomes wider. As it decreases, the parabola becomes narrower. If $a > 0$, the parabola opens upward, and if $a < 0$, it opens downward.

2. As b increases, the graph shifts upward. As b decreases, the graph shifts downward.

3. The vertex of the parabola moves in a parabolic shape with vertex at the origin. For $a > 0$, if $b > 0$, the vertex is in the third quadrant. If $b < 0$, it is in the second quadrant.

Computer Exploration 10: Quadratic Equations

(for use with Lesson 13-1)

1. Graph the related function $y = ax^2 + bx + c$ for each of the following quadratic equations. Then determine where the graph crosses the x-axis, or where $y = 0$, to estimate the solution of each equation.

   a. $y = x^2 + 6x + 9$ **b.** $y = 2x^2 + 3x + 5$ **c.** $y = x^2 - 16$

   d. $y = 2x^2 + 5x + 3$ **e.** $y = 2x^2 + 7x + 4$ **f.** $y = 0.5x^2 - 2x - 1$

   g. $y = 3x^2 - 8x + 6$ **h.** $y = -3x^2 + 14x$ **i.** $y = \frac{1}{3}x^2 - 3$

   j. $y = -7x^2 - 6x - 2$ **k.** $y = -2x^2 - x - 0.5$

   l. $y = 0.2x^2 - x - 3$

2. For each equation in problem 1, calculate $b^2 - 4ac$. What pattern do you notice for the equations whose graphs do not cross the x-axis?

Quadratic Equations

Students can use any function grapher, such as *Master Grapher,* or input the program listed in the *Management and Teaching Aids* supplement.

Answers

Exact answers are given. Actual answers will only be rough estimates unless using *Master Grapher* or some other program with zoom capabilities.

1. a. 3 **b.** No solution **c.** −4, 4 **d.** −1, −1.5 **e.** −0.72, −2.78 **f.** 4.45, −0.45 **g.** No solution **h.** 0, 4.67 **i.** −3, 3 **j.** No solution **k.** No solution **l.** 7.11, −2.11

2. a. 0 **b.** −31 **c.** 64 **d.** 1 **e.** 17 **f.** 6 **g.** −8 **h.** 196 **i.** 4 **j.** −7 **k.** −3 **l.** 3.4

$b^2 - 4ac$ is the determinant. For each of the equations with no solution (b, g, j, and k), the determinant is negative.

Simulation with a Computer

Scientists frequently study mathematical models of physical phenomena instead of the phenomena themselves. A model often approximates a real situation accurately, and data can be produced less expensively. Computer technology has enabled mathematical modeling to produce useful data very quickly.

The first program simulates a coin toss by randomly generating either a 0 or 1. The second program simulates a die toss by randomly choosing an integer from 1 through Q, each of which represents one of the Q sides.

In both programs, line 60 shows a standard way of generating random integers, RND(1) is a random number strictly between 0 and 1. Multiplying by Q then alters its range to strictly between 0 and Q (for the first program, between 0 and 2). Adding R shifts the range so that R is its smallest value (for the second program, $R = 1$ because dice are usually numbered beginning with 1). The INT function is the greatest integer value, insuring that the result will be an integer.

Computer Exploration 11: Simulation with a Computer

(for use with Lesson 15-3)

This program will simulate tossing a coin.When you run the program, you are asked to input the number of times you want to "toss the coin" (the trial) and the number of trials to run.

Program 1

```
10  REM COIN SIMULATION
15  PRINT "HOW MANY TIMES DO YOU WANT TO
    TOSS"
20  INPUT "THE COIN FOR EACH TRIAL? ";N
25  LET Q = 2:R = 0
30  INPUT "HOW MANY TRIALS DO YOU WANT? ";T
40  FOR J = 1 TO T: FOR I = 1 TO N
60  F(I) = INT (Q * RND (1) + R)
70  IF F(I) = 0 THEN P$(I) = "H"
80  IF F(I) = 1 THEN P$(I) = "T"
90  PRINT P$(I);
100 NEXT I: PRINT: NEXT J
110 END
```

This program will simulate rolling a die with 3 to 9 sides. When you run the program, you are also asked to input the number of times you want to "roll the die" (the trial) and the number of trials to run.

Program 2

```
10  REM DIE SIMULATION
12  INPUT "HOW MANY SIDES DOES YOUR DIE
    HAVE? (3 TO 9) ";Q
15  PRINT "HOW MANY TIMES DO YOU WANT TO
    ROLL?"
20  INPUT "THE DIE FOR EACH TRIAL? ";N
30  INPUT "HOW MANY TRIALS DO YOU WANT? ";T
40  FOR J = 1 TO T: FOR I = 1 TO N
60  F(I) = INT (Q * RND (1) + 1)
90  PRINT F(I);
100 NEXT I: PRINT: NEXT J
110 END
```

Computer Exploration 12: Simulating the Birthday Problem

(for use with Lesson 15-2)

What is the probability that two or more people in a group of 35 people will have the same birthday? This situation can be easily simulated on a computer.

The program below is written to simulate this situation. Line 40 generates a random number from 1 to 365 representing the days of the year. Line 70 checks to see if the generated number matches any of the previous numbers.

Program

```
5    DIM M(400)
10   REM BIRTHDAY PROBLEM
20   INPUT "HOW MANY PEOPLE? ";N
30   FOR I = 2 TO (N + 1)
40   LET M(I) = INT ( RND (1) * 365 + 1)
50   PRINT M(I);" ";
55   IF M(I) = 0 THEN PRINT "0";
60   FOR X = 1 TO (I - 1)
70   IF M(X) = M(I) THEN PRINT "MATCH"
80   NEXT X
90   IF (I - 1) / 4 = INT ((I - 1) / 4)
     THEN PRINT
100  NEXT I
110  END
```

PROBLEMS

1. Use the program to determine the probability that two or more people in a group of 35 people will have the same birthday.
   a. RUN the program above, entering 35 for the number of people. This represents one trial. The outcome is favorable if the word "MATCH" appears anywhere in results.
   b. Repeat part **a** as many times as possible. You need at least twenty trials to determine the probability.
   c. Determine the probability by finding the ratio of the favorable outcomes to the number of trials run.
2. Use the program to determine the probability that two or more students in your math class have a birthday on the same day. (Then collect the birthdays of everyone in your class to determine if any two students do in fact have birthdays on the same day.)

Simulating the Birthday Problem

Before running the experiment, ask students to *guess* the probability that two or more people in a group of 35 people will have the same birthday. After running the experiment, determine if any two students in your class have the same birthday. The theoretical probabilities are listed below, and are usually surprising to anyone who is not familiar with this problem.

Note that each time the program is run is only 1 trial. This program must be run at least 20 times to find the experimental probability. This makes an excellent class assignment. Students can run the program once and then combine their results.

Answers

1. The theoretical probability that two or more have the same birthday for a group of 35 people is 0.814.
2. Answers will vary. Below are some theoretical probabilities for two or more people having a birthday on the same day.

Number of people	Probability
16	0.284
17	0.315
18	0.347
19	0.379
20	0.411
21	0.444
22	0.476
23	0.507
24	0.538
25	0.569
26	0.598
27	0.627
28	0.654
29	0.681
30	0.706
31	0.7320
32	0.753
33	0.775
34	0.795
35	0.814
36	0.832
37	0.849
38	0.864
39	0.878
40	0.891

Slope and y-Intercept

You may wish to have students experiment with the TI-Graphing Calculator before they begin this first investigation. You may need to point out that the [ENTER] key replaces the [=] key found on many calculators. Students may notice that when they press the multiplication key, [×], that the symbol * appears in the viewing window.

The default window for graphs shows the x-axis from -10 to 10, and the y-axis from -10 to 10, with the tick marks (Xscl and Yscl) 1 unit apart on each axis. If any calculators are not showing the default window, instruct students to reset the RANGE by pressing [ZOOM] and selecting 6 : Standard by pressing [6].

ANSWERS

Investigate

Answers will vary. The following are possible answers.

1. a. If the coefficient of x is positive, the line slopes upward to the right through the origin.
   b. As the coefficient of x gets larger, the graph gets steeper and approaches being vertical.

TI–81 INVESTIGATION 1

Slope and y-Intercept

(for use with Lesson 7-4)

Objective: Describe the effects of changing the numerical values of a linear equation.

A graphing calculator allows us to graph several equations quickly. We can easily investigate the effects of changing some of the values. To graph an equation on the *TI-81* calculator, press the [Y=] key and follow the steps outlined in the example below.

EXAMPLE Graph the equations $y = x$, $y = 2x$, $y = 3x$, and $y = 4x$ on the same axes.

- Press the [Y=] key.
- Enter Y1 = x, Y2 = $2x$, Y3 = $3x$, Y4 = $4x$. Use the [X|T] key for x. Press [ENTER] to move the cursor to the next line.
- Press [GRAPH] and the graphs will be drawn one at a time from Y1 to Y4.

If you make an error you can use the arrow keys [◀], [▲], [▶], or [▼] to move to the error, and the insert [INS] and delete [DEL] keys as on a word processor. The [CLEAR] key can be used to blank a whole line.

Try This Graph $y = x$, $y = x + 1$, $y = x + 2$, and $y = x + 3$ on the same axes.

Investigate

1. Graph the equations $y = x$, $y = 2x$, $y = 4x$, and $y = 9x$ on the same axis.
   a. What is the effect of a positive coefficient of x on the slope of the line?
   b. Predict what will happen as the coefficient of x gets very large.
   c. Test your conjecture (the prediction that you made in part b) by trying further equations with different coefficients for x.

The *TI-81* distinguishes between the negative sign [(−)] and the subtraction sign [−]. You will get an error message if you use the subtraction sign when a negative sign is intended.

Investigate

2. Graph $y = -x$, $y = -2x$, $y = -4.6x$, and $y = -8x$ on the same axes.

   a. What effect does the negative coefficient of x have on the slope of the line?

   b. Predict what will happen to the graph of a line as the absolute value of the negative slope gets very large. Test your conjecture.

For investigation 3 you will want to change the viewing window. To do this, press the [RANGE] key and set `Xmin=-5`, `Xmax=5`, `Ymin=-5`, and `Ymax=5`. Leave the other settings the same. The graph window will now show the x-axis from -5 to 5 and the y-axis from -5 to 5.

3. Graph $y = x$, $y = 0.5x$, $y = 0.2x$, and $y = 0.05x$ on the same axes.

   a. How do graphs of lines with coefficients of x that are between 0 and 1 compare to the graph of $y = x$?

   b. Describe what happens to the slope of the line as the coefficient of x gets close to 0.

4. Graph $y = -x$, $y = -0.8x$, $y = -0.5x$, and $y = -0.2x$ on the same axes.

   a. How do graphs of lines with coefficients of x that are between -1 and 0 compare to the graph of $y = -x$?

   b. Describe what happens to the slope of the line as negative coefficients of x get close to 0.

   c. Predict what the graph of $y = 0 \cdot x$ looks like.

Press [ZOOM] and select `6:Standard` to set the `RANGE` to the default setting, showing the x-axis from -10 to 10 and the y-axis from -10 to 10.

5. Graph $y = x$, $y = x + 5$, $y = x - 2$, and, $y = x - 6$ on the same axes.

   a. What effect does varying the value of b in $y = x + b$ have on the graph?

   b. Identify the y-value of the point at which the graph of each equation crosses the y-axis. This is called the **y-intercept**. How is the value of b in $y = x + b$ related to the y-intercept?

You may need to adjust the viewing window for the following investigations. You can do this by pressing the [RANGE] key and adjusting the values of `Xmin`, `Xmax`, `Ymin`, and `Ymax`. You can also get a larger viewing window by pressing [ZOOM] and selecting `3:Zoom Out`. (Press [3] [ENTER].)

6. Let Y1 $= 2x + 5$. Determine three equations that have the same slope as Y1 but a different b value. Define the equations as Y2, Y3, and Y4.

   a. What is the y-intercept in each equation?

   b. What effect does varying the value of b have on these graphs?

   c. What relationship do these lines have?

2. a. If the coefficient of x is negative, the line slopes downward to the right through the origin.
b. As the coefficient of x gets larger in absolute value, the graph gets steeper and approaches being vertical.
3. a. The graphs are flatter than $y = x$.
b. As the coefficient of x gets closer to 0, the graph flattens and approaches being horizontal.
4. a. The graphs are flatter than $y = -x$.
b. As the coefficient of x gets closer to 0, the graph flattens and approaches being horizontal.
c. It is a horizontal line.
5. a. The line keeps the same steepness but moves up or down the y-axis as b changes.
b. 0, 5, -2, -6 respectively. They are the same.
6. a. 5; other answers will vary.
b. The line keeps the same steepness but moves up or down the y-axis as b changes.
c. They are parallel.

Solving Systems of Equations

You can use this investigation either before or after completing Lesson 7-4. After completing investigation 2, you may want to introduce the terms consistent, inconsistent, and independent.

TI–81 INVESTIGATION 2

Solving Systems of Equations

(for use with Lesson 8-1)

Objective: Find a solution of a system of linear equations.

The solution to a system of two equations in two variables is the coordinates of the point of intersection, if there is one. These coordinates are solutions for *both* equations. You will sometimes need to change the RANGE settings or use features of the ZOOM menu to locate the point of intersection.

EXAMPLE 1 Find a solution to the system of equations.

$$3x + y = 6$$
$$-x + y = -2$$

- You must enter each equation in slope-intercept form ($y = mx + b$). Therefore, first solve each equation for y.

  $3x + y = 6$ $\quad$ $-x + y = -2$

  $y = -3x + 6$ $\quad$ $y = x - 2$

- Press [Y=] and enter Y1 = −3x + 6
  Y2 = x − 2
- Set the RANGE at the default settings by pressing [ZOOM] and selecting 6:Standard.
- Press [GRAPH] to view the graph. The intersection is in the viewing window.
- Press the [TRACE] key. A blinking cursor will appear. Use the right or left arrow key to move the cursor along the graph until it is at the point of intersection.
- As the blinking cursor moves along the graph, its position is shown at the bottom of the viewing window. The position at the point of intersection is $x = 2$ and $y = 0$. The solution of the system is (2,0) since this point lies on both graphs.
- Check (2, 0) in *both* equations.

  $3(2) + 0 = 6$ ✓ $\quad$ $-2 + 0 = -2$ ✓

  You can also check by tracing the cursor along the second graph.

Press [TRACE] again. Press the down arrow key. The blinking cursor jumps to the second graph. Use the right or left arrow key to move the cursor to the point of intersection as before.

EXAMPLE 2 Solve. $y = \frac{3}{2}x - 3$

$$y = \frac{2}{3}x + 7$$

- Press [Y=] and enter Y1= (3/2)x−3
  Y2= (2/3)x+7

- Press [GRAPH] and view the graphs. The intersection point does not lie in the viewing rectangle. Press [ZOOM] and select `3:Zoom Out`. The point of intersection is in the first quadrant (upper-right corner).
- Since the intersection point does not lie in the viewing rectangle, change the range. The point of intersection is in the upper-right corner. Press [RANGE] and change the settings to `Xmin=0`, `Xmax=20`, `Ymin=0`, and `Ymax=20`. Leave the other settings alone. Press [GRAPH] again.
- Turn on the `TRACE` and move the blinking cursor to the point of intersection, $x = 12$ and $y = 15$.
- Check the point (12, 15) in *both* equations.

$$15 = \frac{3}{2}(12) - 3 \qquad 15 = \frac{2}{3}(12) + 7$$
$$15 = 18 - 3 \checkmark \qquad 15 = 8 + 7 \checkmark$$

Try This Find the solution to the system of equations, if one exists.

a. $y = x + 2$
$y = -x + 8$

b. $x + 2y = 6$
$-2x + y = 8$

c. $x + y = 10$
$x - y = 16$

d. $2x - 3y = -2$
$x + 3y = 35$

Sometimes the cursor only approximates the solution due to the limits of the calculator. Always check any possible solution in the original equations to determine whether the ordered pair does, in fact, solve the system.

Investigate

1. Find the solution of each system of equations to the nearest tenth. Remember to use parentheses when the coefficient of x is a fraction.

a. $y = \frac{5}{4}x - \frac{7}{4}$
$y = -\frac{1}{7}x + \frac{4}{7}$

b. $7x + y = 1$
$-7x + y = -6$

2. Graph each system of equations. Determine how many solutions each system has by noting the number of points the two graphs have in common.

a. $y = 3x - 1$
$y = 3x + 6$

b. $3x + 4y = 7$
$\frac{3}{2}x + 2y = 11$

c. $x + 3y = 5$
$2x + 6y = 10$

d. $-x + 2y = -8$
$\frac{3}{2}x - 3y = -9$

ANSWERS

Try This

a. (3, 5)
b. (−2, 4)
c. (13, −3)
d. (11, 8)

Investigate

1. a. (1.7, 0.3)
b. (0.5, −2.5)
2. a. 0
b. 0
c. All points on the line are solutions; therefore, there are infinite solutions.
d. 0

Solutions of Quadratic Equations

This investigation helps students see the connection between the graph of a quadratic function, $y = ax^2 + bx + c$, and the related equation, $ax^2 + bx + c = 0$.

Students may try to find the x-intercept without using the [ZOOM] feature. They will quickly discover that their answers are not very accurate.

ANSWERS

Try This

a. 3.45

TI–81 INVESTIGATION 3

Solutions of Quadratic Equations

(for use with Lesson 13-4)

Objective: Solve quadratic equations using graphs.

Recall that the graph of a quadratic equation of the form $y = ax^2 + bx + c$ is a parabola, and the value(s) of x where the graph crosses the x-axis are called the **x-intercepts**.

You can locate the x-intercepts with the *TI-81* by using the ZOOM features and the TRACE key.

EXAMPLE Find the x-intercepts of $y = x^2 - 2x - 5$ to the nearest hundredths place.

- Press [Y=] and enter Y1= [X|T] [x²] − 2[X|T] − 5
- View the graph with the standard settings. There are two x-intercepts, one located between −2 and −1, and the other between 3 and 4.
- Press [ZOOM] and select 1:Box This option allows you to draw a small rectangle around a point at which you would like to have a closer look. Move the cursor to the left and down until it is a small distance below and away from the left x-intercept.
- Press [ENTER] to fix that corner of the box. Use the up and right arrows to locate the diagonally opposite corner and complete a box. Be sure to include a portion of the graph in the box. Press [ENTER] to "zoom in" and the box becomes the entire viewing window.
- Repeat the "box" procedure two more times to get a closer look.
- Press [TRACE] and move the blinking cursor to read the x-intercept to the nearest hundredths place: $x = -1.45$.

Try This

a. Use the Zoom Box feature to draw a rectangular box around the right intercept Example 1. Repeat this two more times for a closer look, and find the second x-intercept to the nearest hundredth.

Investigate

1. Enter the equation $y = x^2 - 2x - 8$, and view its graph. Then answer the following questions.
   a. Factor the equation. What relationship do you observe between the factors and the graph of the equation?
   b. What is the value of the y-coordinate where the graph of the quadratic equation crosses the x-axis?
   c. What equation did you solve when you found the x-intercept?
2. Enter the equation $y = x^2 + 7x + 10$, and view its graph. Then answer questions **a**, **b**, and **c** of Investigation 1 for this equation.
3. Enter the equation $y = x^2 - 12x + 32$, and view its graph. Then answer questions **a**, **b**, and **c** of Investigation 1 for this equation.
4. a. How can you solve the equation $2x^2 + 6x - 5 = 0$ using the *TI-81*?
   b. Find the solution(s) to the nearest hundredth.
5. Enter the following equations on the *TI-81* and view their graphs. Then answer the following questions.

   $y = x^2 - 4x + 1$ $\qquad y = -5x^2 + 2x - 1$
   $y = x^2 + 3x - 5$ $\qquad y = 3x^2 + 12x + 1$

   a. If a quadratic polynomial cannot be factored, will it still have an x-intercept?
   b. How does the number of times the graph of a quadratic equation crosses the
   x-axis relate to the number of real-number solutions for a quadratic equation?

Investigate

1. a. $y = (x - 4)(x + 2)$; the x-intercepts are 4 and -2.
   b. 0
   c. $0 = x^2 - 2x - 8$
2. a. $y = (x + 2)(x + 5)$; the x-intercepts are -2 and -5.
   b. 0
   c. $0 = x^2 + 7x + 10$
3. a. $y = (x - 8)(x - 4)$; the x-intercepts are 8 and 4.
   b. 0
   c. $0 = x^2 - 12x + 32$
4. a. Find the x-intercepts of the function $y = 2x^2 + 6x - 5$
   b. -3.68 and 0.68
5. a. It may.
   b. The number of times the graph of a quadratic equation crosses the x-axis is the same as the number of real-number solutions for the related equation.

Analyzing Statistical Data

Students may choose to enter data individually, followed by the frequency of 1 rather than entering each value once followed by the actual frequency.

Remind students that they can use the arrow keys to edit data that has been entered.

TI–81 INVESTIGATION 4

Analyzing Statistical Data

(for use with Lesson 15-6)

Objective: Analyze statistical data using the mean and graphs of the data.

To access the statistical menus press [2nd] [STAT]. The statistical operations are grouped in three menus:

`CALC` for calculating statistical results
`DRAW` for plotting the data
`DATA` for entering or editing the data

To clear the statistical data memory press
[2nd] [STAT] [▶] [▶] `2:ClrStat` [ENTER]

For one-variable statistics, enter new data as the *x*-variable. The frequency of that particular number in the data is assigned to the *y*-variable.

EXAMPLE 1

You want to find your quiz score average for the grading period. Your quiz scores are 91, 93, 98, 87, 93, 93, 87, and 91.

- Press [2nd] [STAT] [▶] [▶] to highlight the DATA menu. Then select `1:Edit` (by pressing [1] or [ENTER])
- Enter
  - x1 = 91 — The score 91. (Press [ENTER])
  - y1 = 2 — The frequency, or number of occurrences of 91.
  - x2 = 93 — The score 93.
  - y2 = 3 — The frequency, or number of occurrences of 93.
  - x3 = 98
  - y3 = 1
  - x4 = 87
  - y4 = 2
- To find the **mean** or the **average** of the data, press [2nd] [STAT], and Select `1:1-Var` (by pressing 1 or [ENTER]). Then press [ENTER].
- The screen displays
  - $\bar{x}$ = 91.625 — the mean of the data
  - Σx = 733 — the sum of the data
  - Σx^2 = 67251
  - Sx = 3.583194903
  - σx = 3.351771919
  - n = 8 — the number of data

Your average quiz score is 91.625 or 92 to the nearest whole number.

The other statistics are used to find measures of variance of the data. (See Lesson 15-6 Challenge).

The menu `DRAW` will display three types of graphs: a histogram, a scatter plot, and a line graph.

EXAMPLE 2 View the three types of graphs for the data in Example 1.

Before selecting a graph, adjust the parameters of the RANGE so the graphs will appear in the graphics window.

- Since the grades range from 87 to 98, set `Xmin = 80` and `Xmax = 100`.
- The difference between 80 and 100 is 20, and there are 10 tick marks in the window. The x-scale will then be $\frac{20}{10} = 2$. Set `Xscl = 2`.
- The frequency, or y values, range from 1 to 3, so set `Ymin = 0` and `Ymax = 5`. The y-scale will then be $\frac{5}{10} = 0.5$. Set `Yscl = 0.5`.
- Go to the [Y=] menu to clear any active graphs that would be graphed at the same time as the statistical graphs. To display the histogram, press [2nd] [STAT] [▶] [1] [ENTER]

To clear a statistical graph, press [2nd] [DRAW], select `1:ClrDraw`, and [ENTER].

To display the *scatter plot*, press [2nd] [STAT] [▶] [2] [ENTER]

To display the *line graph*, first clear any other graphs as above.

- Sort the data first by pressing [2nd] [STAT] [▶] [▶] [3] [ENTER]
- To view the line graph, press [2nd] [STAT] [▶] [3] [ENTER].

Try This Enter the data and find the mean. Then view the three types of graphs.

a. The number of boxes of popcorn sold daily by the junior class were: 115, 126, 115, 158, 131, 115, 126, 118, 115, 126.

b. The twelve highest recorded rainfalls in a 24-hour period in the U.S. were: 43, 38, 38, 35, 27, 27, 22, 22, 20, 19, 18, and 18 inches

Investigate

1. You are working in a cooperative group. Each one in the group will receive as a grade the mean of the group's scores on the unit test. The test scores for Group A are: 91, 81, 83, 22. The test scores for Group B are: 65, 70, 69, 96.
   a. Based on the test scores, which group would you choose to be in, A or B?
   b. Is the mean always a good indicator of central tendency? Explain.
2. Investigate whether there is a relationship between the population of a city and its area in square miles. Collect needed data on 20 U.S. cities from an encyclopedia or a world almanac. View the scatter plot and sketch the graph on paper. Assign population to x values and area to y values.

ANSWERS

Try This

a. $\bar{x} = 124.5$
b. $\bar{x} = 27.25$

Investigate

1. a. Group B has a mean of 75. Group A has a mean of 69.25.
b. No, it is affected by extreme values. Sometimes the median or mode is a better indicator of central tendency.
2. Answers will vary, but there should be a slight positive relationship.

An Introduction to Matrices

You can use this investigation at any point in Chapter 15 to introduce students to the use of matrices for displaying data.

TI–81 INVESTIGATION 5

An Introduction to Matrices

(for use with Chapter 15)

Objectives: Understand the meaning of a matrix; identify the dimensions of a matrix; solve problems by adding matrices.

Real-world data such as that shown in the chart at the right can be shown using a **matrix.** A matrix is a rectangular array of numbers.

ATHLETIC SHOE SALES				
U.S. Sales (million $)				
Quarter	Tennis	Basket-ball	Running	Walking
1st	4.2	12.7	6.3	8.6
2nd	5.3	11.2	7.5	8.6
3rd	5.2	15.8	6.4	7.5
4th	4.9	9.4	5.5	6.9
Foreign Sales (million $)				
Quarter	Tennis	Basket-ball	Running	Walking
1st	5.6	6.4	4.2	6.2
2nd	6.1	5.8	3.1	6.2
3rd	5.9	4.6	2.7	5.9
4th	5.1	5.1	3.6	6.0

Here is how the data for one company's sales of athletic shoes in the U.S. can be shown using a matrix. Notice that brackets are used to indicate a matrix.

$$\begin{bmatrix} 4.2 & 12.7 & 6.3 & 8.6 \\ 5.3 & 11.2 & 7.5 & 8.6 \\ 5.2 & 15.8 & 6.4 & 7.5 \\ 4.9 & 9.4 & 5.5 & 6.9 \end{bmatrix}$$

The number of rows and columns in a matrix determine the dimensions of the matrix. For the matrix above, there are 4 rows and 4 columns, so the dimensions are **4 × 4** (read "four by four"). A matrix that has the same number of rows and columns is called a **square matrix.**

The numbers in a matrix are called **entries.** The position of an entry is identified by its row and its column. In the matrix above, the entry 15.8 is in the 3rd row, 2nd column. We can write (3, 2) to name the position. The entry in position (4, 3) is 5.5.

EXAMPLE 1 Using the data given in the table for Foreign athletic shoe sales, create a matrix and give the dimensions of the matrix. In what position is the entry 6.0? the entry 6.1?

$$\begin{bmatrix} 5.6 & 6.4 & 4.2 & 6.2 \\ 6.1 & 5.8 & 3.1 & 6.2 \\ 5.9 & 4.6 & 2.7 & 5.9 \\ 5.6 & 5.1 & 3.6 & 6.0 \end{bmatrix}$$

The dimensions of the matrix are 4×4.

The entry 6.0 is in position (4, 4); 6.1 is in position (2, 1).

Try This

a. Using the data given in the table below, create a matrix and give the dimensions of the matrix. In what position is the entry 642? the entry 327?

ATHLETIC SHOE SALES IN THE U.S. (in millions of dollars)			
	1986	1987	1988
walking shoes	368	512	752
gym shoes	642	693	783
jogging/running	476	475	460
tennis	448	367	353
aerobic	333	401	327

Data from the Statistical Abtracts of the United States, 1990.

A matrix looks very similar to a table. So, why do we use matrices? When data are written in matrices, we can define operations on the matrices similar to the way we perform operations with rational numbers.

EXAMPLE 2 Find the total of the U.S. and foreign sales by quarter for each type of athletic shoe using the data at the top of page 732.

Since we want to find the total sales, we need to add. Two matrices can be added if they have the same dimensions. To add matrices, add corresponding entries.

$$\begin{bmatrix} 4.2 & 12.7 & 6.3 & 8.6 \\ 5.3 & 11.2 & 7.5 & 8.6 \\ 5.2 & 15.8 & 6.4 & 7.5 \\ 4.9 & 9.4 & 5.5 & 6.9 \end{bmatrix} + \begin{bmatrix} 5.6 & 6.4 & 4.2 & 6.2 \\ 6.1 & 5.8 & 3.1 & 6.2 \\ 5.9 & 4.6 & 2.7 & 5.9 \\ 5.6 & 5.1 & 3.6 & 6.0 \end{bmatrix} = \begin{bmatrix} 9.8 & 19.1 & 10.5 & 14.8 \\ 11.4 & 17.0 & 10.6 & 14.8 \\ 11.1 & 20.4 & 10.1 & 13.4 \\ 10.5 & 14.5 & 9.1 & 12.9 \end{bmatrix}$$

You can use the *TI-81* to add matrices. You can enter and store up to three different matrices in the calculator at a time.

EXAMPLE 3 Find [A] + [B]

$$[A] = \begin{bmatrix} 6 & -1 & -5 \\ 0.4 & 1.7 & 16 \end{bmatrix} \quad B = \begin{bmatrix} -7 & -2 & 11 \\ 4.7 & -0.8 & -5 \end{bmatrix}.$$

- Press the MATRX key. The screen will show two menus: `MATRIX` (for doing matrix operations within a single matrix), and `EDIT` (for entering new matrices or modifying existing matrices).

ANSWERS

Try This

a. $\begin{bmatrix} 368 & 512 & 752 \\ 642 & 693 & 783 \\ 476 & 475 & 460 \\ 448 & 367 & 353 \\ 333 & 401 & 327 \end{bmatrix}$

The dimensions of the matrix are 5×3.
The entry 642 is in position (2, 1).
The entry 327 is in position (5, 3).

b. $\begin{bmatrix} -4.5 & 8.1 & 2.7 \\ 4.9 & 4.2 & 6.1 \end{bmatrix}$

c. $\begin{bmatrix} 6 & -3 \\ 12.25 & -5.6 \\ 0.25 & 8.5 \end{bmatrix}$

d. You can not add these matrices together because they don't both have the same dimensions.

Exercises

1. 4 × 2; 7.5
2. 1 × 3; there is no position (2, 1) in this matrix
3. The difference in sales was the greatest in the 3rd quarter for basketball shoes.
4. Rock-n-Roll CDs were most popular.

- Press the right arrow key [▶] to enter the EDIT menu, and then select 1:[A] to enter the first matrix.
- Set the dimensions of [A] to 2 × 3 by pressing 2 [ENTER] 3 [ENTER].
- Define each entry of the matrix by its row and column. When you finish with a position, press [ENTER] to go to the next position.
- After entering matrix [A], press [MATRX] and follow the same steps to enter [B].
- Return to the Home screen, by pressing [2nd] [QUIT]. To display a stored matrix on the Home screen, press [2nd] [[A]] [ENTER], and matrix [A] will be displayed.
- To add [A] and [B], press [2nd] [[A]] [+] [2nd] [[B]] [ENTER].

  The sum of [A] and [B] is $\begin{bmatrix} -1 & -3 & 6 \\ 5.1 & 0.9 & 11 \end{bmatrix}$.

Try This Add if possible. If it is not possible to add the matrices, tell why.

b. $\begin{bmatrix} -2.1 & 5 & 8.3 \\ 4 & -1.8 & 3.4 \end{bmatrix} + \begin{bmatrix} -2.4 & 3.1 & -5.6 \\ 0.9 & 6 & 2.7 \end{bmatrix}$

c. $\begin{bmatrix} 9 & -11 \\ 7.5 & -2.5 \\ 0 & 3.4 \end{bmatrix} + \begin{bmatrix} -3 & 8 \\ 4.75 & -3.1 \\ 0.25 & 5.1 \end{bmatrix}$

d. $\begin{bmatrix} 6 & 2 \\ 5 & -1 \\ 4 & -4 \\ 3 & -7 \end{bmatrix} + \begin{bmatrix} 2 & 0 & 1 & 5 \\ 8 & -1 & 0 & 11 \\ 1 & 12 & -3 & -2 \end{bmatrix}$

EXERCISES

Add. Give the dimensions of the resulting matrix and the entry in the (2, 1) position.

1. $[A] = \begin{bmatrix} -4.2 & 6.5 \\ 2.8 & 3.7 \\ -5.4 & 7.3 \\ 8.1 & -2.4 \end{bmatrix}$ $B = \begin{bmatrix} -3.6 & 2.4 \\ 4.7 & 5.2 \\ -5.4 & 7.3 \\ 6.4 & 6.8 \end{bmatrix}$

2. $A = [124 \quad 18 \quad -74]$ $B = [56 \quad -33 \quad -29]$

Solve.

3. Find how much greater U.S. sales of athletic shoes were than foreign sales by quarter and for each type of shoe. (Note: You subtract matrices with the same dimensions by subtracting corresponding entries.) In which quarter and for which type of shoe was the difference the greatest?

4. The Be-Bop Music Shoppe collected data on sales for its two biggest sales months. Combine the data to find which type of format and which style of music was most popular.

NUMBER OF UNITS SOLD								
	July				December			
	Jazz	Rock-n-Roll	Classical	Other	Jazz	Rock-n-Roll	Classical	Other
CDs	475	624	450	260	1264	1422	1325	924
CD singles	100	95	120	47	523	764	821	75
Cassettes	270	295	175	98	425	524	600	120
Cassette singles	160	198	46	62	190	220	75	91
Other	69	74	52	61	75	82	90	60

5. ***Write Your Own Problem*** Find data that can be represented in two matrices. Write a problem that can be solved by adding or subtracting matrices.

Investigate

6. If A and B are two matrices with the same dimensions, does A + B = B + A? Give an example and write to explain why or why not.

7. If A and B are two matrices with the same dimensions, does A − B = B − A? Give an example and write to explain why or why not.

8. Suppose A = B. What are the values of x, y, and z. Write an explanation of how you determined the values of the variables?

$$A = \begin{bmatrix} 2x + 1 & 0 & 3z - 2 \\ 3 & y - 7 & -1 \end{bmatrix} \quad B = \begin{bmatrix} 7 & 0 & -5 \\ 3 & -0.25 & -1 \end{bmatrix}$$

5. Answers may vary.

Investigate

6. Yes. Examples and explanations may vary. The Commutative Property holds for addition of matrices.
7. No. Examples and explanations may vary. The Commutative Property does not hold for subtraction of matrices.
8. $x = 3$, $y = 6.75$, $z = -1$; Since A and B are equal, you can set up equations from corresponding entries of the two matrices to find the values of x, y, and z.

Matrix Multiplication

You may need to diagram matrix multiplication manually before having students use the calculator so that students will understand how each entry in the new matrix is found.

TI–81 INVESTIGATION 6

Matrix Multiplication

(for use with Chapter 15)

Objective: To multiply a rational number and a matrix; to multiply two matrices.

The data at the right shows the average monthly income for two school stores in the Yorktown School District. If we represent the data using a matrix and multiply by a rational number, we can gain more information about the school stores.

AVERAGE MONTHLY INCOME			
	Clothing	Supplies	Food
School 1	$1800	$1200	$2500
School 2	$2000	$1800	$3000

EXAMPLE 1

If profits from sales in the school stores average 20% of total sales, use the data in the table to find the average profit from clothing at School 2, the average profit from food at School 1, and the average total profit from all items at School 1.

- We can represent the sales data in a matrix.

$$\text{Let } A = \begin{bmatrix} 1800 & 1200 & 2500 \\ 2000 & 1800 & 3000 \end{bmatrix}$$

The rows represent schools and the columns represent the types of items.

- To find the averge amount of profit, find (0.20)A. To multiply a rational number and a matrix, multiply each entry in the matrix by the rational number.

$$(0.20)A = \begin{bmatrix} (0.20)1800 & (0.20)1200 & (0.20)2500 \\ (0.20)2000 & (0.20)1800 & (0.20)3000 \end{bmatrix}$$

$$= \begin{bmatrix} 360 & 240 & 500 \\ 400 & 360 & 600 \end{bmatrix}$$

The *TI-81* can be used to multiply a rational number and a matrix. For the product above, enter the original matrix in the calculator and press [2nd] [QUIT]. Then press 0.20 [×] [2nd] [[A]] [ENTER].

The average profit from clothing at School 2 is $400. The average profit from food at School 1 is $500. The average profit from all items at School 1 is $1100. (This is the sum of all entries in the first row of the matrix.)

Try This Suppose the profits from sales in the school stores average 17% of total sales.

a. Find the average profit from clothing at School 1.

b. Find the average profit from supplies at School 2.

c. Find the average profit from food at both school stores combined.

ANSWERS

Try This

a. $306
b. $306
c. $935

The tables at the right show data about extracurricular activities at the two schools in the Yorktown School District. We can use matrix multiplication to find the costs associated with extracurricular activities at each school.

NUMBER OF PARTICIPANTS			
	Music	Sports	Clubs
School 1	120	175	230
School 2	140	98	290

EXAMPLE 2

COST PER PUPIL BY SEMESTER		
	1st Semester	2nd Semester
Music	$60	$80
Sports	$120	$100
Clubs	$35	$35

The Superintendent for the Yorktown School District has to prepare a budget summary for the School Board for extracurricular activities. Use the data in the tables to determine which school and which semester the costs were the highest, how much less the costs for the second semester were at School 2 than at School 1, and whether the costs for School 1 were more or less than the costs for School 2 for the entire year.

Solution

- The data can be shown in matrices.

$$A = \begin{bmatrix} 120 & 175 & 230 \\ 140 & 98 & 290 \end{bmatrix} \quad B = \begin{bmatrix} 60 & 80 \\ 120 & 100 \\ 35 & 35 \end{bmatrix}$$

- We need to multiply the matrices to find the cost per school by semester.

$$AB = \begin{bmatrix} 120 & 175 & 230 \\ 140 & 98 & 290 \end{bmatrix} \begin{bmatrix} 60 & 80 \\ 120 & 100 \\ 35 & 35 \end{bmatrix}$$

$$= \begin{bmatrix} 120 \cdot 60 + 175 \cdot 120 + 230 \cdot 35 & 120 \cdot 80 + 175 \cdot 100 + 230 \cdot 35 \\ 140 \cdot 60 + 98 \cdot 120 + 290 \cdot 35 & 140 \cdot 80 + 98 \cdot 100 + 290 \cdot 35 \end{bmatrix}$$

$$= \begin{bmatrix} 36{,}250 & 35{,}150 \\ 30{,}310 & 21{,}325 \end{bmatrix}$$

The color coding shows how the entries in the product matrix were found. Notice that the row number and the column number from the original matrices determine the position of the entry in the product matrix. For example, the **2nd** row taken with the **1st** column produce the entry in the **(2,1)** position in the product matrix.

- You now have to interpret the entries in the product matrix. The number of participants in each activity for each semester was multiplied by the cost per participant for that activity. So, an entry in the product matrix is the cost per semester for each school.

	Total cost 1st semester	Total cost 2nd semester
School 1	\$36,250	\$35,150
School 2	\$30,310	\$21,325

- To multiply two matrices using the *TI-81*, first enter matrix *A*, then enter matrix B. Then press, [2nd] [[A]] [×] [2nd] [[B]] [ENTER].
- Costs were highest during the first semester at School 1. Costs during the second semester at School 2 were \$13,825 less than costs during the second semester at School 1. (Subtract the entries in the second column.) The cost for the year was greater at School 1. (Find the total for each row and compare.)

d. School 2, first semester
e. \$3700
f. \$67,400

Try This Suppose that 150 students participated in music at school 1 and that 125 students participated in sports at school 2.

d. At which school and for which semester were costs the lowest?

e. How much more were the costs for the second semester for School 1 than for School 2?

f. What was the total cost for extracurricular activities for the year at School 2?

Exercises

1. $\begin{bmatrix} 105 & 150 \\ 75 & 165 \end{bmatrix}$

2. $\begin{bmatrix} 15 & 60 \\ 30 & 90 \end{bmatrix}$

3. $\begin{bmatrix} 48 & 40 \\ 2 & -10 \end{bmatrix}$

4. $\begin{bmatrix} 5 & 4 \\ 2 & 3 \end{bmatrix}$

EXERCISES

Find each product.

1. $0.75\begin{bmatrix} 140 & 200 \\ 100 & 220 \end{bmatrix}$

2. $1.5\begin{bmatrix} 10 & 40 \\ 20 & 60 \end{bmatrix}$

3. $\begin{bmatrix} 8 & 4 \\ -2 & 6 \end{bmatrix}\begin{bmatrix} 5 & 5 \\ 2 & 0 \end{bmatrix}$

4. $\begin{bmatrix} 1 & 0 \\ 0 & 1 \end{bmatrix}\begin{bmatrix} 5 & 4 \\ 2 & 3 \end{bmatrix}$

The number of male and female students at Manlius High School are given in matrix S below.

$$\begin{array}{lcccc} \text{Grade:} & 9 & 10 & 11 & 12 \end{array}$$

$$S = \begin{bmatrix} 220 & 195 & 205 & 200 \\ 225 & 190 & 200 & 200 \end{bmatrix} \begin{matrix} \text{males} \\ \text{females} \end{matrix}$$

The average amount of money each student spends in the cafeteria daily is given in matrix D below.

$$D = \begin{bmatrix} 2.90 \\ 2.75 \\ 3.05 \\ 2.50 \end{bmatrix}$$

5. If 42% of all students buy lunch in the school cafeteria, use scalar multiplication find the number of each category of students that buys lunch in the cafeteria. Round to the nearest whole number.

6. Find SD. How much money do the students at Manlius High spend daily on lunch?

Investigate

7. Try to multiply all of the combinations of two of the matrices A, B, and C (AB, BA, AC, CA, BC, CB).

$$A = \begin{bmatrix} 1 & 2 & 3 \\ 2 & 1 & 4 \end{bmatrix} \quad B = \begin{bmatrix} 1 & 0 \\ 2 & 1 \\ 3 & 2 \end{bmatrix} \quad C = \begin{bmatrix} 3 & -1 & 3 \\ 4 & 1 & 5 \\ 2 & 1 & 3 \end{bmatrix}$$

a. Which products were possible? Which were not possible?

b. Write a rule that tells about the conditions necessary for the dimensions of two matrices in order for them to be multiplied.

8. Two matrices are equal when corresponding entries are equal. Does $AB = BA$ for the matrices above? Is multiplication of any two matrices commutative?

9. In which Exercise, 1–4, was the product matrix equal to one of the original matrices? What generalization can be made from this example?

5. $\begin{bmatrix} 92 & 82 & 86 & 84 \\ 95 & 80 & 84 & 84 \end{bmatrix}$

6. $4584.50

Investigate

7. a. AB, BA, AC, and CB are possible; BC and CA are not possible

b. Two matrices may be multiplied if the number of rows in the second matrix is the same as the number of columns in the first matrix.

8. No, AB $\neq$ BA; multiplication of matrices is not commutative.

9. In Exercise 4 the product matrix is equal to the second matrix. The first matrix is the identity matrix.

Milestones in Mathematics

Gauss called mathematics the Queen of the sciences. Clearly then, mathematicians are her courtiers. To fully enjoy mathematics, you need a sense of its development and of the people of genius who have devoted their lives to its exploration. **Milestones in Mathematics** is a partial list of important events in mathematical history. You may want to find additional information in the library to learn more about these and other mathematicians and their contributions to the field of mathematics.

Milestones in Mathematics

c. 30,000+	BC	The knucklebones of animals were used as dice in games of chance.
c. 20,000+	BC	A wolfbone with 55 notches in two rows divided into groups of five was used for counting (discovered at Vestonice in Czechoslovakia).
c. 8,000	BC	First evidence of recorded counting.
c. 2,000	BC	The Egyptians had arrived at the value for pi of $\pi = 4(8/9)^2$.
c. 1,900	BC	Babylonian scholars used cuneiform numerals to the base 60 in the oldest-known written numeration for place value.
c. 1,700	BC	Sumerian notation was used to solve quadratic equations by the equivalent of the formula we use today.
c. 800	BC	Queen Dido founded the great city of Carthage by solving the geometric "Problem of Dido." A rigorous proof of this problem—what closed curve of specified length will enclose a maximum area—did not come until the nineteenth century.
c. 700	BC	Zero appeared in the Seleucid mathematical tables.
c. 550	BC	Pythagoras developed a logical, deductive proof of the Pythagorean theorem.
c. 300	BC	Euclid wrote the first geometry text, *Elements*.
c. 250	BC	Archimedes wrote *On Mechanical Theorems, Method* for his friend Eratosthenes.
c. 250	AD	An initial-letter shorthand for algebraic equations was developed.
c. 300	AD	Pappus of Alexandria discussed the areas of figures with the same perimeter in the *Mathematical Collection*.
c. 375	AD	Earliest known Mayan Initial Series inscriptions for expressing dates and periods of time.
c. 400	AD	Hypatia, the foremost mathematician in Alexandria, lectured on Diophantine algebra.
595		Date of an Indian deed on copper plate showing the oldest known use of the nine numerals according to the place value principle: the first written decimal numeration with the structure used today.

825	A treatise on linear and quadratic equations was published by Mohammed Al-Khwarizmi.
850	Mahavira contributed to the development of algebra in India.
1202	Leonardo of Pisa, also called Fibonacci, wrote *Liber abaci*, introducing Arabic numbers to Europe. This book contains his "rabbit problem" involving the numbers we now call Fibonacci.
1261	Yang Hui of China wrote on the properties of the binomial coefficients.
1557	The equal sign (=) came into general use during the 16th century, A.D. (The twin lines as an equal sign were used by the English physician and mathematician Robert Recorde with the explanation that "noe .2. thynges, can be moare equalle.")
1614	John Napier invented logarithms.
1639	René Descartes published his treatise on the application of algebra to geometry (analytic geometry).
1654	Blaise Pascal described the properties of the triangle we now call Pascal's triangle.
1657	Major contributions to number theory were made by Pierre de Fermat including his formulation of the "Pell" equation.
1670	G. Mouton devised a decimal-based measuring system.
1688	The calculus was published by Isaac Newton in *Principia Mathematica*.
1735	Graph theory was originated by Leonard Euler in his paper on the problem, "The Seven Bridges of Konigsberg."
1784	Maria Agnesi developed new ways to deal with problems involving infinite quantities in her book, *Analytical Institutions*.
1799	The fundamental theorem of algebra was delineated by Carl Friederich Gauss, who also developed rigorous proof as the requirement of mathematics.
1816	Sophie Germain published equations which stated the law for vibrating elastic surfaces.
1832	Evariste Galois wrote the theorem stating the conditions under which an equation can be solved.
1854	George Boole developed the postulates of "Boolean Algebra" in *Laws of Thought*.
1854	Mary Fairfax Somerville wrote books to popularize mathematics and extend the influence of the work of mathematicians.
1859	George F. B. Reimann published his work on the distribution of primes; "Reimann's Hypothesis" became one of the famous unsolved problems of mathematics.

1886 Modern combinatorial topology was created by Henri Poincare.

1888 Sonya Kovalesvskaya was awarded the Prix Bordin for her paper "On the Rotation of a Solid Body About a Fixed Point."

1897 David Hilbert published his monumental work on the theory of number fields and later clarified the foundations of geometry.

1906 Grace Chisholm Young and William Young published the first text on set theory.

1914 Srinivasa Ramanujan went to England to collaborate with G. H. Hardy on analytic number theory.

1925 Hermann Weyl published fundamental papers on group theory.

1931 Gödel showed that there must be undecidable propositions in any formal system and that one of those undecidable propositions is consistency.

1932 A completely general theory of ideal numbers was built up, on an axiomatic basis, by Emmy Noether.

1936 The minimax principle in probability and statistics was developed by Abraham Wald.

1937 Goldbach's conjecture that every even number is the sum of two primes ($12 = 5 + 7$, $100 = 3 + 97$) was established by I. M. Vinogradov for every sufficiently large even number that is the sum of, at most, four primes.

1938 Claude E. Shannon discovered the analogy between the truth values of propositions and the states of switches and relays in an electric circuit.

1942 Jacqueline Ferrand created the concept of preholomorphic functions, using these to produce a new methodology for mathematical proofs.

1951 Elizabeth Scott, Jerzy Newyman, and C. D. Shane applied statistical theories to deduce the existence of clusters of galaxies.

1953 Maria Pastori extended the usefulness of the tensor calculus in the pure mathematical investigation of generalized spaces.

1960 Advances in the application of probability and statistics were made by Florence Nightingale David.

1976 Four color problem proved using electronic computing in concert with human deduction.

1985 A new algorithm for factoring large numbers by using elliptic curves was developed by Hendrik W. Lenstra, Jr.

1985 David Hoffman discovered a fourth minimal surface, the first new minimal surface discovered since the 1700s.

???? "Fermat's Last Theorem" on the impossibility of separating any power above the second into two powers of the same degree is proved.

Tables

TABLE 1: Squares and Square Roots

N	N^2	$\sqrt{N}$	N	N^2	$\sqrt{N}$
1	1	1	51	2,601	7.141
2	4	1.414	52	2,704	7.211
3	9	1.732	53	2,809	7.280
4	16	2	54	2,916	7.348
5	25	2.236	55	3,025	7.416
6	36	2.449	56	3,136	7.483
7	49	2.646	57	3,249	7.550
8	64	2.828	58	3,364	7.616
9	81	3	59	3,481	7.681
10	100	3.162	60	3,600	7.746
11	121	3.317	61	3,721	7.810
12	144	3.464	62	3,844	7.874
13	169	3.606	63	3,969	7.937
14	196	3.742	64	4,096	8
15	225	3.873	65	4,225	8.062
16	256	4	66	4,356	8.124
17	289	4.123	67	4,489	8.185
18	324	4.243	68	4,624	8.246
19	361	4.359	69	4,761	8.307
20	400	4.472	70	4,900	8.367
21	441	4.583	71	5,041	8.426
22	484	4.690	72	5,184	8.485
23	529	4.796	73	5,329	8.544
24	576	4.899	74	5,476	8.602
25	625	5	75	5,625	8.660
26	676	5.099	76	5,776	8.718
27	729	5.196	77	5,929	8.775
28	784	5.292	78	6,084	8.832
29	841	5.385	79	6,241	8.888
30	900	5.477	80	6,400	8.944
31	961	5.568	81	6,561	9
32	1,024	5.657	82	6,724	9.055
33	1,089	5.745	83	6,889	9.110
34	1,156	5.831	84	7,056	9.165
35	1,225	5.916	85	7,225	9.220
36	1,296	6	86	7,396	9.274
37	1,369	6.083	87	7,569	9.327
38	1,444	6.164	88	7,744	9.381
39	1,521	6.245	89	7,921	9.434
40	1,600	6.325	90	8,100	9.487
41	1,681	6.403	91	8,281	9.539
42	1,764	6.481	92	8,464	9.592
43	1,849	6.557	93	8,649	9.644
44	1,936	6.633	94	8,836	9.695
45	2,025	6.708	95	9,025	9.747
46	2,116	6.782	96	9,216	9.798
47	2,209	6.856	97	9,409	9.849
48	2,304	6.928	98	9,604	9.899
49	2,401	7	99	9,801	9.950
50	2,500	7.071	100	10,000	10

TABLE 2: Values of Trigonometric Functions

Degrees	Sin	Cos	Tan	Degrees	Sin	Cos	Tan
0°	0.0000	1.0000	0.0000				
1°	0.0175	0.9998	0.0175	46°	0.7193	0.6947	1.0355
2°	0.0349	0.9994	0.0349	47°	0.7314	0.6820	1.0724
3°	0.0523	0.9986	0.0524	48°	0.7431	0.6691	1.1106
4°	0.0698	0.9976	0.0699	49°	0.7547	0.6561	1.1504
5°	0.0872	0.9962	0.0875	50°	0.7660	0.6428	1.1918
6°	0.1045	0.9945	0.1051	51°	0.7771	0.6293	1.2349
7°	0.1219	0.9925	0.1228	52°	0.7880	0.6157	1.2799
8°	0.1392	0.9903	0.1405	53°	0.7986	0.6018	1.3270
9°	0.1564	0.9877	0.1584	54°	0.8090	0.5878	1.3764
10°	0.1736	0.9848	0.1763	55°	0.8192	0.5736	1.4281
11°	0.1908	0.9816	0.1944	56°	0.8290	0.5592	1.4826
12°	0.2079	0.9781	0.2126	57°	0.8387	0.5446	1.5399
13°	0.2250	0.9744	0.2309	58°	0.8480	0.5299	1.6003
14°	0.2419	0.9703	0.2493	59°	0.8572	0.5150	1.6643
15°	0.2588	0.9659	0.2679	60°	0.8660	0.5000	1.7321
16°	0.2756	0.9613	0.2867	61°	0.8746	0.4848	1.8040
17°	0.2924	0.9563	0.3057	62°	0.8829	0.4695	1.8807
18°	0.3090	0.9511	0.3249	63°	0.8910	0.4540	1.9626
19°	0.3256	0.9455	0.3443	64°	0.8988	0.4384	2.0503
20°	0.3420	0.9397	0.3640	65°	0.9063	0.4226	2.1445
21°	0.3584	0.9336	0.3839	66°	0.9135	0.4067	2.2460
22°	0.3746	0.9272	0.4040	67°	0.9205	0.3907	2.3559
23°	0.3907	0.9205	0.4245	68°	0.9272	0.3746	2.4751
24°	0.4067	0.9135	0.4452	69°	0.9336	0.3584	2.6051
25°	0.4226	0.9063	0.4663	70°	0.9397	0.3420	2.7475
26°	0.4384	0.8988	0.4877	71°	0.9455	0.3256	2.9042
27°	0.4540	0.8910	0.5095	72°	0.9511	0.3090	3.0777
28°	0.4695	0.8829	0.5317	73°	0.9563	0.2924	3.2709
29°	0.4848	0.8746	0.5543	74°	0.9613	0.2756	3.4874
30°	0.5000	0.8660	0.5774	75°	0.9659	0.2588	3.7321
31°	0.5150	0.8572	0.6009	76°	0.9703	0.2419	4.0108
32°	0.5299	0.8480	0.6249	77°	0.9744	0.2250	4.3315
33°	0.5446	0.8387	0.6494	78°	0.9781	0.2079	4.7046
34°	0.5592	0.8290	0.6745	79°	0.9816	0.1908	5.1446
35°	0.5736	0.8192	0.7002	80°	0.9848	0.1736	5.6713
36°	0.5878	0.8090	0.7265	81°	0.9877	0.1564	6.3138
37°	0.6018	0.7986	0.7536	82°	0.9903	0.1392	7.1154
38°	0.6157	0.7880	0.7813	83°	0.9925	0.1219	8.1443
39°	0.6293	0.7771	0.8098	84°	0.9945	0.1045	9.5144
40°	0.6428	0.7660	0.8391	85°	0.9962	0.0872	11.4301
41°	0.6561	0.7547	0.8693	86°	0.9976	0.0698	14.3007
42°	0.6691	0.7431	0.9004	87°	0.9986	0.0523	19.0811
43°	0.6820	0.7314	0.9325	88°	0.9994	0.0349	28.6363
44°	0.6947	0.7193	0.9657	89°	0.9998	0.0175	57.2900
45°	0.7071	0.7071	1.0000	90°	1.0000	0.0000	

TABLE 3: Geometric Formulas

Rectangle
Area: $A = \ell w$
Perimeter: $P = 2\ell + 2w$

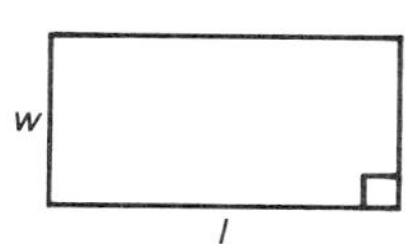

Parallelogram
Area: $A = bh$

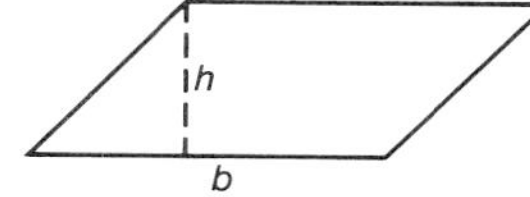

Square
Area: $A = s^2$
Perimeter: $P = 4s$

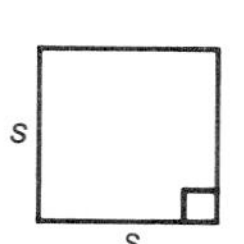

Trapezoid
Area: $A = \frac{1}{2}h(a + b)$

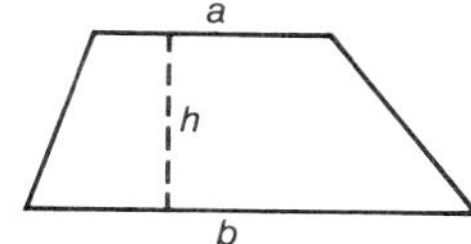

Triangle
Area: $A = \frac{1}{2}bh$
Sum of Angle Measures:

$A + B + C = 180°$

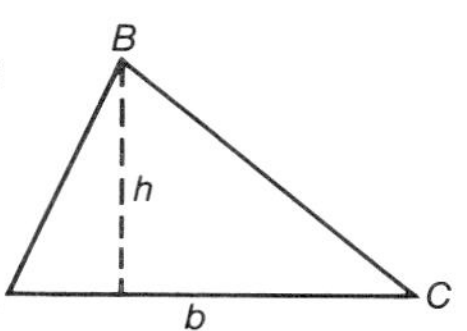

Circle
Area: $A = \pi r^2$
Circumference:
$C = \pi d = 2\pi r$

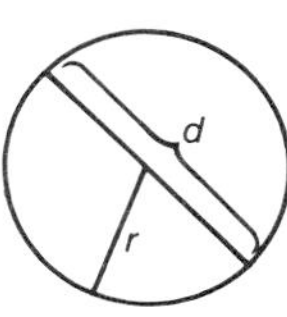

Right Triangle
Pythagorean Property:
$a^2 + b^2 = c^2$

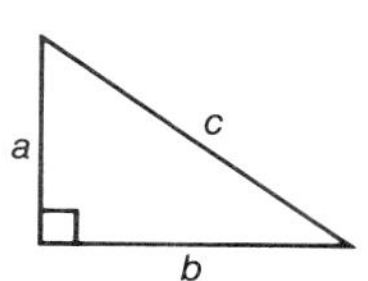

Rectangular Solid
Volume: $V = \ell wh$

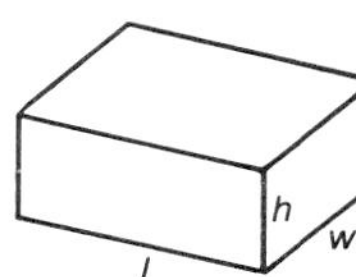

Polygon
Sum of Angle Measures:
$S = 180(n - 2)$
Number of Diagonals:
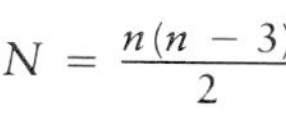
$N = \frac{n(n - 3)}{2}$

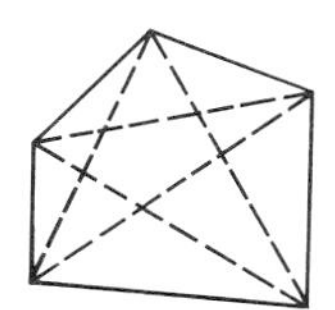

Cylinder
Volume: $V = \pi r^2 h$

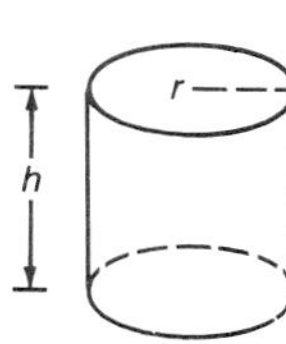

Prism
Volume: $V = Bh$
B = base area

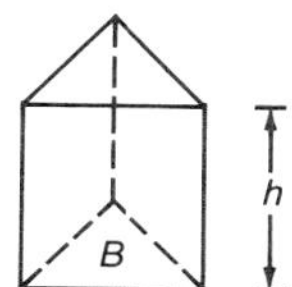

Cone
Volume: $V = \frac{1}{3}\pi r^2 h$

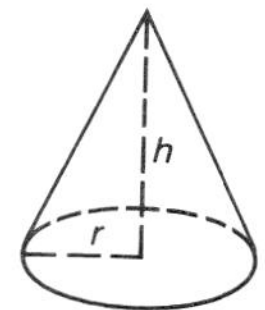

TABLE 4: Symbols

Symbol	Meaning	Symbol	Meaning
$+$	positive	$\{\ \}$	set braces
$-$	negative	$(\ )$	set parentheses
$\cdot$	times ($\times$)	$[\ ]$	set brackets
$\pm$	positive or negative	$\in$	is a member of
$=$	is equal to	$\cap$	the intersection of
$\neq$	is not equal to	$\cup$	the union of
$\approx$	is approximately equal to	$\subset$	is a subset of
$<$	is less than	$\emptyset$	the empty set
$>$	is greater than	(x, y)	ordered pair
$\leq$	is less than or equal to	$f(x)$	f of x, the value of f at x
$\geq$	is greater than or equal to	$\{x \mid x > 1\}$	the set of all numbers x such that $x > 1$
$-n$	additive inverse of n	$\triangle$	triangle
$\lvert n \rvert$	absolute value of n	$\angle$	angle
b^n	n^{th} power of b	$\sim$	is similar to
$a:b$	ratio of a to b	AB	segment AB
$\%$	percent	AB	the length of AB
$^\circ$	degree	$P(A)$	the probability of event A
$\sqrt{\ }$	principal square root	$\sin A$	the sine of A
π	pi, approximately 3.14	$\cos A$	the cosine of A
		$\tan A$	the tangent of A

Glossary

Abscissa (p. 304) See *x-coordinate.*

Absolute value (p. 56) The absolute value of a number n, represented as $|n|$, is its distance from 0 on the number line. For any number n, $|n| = n$ if n is a positive number or zero, and $|n| = -n$ if n is a negative number.

Acute angle (p. 615) An angle whose measure is less than 90°.

Addend Any one of a set of numbers to be added. In the sum $1 + 2 + 3$, 1, 2, and 3 are the addends.

Addition method (p. 367) A method for solving systems of equations in which the equations are added together to obtain an equation with fewer variables. One or both equations may be multiplied by a constant. The result is a *linear combination* of the original equations.

Addition property of equality (p. 114) For all real numbers a, b, and c, if $a = b$ then $a + c = b + c$.

Addition property of inequalities (p. 175) For all real numbers a, b, and c,
if $a < b$, then $a + c < b + c$.
if $a > b$, then $a + c > b + c$.
Similar statements hold for $\leq$ and $\geq$.

Additive identity (p. 10) The number 0 is the additive identity. For any real number a, $a + 0 = n$ and $0 + a = a$.

Additive inverse (p. 66) If the sum of two numbers or expressions is 0, they are additive inverses of each other.

Adjacent sides Two sides of a polygon are adjacent if their endpoints form a vertex.

Algebraic expression (p. 4) An expression that contains at least one variable.

Angle Two rays with a common endpoint called the vertex.

Antecedent (p. 192) See *If-then statement.*

Area The size of a surface expressed in square units.

Ascending order (p. 226) A polynomial is in ascending order for a variable if the term with the smallest exponent for that variable (often a constant term) is first, the term with the next greatest exponent for that variable is second, and so on.

Associative properties (p. 20) For all real numbers a, b, and c,
Addition: $a + (b + c) = (a + b) + c$.
Multiplication: $a \cdot (b \cdot c) = (a \cdot b) \cdot c$.

Axes (p. 304) See *Coordinate axes.*

Axiom (p. 102) A property that is assumed to be true without proof.

Axis of symmetry of a parabola (p. 553) If the graph of a parabola is folded so that its two sides coincide, the line on which the fold occurs is the axis of symmetry. For a parabola defined by the equation $y = ax^2 + bx + c$, the axis of symmetry is the line $x = -\frac{b}{2a}$.

Base (p. 15) In exponential notation n^x, n is the base.

Binomial (p. 221) A polynomial with exactly two terms.

Boundary line (p. 417) A line which separates the plane into two half-planes.

Circumference The distance around a circle.

Closure properties (p. 102) For any real numbers a and b,
Addition: $a + b$ is a real number.
Multiplication: $a \cdot b$ is a real number.

Coefficient (p. 222) In any term, the coefficient is the numeric factor of the term or the number that is multiplied by the variable. In $-3x$, the coefficient is -3; in x^4 the coefficient is 1.

Collect like terms (p. 26) The process of using the distributive property to simplify expressions containing like terms.

Combined variation (p. 566) An equation of the form $z = \frac{kx}{y}$, where k is a nonzero constant, expresses combined variation.

Commutative properties (p. 9) For any real numbers a and b,
Addition: $a + b = b + a$.
Multiplication: $ab = ba$.

Complement (p. 644) Suppose S is a sample space and A is an event in S. The complement of A, symbolized A', is the set of elements in S that are not in A.

Complementary angles (p. 372) Two angles are complementary if their sum is 90°.

Completing the square (p. 586) Adding a constant to an expression of the form $ax^2 + bx + c$ to form a trinomial square.

Complex rational expression (p. 469) An expression with a rational expression in its numerator or denominator or both.

Compound sentence (p. 405) Two simple sentences joined by a connective such as "and" or "or."

Conclusion (p. 192) See *If-then statement.*

Conditional statement (p. 192) A statement in the form of *If a, then b.*

Congruent Two geometric figures are congruent if they have the same size and shape.

Conjunction (p. 405) A conjunction of two statements is formed by connecting them with "and" and is true when *both* statements are true.

Consecutive even integers (p. 158) Numbers that follow each other when counting by twos, beginning with an even number.

Consecutive integers (p. 158) Numbers such as 22, 23, and 24 that follow each other when counting by ones.

Consecutive odd integers (p. 158) Numbers that follow each other when counting by twos, beginning with an odd number.

Consequent (p. 192) See *If-then statement.*

Consistent (p. 361) A system of equations that has one or more solutions is consistent.

Constant (p. 214) A term with no variables.

Constant of variation (p. 557) In an equation of variation $y = kx$ or $y = \frac{k}{x}$, k is the constant of variation.

Converse (p. 192) The converse of a conditional statement is found by interchanging the hypothesis and the conclusion.

Coordinate axes (p. 304) The x- and y-axes in the number plane.

Coordinate of a point on the number line (p. 59) The number that corresponds to the point.

Coordinate plane (p. 304) A plane in which a coordinate system has been set up.

Coordinate system (Cartesian) (p. 304) A system for graphing ordered pairs of numbers as points in a plane using two perpendicular number lines, called the *coordinate axes,* which intersect at the zero point of each.

Coordinates (p. 304) The numbers in an ordered pair, used to locate a point on a plane.

Coordinates of a point on the plane (p. 304) The abscissa and ordinate of a point, used to locate the point on the coordinate plane.

Corner points (p. 424) The corner points of the graph of a system of inequalities are the points where the boundary lines intersect.

Corresponding angles (p. 614) In two similar triangles, the angles with equal measure. See *Similar triangles.*

Corresponding sides (p. 614) In two similar triangles, the sides opposite corresponding angles. See *Similar triangles.*

Cosine (p. 620) In a right triangle, the sine of angle $A = \frac{\text{the length of the side adjacent to } \angle A}{\text{the length of the hypotenuse}}$.

Counterexample (p. 14) An example that shows that a statement is false.

Cube root (p. 494) A number c is a cube root of a if $c^3 = a$.

Data Numerical information, usually about the real world.

Degree of a polynomial (p. 223) The greatest degree of any of its terms after it has been simplified.

Degree of a term (p. 223) The degree of a term is the sum of the exponents of the variables in the term.

Degree of an angle A unit used to measure angles. There are 90 degrees (90°) in a right angle.

Denominator In $\frac{a}{b}$, b is the denominator.

Density property (p. 486) The density property for real numbers states that between any pair of different real numbers, there exists another real number.

Dependent (p. 361) A system of equations that has an infinite number of solutions is dependent.

Descending order (p. 226) A polynomial is in descending order for a variable if the term with the largest exponent for that variable is first, the term with the next smaller exponent for that variable is second, and so on.

Diagonal of a polygon (p. 585) A line segment that connects two nonadjacent vertices of a polygon.

Diameter The diameter of a circle is the length of a line segment that passes through its center and has endpoints on the circle.

Difference (p. 71) For all real numbers a and b, the difference $a - b$ is the number c, such that $c + b = a$.

Direct variation (p. 557) A function that can be described by an equation $y = kx$ where k is a nonzero constant.

Discriminant (p. 591) For a quadratic equation $ax^2 + bx + c = 0$, the expression $b^2 - 4ac$ is the discriminant.

Disjunction (p. 407) A disjunction of two statements is formed by connecting them with "or" and is true when *one or both* statements are true.
Distance formula (p. 513) The distance between any two points (x_1, y_1) and (x_2, y_2) is given by $d = \sqrt{(x_1 - x_2)^2 + (y_1 - y_2)^2}$.
Distributive property of multiplication over addition (p. 24) For any real numbers a, b, and c, $a(b + c) = ab + ac$ and $(b + c)a = ba + ca$.
Distributive property of multiplication over subtraction (p. 89) For any real numbers a, b, and c, $a(b - c) = ab - ac$, and $(b - c)a = ba - ca$.
Division Property for Radicals (p. 498) For any nonnegative real numbers a and b, where $b \neq 0$, $\sqrt{\frac{a}{b}} = \frac{\sqrt{a}}{\sqrt{b}}$ and $\frac{\sqrt{a}}{\sqrt{b}} = \sqrt{\frac{a}{b}}$.
Division Theorem (p. 472) For any number a and any nonzero number b, $\frac{a}{b} = a \cdot \frac{1}{b}$.
Domain (p. 536) The domain of a relation is the set of first coordinates.

Element of a set (p. 400) Any object in the set. Also called *member of a set.*
Empty set (p. 401) The set with no elements, symbolized $\emptyset$.
Equality (p. 103) A mathematical sentence $a = b$ states that a and b are expressions for the same number.
Equation (p. 33) A mathematical sentence that uses an equal sign to state that two expressions represent the same number or are equivalent. An equation may be true, false, or, if it contains a variable, open.
Equilateral triangle A triangle with all 3 sides of equal length.
Equivalent equations (p. 35) Equations with the same solution set.
Equivalent expressions (p. 9) Expressions that always result in the same number for all replacement values of their variables.
Evaluate an expression (p. 4) To evaluate an expression is to replace each variable in the expression by a given value and simplify the result.
Even integer Any integer that has 2 as a factor.
Event (p. 640) A subset of the sample space of an experiment.
Experimental probability (p. 640) See *Probability.*
Exponent (p. 15) In exponential notation n^x, x is the exponent. The exponent tells how many times the base is used as a factor.
Exponential notation (p. 15) The expression x^n is exponential form for the nth power of x.
Expression (p. 4) A number, or two or more numbers together with operation signs.
Extraneous solution (p. 452) When an equation is transformed, for example by squaring both sides, the transformed equation may have solutions that are not solutions to the original equation. These solutions are called extraneous.

Factor (p. 12) When two or more numbers (or expressions) are multiplied, each is a factor of the product.
Factor completely (p. 268) A polynomial is factored completely if the factors have no common factors other than 1.
Factoring (p. 25) To factor a number or expression is to write an equivalent expression that is the product of two or more numbers or expressions.
Factoring by grouping (p. 281) A method for factoring a polynomial in which different terms are first factored from different parts of the polynomial.
Field (p. 103) Any number system with two operations defined in which the field axioms hold.
Field axioms (p. 103) The closure, commutative, associative, identity, inverse, and distributive properties.
FOIL method (p. 241) A method for finding the product of two binomials. The product is written as the product of the first term of each binomial plus the product of the outside terms, plus the product of the inside terms, plus the product of the last terms.
Formula (p. 40) An equation that shows the relationship between two or more quantities.
Fraction See *Rational number.*
Fractional equation See *Rational equation.*
Fractional expression See *Rational expression.*
Frequency distribution (p. 653) A table showing the frequency, or number of occurrences, of a particular set of data.
Frequency polygon (p. 659) A graph used in statistics whose shape is a polygon. The graph shows the frequency of occurrence of data values in a set.
Function (p. 537) A relation that assigns to each member of its *domain* exactly one member its *range.*
Function values (p. 538) The outputs of a function.

Graph of a function (p. 542) A graph of all the ordered pairs that make up a function.
Graph of a number (p. 59) The point on the number line that corresponds to the number.

Graph of an equation (p. 310) The graph of an equation consists of all the points whose coordinates satisfy the equation.

Graph of an inequality (p. 172) The graph of an inequality consists of all the points whose coordinates satisfy the inequality.

Graph of an ordered pair (p. 304) The point on the coordinate plane that corresponds to the ordered pair.

Grouping symbols (p. 5) Symbols, such as parentheses or brackets, that indicate that the operations within them should be done first. When an expression contains more than one grouping symbol, the computations in the innermost grouping should be done first.

Half-plane (p. 417) One of the two regions into which a line separates a plane. The line itself is called a *boundary line* and may or may not be included in the half-plane.

Histogram (p. 658) A bar graph used in statistics to represent the frequency of occurrence of data values.

Horizontal line (p. 315) A line that is parallel to the x-axis.

Hypotenuse (p. 509) The side of a right triangle opposite the right angle.

Hypothesis (p. 192) See *If-then statement.*

Identity (p. 138) An equation that is true for all acceptable replacements of the variables.

Identity properties (p. 10) For any real number a,
Addition: $a + 0 = a$ and $0 + a = 0$.
Multiplication: $1 \cdot a = a$ and $a \cdot 1 = a$.

If-then statement (p. 192) A conditional statement made up of two parts: "If . . . , then . . . ." The first statement, following *if,* is called the *hypothesis* or *antecedent.* The second statement, following *then,* is called the *conclusion* or *consequent.*

Inconsistent (p. 361) A system of equations that has no solution is independent.

Independent events (p. 648) Two events are independent if neither event affects the probability that the other will occur.

Inequality (p. 172) A mathematical sentence containing an inequality symbol between two expressions.

Inequality symbols (p. 172) The symbols $<$, $>$, $\leq$, and $\geq$.

Integers (p. 54) The numbers in the set $\{\ldots, -3, -2, -1, 0, 1, 2, 3, \ldots\}$.

Interest (p. 346) A charge for the use of money, payed by the borrower to the lender.

Interior angles The interior angles of a polygon are those inside the figure.

Intersection (p. 401) The intersection of two sets is the set of all members that are common to both sets, symbolized $A \cap B$.

Interval graph (p. 550) A graph used to solve problems involving the intersections of various time intervals.

Inverse of a sum property (p. 94) For any real numbers a and b, $-(a + b) = -a + (-b)$. (The additive inverse of a sum is the sum of the additive inverses.)

Inverse properties (p. 102)
Addition: For each real number a, there is an additive inverse, $-a$, such that $a + (-a) = 0$.
Multiplication: For each real number a not equal to 0, there is a multiplicative inverse $\frac{1}{a}$ such that $a \cdot \frac{1}{a} = 1$.

Inverse variation (p. 561) A function that can be described by an equation $y = \frac{k}{x}$ where k is a nonzero constant.

Irrational number (p. 483) A real number that *cannot* be written in the form $\frac{a}{b}$ where a and b are integers.

Isosceles triangle A triangle with two sides of equal length.

Joint variation (p. 565) An equation of the form $z = kxy$ where k is a nonzero constant expresses joint variation.

Leading coefficient (p. 223) The coefficient of the leading term.

Leading term (p. 223) The term of a polynomial with the highest degree.

Least common denominator (LCD) of a rational expression (p. 446) The expression of smallest degree that is a multiple of the denominators of the given expressions.

Least common denominator (LCD) of a rational number The smallest positive number that is a multiple of each denominator.

Least common multiple (LCM) of a rational expression (p. 445) The expression of smallest degree that is a multiple of two or more expressions.

Least common multiple (LCM) of a rational number The smallest positive number that is a multiple of two or more given numbers.

Legs of a triangle (p. 509) The two sides of a right triangle that form the right angle.

Like terms (p. 26) Terms whose variable factors are exactly the same.

Line of best fit (p. 334) The line that best approximates a linear relationship among a set of data points.

Line plot (p. 657) A graph used in statistics that shows the frequency of occurrence of data values in a set.

Line segment A set of points containing two points and all the points between them in a line.

Linear combination (p. 368) A constant multiple of one equation added to a constant multiple of second equation results in a linear combination of the two equations.

Linear equation (p. 313) An equation whose graph is a straight line. An equation is linear if the variables occur to the first power only, there are no products of variables, and no variable appears in a denominator.

Linear function (p. 547) A function in the form $f(x) = mx + b$, where m and b are real numbers and $m \neq 0$.

Matrix (p. 732) A rectangular array of numbers.

Mean (p. 661) The average of a set of values.

Measures of central tendency (p. 661) A value that tells what number is at the middle, or center, of a set of data. Measures of central tendency include *Mean, Median,* and *Mode.*

Median (p. 661) The middle value of a set of values when all the values are arranged in order.

Member of a set (p. 400) Any object in the set. Also called *Element of a set.*

Minutes (p. 627) A subdivision of an angle. There are 60 minutes in a degree.

Mode (p. 662) In a set of data, the value that occurs the most often. Some sets of data have more than one mode, and some have no mode.

Moment (p. 87) The product of the force each load exerts on a lever and its distance from the fulcrum. Also known as *torque.*

Monomial (p. 214) An expression that is the product of numerals and variables.

Multiplication property of equality (p. 119) For all real numbers a, b, and c, if $a = b$, then $ac = bc$.

Multiplication property of inequalities (p. 180) For all real numbers a, b, and c, if $a > b$ and $c > 0$ then $ac > bc$. If $a > b$ and $c < 0$, then $ac < bc$.

Multiplicative identity (p. 10) The number 1 is the multiplicative identity. For any real number a, $1 \cdot a = a$ and $a \cdot 1 = a$.

Multiplicative inverse (p. 82) See *Reciprocal.*

Multiplicative property of zero (p. 78) The product of any real number and 0 is 0.

Mutually exclusive events (p. 645) Two events that cannot happen at the same time are mutually exclusive.

Natural numbers (p. 5) The numbers we use for counting. They are 1, 2, 3, 4, and so on.

Negative number (p. 54) Any number that is less than 0.

Negative relationship (p. 665) For a set of data in two variables, the variables have a negative relationship if one decreases as the other increases.

Null set (p. 80) See *Empty set.*

Numeral A symbol that names a number.

Numerator In $\frac{a}{b}$, a is the numerator.

Odd integer An integer that does not have 2 as a factor.

Open sentence (p. 33) An equation or inequality that contains at least one variable.

Opposites (p. 54) Numbers, such as 3 and -3, that are the same distance from 0 but on opposite sides of 0 on the number line.

Order of operations (p. 16) A rule for the order in which operations should be done. The order of operations is: (1) compute within grouping symbols; (2) compute powers; (3) multiply and divide in order from left to right; and (4) add and subtract in order from left to right.

Ordinate (p. 304) See *y-coordinate.*

Origin (p. 304) The point at which the axes of a plane or graph cross; the point (0, 0) in the Cartesian coordinate system.

Parabola (p. 552) The graph of a quadratic equation $ax^2 + bx + c = 0$, $a \neq 0$, is a parabola.

Parallel lines (p. 338) Lines in the same plane that never intersect.

Parallelogram A four-sided polygon in which the opposite sides are parallel and of equal length.

Percent (p. 152) Literally, "per one hundred"; represented by the symbol %.

Perfect square An expression whose square root can be written without radicals.

Perimeter The sum of the lengths of the sides of a polygon.

Perpendicular lines (p. 339) Two lines that intersect to form right angles.

Point-slope equation (p. 329) A nonvertical line that contains a point (x_1, y_1) and has slope m has an equation $y - y_1 = m(x - x_1)$.

Polygon A closed plane figure formed by three or more segments that intersect only at their endpoints so that exactly two segments meet at each endpoint. In a *regular polygon,* all angles are congruent and all line segments are congruent.

Polynomial (p. 221) A monomial or a sum of monomials.

Positive number (p. 54) Any number that is greater than zero.

Positive relationship (p. 665) For a set of data in two variables, the variables have a positive relationship if one increases as the other increases.

Power (p. 15) A number that can be named with exponential notation as x^n. The nth power of x is $\underbrace{x \cdot x \cdot x \cdot \ldots \cdot x}_{n \text{ factors}}$.

Prime number Any integer greater than 1 which has no integral factors other than 1 and itself.

Principal (p. 346) An amount of money that is invested or loaned.

Principal square root (p. 482) The nonnegative square root of a number.

Principle of moments (p. 88) When several parallel forces act on an object, it will be in balance if the sum of the moments is 0.

Principle of squaring (p. 519) If an equation $a = b$ is true, then the equation $a^2 = b^2$ is true.

Principle of zero products (p. 286) For any real numbers a and b, if $ab = 0$ then $a = 0$ or $b = 0$; if $a = 0$ or $b = 0$, then $ab = 0$.

Probability (p. 640) If an event E can occur m ways out of n possible equally-likely ways, the theoretical probability of that event is $P(E) = \frac{m}{n}$. The experimental probability is the estimated likelihood of an event, found by performing a number of trials and dividing the number of successful trials by the total number of trials.

Product Property for Radicals (p. 491) For any nonnegative real numbers a and b, $\sqrt{ab} = \sqrt{a} \cdot \sqrt{b}$.

Proof (p. 342) A convincing argument that a statement is true, using definitions, axioms, and other known facts.

Property of additive inverses (p. 66) For each real number a, there is one and only one real number $-a$ such that $a + (-a) = 0$.

Property of multiplicative inverses (p. 82) For each nonzero real number a, there is one and only one real number $\frac{1}{a}$ such that $a \cdot \frac{1}{a} = 1$.

Property of −1 (p. 93) For any real number a, $-1 \cdot a = -a$.

Proportion (p. 148) An equation that states that two ratios are equal.

Pythagorean theorem (p. 509) In any right triangle, if a and b are the lengths of the legs and c is the length of the hypotenuse, then $a^2 + b^2 = c^2$.

Quadrant (p. 306) One of the four regions into which coordinate axes divide a plane.

Quadratic equation (p. 576) An equation that can be written in the form $ax^2 + bx + c = 0$, where a, b, and c are real numbers and $a \neq 0$.

Quadratic formula (p. 589) A formula for finding the solutions of a quadratic equation $ax^2 + bx + c = 0$. The formula is $x = \frac{-b \pm \sqrt{b^2 - 4ac}}{2a}$.

Quadratic function (p. 552) A function in the form $f(x) = ax^2 + bx + c$, where a, b, and c are real numbers and $a \neq 0$.

Quotient (p. 81) For all real numbers a and b, the quotient $\frac{a}{b}$ (or $a \div b$), if it exists, is the number c such that $cb = a$.

Radical equation (p. 598) An equation that contains a variable in a radicand.

Radical expression (p. 487) When an expression is written under a radical, the result is a radical expression.

Radical sign (p. 482) The symbol $\sqrt{}$. Any expression that contains a radical sign is called a *radical expression*.

Radicand (p. 487) An expression under a radical sign.

Radius The radius of a circle is the distance from any point on the circle to its center.

Range (p. 536) The range of a relation is the set of second coordinates.

Ranked stem-and-leaf diagram (p. 656) A stem-and-leaf diagram in which the values are arranged in order from least to greatest.

Rate A ratio that compares two different units.

Ratio (p. 148) A comparison of one number to another, expressed as a quotient.

Rational equation (p. 451) An equation containing one or more rational expressions.

Rational expression (p. 432) The quotient of two polynomials.

Rational number (p. 59) Any number that can be expressed as the ratio of two integers in the form $\frac{a}{b}$ where $b \neq 0$.

Rationalizing the denominator (p. 499) Simplifying a radical expression so that there are no radicals in the denominator and only whole numbers or variables in the radicand.

Real number (p. 61) The real numbers consist of the rational numbers and the irrational numbers. There is a real number for each point of the number line.

Reciprocal (p. 82) Two expressions are reciprocals if their product is 1. A reciprocal is also called a *multiplicative inverse*.

Reciprocal Theorem (p. 472) For any rational numbers a and b, $\frac{1}{ab} = \frac{1}{a} \cdot \frac{1}{b}$.

Reflexive property of equality (p. 103) For any real number a, $a = a$ is always true.

Regular polygon (p. 432) See *Polygon*.
Relation (p. 536) Any set of ordered pairs.
Relatively prime (p. 264) Two polynomials are relatively prime if they have no common factors other than constants.
Repeating decimal (p. 86) A decimal in which the same number or group of numbers repeats endlessly.
Replacement set (p. 34) The set of all values that may replace the variables in a sentence.
Right angle An angle that measures 90°.
Right triangle (p. 615) A right triangle has one angle of 90°.
Rise (p. 318) The difference between the y-coordinates of two points; used to determine the slope of a line.
Roster notation (p. 400) A listing of all the members in a set.
Run (p. 318) The difference between the x-coordinates of two points; used to determine the slope of a line.

Sample space (p. 640) The set of all possible outcomes of an experiment.
Scatter plot (p. 665) A graph that shows the relationship between two variables. Each variable appears on one of the axes, and data are plotted as points.
Scientific notation (p. 217) A number expressed as the product of a power of 10 and a numeral greater than or equal to 1 but less than 10. The numbers 4.25×10^3 and 2.3×10^{-2} are expressed using scientific notation.
Set (p. 400) A well-defined collection of objects.
Set-builder notation (p. 400) A notation used to express the members of a set of numbers. For example, the set of negative integers can be written $\{x|x \text{ is an integer and } x < 0\}$.
Similar triangles (p. 614) Two triangles that have three pairs of angles of the same size. For similar triangles $\triangle ABC$ and $\triangle XYZ$, $\angle A$ and $\angle X$ have equal measure, $\angle B$ and $\angle Y$ have equal measure, and $\angle C$ and $\angle Z$ have equal measure. The corresponding sides are $\overline{AB}$ and $\overline{XY}$, $\overline{BC}$ and $\overline{YZ}$, and $\overline{AC}$ and $\overline{XZ}$. Corresponding sides are proportional.
Simple interest (p. 346) A percent[illegible] of a sum of borrowed money payed by t[illegible] borrower to the lender. The amount of the loan is called the *principal*.
Simplest form of a radical expression (p. 499) A radical is in simplest form when its radicand contains no perfect square factors and is not fractional, and any fraction does not contain a radical in the denominator.
Simplest form of a rational expression (p. 433) A rational expression is in simplest form when the numerator and denominator have no common factors other than 1 or -1.
Simplest form of an expression (p. 12) An expression is in simplest form when the only common factor of the numerator and denominator is 1.
Simplifying an expression (p. 12) The process of finding the simplest form of an expression.
Simulation (p. 649) A procedure for determining the probability of real events by running experiments that closely resemble the real situation.
Simultaneous equations (p. 358) See *System of equations*.
Sine (p. 619) In a right triangle, the sine of angle $A = \dfrac{\text{the length of the side opposite } \angle A}{\text{the length of the hypotenuse}}$.
Slope (p. 318) A number that tells how steeply a line slants; the ratio of rise to run.
Slope-intercept equation (p. 324) A line with slope m and y-intercept b has a slope-intercept equation $y = mx + b$.
Solution of a system of two equations in two variables (p. 358) An ordered pair that makes both equations true.
Solution of an equation (p. 34) A replacement for the variable that makes the equation true.
Solution of an equation in two variables (p. 309) An ordered pair that makes the equation a true statement.
Solution of an inequality (p. 172) A replacement for the variable that makes the inequality true.
Solution of an inequality in two variables (p. 417) Any ordered pair that makes the inequality true.
Solution set of an equation (p. 34) The set of all replacements for the variable that make the equation true.
Solve an equation (p. 34) To find the solution set of an equation.
Square of a number (p. 482) A number that has been raised to the second power.
Square root (p. 482) A number c is a square root of a if $c^2 = a$.
Standard form of a linear equation (p. 315) The standard form of a linear equation is $Ax + By = C$ where A, B, C are constants and A and B are not both 0.
Standard form of a quadratic equation (p. 576) Standard form for a quadratic equation is $ax^2 + bx + c = 0$.
Standard notation (p. 217) A number such as 100 or 3.21 written in its decimal form is in standard notation.
Statistics (p. 653) The branch of mathematics that deals with the collection, organization, display, and interpretation of data.

Stem-and-leaf diagram (p. 654) A display of data using certain digits (such as in the tens place) as "stems" and the remaining digit or digits as "leaves."
Subset (p. 80) Set A is a subset of set B if every element of set A is an element of set B.
Substitute (p. 4) To replace a variable with a number or expression.
Substitution method (p. 362) A method for solving systems of equations in which one equation is solved for one of the variables and the result is substituted in the other equation.
Symmetric property of equality (p. 103) For any real numbers a and b, if $a = b$, then $b = a$.
System of equations (p. 358) Two or more equations for which a common solution is sought (also called *Simultaneous equations*).
System of inequalities (p. 421) Two or more linear inequalities for which a common solution is sought.

Tangent (p. 621) In a right triangle, the tangent of angle $A = \frac{\text{the length of the side opposite } \angle A}{\text{the length of the side adjacent to } A}$.
Term of a polynomial (p. 222) In a polynomial, each monomial is a term.
Terminating decimal (p. 86) A number that can be written in decimal form with a finite number of digits.
Terms (p. 26) An expression that is the product of numerals and variables.
Tessellation (p. 432) A pattern formed by covering a surface with congruent shapes.
Theorem (p. 102) A property that can be proved using axioms, definitions, and other theorems.
Theoretical probability (p. 640) See *Probability*.
Transitive property of equality (p. 103) For any real numbers a, b, and c, if $a = b$ and $b = c$, then $a = c$.
Trapezoid A four-sided polygon with exactly two parallel sides.
Trial (p. 649) A trial is a simulation of a single event. Experimental probability is found by conducting many trials simulating the event and dividing the number of successful trials by the total number of trials.
Trigonometric ratios (p. 619) Ratios of the lengths of the sides of right triangles. See *sine, cosine,* and *tangent.*
Trinomial (p. 221) A polynomial with exactly three terms.
Trinomial square (p. 270) A trinomial that is the square of a binomial.

Union (p. 402) The union of two sets is the set of all members that are in either set (or in both), symbolized $A \cup B$.

Variable (p. 4) A letter (or other symbol) used to represent one or several numbers.
Variance (p. 664) A measure of how much a set of data varies from the mean of the data.
Velocity (p. 4) The rate of change of distance with respect to time.
Vertex of a parabola (p. 553) The maximum or minimum point of the graph of $y = ax^2 + bx + c$ $(a \neq 0)$. The x-coordinate of the vertex is $-\frac{b}{2a}$.
Vertex of an angle The point at which two rays meet (pl. vertices).
Vertical line (p. 315) A line that is parallel to the y-axis.
Volume (p. 41) The size of a solid expressed in cubic units.

Whole number (p. 5) Any natural number or 0.

x-axis (p. 304) The horizontal axis or number line in a coordinate plane.
x-coordinate (p. 304) The first number in an ordered pair used to locate a point on a plane, also called the *abscissa*.
x-intercept (p. 314) The x-coordinate of the point where a graph intersects the x-axis.

y-axis (p. 304) The vertical axis or number line in a coordinate plane.
y-coordinate (p. 304) The second number in an ordered pair used to locate a point on a plane, also called the *ordinate*.
y-intercept (p. 314) The y-coordinate of the point where a graph intersects the y-axis.

Selected Answers

Chapter 1

Lesson 1-1 Try This

a. 17 **b.** 8 **c.** 11 **d.** 3 **e.** 18 **f.** 9 **g.** 10 **h.** 12 **i.** 6 **j.** 2 **k.** 15 **l.** 16 **m.** 4 **n.** 21 **o.** 15 **p.** 11 **q.** 2

Exercise Set 1-1

1. 13 **3.** 10 **5.** 35 **7.** 7 **9.** 17 **11.** 2 **13.** 48 **15.** 27 **17.** 6 **19.** 3 **21.** 9 **23.** 9 **25.** 16 **27.** 19 **29.** 9 **31.** 26 **33.** 16 **35.** 14 **37.** 30 **39.** 2 **41.** 3 **43.** 1 **45.** 3 **47.** 5 **49.** 6 **51.** 9 **53.** 12 and 5 **55.** 72 **57.** 57 **59.** 14.1 **61.** $1\frac{1}{28}$ **63.** $2\frac{1}{6}$ **65.** $\frac{15}{28}$

Lesson 1-2 Try This

a. $9 + x$ **b.** qp **c.** $yx + t$, $t + xy$, or $t + yx$ **d.** $\frac{28}{20}$ **e.** $\frac{15}{40}$ **f.** $\frac{yz}{2xz}$ **g.** $\frac{2mp}{np}$ **h.** $\frac{2}{3}$ **i.** $\frac{8}{3}$ **j.** $\frac{8}{7}$ **k.** $\frac{1}{2}$ **l.** 4 **m.** $\frac{5y}{3}$ **n.** $\frac{1}{8n}$ **o.** $2a$

Exercise Set 1-2

1. $8 + y$ **3.** nm **5.** $9 + yx$ **7.** $ba + c$ **9.** $\frac{40}{48}$ **11.** $\frac{600}{700}$ **13.** $\frac{st}{20t}$ **15.** $\frac{1}{8}$ **17.** 12 **19.** $\frac{a}{9}$ **21.** $\frac{1}{8p}$ **23.** $\frac{9}{17q}$ **25.** $\frac{3}{s}$ **27.** $\frac{13r}{3b}$ **29.** 8 **31.** No **33.** No **35.** Yes **37.** $\frac{r}{g}$ **41.** 16 **43.** 42 **45.** $\frac{15}{16}$ **47.** 0.48

Lesson 1-3 Try This

a. $5 \cdot 5 \cdot 5 \cdot 5$ **b.** $b \cdot b \cdot b$ **c.** $2 \cdot x \cdot x \cdot x$ **d.** $12 \cdot y \cdot y \cdot y \cdot y$ **e.** 9^3 **f.** y^5 **g.** $4n^5$ **h.** $15x^4$ **i.** $10b^3$ **j.** 100 **k.** 32 **l.** 0 **m.** 29 **n.** 40 **o.** 64 **p.** 1000 **q.** 27 **r.** 48

Exercise Set 1-3

1. $2 \cdot 2 \cdot 2 \cdot 2$ **3.** 3 **5.** $1 \cdot 1 \cdot 1$ **7.** $a \cdot a \cdot a$ **9.** $3 \cdot x \cdot x$ **11.** $2 \cdot m \cdot m \cdot m$ **13.** 10^6 **15.** x^5 **17.** $5m^4$ **19.** 27 **21.** 19 **23.** 248 **25.** 66 **27.** 3 **29.** 32 **31.** 1296 **33.** 20736 **35.** 0 **37.** 10^5 **39.** 8^4 **43.** 9 **45.** 81 **47.** $\frac{7}{8}$ **49.** $12\frac{1}{2}$ **51.** 10 **53.** 8 **55.** $\frac{9}{y}$

Lesson 1-4 Try This

a. 225 **b.** 75 **c.** 32 **d.** 512 **e.** 8 **f.** 36 **g.** 16 **h.** 4 **i.** 139 **j.** 120 **k.** $2\frac{3}{10}$ **l.** 8 **m.** 63 **n.** $(a + b) + 2$ **o.** $(3 \cdot v) \cdot w$ **p.** Ex. $4 \cdot (u \cdot t)$ or $u \cdot (4 \cdot t)$ or $t \cdot (4 \cdot u)$ **q.** Ex. $r + (s + 2)$ or $(2 + s) + r$ or $(r + s) + 2$

Exercise Set 1-4

1. 400 **3.** 80 **5.** 11 **7.** 81 **9.** 9 **11.** 1 **13.** 4 **15.** 125 **17.** 76 **19.** 925 **21.** 66 **23.** 343 **25.** 60 **27.** $\frac{4}{5}$ **29.** 1 **31.** $a + (b + 3)$ **33.** $(3 \cdot a) \cdot b$ **35.** $(2 + b) + a$, $(2 + a) + b$, $b + (a + 2)$ **37.** $v + (w + 5)$, $(5 + w) + v$, $w + (5 + v)$ **39.** $(y \cdot 3) \cdot x$, $x \cdot (3 \cdot y)$, $y \cdot (x \cdot 3)$ **41.** $a \cdot (b \cdot 7)$, $(a \cdot 7) \cdot b$, $b \cdot (7 \cdot a)$ **43.** $c \cdot (2 \cdot d)$, $d \cdot (c \cdot 2)$, $2 \cdot (d \cdot c)$ **45.** $7 \cdot (n \cdot m) + 3$, $3 + m \cdot (7 \cdot n)$ **47.** $6(mp)n$, $m(6n)p$ **49.** $(3 + 5) + 7y + 4$, $5 + 3 + (4 + 7y)$ **51.** Any number except 0 or -2 **53.** Any number except 1. 0 is not acceptable. **55.** 9; 1; No, $9 \neq 1$ **57. a.** No **b.** No **59.** $9\frac{1}{10}$ **61.** $1\frac{5}{12}$ **63.** $\frac{8}{5}$ or $1\frac{3}{5}$ **65.** $\frac{6}{7y}$ **67.** $\frac{6n}{11t}$ **69.** 3375 **71.** 7 **73.** 30 **75.** 2 **77.** 4

Lesson 1-5 Try This

a. $4x + 4y + 4z$ **b.** $5y + 15$ **c.** $16a + 6$ **d.** $6x + 12y + 30$ **e.** $5(x + 2)$ **f.** $3(4 + x)$ **g.** $3(2x + 4 + 3y)$ **h.** $5(x + 2y + 1)$ **i.** $3(3x + y)$ **j.** $5(1 + 2x + 3y)$ **k.** $8y$ **l.** $11x + 8y$ **m.** $14p + 13q$ **n.** $8x^2$

Exercise Set 1-5

1. $2b + 10$ **3.** $7 + 7t$ **5.** $3x + 3$ **7.** $4 + 4y$ **9.** $30x + 12$ **11.** $7x + 28 + 42y$ **13.** $2(x + 2)$ **15.** $5(6 + y)$ **17.** $7(2x + 3y)$ **19.** $5(x + 2 + 3y)$ **21.** $7(2c + 9d + 1)$ **23.** $9(r + 3s + 2)$ **25.** $9(x + 3)$ **27.** $3(3x + y)$ **29.** $8(a + 2b + 8)$ **31.** $11(x + 4y + 11)$ **33.** $5(x + 2y + 9z)$ **35.** $19a$ **37.** $11a$ **39.** $8x + 9z$ **41.** $7x + 15y^2$ **43.** $101a + 92$ **45.** $11a + 11b$ **47.** $14u^2 + 13t + 2$ **49.** $50 + 6t + 8y$ **51.** $1b$ or b **53.** $\frac{13}{4}y$ or $3\frac{1}{4}y$ **55.** $10x + 5y$ **57.** $12p^2 + 6p$ **59.** $9xy + 6x + 3y$ **61.** $9x + 27$ **63.** $12a + 16b$ **65.** $P(1 + rt)$ **69.** $\frac{4}{3}$ **71.** $q(1 + r + rs + rst)$ **73.** $a + ab + abc + abcd$ **75.** 48 **77.** 0 **79.** $\frac{1}{3a}$ **81.** $8x$ **83.** 24 **85.** 15

Lesson 1-6 Try This

a. $n + 7$ **b.** $4n$ **c.** $y - 4$ **d.** $x - 6$ **e.** $m - n$ **f.** $2y$ **g.** $b - a$ **h.** $7n$ **i.** $\frac{a}{7}$ **j.** $c - 24$

Exercise Set 1-6

1. $b + 6$ **3.** $c - 9$ **5.** $q + 6$ **7.** $a + b$ **9.** $y - x$ **11.** $w + x$ **13.** $n - m$ **15.** $r + s$ **17.** $2x$ **19.** $5t$ **21.** $3b$ **23.** $2h$ **25.** $x - y$ **27.** $m - 5$ **29.** $a + 5$ **31.** $m - \$4.50$ **33.** $a + \$45$ **35.** $w - 2$ **37.** $3k$ **39.** $\frac{1}{4}t$ or $\frac{t}{4}$ **41.** $R - 3$ **43.** $y + 2x$ **45.** $2x - 3$ **47.** lw **49.** 2 **51.** $\frac{31}{4}$ **53.** 9 **55.** 24 **57.** $w + 4$ **59.** $t + 3, t - 3$ **61.** 4 **63.** 48 **65.** $3(x + 2)$ **67.** $8(1 + 2x + 5y)$ **69.** $12a + 7b$ **71.** $11y$ **73.** $9 + 7c$

Lesson 1-7 Try This

a. False **b.** True **c.** Open **d.** {3} **e.** {2} **f.** $x = 6$ **g.** $y = 24$ **h.** $y = 5$ **i.** $x = 17$ **j.** 4 was added to both sides. **k.** 5 was subtracted from both sides. **l.** Both sides were divided by 2.

Exercise Set 1-7

1. False **3.** True **5.** {8} **7.** {0} **9.** {12} **11.** $m = 23$ **13.** $y = 27$ **15.** $y = 9$ **17.** $c = 48$ **19.** 5 was added to both sides. **21.** 10 was subtracted from both sides. **23.** Both sides were multiplied by 4. **25.** Both sides were multiplied by 8. **27.** Both sides were multiplied by 4. **29.** $y = 2$ **31.** $y = 31$ **33.** $x = \frac{1}{2}$ **35.** $k = 2$ **37.** Add 12 to both sides. **39.** Divide both sides by 3. **41.** Multiply both sides by 8. **43.** Yes **45.** No **47.** Yes **53.** m^3 **55.** 36 **57.** 18 **59.** $4(x + 3)$ **61.** $5(2t + 5m)$ **63.** $8(a + 2b)$ **65.** $8(1 + 3c)$

Problem Set 1-8

1. The underwater mountain is 5550 ft high. **3.** The booster is 90 ft long, the fuel tank is 75 ft long, and the cargo and navigation section is 15 ft long.

Lesson 1-9 Try This

a. 1695 km/h **b.** 1370 mi/h **c.** $P = 39$ cm **d.** $A = 49$ in.^{2} **e.** $r = 9$ ft/sec **f.** $v = 20$ ft^3

Exercise Set 1-9

1. 440 mi **3.** \$6.80 **5.** 1435 ft/s **7.** 364 m^2 **9.** 198 yd or 594 ft **11.** \$900 **13.** 0.7 mL **15.** 0.6 mL **17.** 56.25 ft **19.** 206.25 ft **21.** 17 ft^2 **23.** $2\frac{1}{2}$ m^2 **25.** 4 cm **29.** $x + y$ **31.** $m - 3$ **33.** $8x + 4$ **35.** 7

Problem Set 1-10

1. 7 **3.** 7 **5.** 8 **7.** 9 **9.** 5 **11.** The numbers are 12 and 48. **13.** 24 in., 12 in. **15.** 45°, 45°, 90° **17.** 22 and 11 **19.** 59 **21.** Eunpyo worked 11 hours of overtime. **23.** Peter earned \$15.25 the first week.

Chapter 1 Summary and Review

1. 11 **3.** 5 **5.** 72 **7.** 2 **9.** 53 **11.** 4 **13.** $8 + x$ **15.** $\frac{36}{45}$ **17.** $\frac{1}{3}$ **19.** $\frac{a}{3c}$ **21.** $\frac{n}{6}$ **23.** 6^5 **25.** 64 **27.** 62 **29.** 216 **31.** 400 **33.** 70 **39.** $7y + 35$ **41.** $6(3x + y)$ **43.** $8a + 9b$ **45.** $5n$ **47.** $n + 4$ **49.** $x + 2x$ or $3x$ **51.** {3} **53.** $a = 7$ **55.** 5 was subtracted from both sides. **57.** 93.75 cm^2

Chapter 2

Lesson 2-1 Try This

a. -12 **b.** 8 **c.** -5 **d.** -3 **e.** $>$ **f.** $>$ **g.** $<$ **h.** 17 **i.** 8 **j.** 14 **k.** 21 **l.** 0 **m.** 21

Exercise Set 2-1

1. -12 **3.** 18 **5.** 2500 **7.** -125 **9.** 3,000,000 **11.** $>$ **13.** $>$ **15.** $>$ **17.** $<$ **19.** $>$ **21.** $>$ **23.** 7 **25.** 11 **27.** 4 **29.** 325 **31.** 5.5 **33.** 120.2 **35.** 340 **37.** 0.3 **39.** 0.07 **41.** 3.75 **43.** 34 **45.** 0 **47.** 11 **49.** $-23, -17, 0, 4$ **51.** $-24, -16, -14, -13, -5, 12, 15$ **53.** 21 **55.** 31 **59.** $<$ **61.** $=$ **63.** $<$ **65.** $=$ **67.** $21m$ **69.** $11x^2 + 7x$ **71.** $4(m + 6c)$ **73.** $7(2x + 4y + 1)$ **75.** {361} **77.** {2.7} **79.** $x = 22$ **81.** $y = 90$ **83.** $x = 24$

Lesson 2-2 Try This

a. $\frac{45}{10}$ or $\frac{9}{2}$ **b.** $-\frac{10}{1}$ **c.** $-\frac{143}{10}$ **d.** $-\frac{1}{100}$

e.
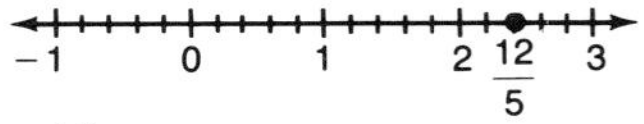

f.
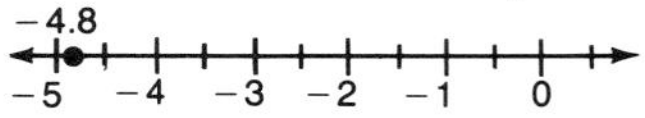

g.
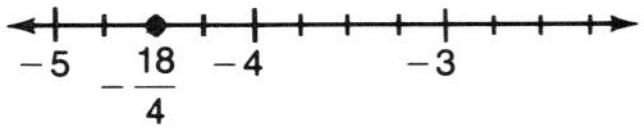

h.
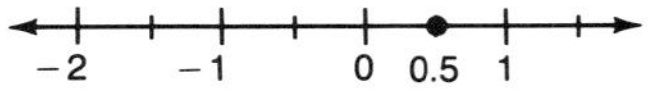

i. $>$ **j.** $>$ **k.** $<$ **l.** $>$

Exercise Set 2-2

1. $\frac{14}{1}$ **3.** $\frac{42}{10}$ or $\frac{21}{5}$ **5.** $-\frac{5}{10}$ or $-\frac{1}{2}$ **7.** $\frac{3444}{1000}$ or $\frac{861}{250}$

$9.\ -\frac{68}{100}$ or $-\frac{17}{25}$ **11.** $\frac{15}{2}$

13. 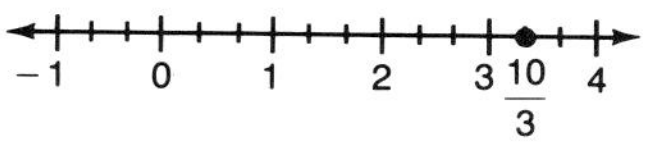

15. 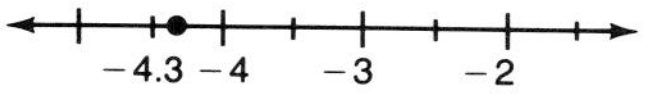

17. > **19.** < **21.** > **23.** > **25.** > **27.** >
29. < **31.** > **33.** < **35.** > **37.** < **43.** $-\frac{7}{5}, -\frac{4}{5}, -\frac{2}{5}, -\frac{1}{5}, \frac{4}{5}, \frac{6}{5}$ **45.** $-\frac{5}{6}, -\frac{3}{4}, -\frac{2}{3}, \frac{1}{6}, \frac{3}{8}, \frac{1}{2}$
49. $m - 11$ **51.** $9 + t$ **53.** 0.06 **55.** 41 **57.** 1
59. 56 **61.** 128 **63.** 135 **65.** 39

Lesson 2-3 Try This

a. 7 **b.** −3 **c.** −2 **d.** −6 **e.** $\frac{4}{4}$ or 1 **f.** 0
g. −20 **h.** −25 **i.** 0.53 **j.** 13 **k.** −7 **l.** $-\frac{2}{4}$ or $-\frac{1}{2}$ **m.** $-\frac{7}{8}$ **n.** $-\frac{3}{35}$ **o.** −58 **p.** −56 **q.** 19
r. −54 **s.** 0 **t.** 7.4 **u.** $\frac{8}{3}$ **v.** −14, 14 **w.** −1, 1
x. 19, −19

Exercise Set 2-3

1. −7 **3.** −4 **5.** 0 **7.** −8 **9.** −7 **11.** −27
13. 0 **15.** −42 **17.** −43 **19.** 5 **21.** −22
23. −7 **25.** 0 **27.** −67 **29.** $-\frac{1}{5}$ **31.** $-\frac{8}{7}$
33. $-\frac{3}{8}$ **35.** $-\frac{29}{35}$ **37.** $-\frac{11}{15}$ **39.** 39 **41.** 50
43. 37.9 **45.** −20 **47.** 118 **49.** −1021 **51.** 64
53. $-\frac{7}{2}$ **55.** −48.2 **57.** 26 **59.** $-\frac{1}{328}$ **61.** 0
63. 29 **65.** −9.1 **67.** 542 above last year's
69. $1715 **71.** 999 mb **73.** When x is positive
75. Positive **77.** Positive **79.** −1 **81.** 0 **83.** 3
85. Yes **87.** 4.31 **89.** < **91.** < **93.** < **95.** 4
97. 0

Lesson 2-4 Try This

a. −8 **b.** −6 **c.** −5 **d.** −5 **e.** 10 **f.** −21
g. 9 **h.** $\frac{5}{8}$ **i.** −9 **j.** 21.6 **k.** $5x + 5$ **l.** $90

Exercise Set 2-4

1. −4 **3.** −7 **5.** 7 **7.** 0 **9.** 0 **11.** 14 **13.** 11
15. −14 **17.** 5 **19.** −7 **21.** −1 **23.** 18
25. −5 **27.** −49 **29.** −193 **31.** 500 **33.** −2.8
35. −3.53 **37.** $-\frac{1}{2}$ **39.** 0 **41.** $-\frac{41}{30}$ **43.** $-\frac{1}{156}$
45. 37 **47.** −62 **49.** −139 **51.** 6 **53.** $10x + 7$
55. $15x + 66$ **57.** $330.54 **59.** 7° **61.** 116 males
63. 116 m **65. a.** 10.7 **b.** 5.7 **c.** 6.6 **d.** 19.4
e. −15.3 **f.** −14.8 **67.** False **69.** True
71. True **73.** No **75.** $-[-(-5)] = -5$; $-\{-[-(-5)]\} = 5$ **77.** Yes **79.** 116 **81.** 32
83. 0 **85.** 6 **87.** $a = 8$ **89.** $7x^2 + 8x$
91. $c(3c + 5)$ **93.** $3(2m + 3p)$

Lesson 2-5 Try This

a. −18 **b.** −100 **c.** −90 **d.** $-\frac{3}{2}$ **e.** 20 **f.** 0
g. 12.6 **h.** $\frac{3}{56}$ **i.** −90 **j.** 120 **k.** −6

Exercise Set 2-5

1. −16 **3.** −42 **5.** −24 **7.** −72 **9.** 16 **11.** 42
13. −120 **15.** −238 **17.** 1200 **19.** 98 **21.** $-\frac{2}{45}$
23. 1911 **25.** 50.4 **27.** $\frac{10}{189}$ **29.** −960 **31.** 17.64
33. $-\frac{5}{784}$ **35.** 0 **37.** −0.104 **39.** 72 **41.** −6
43. 1944 **45.** −32 **47.** 13 **49.** −79 **51.** −69
55. Both m and n are positive or both are negative.
57. $0 < x < 2$ **59.** −5 **61.** −4 **63.** 8 **65.** 59
67. > **69.** = **71.** $5(2a + 3b + 1)$ **73.** 5

Lesson 2-6 Try This

a. −5 **b.** 3 **c.** 4 **d.** −7 **e.** 2 **f.** −5 **g.** 3
h. −21 **i.** $\frac{6}{3}$ or 2 **j.** $-\frac{1}{4}$ **k.** −2 **l.** $\frac{3}{4}$ **m.** $\frac{y}{x}$
n. $-6(5)$ **o.** $-5\left(\frac{1}{7}\right)$ **p.** $(x^2 - 2)\frac{1}{3}$ **q.** $x\left(\frac{1}{y}\right)$
r. $-15x$ **s.** $-\frac{4}{7}\left(-\frac{5}{3}\right)$ **t.** $13\left(-\frac{3}{2}\right)$ **u.** ab **v.** $\frac{11}{20}$
w. $-\frac{12}{5}$ **x.** −16.2 **y.** −26.2

Exercise Set 2-6

1. −6 **3.** −13 **5.** −2 **7.** 4 **9.** −8 **11.** 2
13. −12 **15.** −8 **17.** 15 **19.** $\frac{7}{15}$ **21.** $\frac{13}{47}$ **23.** $\frac{1}{13}$
25. $\frac{10}{3}$ **27.** $\frac{2}{3}$ **29.** $\frac{q}{p}$ **31.** $4y$ **33.** $\frac{3b}{2a}$ **35.** $3\left(\frac{1}{19}\right)$
37. $6\left(-\frac{1}{13}\right)$ **39.** $13.9\left(-\frac{1}{1.5}\right)$ **41.** $x \cdot y$
43. $\frac{1}{5}(3x + 4)$ **45.** $(5a - b)\left(\frac{1}{5a + b}\right)$ **47.** $-\frac{9}{8}$
49. $\frac{5}{3}$ **51.** $\frac{9}{14}$ **53.** $\frac{9}{64}$ **55.** −2 **57.** None **59.** −1
61. $-\frac{10}{9}$ **63.** $-\frac{17}{2}$ **65.** −9 **67.** $\frac{40}{49}$ **69.** $\frac{1}{8}$
71. 0.238095238 **73.** No **75.** No **79.** 7 **81.** 7
83. $2m$ **85.** $25 - x$ **87.** $\frac{1}{2}$ **89.** $\frac{1}{3}$

Bonus Topic

1. $0.\overline{36}$ **3.** $2.\overline{5}$ **5.** $0.\overline{4}$

Problem Solving: Application

3. 600 lb **5.** The fulcrum would have to be 60 cm from the 10-kg weight and 40 cm from the 15-kg weight.

Lesson 2-7 Try This

a. $8y-56$ **b.** $\frac{5}{6}x - \frac{5}{6}y + \frac{35}{6}z$
c. $-5x + 15y - 40z$ **d.** $4(x - 2)$
e. $3(x - 2y - 5)$ **f.** $b(x - y + z)$
g. $-2(y - 4z + 1)$ or $2(-y + 4z - 1)$
h. $4(3z - 4x - 1)$ **i.** $5a, -4b, 3$ **j.** $-5y, -3x, 5z$
k. $3x$ **l.** $6y$ **m.** $0.56m$ **n.** $3x + 3y$
o. $-4x - 5y - 15$

Exercise Set 2-7

1. $7x - 14$ **3.** $-7y + 14$ **5.** $45x + 54y - 72$
7. $-4x + 12y + 8z$ **9.** $-3.72x + 9.92y - 3.41$
11. $2a - 4b + 6$ **13.** $\frac{2}{5}x - \frac{8}{15}y + \frac{4}{5}$ **15.** $8(x - 3)$
17. $4(8 - y)$ **19.** $2(4x + 5y - 11)$ **21.** $a(x - 7)$
23. $a(x - y - z)$ **25.** $\frac{1}{4}(3x - y - 1)$ **27.** $4x, 3z$
29. $7x, 8y, -9z$ **31.** $12x, -13.2y, \frac{5}{8}z, -4.5$
33. $-2x$ **35.** $5n$ **37.** $4x + 2y$ **39.** $7x + y$
41. $0.8x + 0.5y$ **43.** $-2y - 3x$ **45.** $-9t + 5p$
47. $32a - 17b - 17c$ **49.** $8.5d + 3a$ **51.** $\frac{3}{5}x + \frac{3}{5}y$
53. $8(x - y)$ **55.** $3(a + b) - 7a$ or $3b - 4a$
59. $18.292.50 **61.** $-\frac{11}{6}$ **63.** $3c$ **65.** $12x$
67. $-\frac{3}{16}$ **69.** 2

Lesson 2-8 Try This

a. $-x - 2$ **b.** $-5x - 2y - 8$ **c.** $-a + 7$
d. $-3c + 4d - 1$ **e.** $-6 + t$ **f.** $4a - 3t + 10$
g. $-18 + m + 2n - 4t$ **h.** $2x - 9$
i. $8x - 4y + 4$ **j.** $-9x - 8y$ **k.** $-16a + 18$
l. -1 **m.** 4 **n.** $2x - y + 4$

Exercise Set 2-8

1. $-2x - 7$ **3.** $-5x + 8$ **5.** $-4a + 3b - 7c$
7. $-6x + 8y - 5$ **9.** $-3x + 5y + 6$
11. $8x + 6y + 43$ **13.** $5x - 3$ **15.** $-3a + 9$
17. $5x - 6$ **19.** $-19x + 2y$ **21.** $9y - 25z$
23. $-2x + 6y$ **25.** $3m - 6n$ **27.** 0 **29.** $a + 4b$
31. 7 **33.** -40 **35.** 19 **37.** $12x + 30$
39. $3x + 30$ **41.** $x - (y + a + b)$
43. $6m - (-3n + 5m - 4b)$ **45.** $2a + 4$
49. $-2x - t$ **51.** $5y - 4$ **53.** $2(a - 3b + 6)$
55. 54 **57.** 50 **59.** -8 **61.** $-\frac{7}{45}$ **63.** $2x^2 + x$
65. $3x - 5$

Problem Set 2-9

1. (B) or (C) **3.** (A) or (B) **5.** (B) or (C)
Problems 7–24: Answers may vary.
7. $127 + d = 318$ **9.** $12c = 3.12$
11. $80c = 53{,}400$ **13.** $2.5t = 16.6$
15. $b + 13.5 = 78.3$ **17.** $391d = 150{,}000{,}000$
19. $325 = 50t$ **21.** $7q = 45$ **23.** $1087t = 10{,}000$

Lesson 2-10 Try This

a. Associative property of addition **b.** Inverse property of multiplication **c.** Inverse property of addition **d.** Commutative property of multiplication **e.** Reflexive **f.** Transitive **g.** Symmetric **h.** 2. Distributive property 3. Distributive property **i.** 4. Distributive property 6. Multiplicative identity 7. Additive inverses

Exercise Set 2-10

1. Commutative property of addition **3.** Distributive property of multiplication over addition **5.** Additive inverses **7.** Additive inverses **9.** Associative property of multiplication **11.** Distributive property of multiplication over addition **13.** Multiplicative inverse **15.** Reflexive property of equality **17.** Commutative property of multiplication **19.** Reflexive property of equality **21.** 1. Additive identity 3. Associative property of addition 5. Distributive property 7. Mult. property of zero 8. Additive identity **23.** No. $1 + 3 = 4$. 4 is not in the set of odd whole numbers.
25. Yes
27.

Statement	*Reason*
1. $-(a - b) = -[a + (-b)]$	Subtraction rule
2. $= -a + -(-b)$	Inverse of a sum
3. $= -a + b$	Inverse of inverse
4. $= b + -a$	Comm. property of addition
5. $= b - a$	Subtraction rule
6. $-(a - b) = b - a$	Transitive property of equality

29. $16(a - 3)$ **31.** $15(3 - n)$ **33.** $9 - 17c$

Chapter 2 Summary and Review

1. -25 **3.** 38 **5.** 0.02
7.
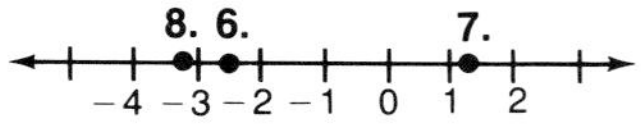

9. > **11.** < **13.** $\frac{8}{5}$ **15.** -19 **17.** 3.5 **19.** -6.4
21. 7.45 **23.** 34 **25.** 8 yd gain **27.** -4 **29.** 19
31. 4000 ft **33.** -24 **35.** 210 **37.** 5 **39.** $12x - 2$
41. $-6a + 9b - 3c$ **43.** $8(x - 4y - 1)$ **45.** $7x$

47. $2m + 6$ **49.** $-7a - 12b - c$ **51.** $-5a - 3$ **53.** $-4a - 5b$ **55.** 1 **57.** (A) or (C)

Chapter 3

Lesson 3-1 Try This

a. -5 **b.** 5 **c.** 9 **d.** $x + 32 = 475$: \$443

Exercise Set 3-1

1. 4 **3.** 11 **5.** -14 **7.** -18 **9.** 15 **11.** -14 **13.** 2 **15.** 20 **17.** -6 **19.** 13 **21.** 27 **23.** 19 **25.** 19 **27.** 37 **29.** 4.6 **31.** 5.9 **33.** -6.5 **35.** 9.3 **37.** $\frac{7}{3}$ **39.** $-\frac{7}{4}$ **41.** $\frac{41}{24}$ **43.** $\frac{5}{8}$ **45.** $\frac{4}{9}$ **47.** $x - 18 = -53; -35$ **49.** $x + 42 = -100$; -142 **51. d.** $c + 15{,}918{,}215 = 18{,}870{,}730$ **f.** $c = 2{,}952{,}515$ **53.** -4 **55.** -8 **57.** $b + 3$ **59.** 386 **63.** Subtraction is the addition of inverses. **65.** 11,074 **67.** Any value **69.** $7y - 4$ **71.** $-7w + 24$ **73.** $51 - 12y$ **75.** 100 **77.** 32 **79.** $\frac{1}{5}$ **81.** -2 **83.** $-\frac{98}{75}$

Lesson 3-2 Try This

a. 5 **b.** $-\frac{7}{4}$ **c.** 14 **d.** -12 **e.** $-\frac{5}{4}$ **f.** -6 **g.** 50 **h.** 36 **i.** -24 **j.** $12x = \$6.72$; \$0.56

Exercise Set 3-2

1. 6 **3.** 9 **5.** 12 **7.** -40 **9.** 1 **11.** -7 **13.** -6 **15.** 6 **17.** -63 **19.** 36 **21.** -21 **23.** $\frac{-3}{5}$ **25.** $\frac{3}{2}$ **27.** $\frac{9}{2}$ **29.** 7 **31.** -7 **33.** 8 **35.** 45 **37.** $18x = -1008; -56$ **39. d.** $8p = 170$ **f.** $p = \$21.25$ **41. d.** $30e = 164{,}275$ **f.** $e \approx 5476$ **43.** $1131 = \frac{1}{3}f$; 3393 **45.** $\frac{3}{5}a = 16{,}856$; $\approx 28{,}093$ **47.** 36 **49.** 24 **51.** $\frac{b}{3a}$ **53.** $\frac{1}{ab}$ **55.** No value **57.** Division is multiplication by reciprocal. **59.** $4x + 9y$ **61.** $5r - 5s$ **63.** -80 **65.** 2.52 **67.** -44 **69.** 17 **71.** 24 **73.** -3 **75.** $3(2a - 4b - 3c)$

Lesson 3-3 Try This

a. 5 **b.** -4 **c.** 13 **d.** -1 **e.** 3 **f.** 4 **g.** -3 **h.** 7 **i.** 2

Exercise Set 3-3

1. 5 **3.** 8 **5.** 10 **7.** 14 **9.** -8 **11.** -8 **13.** -7 **15.** 15 **17.** 18 **19.** 6 **21.** 4 **23.** 6 **25.** 5 **27.** -3 **29.** 1 **31.** -20 **33.** 3 **35.** 5 **37.** 1 **39.** 0 **41.** 6 **43.** 2 **45.** 32 **47.** 1 **49.** 2 **51. a.** Using the multiplication property **b.** Simplifying **c.** Using the addition property **d.** Simplifying **e.** Using the multiplication property **53. a.** Using the distributive property **b.** Collecting like terms **c.** Using the addition property **d.** Simplifying **e.** Using the multiplication property **f.** Simplifying **55.** $-\frac{7}{2}$ **57.** -7 **59.** -2 **63.** $x = -\frac{1}{3}, y = -5$ **65.** $<$ **67.** $>$ **69.** $\frac{5}{9}$ **71.** $-\frac{4}{9}$ **73.** $t = 156$ **75.** $4(t + n - 3m)$ **77.** $4(c - 3d)$ **79.** $6q - 3r - 12$

Lesson 3-4 Try This

a. $2n - 3$ **b.** $\frac{1}{2}(n - 1)$ **c.** $\frac{n}{3} - 5$ **d.** $10n - 2$ **e.** $2n - 5$ **f.** $\frac{1}{2}t + 2$ **g.** $\frac{1}{2}S + 80$ **h.** 7 **i.** 3

Exercise Set 3-4

1. $5n - 3$ **3.** $\frac{1}{2}n - 18$ **5.** $\frac{n}{5} - 3$ **7.** $4(n - 1)$ **9.** $\frac{1}{2}(n + 6)$ **11.** $\frac{1}{3}n - 4$ **13.** $2y + 2$ **15.** $\frac{1}{2}c + 25$ **17.** $2(r + 3)$ **19.** $3\frac{1}{2}$ hours **21.** 70 **23.** \$1.50 **27.** 140 customers **29.** 3 **31.** 2 **33.** y^3x **35.** $12r^2$ **37.** -4 **39.** $\frac{9}{2}$

Lesson 3-5 Try This

a. 1 **b.** 2 **c.** 2 **d.** 9 **e.** -2 **f.** $-\frac{1}{2}$

Exercise Set 3-5

1. 7 **3.** 2 **5.** 5 **7.** 2 **9.** 10 **11.** 4 **13.** 8 **15.** 4 **17.** 1 **19.** 17 **21.** -8 **23.** -3 **25.** -3 **27.** 2 **29.** 5 **31.** 2 **33.** $\frac{1}{6}$ **35.** $2\frac{1}{2}$ hours **37.** $x = \frac{bc + d - a}{-b}$ **39.** $-\frac{1}{5}x + \frac{3}{7}y$ **41.** $\frac{1}{3}a + \frac{1}{3}$ **43.** $5(n - 2)$

Lesson 3-6 Try This

a. 2 **b.** 21 **c.** 6 **d.** -4.3

Exercise Set 3-6

1. -1 **3.** -2 **5.** 4 **7.** $\frac{1}{2}$ **9.** $-\frac{2}{3}$ **11.** 28 **13.** -4 **15.** 0.8 **17.** 3 **19.** 12 **21.** 5 **23.** $\frac{5}{4}$ **27.** 72 **29.** $<$ **31.** $<$ **33.** $2n - 5$ **35.** -3 **37.** 6 **39.** $\frac{8}{3}$ **41.** 28

Lesson 3-7 Try This

a. $r = \frac{C}{2\pi}$ **b.** $l = \frac{P - 35}{2}$ **c.** $c = 4A - a - b - d$ **d.** $n = \frac{y}{r}$

Exercise Set 3-7

1. $\frac{A}{b}$ **3.** $\frac{d}{t}$ **5.** $\frac{1}{rt}$ **7.** $\frac{F}{m}$ **9.** $\frac{P - 2l}{2}$ **11.** $\frac{A}{\pi}$ **13.** $\frac{2A}{b}$ **15.** $\frac{E}{c^2}$ **17.** $3A - a - c$ **19.** $\frac{3K}{v}$ **21.** $\frac{360A}{\pi r^2}$ **23.** $\frac{2.5H}{N}$ **25.** $\frac{ax}{c - 1}$ **27.** $\frac{d - a + l}{d}$ **29.** $\frac{t^2}{v}$ **31.** $t = \frac{R - 3.85}{-0.00625}$ or $-160R + 616$ **33.** $\frac{g - 40n}{20}$ **35.** $\frac{y}{1 - b}$ **37.** $\frac{1}{d} - e$ **39.** $\frac{m - ax^2 - c}{x}$ **41.** $4(x + 3)$ **43.** $3y - 2x$ **45.** 3 **47.** 5 **49.** 3

Lesson 3-8 Try This

a. 17, −17 **b.** 6, −6 **c.** 7, −7

Exercise Set 3-8

1. 19, −19 **3.** 4, −4 **5.** 0 **7.** 12, −12 **9.** 2, −2 **11.** 7, −7 **13.** 28, −28 **15.** 2, −2 **17.** 6, −6 **19.** 0 **21.** 7, −7 **23.** 3, −3 **25.** 20, −20 **27.** $\frac{5}{4}, -\frac{5}{4}$ **29.** $\frac{1}{2}, -\frac{1}{2}$ **31.** 1, −1 **33.** 3, −3 **35.** 4, −4 **37.** 2, −2 **39.** 2, −2 **41.** 4, −4 **43.** $\frac{24}{5}, -\frac{24}{5}$ **45.** $m = 2, -2$ **47.** $m = 5, -5$ **51.** $-x$ **53.** 5, −9 **55.** 2, −3 **57.** No **59.** −3 **61.** 12 **63.** 14 **65.** $\frac{5}{2}a - \frac{32}{5}b$ **67.** 46, 48 **69.** 30°, 60°, 90°

Lesson 3-9 Try This

a. 20 **b.** $\frac{5}{2}$ **c.** $\frac{14}{3}$ **d.** 250 km **e.** $133\frac{1}{3}$ miles

Exercise Set 3-9

1. 1 **3.** $\frac{27}{2}$ **5.** $\frac{18}{5}$ **7.** 25 **9.** $\frac{5}{2}$ **11.** $\frac{55}{9}$ **13.** 24 **15.** 63 **17.** 12 **19.** 25 **21.** $\frac{63}{4}$ **23.** 35 **25.** 40 **27.** $\frac{4}{15}$ minute **29.** 80 **31.** 24 **33.** 5075 **35.** 1 second **37.** 225 **41.** 28 minutes **43.** 95 minutes or 1 hour 35 minutes **45.** $-\frac{7}{2}$ or $-3\frac{1}{2}$ **47.** 3 **49.** 12 **51.** ±3 **53.** 0 **55.** $x = \frac{55}{2}$ **57.** $m = \frac{y - b}{x} = \frac{y}{x} - \frac{b}{x}$ **59.** $r = \frac{I}{Pt}$ **61.** $-6x - 16$

Lesson 3-10 Try This

a. 0.48 **b.** 0.03 **c.** 1.45 **d.** 0.005 **e.** 75% **f.** 37.5% **g.** 490% **h.** 49.6% **i.** 0.004% **j.** 7.5% **k.** 37.5% **l.** 18.75 **m.** 6 **n.** 5 **o.** 30% **p.** 30%

Exercise Set 3-10

1. 0.41 **3.** 0.07 **5.** 1.25 **7.** 0.008 **9.** 0.015 **11.** 75% **13.** 96% **15.** 33.3% **17.** 62.5% **19.** 18.8% **21.** 25% **23.** 24% **25.** 150 **27.** 2.5 **29.** 125% **31.** 0.8 **33.** 5% **35.** 86.4% **37.** $800 **39.** 36 cm^3; 436 cm^3 **41.** $30 **43.** $20 **45.** 4% **47.** 20 cm by 33.3 cm **51.** 40%. Successive 20% discounts mean you pay 80% of 80%, or 64%, which is only 36% discount. **53.** Equal. Both earn $62 interest over two years. **55.** 9 **57.** $9x + 5$ **59.** $3x - 6$ **61.** 20.4 **63.** −32 **65.** −24

Lesson 3-11 Try This

a. $\frac{1}{2}g + g$ or $2b + b$ **b.** $x + x + 2 + x + 4 = 3x + 6$ **c.** width is 30 cm; length is 45 cm **d.** 9, 10 **e.** $9000

Exercise Set 3-11

1. Let r = cost of one record; $r + (r - 3.50)$ or $2r - 3.50$ **3.** Let e = # of English books; $e + (e - 9)$ or $2e - 9$ **5.** Let p = cost of paperback book; $p + 3(p + 7)$ or $4p + 21$ **7.** $x + (x + 2) = 2x + 2$ **9.** $x + 2(x + 2) = 3x + 4$ **11.** $x + (x + 2) + (x + 4) = 3x + 6$ **13.** $x + \frac{1}{2}(x + 2) + \frac{1}{4}(x + 4) = \frac{7}{4}x + 2$ **15.** $2x + \frac{2}{3}(x + 1) + 3(x + 2) = \frac{17}{3}x + \frac{20}{3}$ **17.** 36 **19.** 52, 54 **21.** 61, 63, 65 **23.** 18° **25.** McEnroe: $1,289,109; Navratilova: $2,173,556 **27.** $7500 **29.** $12,000 **31.** 41 million **33.** 19¢ **35.** 12 cm, 9 cm **39.** $1.09p = 10.00$, $p = \$9.17$, not $9.10 **41.** $1056 **43.** $\frac{10}{7}$ **45.** 9 **47.** 4 **49.** 36

Problem Set 3-12

1. There will be 72 games played when each team has played each other team twice. **3.** The 5 orange tiles can be arranged 12 different ways. **5.** The garden's measurements were 10 m by 12 m. **7.** Charles and Eva will both be off on a Monday five weeks later.

Chapter 3 Summary and Review

1. −20 **3.** 25 **5.** $591 **7.** 4 **9.** $-\frac{3}{2}$ **11.** 27 **13.** −3 **15.** 3 **17.** 3 **19.** $5n - 18$ **21.** $\frac{1}{2}(n + 10)$ **23.** $2x + 10$ **25.** 4 h 10 min or 250 min **27.** 2

29. 6 **31.** -1 **33.** 7 **35.** $h = \frac{V}{B}$ **37.** $x = \frac{P - 2w}{2}$
39. 5, -5 **41.** 11, -11 **43.** 10 **45.** 702 km
47. 0.07 **49.** 33.3% **51.** 1.2% **53.** 250
55. $2x + x = 3x$ **57.** 57, 59

Chapter 4

Lesson 4-1 Try This

a. (1) Yes (2) Yes (3) Yes (4) No (5) No
b. (1) Yes (2) No (3) No (4) Yes (5) No
c.

d.

Exercise Set 4-1

1. a. No **b.** No **c.** No **d.** Yes **3. a.** No **b.** No **c.** Yes **d.** Yes **5. a.** No **b.** No **c.** Yes **d.** No **7. a.** Yes **b.** Yes **c.** Yes **d.** No

9.

11.

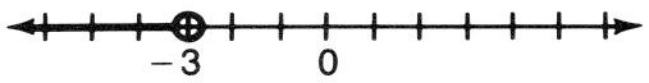

13.

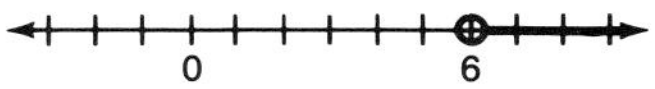

15.

17.

19.

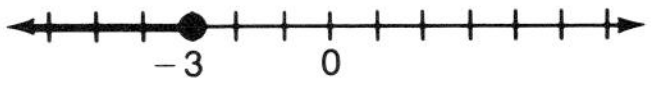

21. T **23.** F **25.** $x \geq 2$ **27.** $x \leq -2$ **29.** $x < 0$
31. $x \leq 7$
33.

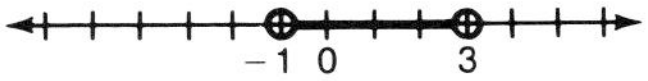

35.

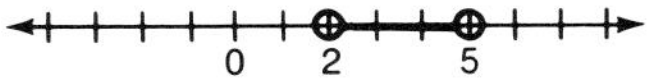

37. $-\frac{1}{6}$ **39.** 12 **41.** ± 15 **43.** No solution **45.** 6

Lesson 4-2 Try This

a. $x > 2$

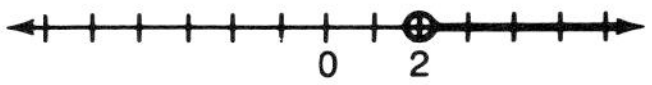

b. $x \leq 13$

c. $x \geq 9$

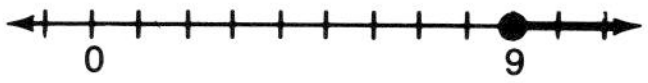

d. $x < 2$

e. $y < -\frac{1}{2}$

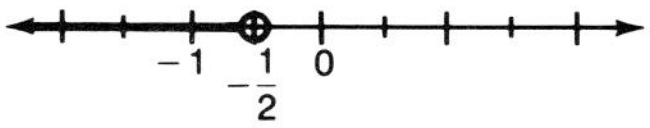

f. $y \geq \frac{1}{2}$

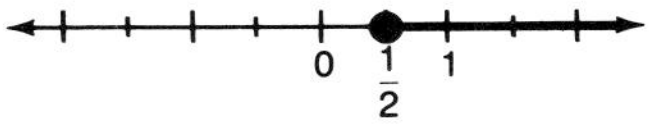

g. $y \leq -3$

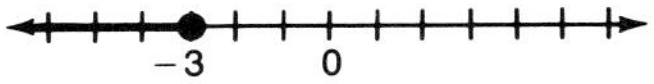

h. $x < -3$

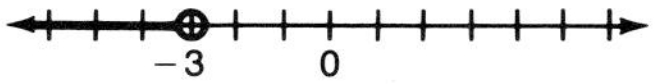

Exercise Set 4-2

1. $x > -5$ **3.** $y > 3$ **5.** $x \leq -18$ **7.** $a < -6$
9. $x \leq 16$ **11.** $x > 8$ **13.** $y > -5$ **15.** $m < 2$
17. $x \leq -3$ **19.** $n < 4$ **21.** $y \leq -11$ **23.** $m \leq \frac{1}{4}$
25. $x > \frac{7}{12}$ **27.** $c \leq -\frac{1}{2}$ **29.** $r < -2$ **31.** $a \geq -5$
33. $x > -8$ **35.** $a \leq 0$ **37.** 7 **39.** 0 **41.** $a - 4$
45. False **47.** $y \leq 4$ **49. a.** $x \leq 5$ **b.** $x \geq -3$
c. $x < \frac{-3}{2}$ or $x > \frac{-3}{2}$ **d.** $x \geq y$ **e.** $x \leq -y$
f. $-x > y$ or $-x < y$ **51.** 9 **53.** $-\frac{1}{21}$ **55.** ± 25
57. 5 **59.** $2x + 3$ **61.** 42

Lesson 4-3 Try This

a. $x < 8$ **b.** $y \geq 32$ **c.** $t < 28$ **d.** $s > 9$
e. $x \leq -6$ **f.** $y > -\frac{13}{5}$ **g.** $t > 5$ **h.** $n < -2$
i. $y \leq -\frac{1}{2}$ **j.** $x > -\frac{1}{18}$ **k.** $x \geq -\frac{5}{16}$ **l.** $y \leq \frac{3}{28}$

Exercise Set 4-3

1. $x < 7$ **3.** $y \leq 9$ **5.** $y > 12$ **7.** $x < \frac{13}{7}$
9. $y \geq \frac{15}{4}$ **11.** $y \leq \frac{1}{2}$ **13.** $y \geq -3$ **15.** $x < -3$
17. $y \geq -\frac{2}{5}$ **19.** $x \geq -6$ **21.** $y \geq -4$
23. $y < -60$ **25.** $x > 2$ **27.** $y \leq 2$ **29.** $x > \frac{17}{2}$
31. $y \leq \frac{31}{8}$ **33.** $y > -\frac{1}{21}$ **35.** $y \geq \frac{9}{10}$ **37.** $x \leq \frac{1}{6}$
39. $y > 3$ **41.** $n \leq -\frac{1}{2}$ **45.** False. $6 < 10$ but $\frac{6}{-2} > \frac{10}{-2}$ **47.** $5m$ **49.** $33y$ **51.** 26

Lesson 4-4 Try This

a. $x > 2$ **b.** $a \geq -1$ **c.** $m > 6$ **d.** $n > 2$

Exercise Set 4-4

1. $x < 8$ **3.** $y \geq 6$ **5.** $x \leq 6$ **7.** $y > 4$ **9.** $x < -3$ **11.** $x \geq -2$ **13.** $y < -3$ **15.** $x > -3$ **17.** $y < -\frac{10}{3}$ **19.** $x \leq 7$ **21.** $x > -10$ **23.** $y < 2$ **25.** $y \geq 3$ **27.** $y > -2$ **29.** $y > -2$ **31.** $y \leq \frac{33}{7}$ **33.** $x < \frac{9}{5}$ **35.** $t \leq 0$ **37.** $y < \frac{2.2}{7}$ **39.** $x \leq 9$ **41.** $y \leq -3$ **43.** $x > \frac{8}{3}$ **45.** $1.8 \geq y$ **47.** $a < -5$ **49.** $2 \leq z$ **51.** $c > -13$ **53.** $x < 2$
55. a. Simplifying **b.** Using the addition property **c.** Simplifying **d.** Using the multiplication property **e.** Simplifying **57. a.** Using the distributive property **b.** Using the addition property **c.** Simplifying **d.** Using the addition property **e.** Simplifying **f.** Using the multiplication property **g.** Simplifying **61.** $x > 7$ **63.** $x > \frac{y - b}{a}$ if $a > 0$; $x < \frac{y - b}{a}$ if $a < 0$ **65.** $x^2 < x$ **67.** 3 **69.** 18 **71.** $z < -3$ **73.** 4 **75.** $\frac{9}{5}$, 180% **77.** $\frac{3}{5}$, 60% **79.** $M - 2$ **81.** $3L$

Lesson 4-5 Try This

a. $x \geq 8$ **b.** $t < 12$ **c.** $x \leq 4\frac{1}{2}$ **d.** $n \geq 0$ **e.** $n - 3 > 4$ **f.** $p \geq 10$; at least 10 **g.** $s \geq 94$; at least 94 **h.** 16, 17

Exercise Set 4-5

1. $y > 3$ **3.** $h \geq 4\frac{5}{6}$ **5.** $x \geq 0$ **7.** $x + 2 > 9$ **9.** $\frac{x}{2} \leq 6$ **11.** $2x - 4 \leq 18$ **13.** $3x + 2 \leq 11$ **15.** 97 **17.** 9, 18 **19.** 0, 2, 4, 6; 2, 4, 6, 8; 4, 6, 8, 10 **21.** $A > 12$, $D > 15$; Armando worked more than 12 hours, and Drew worked more than 15 hours. **23.** $w > 14$ cm **25.** $b > 4$ cm **27.** Cut all three links of one section (30¢). Use each link to join the remaining 4 sections, requiring 3 welds (60¢). The total cost will be 90¢. **29.** $-\frac{5}{6}$ **31.** $-\frac{1}{15}$ **33.** -1 **35.** $a \geq -4$

Connections: Discrete Math

1. If we can't play soccer, then it's raining; False. Counterexample: It is a sunny day but we can't play soccer because no one can find the ball. **3.** If a number is even, then it is divisible by 4; False. Counterexample: 10 is even and is not divisible by 4. **5.** If $x < 10$, then $x < 5$; False. Counterexample: 7 is less than 10 and is not less than 5.

Problem Solving: Application

1. 800 customers on Memorial Day, 1000 customers on the Fourth of July, 500 customers on Labor Day **3.** About 7 checks were returned. **5.** April cheese sales: \$28,000, May cheese sales: \$22,000 **7.** The average amount of ice cream sold is \$31,000.

Problem Set 4-6

1. William coaches racquetball. Carrie coaches tennis. Lester coaches volleyball. Rosa coaches basketball. **3.** The student earned \$56.70 for painting the house numbers. **7.** Nellie lives in Jackson, Meg lives in Springstown, Scott lives in Mowetown, and Jeff lives in Newton.

Chapter 4 Summary and Review

1. a. Yes **b.** Yes **c.** Yes **d.** No
3. 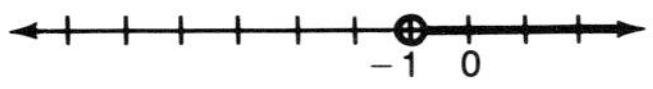 −1 0
5. 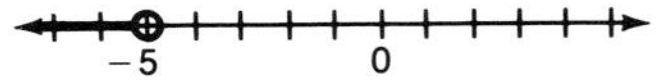 −5 0
7. $b \geq \frac{9}{4}$ **9.** $x > -4$ **11.** $y \leq 20$ **13.** $b \leq -7$ **15.** $y < 7$ **17.** $y < 3$ **19.** $x > -\frac{11}{7}$ **21.** 120 lbs **23.** 12, 14, 16

Chapters 1-4 Cumulative Review

1. $\frac{3}{2}$ **3.** 8 **5.** $y + 12$ **7.** $\frac{3x}{4z}$ **9.** 16 **11.** 10,000 **13.** 1000 **15.** $3 \cdot (y \cdot z)$ **17.** $15x + 25y + 10z$ **19.** $6(9y + 1)$ **21.** $15b + 22y$ **23.** $2w - 4$ **25.** {9} **27.** {6} **29.** Both sides were multiplied by 7. **31.** $p = 40.8$ m **33.** > **35.** 14 **37.** > **39.** -3.5 **41.** 3 **43.** 1 **45.** $3 - 10x$ **47.** 420 **49.** -105 **51.** $-\frac{32}{125}$ **53.** $-12x - 8$ **55.** $5x + 5$ **57.** $-2(x + 4)$ **59.** $-9d - 3a + 1$ **61.** $-2x - y$ **63.** $8x$ **65.** Transitive property **67.** $3\frac{5}{6}$ **69.** 12 **71.** $-\frac{12}{5}$ **73.** 7 **75.** $-3\frac{1}{3}$ or $-3.\overline{3}$ **77.** $r = \frac{L}{2h}$ **79.** 9, −9 **81.** $\frac{32}{3}$ **83.** 56.9L **85.** 50 **87.** \$1500 **89.** No **91.** Yes **93.** $x \geq \frac{5}{6}$ **95.** $x > -6$ **97.** $l > 20$ ft, $w > 16$ ft

Chapter 5

Lesson 5-1 Try This

a. 5^6 **b.** a^8 **c.** y^{10} **d.** m^5n^8 **e.** 7^4 **f.** a^5

g. m^2 **h.** x^2y **i.** $\frac{1}{2^2}$ **j.** $\frac{1}{y^4}$ **k.** $\frac{3}{c^2}$ **l.** $\frac{1}{16}$ **m.** 1 **n.** 1

Exercise Set 5-1

1. 2^7 **3.** 8^{14} **5.** x^7 **7.** n^4 **9.** x^4 **11.** m^7 **13.** x^7 **15.** a^9 **17.** a^8b^7 **19.** $p^3q^4r^5$ **21.** $5^2s^4t^4$ **23.** 7^3 **25.** 8^6 **27.** 1 **29.** y^4 **31.** a^2 **33.** x^2 **35.** 1 **37.** 1 **39.** x^2y^2 **41.** ab^4 **43.** a^2b^3 **45.** $4x^2$ **47.** $\frac{1}{3^2}$ **49.** $\frac{1}{2^4}$ **51.** $\frac{1}{a^3}$ **53.** $\frac{1}{x^4}$ **55.** $\frac{3}{a}$ **57.** $\frac{1}{2y}$ **59.** $\frac{5}{c^4}$ **61.** $\frac{1}{3a}$ **63.** $\frac{1}{16}$ **65.** $\frac{1}{7}$ **67.** 1 **69.** $\frac{1}{16}$ **71.** 1 **73.** 1 **75.** 64 **77.** 9 **79.** $\frac{1}{16}$ **81.** $-\frac{1}{8}$ **83.** (a) x^{-4} (b) $\frac{1}{x^4}$ **85.** (a) a^{-4} (b) $\frac{1}{a^4}$ **87.** 256 **89.** 64 **91.** 256 **93.** b^{-2} or $\frac{1}{b^2}$ **95.** 256 **97.** x^2 **101.** 2^6 **103.** 2^{13} **105.** 3^{10} **107.** $\frac{b^3}{a^3}$ **109.** $-(m + 3n)$ **111.** $12a^2 + 14a$ **113.** $ac - 8$ **115.** 369 **117.** 5 **119.** $27 or less

Lesson 5-2 Try This

a. 5^{12} **b.** 2^{10} **c.** a^{18} **d.** n^{16} **e.** $9y^2$ **f.** $1296m^4$ **g.** $8a^9$ **h.** $16x^6$ **i.** $256y^{12}$ **j.** $243x^{20}y^{35}z^{30}$ **k.** $49x^{18}y^{12}$ **l.** $-y^{45}$ **m.** $\frac{y^6}{4}$ **n.** $\frac{a^{15}}{27}$ **o.** $\frac{x^4}{y^6}$

Exercise Set 5-2

1. 2^{10} **3.** 5^6 **5.** y^{45} **7.** m^{32} **9.** a^{30} **11.** p^{100} **13.** $81y^4$ **15.** $343y^3$ **17.** $25m^2$ **19.** $2401x^4$ **21.** $4m^4$ **23.** $125y^{12}$ **25.** $-216t^6$ **27.** $512k^{12}$ **29.** $4x^{16}y^6$ **31.** $-8x^6y^{12}$ **33.** $256x^8y^{12}z^4$ **35.** $\frac{27}{a^6}$ **37.** $\frac{x^8}{256}$ **39.** $\frac{m^{12}}{n^6}$ **41.** $\frac{1728}{125}$ **43.** $\frac{x^3y^6}{z^3}$ **45.** $\frac{4x^4y^{12}}{25}$ **47.** $-\frac{64m^6n^{15}}{27}$ **49.** x^{30} **51.** $-\frac{x^3}{27y^3}$ **53.** $\frac{x^6y^3}{z^3}$ **55.** $\frac{9a^4b^8}{16c^6}$ **57.** $54n^7$ **59.** $19a^2$ **61.** $8z^8$ **63.** $6z^7 - 25z^6$ **65.** $18c^9$ **67.** $-432a^{12}b^{14}$ **69.** x^{2a+4} **71.** x^{a+7} **73.** $a^{3n+3}b^{3m+6}$ **75.** $c^{4a}d^{8a}$ **77.** $a = 8$ **79.** $a = \frac{3}{2}$ **81.** $c - 8m$ **83.** $\frac{y}{x}$ **85.** $-\frac{2a}{5}$ **87.** $\frac{t}{7}$ **89.** $x = 2$

Lesson 5-3 Try This

a. $-15x$ **b.** $-m^2$ **c.** y^2 **d.** x^5 **e.** $12p^7q^5$ **f.** $-8x^{11}y^9$ **g.** $14y^8$ **h.** $-21a^{13}$ **i.** x^3 **j.** $\frac{3}{2m^3}$ **k.** xy^3 **l.** $-4xy$

Exercise Set 5-3

1. $42x^2$ **3.** x^4 **5.** $-x^8$ **7.** $6a^6$ **9.** $28t^8$ **11.** $-18g^7$ **13.** $-6x^{11}$ **15.** $25n^8$ **17.** x^7y^6 **19.** $8a^8b^{10}$ **21.** $6y^8$ **23.** $40m^9$ **25.** x^4 **27.** $2x^3$ **29.** 3 **31.** $\frac{5}{a^4}$ **33.** $-\frac{1}{2}b$ **35.** $\frac{1}{4}x^5$ **37.** -4 **39.** $3x$ **41.** $5x^2y^3$ **43.** $-4b^6$ **45.** $\frac{-3p^2}{r}$ **47.** $\frac{-5a^6}{7b^2}$ **49.** x^{11} **51.** a^{18} **53.** $18x^8$ **55.** $36x^{18}$ **57.** $6x^6y^6$ **59.** a^9b^{14} **61.** $4x$ **63.** y^2 **65.** $\frac{a^2}{3b}$ **67.** $\frac{1}{2mn^6}$ **71.** $\frac{-32}{m^3}$ **73.** $-\frac{3}{m^{15}}$ **75.** 15 **77.** $\frac{5r^6}{qs}$ **79.** 0.0004 **81.** $x < -7$ **83.** $x > -1$ **85.** $J - 14$

Lesson 5-4 Try This

a. 1250 **b.** 700,000 **c.** 0.0048 **d.** 0.00018 **e.** 3.2×10^3 **f.** 1.39×10^5 **g.** 3.07×10^{-2} **h.** 2.004×10^{-1} **i.** 5.5×10^{-15} **j.** 2.0×10^3

Exercise Set 5-4

1. 5543 **3.** 0.00235 **5.** 57,000 **7.** 0.000034 **9.** 0.0006 **11.** 0.003007 **13.** 4.25×10^2 **15.** 1.24×10^4 **17.** 4.5×10^{-2} **19.** 1.25×10^5 **21.** 5.2×10^6 **23.** 5.6×10^{-6} **25.** 1.4×10^7 **27.** 3.2×10^{11} **29.** 1.0×10^{-10} **31.** 2.0×10^5 **33.** 4.2×10^{-2} **35.** 5.0×10^1 **37.** $4.08 \times 10^4 = 40{,}800$ **39.** $8.32 \times 10^{-8} = 0.0000000832$ **41.** 1.5×10^8 km = 150,000,000 km **45.** 7.2917×10^2 days = 729.17 days **47.** $1.5 \times 10^4 = 15{,}000$ s **49.** 8×10^2 **51.** 2.5×10^{-1} **53.** $3(3a + 2)$ **55.** $4(3m - n)$ **57.** $7x - 6$ **59.** $a - 15$

Lesson 5-5 Try This

a. No **b.** Yes; binomial **c.** Terms: $5y^3$, $6y$, -3; Coefficients: 5, 6, -3 **d.** Terms: m^4, $-3m$, -6; Coefficients: 1, -3, -6 **e.** Terms: $-3m^4n^2$, $-m^2n$, $2n$; Coefficients: -3, -1, 2 **f.** $2x - 10x^3 - 24$ **g.** $6m^2 - m - 7$ **h.** $4x^2y^2 - y^2 + y^3 - 1$ **i.** $b^5 + 5ab^3$ **j.** 4, 2, 1, 0; 4 **k.** 11, 7, 7, 1; 11

Exercise Set 5-5

1. No **3.** Yes; binomial **5.** No **7.** Yes; binomial **9.** Yes; monomial **11.** Yes; trinomial **13.** Yes; monomial **15.** Terms: $-4m^9$, $6m$, -1; Coefficients: -4, 6, -1 **17.** Terms: $2x^2y$, $5xy^2$, $-6y^4$; Coefficients: 2, 5, -6 **19.** Terms: $8p^3$, $2pq$, -4; Coefficients: 8, 2, -4 **21.** Terms: $-3n^6$, $3n$, -3; Coefficients: -3, 3, -3 **23.** Terms: x^8y^6, $-2x^6y^6$, $8x^4y^7$, $-4xy^8$; Coefficients: 1, -2, 8, -4 **25.** $-3x$ **27.** $10x^2$ **29.** $-x^3 - 5x$ **31.** $3x^4 + 7$ **33.** $3x^3 - 3$ **35.** $4a^4$ **37.** $3xy^2 + 5x^2y$ **39.** $6ab^2 + 3ab - 5a^2b$ **41.** 1, 0; 1 **43.** 2, 1, 0; 2

45. 3, 2, 1, 0; 3 **47.** 2, 1, 6, 4; 6 **49.** 6, 4, 2, 0; 6
51. 9, 9, 4; 9 **53.** $\frac{3}{4}x^5 - 2x - 5$

55. $\frac{7}{6}a^4 - 4a^2 - 3$ **57.** $14y + 17$; $11\frac{1}{2}a + 10$
59. $n(n + 2) - 3 = n^2 + 2n - 3$ **61.** c^{10}
63. x^7y^{11} **65.** $9c^{-4}$ or $\frac{9}{c^4}$ **67.** $-\frac{1}{12}$ **69.** $\frac{11}{8}$
71. $a \geq 3$

Lesson 5-6 Try This

a. $6x^7 + 3x^5 - 2x^4 + 4x^3 + 5x^2 + x$
b. $7x^5 - 5x^4 + 2x^3 + 4x^2 - 3$
c. $-14x^7 - 10x^3y^2 + 7x^2y^3 - 14y$
d. $-2m^2 - 3m + 2$ **e.** $3m^3y - 6m^2y$ **f.** -19
g. -14 **h.** 56 **i.** 196 ft **j.** ≈23.9¢ per mile
k. 3.83L

Exercise Set 5-6

1. $x^5 + 6x^3 + 2x^2 + x + 1$
3. $15x^9 + 7x^8 + 5x^3 - x^2 + x$
5. $-5y^8 - y^7 + 9y^6 + 8y^3 - 7y^2$ **7.** $m^6 + m^4$
9. $13m^3 - 9m + 8$ **11.** $-5m^2 + 9mp$
13. $12m^4 - 2m + \frac{1}{4}$ **15.** 98 **17.** 78 **19.** 9
21. -448 **23.** -18 **25.** 19 **27.** -12 **29.** -13
31. 5 **33.** 2 **35.** 448.6 **37.** $x^2 - 16$ **41.** 24
45. $\frac{x^9}{8}$ **47.** $\frac{3c^3}{a^3}$ **49.** 0.007662

Lesson 5-7 Try This

a. $-x^2 + 5$; $2x^2 + 2x$; Sum: $x^2 + 2x + 5$
b. $x^2 + 7x + 3$ **c.** $24m^4 + 5m^3 + m^2 + 1$
d. $2a^2b - 7a - 1$ **e.** $8n^3 - m^3n^2 - 7n - 3m - 5$
f. $m^4 - 2m^3 - 11m^2 + 5m - 14$
g. $-2x^4y^3 + x^2 - 3xy + 7$

Exercise Set 5-7

1. $x^2 + 4x + 5$; $2x^2 + x + 3$; Sum: $3x^2 + 5x + 8$
3. $x^2 + 5$; $x^2 + 4x$; Sum: $2x^2 + 4x + 5$
5. $-x + 5$ **7.** $-4x^4 + 6x^3 + 6x^2 + 2x + 4$
9. $12x^2 + 6$ **11.** $5x^4 - 2x^3 - 7x^2 - 5x$
13. $9x^8 + 8x^7 - 3x^4 + 2x^2 - 2x + 5$
15. $-3cd^4 + 3d^2 + 4cd$
17. $3x^5y^5 - 3x^4y^3 + 4y - 3y^4$
19. $-9x^2y^2 + 5xy + 5y^3 + 7$
21. $4m^4 + 3m^3 - 2m^2 + 2m - 3$
23. $-3x^4 - 3x^2 + 4x + 1$
25. $7y^5 - y^3 + 6y^2 + 4$
27. $x^4 + x^3y^2 + 3x^2 + 3x + 7$
29. $5x^5 - 3x^4y^3 + 3x^3y^3 - 6x^2 + 1$
31. $9b^5c^3 + 4b^4c^4 + 5b^3c^5 + 4b^2c^6 - 4b$
33. $3x^2 + x^2 + x^2 + 4x = 5x^2 + 4x$
35. 20, 25, 30 **39.** $2n^2 + 6n - 4$ **47.** Additive inverse **49.** Commutative property of multiplication
51. Commutative property of addition **53.** $18a^7$
55. $12m^2n^2$ **57.** $y(xz + 5 - 9z)$

Lesson 5-8 Try This

a. $-12x^4 + 3x^2 - 4x$
b. $13x^6y^4 - 2x^4y + 3x^2 - xy + \frac{5}{13}$
c. $5x^4 - 2x^2 + 5$ **d.** $-5m^3 + 2m + 8$
e. $4a^3 - 14a^2b^4 + 5ab + 2a + 2$
f. $2x^3 + 5x^2 - 2x - 5$ **g.** $-ab^2 + 4ab - 4a - 4$

Exercise Set 5-8

1. $5x$ **3.** $x^2 - 10x + 2$ **5.** $-12x^4y + 3x^3 - 3$
7. $2x^2 + 14$ **9.** $-2x^5 - 6x^4 + x + 2$
11. $9b^2 + 9b - 8$ **13.** $7m^3 - 3m - 11$
15. $3y^4 + 8y^3 - 5y - 3$ **17.** $6v^4u + 9v^2 - 7$
19. $9mn^5 + n^4 + mn^4 - 3mn^3 + 3n^2 + 1$
21. $3x + 6$ **23.** $4c^3 - 3c^2 + c + 1$
25. $11x^4 + 12x^3 - 9x^2 - 8x$
27. $-4m^5 + 9m^4 + 6m^2 + 16m + 6$
29. $x^4y^2 + x^2y$ **31.** $y - 9$ **33.** $11a^2 - 18a - 4$
35. $-10y^2 - 2y - 10$ **37.** $-3xy^4 - y^3 + 5y - 2$
39. $2x^2 + 3x - 1$, $x^2 + 3x$, $x^2 - 1$
41. $2x^2 + 4$, $x^2 - 2x + 5$, $x^2 + 2x - 1$
43. No, $-3(-x)^2 = 3x^2$ **45.** 1.594×10^3
47. 9.361×10^4 **49.** Terms: $5n^4m$, $7n^2m^2$, $-2m$, 3; Coefficients: 5, 7, -2, 3; Factors: 5, n^4 and m; 7, n^2 and m^2; -2, and m; 3 **51.** 3

Lesson 5-9 Try This

a. $8x^2 + 16x$ **b.** $-15a^5 + 6a^3 - 21a^2$
c. $40st^4 - 20s^3 - 45st - 55s$ **d.** $x^2 + 7x + 12$
e. $x^2 - 2x - 15$ **f.** $2x^2 + 9x + 4$
g. $2x^3 - 4x^2 - 3x + 6$ **h.** $12x^5 + 10x^3 + 6x^2 + 5$
i. $y^6 - 49$ **j.** $-2x^8 + 2x^6 - x^5 + x^3$
k. $-6a^2 - 14ab - 4b^2$ **l.** $2xy^3 - 8xy$
m. $3r^3s + 2r^3 + 6r^2s^3 + 4r^2s^2$ **n.** $5x^2 - 17x - 12$
o. $6y^3 - 10y^2 - 9y + 15$ **p.** $6a^2 - ab - b^2$
q. $18m^3 - 6m^2n^2 + 3mn - n^3$
r. $4p^2q^2 + 3p^3q - p^4$ **s.** $\frac{1}{4}r^4s^2 - s^2$

Exercise Set 5-9

1. $-3x^2 + 15x$ **3.** $12x^3 + 24x^2$
5. $-6m^4 - 6m^2x$ **7.** $3x^6 + 15x^3$ **9.** $18y^6 + 24y^5$
11. $6x^3 + 8x^2 - 6x$ **13.** $15a^4 + 30a^3 - 35a^2$
15. $-8y^9 - 8y^8 + 4y^7 - 20y^6$
17. $-7h^4k^6 + 7h^4k^4 + 7h^4k^3 - 7h^4k$
19. $-10a^9b + 2a^3 - 24a^2b$ **21.** $x^3 + x^2 + 3x + 3$
23. $x^4 + x^3 + 2x + 2$ **25.** $a^2 - a - 6$
27. $9x^2 + 15x + 6$ **29.** $5x^2 + 4x - 12$
31. $9x^2 - 1$ **33.** $4x^2 - 6xy + 2y^2$ **35.** $x^2 - \frac{1}{16}$
37. $x^2 - 0.01$ **39.** $2x^3 + 2x^2 + 6x + 6$

41. $-2x^2 + 13x - 6$ **43.** $x^2 + 14xy + 49y^2$
45. $6x^7 + 18x^5 + 4x^2 + 12$ **47.** $8x^6 + 65x^3 + 8$
49. $4x^3 - 12x^2 + 3x - 9$
51. $4x^6 + 4x^5 + x^4 + x^3$ **53.** $a^2b^2 - 9b^4$
55. $a^2 + 2ab + b^2$ **57.** $4x^2 + 12x + 9$
59. $84y^2 - 30y$ **61.** $m^2 - 28$ **63.** $2x + 1$
65. a. $2x^2 + 18x + 36$ **b.** 0
67. a. $2x^2 + 4x - 30$ **b.** 0 **69.** 3 **71.** 0
73. $6n + 9$ **75.** $n + (n + 1)$ **77.** 10 **79.** -4

Lesson 5-10 Try This

a. $x^2 - 4$ **b.** $x^4 - 49$ **c.** $9t^2 - 25$ **d.** $4x^6 - y^2$
e. $x^2 + 4x + 4$ **f.** $y^2 - 18y + 81$
g. $16x^2 - 40x + 25$ **h.** $a^2 - 8a + 16$
i. $25x^4 + 40x^2 + 16$ **j.** $16x^4 - 24x^3 + 9x^2$

Exercise Set 5-10

1. $x^2 - 16$ **3.** $d^2 - 36$ **5.** $36 - m^2$ **7.** $4x^2 - 1$
9. $16a^2 - 49$ **11.** $16x^4 - 9$ **13.** $9x^8 - 4$
15. $x^{12} - x^4$ **17.** $49c^2 - 4d^2$ **19.** $36t^2 - s^2$
21. $x^2 + 4x + 4$ **23.** $t^2 - 6t + 9$
25. $4x^2 - 4x + 1$ **27.** $16a^2 - 24ab + 9b^2$
29. $16s^2 + 40st + 25t^2$ **31.** $x^2 - \frac{1}{2}x + \frac{1}{16}$
33. $4x^2 + 28x + 49$ **35.** $9x^2 - 4y^2$
37. $25x^4 - 10x^2 + 1$ **39.** $4x^2 - \frac{4}{5}x + \frac{1}{25}$
41. $4x^6 - 0.09$ **43. a.** ac, ad, bc, bd
b. $ac + ad + bc + bd$ **c.** $ac + ad + bc + bd$, equal **47.** $100x^2 + 100x + 25 = 100(x^2 + x) + 25$ Add the first digit to its square, multiply by 100, add 25. **49. a.** $w(w + 1)(w + 2) = w^3 + 3w^2 + 2w$
b. $l(l - 1)(l + 1) = l^3 - 1$
c. $h(h - 1)(h - 2) = h^3 - 3h + 2h$
51. $2y^3 + 5y^2 - 7y$ **53.** $a^5b^6c^3$ **55.** -73
57. -11 **59.** 0 **61.** 60

Lesson 5-11 Try This

a. $b^4 + 3b^3 + b^2 + 15b - 20$
b. $6x^2 - xy - 12y^2 + 15x + 20y$
c. $3a^4 + 13a^3 - 3a^2 + 18a + 4$
d. $-20x^4 - 11x^3 - 44x^2 - 30x - 16$
e. $8n^5 + 4n^4 - 20n^3 - 16n^2 + 7n + 10$
f. $3x^7y^2 + 3x^6y^3 - 4x^5 - 4x^4y - 5x^3 - 5x^2y$
g. $x^2 + 11x + 30$ **h.** $x^2 - 16$
i. $-8x^5 + 20x^4 + 40x^2$ **j.** $81x^4 + 18x^2 + 1$
k. $4x^2 + 6x - 40$ **l.** $3x^3 - 14x^2 - x + 6$

Exercise Set 5-11

1. $x^3 - 1$ **3.** $4x^3 + 14x^2 + 8x + 1$
5. $3y^4 - 6y^3 - 7y^2 + 18y - 6$ **7.** $x^6 + 2x^5 - x^3$
9. $a^4 - b^4$ **11.** $x^4 - x^2 - 2x - 1$
13. $4x^4 + 8x^3 - 9x^2 - 10x + 8$
15. $6t^4 + t^3 - 16t^2 - 7t + 4$
17. $-4x^4 + 6x^3 - 2x^2 - 13x + 10$
19. $x^9 - x^5 + 2x^3 - x$ **21.** $b^4 - 1$
23. $x^4y - 2x^3y - 4x^2y + 9y$ **25.** $x^2 - 16x + 64$
27. $x^2 - 64$ **29.** $x^2 - 3x - 40$
31. $4x^3 + 24x^2 - 12x$ **33.** $4x^4 - 2x^2 + \frac{1}{4}$
35. $36a^6 - 1$ **37.** $-9x^2 + 4$
39. $36x^8 + 48x^4 + 16$ **41.** $-6x^5 - 48x^3 + 54x^2$
43. $12q^5 + 6q^3 - 2q^2 - 1$ **45.** $\frac{9}{16}x^2 + \frac{9}{4}x + 2$
47. $4x^3 + 13x^2 + 22x + 15$
49. $3x^5 - 14x^4 + 13x^3 - 20x^2$
51. $x^3 + 3x^2y + 3xy^2 + y^3$
55. $x^4 + x^3 + x^2 + x + 1$
57. $x^5 + x^4 + x^3 + x^2 + x + 1$ **61.** $x^2 + 6x + 9$
63. $-7a$ **65.** $-3y^2 + 9y - 1$ **67.** 21,000,000
69. 7, 3, 0; 7 **71.** 9 ft

Problem Solving

1. 14.938% ≈ 15% **3.** 2.4747 Liters ≈ 2.5 L

Problem Set 5-12

1. Job B will pay more money for the 10-year period.
3. Seven people bought the stamp, each paying $29.
5. The company would have 204,775 salespeople after 12 weeks.

Chapter 5 Summary and Review

1. 7^6 **3.** x^{11} **5.** x^8y^{10} **7.** 7^2 **9.** x^7y^4 **11.** $\frac{1}{y^2}$
13. 5^6 **15.** x^{12} **17.** $9a^2$ **19.** $8x^9$ **21.** $9x^4y^2z^8$
23. n^{30} **25.** $6a^2$ **27.** $-20b^3c^6$ **29.** $15w^3z^7$ **31.** a^3
33. $-3x^2y^3$ **35.** $-6b^7c^4$ **37.** 3250
39. 2.426×10^6 **41.** $4x^3 + 4$ **43.** 5, 3, 0; 5
45. $7x^5 - 2x^4 + 3x^2 - 2x + 5$
47. $-x^5 + 10x^4 - 7x - 1$ **49.** 25
51. $7x^3 + 4x^2 + 4x$
53. $3x^5 - x^4 - 4x^3 + 3x^2 - 3$ **55.** $4y^3 + 14$
57. $x^5 + 8x^4 - 3x^3 - 2x^2 + 8$
59. $-x^5 + x^4 - 5x^3 - 2x^2 + 2x$
61. $15x^6 - 40x^5 + 50x^4 + 10x^3$ **63.** $a^2 - 9$
65. $6x^4 + 15x^3y - 6x^2 - 15xy$ **67.** $a^2 - 64$
69. $9x^4 - 16$ **71.** $4 - 9y^2$ **73.** $9x^2 + 36x + 36$
75. $2a^4 + 3a^3 - 10a^2 - 12a + 8$
77. $x^7 + x^5 - 3x^4 + 3x^3 - 2x^2 + 5x - 3$

Chapter 6

Lesson 6-1 Try This

a. $(4x^2)(2x^2)$, $(4x)(2x^3)$, $(8x)(x^3)$ **b.** $(2m)(3m^4)$, $(m^2)(6m^3)$, $(2m^3)(3m^2)$ **c.** $(6ab)(2ab)$, $(6a^2)(2b^2)$, $(12)(a^2b^2)$ **d.** $x(x + 3)$ **e.** $ab(a + 2)$
f. $x^2(3x^4 - 5x + 2)$ **g.** $3x^2(3x^2 - 5x + 1)$
h. $pq(2p^2q + p + 1)$ **i.** $3m^2n^2(4m^2n^2 + m + 2)$

Exercise Set 6-1

11. $y(y + 8)$ **13.** $3p(p - 1)$ **15.** $5(x^2 + 2x + 6)$ **17.** $7y^2(4 + 3y^2)$ **19.** $x^3(9 + 25x^4)$ **21.** $18y^4$ **23.** $3(2x^2 + x - 5)$ **25.** $a^2b(4a^2b + 1)$ **27.** $5m^3(m^2n + 2)$ **29.** $2xy^2(x^2 + 3y + 4)$ **31.** $16x(x^5 - 2x^4 - 3)$ **33.** $x(5x^4 + 10x - 8)$ **35.** $x^3(x^6 - x^4 + x + 1)$ **37.** $5(2x^3 + 5x^2 + 3x - 4)$ **39.** $5pq^2(p^2 + 2p - 4)$ **41.** $m^2n^2(6mn + 3m + 1)$ **43.** Yes **45.** Yes **47.** Yes **49.** No **51.** No **53.** No **57.** No common factor **59.** No common factor **61.** $9m^4n^6$ **63.** 4.37×10^{-3} **65.** 5.613×10^3 **67.** $m^2 + 119$

Lesson 6-2 Try This

a. Yes **b.** No **c.** No **d.** No **e.** Yes **f.** Yes **g.** $(x + 3)(x - 3)$ **h.** $(y + 8)(y - 8)$ **i.** $(2y + 7)(2y - 7)$ **j.** $(4x - 5y)(4x + 5y)$ **k.** $(a^4b^2 - 2)(a^4b^2 + 2)$ **l.** $(5a^5 - 6b^4)(5a^5 + 6b^4)$ **m.** $8y^2(2 + y^2)(2 - y^2)$ **n.** $5(1 + 2y^3)(1 - 2y^3)$ **o.** $ab(a + 2b)(a - 2b)$ **p.** $x^4y^4(8 - 5xy^2)(8 + 5xy^2)$ **q.** $(3x + 1)(3x - 1)(9x^2 + 1)$ **r.** $(4m^2 + n^4)(2m - n^2)(2m + n^2)$

Exercise Set 6-2

1. Yes **3.** No **5.** No **7.** Yes **9.** $(x + 2)(x - 2)$ **11.** $(x + 3y)(x - 3y)$ **13.** $(4a + 3)(4a - 3)$ **15.** $(2x + 5)(2x - 5)$ **17.** $(5m + 7)(5m - 7)$ **19.** $(x^2 + 3)(x^2 - 3)$ **21.** $(m^8 + 5)(m^8 - 5)$ **23.** $(2x^2 + 4)(2x^2 - 4)$ **25.** $(8y^2 + 9)(8y^2 - 9)$ **27.** $(6x^6 + 7)(6x^6 - 7)$ **29.** $x(6 + 7x)(6 - 7x)$ **31.** $y^2(9y^2 + 5)(9y^2 - 5)$ **33.** $2(2x + 7y)(2x - 7y)$ **35.** $2(4x + 5y)(4x - 5y)$ **37.** $3(5m^3n + 7)(5m^3n - 7)$ **39.** $(x^2 + 1)(x + 1)(x - 1)$ **41.** $4(x^2 + 4)(x + 2)(x - 2)$ **43.** $(4 + y^2)(2 + y)(2 - y)$ **45.** $(25 + m^2)(5 + m)(5 - m)$ **47.** $x(4 + 9x)(4 - 9x)$ **49.** $(b^4 + a^2)(b^2 + a)(b^2 - a)$ **51.** $x^2(x^7 + 3)(x^7 - 3)$ **53.** $(7a^2 + 9)(7a^2 - 9)$ **55.** $(x^6 + 4)(x^3 + 2)(x^3 - 2)$ **57.** $a^2(a^5 + 2)(a^5 - 2)$ **59.** $(5a^2 + 3)(5a^2 - 3)$ **61.** $(3c^4 + 7)(3c^4 - 7)$ **63.** $3x^3(x + 2)(x - 2)$ **65.** $2x\left(3x + \frac{2}{5}\right)\left(3x - \frac{2}{5}\right)$ **67.** $x\left(x + \frac{1}{4}\right)\left(x - \frac{1}{4}\right)$ **69.** $(0.8x + 1.1)(0.8x - 1.1)$ **71.** $x(x + 6)$ **73.** $3(a - 1)(3a + 11)$ **75.** $(y^4 + 16)(y^2 + 4)(y + 2)(y - 2)$ **83.** $x^2 + 14x + 49$ **85.** 1, 0; 1 **87.** 5, 2, 0; 5 **89.** 0.08 **91.** 0.065 **93.** 5 **95.** The base is 18 cm.

Lesson 6-3 Try This

a. Yes **b.** Yes **c.** No **d.** Yes **e.** No **f.** Yes **g.** $(x + 1)^2$ **h.** $(x - 1)^2$ **i.** $(5x - 7)^2$ **j.** $3(4m + 5n)^2$

Exercise Set 6-3

1. Yes **3.** No **5.** Yes **7.** No **9.** No **11.** $(x - 7)^2$ **13.** $(x + 8)^2$ **15.** $(x - 1)^2$ **17.** $(x + 2y)^2$ **19.** $(y - 3x)^2$ **21.** $2(x - 1)^2$ **23.** $x(x - 9)^2$ **25.** $5(2x + 5)^2$ **27.** $(7y - 3x)^2$ **29.** $5(y^2 + 1)^2$ **31.** $(y^3 + 13)^2$ **33.** $(4x^5 - 1)^2$ **35.** $(2x^2 + 1)^2$ **37.** $(9x^3 + 4y)^2$ **39.** Not possible **41.** $(x + 11)^2$ **43.** Not possible **45.** $7(9x - 4)$ **47.** $y^4(x^2 - 3)(x^2 + 3)$ **49.** $(x^4 + 16)(x^2 + 4)(x + 2)(x - 2)$ **51.** $(y + 4)^2$ **53.** $(2a + 15)^2$ **55.** $(x + 5)^2$ **59.** $(x^n + 5)^2$ **61.** $(y + 3)^2 - (x + 4)^2 = (y + x + 7)(y - x - 1)$ **63.** 16 **65.** $-2x^3 - x^2 + 18x + 9$ **67.** $3x(2x - 3)$ **69.** $3y(3y^2 + 1)$ **71.** 359,400

Lesson 6-4 Try This

a. $(x + 4)(x + 3)$ **b.** $(x + 9)(x + 4)$ **c.** $(x - 5)(x - 3)$ **d.** $(x - 4)(x - 5)$ **e.** $(x - 3)(x - 4)$ **f.** $(m + 3n)(m + 5n)$ **g.** $(a + 3b)(a + 2b)$ **h.** $(p + 4q)(p + 2q)$ **i.** $(x + 6)(x - 2)$ **j.** $(x - 6)(x + 2)$ **k.** $(a + 7b)(a - 2b)$ **l.** $(x - 6y)(x + 5y)$

Exercise Set 6-4

1. $(x + 5)(x + 3)$ **3.** $(x + 4)(x + 3)$ **5.** $(x - 3)^2$ **7.** $(x + 7)(x + 2)$ **9.** $(b + 4)(b + 1)$ **11.** $(a - 8)(a - 6)$ **13.** $(m + 7)(m + 3)$ **15.** $(z - 4)(z - 6)$ **17.** $(a - 5b)(a - 4b)$ **19.** $(c - 5d)(c - 2d)$ **21.** $(y - 10z)(y - z)$ **23.** $(x + 7)(x - 6)$ **25.** $(x - 9)(x + 2)$ **27.** $(x - 8)(x + 2)$ **29.** $(y - 9)(y + 5)$ **31.** $(x - 11y)(x + 9y)$ **33.** $(c + 8d)(c - 7d)$ **35.** $(a + 7b)(a - 5b)$ **37.** $(x + 10)^2$ **39.** $(x - 25)(x + 4)$ **41.** $(x - 24)(x + 3)$ **43.** $(x - 16)(x - 9)$ **45.** $(a + 12)(a - 11)$ **47.** $(15y - x)(8y - x)$ **49.** $(12y + x)(9y - x)$ **53.** $-49, -23, -5, 5, 23, 49$ **55.** $-x(x - 23)(x + 1)$ **57.** $8y(y^2)$, $(4y^2)(2y)$, $(2y^2)(4y)$, etc. **59.** a^4b **61.** $5y^2 + 8$ **63.** c **65.** $2, -2$

Lesson 6-5 Try This

a. $(3x + 2)(2x + 1)$ **b.** $(4x - 1)(2x + 3)$ **c.** $(6x + 1)(x - 7)$ **d.** $3(x - 3)(x - 4)$ **e.** $2(2x + 1)(2x - 1)$ **f.** $3(3a + 1)(a - 2)$ **g.** $2(x + 3)(x - 1)$ **h.** $2(2a + 3)(a - 1)$ **i.** $3(2m - n)(m + 3n)$

Exercise Set 6-5

1. $(2x + 1)(x - 4)$ **3.** $(5x - 9)(x + 2)$ **5.** $(2x + 7)(3x + 1)$ **7.** $(3x + 1)(x + 1)$ **9.** $(2x + 5)(2x - 3)$ **11.** $(2x + 1)(x - 1)$ **13.** $(3x + 8)(3x - 2)$ **15.** $(3x + 1)(x - 2)$ **17.** $(3x + 4)(4x + 5)$ **19.** $(7x - 1)(2x + 3)$

21. $(3p + 4)(3p + 2)$ **23.** $(7 - 3b)^2$
25. $(x + 2)(24x - 1)$ **27.** $(7x + 4)(5x - 11)$
29. $2(5 - x)(2 + x)$ **31.** $4(3x - 2)(x + 3)$
33. $6(5x - 9)(x + 1)$ **35.** $2(3x + 5)(x - 1)$
37. $(3a - 1)(a - 1)$ **39.** $4(3x + 2)(x - 3)$
41. $(2x - 1)(x + 1)$ **43.** $(3b - 8)(3b + 2)$
45. $5(3x + 1)(x - 2)$ **47.** $(6x + 5y)(3x - 2y)$
49. $(5m + 2n)(3m - 5n)$ **51.** $(5x - 2y)(7x - 4y)$
53. $(3x^2 + 2)(3x^2 + 4)$ **55.** $(3x - 7)^2$
57. $2a(3a + 5)(a - 1)$ **59.** Not factorable
61. $x(x^2 + 3)(x^2 - 2)$ **65.** $(-3x^m + 4)(5x^m - 2)$
67. $x(x^n - 1)^2$ **69.** $mn + 11$ **71.** $(x - y)^2$
73. $y > -1$ **75.** $y \geq 2$

Lesson 6-6 Try This

a. $(4x + 1)(2x^2 + 3)$ **b.** $(2x - 3)(2x^2 - 3)$
c. $(x + 1)(x + 1)(x - 1)$ **d.** $(a - 2b)(3 + 5a)$

Exercise Set 6-6

1. $(x + 3)(x^2 + 2)$ **3.** $(y + 3)(2y^2 + 1)$
5. $(2a - 3)(4a^2 + 3)$ **7.** $(3x - 4)(4x^2 + 1)$
9. $(b + 8)(b^2 - 3)$ **11.** Not factorable
13. $(x - 4)(2x^2 - 9)$ **15.** $(a - b)(x + y)$
17. $(n + p)(n + 2)$ **19.** $(a + y)(a - 3)$
21. $(2x^2 + 3)(2x^3 + 3)$
23. $(c^2 + 1)(c + 1)(c + 1)(c - 1)(c - 1)$
25. $(x - y + z)(x - y - z)$
27. $(a + b + 1)(a + b - 1)$
31. $28x^3 + 20x^2 + 7x + 5$, $(7x + 5)(4x^2 + 1)$
33. $m^2 + 2mn + n^2$ **35.** $m^2 - n^2$
37. $(y + 3)(y + 3)$ or $(y + 3)^2$ **39.** $(c + 9)(c - 10)$
41. $(5 - x)(4 - y)$ **43.** $(3a^2 + b)(3a^2 - b)$

Lesson 6-7 Try This

a. $3(m^2 + 1)(m + 1)(m - 1)$ **b.** $(x^3 + 4)^2$
c. $2x^2(x + 3)(x + 1)$ **d.** $(x + 4)(3x^2 - 2)$
e. $8x(x + 5)(x - 5)$ **f.** $y^3(y - 7)(y + 5)$

Exercise Set 6-7

1. $2(x + 8)(x - 8)$ **3.** $(a - 5)^2$ **5.** $(2x - 3)(x - 4)$
7. $x(x + 12)^2$ **9.** $(x - 2)(x + 2)(x + 3)$
11. $6(2x + 3)(2x - 3)$ **13.** $4x(x - 2)(5x + 9)$
15. Not factorable **17.** $x(x - 3)(x^2 + 7)$
19. $x^3(x - 7)^2$ **21.** Not factorable
23. $4(x^2 + 4)(x + 2)(x - 2)$
25. $(y^4 + 1)(y^2 + 1)(y + 1)(1 - y)$
27. $x^3(x - 3)(x - 1)$
29. $(a + 1)(a + 1)(a - 1)(a - 1)$
31. $-2(x - 2)(x + 5)$ or $2(2 - x)(5 + x)$
33. $(y - 2)(y + 3)(y - 3)$ **35.** $(a + 4)(a^2 + 1)$
37. $2ab(2ab - 1)(3a + 1)$ **39.** $x^2y(x + 1)(3x - 2y)$
43. $(x^4 + 16)(x^2 + 4)(x + 2)(x - 2)$ **45.** $\frac{1}{x}$
47. $6a^5 - 3a^3$

Connections: Discrete Math

1. $m^5 + 5m^4n + 10m^3n^2 + 10m^2n^3 + 5mn^4 + n^5$
3. $a^4 + 16a^3 + 96a^2 + 256a + 256$
5. $a^6 + 6a^5b + 15a^4b^2 + 20a^3b^3 + 15a^2b^4 + 6ab^5 + b^6$

Lesson 6-8 Try This

a. 3, −4 **b.** 7, 3 **c.** 0, $\frac{17}{3}$ **d.** $-\frac{1}{4}, \frac{2}{3}$ **e.** 3, −2
f. 8, −7 **g.** 7, −4 **h.** 3 **i.** 0, 4 **j.** $\frac{4}{5}, -\frac{4}{5}$

Exercise Set 6-8

1. −8, −6 **3.** 3, −5 **5.** −12, 11 **7.** 0, −5
9. 0, 13 **11.** 0, −10 **13.** 4, $\frac{1}{4}$ **15.** 0, $\frac{2}{3}$ **17.** 0, 18
19. $\frac{1}{9}, \frac{1}{10}$ **21.** 2, 6 **23.** $\frac{1}{3}$, 20 **25.** 0, $\frac{2}{3}, \frac{1}{2}$
27. −5, −1 **29.** 2, −9 **31.** 5, 3 **33.** 0, 8
35. 0, −19 **37.** 4, −4 **39.** $\frac{2}{3}, -\frac{2}{3}$ **41.** −3
43. $\frac{2}{3}, -\frac{1}{4}$ **45.** 7, −2 **47.** $\frac{9}{8}, -\frac{9}{8}$ **49.** $-\frac{9}{4}, \frac{1}{2}$
51. 0, $\frac{6}{5}$ **53.** 3, $-\frac{1}{5}$ **55.** 3, −3 **57.** $\frac{5}{3}$, −1
59. $-\frac{9}{2}$, −8 **61.** 4, −5 **63.** 9, −3 **65.** $\frac{1}{8}, \frac{-1}{8}$
67. 4, −4 **71. a.** (3) **b.** (5) **c.** (1) **d.** (2) **e.** (4)
f. (6) **73.** $3(n + 8)$ **75.** $(a + b)^2$ **77.** $a^2 - b^2$
79. $(2x - y)(2x + y)$

Lesson 6-9 Try This

a. 7, 8 **b.** 0, 1 **c.** 5, −5 **d.** 5, −4 **e.** 6, −6
f. 5 cm, 3 cm **g.** 21, 22; −21, −22

Exercise Set 6-9

1. $-\frac{3}{4}$ or 1 **3.** 2 or 4 **5.** 13 and 14, −13 and −14
7. 12 and 14, −12 and −14 **9.** 15 and 17, −15 and −17 **11.** 12 m, 8m **13.** 5 ft **15.** 4 cm, 14 cm
17. 6 m **19.** 5 and 7 **21.** $7x + 1 = (x + 1)^2, x = 5$
23. $x^3 = 2x^2, x = 0$ or $x = 2$ **25. a.** 1 second (on the way up); 3 seconds (on the way back down)
b. 4 seconds **27.** 7 in. **29.** $2\frac{1}{2}$ cm **31.** 5 in.
33. 5.59×10^{-3} **35.** $80x^8$ **37.** 24 **39.** $(a - 4)^2$
41. $x^2(x - 1)(x + 1)$ **43.** $9(4y^4 - 7)$

Problem Solving College Entrance Exams

1. (C) **3.** (B) **5.** (C) **7.** (B) **9.** (D)

Chapter 6 Summary and Review

3. $x(x - 3)$ **5.** $4x^4(2x^2 - 8x + 1)$ **7.** No
9. $(3x - 2)(3x + 2)$ **11.** $2(x - 5)(x + 5)$
13. $(x^2 + 9)(x - 3)(x + 3)$ **15.** No **17.** Yes

19. $(x - 3)^2$ **21.** $(3x - 5)^2$ **23.** $2(3x - 1)^2$
25. $(x - 5)(x - 3)$ **27.** $(y + 4)(y + 5)$
29. $(m + 7)(m + 8)$ **31.** $(2x + 1)(x - 4)$
33. $2(a - 6)(3a + 4)$ **35.** $(x^3 - 2)(x + 4)$
37. $(3x + 2)(2x^2 + 1)$ **39.** $-3x(5x - 2)^2$
41. $(x + 15)(x - 13)$
43. $(1 + a^4)(1 + a^2)(1 + a)(1 - a)$ **45.** $0, \frac{3}{2}$
47. $-4, 3$ **49.** $\frac{4}{3}, -\frac{4}{3}$ **51.** $-18, -16$ or $16, 18$
53. $\frac{5}{2}, -2$

Chapter 7

Lesson 7-1 Try This

a.–e.

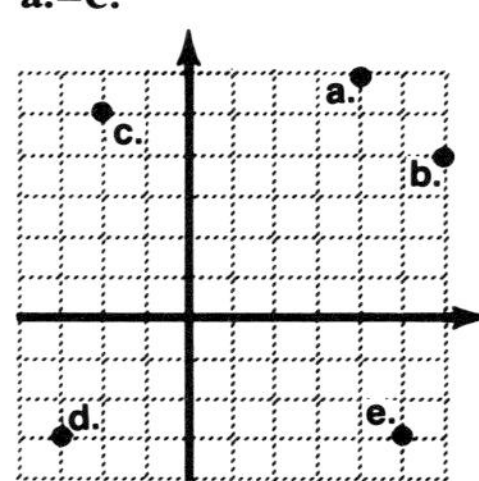

f.–i.

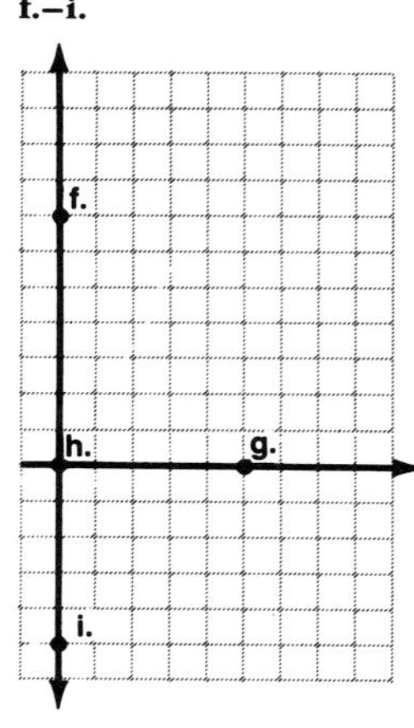

j. I **k.** III **l.** IV **m.** II **n.** (4, 3), (−4, −3), (2, −4), (1, 5), (−2, 0), (0, 3)

Exercise Set 7-1

1–15.

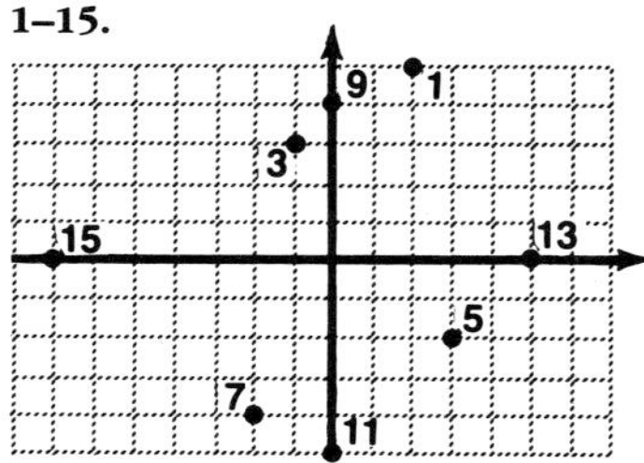

17. II **19.** IV **21.** III **23.** I **25.** Negative, positive
27. A (3, 3), B (0, −4), C (−5, 0), D (−1, −1), E (2, 0) **37.** 32.5 **39.** $(x^2 + 2)(x - 5)$
41. $4ab - 3bc$ **43.** $-4mn - 3pq$

Lesson 7-2 Try This

a. No **b.** Yes **c.** Answers may vary. Ex. (0, 3), (1, 5), (−1, 1), (−2, −1)

d.

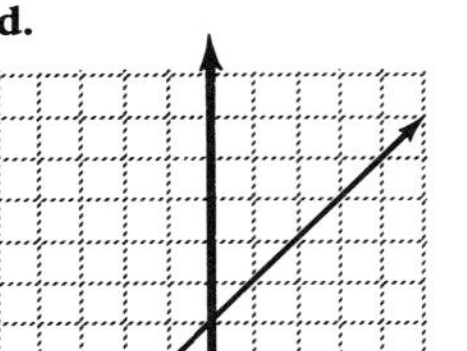

e.

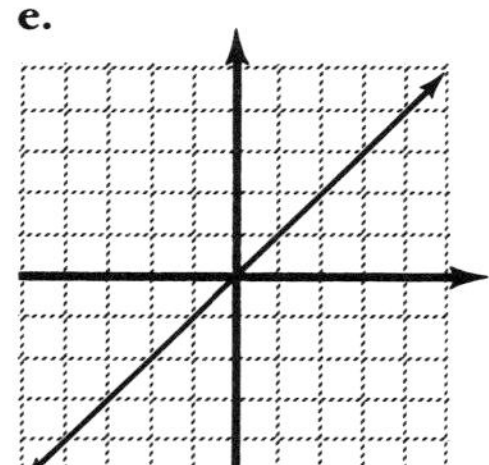

Exercise Set 7-2

1. Yes **3.** No **5.** Yes

17.

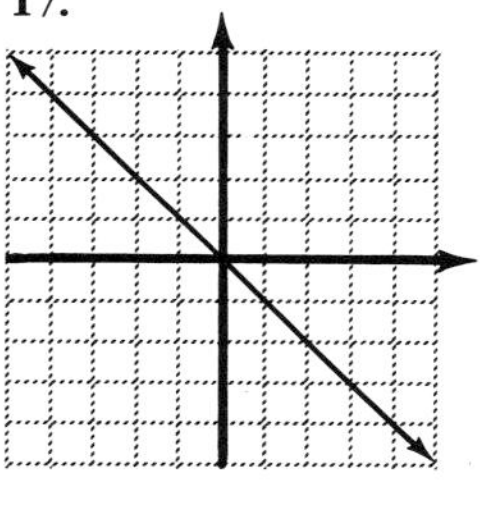

19.

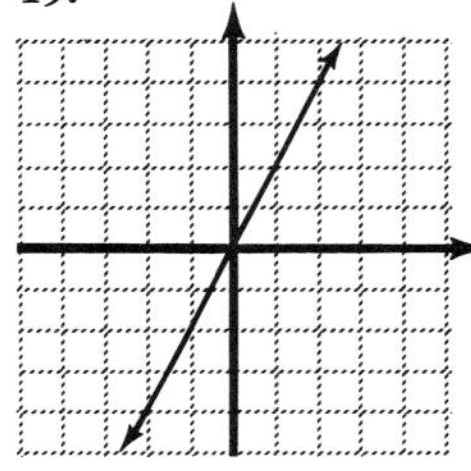

21.

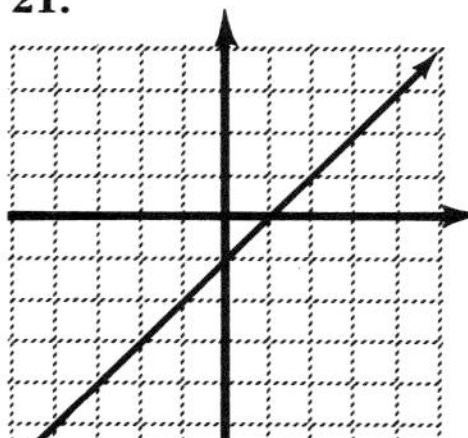

23.

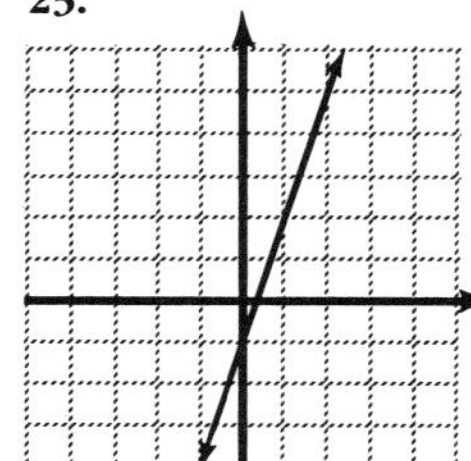

25.

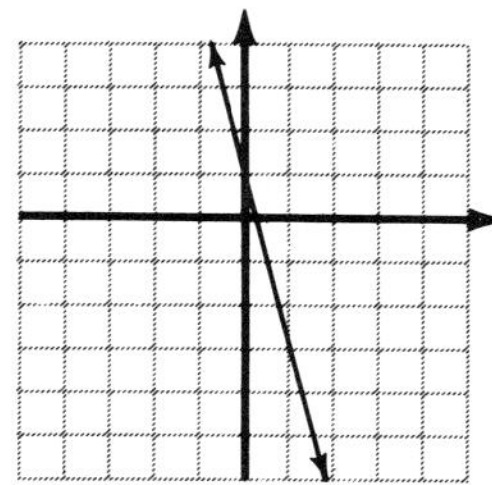

27.

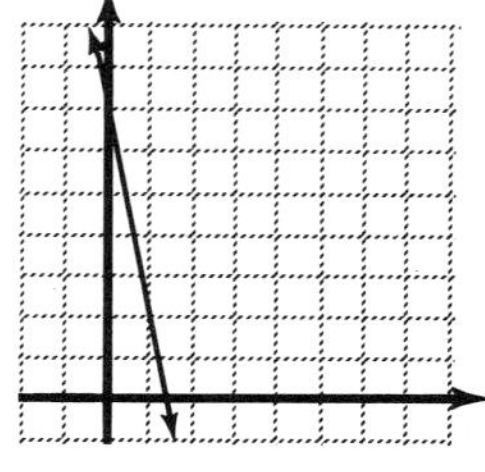

29.

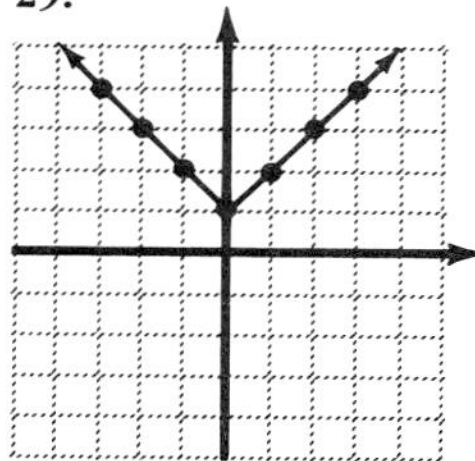

33. $68x + 76y = 864$, Let $x = y$, 6 h each machine
35. 1 **37.** $x(7x^3 + 1)$ **39.** 0 **41.** $-6, 3$
43. $-1, -3$ **45.** $(mn^2)(mn + 2)$ **47.** $(x + 3y)^2$
49. $(3x - 2)(2x - 1)$ **51.** $r = \frac{A - P}{Pt}$

Lesson 7-3 Try This

a.

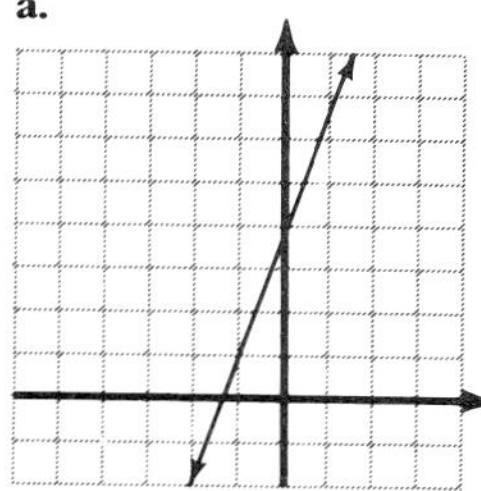

b.

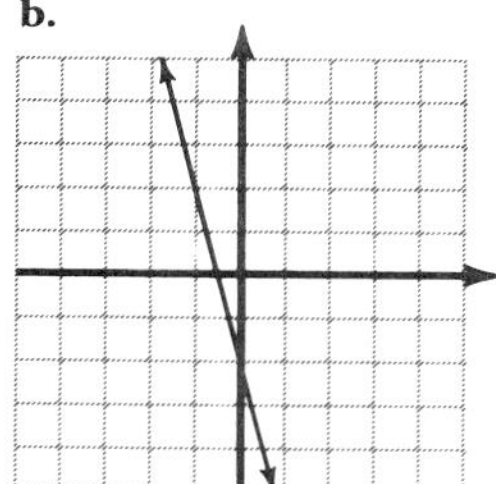

c.

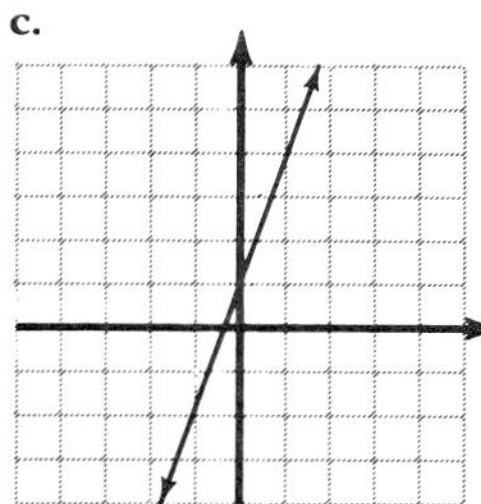

d.

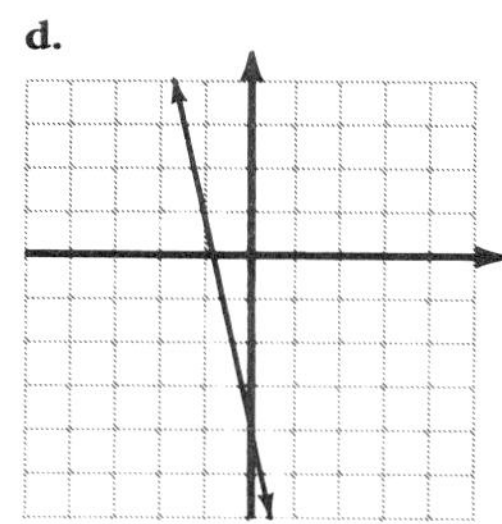

Exercise Set 7-3

1.

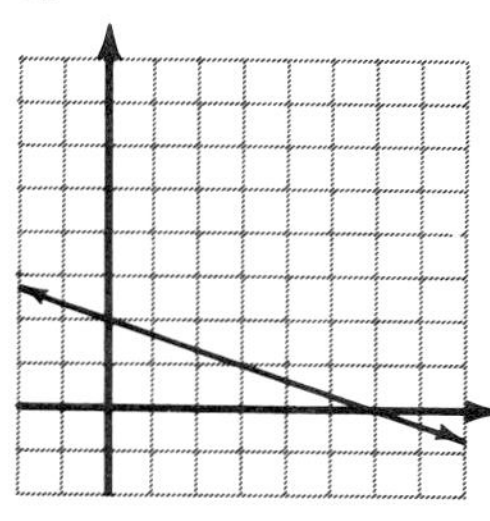

3.

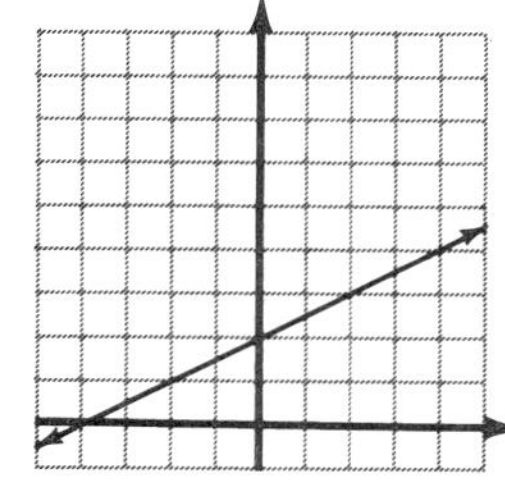

5.

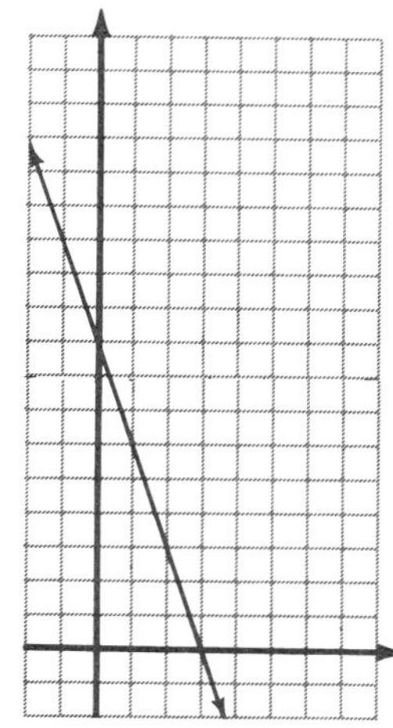

7.

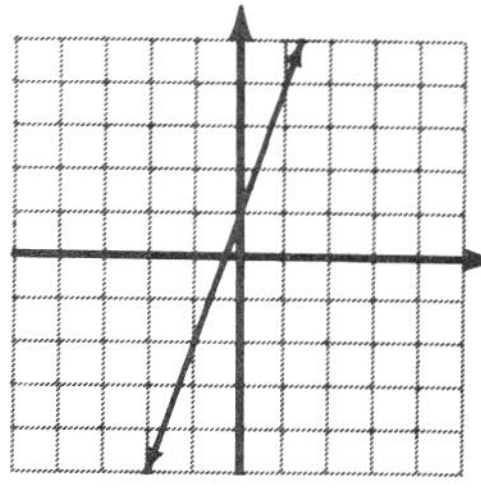

9.

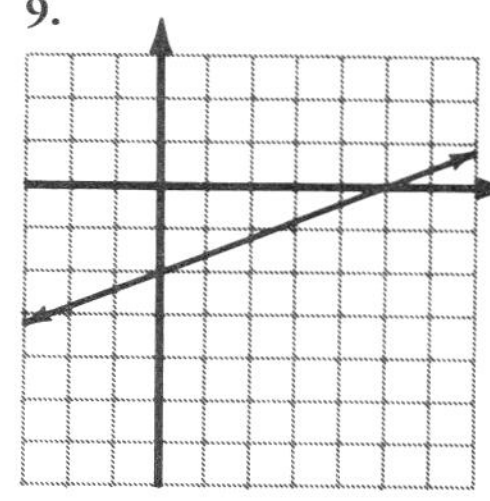

11.

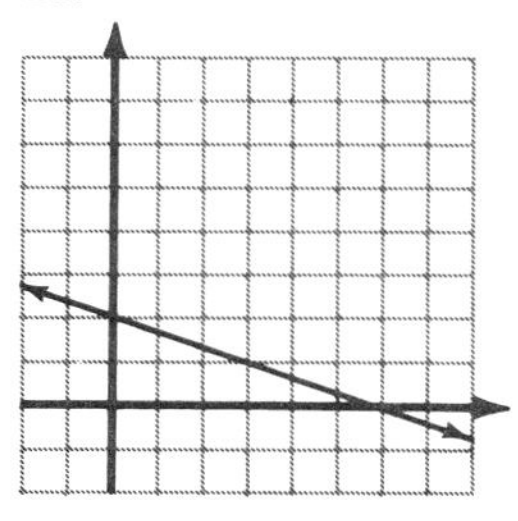

13.

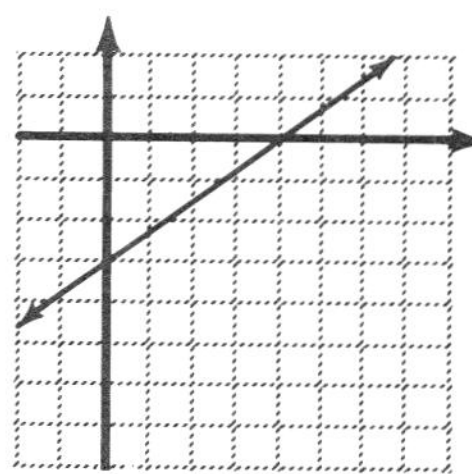

15.

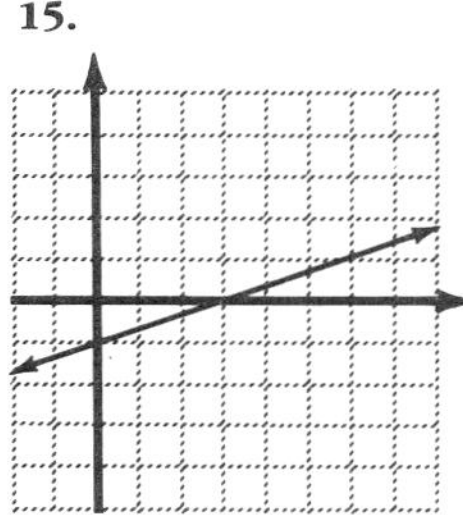

17.

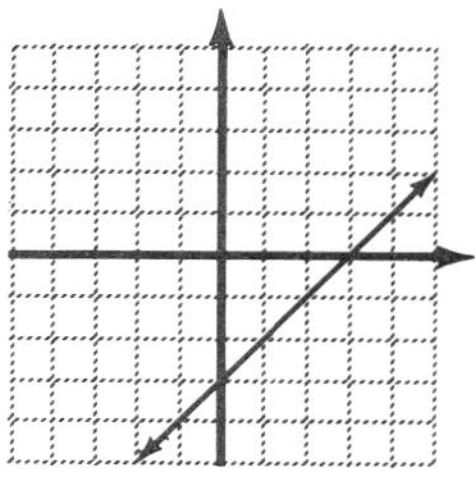

19.

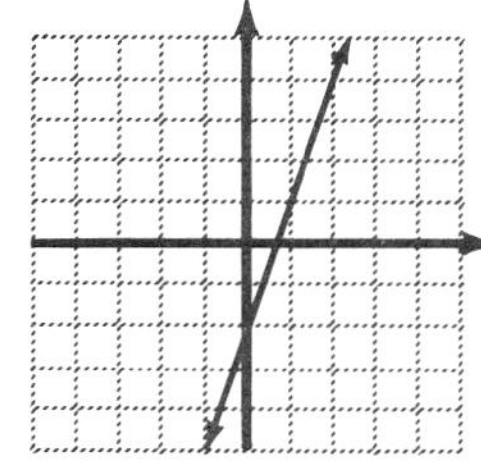

21.

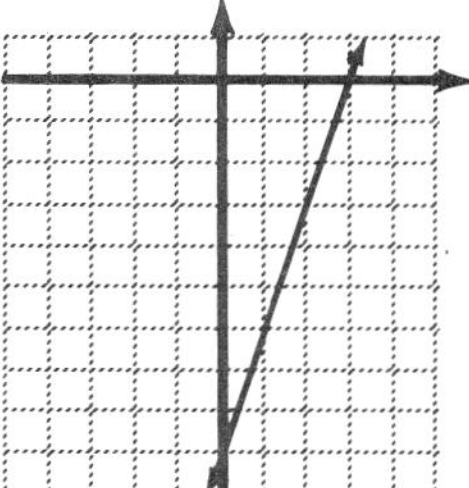

23.

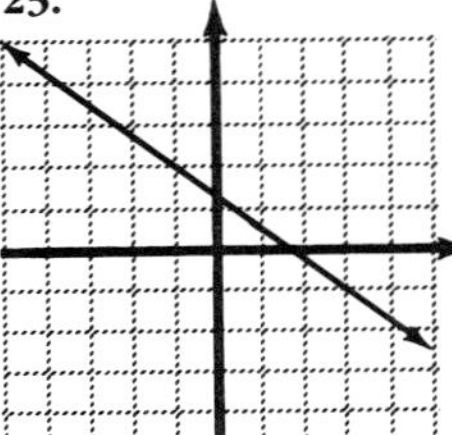

25.

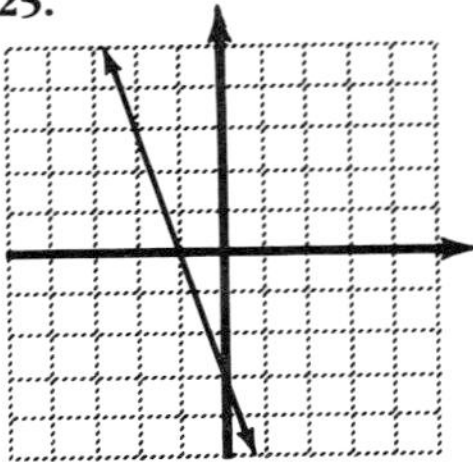

27.

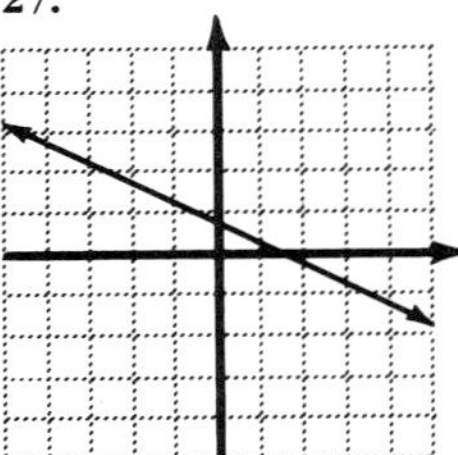

29.

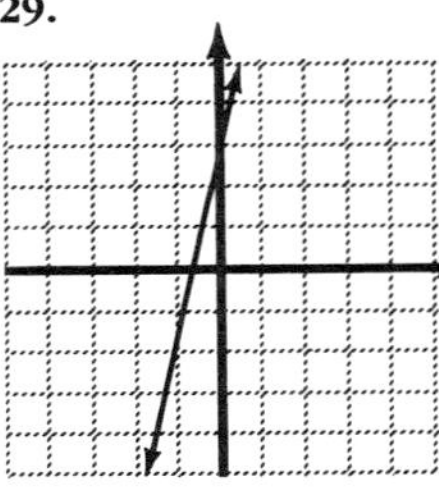

31.

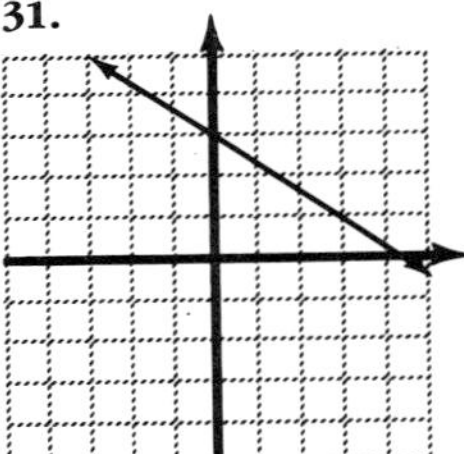

33.

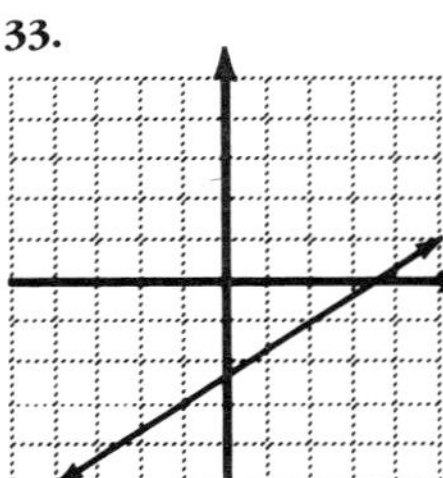

35.

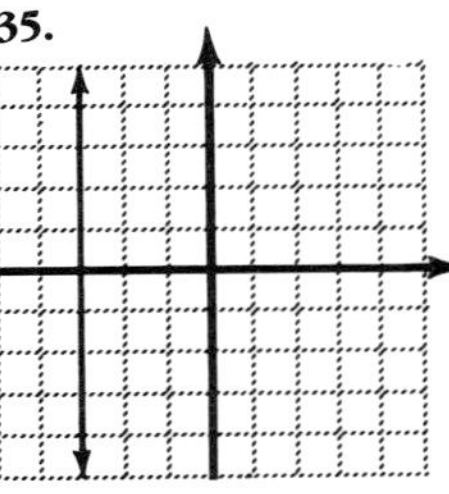

37.

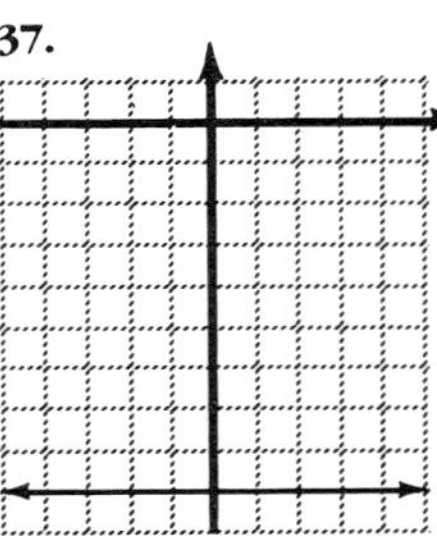

39.

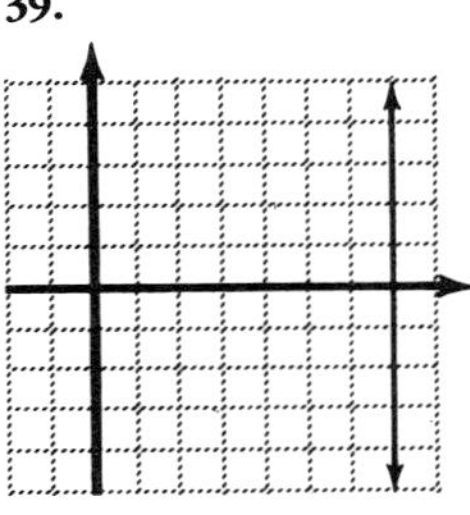

41.

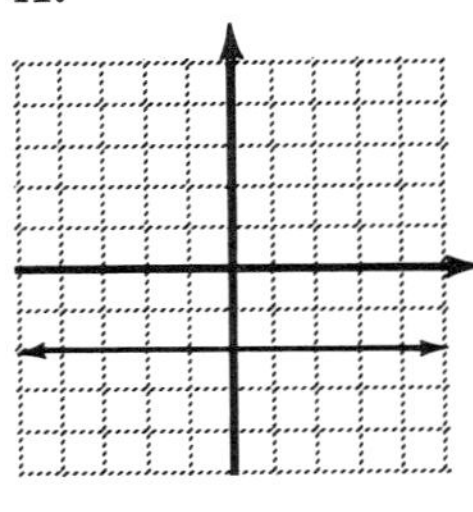

43. b **45.** a **47.** $x = 0$ **49.** $y = -5$ **51.** $y = 2.8$

53.

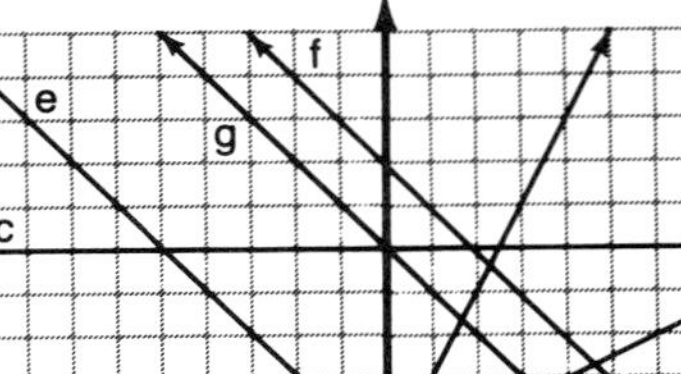

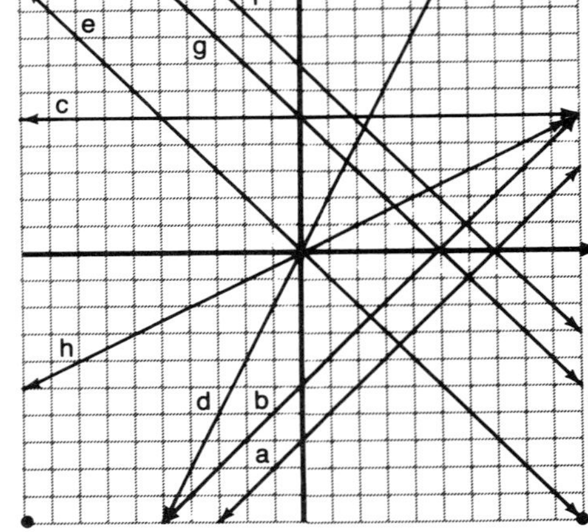

55. Yes **57.** Yes **59.** $(xy + 2)(xy - 4)$ **61.** $r = \frac{v^2}{a}$

63. About 38.5 minutes

Lesson 7-4 Try This

a. Slope $= \frac{2}{5}$ **b.** Slope $= -\frac{5}{3}$ **c.** $\frac{7}{6}$ **d.** $\frac{4}{7}$ **e.** $-\frac{1}{2}$

f. $-\frac{15}{14}$ **g.** 0 **h.** No slope **i.** $-\frac{1}{3}$

Exercise Set 7-4

1. $m = 3$ **3.** $m = -\frac{9}{7}$ **5.** $m = -\frac{5}{6}$ **7.** $m = -\frac{4}{5}$

9. $m = 2$ **11.** 7 **13.** $-\frac{2}{3}$ **15.** -2 **17.** 3 **19.** 2

21. No slope **23.** Zero slope **25.** No slope

27. Zero slope **29.** 6 **31.** 12 **33.** 39% **37.** $2, \frac{1}{2}$,

$-\frac{1}{2}, 2$ **39.** $(ab + 2)(ab - 1)$ **41.** Yes

43. 0.002575 **45.** $-2, 9$ **47.** -2

Lesson 7-5 Try This

a. $-\frac{4}{5}$ **b.** $-\frac{3}{8}$ **c.** $-\frac{1}{5}$ **d.** $\frac{5}{4}$ **e.** 5, 0 **f.** $-\frac{3}{2}, -6$

g. $-\frac{3}{4}, 4$ **h.** $-\frac{7}{5}, -5$

i.

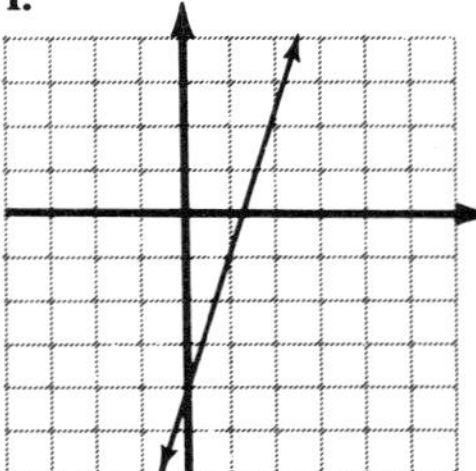

j.

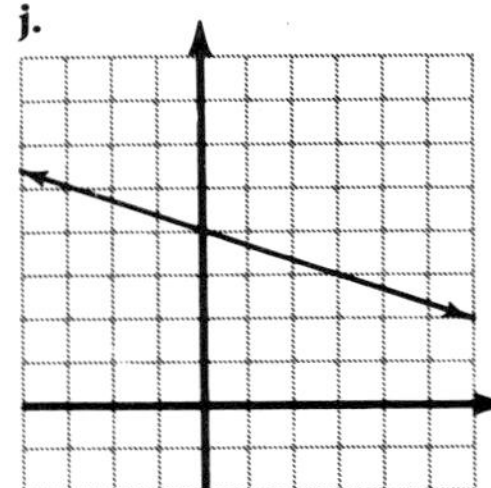

k.

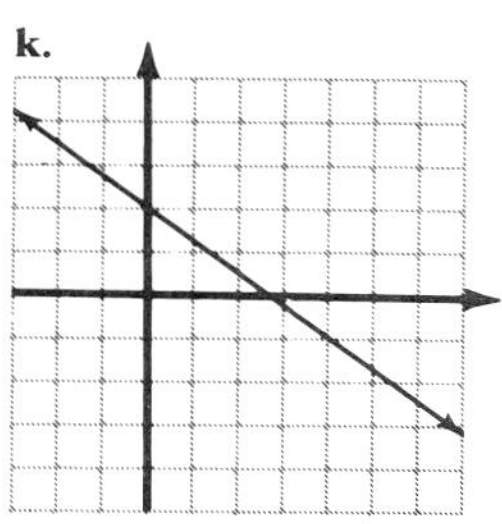

Exercise Set 7-5

1. $-\frac{3}{2}$ **3.** $-\frac{1}{4}$ **5.** 2 **7.** $\frac{4}{3}$ **9.** $\frac{1}{2}$ **11.** $\frac{1}{2}$ **13.** $\frac{7}{5}$
15. $-\frac{2}{3}$ **17.** $-\frac{8}{9}$ **19.** $m = -4, b = -9$
21. $m = -\frac{2}{3}, b = 3$ **23.** $m = -\frac{8}{7}, b = -3$
25. $m = 3, b = -\frac{5}{3}$ **27.** $m = -\frac{3}{2}, b = -\frac{1}{2}$

29.

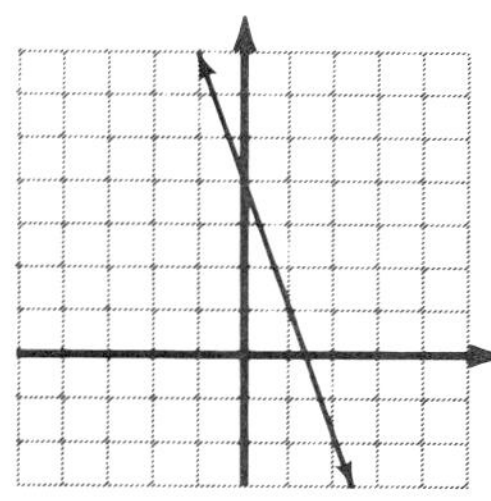

31.

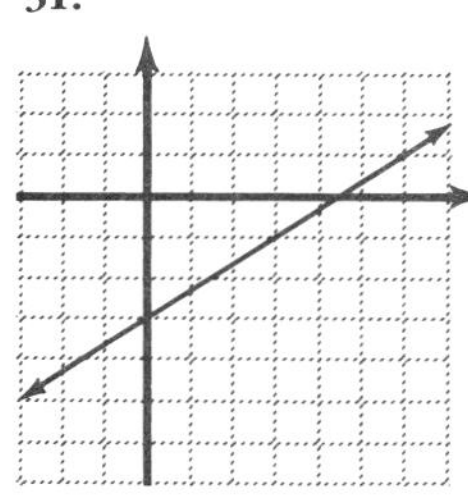

33.

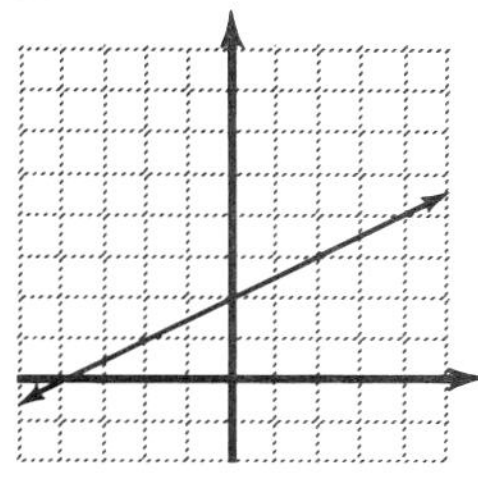

35.

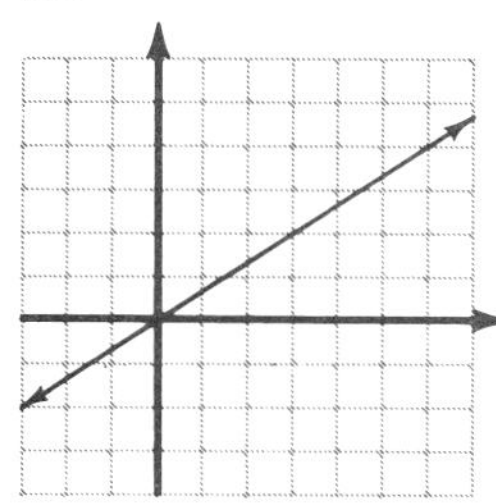

37.

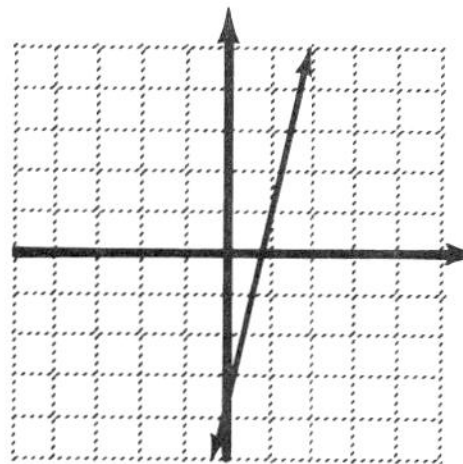

39.

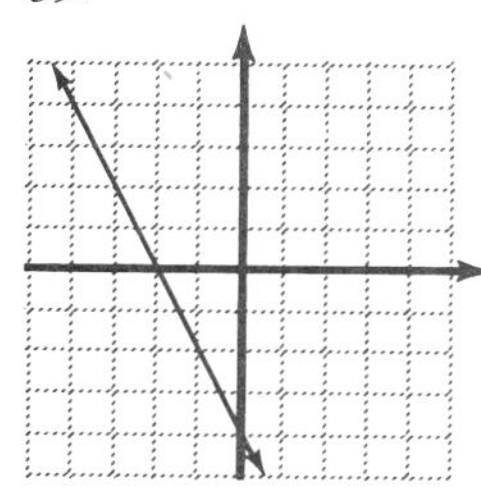

41.

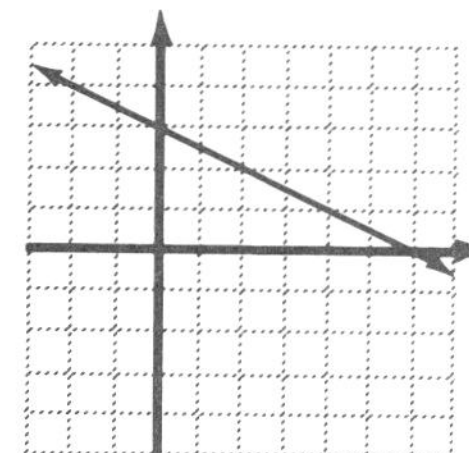

43.

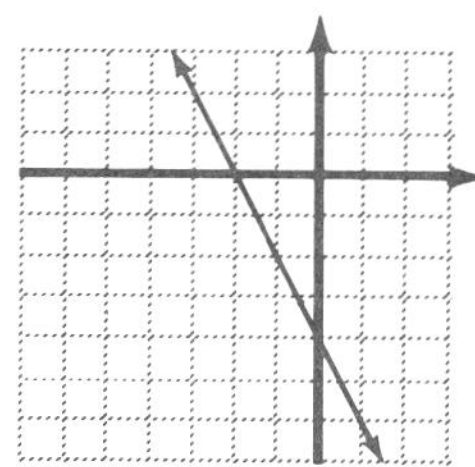

45.

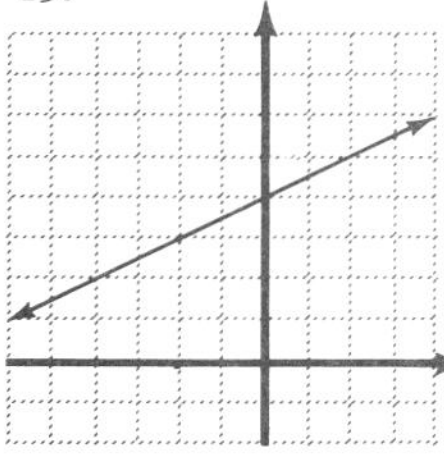

47. -2 **49.** $y = 8x$ **51.** $y = -7x + 4$
53. $y = -6x + \frac{3}{4}$ **55.** $m = 7, b = -8$
57. $m = -\frac{A}{B}, b = \frac{C}{B}$ **59.** IV **61.** I **63.** IV
65. Ex: $(-1, 3), (1, 2), \left(2, \frac{3}{2}\right)$ **67.** Ex: $(0, 2)$, $(1, -1), (-1, 5)$ **69.** $(5b + 4a)(5b - 4a)$
71. $(m + 3)(n + 5)$ **73.** $-3, 3$ **75.** $-5, 5$

Lesson 7-6 Try This

a. $y = 5x - 18$ **b.** $y = -3x - 5$
c. $y = -\frac{2}{3}x + \frac{22}{3}$ **d.** $y = \frac{9}{2}x + \frac{17}{2}$
e. $y = 6x - 13$ **f.** $y = -\frac{2}{3}x + \frac{14}{3}$
g. $y = x + 2$ **h.** $y = -\frac{7}{6}x - \frac{2}{3}$

Exercise Set 7-6

1. $y = 5x - 5$ **3.** $y = \frac{3}{4}x + \frac{5}{2}$ **5.** $y = x - 8$
7. $y = -3x - 9$ **9.** $y = \frac{3}{4}x$ **11.** $y = \frac{5}{6}x + \frac{16}{3}$
13. $y = -\frac{3}{5}x - \frac{34}{5}$ **15.** $y = 3x + \frac{3}{2}$
17. $y = x + 4$ **19.** $y = \frac{1}{2}x$ **21.** $y = x + 5$
23. $y = \frac{5}{3}x + \frac{4}{3}$ **25.** $y = -4x - 7$
27. $y = -\frac{2}{3}x + \frac{14}{3}$ **29.** $y = -\frac{2}{7}x + \frac{8}{7}$
31. $y = \frac{1}{5}x - 2$ **33.** $y = \frac{2}{3}x - \frac{31}{3}$ **35. a.** $(1, -3)$
b. $(0, 0)$ **c.** $(1, 2)$ **d.** $(0, 0)$ **37.** $b = 3, \left(0, \frac{19}{3}\right)$

39.

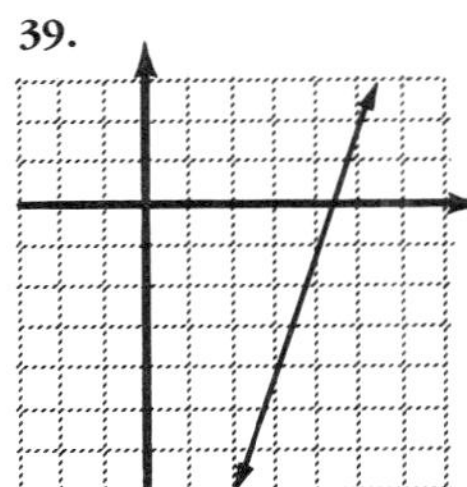

41. 163.2 **43.** $-7, 7$ **45.** $-9, 4$ **47.** $9, -\frac{5}{3}$
49. $4(m - 4)(m - 5)$ **51.** $(3c^2 - 1)(3c - 1)$
53. $(xy - z)(xy + z)$ **55.** p^2 **57.** 50 million

Lesson 7-7 Try This

a. (1) $r = -0.01t + 30$ (2) 10.1 s

b. $c = \frac{5}{6}d$

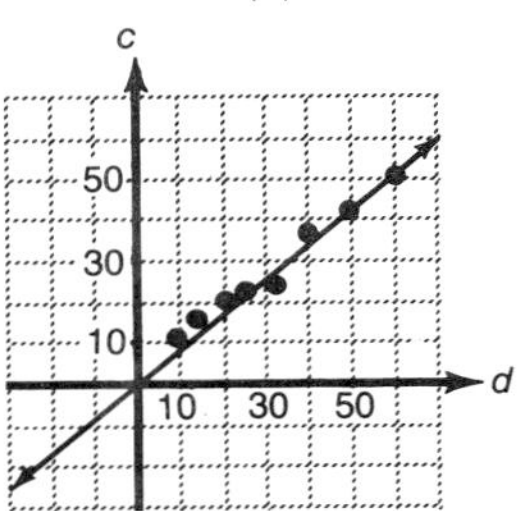

Exercise Set 7-7

1. a. $p = 0.05m + \$0.60$ **b.** \$1.60
2. a. $F = \frac{9}{5}C + 32$ **b.** 86°F
3. a. $t = -\frac{1}{100}h + 15$ **b.** 0°C
4. a. $b = \frac{3}{20}a + 25$ **b.** 130
5. a. $r = -0.0075t + 18.5$ **b.** 3.575
6. a. $t = \frac{7}{50}l - 2$ **b.** 26 mm **c.** 47 mm
7. Answers may vary; using (10, 5) and (40, 20), $y = \frac{1}{2}d$. **9.** Answers may vary; using (3, 60) and (6, 35), $c = \frac{25}{3}d + 85$. **11.** \$250 **15.** (0, 0), $\left(1, \frac{21}{20}\right), \left(2, \frac{11}{5}\right), \left(3, \frac{69}{20}\right), \left(4, \frac{24}{5}\right), \left(5, \frac{25}{4}\right)$; No
17. $m = -4$ **19.** $3y^5 - 6y^4$
21. $2y^2(5y + 6)(5y - 6)$ **23.** $(a - 6)(b + 3)$
25. $n(n + 1) = 110$; 10, 11 or $-11, -10$

Lesson 7-8 Try This

a. Yes **b.** No **c.** Yes **d.** No

Exercise Set 7-8

1. Yes **3.** No **5.** No **7.** Yes **9.** Yes **11.** Yes
13. No **15.** Yes **17.** Yes **19.** No **21.** No
23. No **25.** No **27.** $y = 2x + 8$ **29.** $y = \frac{1}{2}x - \frac{1}{2}$
35. 16 **37.** $4y + 3x = -1$; $3y - 4x = -7$
39. $m = -\frac{1}{2}, b = \frac{5}{4}$ **41.** $m = 2, b = \frac{2}{3}$
43. $m = \frac{2}{3}, b = -\frac{4}{3}$ **45.** $y = -2x + 5$
47. $(3a - 7b)(3a + 7b)$
49. $(2m + 3)(m + 3)(m - 3)$ **51.** $9t^6$ **53.** $6x^5y^2z^3$
55. $6x^2 + 9xy + 3y^2$

Lesson 7-9 Try This

a. The y-intercept of a line is the point where the line crosses the y-axis. Thus, the x-coordinate of the point is zero. Let $x = 0$ in the equation $y = mx + b$. $y = 0 \cdot x + b$, $y = 0 + b$, $y = b$. Thus b is the y-intercept. **b.** Suppose that (x_1, y_1) and (x_2, y_2) are any two points on a vertical line. The slope of the line is $\frac{y_2 - y_1}{x_2 - x_1}$. Since the line is vertical, the x-coordinates are the same, so the slope is $\frac{y_2 - y_1}{0}$. Division by 0 is not allowed, so the line has no slope.

Exercise Set 7-9

3. 2, 0; 2 **5.** 6, 3; 6 **7.** $-35 + 8c$ **9.** $3(a^3)$, $(3a)(a^2)$, $(3a^2)(a)$, etc. **11.** $\left(-4, -\frac{3}{4}\right)$, (3, 1), $\left(4, \frac{5}{4}\right)$, etc. **13.** $(2y + 3)(2y - 3)$

Lesson 7-10 Problem Set

1. The perimeter would be 72. **3.** 18 different matches could be played. **5.** Five baseball fans are neither soccer fans nor football fans. **7.** There are 140 different squares.

Chapter 7 Summary and Review

1.–6

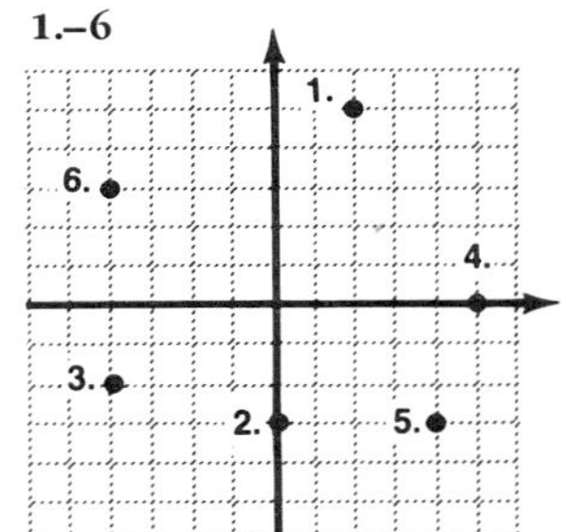

7. IV **9.** I **11.** (4, 3) **13.** $(-4, -3)$ **15.** No

17.

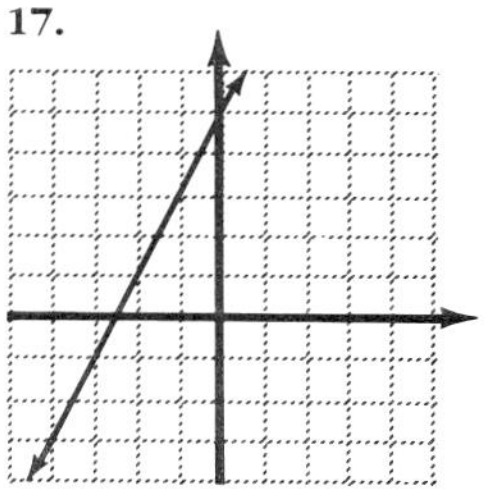

19.

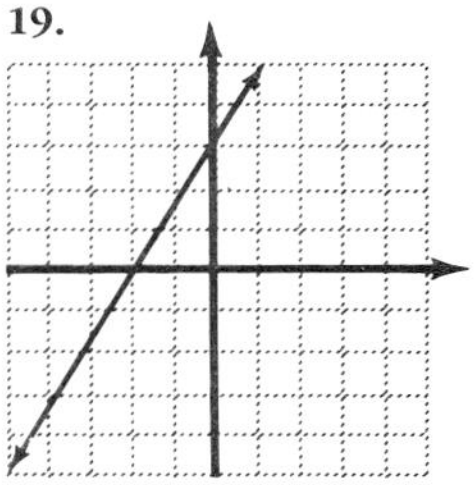

21.

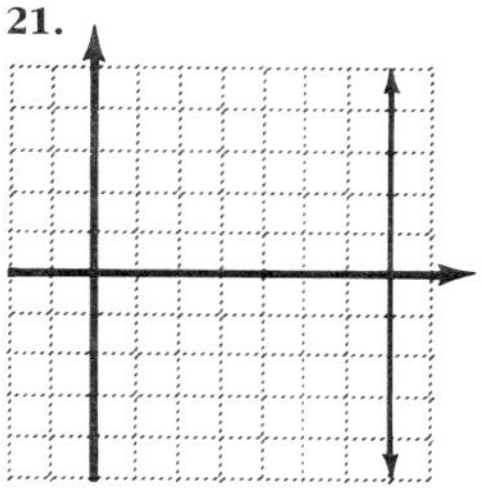

23. 0 **25.** −6 **27.** $-\frac{5}{3}$ **29.** −2

31.

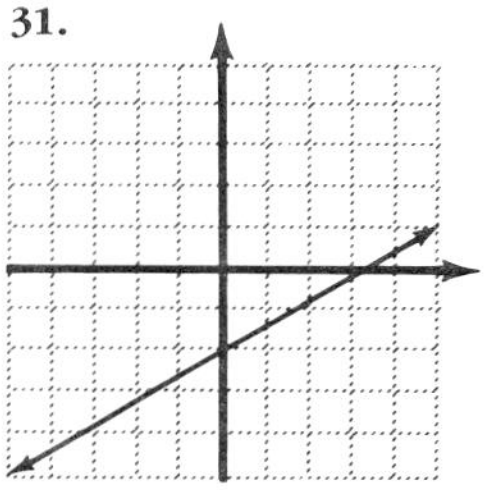

33. $y = 3x - 4$ **35.** $y = 3x - 1$

37. $y = -\frac{1}{2}x + 3$ **39.** $y = \frac{1}{2}x - 1$

41. $y = -\frac{2}{3}x + 2$ **43.** 25°C **45.** No **47.** No

49. Perpendicular **51.** Neither

Chapters 1–7 Cumulative Review

1. 22 **3.** Ex. $4x + y \cdot 3$, $x \cdot 4 + 3y$, $3y + 4x$ **5.** $\frac{1}{12}p$

7. 4 **9.** 25 **11.** $12x + 16y + 4z$
13. $9x^2 + 2y + 2z$ **15.** $x - 3y$ **17. a.** Open
b. False **c.** Open **19.** No solution **21.** 59°F

23. > **25.** 18 **27.** > **29.** < **31.** −15 **33.** $-\frac{2}{3}$

35. 1 **37.** 6 **39.** 1 **41.** $-2(3 + x + 6y)$ or $2(-3 - x - 6y)$ **43.** $-5y - 6$ **45.** Distributive property **47.** 2.6 **49.** $\frac{9}{2}$ **51.** $-\frac{1}{2}$ **53.** 10

55. $12d = 9$; $0.75 **57.** $-\frac{33}{4}$ **59.** $-\frac{2}{7}$

61. $r = \frac{c}{2\pi}$ **63.** 61, −61 **65.** 28 **67.** 60%

69.

71.

73. 31, 33, 35 **75.** $\frac{1}{z^3}$ **77.** $27x^6y^3$ **79.** $24b^5c^7$

81. $-6m^2$ **83.** $\frac{1}{3p^3r^5}$ **85.** 3.75×10^{-5}

87. $-4x^3 - x^2 - 2$ **89.** $x^4 + 2x^3 - 9x^2 - 7$
91. $-y^3 - 2y^2 - 2y + 7$ **93.** $8x^5 - 4x^4 + 28x^3$
95. $x^2y^2 - 49y^4$ **97.** $4a^2 - 20ab + 25b^2$
99. $2 - 10x^2 + 12x^4$ **101.** $4x^6 - 1$
103. $36x^2 - 60x + 25$ **105.** $x(x - 4)$
107. $4x(3 - x - 12x^3)$ **109.** $2(x - 2)(x + 2)$
111. $(x - 7)^2$ **113.** $(x - 4y)^2$ **115.** $2(3x - 4)^2$
117. $(x - 7)(x + 5)$ **119.** $(2x + 1)(4x + 3)$
121. $2(3x - 2)(x - 4)$ **123.** $(x^3 - 3)(x + 2)$
125. $(x + 5)(x + y)$ **127.** 2, −6 **129.** 14, 16 or −16, −14 **131.** II

133.

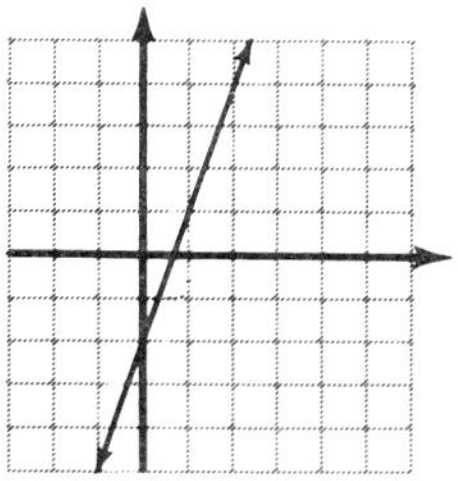

135.

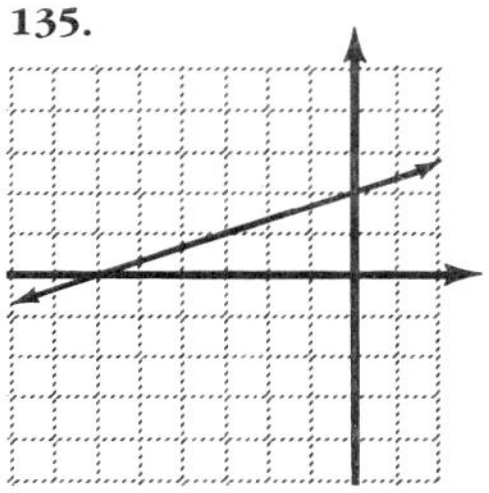

137. $\frac{3}{4}$ **139.** $m = -2, b = 4$ **141.** $y = -x + 3$

143. $y = \frac{2}{3}x + \frac{11}{3}$ **145.** Parallel

Chapter 8

Lesson 8-1 Try This

a. Yes **b.** No **c.** (−2, −1) **d.** (0, 5)
e. No solution **f.** Infinite solutions

Exercise Set 8-1

1. Yes **3.** No **5.** Yes **7.** Yes **9.** Yes **11.** (2, 1)
13. (−12, 11) **15.** (4, 3) **17.** (−3, −3) **19.** No solution **21.** (2, 2) **23.** (5, 3) **25.** $\left(\frac{1}{3}, 1\right)$ **27.** No solution **29.** All except 19, 27, and 28 **31.** Ex. 19, 27, and 28 **37.** $m = 1, b = -3$ **39.** $y = -3x + 2$

41. $2(a + 1)(2a - 9)$
43. $(4m^2 + 1)(2m + 1)(2m - 1)$ **45.** $5, -\frac{1}{2}$

Lesson 8-2 Try This

a. (3, 2) **b.** (1, −3) **c.** (3, 5) **d.** $\left(\frac{24}{5}, -\frac{8}{5}\right)$
e. $\left(\frac{5}{2}, 5\right)$ **f.** (1, 6) **g.** (2, −1) **h.** 63, 21

Exercise Set 8-2

1. (1, 3) **3.** (1, 2) **5.** (4, 3) **7.** (−2, 1) **9.** (5, 3)
11. (2, −4) **13.** $\left(\frac{17}{3}, \frac{2}{3}\right)$ **15.** (−12, 11)
17. (4, −2) **19.** (1, 2) **21.** $\left(\frac{3}{4}, 0\right)$ **23.** 19, 17
25. 37, 29 **27.** 22, 4 **29.** Substitution yields 15 = 15. Since this equation is true for all values of x, there are infinitely many solutions.
33. (30, 50, 100) **35.** Yes **37.** No
39. $y^2(6y - 5)(6y + 5)$ **41.** $(3x + 2z^3)^2$ **43.** 5
45. $\frac{7}{2}, -\frac{7}{2}$ **47.** 5 in.

Lesson 8-3 Try This

a. (3, 2) **b.** (1, −1) **c.** (1, 4) **d.** $\left(3, \frac{13}{11}\right)$ **e.** (1, 1)
f. (13, 3) **g.** (−1, 2) **h.** (1, −1) **i.** (2, −4)
j. 126, 90

Exercise Set 8-3

1. (9, 1) **3.** (3, 5) **5.** (3, 0) **7.** $\left(-\frac{1}{2}, 3\right)$
9. $\left(-1, \frac{1}{5}\right)$ **11.** No solution **13.** (−3, −5)
15. (4, 5) **17.** (4, 1) **19.** (4, 3) **21.** (1, −1)
23. (−3, −1) **25.** (2, −2) **27.** $\left(5, \frac{1}{2}\right)$ **29.** (4, 8)
31. 68, 47 **33.** 56, 36 **35.** $\frac{37}{3}$ in., $\frac{20}{3}$ in. **37.** 62°, 28°
39. (5, 2) **41.** (1, −1) **43.** (525, 1000)
45. $\left(\frac{b - c}{1 - a}, \frac{b - ac}{1 - a}\right)$ **47.** (4, 3) **49.** (110, −106)
51. Yes **53.** (5, 2) **55.** $(2m^2 - 1)(m - 2)$
57. $xz(x - z)$ **59.** $y^2 + 4xy + 3x$

Lesson 8-4 Try This

a. 70 trucks, 110 vans **b.** 16 km **c.** 4 **d.** 14, 21
3. \$0.08, \$0.21 **f.** 75 miles

Exercise Set 8-4

1. c. $n + d = 150, n + 12 = d$ **d.** 69 nickels, 81 dimes **3.** 20¢, 24¢ **5.** 48, 24 **7.** $71\frac{1}{9}$ ft, $8\frac{8}{9}$ ft
9. 150 mi **11.** \$0.21, \$0.17 **13.** 18 \$7 tickets, 11 \$9 tickets **15.** 4 12-oz, 6 16-oz **17.** 120, 121
19. No solution
21. $1100x + 1800(x + 0.015) = 288$; 9%, 10.5%
23. glove \$79.95, bat \$14.50, ball \$4.55 **25.** 2
27. $y = x + 4$ **29.** x^4 **31.** 1
33. $7m^2n^2(m + n)(m - n)$

Lesson 8-5 Try This

a. 168 km **b.** 275 km/h **c.** $35t + 40t = 200$, $t = 2\frac{2}{3}h$ **d.** $d = 35t, d + 15 = 40t, t = 3$ h

Exercise Set 8-5

1. c. $48t + 55t = 206$ **d.** $t = 2$; in 2 hours they will be 206 miles apart. **3. c.** $d = 72(t + 3)$; $d = 120t$ **d.** $t = 4.5$; 4.5 hours after the second train leaves, the second train will overtake the first train. **5.** 4.6 h
7. 14 km/h **9.** 384 km **11.** 330 km/h **13.** 15 mi
15. ≈317.03 km/h **17.** 90 mi, 48 mi **19.** After 40 min **21.** 6:34 a.m. **23.** Yes **25.** 9, −2
27. a^5b^6 **29.** $x^9y^2z^2$

Lesson 8-6 Try This

a. 14 **b.** 43 **c.** 7 quarters, 13 dimes **d.** 8 dimes, 11 nickels **e.** 135, 31

Exercise Set 8-6

1. 18 **3.** 75 **5.** 70 dimes, 33 quarters **7.** 8 nickels, 40 dimes **9.** 226 children, 203 adults **11.** 130 adults, 70 students **13.** 130 5-g bolts, 170 10-g bolts **15.** 86
17. 54 **19.** 336 **21.** 100 dimes, 40 quarters
23. $4(2a^4 + 3)(2a^4 - 3)$ **25.** $c(c - 5)$
27. $(5m - 9)(9m - 5)$ **29.** 0, −4 **31.** 2, −5
33. $x^3y^3z^3$ **35.** $x^2 + 2x + 1$ **37.** $a^2 + 14a + 49$
39. $2a^2 - 6a - 20$ **41.** $x = 2, y = -1$

Problem Solving: College Entrance Exams

1. (C), variation **3.** (C), variation **5.** (B), substitution
7. (D), variation **9.** (C), variation **11.** (D), variation

Problem Solving: Application

1. No **3.** Yes **5.** \$1.42 **7.** \$2.84 **9.** \$0.71

Chapter 8 Summary and Review

1. No **3.** Yes **5.** (6, −2) **7.** (2, −3) **9.** (0, 5)
11. (1, −2) **13.** (1, 4) **15.** (35, −5) **17.** (1, 4)
19. (−4, 1) **21.** (−2, −6) **23.** (2, −4)
25. Roberta 46, Cindy 21 **27.** 135 mi/h
29. 60 quarters, 100 dimes

Chapter 9

Lesson 9-1 Try This

a. (a) $G = \{6, 7, 8, \ldots\}$; (b) $G = \{x|x$ is a whole number and $x > 5\}$ **b.** (a) $T = \{20, 15, 10, 5, 0, -5, \ldots\}$; (b) $T = \{x|x$ is a multiple of 5 and $x < 24\}$ **c.** (a) $P = \{2, 3, 5, 7, 11, 13, 17, 19\}$; (b) $P = \{x|x$ is a prime number and $x < 20\}$ **d.** $\{0, 1\}$ **e.** $\{1, 6\}$ **f.** $\{-3, 1\}$ **g.** $\emptyset$ **h.** E **i.** $\{0, 2\}$ or T **j.** $\emptyset$ **k.** S **l.** T **m.** $\{-4, -3, -2, 0, 4, 5, 6\}$ **n.** $\{-3, -2, 0, 1, 3, 4, 5\}$ **o.** D **p.** $\{x|x$ is a whole number$\}$ **q.** M

Exercise Set 9-1

1. (a) $A = \{0, 1, 2, 3\}$; (b) $A = \{x|x$ is a whole number and $x < 4\}$ **3.** (a) $N = \{-1, -2, -3, -4\}$; (b) $N = \{x|x$ is an integer and $-5 < x < 0\}$ **5.** (a) $H = \{3, 6, 9, 12, 15, 18, 21\}$; (b) $H = \{x|x$ is a multiple of 3 and $0 < x \leq 21\}$ **7.** (a) $E = \{2, 4, 6, 8, \ldots\}$; (b) $E = \{x|x$ is an even integer and $x > 0\}$ **9.** (a) $m = \{2\}$; (b) $m = \{x|x$ is an even prime number$\}$ **11.** $\{1, 2\}$ **13.** $\{4, 5\}$ **15.** $\emptyset$ **17.** $\emptyset$ **19.** $\{0, 2, 4, 6, 8, \ldots\}$ or E **21.** $\{-5, -4, -3, -2, -1, 0\}$ or P **23.** $\{-5, -4, -3, -2, -1, 0, 5, 6, 7, 8\}$ **25.** $\{-1, 0, 1, 2, 3, 4, 5, 6, 7, 8\}$ **27.** $\{-5, -4, -3, -2, -1, 0\}$ or P **29.** W **31.** T **33.** T **35.** T **37.** T **39.** F **41.** T **43.** A **45.** A **47.** $\{2, 4, 6, 8, \ldots\}$

51.

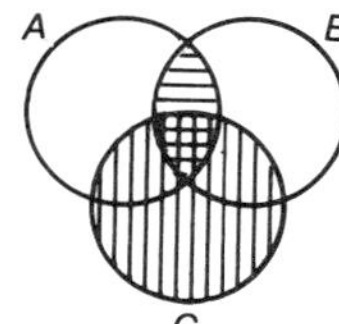

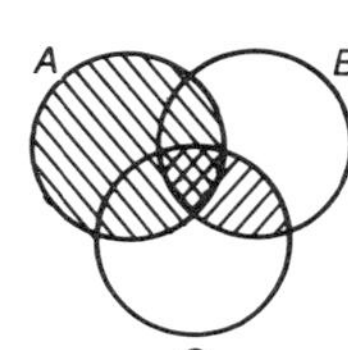

53. $B = \{3, 7, 10, 15\}$ **55.** $(7 - 2c)(7 + 2c)$ **57.** $(2a - 3)^2$ **59.** $2(x + 3y)(4x - 3y)$ **61.** $(5, 3)$ **63.** $y = 3x$ **65.** $y = \frac{1}{3}x - 4$ **67.** 9, 4

Lesson 9-2 Try This

a. −3 0 4

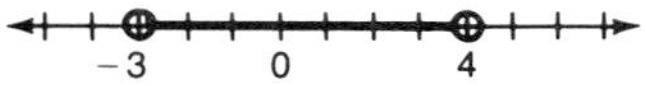

b. −2 0 7

c. −2 0 4

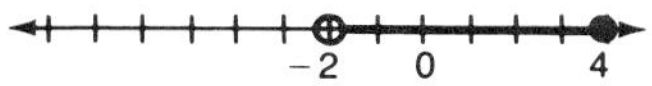

d. −7 −3 0

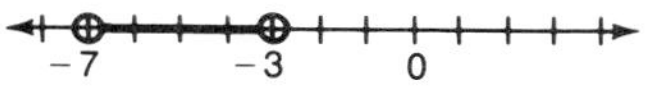

e. $\{x|-4 < x \leq 1\}$ Art 9T-16

−4 0 1

f. $\emptyset$

g.

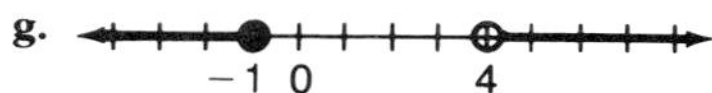

h. $\{x|x < -5$ or $x > 3\}$

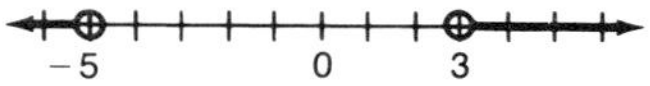

−5 0 3

i. $\{x|x < -5$ or $x > 5\}$

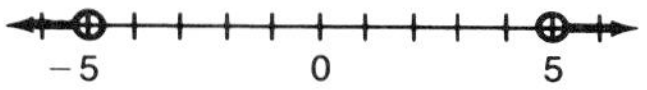

−5 0 5

Exercise Set 9-2

1.

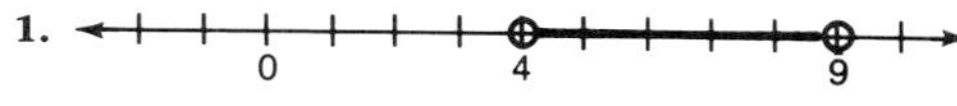

3. 0 5

5. −3 0 2

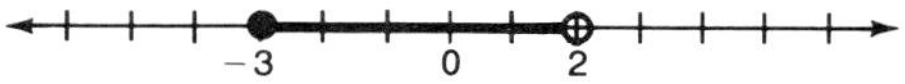

7. 0 3 12

9. $\{x|1 < x < 3\}$ 0 1 3

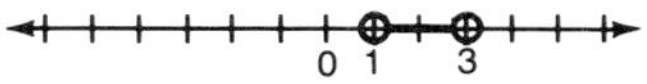

11. $\{x|-1 \leq x < 4\}$ −1 0 4

13. $\{x|-6 < x < 1\}$ −6 0 1

15. $\{x|1 < x < 6\}$ 0 1 6

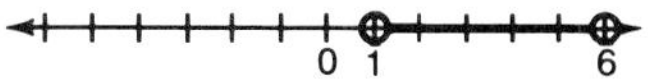

17. $\{x|0 < x \leq 3\}$ 0 3

19. $\{x|0 < x \leq 4\}$ 0 4

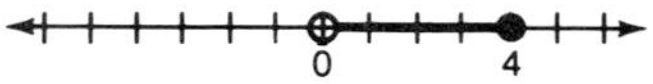

21. −1 0 2

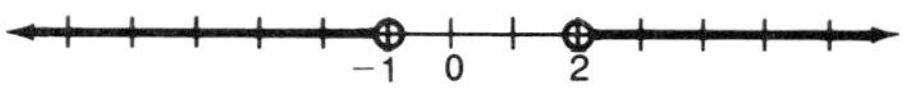

23. −4 0 4

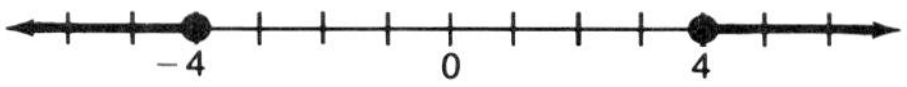

25. −6 0 2

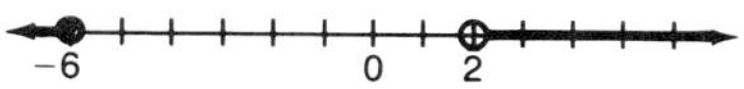

27. $\{x|x < 2$ or $x > 7\}$ 0 2 7

29. $\{x|x \leq -1$ or $x > 9\}$ −1 0 9

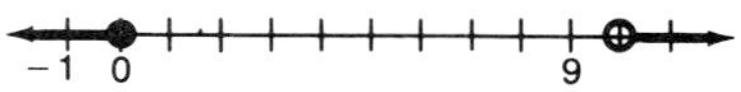

31. $\{x|x < 4 \text{ or } x > 5\}$

33. $\{x|x \le -5 \text{ or } x > 3\}$

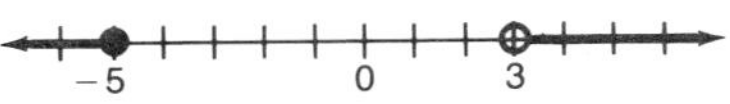

35. $\{x|x \text{ is any rational number}\}$ **37.** $\emptyset$ **39.** $\emptyset$ **41.** $-5 < x$ and $x \le 2$ or $-5 < x \le 2$ **43.** $x \le -2$ or $x > 1$ **45.** $x < 0$ or $x > 6$ **47.** $20 < l$ and $l < 25$ or $20 < l < 25$ **49.** $300 \le L$ and $L \le 1700$ or $300 \le L \le 1700$ **53.** $x = -4$ or $x > 4$ **55.** $-8 < x$ and $x < 4$ **57.** $-2 \le x$ and $x \le 3$ **59.** 5, 3, 1, 0; 5 **61.** $y = \frac{1}{7}x + \frac{10}{7}$ **63.** $(1, -2)$ **65.** $(1, -1)$ **67.** 5, 13 or -5, -13

Connections: Discrete Math

1. False **3.** True **5.** True

Lesson 9-3 Try This

a. $\{-2, -14\}$ **b.** $\{16, -4\}$ **c.** $\emptyset$

Exercise Set 9-3

1. $\{9, -27\}$ **3.** $\{-17, -5\}$ **5.** $\emptyset$ **7.** $\{5, -1\}$ **9.** $\left\{1, -\frac{3}{7}\right\}$ **11.** $\left\{2, \frac{8}{5}\right\}$ **13.** $\left\{\frac{3}{8}, \frac{5}{8}\right\}$ **15.** $\left\{-\frac{1}{6}, -\frac{1}{2}\right\}$ **17.** $\emptyset$ **19.** $\{-1, -9\}$ **21.** $\{0.2, -0.28\}$ **23.** $\left\{\frac{19}{3}, -5\right\}$ **25.** $\{0, 2\}$ **27.** $\{1, -7\}$ **29.** $\{3, 1\}$ **31.** $\emptyset$ **33.** $\{1, -3\}$ **35.** $\{x|x \ge 4\}$ **37.** $\left\{-\frac{3}{5}, -1\right\}$ **39.** $m = -4$, $b = -7$ **41.** $m = \frac{2}{5}$, $b = -1$ **43.** $2x(x - 3)(x + 1)$ **45.** $(3a + 2)(3a - 2)$ **47.** $(1, -4)$ **49.** 1, -2 **51.** 25 yr

Lesson 9-4 Try This

a. $\{x|-7 < x < 7\}$

b. $\{x|-6 < x < 6\}$

c. $\{x|-14 \le x \le 4\}$

d. $\left\{x\middle|\frac{2}{3} \le x \le 2\right\}$

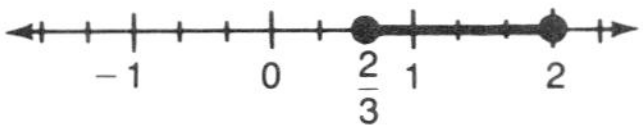

e. $\{x|x < -1 \text{ or } x > 1\}$

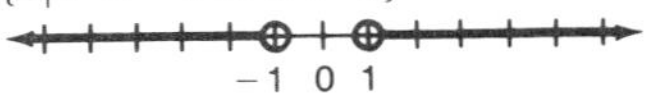

f. $\{x|x \le -3 \text{ or } x \ge 3\}$

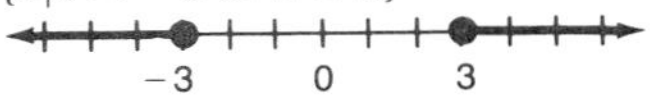

g. $\{x|x < -5 \text{ or } x > 5\}$

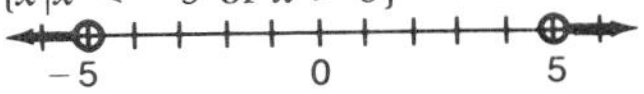

h. $\{x|x < -5 \text{ or } x > 5\}$

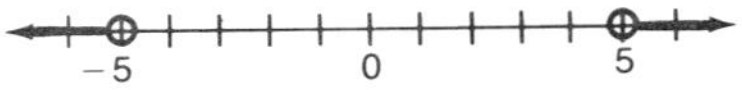

i. $\{x|x \le -1 \text{ or } x \ge 9\}$

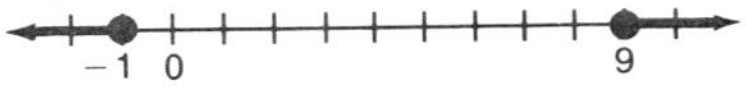

j. $\{x|x \le -10 \text{ or } x \ge 6\}$

Exercise Set 9-4

1. $\{x|-1 < x < 1\}$

3. $\{x|-4 \le x \le 4\}$

5. $\left\{x\middle|-\frac{11}{2} < x < \frac{11}{2}\right\}$ **7.** $\{t|-7 < t < 7\}$ **9.** $\{x|-5 \le x \le 5\}$ **11.** $\{x|-7 \le x \le 3\}$ **13.** $\{x|-8 < x < -4\}$ **15.** $\left\{y\middle|-\frac{5}{4} < y < \frac{9}{4}\right\}$ **17.** $\{x|-3 \le x \le 2\}$ **19.** $\{d|0.989 < d < 1.011\}$ **21.** $\{d|1.999 \le d \le 2.001\}$

23.

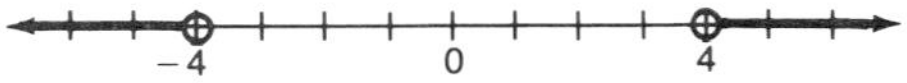

25.

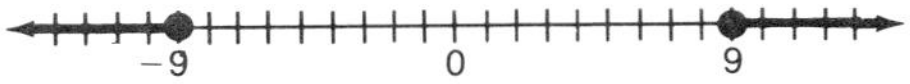

27. $\{x|x \le -6 \text{ or } x \ge 6\}$

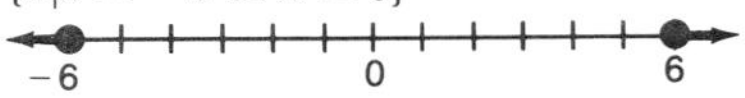

29. $\{x|x < -2 \text{ or } x > 2\}$

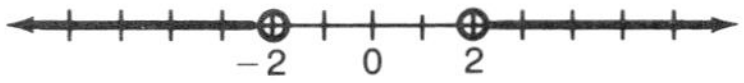

31. $\{x|x < -14 \text{ or } x > 4\}$ **33.** $\left\{t\middle|t \le -\frac{5}{2} \text{ or } t \ge \frac{7}{2}\right\}$

35. $\left\{x \middle| x \leq -\frac{5}{2} \text{ or } x \geq 4\right\}$ **37.** $\left\{x \middle| x < -\frac{15}{4} \text{ or } x > \frac{25}{4}\right\}$ **39.** $\{x \mid -6 \leq x \leq 3\}$ **41.** $\{y \mid y \leq -8 \text{ or } y \geq 7\}$ **43.** $\left\{-\frac{3}{2}, -\frac{7}{4}\right\}$ **45.** $\emptyset$ **49.** $\{11, 13, 17, 19, 23, 29\}$ **51.** $\{0, 2\}$ **53.** $\{-2, -1, 0, 1, 2, 4, 6\}$
55. $\{-6, -4, -2, -1, 0, 1, 2\}$

Lesson 9-5 Try This

a. Yes **b.** No

c.

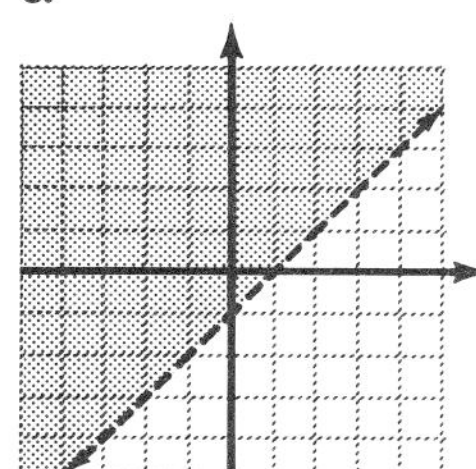

d.

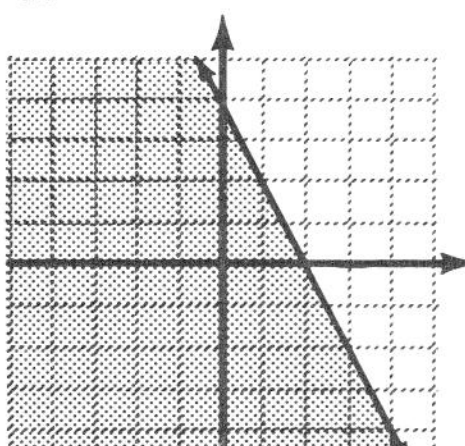

e.

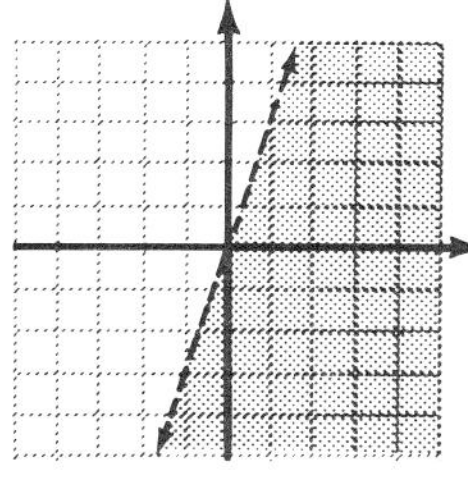

f.

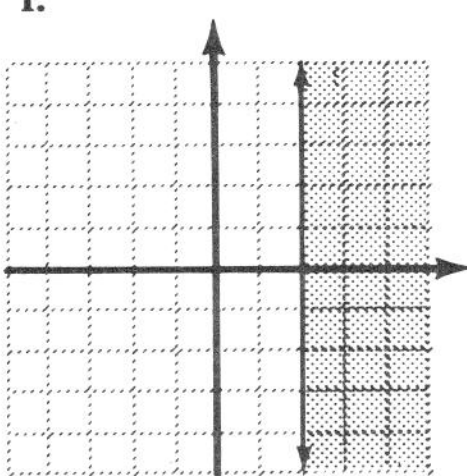

Exercise Set 9-5

1. No **3.** No

5.

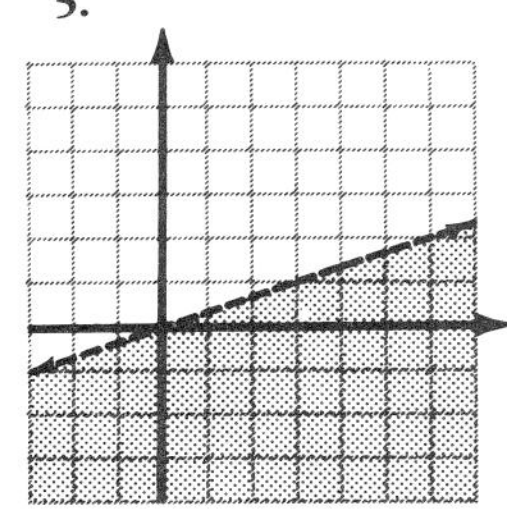

7.

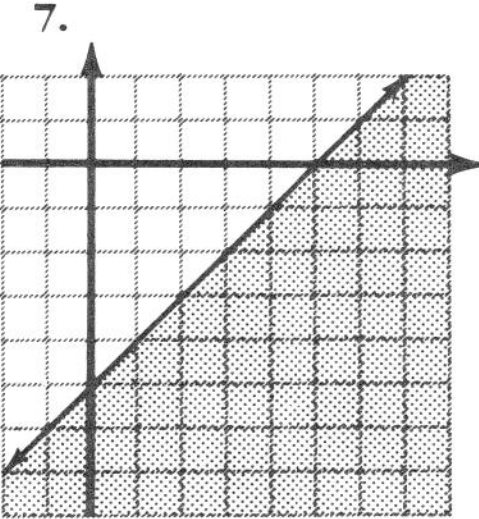

9.

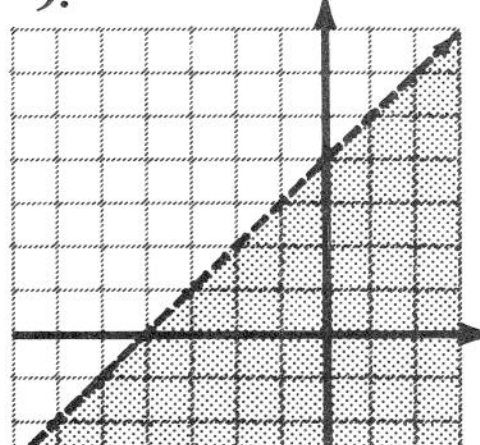

11.

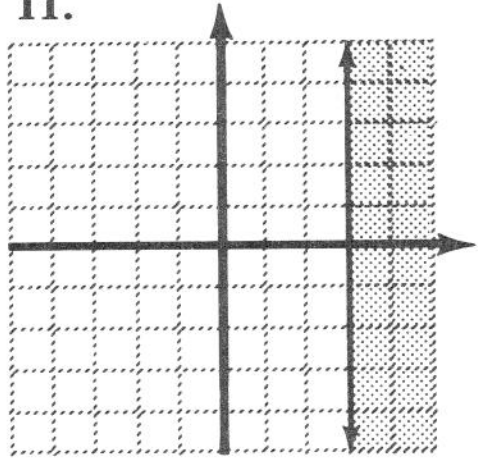

13.

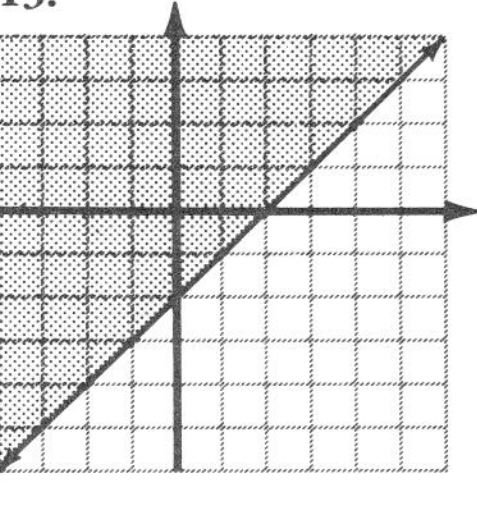

15.

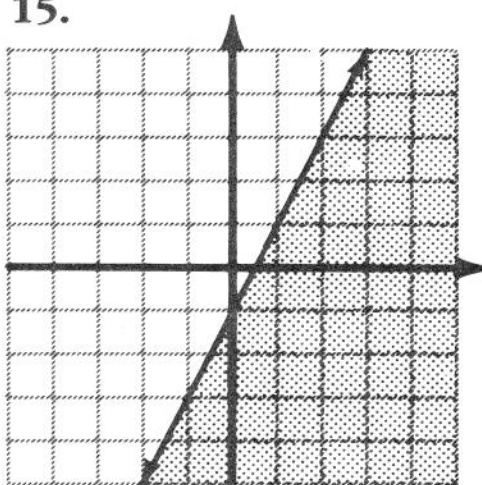

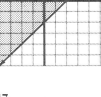

17.

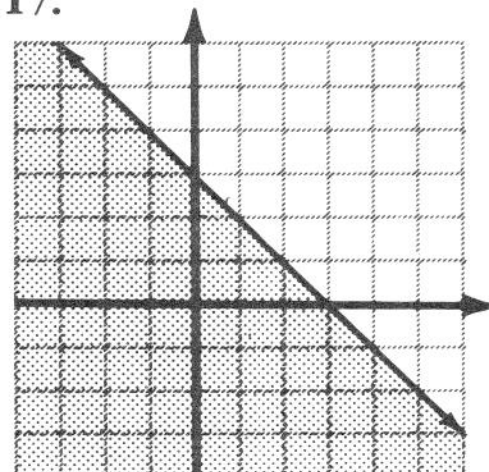

19.

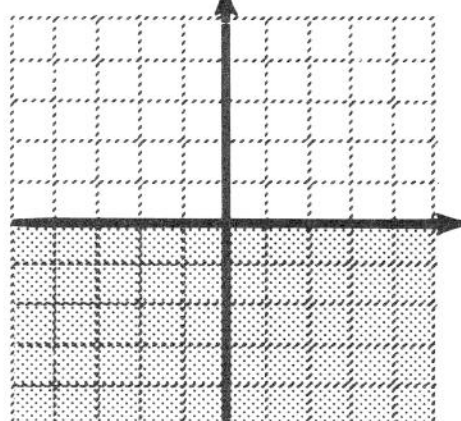

21.

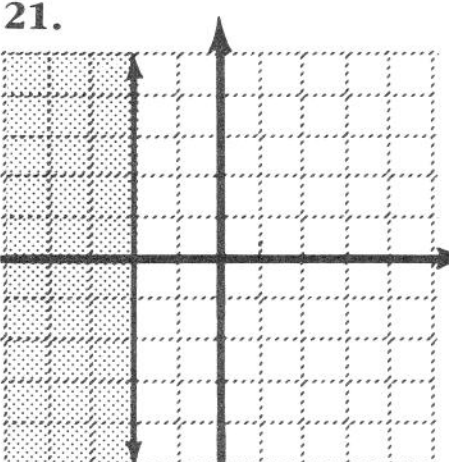

23.

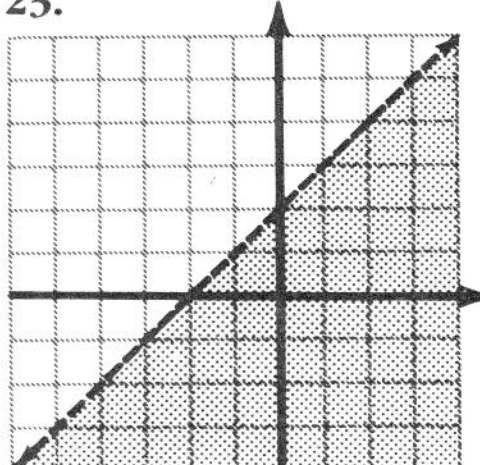

25.

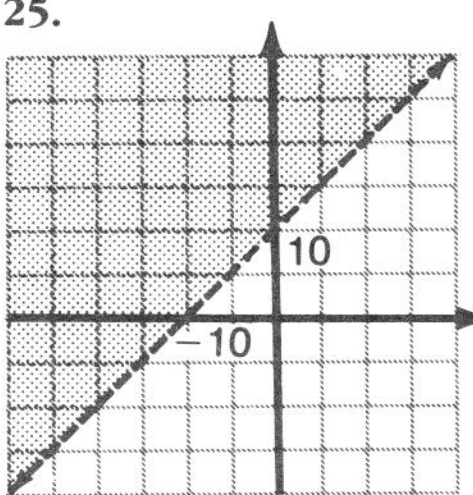

27.

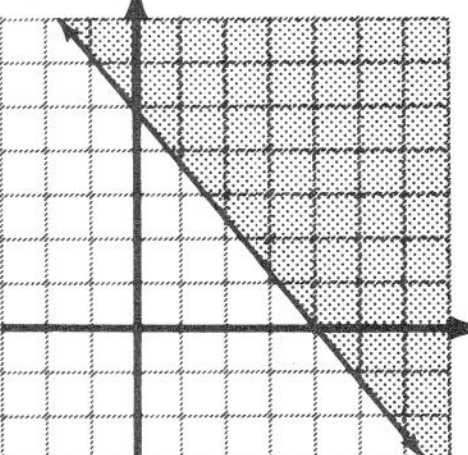

29.

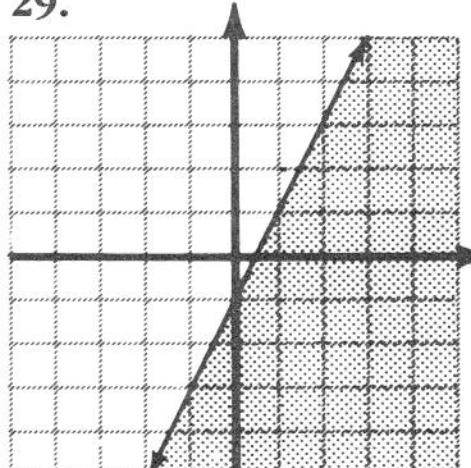

31.

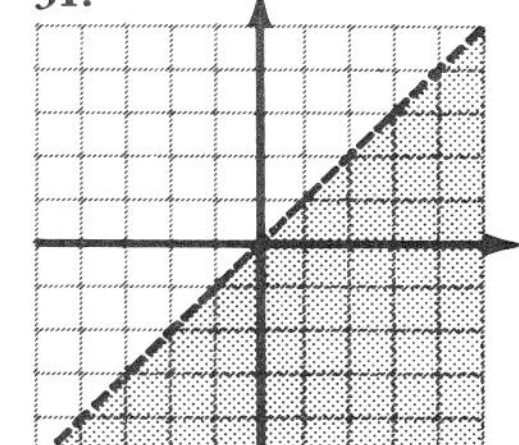

33.

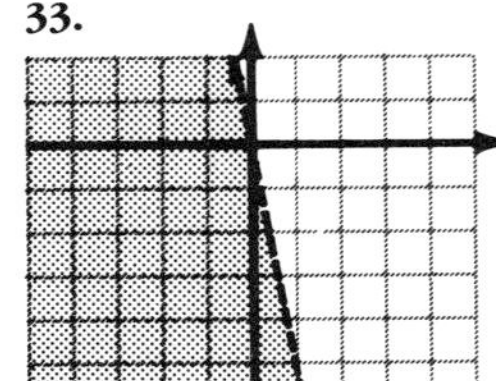

e. i. $0 \le b \le 300$
$0 \le r \le 400$
$b + r \ge 100$
$b + r \ge 200$

iii. Yes

ii.

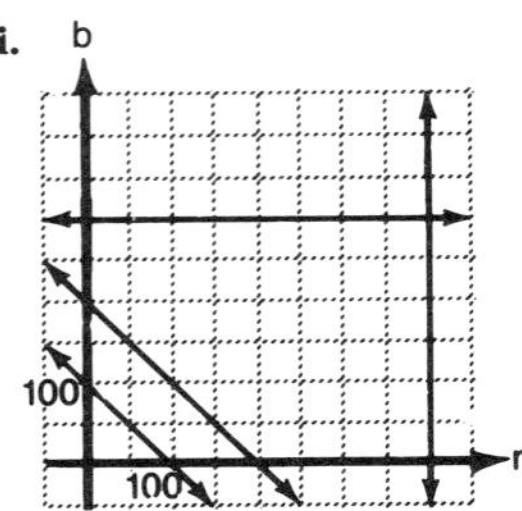

35. $y \le x - 4$ 37. $y \ge x + 4$ 39. $x > -2$

41.

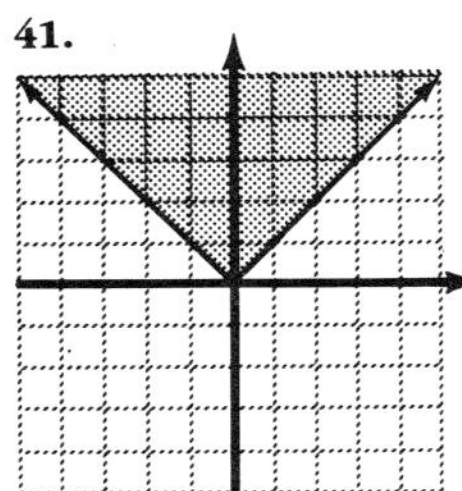

43.

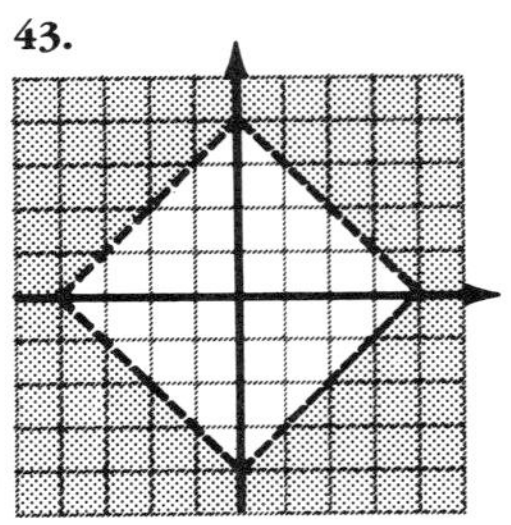

45.

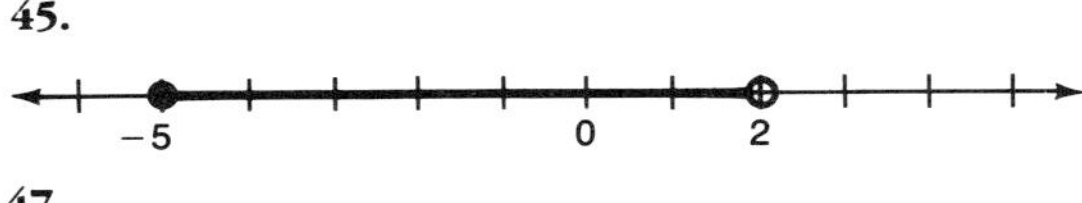

47.

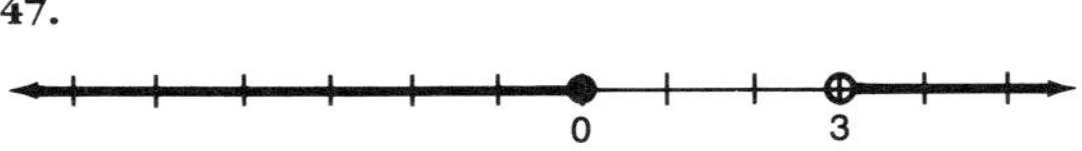

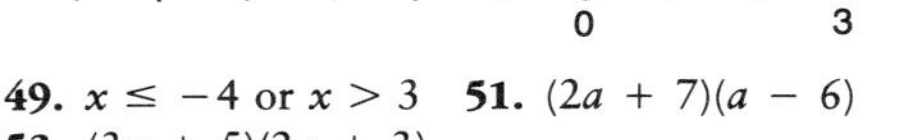

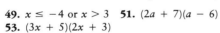

49. $x \le -4$ or $x > 3$ 51. $(2a + 7)(a - 6)$
53. $(3x + 5)(2x + 3)$

Lesson 9-6 Try This

a.

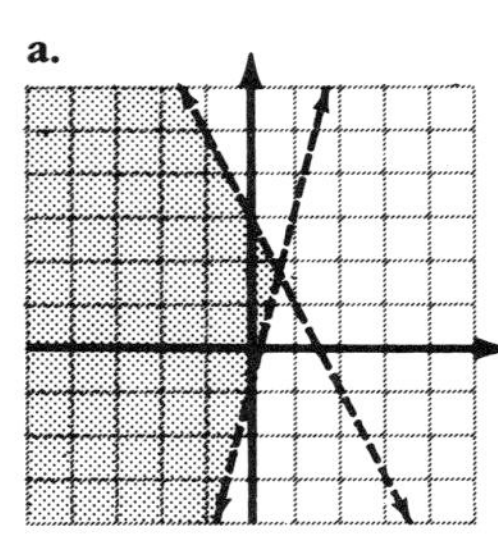

b.

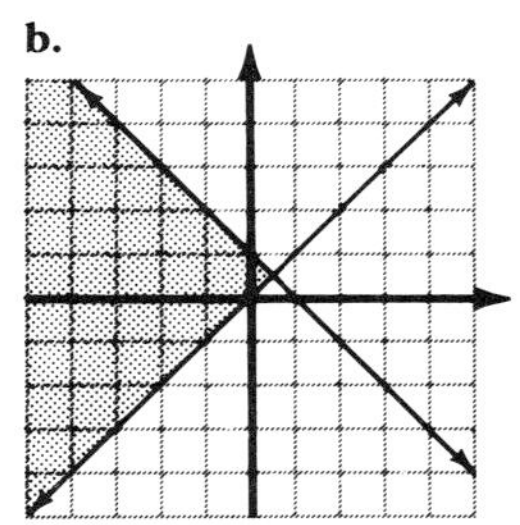

c.

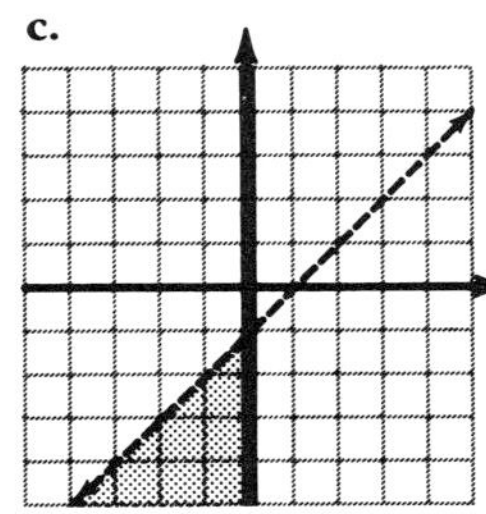

d.

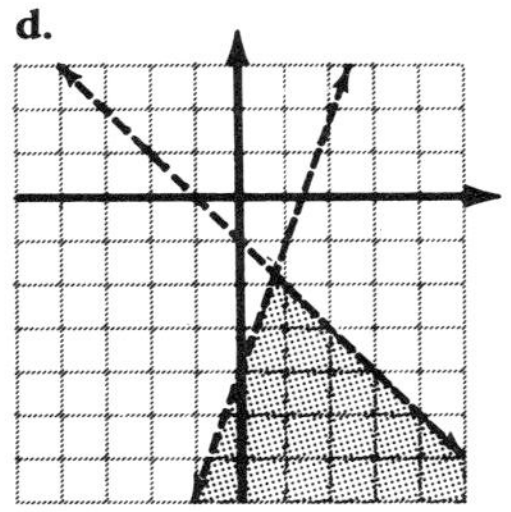

Exercise Set 9-6

1.

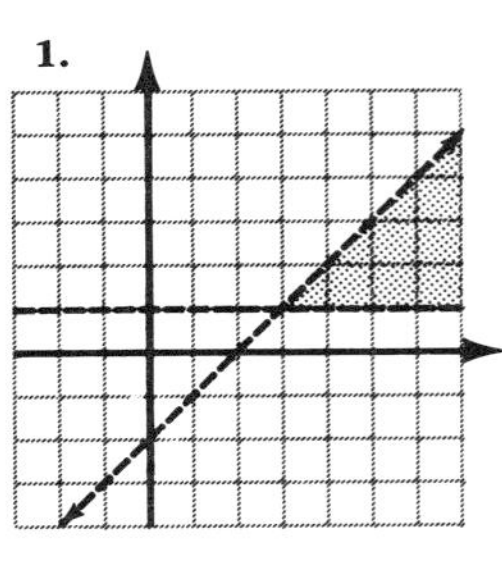

3.

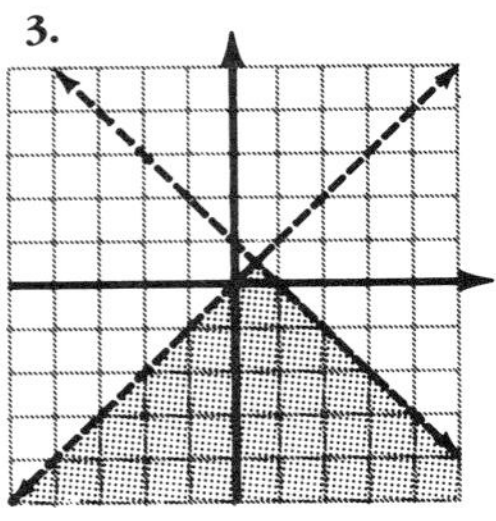

5.

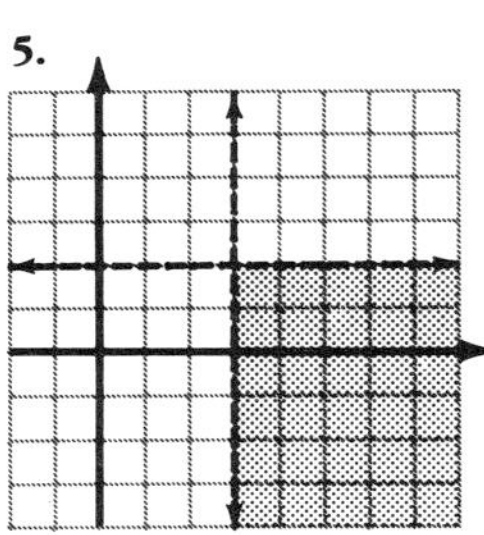

7.

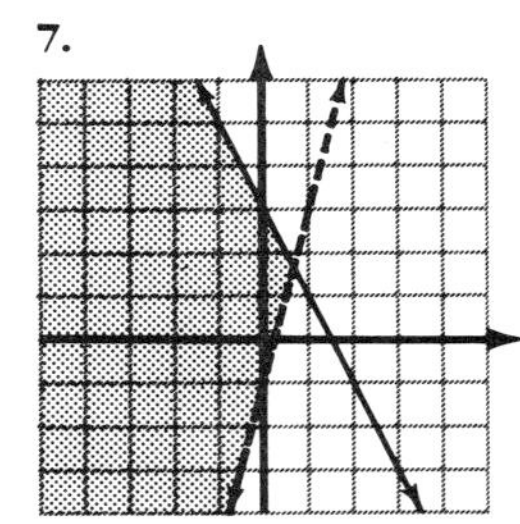

9.

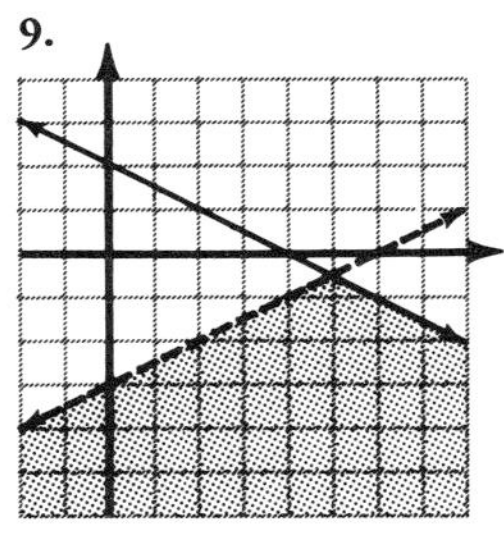

11.

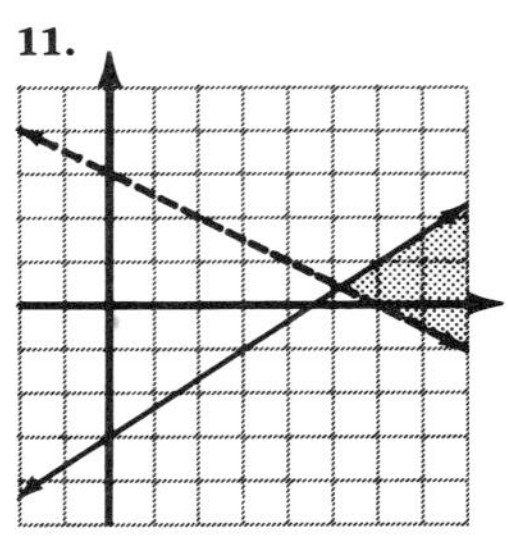

13.

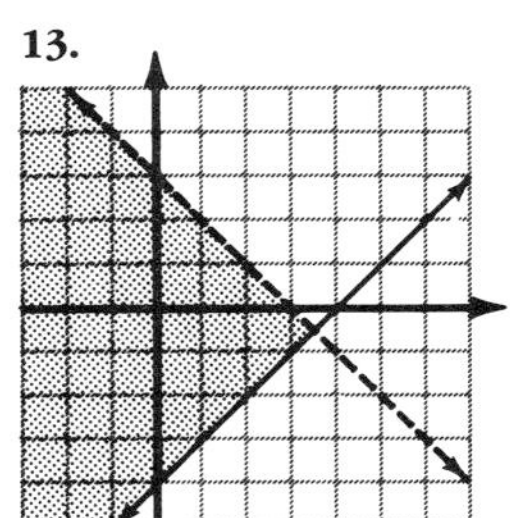

15.

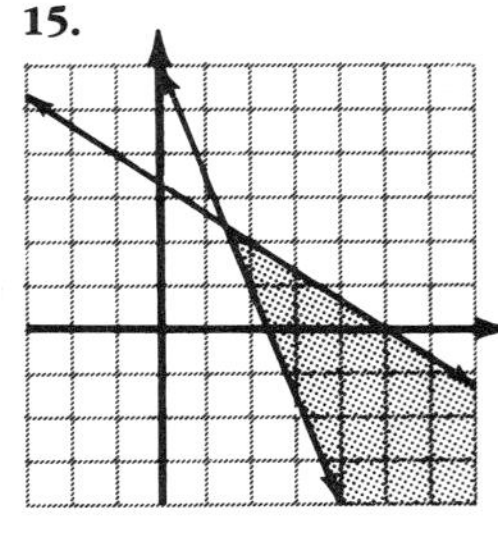

17.

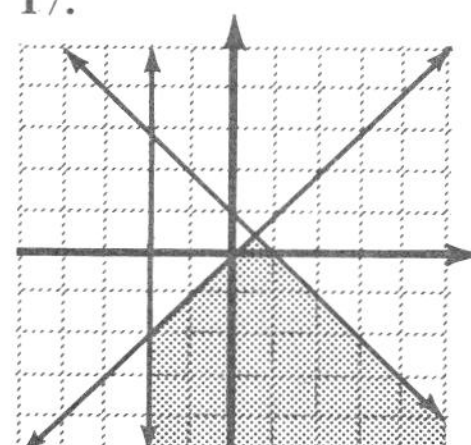

19.

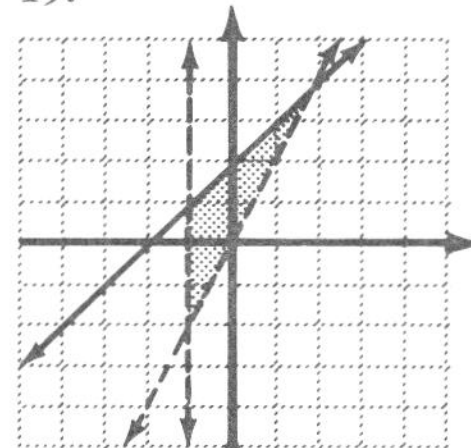

21.

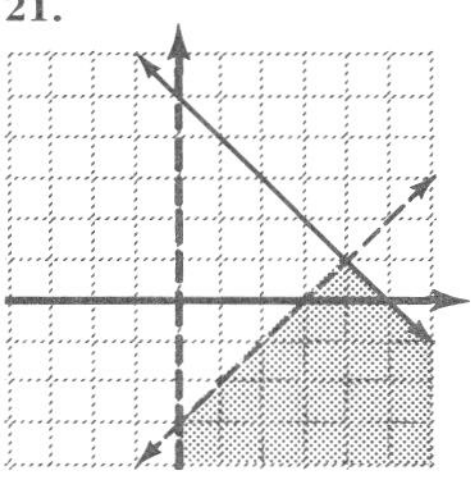

23. a. $x + y \geq 20$
$x \geq 12$
$y \leq 2x$
$x + y \leq 50$
$x \geq 0, y \geq 0$

c. No

b.

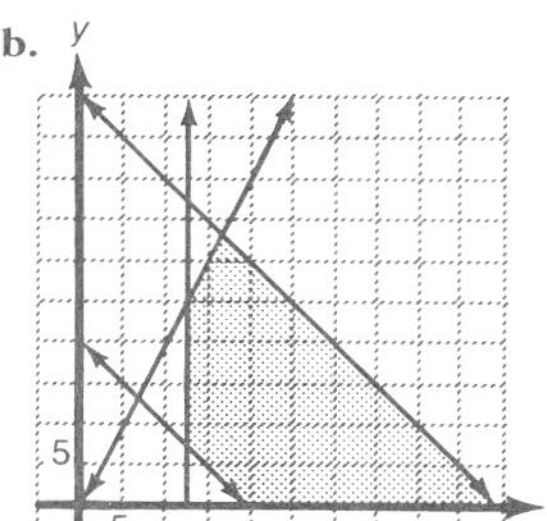

25. $y \geq 0; x > y$ **27.** $x < 3; y \leq 2; y \geq \frac{1}{2}x$

29.

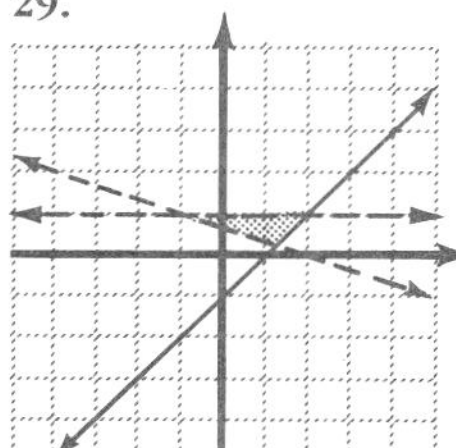

31.

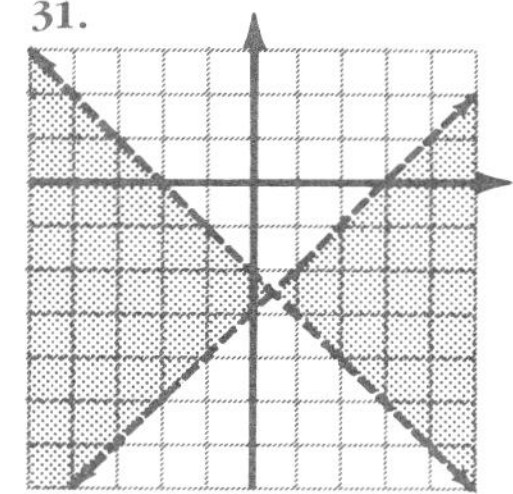

33. $1 < x \leq 3$ **35.** $-2 < x < 2$ **37.** $-5 < y < 4$ **39.** $(b + 2)^2$ **41.** 27 dimes, 54 quarters

Problem Solving: College Entrance Exams

1. (D) **3.** (D) **5.** (B) **7.** (A) **9.** (D)

Chapter 9 Summary and Review

1. a) $A = \{0, 1, 2, 3, 4, 5, 6, 7, 8\}$; b) $A = \{x|x$ is a whole number and $x < 9\}$ **3.** a) $C = \{7, 14, 21, 28\}$; b) $C = \{x|x$ is a positive multiple of 7 and $x < 30\}$ **5.** $\{2, 4, 8, 12, 16, 20, 32\}$ **7.** $\{4, 8, 16\}$ **9.** $W \cap P = P$

11.

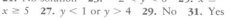

13.

15. $-5 \leq x < 0$

17. All numbers on the number line **19.** $\{-4, 8\}$ **21.** No solution **23.** $-2 < y < 8$ **25.** $x \leq -5$ or $x \geq 5$ **27.** $y < 1$ or $y > 4$ **29.** No **31.** Yes

33.

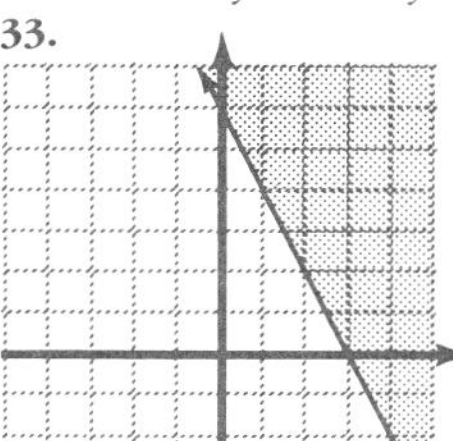

35.

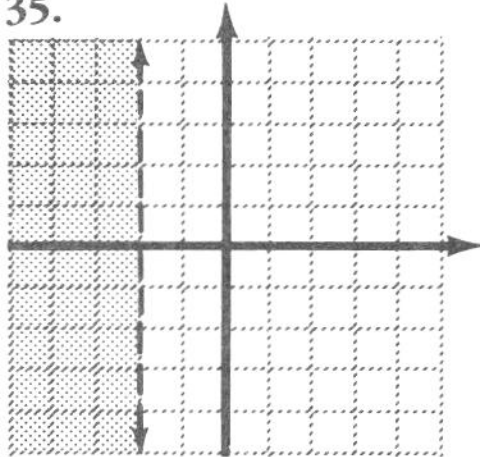

37.

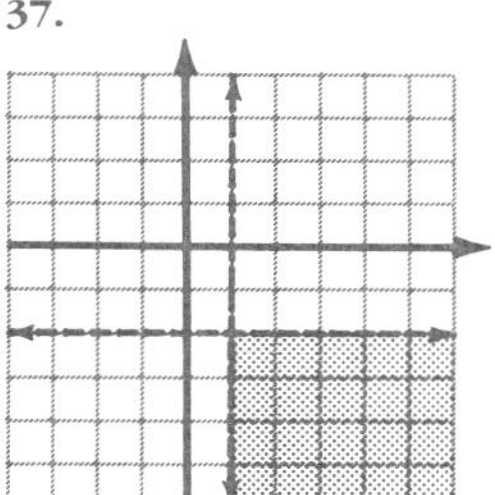

Chapter 10

Lesson 10-1 Try This

a. $\frac{y + 2}{4y}$ **b.** $\frac{2x + 1}{3x + 2}$ **c.** $\frac{a + 1}{2a + 1}$ **d.** -1 **e.** $-\frac{1}{3}$ **f.** -2

Exercise Set 10-1

1. $\frac{2x}{y^2}$ **3.** $\frac{x - 3}{x}$ **5.** $\frac{m + 1}{2m + 3}$ **7.** $\frac{x^3(6x - 1)}{x - 1}$ **9.** $\frac{1}{d - 7}$ **11.** $\frac{t - 5}{t - 4}$ **13.** $a + 1$ **15.** Already simplified **17.** $\frac{3}{2}$ **19.** $\frac{6}{x - 3}$ **21.** $\frac{b - 3}{b - 4}$ **23.** $\frac{y - 6}{y - 5}$ **25.** $\frac{a - 3}{a + 3}$ **27.** $\frac{-1}{y + 4}$ **29.** Already simplified **31.** $-a^2 - b^2$ **33.** $\frac{m^2 - n^2}{4}$ **35.** $\frac{(t - 3)^3}{(t - 1)(t - 2)^2}$ **37.** 7; 7 **41.** $-3, 1$ **43.** 5, 7 **45.** $\frac{1}{2}, -\frac{1}{3}$ **47.** $(-2, -3)$ **49.** $(-2, 5)$

Lesson 10-2 Try This

a. $\frac{8a^2}{5}$ **b.** $\frac{(x+3)(x+2)}{x+4}$ **c.** $\frac{-6}{(2m+1)(2m-1)}$

Exercise Set 10-2

1. $\frac{56x}{3}$ **3.** $\frac{2}{c^2d}$ **5.** $2y$ **7.** $\frac{-2n}{n+2}$ **9.** $\frac{(a-6)(a+2)}{a^2(a+1)}$ **11.** $\frac{2(y-3)}{5}$ **13.** $\frac{m+5}{m-5}$ **15.** $\frac{15}{(3y-2)(5y+6)}$ **17.** $\frac{t+3}{(t^2-2)(t-3)}$ **19.** $\frac{x-1}{x+4}$ **21.** $\frac{x-3}{x-4}$ **23.** $\frac{12(x+2)}{5}$ **25.** $\frac{(y-4)(y-2)}{3y(y+4)}$ **27.** $\frac{5}{(m+3)(m-1)}$ **29.** $\frac{5+x}{2}$ **31.** $-\frac{1}{2}$ **33.** $14x$ **35.** $\frac{x+2}{x-2}$ **37.** $\frac{(a-3)(a+3)}{a(a+4)}$ **39.** $\frac{2a}{a-2}$ **41.** $\frac{(x-2)(x+2)}{(x-1)(x+1)}$ **43.** $\frac{(t-2)}{(t-1)}$ **45.** $(m-n)(m-3)$ **47.** $\frac{1}{x-y}$ **49.** -2 **51.** 0, 2, 7 **53.** $\{-2, 0, 1, 2, 3, 4, 5\}$ **55.** $\{0, 1\}$ **57.** 4, -1 **59.** $\frac{5}{3}$, -1 **61.** (4, 4) **63.** 11, -5 **65.** (a) $p = 18y + 12$, (b) \$246

Lesson 10-3 Try This

a. $2a^2$ **b.** 8 **c.** $\frac{3(x-1)}{2(x+2)(x-2)}$ **d.** $x + 3$

Exercise Set 10-3

1. $2x^2$ **3.** $\frac{1}{a^3}$ **5.** $\frac{3m^3}{5}$ **7.** $\frac{15}{8}$ **9.** $\frac{15}{4}$ **11.** $\frac{a-5}{3(a-1)}$ **13.** $\frac{(x+2)^2}{x}$ **15.** $\frac{3}{2}$ **17.** $\frac{c+1}{c-1}$ **19.** $\frac{3(a-4)}{2}$ **21.** $\frac{y-3}{2y-1}$ **23.** $\frac{x+12}{x+2}$ **25.** $\frac{1}{(c-5)^2}$ **27.** $\frac{c+2}{c-2}$ **29.** $\frac{t+5}{t-5}$ **31.** $\frac{4(a+7)}{27}$ **33.** $\frac{4^4(b-3)}{3^5}$ **35.** $\frac{a}{(c-3d)(2a+5b)}$ **37.** 1 **39.** $\frac{(z+4)^3}{(z-4)^3}$ **41.** $\frac{(a-7)^2}{a+b}$ **43.** $\frac{x(x^2+1)}{3(x+y-1)}$ **45.** $\frac{a-3b}{c}$ **47.** No **49.** Yes **51.** Yes **53.** $c = \frac{ad}{b}$ **55.** $(-2, 4)$ **57.** ± 3 **59.** $x > 1$, $x < -4$

Lesson 10-4 Try This

a. $\frac{5a}{2}$ **b.** $\frac{10x^2}{x+4}$ **c.** $x + 4$ **d.** $\frac{2(m+3)}{m-1}$ **e.** $y + 3$

Exercise Set 10-4

1. a **3.** $\frac{s}{2}$ **5.** $\frac{13b^2}{c}$ **7.** $\frac{7(x+1)}{x+2}$ **9.** -2 **11.** $y - 6$ **13.** $\frac{5a-1}{a-1}$ **15.** -2 **17.** $\frac{-y+4}{y+5}$ **19.** $\frac{(3n+2)(n-4)}{n+4}$ **21.** $\frac{2(x-2)(x-1)}{2x-1}$ **23.** $\frac{-2(a-2)}{(a-1)(a-1)}$ **25.** $\frac{2(5a+3)}{a-2}$ **27.** $\frac{a^2+a+9}{a+2}$ **29.** $\frac{2x^2+4x+3}{x-1}$ **31.** $\frac{-y(3y+10)}{2y+1}$ **33.** $\frac{2(2x-1)}{x-1}$ **37.** $\frac{30}{(x+4)(x-3)}$ **39.** $\frac{m-6}{4}$ **41.** $81t^8$ **43.** $\frac{m^{24}n^{12}}{64}$ **45.** $\frac{4x^2}{y^2}$ **47.** 11, 9

Lesson 10-5 Try This

a. $60x^3y^2$ **b.** $(y+1)^2(y+4)$ **c.** $(t^2+16)(t-2)$ **d.** $3(a-b)(a+b)$ or $3(b-a)(b+a)$ **e.** $(x+1)(x-1)^2$ **f.** $\frac{56x^2+9x}{48}$ **g.** $\frac{x^2+6x-8}{(x-2)(x+2)}$ **h.** $\frac{4x^2-x+3}{x(x-1)(x+1)^2}$ **i.** $\frac{8(x+11)}{(x+16)(x+1)(x+8)}$ **j.** $\frac{(2+x)(2-x)}{(x+4)(x-4)}$ **k.** $\frac{3a^2+8a-4}{(a-2)(a+2)}$ **l.** $\frac{6t-13}{t-2}$

Exercise Set 10-5

1. c^2d^2 **3.** $(x-y)(x+y)$ **5.** $6(y-3)$ or $6(3-y)$ **7.** $(t+2)(t-2)$ **9.** $(x+2)(x-2)(x+3)$ **11.** $t(t+2)^2(t-4)$ **13.** $(a-1)(a+1)$ **15.** $(m-2)^2(m-3)$ **17.** $\frac{7a^2}{8}$ **19.** $\frac{44c}{75}$ **21.** $\frac{4(x+2)}{x^2}$ **23.** $\frac{37}{18t}$ **25.** $\frac{c^2+3cd-d^2}{c^2d^2}$ **27.** $\frac{4x}{(x-1)(x+1)}$ **29.** $\frac{11x+15}{4x(x+5)}$ **31.** $\frac{2x^2-10x+25}{x(x-5)}$ **33.** $\frac{x(x-1)}{(x+5)(x-5)}$ **35.** $\frac{4t+5}{4(t-3)}$ **37.** $\frac{2(x+5)}{(x+3)^2}$ **39.** $\frac{9a}{4(a-5)}$ **41.** $\frac{12a-11}{(a+2)(a-1)(a-3)}$ **43.** $\frac{a+8}{4}$ **45.** $\frac{-7x-13}{4x}$ **47.** $\frac{3x-8}{12x}$ **49.** $\frac{4x^2-13xt+9t^2}{3x^2t^2}$ **51.** $\frac{z(5-z)}{(z-1)(z+1)}$ **53.** $\frac{3x+20}{(x-4)(x+4)}$ **55.** $\frac{4-3b}{5b(b-1)}$ **57.** $\frac{8-3b}{b-7}$ or $\frac{3b-8}{7-b}$ **59.** $\frac{t^2+4}{t-2}$ **61.** 0 **63.** 3 **65.** $\frac{x-3}{(x+1)(x+3)}$ **67.** $120(x+1)(x-1)^2$ **69.** $10x^3(x+1)^2(x-1)$ **71.** $\frac{(z+6)(2z-3)}{z^2-4}$ **73.** $\frac{11z^4-22z^2+6}{(2z^2-3)(z^2+2)(z^2-2)}$ **77.** Every 60 years **79.** Yes **81.** No **83.** $\left\{x \middle| x \geq 3 \text{ or } x \leq \frac{1}{3}\right\}$ **85.** $\{x|x \neq 0\}$ **87.** $\frac{a+4}{a-3}$ **89.** -3

Lesson 10-6 Try This

a. $\frac{33}{2}$ **b.** 3 **c.** 1 **d.** 2 **e.** $-\frac{1}{8}$

Exercise Set 10-6

1. $\frac{47}{2}$ **3.** -6 **5.** $\frac{24}{7}$ **7.** -4; -1 **9.** 4, -4 **11.** 3 **13.** $\frac{14}{3}$ **15.** 10 **17.** 5 **19.** $\frac{5}{2}$ **21.** -1 **23.** $\frac{17}{2}$ **25.** No solution **27.** -5 **29.** $\frac{5}{3}$ **31.** $\frac{1}{2}$ **33.** No solution **35.** 7 **37.** 4, -2 **39.** 0, -1 **41.** $\frac{4}{3}$, $-\frac{7}{3}$ **47.** $\frac{(x+1)(x-3)}{x-5}$ **49.** $\frac{1}{4}$ **51.** -2, 3 **53.** $x < -4$ or $x > 0$ **55.** $y > -2$ **57.** 2, 6

Lesson 10-7 Try This

a. $3\frac{3}{7}$ h **b.** $34\frac{2}{7}$ km/h, $44\frac{2}{7}$ km/h **c.** -3

Exercise Set 10-7

1. $1\frac{7}{8}$ h **3.** $10\frac{2}{7}$ h **5.** 30 km/h, 70 km/h

7. p: 80 km/h, f: 66 km/h **9.** $\frac{1}{2}x + \frac{1}{x} = \frac{51}{x}$, $x = 10$ or -10 **11.** 24 h **13.** 12 min, 24 min **15.** 20 h **19.** 45 mi/h **21.** $\frac{(8x-3)}{(x-1)}$ **23.** $x - 1$ **25.** 7, -2 **27.** 0, -1, -2

Lesson 10-8 Try This

a. 120 mL **b.** 75 lb, 100 lb

Exercise Set 10-8

1. 50 L of 60%, 50 L of 40%
3. e. $0.50x + 0.80(100 - x) = 0.68(100)$; 40 mL of A, 60 mL of B **5.** 80 L of 30%, 120 L of 50% **7.** 6 kg of cashews, 4 kg of pecans **9.** 590 from Southern Maywood **11.** 1770 **13.** 4, -10 **15.** 6, -6 **17.** $-3 \le x \le \frac{17}{13}$ **19.** 46 dimes, 37 quarters

Lesson 10-9 Try This

a. $2x^3 + 3x - \frac{5}{2}$ **b.** $x^2 + 3x + 2$ **c.** $x + 4 + \frac{-1}{x-2}$ **d.** $x^2 + x + 1$

Exercise Set 10-9

1. $3x^4 - \frac{x^3}{2} + \frac{x^2}{8} - 2$ **3.** $1 - 2u - u^4$ **5.** $5t^2 + 8t - 2$ **7.** $-4x^4 + 4x^2 + 1$ **9.** $6x^2 - 10x + \frac{3}{2}$ **11.** $-3rs - r + 2s$ **13.** $x + 2$ **15.** $x - 5 + \frac{-50}{x-5}$ **17.** $x - 2 + \frac{-2}{x+6}$ **19.** $x - 3$ **21.** $x^4 - x^3 + x^2 - x + 1$ **23.** $a^2 + 4a + 4$ **25.** $3x^2 - 2x + 7$ **27.** $2x^2 - 7x + 4$ **29.** $x^3 - 6$ **31.** $x^3 + 2x^2 + 4x + 8$ **33.** $t^2 + 1$ **35.** $x^2 + 5$ **37.** $a + 3 + \frac{5}{5a^2 - 7a - 2}$ **39.** $2x^2 + x - 3$ **41.** $a^5 + a^4b + a^3b^2 + a^2b^3 + ab^4 + b^5$ **45.** -5 **47.** 1 **49.** $-18(y - 1)$ or $18(y - 1)$ **51.** $\frac{9}{14m}$ **53.** $\frac{-1(2x-1)}{(x+3)(x-3)}$ **55.** -1, 3 **57.** 6

Lesson 10-10 Try This

a. $\frac{5x}{3}$ **b.** $\frac{x}{x-1}$

Exercise Set 10-10

1. $\frac{20}{21}$ **3.** $\frac{4(x+2)}{3x}$ **5.** $\frac{25}{4}$ **7.** $\frac{1+3x}{1-5x}$ **9.** $\frac{28}{y+8}$ **11.** $\frac{9+3s^2}{4s^2}$ **13.** $\frac{2x+1}{x}$ **15.** $\frac{a-b}{2}$ **17.** $x - y$ **19.** $\frac{a}{b(2a+1)}$ **21.** $\frac{st(pr+q^2)}{qr(rt+s^2)}$ **23.** $\frac{4f + 3fg + g}{2(fg^2 + 2fg + 3f + 2g + 3)}$ **25.** $\frac{a+b}{a-b}$ **27.** $\frac{-ac}{bd}$ **29.** $\frac{27}{10}$ **31.** $\frac{3(x-2)}{(x+5)}$ **33.** $(m + 5)$ **35.** $\frac{-1(x+7)}{2x}$ **37.** 3 **39.** -17, 4

Lesson 10-11 Try This

a. 3. Associative and commutative properties
4. Reciprocal theorem 5. Division theorem
6. Transitive property of equality
b.

1. $[a + (-b)] + b$ $= a + [(-b) + b]$	Asso. prop.
2. $= a + 0$	Prop. of add. inv.
3. $= a$	Identity prop.
4. $[a + (-b)] + b = a$	Transitive prop.

Thus, by the definition of subtraction, $a + (-b) = a - b$.

Exercise Set 10-11

1. c) Distributive property, d) Division theorem, e) Transitive property of equality **5.** $32w^5$ **7.** y^{81} **9.** $(9c + 4)(9c - 4)$ **11.** $(2x + 5)(x - 1)$ **13.** $(3x + 1)(2x + 3)$ **15.** 7, -7 **17.** 5 **19.** $(-1, 1)$

Problem Set 10-12

1. Together they found 44 new stores. They did not get the bonus. **3.** Before entering the first turnpike, Ramon had \$22.50. **5.** The number is 42.

Chapter 10 Summary and Review

1. $\frac{x+3}{x}$ **3.** $\frac{x-1}{x+2}$ **5.** $\frac{3(y-3)}{5}$ **7.** $\frac{28m}{5}$ **9.** $\frac{y+1}{y-3}$ **11.** $\frac{1}{b(b+2)}$ **13.** $\frac{x-y}{y^3}$ **15.** $\frac{4b+3}{2+b}$ **17.** $\frac{2a}{a-1}$ **19.** $\frac{x+1}{2x}$ **21.** $\frac{-x^2 + x + 26}{(x-5)(x+5)(x+1)}$ **23.** $(-5, 3)$ **25.** $(-1, -5)$ **27.** $5\frac{1}{7}$ hours **29.** 40 liters of each **31.** $2x - 5$ **33.** $\frac{y(xy+3)}{xy^2 - 2}$

Chapter 11

Lesson 11-1 Try This

a. 13, -13 **b.** -10 **c.** 16 **d.** Irrational **e.** Rational **f.** Irrational **g.** Irrational **h.** 2.646 **i.** 8.485 **j.** 4.243 **k.** 6.708

Exercise Set 11-1

1. 1, −1 **3.** 4, −4 **5.** 10, −10 **7.** 13, −13 **9.** 18, −18 **11.** 15, −15 **13.** 2 **15.** −3 **17.** −8 **19.** −15 **21.** 19 **23.** 14 **25.** −18 **27.** −6 **29.** Irrational **31.** Irrational **33.** Rational **35.** Irrational **37.** Rational **39.** Irrational **41.** Irrational **43.** Irrational **45.** 2.236 **47.** 4.123 **49.** 9.644 **51.** 6.325 **53.** 7.746 **55.** 10.536 **57.** Rational, integer **59.** Rational, rational **61.** Rational, rational **63.** 2 **65.** 7 **67.** −5, −6 **71.** $\sqrt{17}$ **73.** $\sqrt{26}$ **75.** $\sqrt{44}$ **77.** $\frac{x+y}{2}$ **79.** $\sqrt{5} \approx 2.2$ **81.** $\frac{x^4y}{-3}$ **83.** $\frac{x^2(x+1)}{15}$ **85.** $\frac{-2x}{(x+2)(x-2)}$ **87.** $(a+c)(a-c)$ **89.** 27 **91.** $\frac{15}{7}$ **93.** $-\frac{12}{7}$ **95.** $y^3 + 3y^2 + 9y + 27$ **97.** $\left(-\frac{3}{2}, 2\right)$

Lesson 11-2 Try This

a. $\sqrt{-1}$; No **b.** $x \geq -1$ **c.** $x \geq 3$ **d.** $x \geq \frac{5}{2}$ **e.** All replacements **f.** $|xy|$ **g.** $|xy|$ **h.** $|x-1|$ **i.** $|x+4|$ **j.** $5|y|$ **k.** $\frac{1}{2}|t|$

Exercise Set 11-2

1. 0; Yes **3.** $\sqrt{6}$; Yes **5.** $x \geq 0$ **7.** $t \geq 5$ **9.** $y \geq -8$ **11.** $x \geq -20$ **13.** $y \geq \frac{7}{2}$ **15.** Any value **17.** $|t|$ **19.** $3|x|$ **21.** 7 **23.** $4|d|$ **25.** $|x+3|$ **27.** $|a-5|$ **29.** $|2a-1|$ **31.** 6, −6 **33.** 3, −3 **35.** −2, 8 **37.** $3|a|$ **39.** $\frac{2x^4}{|y^3|}$ **41.** $\frac{13}{m^8}$ **43.** $m \geq 0$ or $m \leq -3$ **b.** $x \geq 3$ or $x = 0$ **45.** $x \geq 2$ or $x \leq -3$ **47.** $x \geq 2$ or $x \leq -2$ **49. a.** Real **b.** Real **c.** Not real **d.** Not real **e.** Real **f.** Not real **51.** No solution **53.** −2 **55.** $\frac{5y+27}{(y+5)^2}$ **57.** 6, −1 **59.** 7

Lesson 11-3 Try This

a. $4\sqrt{2}$ **b.** $5x$ **c.** $2\sqrt{15x}$ **d.** $3x\sqrt{5}$ **e.** $\sqrt{7}(x-1)$ **f.** y^4 **g.** $(x+y)^7$ **h.** $t^7\sqrt{t}$ **i.** $a^{12}\sqrt{a}$

Exercise Set 11-3

1. $2\sqrt{3}$ **3.** $2\sqrt{5}$ **5.** $5\sqrt{3}$ **7.** $10\sqrt{2}$ **9.** $x\sqrt{3}$ **11.** $4\sqrt{a}$ **13.** $x\sqrt{13}$ **15.** $3\sqrt{x}$ **17.** $8y$ **19.** $2t\sqrt{2}$ **21.** $2(x+1)$ **23.** $(x+3)\sqrt{2}$ **25.** $2x+3y$ **27.** x^3 **29.** x^6 **31.** $x^2\sqrt{x}$ **33.** $t^9\sqrt{t}$ **35.** $(y-2)^4$ **37.** $2(x+5)^5$ **39.** $6m\sqrt{m}$ **41.** $2a^2\sqrt{2a}$ **43.** $8x^3y\sqrt{7y}$ **45.** $30\sqrt{2}$ **47.** $8\sqrt{3}$ **49.** $-20\sqrt{10}$ **51.** $8m^2\sqrt{5}$ **53.** $20r^4s\sqrt{2s}$ **55.** $2\sqrt{7}$ **57.** $\sqrt{10}$ **61.** = **63.** > **65.** < **67.** = **69.** < **71.** (4, 1) **73.** $\frac{a^2+4}{2a^2+3a+7}$ **75.** 35, 16

Bonus Topic

1. 2 **3.** 5 **5.** −2 **7.** −1 **9.** x **11.** ab **13.** $3x^2y$ **15.** $-2a^2b^3$ **17.** xy^2 **19.** $a^2b^3\sqrt[3]{30ab^2}$

Lesson 11-4 Try This

a. $\sqrt{21}$ **b.** $\sqrt{25}$ or 5 **c.** $\sqrt{x^2+x}$ **d.** $\sqrt{x^2-1}$ **e.** $3\sqrt{2y}$ **f.** $10x$ **g.** $4x^3y^2$ **h.** $5xy^2\sqrt{2xy}$ **i.** $6x^2y^4\sqrt{x}$

Exercise Set 11-4

1. $\sqrt{6}$ **3.** 17 **5.** $\sqrt{2x}$ **7.** $\sqrt{x^2-3x}$ **9.** $\sqrt{x^2+3x+2}$ **11.** $\sqrt{2x^2-2x-12}$ **13.** $\sqrt{2xy+y^2}$ **15.** $\sqrt{3x^2+4xy}$ **17.** $\sqrt{a^2-b^2}$ **19.** $3\sqrt{6}$ **21.** $3\sqrt{10}$ **23.** $6\sqrt{7x}$ **25.** $6\sqrt{xy}$ **27.** 10 **29.** $5b\sqrt{3}$ **31.** $2t$ **33.** $a\sqrt{bc}$ **35.** $2xy\sqrt{2xy}$ **37.** $6xy^3\sqrt{3xy}$ **39.** $10ab^2\sqrt{5ab}$ **41.** $12x\sqrt{y}$ **43.** $8xy^4\sqrt{7x}$ **45.** $3x^2y^8\sqrt{5y}$ **47.** $2x^2y^3z\sqrt{15y}$ **49.** $42x^5\sqrt{2}$ **51.** $4y\sqrt{3}$ **53.** $18(x+1)\sqrt{y(x+1)}$ **55.** $2x^3\sqrt{5x}$ **57.** $2^{54}x^{158}\sqrt{2x}$ **59.** $(x+9)^{51}\sqrt{x+9}$ **61.** $x^ny^n\sqrt{y}$ **65.** $y^{\frac{n-1}{2}}\sqrt{y}$ **67.** m^8 **69.** $4x^5$ **71.** $(a+b)(a-b)$ **73.** $(2m+3n)(2m-3n)$ **75.** $\frac{4x+3}{x^2}$ **77.** ±6 **79.** ±25 **81.** −6 **83.** 9

Bonus Topic

1. 11.180 **3.** 13.416 **5.** 18.974 **7.** 10.247 **9.** 67.082 **11.** 122.474

Lesson 11-5 Try This

a. $\frac{4}{3}$ **b.** $\frac{1}{5}$ **c.** $\frac{1}{3}$ **d.** $\frac{3}{4}$ **e.** $\frac{15}{16}$ **f.** 5 **g.** $x\sqrt{6}$ **h.** $\frac{\sqrt{35}}{7}$ **i.** $\frac{4\sqrt{6}}{3}$ **j.** $\frac{\sqrt{xy}}{y}$ **k.** $\frac{\sqrt{21}}{7}$ **l.** $\frac{\sqrt{10}}{4}$ **m.** $\frac{\sqrt{6}}{9}$ **n.** $\frac{\sqrt{10a}}{2a}$ **o.** $\frac{\sqrt{21b}}{3b^3}$ **p.** $\frac{\sqrt{2xy}}{6y^2}$

Exercise Set 11-5

1. $\frac{3}{7}$ **3.** $\frac{1}{6}$ **5.** $-\frac{4}{9}$ **7.** $\frac{8}{17}$ **9.** $-\frac{3}{10}$ **11.** $\frac{3}{5}$ **13.** 3 **15.** 2 **17.** $\sqrt{5}$ **19.** $\frac{1}{5}$ **21.** $\frac{2}{5}$ **23.** 2 **25.** $3y$ **27.** $x^2\sqrt{5}$ **29.** $\frac{1}{3}\sqrt{21}$ **31.** $\frac{3}{4}\sqrt{2}$ **33.** $\frac{1}{5}\sqrt{10}$ **35.** $\frac{1}{4}\sqrt{6}$ **37.** $\frac{1}{6}\sqrt{21}$ **39.** $\frac{1}{6}\sqrt{2}$ **41.** $\frac{1}{2}\sqrt{2}$ **43.** $\frac{2}{3}\sqrt{6}$ **45.** $\frac{1}{x}\sqrt{3x}$ **47.** $\frac{1}{y}\sqrt{xy}$ **49.** $\frac{x\sqrt{2}}{6}$ **51.** $\frac{\sqrt{3cd}}{d^2}$ **53.** $\frac{\sqrt{10}}{5}$ **55.** $\sqrt{2}$ **57.** $\frac{\sqrt{6}}{2}$ **59.** 5 **61.** $\frac{\sqrt{3x}}{x}$

63. $\frac{4y\sqrt{3}}{3}$ **65.** $\frac{a\sqrt{2a}}{4}$ **67.** $\frac{\sqrt{42x}}{3x}$ **69.** $\frac{3\sqrt{6}}{8c}$
71. $\frac{y\sqrt{xy}}{x}$ **73.** $\frac{\sqrt{6}}{9}$ **75.** $\frac{\sqrt{10}}{3}$ **77.** $6\sqrt{2}$
81. -4 **83.** $5 + 2\sqrt{6}$ **85.** Irrational **87.** Irrational
89. Rational **91.** Rational **93.** $(x + 3)(x - 5)$
95. $(m - 3n)(2a + b)$ **97.** 4 **99.** $x \geq 0$
101. $x \geq 2$

Bonus Topic

1. 4 **3.** 3 **5.** 7 **7.** 8 **9.** 9

Lesson 11-6 Try This

a. $12\sqrt{2}$ **b.** $5\sqrt{5}$ **c.** $-12\sqrt{10}$ **d.** $5\sqrt{6y}$
e. $\sqrt{x + 1}$ **f.** $\frac{3}{2}\sqrt{2}$ **g.** $\frac{2\sqrt{15}}{15}$ **h.** $2\sqrt{x}$

Exercise Set 11-6

1. $7\sqrt{2}$ **3.** $4\sqrt{5}$ **5.** $13\sqrt{x}$ **7.** $-2\sqrt{x}$ **9.** $25\sqrt{2}$
11. $\sqrt{3}$ **13.** $\sqrt{5}$ **15.** $13\sqrt{2}$ **17.** $3\sqrt{3}$
19. $-24\sqrt{2}$ **21.** $6\sqrt{2} - 6\sqrt{3}$ **23.** $(2 + 9x)\sqrt{x}$
25. $(3 - 2x)\sqrt{3}$ **27.** $3\sqrt{2x + 2}$
29. $(x + 3)\sqrt{x^3 - 1}$ **31.** $(-x^2 + 3xy + y^2)\sqrt{xy}$
33. $(2 - a - b)\sqrt{a + b}$ **35.** $\frac{2\sqrt{3}}{3}$ **37.** $\frac{13\sqrt{2}}{2}$
39. $\frac{\sqrt{6}}{6}$ **41.** $\frac{\sqrt{3}}{18}$ **43. a.** None **b.** $\sqrt{10} + 5\sqrt{2}$
45. $16\sqrt{2}$ **47.** $11\sqrt{3} - 10\sqrt{2}$ **49.** 0
51. $\frac{x + 1}{x}\sqrt{x}$ **53.** $\frac{\sqrt{30}}{12}$ **55. a.** $\sqrt{5}$, 3 **b.** $\sqrt{13}$, 5
c. $\sqrt{17}$, 5 **d.** 5, 7 **e.** $\sqrt{10}$, 4 **f.** $2\sqrt{5}$, 6
57. $\frac{24 + 3\sqrt{3} + 8\sqrt{2} + \sqrt{6}}{7}$ **59.** 6 **61.** $y + 5$
63. $4\sqrt{3}$ **65.** $\sqrt{a^2 - c^2}$ **67.** $4x\sqrt{y}$
69.

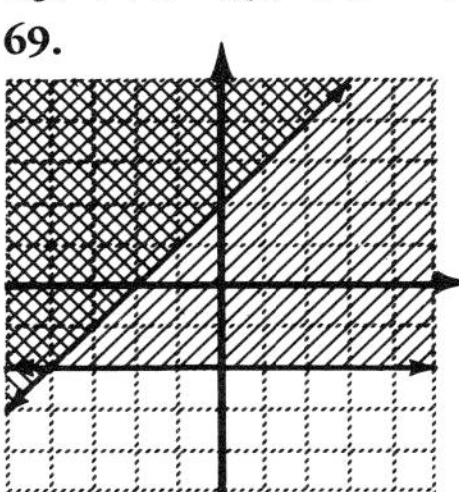

71.

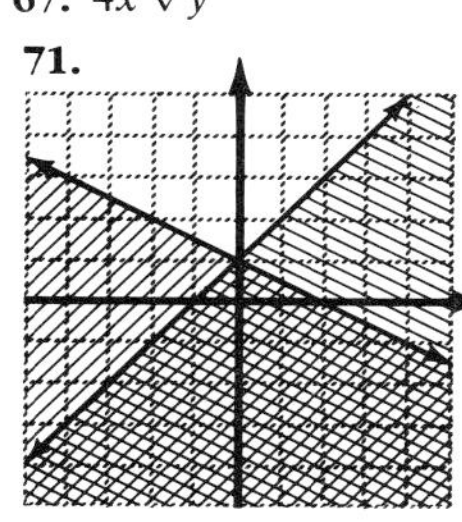

Problem Solving: Application

1. 35 **3.** 62 **5.** 38 **7.** 43 **9.** 50 **11.** From the highest score to lowest: 8, 6 or 9, 7, 5, 10

Lesson 11-7 Try This

a. $\sqrt{65} \approx 8.062$ **b.** $\sqrt{75} = 8.660$ **c.** $\sqrt{10} \approx 3.162$
d. $\sqrt{175} = 5\sqrt{7} \approx 13.229$

Exercise Set 11-7

1. 17 **3.** $4\sqrt{2}$ or 5.657 **5.** 12 **7.** 4 **9.** 26
11. 12 **13.** 2 **15.** $\sqrt{2}$ **17.** 5 **19.** $\frac{a}{2}\sqrt{3}$
21. $A = \frac{b^2\sqrt{3}}{3}$ **25.** $12 - 2\sqrt{6} \approx 7.1$ **27.** 6
29. $x + 3$ **31.** $4a\sqrt{2}$ **33.** a^{10} **35.** $(x - 3)\sqrt{x - 3}$
37. $6x^2\sqrt{6}$ **39.** $3ab^2\sqrt{2a}$ **41.** 3 **43.** 14, 15

Bonus Topic

1. 13 **3.** $3\sqrt{2}$ **5.** $8\sqrt{2}$

Lesson 11-8 Try This

a. $\approx$18.0 ft **b.** $\approx$9.7 ft

Exercise Set 11-8

1. $\approx$8.7 m **3.** $\approx$76.5 ft **5.** $\approx$68.0 m **7.** $\approx$77.6 mi
9. $\approx$14.5 km **11.** $\sqrt{39} \approx 6.2$ ft
13. $8\sqrt{10} + 2 \approx 27.3$ ft **15.** $\sqrt{193} \approx 13.9$ in.
19. $\sqrt{1525} = 5\sqrt{61} \approx 39.05$ mi, 1.28 h **21.** $\frac{2\sqrt{y}}{y}$
23. $5\sqrt{6}$ **25.** $5\sqrt{2}$ **27.** $8\sqrt{3}$ **29.** $22\sqrt{2}$ **31.** $-\sqrt{2}$

Lesson 11-9 Try This

a. $\frac{64}{3}$ **b.** 2 **c.** 66 **d.** $\approx$313 km **e.** $\approx$16 km
f. About 300 m

Exercise Set 11-9

1. 25 **3.** 38.44 **5.** 397 **7.** 310.5 **9.** 5 **11.** 3
13. $\frac{17}{4}$ **15.** No value **17.** No value **19.** $\approx$346 km
21. $\approx$10,000 m **23.** 125 ft, 245 ft **25.** 2 or -2
27. 49 **29.** 2.1 ft **33.** $\frac{1}{2}$ **35.** 5 **37.** 0 or 4 (1 is not a solution) **39.** $\frac{t^2g}{2}$ **41.** 1610 ft **43.** $x \geq 1$
45. Any real number **47.** m **49.** $9a$ **51.** $3(y + 7)^2$
53. $\frac{1}{3}, \frac{1}{5}$

Problem Solving: College Entrance Exams

1. (D) **3.** (B) **5.** (C)

Chapter 11 Summary and Review

1. 6 **3.** 7 **5.** Irrational **7.** Irrational **9.** $x \geq -7$
11. $|m|$ **13.** $|p|$ **15.** $-4\sqrt{3}$ **17.** $8x$ **19.** x^6
21. $(x - 2)^2$ **23.** $5x^4\sqrt{x}$ **25.** $\sqrt{21}$ **27.** $\sqrt{x^2 - 9}$
29. $\sqrt{\frac{15}{28}}$ **31.** $3\sqrt{2}$ **33.** $b\sqrt{ac}$ **35.** $\frac{3}{4}$ **37.** $\frac{2}{3}$
39. 4 **41.** 2 **43.** $\frac{\sqrt{15}}{5}$ **45.** $\frac{2\sqrt{2x}}{x}$ **47.** $\frac{\sqrt{2}}{4}$
49. $13\sqrt{5}$ **51.** $4\sqrt{x}$ **53.** $4\sqrt{x + 1}$ **55.** $c = 25$
57. $b = 8$ **59.** $a = 8\sqrt{2}$ **61.** $\sqrt{128} \approx 11.3$ ft
63. 52 **65.** 466.56 m

Chapter 1–11 Cumulative Review

1. 102 **3.** $11(11a + 8b)$ **5.** $\frac{x(y-4)}{x-8y}$ **7.** 70
9. -72 **11.** 8 **13.** $-7(3x + 4w)$ **15.** $-5x + 7$
17. 3 books **19.** 0 **21.** 250 **23.** 770 oranges
25. $x \leq -6$ **27.** $x < 4$ **29.** a^3b^9 **31.** a^3b
33. $\frac{1}{7^4}$ **35.** $-27x^{15}y^6$ **37.** 3.46×10^5 **39.** a
41. $3c + 2bc + c^2 - 4 - 2b$
43. $5x^2 + 4xy - 12y^2$ **45.** $h^2 - 8hk + 16k^2$
47. $x^4 - 9$ **49.** $xy(x^2y^2 + xy - 4)$
51. $(2 - 3m^2)(2 + 3m^2)$ **53.** $(x - 6)(x + 2)$
55. $t(t - 2)(t - 3)$ **57.** $(4y + 3)(5y + 1)$
59. $-2, 5$ **61.** $y = 5x$ **63.** $y = -x - 12$
65. $y = 3x + 5$ **67.** $(3, -3)$ **69.** 37 **71.** $\{0\}$
73. $6, -1$
75. $x \leq -5$ or $x \geq 5$

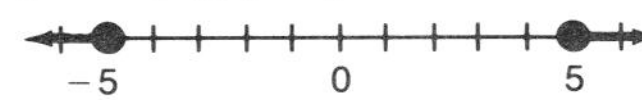

77. $-\frac{2}{3}$ **79.** x^3y^2 **81.** $\frac{3y^2 - 5y - 6}{(y + 1)(y - 1)}$ **83.** -10
85. $26\frac{2}{3}$ h or 26 h 40 min **87.** $\frac{1 + 3x}{1 - 2x}$ **89.** -11
91. $7|c|$ **93.** $|x - 3|$ **95.** x^4 **97.** $2x^2y^2\sqrt{5y}$
99. $3|ab|\sqrt{2a}$ **101.** $\sqrt{2x^2 + 3xy - 20y^2}$
103. $2|x|\sqrt{2}$ **105.** $\frac{1}{3}$ **107.** $8\sqrt{2}$ **109.** $\frac{-\sqrt{3}}{6}$
111. $c = 34$ **113.** 14

Chapter 12

Lesson 12-1 Try This

a. Yes **b.** No **c.** $8, -5, 1$ **d.** $0, -10, 2$
e. $11, 35, 5$ **f.** $-1, 5, 20$

Exercise Set 12-1

1. Yes **3.** Yes **5.** No **7.** $8, 12, -4$ **9.** $-6, 15, 72$
11. $6, -10, 16$ **13.** $2, 7, 4$ **15.** $4, 4, 3$
17. $1, 91, 98$ **19.** $-3, -2, 78$ **21.** \$45.15
23. \$54.24 **25.** $1\frac{20}{33}, 1\frac{30}{33}, 4\frac{1}{33}$ **27.** 70°, 220°, 10,020°
29. 5, 8, 11, 14 **31.** 0, 2 **35.** 100 **37.** 880
39. -64 **41.** $(-1, 6)$ **43.** $(-2, 7)$ **45.** $\sqrt{y^2 - 2y}$
47. $\sqrt{m^2 - n^2}$ **49.** $\sqrt{3x^2 - 10x - 8}$ **51.** $y = 1$
53. $x = 3$ **55.** $12|m|$ **57.** $4|a|\sqrt{2a}$

Lesson 12-2 Try This

a.
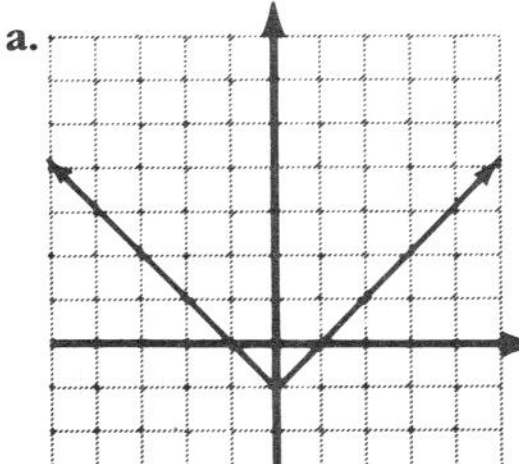

b.
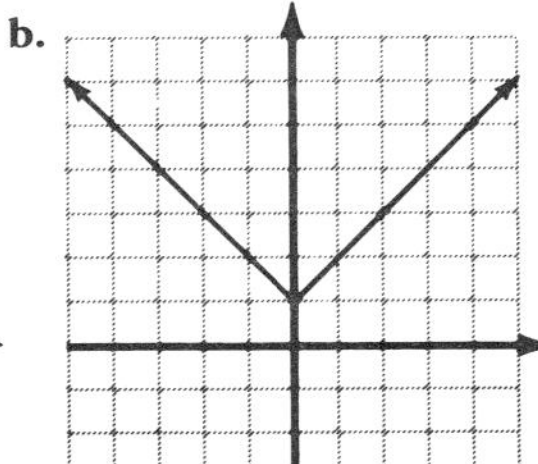

c. Yes **d.** No **e.** No

Exercise Set 12-2

1.
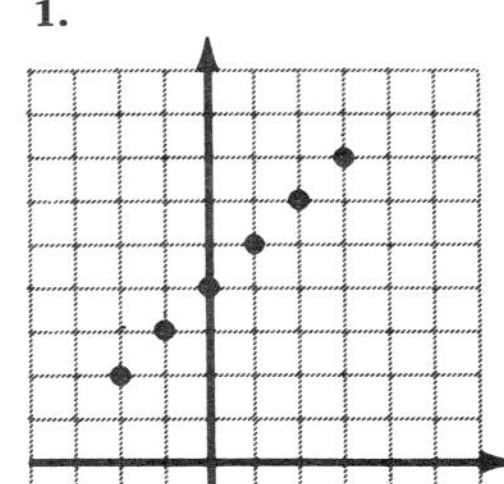

3.
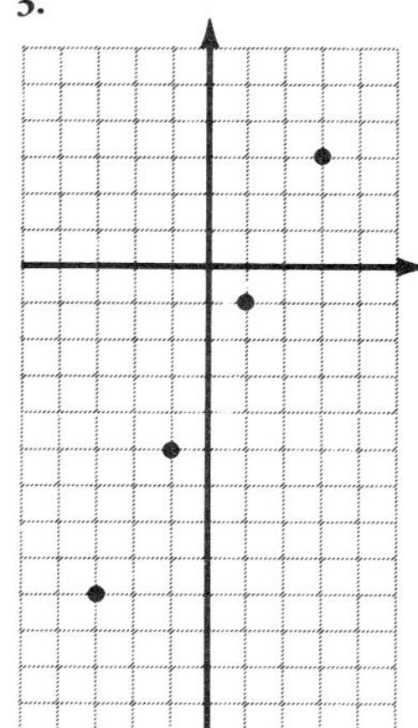

5.
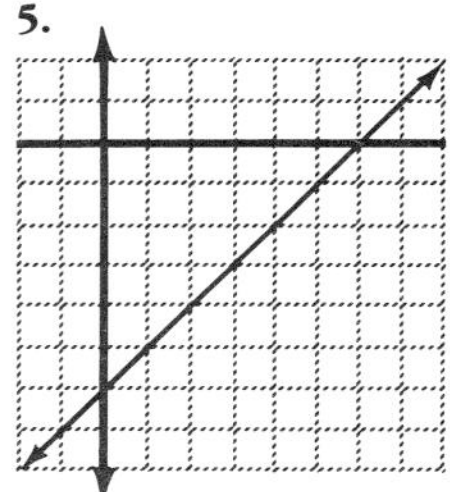

7.
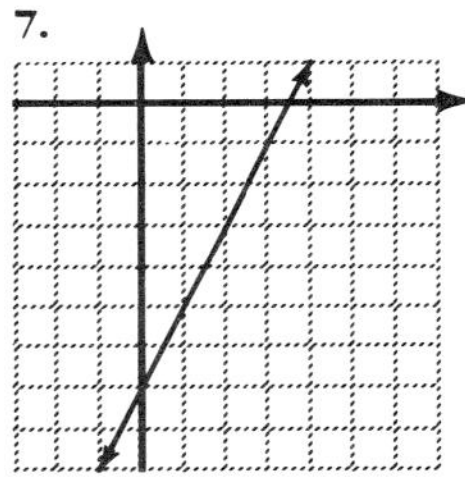

9.
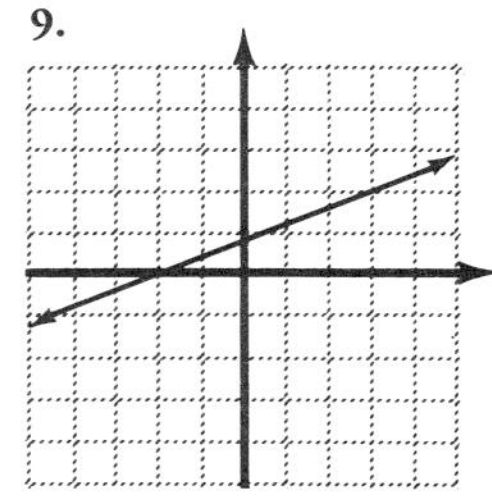

11.
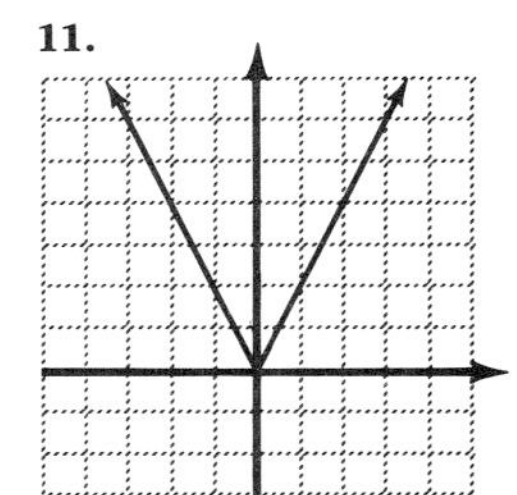

13.
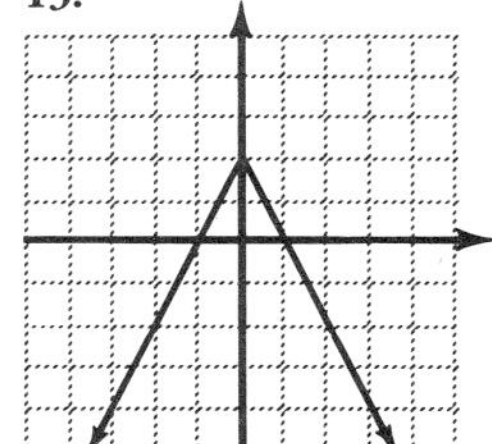

15. Yes **17.** No **19.** No **23.** If $|a|$ increases, the graph gets thinner; if b increases, the graph is moved upwards. **25.** $\frac{2}{3}$ **27.** $\frac{\sqrt{7xy}}{xy}$

29. $y^3 + 3y^2 + 9y + 27 + \frac{72}{y - 3}$ **31.** $\frac{y + 10}{y^2 - 25}$

Bonus Topic

1. $(0, 0)$; $(-1, 0)$ **3.** The constant b moves the vertex to $(-b, 0)$. **5.** The constant a changes the slope of the legs of the graph to $\pm a$. **7.**

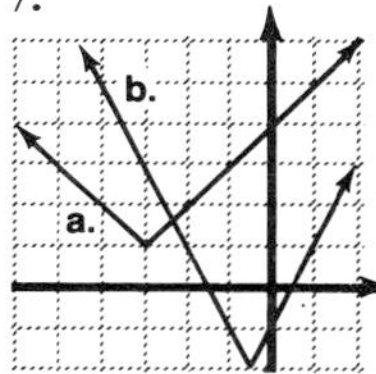

Lesson 12-3 Try This

a. $c(h) = 3.50 + 1.65h$; $c(9) = \$18.35$

Exercise Set 12-3

1. $c(k) = 35 + 0.21k$; $c(340) = \$106.40$

3. $L(w) = \frac{1}{3}w + 40$; $L(15) = 45$ cm

5. $c(h) = 5.50 + 4.25h$; $c(4.5) = \$24.63$

7. $c(h) = 6.50 + 3.90h$; $c(7.5) = \$35.75$

9. \$8.70; \$20.10 **11.** \$12.50 **13.** A horizontal line

15.

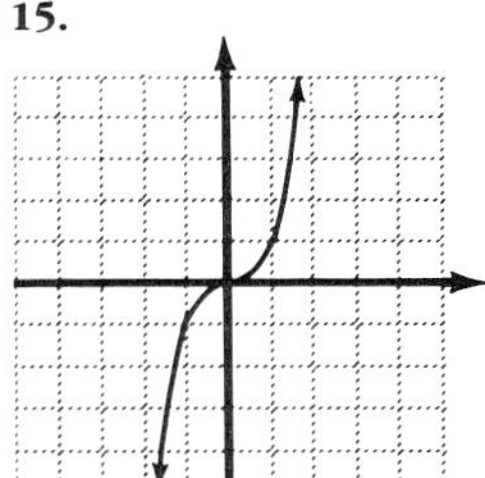

17. $8\sqrt{2}$ **19.** 5.47×10^6 **21.** 2 **23.** $x > 4$ or $x < -4$ **25.** $x > 4$ or $x < -2$

Lesson 12-4 Try This

a.

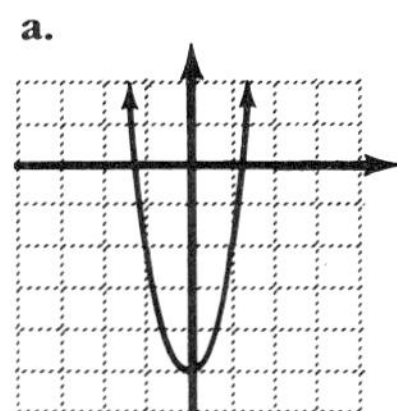

b.

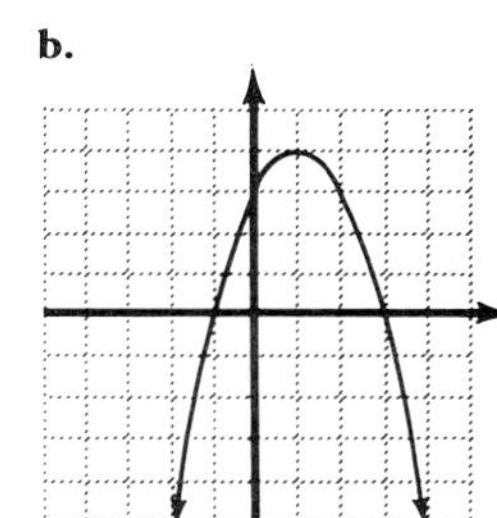

c.

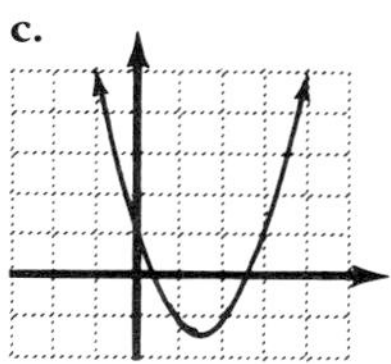

Exercise Set 12-4

1.

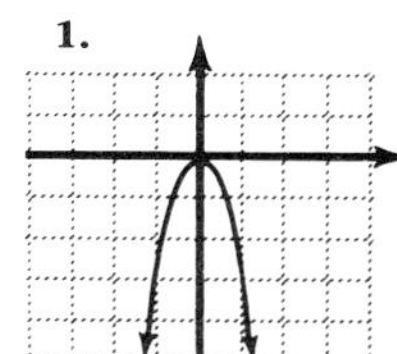

3.

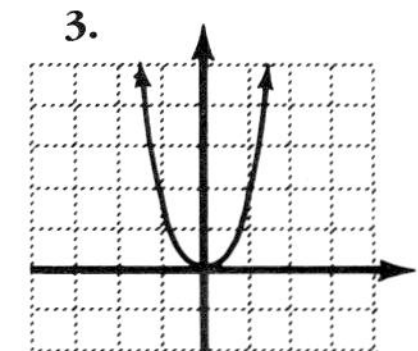

5.

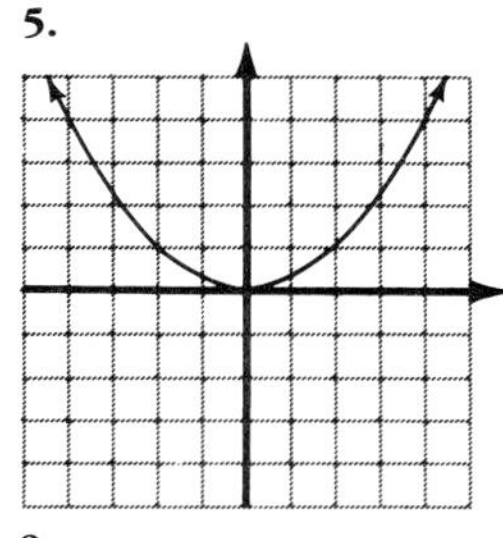

7.

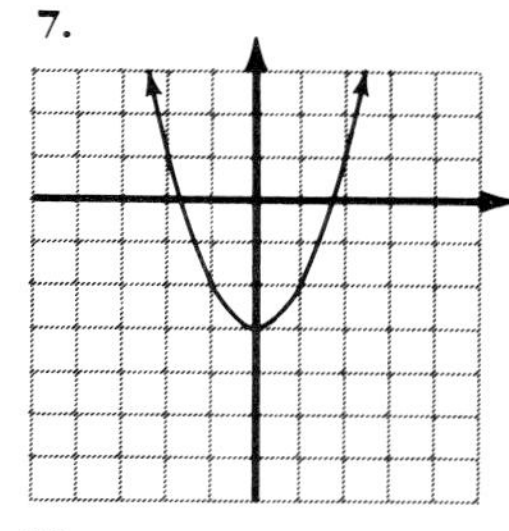

9.

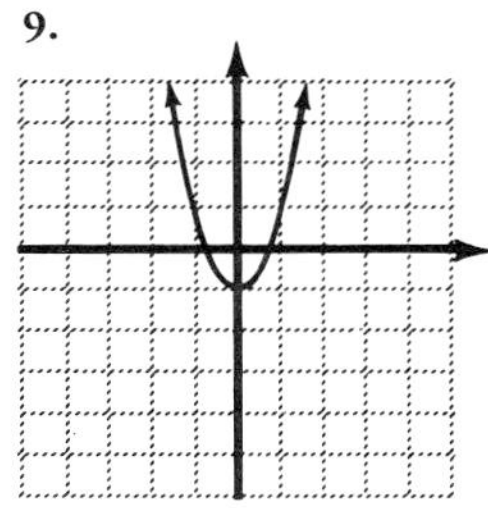

11.

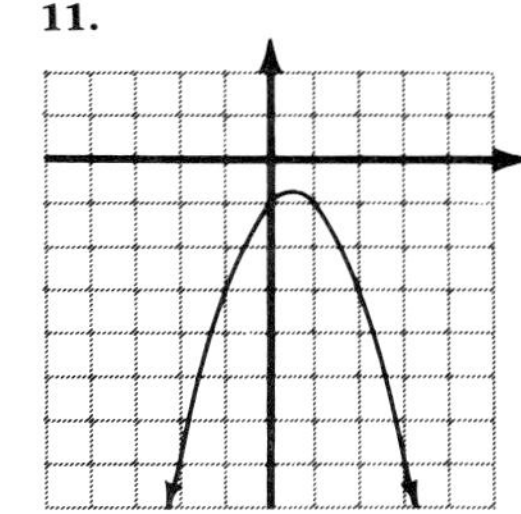

13.

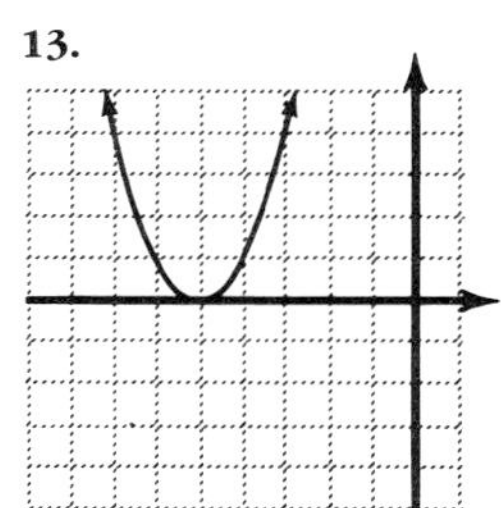

15.

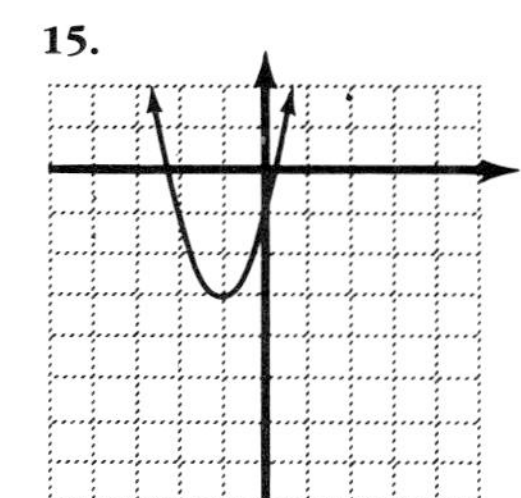

17.

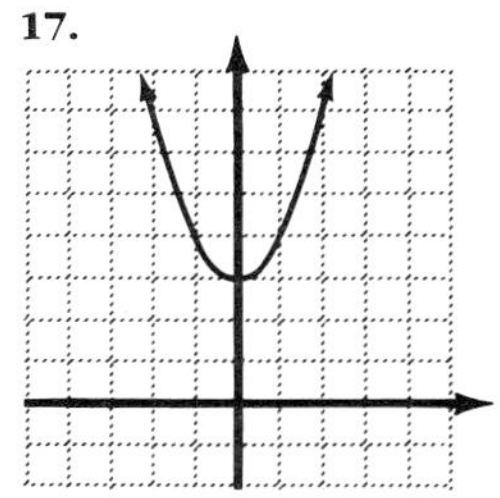

19. When the function is in standard form, the y-intercept is the constant term. **21.** Graphs that open upward have a minimum point. Graphs that open downward have a maximum point. **23.** Axis is parallel to y-axis and contains maximum or minimum points. **25.** 3 s; 144 ft

27.

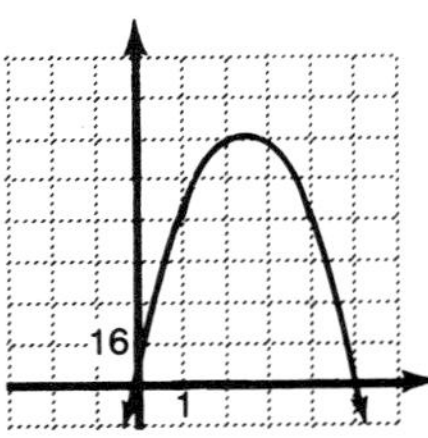

29. 2.5 s **33.** If the graph of the function does not cross the x-axis, then the equation has no real-number solution. **35.** 0.0000005115 **37.** 289 **39.** 80 **41.** 7 **43.** $\frac{-2\sqrt{35}}{35}$ **45.** $\frac{3\sqrt{10}+\sqrt{15}}{15}$ **47.** -1, 11, 5, -10 **49.** $|x-5|$ **51.** $9|m|\sqrt{3m}$

Lesson 12-5 Try This

a. $y = 7x$ **b.** $y = 0.625x$ **c.** $46\frac{2}{3}$¢, $1\frac{17}{18}$¢ **d.** 132.5 lb

Exercise Set 12-5

1. $y = 4x$ **3.** $y = 1.75x$ **5.** $y = 3.2x$ **7.** $y = \frac{2}{3}x$ **9.** \$183.75 **11.** Approx. 25 servings **13.** Approx. 25 lb **15.** 68.4 kg **17.** 2500 miles **19.** Yes **21.** No **23.** No **25.** $C = kr(k = 2\pi)$ **27.** $C = kA$ **29.** $S = kV^6$ **31.** $A = kr^2$ **33.** $t \geq 0$ **35.** $a \geq 7$ **37.** Any real number **39.** Any real number **41.** $\sqrt{3xy}$ **43.** $7\sqrt{3}$ **45.** 9 **47.** -2, 2, 0, 4

Lesson 12-6 Try This

a. $y = \frac{63}{x}$ **b.** $y = \frac{900}{x}$ **c.** $7\frac{1}{2}$ hr **d.** 3.2 h or $3\frac{1}{5}$ h

Exercise Set 12-6

1. $y = \frac{75}{x}$ **3.** $y = \frac{80}{x}$ **5.** $y = \frac{1}{x}$ **7.** $y = \frac{1050}{x}$ **9.** $y = \frac{0.06}{x}$ **11.** $y = \frac{3.2}{x}$ **13.** $y = \frac{1}{x}$ **15.** $5\frac{1}{3}$ hr **17.** 320 cm^3 **19.** 54 min **21.** $C = \frac{k}{N}$ **23.** $I = \frac{k}{R}$ **25.** No **27.** Yes **31.** $L = \frac{kwf^2}{d}$ **33.** $|a|c^2\sqrt{a}$

35. 33 **37.** Yes **39.** No **41.**

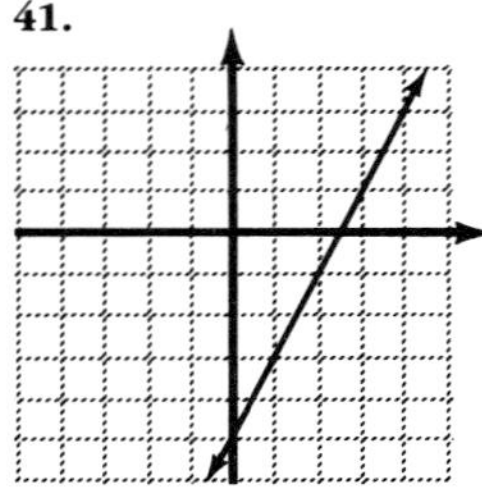

Lesson 12-7 Try This

a. $w = 0.4xyz$; 32 **b.** $P = \frac{0.02\,q}{r}$; 0.024 **c.** 420 K

Exercise Set 12-7

1. $r = \frac{1}{2}st$; 54 **3.** $q = 5rs$; 0.8 **5.** $x = \frac{3}{10}wyz$; 54 **7.** $a = \frac{6b}{c}$; 3 **9.** $w = \frac{2x}{3y}$; 2 **11.** $u = \frac{1.5v}{w}$; 0.9375 **13.** 2.8 **15.** 28 cm^3 **17.** 8 in. **19.** $\frac{\pi}{4}$ **21.** y is quadrupled **23.** 10 m **25.** $\frac{\sqrt{5x}}{x}$ **27.** $\frac{3\sqrt{y}}{y}$ **29.** $\frac{x\sqrt{xy}}{y}$ **31.** $\frac{2\sqrt{cd}}{c^2d^2}$ **33.** 13 **35.** 3 **37.** 9

39.

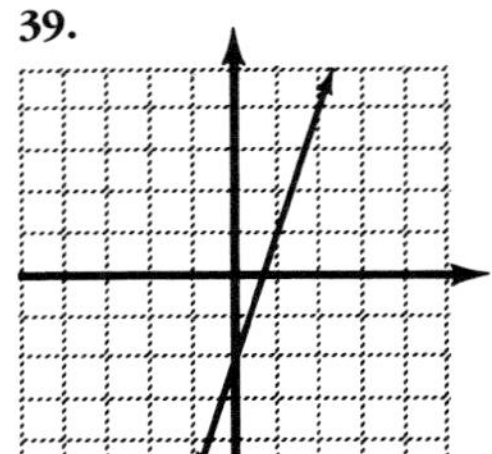

Chapter 12 Summary and Review

1. No **3.** 2; -4; -7 **5.** -7; 1; 0

7.

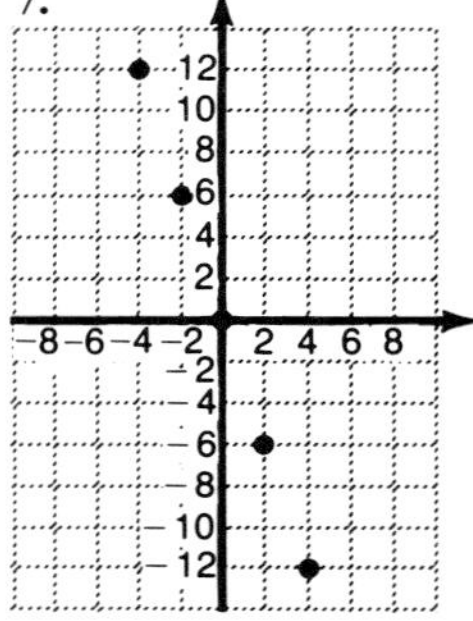

9.

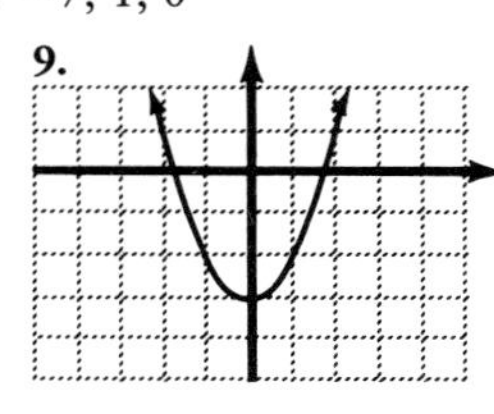

11. No **13.** $c(m) = 0.35 + 0.25(m - 1)$; \$1.35

15.

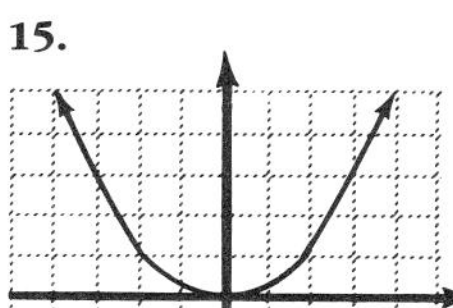

17. $y = \frac{1}{2}x$ **19.** $y = \frac{30}{x}$ **21.** 1 h **23. (a)** $k = 27$ **(b)** $W = 72$

Chapter 13

Lesson 13-1 Try This

a. $x^2 - 7x = 0; a = 1, b = -7, c = 0$
b. $x^2 + 9x - 3 = 0; a = 1, b = 9, c = -3$
c. $5x^2 + 0x + 4 = 0; a = 5, b = 0, c = 4$
d. $-\frac{5}{3}, 0$ **e.** $\frac{3}{5}, 0$ **f.** $-1, \frac{2}{3}$ **g.** $7, -3$

Exercise Set 13-1

1. $x^2 - 3x + 2 = 0; a = 1, b = -3, c = 2$
3. $2x^2 - 3 = 0; a = 2, b = 0, c = -3$
5. $7x^2 - 4x + 3 = 0; a = 7, b = -4, c = 3$
7. $2x^2 - 3x + 5 = 0; a = 2, b = -3, c = 5$
9. $3x^2 - 2x + 8 = 0; a = 3, b = -2, c = 8$
11. $0, -5$ **13.** $0, -2$ **15.** $0, \frac{7}{3}$ **17.** $0, 1$ **19.** $0, 5$
21. $0, -\frac{1}{3}$ **23.** $0, \frac{8}{17}$ **25.** $4, 12$ **27.** $-1, -6$
29. $3, -7$ **31.** $2, 7$ **33.** -5 **35.** 1 **37.** $\frac{3}{2}, 5$
39. $4, -\frac{2}{3}$ **41.** $4, -\frac{5}{3}$ **43.** $-1, -5$ **45.** $\frac{1}{3}, -\frac{1}{2}$
47. $-5, \frac{7}{2}$ **49.** $-2, 7$ **51.** $3, -\frac{5}{3}$ **53.** $4, -5$
55. $\frac{3}{2}, 3$ **57.** $-1, -\frac{5}{2}$ **59.** $\pm\sqrt{3}$ **61.** $\frac{\sqrt{5}}{5}, 0$
63. $-\frac{\sqrt{5}}{5}, 0$ **71.** $x \geq 3$ **73.** $x \geq \frac{2}{3}$
75. $(c + 9)(c - 10)$ **77.** $9(x + 1)(x + 6)$
79. $(2b + 3d)(a + c)$ **81.** $\{25, 36, 49\}$

Lesson 13-2 Try This

a. $\pm\sqrt{10}$ **b.** $\pm\frac{\sqrt{15}}{3}$ **c.** ± 5 **d.** 0 **e.** $7, -1$
f. $-3 \pm \sqrt{10}$ **g.** $1 \pm \sqrt{5}$ **h.** $7 \pm \sqrt{3}$ **i.** $2, -24$
j. 15%

Exercise Set 13-2

1. ± 11 **3.** $\pm\sqrt{7}$ **5.** $\pm\frac{\sqrt{15}}{5}$ **7.** $\pm\frac{5}{2}$ **9.** $\pm\frac{7\sqrt{3}}{3}$
11. $\pm\sqrt{3}$ **13.** $\pm\frac{6}{5}$ **15.** $\pm\frac{\sqrt{5}}{10}$ **17.** $-1 \pm \sqrt{6}$
19. $3 \pm \sqrt{6}$ **21.** $21, 5$ **23.** $-1 \pm \sqrt{14}$
25. $2, -10$ **27.** $5 \pm 2\sqrt{5}$ **29.** $-3, 5$ **31.** $13, -1$
33. $-8 \pm \sqrt{15}$ **35.** $7 \pm \sqrt{19}$ **37.** $-12 \pm 2\sqrt{2}$
39. 20 **41.** 10% **43.** 8% **45.** 12.6% **47.** 5.25%
49. $1, -\frac{1}{3}$ **51.** $\frac{1}{3}, -1$ **53.** $\frac{1}{3}(4 \pm \sqrt{2})$ **55.** $4, -2$
57. ± 9 **59.** 7.81 s **61.** $a = 1$ **65.** \$2682.63
67. \$1171.66 **69.** $A = P\left(1 + \frac{r}{q}\right)^{qt}$
71.

73. $3|y|$ **75.** $\frac{4\sqrt{3}}{3}$ **77.** $2, -3, -4$

Lesson 13-3 Try This

a. $x^2 - 8x + 16 = (x - 4)^2$
b. $x^2 + 12x + 36 = (x + 6)^2$
c. $y^2 + 7y + \frac{49}{4} = \left(y + \frac{7}{2}\right)^2$
d. $m^2 - 3m + \frac{9}{4} = \left(m - \frac{3}{2}\right)^2$ **e.** $-2, -6$
f. $\frac{-3 \pm \sqrt{33}}{4}$ **g.** $\frac{1 \pm \sqrt{10}}{3}$

Exercise Set 13-3

1. $x^2 - 6x + 9$ **3.** $m^2 + 7m + \frac{49}{4}$ **5.** $x^2 + 4x + 4$
7. $z^2 - 20z + 100$ **9.** $x^2 + 15x + \frac{225}{4}$
11. $-5, -3$ **13.** $-15, 1$ **15.** $2 \pm \sqrt{15}$
17. $9 \pm \sqrt{7}$ **19.** $5 \pm \sqrt{29}$ **21.** $\frac{-7 \pm \sqrt{57}}{2}$
23. $-4, 7$ **25.** $\frac{3 \pm \sqrt{17}}{4}$ **27.** $\frac{2 \pm \sqrt{13}}{3}$ **29.** $-\frac{3}{2}, 4$
31. $\pm 2x\sqrt{55}$ **33.** $\pm 16x$ **35.** $\pm 2x\sqrt{ac}$
37. $3a, -2a$ **39.** $c + 1, -c$ **41.** $-\frac{m \pm \sqrt{m^2 - 4nk}}{2k}$
43. $y = \frac{11}{4}x$ **45.** Irrational **47.** Rational
49. No real-number solution

Lesson 13-4 Try This

a. $\frac{1}{2}, -4$ **b.** $4, -\frac{2}{3}$ **c.** $2.9, -0.9$ **d.** $-0.7, -4.3$
e. 56, two real-number solutions **f.** -7, no real-number solutions **g.** 0, one real-number solution

Exercise Set 13-4

1. $-3, 7$ **3.** 3 **5.** $-\frac{4}{3}, 2$ **7.** $-\frac{7}{2}, \frac{1}{2}$ **9.** $-3, 3$

11. 1 **13.** $5 \pm \sqrt{3}$ **15.** $-2 \pm \sqrt{7}$ **17.** $\frac{-4 \pm \sqrt{10}}{3}$
19. $\frac{5 \pm \sqrt{33}}{4}$ **21.** $\frac{1 \pm \sqrt{2}}{2}$ **23.** $-\frac{5}{3}, 0$ **25.** No real-number solutions **27.** $-5, 5$ **29.** $\frac{5 \pm \sqrt{73}}{6}$
31. $\frac{3 \pm \sqrt{29}}{2}$ **33.** $\frac{-1 \pm \sqrt{10}}{3}$ **35.** $-1.3, 5.3$
37. $-0.2, 6.2$ **39.** $-1.2, 0.2$ **41.** $-1.7, 0.4$
43. $-1.8, 0.8$ **45.** $-1.7, -6.2$ **47.** 1.2, 3.8
49. $-0.9, 1.3$ **51.** -3, no real-number solutions
53. 0, one real-number solution **55.** -39, no real-number solutions **57.** -39, no real-number solutions
59. 0, 2 **61.** $\frac{3 \pm \sqrt{5}}{2}$ **63.** $\frac{-7 \pm \sqrt{61}}{2}$ **65.** $\frac{-2 \pm \sqrt{10}}{2}$
67. No real-number solutions **69.** $\frac{-1 \pm \sqrt{3a + 1}}{a}$
71. $\frac{c \pm |d|\sqrt{3}}{2}$ **75.** $b = 9.4$, so $x = 0.3$
77. $4x^2 + 5x + 16 = 0; a = 4, b = 5, c = 16$
79. $y = \frac{64}{x}$ **81.** 6 **83.** $5(m - 3)^2$ **85.** 120 adults, 65 children

Lesson 13-5 Try This

a. $-5, 2$ **b.** $-3, 4$ **c.** $6, -1$

Exercise Set 13-5

1. $4, -4$ **3.** $3, -1$ **5.** $5, -1$ **7.** $3 \pm \sqrt{5}$
9. $\pm\sqrt{7}$ **11.** No real solution **13.** $10, -\frac{2}{5}$
15. 2 **17.** 0, 5 **19.** No real solution
21. $-3 \pm 2\sqrt{3}$ **23.** $\frac{3 \pm \sqrt{33}}{2}$ **25.** $-1, 6$
27. $4 \pm 2\sqrt{5}$ **29.** 0 **31.** $\frac{1}{2}$ **33.** $\frac{7 \pm \sqrt{13}}{2}$
35. $\frac{3}{4}$ **37.** $3 \pm \sqrt{13}$ **39.** $9 \pm \sqrt{59}$ **41.** $-3, 0$
43. $7, -2$ **45.** $\pm\frac{2\sqrt{5}}{3}$
47.

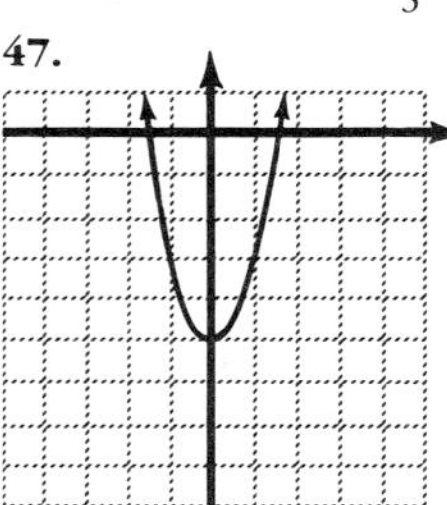

49.

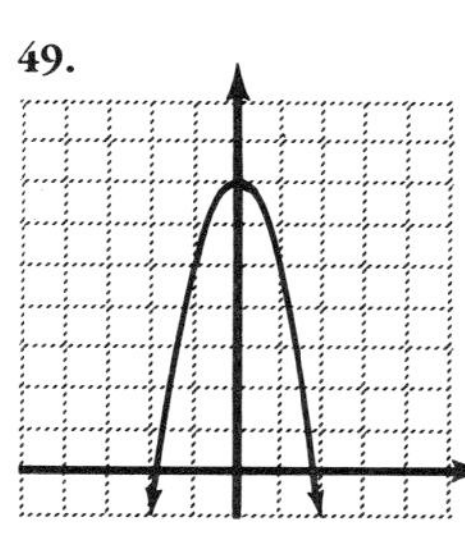

51. $y = 1.5x$ **53.** $y = \frac{10}{x}$ **55.** 3.485117×10^6
57. $m = \frac{5}{3}$

Lesson 13-6 Try This

a. 2 **b.** 7 **c.** $\frac{r^2}{20}$ **d.** $\frac{T^2g}{4\pi^2}$ **e.** $\frac{E}{c^2}$ **f.** $\sqrt{\frac{A}{\pi}}$
g. $1 \pm \sqrt{\frac{C}{P}}$

Exercise Set 13-6

1. 18 **3.** 7 **5.** 12 **7.** 8 **9.** 3 **11.** 106 **13.** 9
15. 7 **17.** 3 **19.** 13, 25 **21.** 0, 8
23. $a = \sqrt{c^2 - b^2}$ **25.** $b = \sqrt{c^2 - a^2}$
27. $r = \sqrt{\frac{V}{\pi h}}$ or $\sqrt{\frac{V\pi h}{\pi h}}$ **29.** $\sqrt{r^2 - y^2 - z^2}$
31. $\sqrt{\frac{GmM}{F}}$ **33.** $\frac{P}{I^2}$ **35.** $\sqrt{\frac{P}{R}} - 4$ **37.** 13
39. $\sqrt{\frac{3}{5}}$ or $\frac{\sqrt{15}}{5}$ **41.** 63 **43.** 0 **47.** 3
49. $\frac{-v \pm \sqrt{v^2 + 32h}}{16}$ **51.** $m = 49, n = 4$
53. $(-2, -3), (2, -3), (-2, 3), (2, 3)$
55. $m^2 - 5m + \frac{25}{4}$ **57.** 2, 0 **59.** $\pm\frac{5\sqrt{2}}{2}$
61. $5 \pm \sqrt{17}$ **63.** $-\frac{2}{11}$ **65.** $\sqrt{7}$ **67.** (3, 2)
69. $(4, -3)$

Lesson 13-7 Try This

a. 20 m **b.** 2.3 cm, 3.3 cm **c.** 3 km/h

Exercise Set 13-7

1. 3 cm **3.** 7 ft, 24 ft **5.** 8 cm, 10 cm **7.** 4.6 m, 6.6 m **9.** 7 km/h **11.** 4 km/h **13.** $3 + 3\sqrt{2}$ or 7.243 cm **15.** 14.14 in.; a 15 in. pizza **17.** 15 mi/h, 20 mi/h **19.** 100 m **21.** -25 m or 25 m below the starting point **23.** 3 **25.** $3, -5$ **27.** $\frac{-5 \pm \sqrt{17}}{2}$
29. $y = -\frac{2}{5}x - \frac{16}{5}$

Problem Solving: Application

1. \$130.20 **3.** 4.18% compounded monthly

Chapter 13 Summary and Review

1. $3x^2 + 6x + 4 = 0$ **3.** $0, \frac{7}{5}$ **5.** $\frac{3}{5}, 1$ **7.** $2\sqrt{2}, -2\sqrt{2}$ **9.** $-8 \pm \sqrt{13}$ **11.** $-\frac{1}{2}, -\frac{9}{2}$ **13.** 30%
15. $c^2 + 22c + 121$ **17.** $1 \pm \sqrt{11}$ **19.** $\frac{5}{3}, -1$
21. $3 \pm 3\sqrt{2}$ **23.** $\frac{3 \pm \sqrt{33}}{2}$ **25.** $-3 \pm \sqrt{2}$
27. 24, two real-number solutions **29.** $3, -5$
31. 52 **33.** $F = \frac{mV^2}{qr}$ **35.** 10 m, 7 m **37.** 10 in., 24 in. or 2 ft

Chapter 14

Lesson 14-1 Try This

a. $\frac{p}{x} = \frac{q}{y}, \frac{r}{z} = \frac{p}{x}, \frac{q}{y} = \frac{r}{z}$; there are others. **b.** 75

Exercise Set 14-1

1. Corresponding angles; $\angle B$ and $\angle E$, $\angle C$ and $\angle F$, $\angle A$ and $\angle D$; corresponding sides: $\overline{BC}$ and $\overline{EF}$, $\overline{CA}$ and $\overline{FD}$, $\overline{AB}$ and $\overline{DE}$ **3.** Ex. $\frac{t}{m} = \frac{u}{n}, \frac{s}{u} = \frac{l}{n}, \frac{u}{t} = \frac{n}{m}$
5. 16 **7.** 66 m **9.** 8, 10 **11.** $\triangle BAC$, $\triangle DAB$, $\triangle DBC$
13. 36 **15.** $-3 \pm \sqrt{14}$ **17.** 1 real-number solution
19. $y = \frac{21}{x}$ **21.** $y = 0.3x$ **23.** $(a - 6)^2(a + 6)^2$

Lesson 14-2 Try This

a. $\frac{9}{41} \approx 0.2195$ **b.** $\frac{15}{39} \approx 0.3846$ **c.** $\frac{7}{24} \approx 0.2917$

Exercise Set 14-2

1. $\frac{\sqrt{3}}{2}$ or 0.8660 **3.** $\frac{4}{5}$ or 0.8 **5.** $\frac{8}{17}$ or 0.4706
7. $\frac{44}{55} = 0.8$ **9.** $\frac{20}{52} \approx 0.3846$ **11.** $\frac{36}{39} \approx 0.9231$
13. $\frac{40}{42} \approx 0.9524$ **15.** $\frac{60}{11} \approx 5.4545$ **17.** $\frac{32}{60} \approx 0.5333$
19. 0.2925 **21.** 15; 0.6; 0.8 **23.** 13.9; 0.4; 0.9
25. 40; 0.6; 0.8 **29.** 0.88 **31.** $-2, 4$ **33.** $3 \pm \sqrt{3}$
35. ± 5

37.
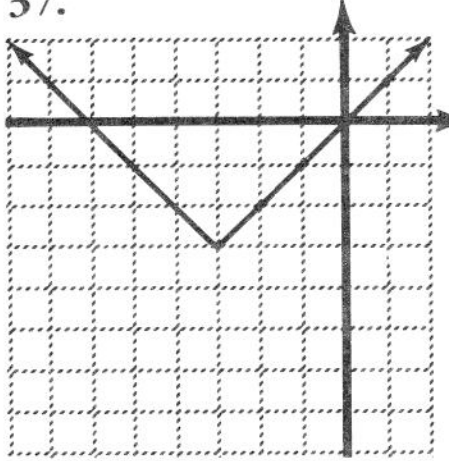

39. $|a|\sqrt{6a}$ **41.** $\frac{2\sqrt{3}}{9}$ **43.** After 6 h

Lesson 14-3 Try This

a. 0.8387 **b.** 0.2250 **c.** 1.0355 **d.** 46° **e.** 21°
f. 56° **g.** 72°

Exercise Set 14-3

1. 0.6157 **3.** 1.4826 **5.** 0.9877 **7.** 0.8660
9. 1.0000 **11.** 0.9998 **13.** 0.9455 **15.** 0.2588
17. 70° **19.** 81° **21.** 66° **23.** 11° **25.** 50° **27.** 5°
29. 61° **31.** 38° **33.** 65° **35.** 70° **37.** 0.6041, 0.6064, 0.6134 **39.** 30° **41.** 5, 9 **43.** 0, 10
45. 2, -6 **47.** -7, -13 **49.** No **51.** Yes

Lesson 14-4 Try This

a. 6.7 cm **b.** 37.1 m **c.** 152.6 m

Exercise Set 14-4

1. 22.8 cm **3.** 54.0 cm **5.** 35° **7.** 3.3 km
9. 338.5 m **11.** 5.3 m **13.** 211.3 m **15.** 2.4 km
17. 36.8 **19.** 33.7 **25.** $x = 3$ **27.** (4, 2)
29. $(-2, 3)$ and (0, 7) **31.** 16

Problem Solving: Application

1. 26.4 m **3.** 2531 ft

Chapter 14 Summary and Review

1. $\overline{PQ}$ and $\overline{ST}$, $\overline{QR}$ and $\overline{TV}$, $\overline{RP}$ and $\overline{VS}$, $\angle P$ and $\angle S$, $\angle Q$ and $\angle T$, $\angle R$ and $\angle V$ **3.** 0.3846 **5.** 0.2250
7. 0.4540 **9.** 28.6363 **11.** 44° **13.** 45°
15. 28.8 cm **17.** 30° **19.** 329.7 m

Chapter 15

Lesson 15-1 Try This

a. $\frac{4}{6}$ or $\frac{2}{3}$ **b.** $\frac{3}{6}$ or $\frac{1}{2}$ **c.** $\frac{26}{52}$ or $\frac{1}{2}$ **d.** $\frac{20}{52}$ or $\frac{5}{13}$
e. $\frac{0}{52}$ or 0

Exercise Set 15-1

1. $\frac{4}{8}$ or $\frac{1}{2}$ **3.** $\frac{2}{8}$ or $\frac{1}{4}$ **5.** $\frac{4}{8}$ or $\frac{1}{2}$ **7.** $\frac{0}{8}$ or 0
9. $\frac{16}{52}$ or $\frac{4}{13}$ **11.** $\frac{12}{52}$ or $\frac{3}{13}$ **13.** $\frac{12}{52}$ or $\frac{3}{13}$ **19.** $\frac{0}{36}$ or 0
21. $\frac{3}{36}$ or $\frac{1}{12}$ **23.** 0, 8 **25.** $-\frac{1}{4}, -\frac{1}{3}$ **27.** $-7 \pm 2\sqrt{5}$
29. 2 real-number solutions **31.** 1 real-number solution **33.** 1 **35.** $\frac{\sqrt{2}}{2}$ **37.** $\frac{\sqrt{2}}{2}$

Lesson 15-2 Try This

a. $\frac{3}{7}$ **b.** 0.92 **c.** $\frac{2}{6}$ or $\frac{1}{3}$ **d.** $\frac{10}{22}$ or $\frac{5}{11}$ **e.** $\frac{5}{8}$
f. $\frac{28}{52}$ or $\frac{7}{13}$

Exercise Set 15-2

1. $\frac{5}{8}$ **3.** 0.42 **5.** $\frac{8}{52}$ or $\frac{2}{13}$ **7.** $\frac{4}{52}$ or $\frac{1}{13}$ **9.** $\frac{5}{10}$ or $\frac{1}{2}$
11. $\frac{7}{10}$ **13.** $\frac{14}{52}$ or $\frac{7}{26}$ **15.** $\frac{26}{52}$ or $\frac{1}{2}$ **17.** $\frac{24}{52}$ or $\frac{6}{13}$
21. $\frac{15}{36}$ **23.** $\frac{1}{4}$ **25.** $b = \sqrt{c^2 - a^2}$ **27.** $b = \frac{2A}{h}$
29. $\pm\sqrt{5}$ **31.** $-3 \pm \sqrt{5}$ **33.** $\pm\sqrt{2}$ **35.** 0.9397
37. 0.6018 **39.** 0.0875

Lesson 15-3 Try This

a. Answers may vary. Theoretical probability is $\frac{1}{8}$.
b. $\frac{20}{50}$ or $\frac{2}{5}$

Exercise Set 15-3

1. a. The probability that out of 3 children, 2 will be boys **b.** A coin toss **c.** A trial is 3 tosses of a coin.

Heads can represent either boys or girls. **d.** Answers may vary. The theoretical probability is $\frac{3}{8}$.

3.–10. Answers may vary. The theoretical probability for each problem is given. **3.** $\frac{4}{27}$ **5.** $\frac{4}{27}$ **7.** $\frac{1}{2}$

9. $\frac{1}{2}$ **13.** Answers may vary. The theoretical probability is 0.1001.

15. $2x^2 + 3x - 10 = 0; 2, 3, -10$

17. $5x^2 - 3x - 39 = 0; 5, -3, -39$

Lesson 15-4 Try This

a.

Pulse Rates	Frequency
68	3
69	3
70	3
71	1
72	5
73	4
74	3
75	2
76	1

b.

Salaries	Frequency
900–999	3
1000–1099	0
1100–1199	9
1200–1299	8
1300–1399	3
1400–1499	4
1500–1599	3
1600–1699	3

c.

Stem	Leaf
10	8, 6, 6, 9
11	2, 8, 8, 4, 6, 3, 6, 8
12	4, 4, 9, 1, 6, 7, 9
13	2, 2, 0, 7, 4
14	8, 1
15	2, 0

Exercise Set 15-4

7.

Stem	Leaf
40	2, 9, 3, 0
41	7, 6, 2
42	3, 6, 9, 7
43	9, 8, 9
44	8
45	6, 6
46	7, 3, 7
47	8, 6, 6, 1
48	9, 7
49	8, 9

11. $P(1) = \frac{12}{120} = \frac{1}{10}$

$P(3) = \frac{15}{120} = \frac{1}{8}$

$P(6) = \frac{30}{120} = \frac{1}{4}$

It appears that the die may not be fair as 6 is rolled ten more times than would be expected. However, this is not conclusive evidence to prove that the die is not fair. The die would need to be rolled 120 more times to see if this pattern continues.

13. $\frac{-5 \pm \sqrt{37}}{2}$ **15.** $\frac{12}{13}$ **17.** $\frac{5}{13}$ **19.** $\frac{5}{13}$ **21.** $y = 6$

23. $\{1, 2, 3, 4, 6, 8, 12, 24\}$

Lesson 15-5 Try This

a.

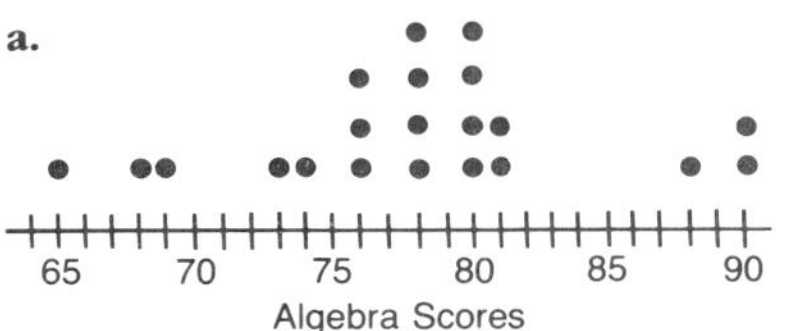

b.

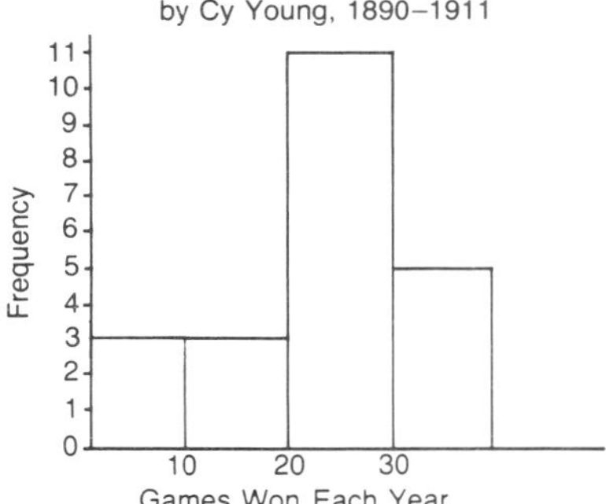

c.

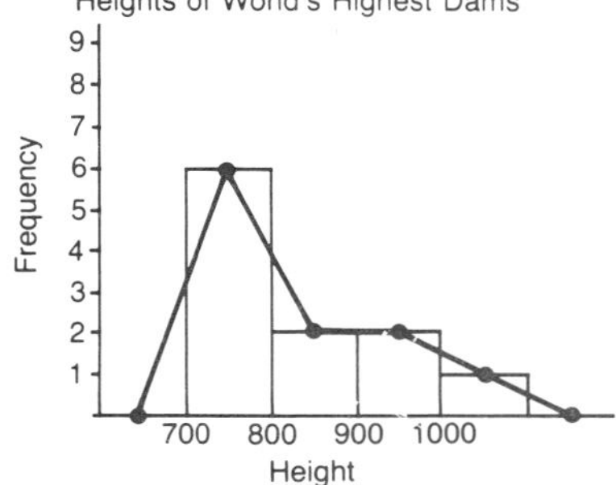

Exercise Set 15-5

17. $11\sqrt{2}$ **19.** 0.4 **21.** 73° **23.** 69° **25.** $\frac{1}{2}$

Lesson 15-6 Try This

a. 58.7 mi/h **b.** 2.75 min. **c.** 13

Exercise Set 15-6

1. Mean: 32.8, median: 34, mode: 44
3. Mean: 12.5, median: 10, mode: 8, 4
5. Mean: 162.2, median: 164.2, mode: 133.1, 153.1
9. Exercise 3 and Exercise 5 **11. a.** 0.40 **b.** 36.7
c. Ex. 2 **15.** $y = -x + 5$ **17.** $y = \frac{5}{2}x - 3$

19. 3 **21.** $-3, -5$ **23.** $0, -4$ **25.** $x = \frac{2}{3}, -5$

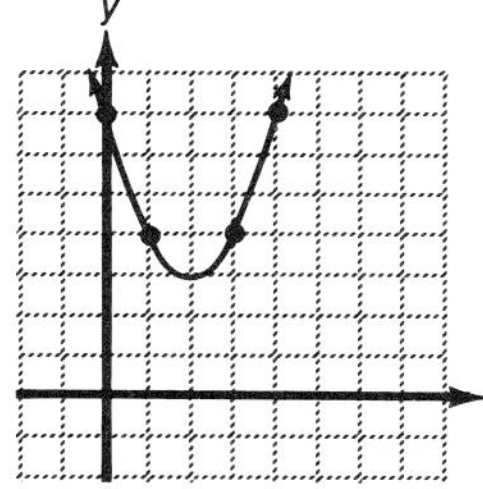

29. $\frac{1}{2}$ **31.** $\frac{1}{4}, -\frac{1}{4}$

Lesson 15-7 Try This

a. Negative **b.** None **c.** Positive
d.

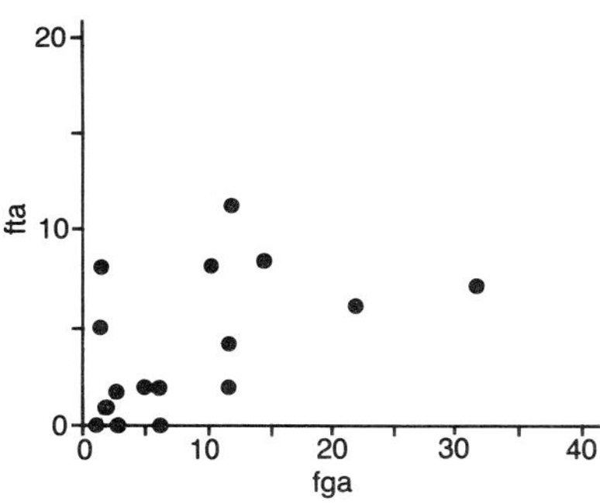

There appears to be no relationship between field goals attempted and free throws attempted.

Exercise Set 15-7

1. Negative **3.** Negative **5.** None **7.** Positive
9. None **11.** There appears to be no relationship between grade point average and shoe size. **15.** 24
17. 26 **19.** 0.5592 **21.** 0.9205 **23.** 4.3315

Problem Solving: Application

1. Solar radiation level of about 150, moderate temperature, low winds in northwesterly direction
3. Days shown by glyphs D, E, and F; solar radiation level ranges from about 50 to about 120; similar temperatures **7.** Not necessarily

Problem Solving: College Entrance Exams

1. (A) **3.** (E) **5.** (A) **7.** (C) **9.** (D)

Chapter 15 Summary and Review

1. $\frac{1}{8}$ **3.** $\frac{4}{8}$ or $\frac{1}{2}$ **5.** $\frac{26}{52}$ or $\frac{1}{2}$ **7.** $\frac{11}{16}$ **9.** $\frac{2}{6}$ or $\frac{1}{3}$

11. $\frac{5}{8}$ **13.** $\frac{32}{52}$ or $\frac{8}{13}$

15.

Stem	Leaf
42	.0, .5
43	.5
44	
45	
46	.5
47	.5
48	.0
49	.5, .0, .5, .0
50	.0, .5, .0
51	.0, .0

17.

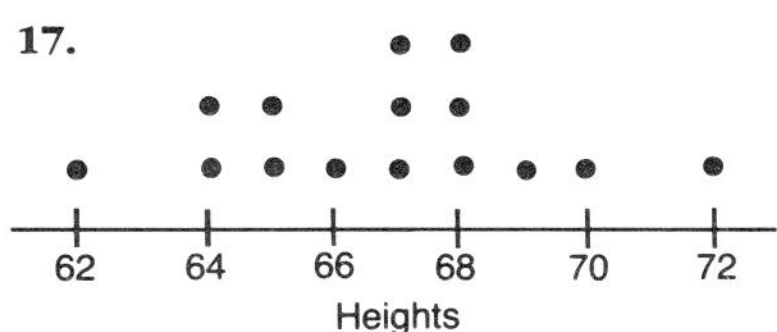

19.

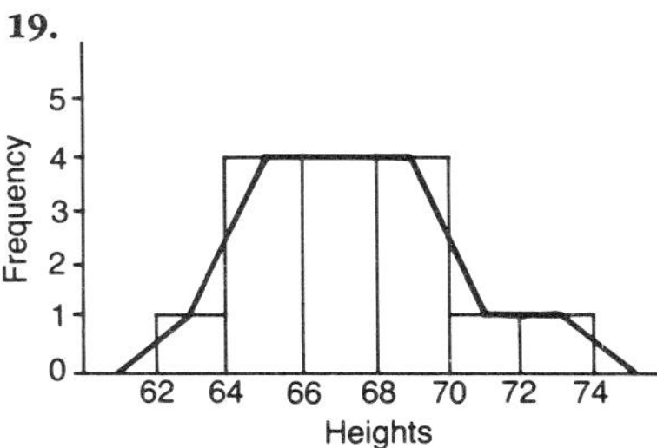

21. 24.86 **23.** Positive

Chapters 1–15 Cumulative Review

1. 54 **3.** 88 **5.** $(a \cdot b) \cdot c$ **7.** $-8\frac{5}{8}$ **9.** $20a + 6b$

11. -34.72 **13.** $\frac{8}{3}$ **15.** 8 **17.** 6090 cars

19. $h = \frac{A}{2\pi r} - r$ or $\frac{A - 2\pi r^2}{2\pi r}$ **21.** 25% **23.** $8\frac{1}{3}\%$

25. 10 **27.** $x < 21$ **29.** $y \leq \frac{1}{2}$ **31.** $y > -5$

33. $l \geq 15$ **35.** $4m^2$ **37.** $8y^{18}$ **39.** $27x^{15}y^{12}$
41. $12ab^4c^5$ **43.** $6xy^2$ **45.** $-a^3 + 4a^2 - 2a$
47. $2m^2 - 9m - 18$ **49.** $a^2 + 4a + 4$
51. $9m^2 + 30m + 25$ **53.** $(7x + 8)(7x - 8)$
55. $(2x - 9)(x + 11)$ **57.** $(3x - 4)^2$
59. $x(10x + 3)^2$
61.

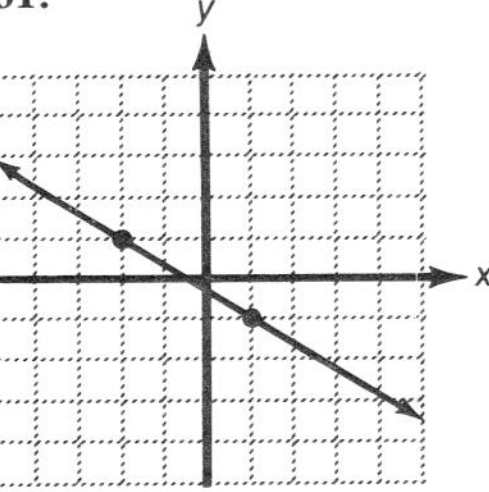

63. $m = -\frac{1}{2}, b = \frac{25}{4}$ **65.** $y = 10$

67. $y = -\frac{2}{3}x - \frac{14}{3}$ **69.** $(-2, 1)$ **71.** $(-2, 1)$

73. $(-2, 5)$ **75.** Dorothy is 60 years old; Stan is 10 years old. **77.** 350 student tickets, 250 adult tickets
79. {99, 100, 102, 105, 108, 110, 111, 115, 120}
81. {100, 110} **83.** {102, 108}
85. $x < -5$ or $x > 5$

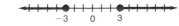

−5 0 5

87. $x \leq -3$ or $x \geq 3$

−3 0 3

89. $\frac{x^2 + 6x + 9}{x^4 - 4x^2 + 4}$ **91.** $\frac{10}{a + 1}$ **93.** $\frac{28}{3}$ **95.** $x + 3$

97. $\frac{-5x + 17}{(x - 4)(x + 3)(x - 3)}$ **99.** -5 **101.** 17 km/h, 22 km/h **103.** 7 **105.** $x \geq -4$ **107.** $|cd|$ **109.** $8|x|$
111. $3\sqrt{y}$ **113.** $y^3\sqrt{y}$ **115.** $3(a + 4)$

117. $8a^2b\sqrt{3ab}$ **119.** $\frac{\sqrt{10}}{6}$ **121.** $13\sqrt{a}$

123. $(3x^2 - x^2y - 2y)\sqrt{y}$ **125.** -4 **127.** -10

129.

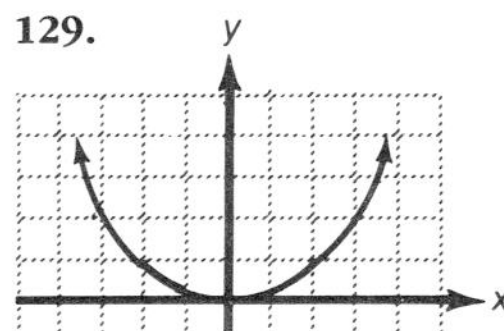

131. 9 psi **133.** $\sqrt{10}, -\sqrt{10}$ **135.** 2

137. $3 \pm \sqrt{6}$ **139.** $\frac{2 \pm \sqrt{6}}{3}$ **141.** $\frac{\pm 2\sqrt{6}}{3}$ **143.** 1, 3

145. 2 km/h **147.** $\frac{1}{2}\sqrt{33} \approx 2.9$ **149.** 15.7 m

151. $\frac{20}{52}$ or $\frac{5}{13}$ **153.** $\frac{5}{8}$

155.

Data	Frequency
180–189	5
190–199	5
200–209	4
210–219	2
220–229	1
230–239	2
240–249	2

157.

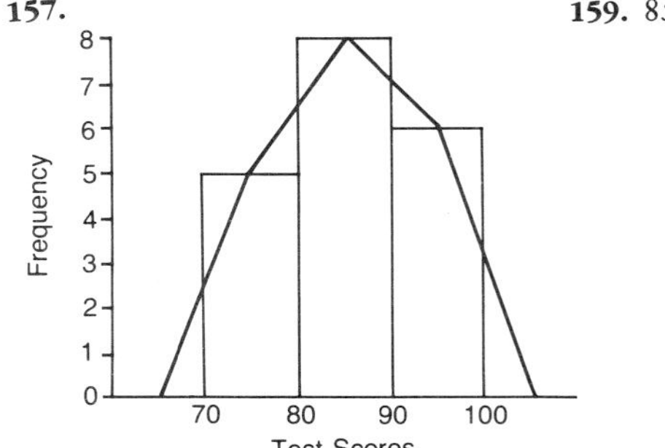

159. 85

T1-81 Investigation 2 Try This
a. (3, 5) **b.** (−2, 4) **c.** (13, −3) **d.** (11, 8)

TI-81 Investigation 3 Try This
a. 3.45

TI-81 Investigation 4 Try This
a. $\bar{x} = 124.5$ **b.** $\bar{x} = 27.25$

TI-81 Investigation 5 Try This

a. $\begin{bmatrix} 368 & 512 & 752 \\ 642 & 693 & 783 \\ 476 & 475 & 460 \\ 448 & 367 & 353 \\ 333 & 401 & 327 \end{bmatrix}$

The dimensions of the matrix are 5×3.
The entry 642 is in position (2, 1).
The entry 327 is in position (5, 3).

b. $\begin{bmatrix} -4.5 & 8.1 & 2.7 \\ 4.9 & 4.2 & 6.1 \end{bmatrix}$

c. $\begin{bmatrix} 6 & -3 \\ 12.25 & -5.6 \\ 0.25 & 8.5 \end{bmatrix}$

d. You can not add these matrices together because they don't both have the same dimensions.

TI-81 Investigation 6 Try This
a. \$306 **b.** \$306 **c.** \$935
d. School 2, first semester
e. \$3700 **f.** \$67,400

Index